The Complete Guide to Electronics Troubleshooting

The Complete Guide to Electronics Troubleshooting

James Perozzo

Delmar Publishers Inc.™
I(T)P™

NOTICE TO THE READER

Publisher does not warrant or guarantee any of the products described herein or perform any independent analysis in connection with any of the product information contained herein. Publisher does not assume, and expressly disclaims, any obligation to obtain and include information other than that provided to it by the manufacturer.

The reader is expressly warned to consider and adopt all safety precautions that might be indicated by the activities described herein and to avoid all potential hazards. By following the instructions contained herein, the reader willingly assumes all risks in connection with such instructions.

The publisher makes no representations or warranties of any kind, including but not limited to, the warranties of fitness for particular purpose or merchantability, nor are any such representations implied with respect to the material set forth herein, and the publisher takes no responsibility with respect to such material. The publisher shall not be liable for any special, consequential or exemplary damages resulting, in whole or in part, from the readers' use of, or reliance upon, this material.

Cover photos by Bruce Parker
Cover and text design by Spiral Design

Delmar Staff
Administrative Editor: Wendy J. Welch
Senior Project Editor: Christopher Chien
Senior Production Supervisor: Larry Main
Art/Design Coordinator: Lisa Pauly
Editorial Assistant: Jennifer Daniels

Printed in the United States of America
Published simultaneously in Canada
by Nelson Canada,
a division of The Thomson Corporation

10 9 8 7 6 5 4 3 2 XX 95 96 97 98 99
Library of Congress Cataloging-in-Publication Data:

Perozzo, James.
The complete guide to electronics troubleshooting / James Perozzo.
p. cm.
Includes index.
ISBN 0-8273-5045-7
1. Electronic apparatus and appliances—Maintenance and repair.
I. Title
TK7870.2.P467 1994
621.3815'4—dc20 93-33977
CIP

CONTENTS

Preface

This book is intended as a reference that new or experienced technicians will find valuable in the classroom and on the job. The material in this text can be covered with acceptable depth in as little as 8 weeks with advanced students, yet also serves well as a basic text for those just beginning a career in electronics repair. Together with suitable texts on basic theory, this volume is particularly valuable during the hands-on repair of actual equipment.

The basic difference in using this text as a supplement with either an 8-week or a full 2-year electronics program will be determined by the depth to which the students will be taken into real-world troubleshooting situations. It is strongly suggested that students be given the opportunity to actually try the methods presented herein, and that hands-on experience be interspersed with lectures covering the material in detail.

Unlike most texts, the instructor can choose to begin at the front, middle, or back without necessarily having to build on previous information to enhance other subjects besides troubleshooting that may be taught concurrently. The order of topics in this book begins with system troubleshooting and progresses to component removal and replacement. Each topic is covered at the point where it is most appropriate. The use of a bench power supply, for instance, is covered when it is most timely, after the equipment is opened and before the technician begins to troubleshoot with a voltmeter. Thus, *the flow of the book may appear to be somewhat scattered to those accustomed to topics being covered in a less chronological, modular form.* However, the topics are ranged, as closely as possible, in a logical, connected order.

Side-barred text identifies basic concepts and material pertinent to the troubleshooting topic of the moment, information that will prove beneficial for the entry-level technician. More advanced students may chose to review, scan, or skip these subjects entirely.

Prerequisites for the use of this book are training in basic electronics, including bipolar transistors, and in digital circuits. Other subjects and special components are explained in this text as they directly apply to practical troubleshooting.

There are three general types of jobs involving electronic problem detection and repair. The first is the one that most commonly comes to mind when one describes an electronic technician, that of returning "veteran" equipment to service. "Veteran" equipment has worked at one time, but because of a normal failure or abuse, it no longer functions properly or has failed altogether. The majority of electronic technicians find employment in this kind of job. There are two subdivisions of this kind of work: that of the field technician who goes to the customer's site to repair equipment and the bench technician who repairs incoming equipment at a fixed location. Some jobs require both field and bench work.

The second kind of job is the production-line technician, who detects problems in brand-new circuits that have just come off the end of the assembly line at a factory. This job is explored in Chapter 24. A detailed knowledge of troubleshooting is not usually required to be an assembly-line technician. The defective unit is simply detected and put aside in order to keep the assembly line moving. Defective circuits may then go to a bench technician if the assembly-line technician does not have the troubleshooting skills or the time necessary to pursue the problems further.

The third kind of job is the engineering assistant. This technician must be very familiar with the troubleshooting procedures within this book, plus a great deal more. This is the highest level that a technician can achieve. Advancement beyond this position will usually require an engineering degree.

An electronic technician can be thought of as an electronic "doctor." Just as the medical profession consists of general practitioners and specialists, so does the electronic technician profession. Within the overall job classification of electronic technician can be found many specialties, including analog, radio-frequency, digital, and microprocessor technicians, and field and bench technicians. This book is intended to serve as the basic troubleshooting reference for all technicians, regardless of specialty.

The author wishes to thank the following reviewers for their suggestions and constructive comments during the development of this book: Arthur H. Aske, Patrick Atchison, Louis D. Bean, Scott G. Bisland, James A. Duffy, John Dyckman, Gordon Fish, John A. Hamilton, Edward T. Karsin, Daniel L. Metzger, and Marshall Seawright. The author would also like to thank his students for their valuable assistance: Steve Dixon, David Gower, Dan Hassler, Tom Kornell, John Matley, Andy Selzler, Jack Suprenant, and Do Vo.

I would like to thank that very Special Person in my life, my wife Sandi, and my daughters Amber and Tina, for their understanding of the many hours I spent slaving over a hot computer during the preparation of this work.

The John Fluke Company of Everett, WA and their Philips Alliance were exceptionally helpful in the development of information on digital multimeters, frequency counters, digital storage oscilloscopes and logic analyzers. Tak Tsang, Bill Dunn, Hans Toorens, Mike Marino, and Bob Roth of the Fluke and Philips Alliance provided invaluable assistance in the form of equipment and tutoring in the latest techniques and instruments available today.

Mr. Bill Hunt of Huntron Instruments continued to encourage me in this work. I especially wish to thank my fellow instructors Arthur Thompson and Richard Francis, who assisted in assuring the correctness and completeness of much of this material. "CJ" Lemmon, in particular, proof-read and edited my work, assuring its understandability and accuracy from a fresh, practical viewpoint. I owe a great deal to him for his honesty and friendship.

About the Author

Mr. Perozzo has 35 years experience in repairing electronic equipment and teaching all manner of electronic troubleshooting. After 20 years service in the

Coast Guard as a Chief Electronics Technician and later as an officer, he broadened his experience by working in the repair of marine and aviation electronics, microwave voice carriers, industrial electronics and microcomputer repair. A native of the Pacific Northwest, his qualifications include an FCC General Radiotelephone Certificate since 1959, an Amateur Extra Class license (K7QJP), an FAA Avionics Repair Certification, and an Electronics Teaching Certificate. Mr. Perozzo currently teaches electronics at Renton Technical College in Renton, Washington. Correspondence may be addressed to him there at 3000 4th St., Renton, WA 98056.

Some Necessary Basics

1

CHAPTER OBJECTIVES

This chapter provides a review of important, fundamental facts that must be clearly understood before beginning a study of electronic troubleshooting. At the conclusion of this chapter, the student will have a clearer understanding of terms and concepts, including:

- The need to first understand basic component operation: resistors, capacitors, inductors, and bipolar transistors.
- Basic safety and cautions to protect you and your equipment.
- Conversion between metric units.
- The definitions of ground, common, neutral, and chassis.
- The concepts of circuit impedance and internal resistance.
- Real-world definitions of shorts and opens.
- The methods used to number and identify component and integrated circuit leads.
- Memorizing a few simple, typical circuits.
- The importance and use of color codes.
- The importance of thoroughly understanding logic functions for basic gates.

- The understanding of classes of analog amplifier operation: A, B, and C.
- Number and type of hand tools for a minimal toolbox.
- Test equipment requirements, as determined by the type of equipment to be repaired.

1.1 ELECTRONIC KNOWLEDGE REQUIRED

Troubleshooting of electronic equipment only to the equipment or the card level can be done easily and requires little electronic knowledge. A simple substitution of suspected equipment or cards is generally sufficient to find and replace a malfunctioning unit and get the system back into operation quickly. However, repair to the component level demands knowledge far above a simple replacement of equipment or a card.

KNOW HOW COMMON ELECTRONIC COMPONENTS WORK

A really competent electronics technician must be able to troubleshoot to the component level if necessary. For that, the technician must have a thorough knowledge of how individual electronic components function. Resistors, capacitors, inductors, diodes, transistors, bipolar transistors, insulated-gate transistors, and silicon-controlled rectifiers are only a few of the basic components that must be understood before troubleshooting to the component level can be done competently. Most electronic schools offer these subjects.

The actual repair of equipment entails much more than a knowledge of components. Understanding the operation of electronic systems and the functions of equipment within those systems is necessary before component-level troubleshooting can be done productively.

1.2 SOME BASIC DOS AND DON'TS

The following tips are not a complete list of what should or should not be done to prevent damage to you and your equipment. However, they are items that should be kept in mind and applied when appropriate.

1. Always turn off all power before removing or inserting circuit boards into equipment.

2. Remove rings or metal watchbands when working near high-voltage or high-current equipment because of the danger of shocks or burns.
3. Always connect the negative or ground lead of test equipment before contacting high voltage with the "hot" lead.
4. Always connect a suitable dummy load to a radio transmitter. This prevents damage to the final amplifier and interference to normal on-air signals.
5. When interconnecting equipment to a computer system, never connect a parallel device to a serial port or a serial device to a parallel port.
6. Discharge static electricity to ground before touching modern solid-state devices or boards. Use static-prevention products when available.
7. When turning on audio equipment, be sure the volume controls are turned down. Speakers can be damaged by excessive power settings.
8. Apply power to CMOS circuits before applying input signals.

1.3 CONVERTING ELECTRONIC TERMS

It is important to be able to convert both ways without error, from one metric multiple to another, when dealing with electronic quantities. The following figure may help in visualizing these conversions; the method an experienced technician carries out mentally. See Figure 1–1.

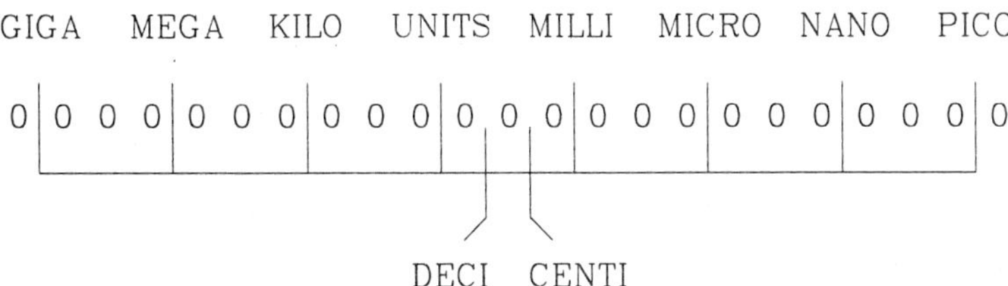

Place the value you have with the decimal point on the end of the line beneath the proper current multiple.

Now move the decimal point alone to under the new multiple and place it on the end of that line.

Example: Convert 0.5 milliwatts to watts.

UNITS MILLI

.5

0 0 | 0 0 0 | 0

UNITS MILLI

0 0 0.5

0 0 | 0 0 0 | 0

Answer: .0005 watt

Figure 1–1 A graphic means of converting between metric multiples.

Practice converting terms up and down the metric scale until you are confident in your ability to do them free of errors. In particular, practice converting between the multiples as shown, for they are the most common in electronics:

Converting between hertz (Hz), kilohertz (kHz), megahertz (MHz), and gigahertz (gHz).

Converting between ohms (Ω), kilohms (kΩ), and megohms (MΩ).

Converting between microfarads (MFd) and picofarads (pFd).

Converting between seconds (s), milliseconds (ms), microseconds (μs and nanoseconds (ηs).

1.4 COMMON SCHEMATIC SYMBOLS

It will be necessary to be able to recognize the common schematic symbols that you will see on schematics. See Appendix II for a complete listing of these symbols.

1.5 THE VOCABULARY OF ELECTRONICS

The field of electronics, as with any profession, has its own vocabulary. New electronic terms are defined in most electronics dictionaries, which are often available at local specialty electronics stores. Some terms used are very important to troubleshooting, as explained in the following paragraphs.

To clarify any possible misunderstanding, study the following terms and definitions, which will be used in this text.

LIVE AND DEAD CIRCUITS

For the remainder of this book, the term *live* will simply mean that all operating voltages are present to operate the circuits under test. A *dead* circuit is one that has no external operating voltages connected to it at all.

IN-CIRCUIT AND OUT-OF-CIRCUIT

If you can hold a single component in your hand, separate from any other equipment, it is *out-of-circuit*. If one lead of the component remains connected to the circuit but all other leads are disconnected, the component is still out-of-circuit. This is a common situation when testing components with an ohmmeter. Disconnect all component leads or leave no more than one lead connected to the circuit. The component is then effectively out of the circuits for further individual testing. An in-circuit component is fully

BASIC INFORMATION

installed and may show unexpected ohmmeter test results because of the other components connected to it and the parallel paths they present to the instrument.

STATIC VERSUS DYNAMIC TESTING

Static testing is done when the circuit under test is not "moving." Voltages are constant, and troubleshooting is accomplished primarily with a direct current (DC) voltmeter. Dynamic troubleshooting, on the other hand, requires the circuit to be in full operation. Troubleshooting in a dynamic circuit usually requires at least an alternating (AC) voltmeter or an oscilloscope.

Analog circuits can be analyzed by either method. For example, a power supply is usually analyzed by the use of a DC voltmeter to find the problem. An audio circuit may require an input signal to find the problem, therefore involving dynamic troubleshooting instruments in most cases. Pulse circuits usually require dynamic troubleshooting methods for successful faultfinding. Digital circuits can be tested by either method. Simple shorts and opens are best found by static troubleshooting methods, while more complex problems, particularly those of a microprocessor-driven circuit, will require dynamic troubleshooting instruments such as a logic analyzer.

SIGNAL AND NO-SIGNAL TESTING

Depending upon the tests desired, the technician may or may not require input signals to the circuits under test. Direct-current voltage measurements do not require that the circuits being tested have signals flowing through them. As a matter of fact, the presence of a signal flowing through the circuit may complicate troubleshooting by producing misleading indications. This is particularly true of radio frequency (RF) circuits. Strong RF fields can cause some volt-ohm-milliammeter (VOM) meters to strike a needle end-stop violently, or digital types of meters to register strange, erratic readings that have nothing to do with the voltages to be measured.

CIRCUIT COMMON, GROUND, NEUTRAL, AND CHASSIS

Circuit common is the central point to which individual circuits connect. It is often, but not always, the external metal portion of the chassis. Common is that point to which the grounded or negative side of test equipment, such as oscilloscopes and signal generators, is usually connected. These instruments are often operated from the 120-V AC power line. Operation with their grounds connected to anything but the common bus of the circuit under test can cause problems, such as damaged printed circuit traces, or ruin semiconductors or integrated circuits (ICs).

Ground is, technically speaking, a connection that can be traced back along wiring *that does not normally carry current* to an actual connection to the earth. The round connector of the modern 120-V AC outlet is an example. It is physically connected to a shaft sunk into the ground at the power distribution panel, somewhere near where the power comes into the building. The term *ground* is often used incorrectly for *common*, the point in a circuit where the negative side of test equipment is connected. If the common point of a circuit is indeed connected back to an earth ground, then the term is being used correctly.

Chassis is the term used to describe the metal framework of the equipment under test. In many cases, the chassis is connected back to an earth ground via the round connector of the 120-V AC outlet. In this case, the chassis can also be called a ground. For safety reasons, a technician should never assume that the chassis of a piece of equipment is connected to earth ground.

Neutral describes a connection of one side of an AC power line which is near earth ground potential. See Figure 1–2.

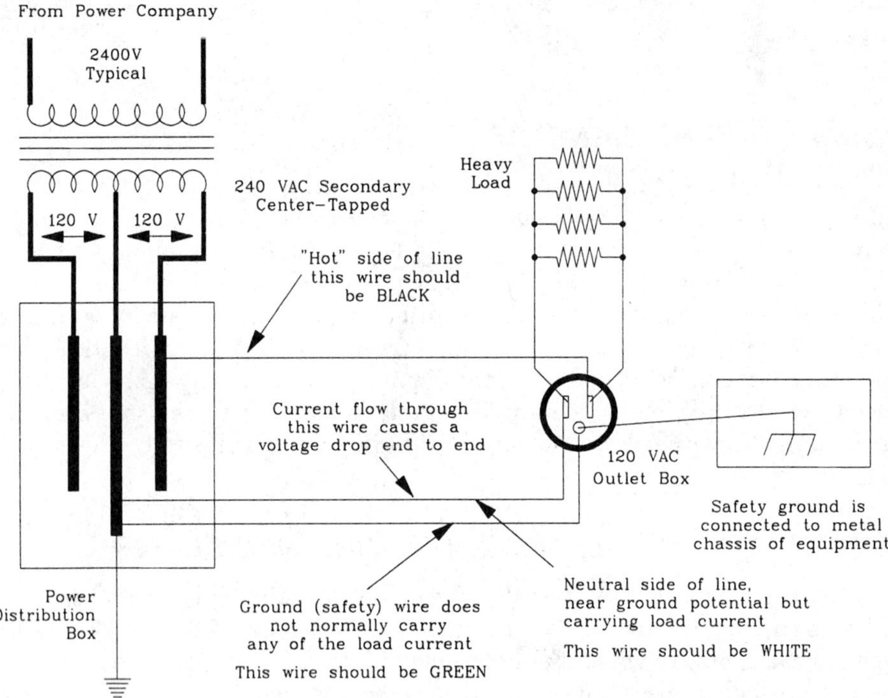

Figure 1–2 The third wire of a three-wire power cord is connected to an earth ground at the power distribution panel at one end and to the equipment chassis at the other.

The neutral wire carries current, and therefore may at any given point be several volts away from earth ground, positive or negative as the current alternates.

Circuits that use relays or photo-isolators usually have two completely isolated circuits connected to the ends of the isolator. One of the primary purposes for these components is to provide isolation, as one or both of the circuits may have dangerous voltages with respect to ground. Thus, the presence of an optical isolator may indicate a potentially dangerous circuit.

Test instruments that do not use ground or are completely isolated (DC and AC isolation) from the power-line ground may be connected into most circuits at any point without incurring any damage due to grounding problems. Instruments that meet this requirement include battery-operated, portable VOMs and DMMs (digital multimeters). When measuring voltages with the VOM or DMM, the black lead is the one usually connected to the circuit common.

SHORTS AND OPENS

A *short* is an unintentional current path of very low, essentially zero, resistance, which in some instances can cause excessive current and serious damage to components. The resultant blown fuse and burned wires are results of short circuits. In other cases, a short may simply eliminate a signal or DC voltage without any damage at all. Troubleshooting techniques sometimes take advantage of this fact.

An *open* is a path of extremely high resistance that prevents any appreciable current flow. A switch in the "off" position is an example of an open circuit.

CIRCUIT IMPEDANCES

Throughout this book, the terms *high impedance* and *low impedance* will be used. These are relative terms with no definite dividing line between them. They are rather like the terms *high* and *low*: it depends on where you happen to be standing at the time.

A high-impedance circuit will be "weak." It will have high internal resistance, and its output voltage will be easily changed by external loading resistances. Figure 1–3 shows how an average VOM will give very inaccurate readings when connected to a high-impedance voltage source. Examples of high-impedance circuits are the inputs to FETs (field effect transistors), and CMOS (complementary metal oxide semiconductor) integrated circuits, as well as the inputs to vacuum tubes.

A low-impedance circuit will be "strong." On such circuits the loading effect of a voltmeter will be negligible. Examples of low-impedance circuits are power supplies, bipolar transistor circuits, and TTL (transistor-transistor logic) integrated circuits.

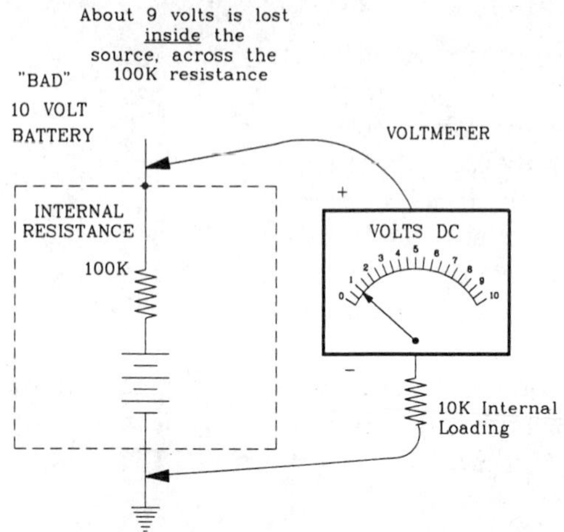

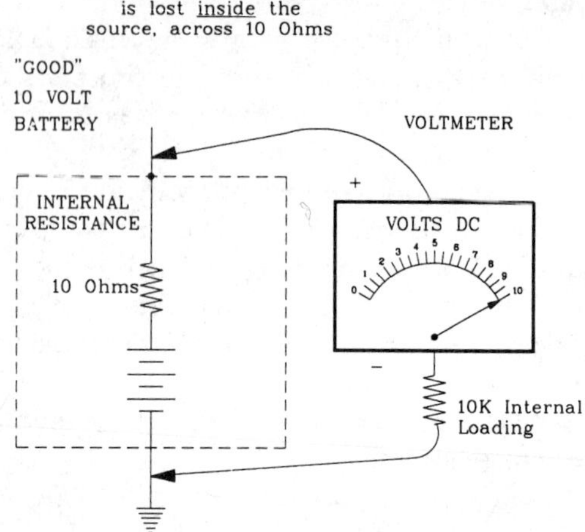

Figure 1–3 Loading effects of the volt-ohm-milliammeter (VOM) due to internal impedance of a source.

BASIC INFORMATION

The main point to keep in mind is that high-impedance circuits are loaded down by external loads, such as test equipment input circuits. Instances in which high and low impedances are critical are pointed out in the text when appropriate.

INTERNAL RESISTANCE

A source of electrical power cannot provide infinite power. If its terminals are shorted together with a perfect short, there is no way that the resulting current can be infinite. What limits this current is the *internal resistance* of the source. Every source has an internal resistance. A 6-volt (V) lantern battery has the same voltage as a 6-V car battery, but the car battery can produce much more current under heavy loads than the lantern battery because the car battery has a much lower internal resistance. It is important to remember this term when troubleshooting voltage sources such as batteries and power supplies.

MOCKUPS

A *mockup* is a series of connectors, signal generators, cables, connectors, and power supplies that are required to bench test a printed circuit card or other equipment. The mockup simulates the circuit's normal external operating conditions as closely as possible.

1.6 COMPONENT LEAD IDENTIFICATION

In addition to the schematic symbols shown in Appendix II, it is necessary to know how the leads of a given kind of component are laid out. For instance, it is useless to know that on a transistor there are three leads called the emitter, base, and collector if you don't know which is which. Likewise, the location of the first pin of an integrated circuit must be identified before you can figure out the location of all the other pins. See Figure 1–4 to find the first lead of a component and determine in which direction to count to find other leads.

1.7 STANDARD CIRCUITS

There are a few simple circuits that should be memorized because they are encountered so often, and a technician should be able to work with them without a schematic. The circuits of Figure 1–5 are the ones that should be learned thoroughly. Other circuits may be obtained from actual equipment schematics.

1.8 COLOR AND COMPONENT VALUE CODES

SURFACE-MOUNTED DEVICE VALUE CODES

See Appendix V for information on this subject.

RESISTOR COLOR CODE

It is important to be able to read resistor values without having to look them up in a color code table each time. *Take the time to memorize the color code,* as it is one of the few things that the technician should commit to memory. Besides enabling the fast identification of parts, memorizing the color code will make a technician more efficient as a troubleshooter. As an example, knowing the code will prevent wasting time on the wrong resistor: for example, the experienced technician knows that the 10,000 Ω resistor being sought is not the one with yellow, violet, and orange bands.

Appendix I gives color codes for resistors and capacitors. There are two different color-coding systems in present use for resistors: the two-significant figure system for carbon resistors and the three-significant figure system for precision and metal film resistors. Learn these color code systems well, as they are frequently used during troubleshooting.

If in doubt as to the color code value of a resistor out-of-circuit, do as any good technician would do: take a shortcut. Use an ohmmeter. A digital ohmmeter will give a more accurate resistance reading with less chance of misreading the value than an analog ohmmeter can provide. When measur-

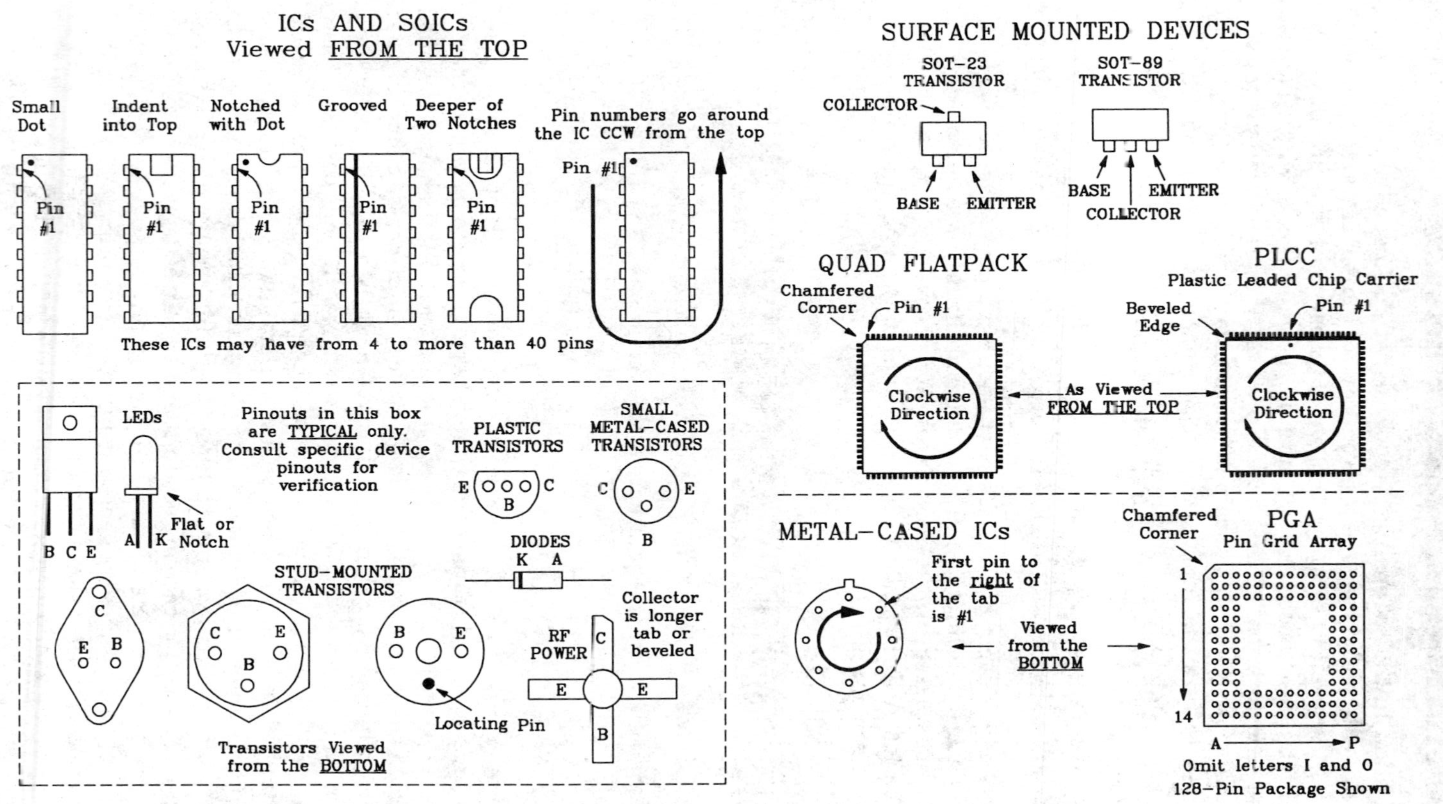

Figure 1–4 Component lead identification.

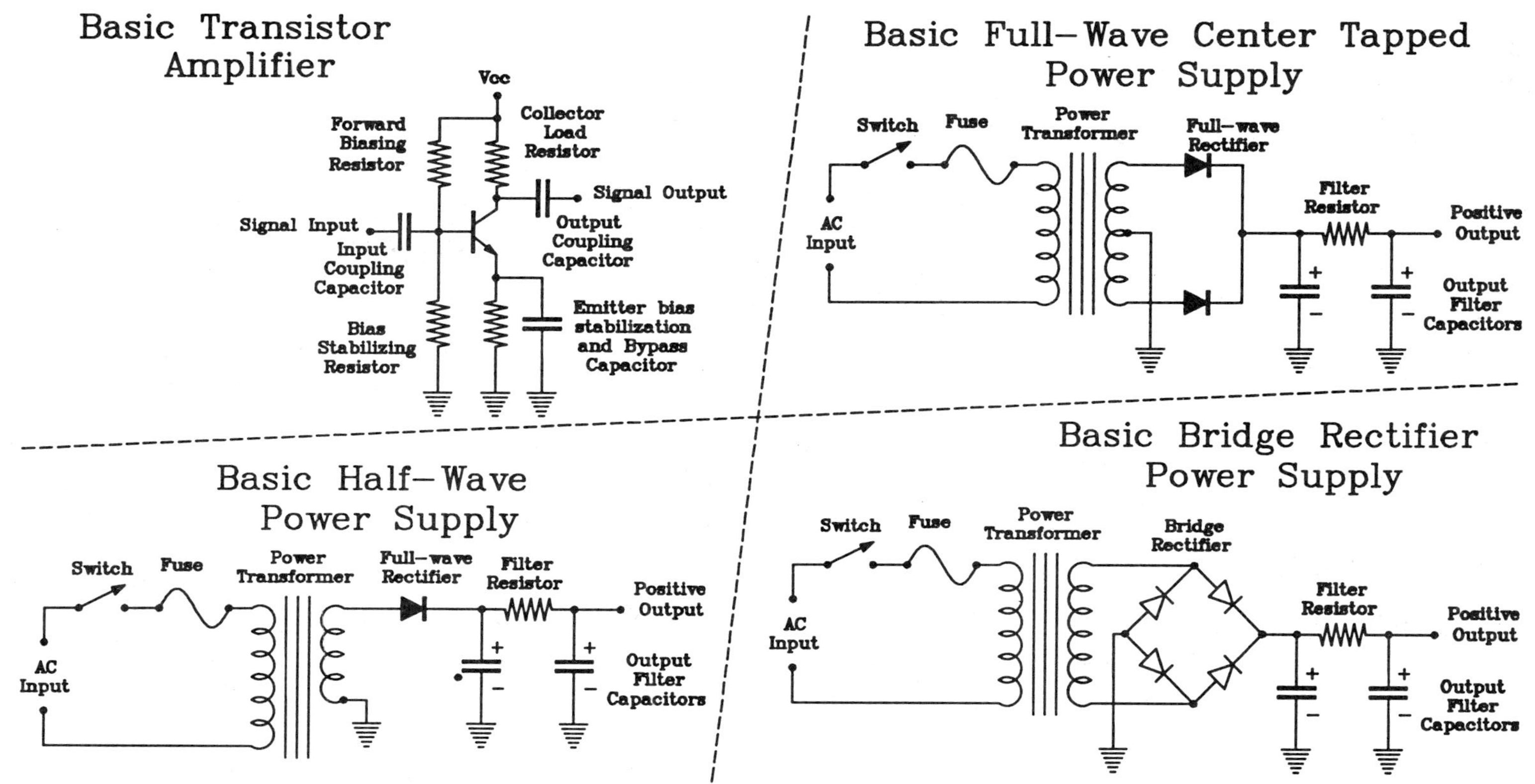

Figure 1–5 These common circuits should be learned thoroughly.

ing high resistances, remember to keep your fingers off the ohmmeter connections to eliminate placing the hand-to-hand resistance of your body in parallel with the circuit.

Some resistors, particularly the larger sizes, may have the resistance value written directly on the component. Several different methods of marking are listed in the following:

Resistance value expressed as two significant figures and a multiplier (very similar to the two-significant figure resistor color code):

103 = 10,000 ohms
122 = 1,200 ohms

Resistance value expressed as three significant figures and a multiplier (very similar to the three-significant figure resistor color code):

6832 = 68,300 ohms
1221 = 1,220 ohms

Since a decimal is easily overlooked, the letter *K* for thousand or *M* for million may be used instead of the decimal:

68K3 = 68,300 ohms
1K22 = 1,220 ohms

Resistance values of less than 10 ohms (these resistors are commonly wire-wound, and are often relatively large and gray or white in color) may be marked as follows:

3R6 = 3.6 ohms
0R5 = 0.5 ohms

CAPACITOR COLOR AND NUMBER CODES

The same basic number coding used with resistors also applies to capacitor color coding. The major problem with color coding of capacitor values is that there are so many different coding schemes in use. See Appendix I for examples of some of the capacitor color-coding schemes used.

Fortunately, capacitors are often marked with their values. Large capacitors, such as electrolytics, are simply marked with their capacitance and voltage ratings. Small capacitors are sometimes marked with the numerical capacitance value as follows, (giving the first and second significant figures and a multiplier) with the answer in picofarads (pFd):

103 = 10,000 pFd
10K = 10,000 pFd

Capacitors, particularly disc ceramics, will often use a letter code to denote the tolerance of the component. See Appendix I for these tolerance codes.

INDUCTOR COLOR CODE

Inductor color codes are also included in Appendix I. These codes are used only on very small inductors.

FUSE COLOR CODES

Miniaturization has extended to fuses, as well. Appendix I also provides information on determining fuse ratings by color coding.

WIRE COLOR CODE

Chassis wiring also sometimes uses color coding. Wires from a channel switch, for instance, might be wired such that channel one is brown, two is red, and so on. Watch for this, as it can be a help in tracing wiring.

When vacuum tubes were in general use, there was a color code for various different circuits in the equipment. With today's solid-state technology, however, all that remains of the old code is that black is still usually the circuit common (or ground) and red is often the "hot" side of the supply; this is called B+ in vacuum tube circuits and Vcc or Vdd in solid-state circuits. Test leads of instruments using direct current, VOMs, DMMs, and power supplies use black wires to indicate negative and red for positive.

Here is an important point to keep in mind for safety's sake, since it is just the opposite of conventional electronic wire color coding: 120-V AC power-line wiring uses black for the "hot" wire, white for the neutral, and green for earth (safety) ground. Again, refer back to Figure 1–1. Erroneously assuming that a black wire is always ground can set the stage for a very bad accident.

1.9 DIGITAL CIRCUITS ARE UNIQUE

When working with digital circuits, the technician is required to think in a different way than when working with analog circuits. There is no "gray area," as digital circuits operate with either "yes" or "no" conditions. This kind of thinking is necessary for understanding and troubleshooting in digital circuitry.

A FEELING FOR LOGIC

When troubleshooting in digital logic circuits, the technician will be using the terms *active high* and *active low*. Since logic circuits use either a high or a low voltage level, either state might be the desirable one. To

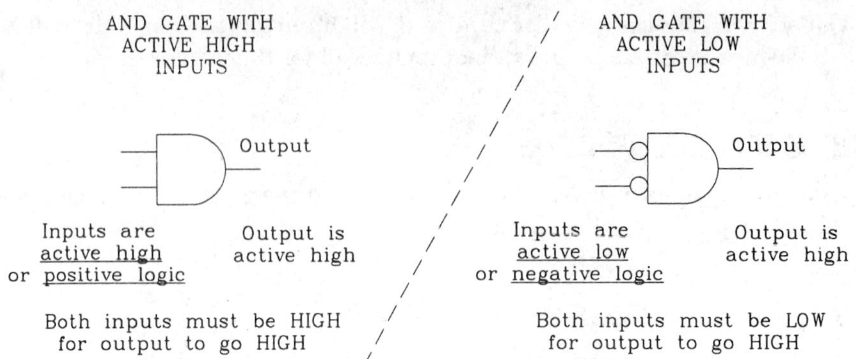
AND GATE WITH
ACTIVE HIGH
INPUTS
Output
Inputs are
active high
or positive logic
Output is
active high
Both inputs must be HIGH
for output to go HIGH
AND GATE WITH
ACTIVE LOW
INPUTS
Output
Inputs are
active low
or negative logic
Output is
active high
Both inputs must be LOW
for output to go HIGH

Figure 1–6 Sample logic symbols showing active high and active low signals.

better clarify this point, consider the two inputs to a digital circuit shown in Figure 1–6.

For a desired high output from the circuit, the input must also be in the high, or positive, state. This is the most logical way to do things in terms of easy understanding by humans. These inputs would be called *active high* inputs.

The opposite case is possible; the two inputs must be *low* to give the desired AND output from the gate. This is called negative logic, and would be indicated by either a small circle at the input of the circuit symbol or a small bar over any identifying letters next to that connection. This is called an *active low* input.

TRUTH TABLES

A technician who works on digital equipment must be very familiar with the truth tables for the digital building blocks that will be encountered. The common ones that must be thoroughly understood are AND, NAND, OR, NOR, and EXCLUSIVE OR (XOR). It is not enough to memorize the tables themselves. Rather, the tables must be *understood* so well that the technician will be able to state without hesitation what the inputs of a given gate would have to be to obtain the desired output. See Figure 1–7.

The tables themselves can often be boiled down to a simple statement. For instance, the truth table for an AND gate simply means that *both inputs must be high for the output to go high.*

1.10 CLASSES OF AMPLIFIER OPERATION

It is necessary to be familiar with the *classes of operation* of amplifiers. It is the biasing of these stages that determines their behavior in a circuit, and proper bias determination is one of the primary troubleshooting steps.

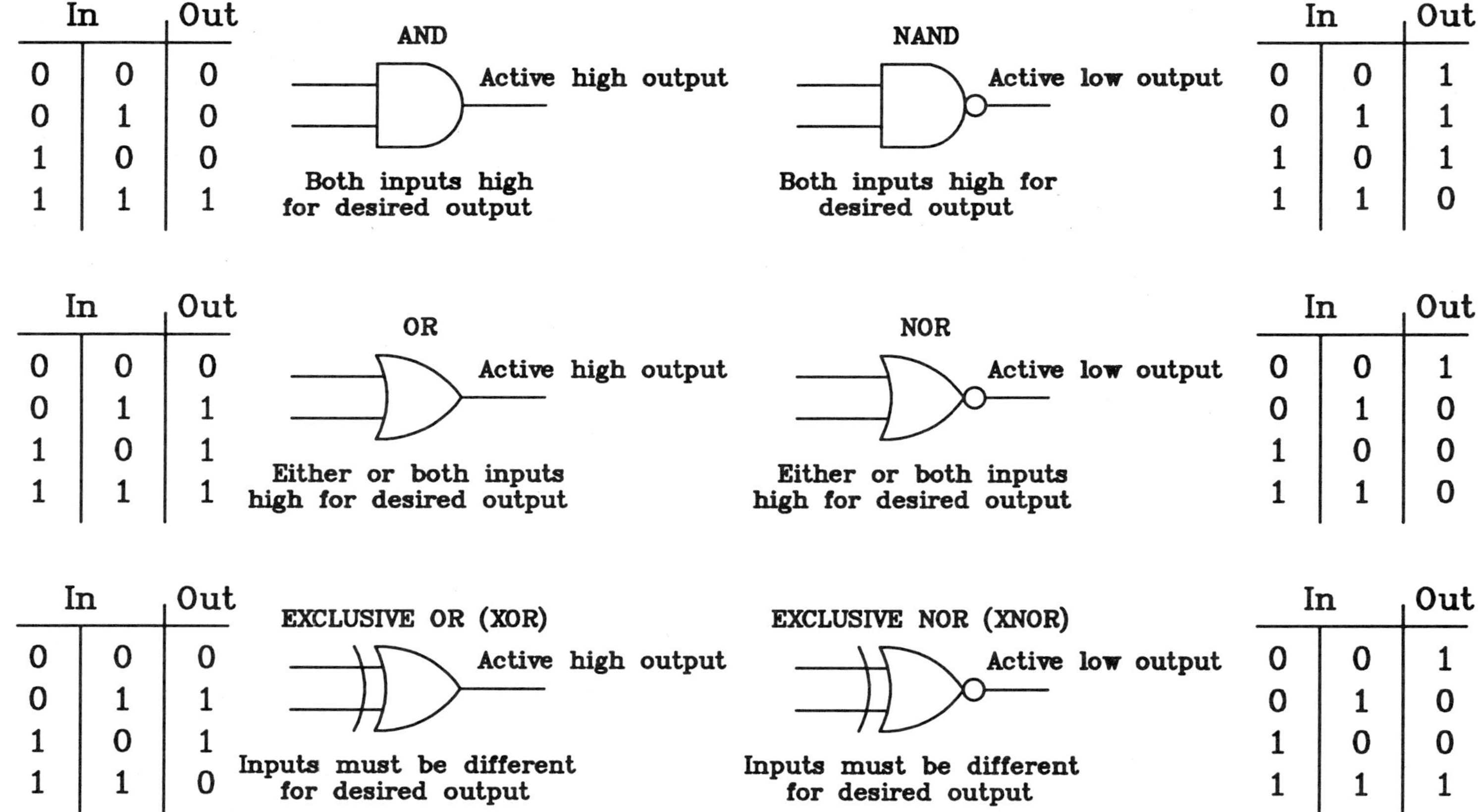

AND

In		Out
0	0	0
0	1	0
1	0	0
1	1	1

NAND

In		Out
0	0	1
0	1	1
1	0	1
1	1	0

OR

In		Out
0	0	0
0	1	1
1	0	1
1	1	1

NOR

In		Out
0	0	1
0	1	0
1	0	0
1	1	0

XOR

In		Out
0	0	0
0	1	1
1	0	1
1	1	0

XNOR

In		Out
0	0	1
0	1	0
1	0	0
1	1	1

Figure 1–7 Input conditions for desired logical outputs: The technician should know these well.

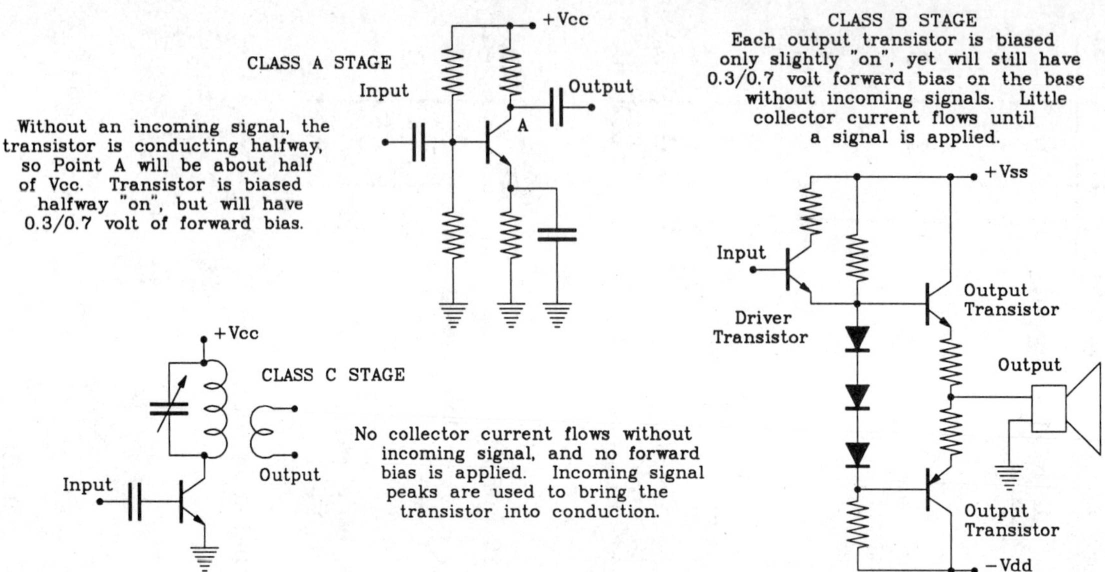

Figure 1–8 Classes of amplifier operation.

Briefly, the *Class A* amplifier is biased so that the amplifier is only turned on halfway. This makes it possible for the stage to operate toward either more conduction or less, following the input signal faithfully. The *Class B* stage is biased just barely above the cutoff point and requires a signal of a particular polarity to make it conduct heavily and produce an output. An input signal of the opposite polarity will merely turn it completely "off," producing no useful signal in the output circuit. The *Class C* stage also requires an input signal of the proper polarity, just like the Class B stage, but the initial turnoff bias on the Class C stage is so great that the incoming signal must be much larger to produce an output from the stage. Therefore, the Class C stage will require more amplitude of the input signal to turn it on. Of course, an opposite input signal polarity will serve only to keep the stage turned off. Figure 1–8 shows typical applications for the three classes of operation.

These classes of operation will be used often in the text. Figure 1–9 shows a water valve analogy of transistor biasing, which can be more easily understood. Figures 1–10, 1–11, and 1–12 expand upon this analogy, showing a water analogy of typical circuits of the three classes of operation.

1.11 THE TECHNICIAN'S WORKING ENVIRONMENT

There are three things required to work on electronic equipment: a decent place to work, the instruments appropriate to the kind of troubleshooting job, and a minimum of hand tools.

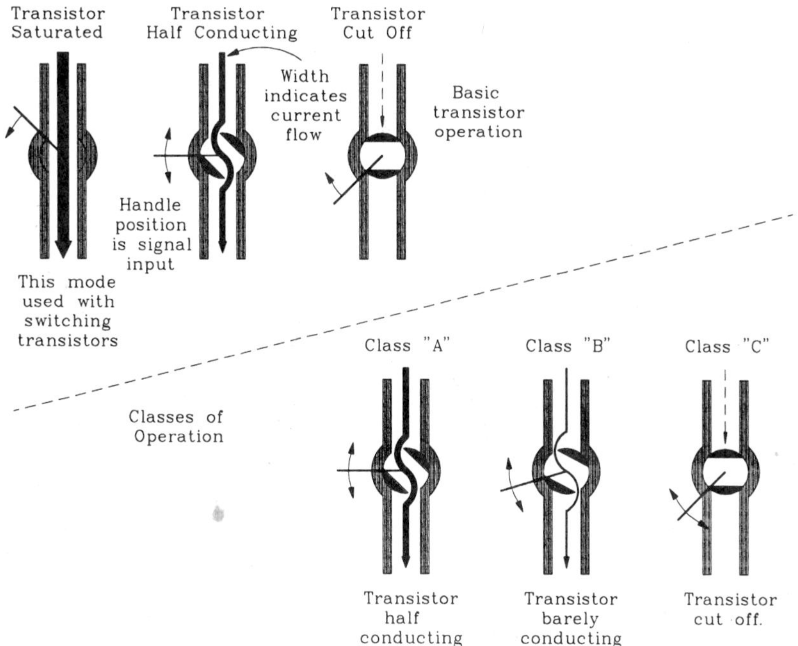

Figure 1–9 How transistor biasing may be compared to a water valve.

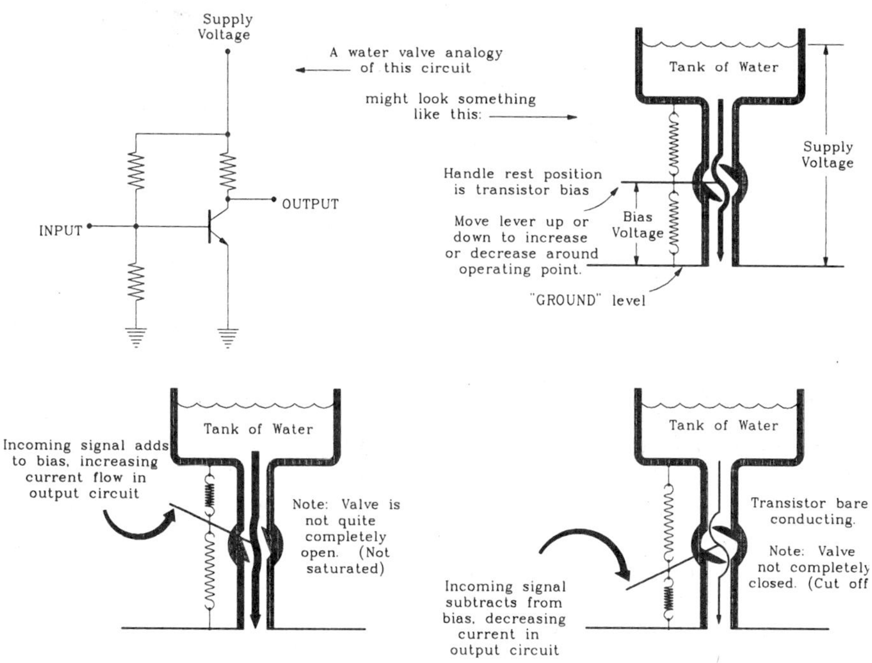

Figure 1–10 A water valve analogy of Class A amplifier operation.

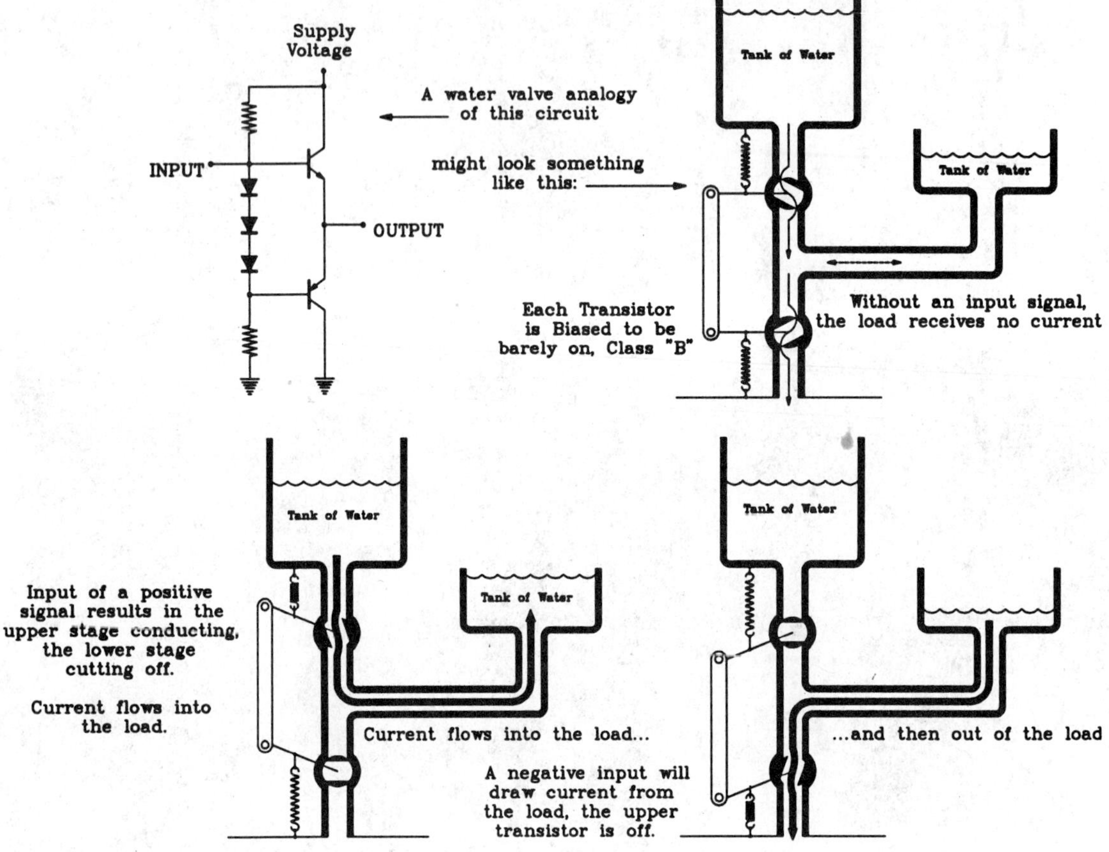

Figure 1–11 A water valve analogy of Class B amplifier operation.

THE TEST BENCH: A DECENT PLACE TO WORK

While much troubleshooting is done in the field without the benefit of a fixed and convenient location to be effective, the bench technician needs basic furniture and tools. A slanted shelf above the bench should be mounted at a convenient level and angle to make instruments on it approximately perpendicular to the technician's line of sight. By doing this, errors due to viewing the instrument needles from the side (parallax errors) will be minimized. Outlets for supply AC power to the instruments should be available in the rear of the bench to avoid a tangle of line cords across the working surface. It is also a good idea to provide a switch to turn off all the outlets to any equipment that is not needed at the end of the work shift.

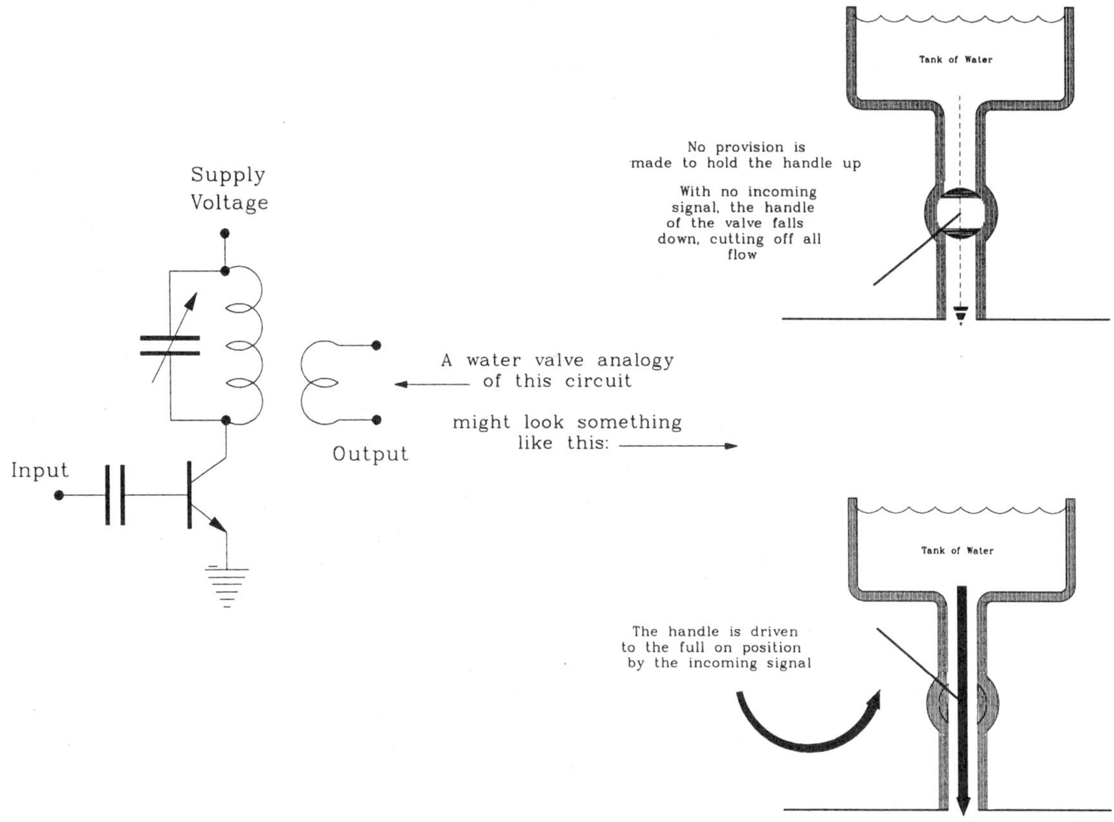
Supply
Voltage
Input
Output
A water valve analogy
of this circuit
might look something
like this:
Tank of Water
No provision is
made to hold the handle up
With no incoming
signal, the handle
of the valve falls
down, cutting off all
flow
Tank of Water
The handle is driven
to the full on position
by the incoming signal

Figure 1–12 A water valve analogy of Class C amplifier operation.

An outlet or two that is always on may be desirable for items such as battery chargers and power supplies needed for running equipment that is under test overnight.

A small vise mounted on the end of the bench or on a heavy metal plate is a valuable "third hand" for such jobs as soldering. Plenty of leg room and a place to put the feet makes sitting for long periods more comfortable. The stool should provide back support for the technician in order to prevent back fatigue. A rotatable stool is best for mobility.

Good lighting is important. A technician must be able to see very tiny broken circuit traces when troubleshooting printed circuit boards. Fluorescent lighting is very good, and incidentally, it provides the strobing effect that is sometimes required to check the speed of rotating parts.

Insulated floor matting is highly recommended, especially if the technician will be working on equipment that is operated from the AC power lines. A voltage breakdown rating of at least 1,000 V is considered the minimum for routine working safety.

ELECTRONIC TEST INSTRUMENTS REQUIRED

The test equipment needed for a given job will depend on the kind of equipment that needs repair. Troubleshooting DC circuits (for example, wiring on automobiles) requires a minimum of test equipment, while the maintenance of radio frequency equipment requires a large equipment investment. The following is a list suggesting typical test instruments required according to the kind of equipment being serviced. Consult Appendix III for a listing of companies that make quality equipment and that will be a pleasure to work with and will stand behind their products.

DC Circuits: power supply, VOM or DMM, solid-state tester.

Low-Frequency (Audio) Circuits: power supply, VOM or DMM, oscilloscope, audio-frequency (AF) oscillator or function generator.

Radio Frequency Circuits: power supply, VOM or DMM, oscilloscope, standing wave ratio (SWR) meter or directional RF power meter, 50 Ω dummy load, frequency counter, RF signal generator. (The final four instruments may be combined in a single *station monitor* instrument.)

Pulse Circuits: power supply, VOM or DMM, oscilloscope, digital storage oscilloscope, pulse generator, frequency counter, function generator.

Digital Circuits: power supply, VOM or DMM, solid-state tester, oscilloscope, logic probe, logic clip, current tracer, logic pulser.

ELECTRONIC TOOLS REQUIRED

The majority of bench repairs to electronic equipment require only a few tools. Specialized jobs may require additional tools, but the following list will cover most repairs.

Diagonal cutters, 4" or 6".

Long-nose pliers, 4" or 6".

Nut-driver, 1/4".

Standard (-) screwdriver, 1/8" tip (shirt pocket type).

Standard (-) screwdriver, 3/16" tip.

Phillips (+) screwdriver, size #0 (shirt pocket type).

Phillips screwdriver, #1.

Phillips screwdriver, #2.

Set of small hex wrenches.

Tweezers.

Temperature-controlled soldering iron for printed circuit (PC) board repairs.

NOTE: Be sure to get Phillips screwdrivers, not Reed and Prince types.

CHAPTER SUMMARY

- It is important to be able to accurately and quickly convert between the metric prefixes of giga, mega, kilo, milli, micro, nano, and pico.
- The definitions of common, neutral, ground, and chassis are very important to prevent damage to circuits and test instruments, and for the technician's safety.
- Circuit impedances and internal resistance are fundamental concepts that are very important when working within circuitry.
- The servicing technician must be familiar with all of the common schematic symbols and with the most common bipolar transistor lead configurations.
- The method of numbering integrated circuits must be understood to properly identify the pins of these components.
- The common circuits of the bridge and half-wave power supply and of the typical bipolar transistor amplifier should be memorized because they are so common.
- Color code should also be memorized because it makes possible the identification of resistors, capacitors, inductors, and sometimes even circuit wiring.
- Logic troubleshooting requires that the technician be able to accurately tell what inputs are required for a given circuit output.
- The classes of amplifier operation are determined by the transistor biasing used, the understanding of which is important for quick and effective troubleshooting.
- To work effectively, a technician needs a decent work area, test equipment as required for the kind of equipment to be repaired, and a minimum of hand tools.

REVIEW QUESTIONS

1. What class of amplifier operation can be described as "half-on"?
2. What class of operation can be called "turned off" until a signal turns it on?
3. What class of operation can be described as "just barely turned on"?
4. What are the two dangers of wearing metal jewelry?
5. Convert the following:

   1500 kHz = _______ MHz

   .47 MΩ = _______ kilohms

   .0047 μFd = _______ picofarad

   40 μS = _______ nanosecond
6. What is the definition of electrical ground?
7. What is the definition of electrical common?
8. In terms of shorts and opens, which cannot blow a fuse?

9. What is the electrical difference between a large and a small flashlight cell if they both produce 1.5 volts?
10. What is a mockup?
11. If you know where pin #1 of a 16-pin dual in-line plastic (DIP) IC is located, where is #2 pin?
12. Draw from memory the circuit for a "standard" transformer-rectifier power supply, using a bridge rectifier and resistor-capacitor filter.
13. Where can you find color codes for electronic components?
14. A small, resistor-like component has a color coding that begins with a double-width silver band. What is it?
15. A small, resistor-like component has a color coding that begins with a double-width red band. What is it?
16. A 2-watt resistor has a double-width first band. What does this mean?
17. If the output of a NAND gate is low, what are the logic levels on the two inputs?
18. One input of an XOR gate is high, and the other is low. What is the logic output?
19. What determines the kind of test instruments that are required for a given job?
20. A small, resistor-like component has a single black band around it in the middle. What is it?

2

Kinds of Electronic Problems

CHAPTER OBJECTIVES

This chapter familiarizes the technician with the common problems and troubleshooting methods involved with each kind of failure. At the conclusion of this chapter, the student should be able to recognize the failures and troubleshooting methods for the following typical problems:

- Complete failures
- Poor performance
- Tampered equipment
- Intermittents
- Motorboating
- Traumatic failures
- Transients
- Overheated parts
- Hum
- Distortion
- Microphonics
- Noisy controls
- Operator-induced problems

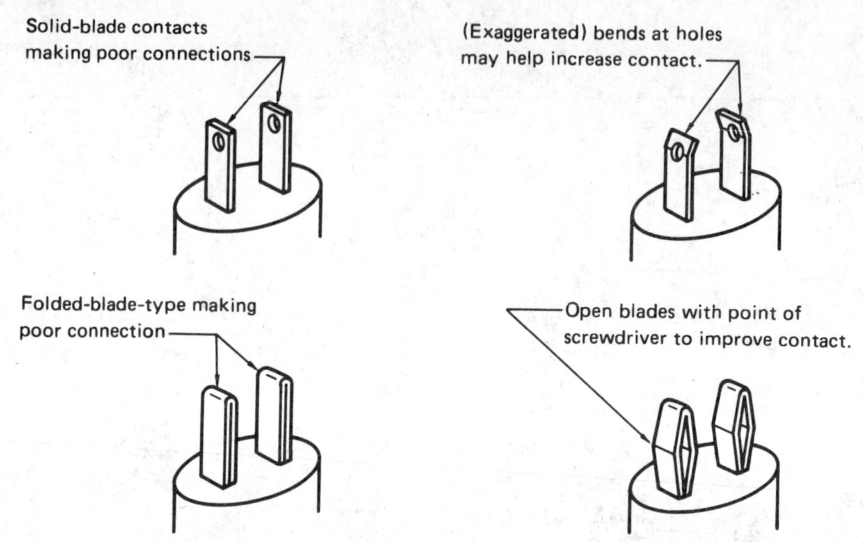
Solid-blade contacts
making poor connections
(Exaggerated) bends at holes
may help increase contact.
Folded-blade-type making
poor connection
Open blades with point of
screwdriver to improve contact.

Figure 2–1 Poor contacts at the wall socket can sometimes be improved.

2.1 COMPLETE FAILURES

A complete failure is the easiest problem to correct. If everything is completely inoperative—panel lights, light emitting diodes (LEDs), meter, and all other indications, it might suggest that you forgot to pay the electric bill. Almost anyone could begin to troubleshoot this problem. Be sure the plug is in the wall, the fuses are good, and the circuit breakers are closed.

After this initial check, a technician should usually check the power supply for proper output voltages. Sometimes a poor connection at the wall socket is responsible. This can often be temporarily cured by spreading apart the tabs of the plug, by putting a small amount of "dogleg" in them, or by spreading apart the layers of some tabs. If this is necessary, replacing the outlet is the best cure. See Figure 2–1.

2.2 POOR PERFORMANCE

Poor performance of equipment is usually a more difficult problem to solve than a complete failure. It generally becomes even more difficult if the performance is only slightly degraded and approaches normal operation. For example, it is much more difficult to discover why a radio receiver is only slightly weak in receiving signals than to find the cause of a completely dead receiver.

Poor performance is best compared against the specifications for the equipment. Since *poor performance* is a term usually associated with RF equipment more than other kinds, this problem is dealt with specifically in Chapter 13.

2.3 TAMPERED EQUIPMENT

Some people are just naturally curious. They like to look inside their equipment. There is no problem with just looking, but the trouble starts when a curious, unqualified person begins to think it might be possible to squeeze just a bit more performance from a piece of equipment by "touching up" some of the adjustments inside. The chances are very good that such efforts will be rewarded with the exact opposite result. By the time a technician gets the equipment, it may be completely inoperative. Rare indeed is the person who will attach a note confessing to the deed of tinkering!

The servicing technician should watch for tell-tale signs of tampering like chipped or cracked RF transformer tuning slugs or broken paint seals on them or on other adjustable components, such as internal adjustable resistors. These signs may indicate that a realignment of the equipment will be required to get it back to the manufacturer's specifications.

2.4 INTERMITTENTS

The key to repairing any kind of intermittent problem is to be able to *make the equipment stay inoperative long enough* to pinpoint the cause. There is little to be gained by working on an intermittent problem when the failed symptoms will not appear.

THE MECHANICAL INTERMITTENT

Have you ever seen a television set that quit working, only to respond favorably to a solid thump on the cabinet? This is called a mechanical intermittent because it responds to a mechanical thump. It is possible to narrow down the problem to the defective component in most cases by very carefully noting, first, the general area of the equipment, and then the printed circuit board (PC board) that is most sensitive to applied mechanical stress. Take special note of the direction of flexing and the amount of force required to produce the problem when tracing the mechanical intermittent. As you approach the exact location of the problem, the amount of force necessary to cause the symptoms will decrease.

Circuit boards with SMDs (surface-mounted devices) should never be flexed because of the likely damage that would be caused. The ends of these tiny components can be broken loose or the components themselves can be fractured.

The mechanical intermittent may respond to pulling and pushing the wiring as it enters plugs and jacks or to cleaning the plug contacts. Printed circuit boards are subject to excessive mechanical stresses by the kind of connector that mounts directly on the PC board. Many of these connectors depend on the traces of the board for support. Indeed, some of these connectors depend entirely on the circuit traces for mounting. Pushing and pulling on these connectors can easily cause a hairline break in the board traces where they attach. This is a particularly good area to inspect visually, using a magnifying glass. *Gently* stressing the connector back and forth can sometimes make a break easier to see.

Some plugs are prone to breaking contact between mating surfaces. These contacts can sometimes be resprung so that their mating surfaces fit tightly together again. The methods of bending to restore normal tension in the contacts will be left to the common sense of the technician, as there are many different types of connectors. A soft eraser makes a very good abrasive with which to clean contacts, especially the edge connectors on a printed circuit board.

THE THERMAL INTERMITTENT

The principal characteristic of a thermal intermittent problem is that the problem usually occurs after the equipment has been operated for some time. If turned off for a time, the problem will be gone when the power is again applied. This thermal cycling can be simulated by the application of heat and/or cold in an effort to produce the problem symptoms. By selectively directing the heat or cold to progressively smaller areas of the equipment or board, it should eventually be possible to isolate the defective component. Wide area cooling may done using a commercial aerosol product specifically manufactured for this purpose. See Figure 2–2.

Figure 2–2 An aerosol product designed to help track down thermal intermittents.

Heating should be done with a heat gun or possibly a hair dryer. As the temperature-sensitive area is selectively narrowed, the tip of a small soldering iron can be used to heat individual components. Be very careful when using an iron near plastic parts and components.

Cooling agents for use on circuits having surface-mounted devices (SMDs) should be marked as being "antistatic." Cooling of SMD circuits should be done carefully. Use a bare minimum of cooling because of the thermal expansion and contraction that will result. Expansion and contraction can easily damage these tiny components.

THE ERRATIC INTERMITTENT

The erratic intermittent is perhaps the most difficult electronic problem to repair. The symptoms seem somehow to disappear when the technician appears on the scene. The erratic equipment will not respond to normal changes in heat or cold, nor to thumping the equipment. It is simply there sometimes and gone at others. The erratic intermittent is the source of many customer disputes. The customer may assume that the technician cannot find the problem because of incompetence, and the technician may wonder if there really *is* a problem or if the customer is imagining it. Even if the technician believes the customer, the former can often only make an educated guess and replace a card or other likely cause of the problem in view of the customer's description of the symptoms. Automotive dealerships commonly use this approach on intermittent problems, leaving the customer with an inflated bill as a result.

Techniques to finding an erratic problem include:

1. Operate the equipment at full ratings (as appropriate for the piece in question) for long periods of time under a watchful eye;
2. Place the equipment in an enclosure designed to subject it to higher- or lower-than-normal temperatures; or
3. Apply higher- or lower-than-normal supply voltages to the equipment.

Each of these techniques is explained as follows.

Operating the Equipment at Full Ratings for Long Periods

Equipment suspected of having an erratic intermittent should be tested for extended periods of time as a first try in making the symptoms appear. If the technician cannot afford to spend time just watching the equipment, put it aside in full operation. Work can proceed on other projects, checking the suspect equipment now and then for the failure. It may even be necessary to leave the equipment on overnight to coax the problem to appear.

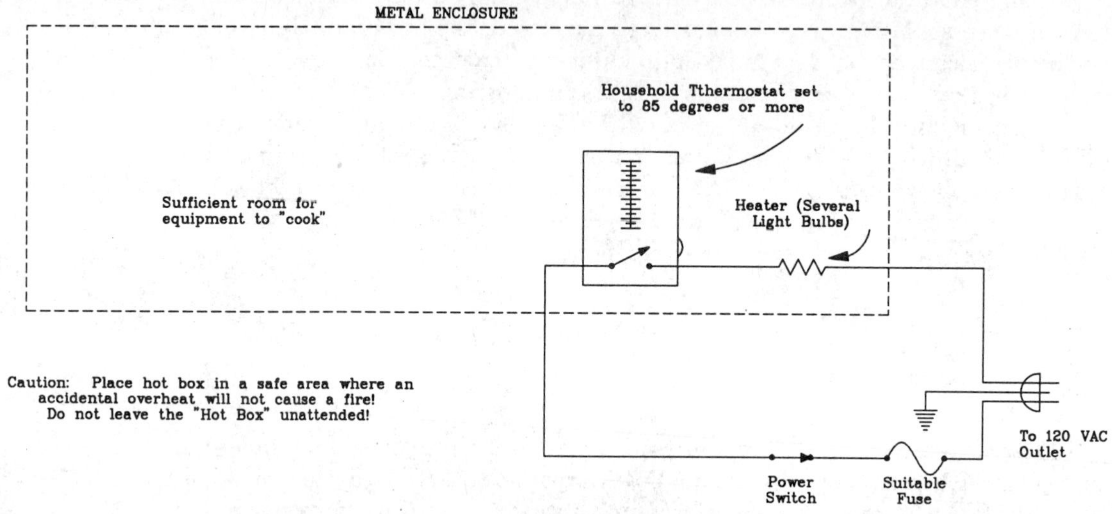

Figure 2–3 An idea for a "hot-box," an aid in identifying an erratic intermittent.

Subjecting the Equipment to Abnormally High or Low Temperatures

If extended operation does not cause the problem to appear, the next step might be to heat the equipment to higher-than-normal temperatures and see if that causes it to fail. Temperatures up to 150 degrees Fahrenheit can be encountered in real-life locations on a hot day, and such conditions may exist on the customer's site.

A "hot-box" can be constructed from inexpensive scrap material. This box will heat equipment placed within it to high temperatures and may make the problem occur if it is due to a component that is failing only at these higher temperatures. See Figure 2–3 for suggestions for wiring the hot-box.

A similar approach can be taken by placing the equipment in a refrigerator, or, in extreme cases, a freezer.

Applying Higher- or Lower-than-Normal Input Voltages

The final attempt at making an erratic intermittent appear may be the application of slightly higher- or lower-than-normal supply voltages. This must be done with great care to prevent doing any additional damage. Some components such as integrated circuits will not tolerate overvoltage without sustaining permanent damage. TTL digital chips, for instance, cannot sustain more than 5 percent over- or undervoltage without damage or circuit failure due to "glitches." Figure 2–4 shows the circuitry for a

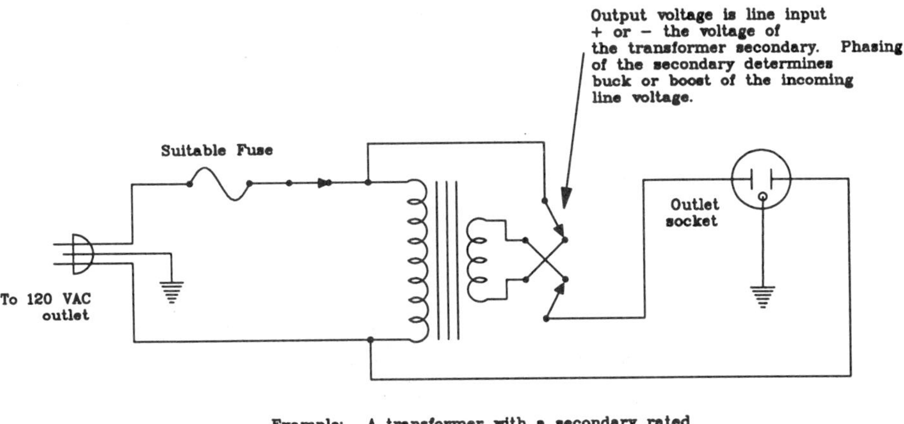
Output voltage is line input
+ or − the voltage of
the transformer secondary. Phasing
of the secondary determines
buck or boost of the incoming
line voltage.
Suitable Fuse
Outlet
socket
To 120 VAC
outlet
Example: A transformer with a secondary rated
at 12 VAC, 3 Amperes will provide
either 132 VAC at 3 amperes or
108 VAC at 3 amperes.

Figure 2–4 Normal AC line voltage can be boosted or bucked by the voltage of the secondary of a transformer.

simple over- or undervoltage source suitable for use on equipment that operates from 120-V AC.

Other Things to Check

High-impedance CMOS circuits, FET gates, and vacuum-tube grid circuits are subject to erratic behavior if an input is disconnected for any reason. A break in a circuit board can produce such an open, which will behave very erratically. Be aware of this unique possibility when looking for the cause of an erratic intermittent in these high-impedance circuits.

In digital circuits, a voltage level that is between the "on" and "off" levels can cause intermittent symptoms that will be erratic in nature. This can happen when two digital outputs are inadvertently connected together, resulting in a situation in which each attempts to take a different logic level. *Bus contention,* as this is called, can occur when a circuit failure causes the two chips to be enabled at the same time. This problem can sometimes be detected with the help of an oscilloscope.

If an intermittent is general in nature (i.e., all parts of the circuitry or equipment seem to be affected), the power supply is a likely suspect and should be given a detailed investigation. See Chapters 6 and 7.

If all attempts to correct an erratic intermittent fail, it will be necessary to give the equipment back to the customer with an explanation of the situation and ask to be called if the problem recurs.

Another tip that may prove helpful is to use the digital meter shown in Figure 5–4, the Fluke 87. This meter will monitor power-line voltage over long periods, recording the root mean square (RMS) voltage as sampled over a selectable period of time of 100 milliseconds or a full second. The maximum and minimum voltages that occur will be recorded, making them available for inspection at any time.

2.5 MOTORBOATING

Motorboating describes the "plup-plup-plup" sound that sometimes occurs when the batteries in a radio become weak or the electrolytic capacitors in a 120-V AC power supply filter dries out and ceases to filter effectively. If the situation is extreme, the oscillation can manifest as a squeal instead of a low-frequency plupping sound.

The technical reason for motorboating is that the final amplifier stage of the audio amplifier is loading the power supply down and the filter or batteries are unable to maintain the proper voltage for the very short period of time required until the audio waveform changes polarity. When the power supply cannot maintain the voltage, there is a feedback path for audio frequencies through the power supply that can enter earlier audio stages, resulting in oscillation. Oscillations are particularly likely at high settings of the volume control.

The cure for a motorboating problem is to replace either the filter capacitors that are not doing their job or the battery, which may have developed too much internal resistance.

2.6 TRAUMATIC FAILURES

Traumatic failures are the result of accidents that cause more than just one or two components to fail, such as:

FIRE OR SMOKE DAMAGE

A close visual inspection of the equipment will determine if it is economical to put it back into service. If plastic parts of the equipment are melted or burned off, it is best to let the insurance company pay off the equipment, wasting no further effort on its repair. If there is no evidence of excessive heat, then the equipment may be only smoke-damaged and may possibly be worth an effort to return it to service. The approach to use is to begin testing the equipment by replacing any obviously damaged parts, and then applying power and watching for any unusual indication. The use of a "soft fuse," as described in Chapter 6, may also be a good idea at this point.

PRIMARY DC POLARITY REVERSAL

For the purposes of this explanation, assume that the DC primary voltage is 12 V, though it could be 6, 24, 48, or any voltage specified by the

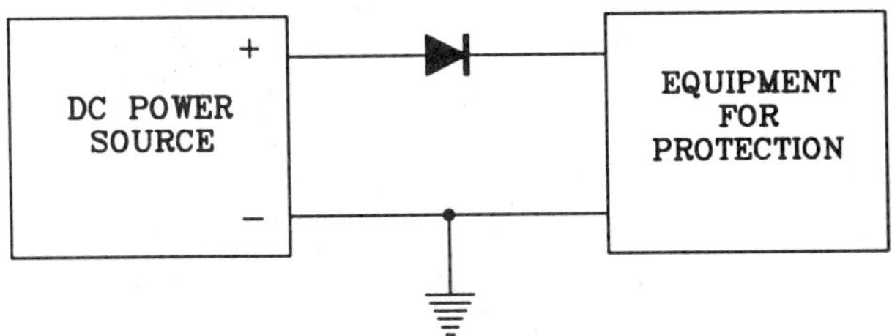

Diode passes only correct polarity on to equipment. This method reduces the available voltage for the equipment by about 0.7 volt.

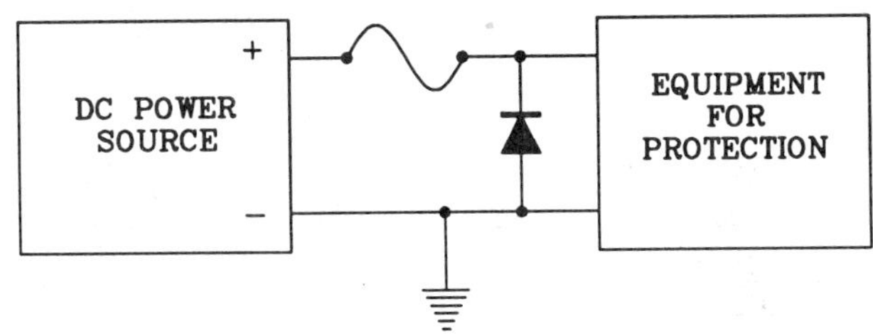

While open for normal polarity input voltage, the diode will conduct and blow the fuse if input polarity is reversed.

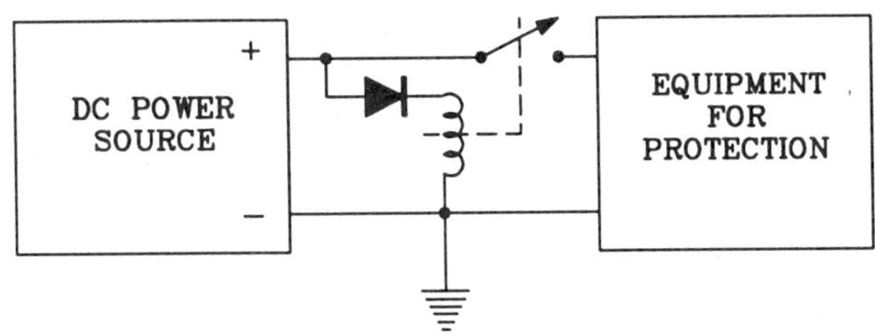

Input polarity must be correct for relay to be energized and pass full power to the equipment

Figure 2–5 Typical protection circuits for the accidental reversal of input polarity.

manufacturer. Accidental reversal of the 12-V input to equipment will probably not harm it *if* the circuit has built-in protection to guard against the possibility. There are three common ways to protect equipment from accidental input polarity reversal, as shown in Figure 2–5.

It is a simple matter to add one of these circuits to existing equipment if there is a chance that the input polarity could be accidentally reversed.

If the shunt diode of Figure 2–5 is not also used with a properly rated fuse (an external in-line fuse is common, which could be accidentally omitted), the application of reversed polarity could burn open the protection diode and thereby subject the entire equipment to the uninhibited rush of reversed current. Extensive damage could be expected in this case.

Circuits without reverse-current protection can suffer greatly from a current flow in the wrong direction. The following components are most susceptible to reverse current damage: electrolytic capacitors, diodes, transistors of any type, and all ICs of any type, including regulators. Every one of these components should be tested for damage. Simple testing for shorted and opened components is not sufficient, as there may be internal damage that will not show during DC voltage testing, as with an ohmmeter. After a mass parts replacement, signal tracing through the circuitry will be the best way to verify operation stage by stage. Be sure to begin troubleshooting with the assumption that the primary input circuit may be shorted and will likely overload the power supply. Chapter 6 gives the techniques to use in applying power to a shorted load.

DROPPED EQUIPMENT

Solid-state equipment is amazingly resistant to damage from dropping as far as the semiconductors are concerned. (Vacuum tubes do not fare so well.) If the equipment is not completely smashed and obviously junk, a simple drop and the resulting lack of operation may not necessarily be as serious as one might think.

Likely problems are that the heavier components have pulled loose from the circuit board, wiring has pulled loose, or the printed circuit board has developed open or intermittent circuits. If there is no extensive mechanical damage, such as binding of mechanical parts, the equipment should be treated as a normal failure and troubleshooting should be done in a routine manner, using signal tracing to find any faults.

WATER IMMERSION

The first thing to do with equipment that has been submerged is to rinse off any damaging salts and contaminants as soon as possible. If the immersion was in salt water, then the equipment should be thoroughly rinsed by submerging and agitating it in warm fresh water. If the original accident involved fresh water or if the equipment has already been rinsed clean of salt, then it may be submerged in a commercial liquid specifically made for the purpose.

Several factors will determine the amount of damage sustained and the feasibility of returning the equipment to service:

1. Did the equipment have power applied during immersion?
2. How long was the equipment submerged?
3. What kind of water was it?
4. What does a close visual inspection reveal?
5. What was the equipment originally worth?
6. With depreciation, what is it worth now?
7. Will any possible future failures as a result of the immersion be tolerable?

The answers to these questions will aid in the owner's final decision whether to attempt repair or scrap the equipment without further investment of a technician's time.

Let us consider each of these items further. The application of power during immersion will cause current flow between portions of the circuit where it does not belong. The resulting corrosion can have a ruinous effect. Current flow within liquids causes the migration of metal molecules from one point to another in great quantities. (This principle is used in electroplating.) It can render equipment useless by completely erasing printed circuit traces. The amount of damage increases with immersion time or if the liquid is salt rather than fresh water. Pure water is a good insulator and will not cause the extensive damage that salt water will. A close visual inspection may show corrosion damage or other problems, such as rusted transistor leads. Leads can rust completely off the board in severe cases. Remember that this kind of deterioration may take place under components where it cannot be seen.

A decision will have to be made whether to proceed with repairs based upon the technician's findings. It is best to set water-damaged equipment aside after further damage has been halted and await the decision of the owner and the insurance company. They will take into account the original value of the equipment and its depreciation value. This decision should also consider the acceptability of probable future unreliability.

APPLICATION OF OVERVOLTAGE IN THE WRONG PLACE

When a technician is using a probe or any metal tool within equipment while it is in operation, there is a risk of shorting a pair of IC pins or printed circuit traces together. Often this does no damage, but once in a while, the wrong combination occurs and, in a few milliseconds, a great deal of damage is done. As a simple precautionary measure, the technician should not use anything to probe into live circuitry other than a test probe designed for the job. A good probe will be needle-sharp at the tip and very small in diameter. Ideally, it should be small enough that it will not short IC pins together if placed directly between them.

If the equipment suddenly emits a strange noise, smokes, or otherwise ceases operation after the technician has "slipped," there is a very good chance that a big job will lie ahead just to get back to the original problem. A slip of a tool like this can cause a string of many ICs to fail instantly. TTL ICs, for example, will not tolerate 12-V DC applied to them without permanent damage. A slip from input to output pins of a regulator, for instance, can result in this happening. Be careful when probing in live circuits!

Investigation into the problems caused by such an accident should begin by noting exactly where the overvoltage was applied, if this is possible to determine. Carefully note the points that were shorted together on the schematic diagram and then determine which components would most likely be damaged as a result. These components will usually be ICs, regulators, and electrolytic capacitors. Other components are more tolerant of such accidents. If, by chance, the accidental voltage applied is reversed from normal, one can expect the results previously discussed in the section titled "Primary DC Polarity Reversal."

LIGHTNING DAMAGE

Equipment on the receiving end of a lightning strike or near-strike should generally be written off as an act of God and replacements should be procured. The amount of damage caused by lightning has to be seen to be believed. Seldom can the many hours of technician time required to place equipment back in operation be justified. Partially operative equipment from the vicinity of a strike may be evaluated as covered in the following topic.

2.7 TRANSIENTS

The transients that cause failures of electronic equipment are actually voltage "spikes" on the primary power line. These spikes are high-voltage pulses that can cause failures of filter capacitors, semiconductors, insulation in transformers, and components farther into the circuitry from the power source.

Transients are common in mobile installations. The normal operation of the starter motor on a vehicle can cause great amplitudes of spikes on the 12-V wiring, which are often sufficient to damage semiconductor equipment. For this reason, any equipment that contains semiconductors must be turned off while cranking the engine. Turning off equipment isolates it from potentially damaging transients.

Typical equipment failures that may point to possible transient damage as the cause include shorted silicon-controlled rectifiers (SCRs), rectifier diodes, and diode bridges. Most well-designed solid-state equipment operated from AC power lines will include one form or another of transient suppression. Transient suppression components should be tested for proper operation if other semiconductors have failed in the circuit and might have been caused to fail by transients. This may indicate that the suppressors could be open or otherwise not performing their intended function. Figure 2–6 shows two methods of suppressing transients and Figure 2–7 shows the most common suppression components, metal oxide varistors (MOVs).

The digital multimeter shown in Figure 5–4 has a special function which may be of help in detecting transients on the power line. When placed in the Peak "Record" mode, the Fluke 87 will "remember" the highest positive and negative voltages (of more than one millisecond duration) that may occur. These values can then be read at any time. The instrument even "beeps" when a new, higher value is recorded.

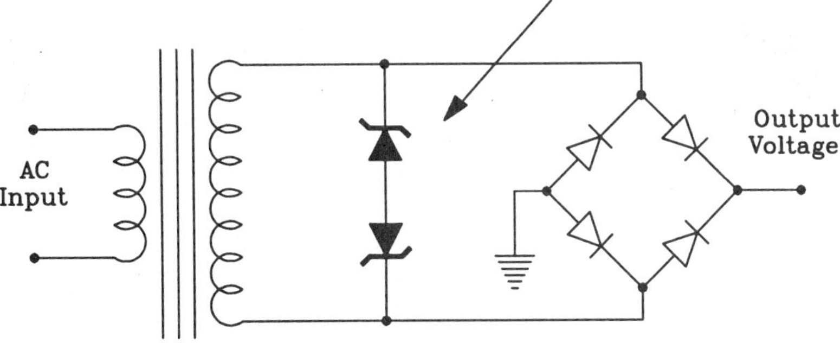
Two zener diodes placed here will protect the circuits and components to the right against voltage transients
Output Voltage
AC Input

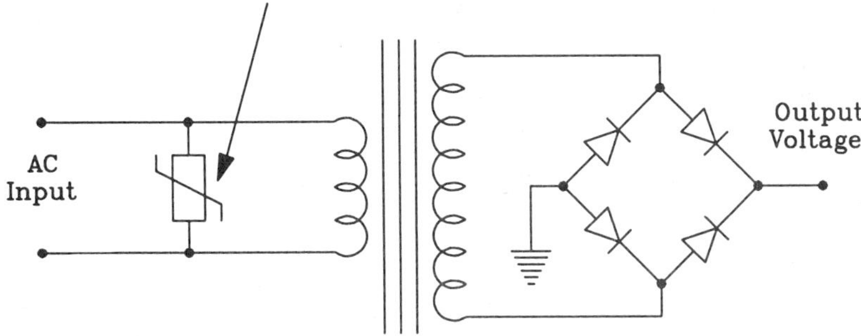
The MOV is a more effective component to protect against voltage transients because of its extremely low internal inductance. This makes it able to clamp extremely short pulses.
Output Voltage
AC Input

Figure 2–6 Common transient-suppression circuits.

2.8 OVERHEATED PARTS FAILURES

Resistors are made to throw off heat. The bigger they are, the more heat they can safely dissipate without overheating and burning up. If hot resistors are mounted directly on a circuit board, they may burn and discolor the board.

Small resistors should not become hot in normal operation. Small resistors are used when the wattage rating is less than about a quarter watt, which is not enough heat to cause any problems with a printed circuit board or nearby wiring. Any small resistor that is burned is almost always

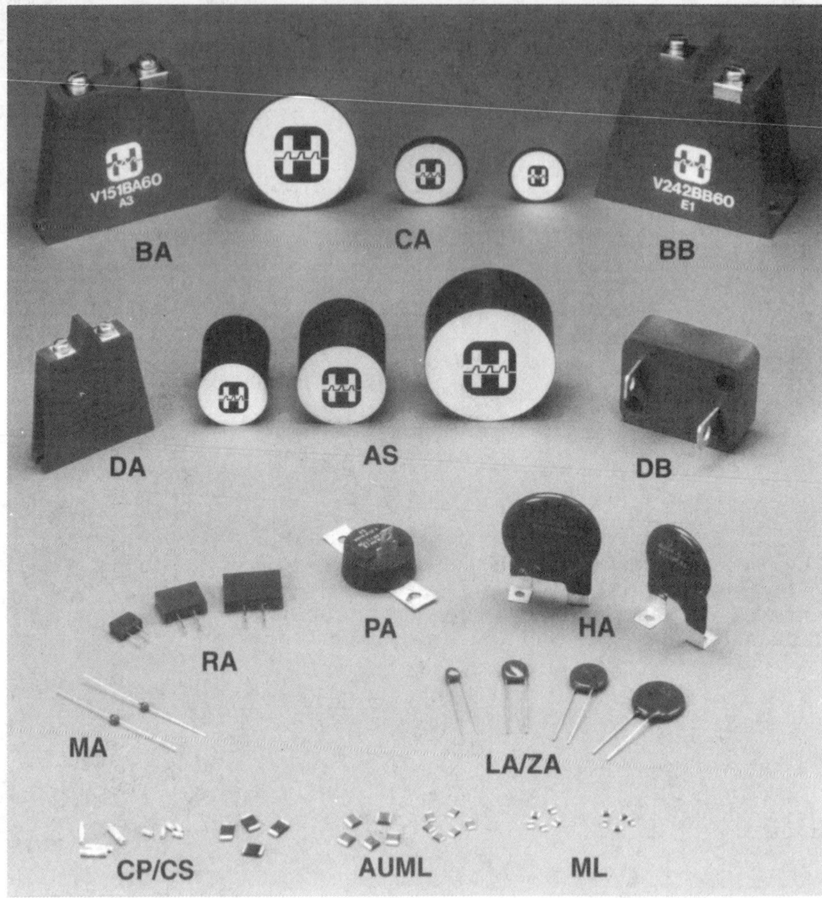

Figure 2–7 Examples of metal oxide varistors used in modern equipment to protect against voltage transients on the power line. (Photo courtesy of Harris Semiconductor.)

caused by the failure of another component. The other component is usually a shorted transistor or an electrolytic capacitor. See Figure 2–8 for a typical failure that will cause a resistor to burn open.

A large carbon composition resistor may produce its own problems. A carbon resistor operated at or near it maximum power rating can change resistance value with time. In some circuits, this effect can accumulate, causing increasing amounts of heat. It is not unusual to find a 10,000 Ω carbon resistor that has decreased to 1,000 Ω or less due to this avalanche effect. These resistors also commonly fail by increasing in resistance or by opening.

Transistors can become hot in normal operation and fail simply because of their own heat. The cause is not always just the transistor. Transistors

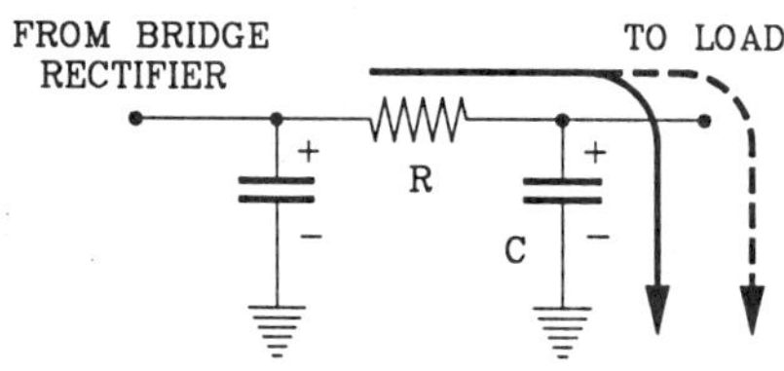
FROM BRIDGE RECTIFIER
TO LOAD
R
C
If C or the load shorts to ground, all of the current capability of the power supply can flow through the filter resistor, burning it up.

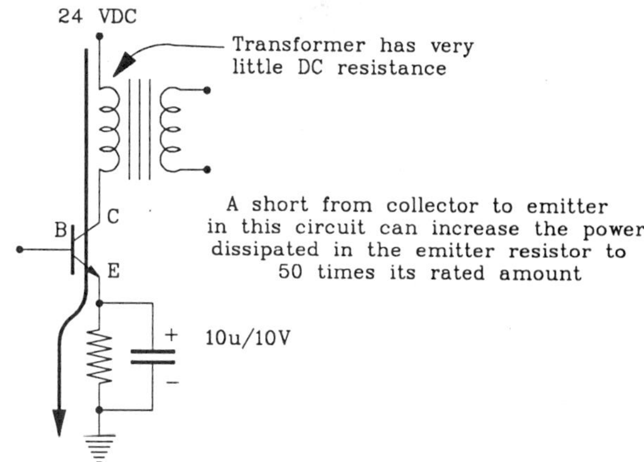
24 VDC
Transformer has very little DC resistance
A short from collector to emitter in this circuit can increase the power dissipated in the emitter resistor to 50 times its rated amount
B
C
E
10u/10V

Figure 2–8 Other components usually cause resistors to fail.

often fail because of defective transistor biasing. Therefore, biasing should always be checked when replacing a defective transistor.

Capacitors should not feel hot. If hot capacitors are not being overheated by nearby components, they are probably very leaky and, thus, defective. When replacing a capacitor, be sure that there is no associated failure causing too much voltage to be applied to that part. For instance, this would be the case if the transistor of Figure 2–8 should develop an emitter-to-collector short.

Burned or overheated wiring should be replaced. Even though the insulation may be intact, it is probably brittle and may flake off later and cause problems by shorting to other circuits.

A burned PC board can usually be repaired. Charred portions of the board accumulate moisture and dirt more easily than clean portions. The charred portion may even be somewhat conductive. Repair consists of the removal of all the burned portion by cutting or filing. The remaining edges of the board should be sealed with lacquer, clear acrylic, or another suitable moisture barrier.

After experiencing the smell of a burned transformer once or twice, a technician will be able to instantly recognize it again and to diagnose such a problem faster, knowing right away that there was excessive current flow through a transformer or inductor.

If you suspect that a component is overheating just slightly, you can get a good idea of its heat by holding your finger on the component for a few moments. If your finger is not sensitive enough, immediately touch that finger to your upper lip, just below your nose. Your lip is extremely sensitive to minute temperature changes.

2.9 HUM PROBLEMS

Hum problems have five general causes:

1. Insufficient filtering of an AC-operated power supply;
2. An overload condition on an AC-operated power supply;
3. Absence of an earth or chassis ground connection where there should be one;
4. Presence of more than one common ground where there should be only one; and
5. An open circuit in a high-gain, high-impedance circuit.

The electrolytic capacitors used in the filters of an AC power supply can dry out with age and lose their capacity to store a charge. This effectively removes them from a circuit and passes on any AC ripple to following stages. The cure is simple: replace the bad capacitors. Testing for this condition is also simple. Since the capacitor is suspected of being open, it is already effectively out of the circuit. Parallel a good capacitor with another one of similar capacitance and voltage rating, directly across the good one. This procedure is called "bridging" the bad capacitor. If the hum disappears, you have verified that the original capacitor is open or nearly so.

An overloaded power supply will have similar hum problems as one with an open filter capacitor. Paralleling the existing filter capacitor with a good one will not cure the problem, although it may diminish the intensity of hum somewhat. Along with this hum problem, an overloaded power supply will probably draw substantially more current than normal. This condition would be signaled by the occasional blowing of the fuse, the overheating of the power transformer, or both. Troubleshooting an overloaded power supply is covered in Chapter 6.

Ground loops may also inject hum signals into a circuit due to the presence of too many grounding points. This sort of problem sometimes occurs in high-gain circuits such as microphone inputs. Grounding the shield on a low-level signal cable at more than one point is one cause of this problem. This sets up a loop circuit that can be very sensitive to magnetic fields such as those near power transformers. See Figure 2–9.

2.10 DISTORTION PROBLEMS

Distortion refers to unwanted changes in a waveform that alter its original shape. Audio waveforms are among those that we wish to have amplified from a source such as a tape player to a load such as a speaker without changing the shape of the waveform along the way. A common distortion that is easily demonstrated occurs when a small transistor radio is turned up too loud. The waveform, as seen on an oscilloscope, will no longer be

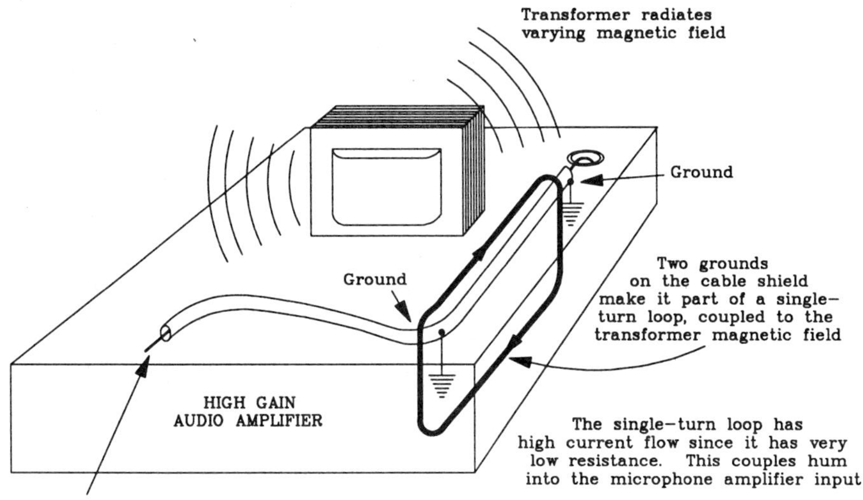
Transformer radiates varying magnetic field
Ground
Ground
Two grounds on the cable shield make it part of a single-turn loop, coupled to the transformer magnetic field
HIGH GAIN AUDIO AMPLIFIER
The single-turn loop has high current flow since it has very low resistance. This couples hum into the microphone amplifier input
Shielded lead to Microphone

Figure 2–9 An example of how two grounds on a shielded cable can produce heavy currents in the shield, thereby introducing hum into the amplifier input.

rounded but will be flattened on the top, bottom, or both, as shown in Figure 2–10.

A distortion analyzer is a precision instrument that analyzes sine waves for harmonic distortion and provides a reading in percentages. Principally used in the design of new circuits, the distortion analyzer is not used for routine troubleshooting. To use an audio distortion analyzer, the source of the sine wave (usually an audio oscillator) is first measured and the percentage of original distortion is noted. Then, the sine wave is applied to the input of the circuit under test and the distortion coming out of the circuit is measured. Since the circuit will always produce at least a little distortion, the percentage indicated on the analyzer will increase. Comparing the two readings, before and after the circuit, provides a measure of the amplifier's quality and an indication as to its condition.

These distortion readings can then be compared to the manufacturer's specifications to determine if the circuit needs repair. This procedure is used only in critical applications such as preventive maintenance of the audio amplifiers used in a broadcast station.

Moderate audio distortion can sometimes be seen on an oscilloscope by a trained eye. Using a pure sine-wave tone with minimal original distortion as an input signal, trace the signal through an amplifier using an oscilloscope and watch for the stage that introduces distortion. Since distortion is usually caused by improper biasing of a transistor, the technician should

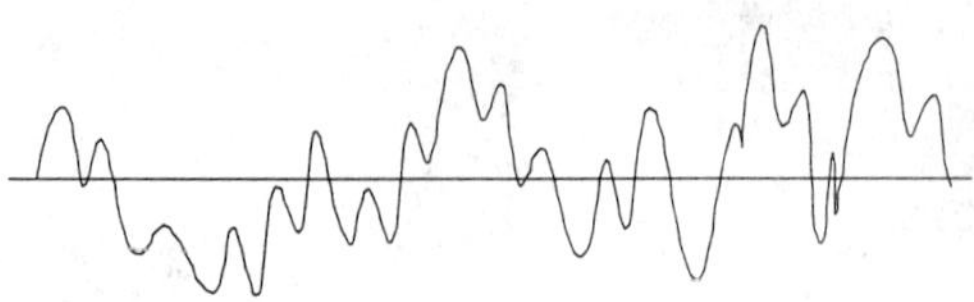

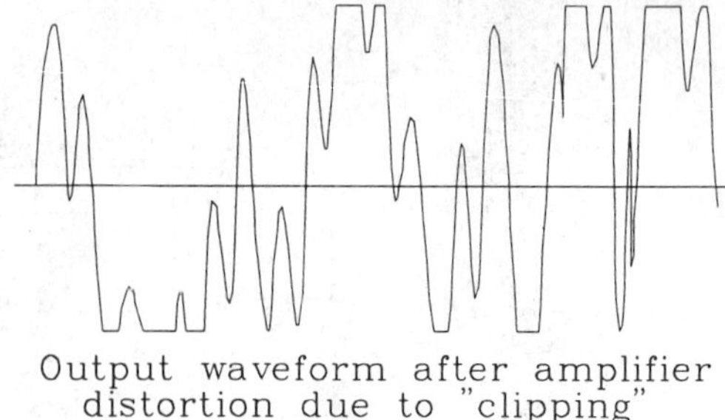

Output waveform after amplifier
distortion due to "clipping"

Figure 2–10 Amplitude distortion due to improper circuit operation.

look for improper bias voltages. One of a pair of balanced or push-pull transistors could also be bad, producing very pronounced distortion.

Distortion of sine waves in radio frequency amplifiers will produce harmonics of the frequency applied to the circuit. In straight-through, large-signal RF amplifier circuits, the amplifying transistor is often operated as Class C. Any harmonic frequency produced at the output of the stage other than the frequency desired is usually filtered out by the inductance and capacitance tuning in the output of the circuit. The production of harmonics is actually encouraged by radio frequency multiplier circuits. Distortion is also deliberately used in RF mixer circuits to produce sum-and-difference frequencies.

Unintentional distortion of RF waveforms in radio power transmitting equipment can cause interference on other radio frequencies, some of which can be quite different from the fundamental frequency of operation. This problem is best detected by using an RF spectrum analyzer. This instrument allows the technician to see the unwanted frequencies along with the desired one. Changes such as retuning are then made to the circuitry to reduce the unwanted frequency strengths to acceptable levels. It is common practice in the design of radio frequency transmitters to include a filter in the output circuits to attenuate (reduce) unwanted frequencies.

2.11 MULTIPLE PROBLEMS

Once a problem has been identified and repaired, it is reasonable to assume that the equipment will work properly when assembled into its cabinet. This is not always the case, however. Once in a while in the course of finding and curing one problem, the technician may be responsible for inadvertently causing another, for instance, by carelessly causing damage to static-sensitive circuits.

The broken wire is probably the most common new problem that a technician can cause. During the opening of equipment and dismantling of circuit boards from the chassis, the wiring takes a considerable punishment. Be careful of internal wiring while dismantling and reassembling equipment. It is a sure indication of a technician-induced problem if the equipment was working fine after the repair but ceased operation when inserted into the cabinet. Watch particularly for pinched wiring that could cause a short to ground or broken wires.

Multiple problems would be responsible if a clearly defective component is discovered and replaced, and yet the equipment still does not work properly after the repair. Perhaps the technician has replaced one of two bad components and neglected to find the second, principal cause of the problem. The new part just installed can be ruined by such a situation. Troubleshooting must continue to find the second problem before reapplying power. If the second problem that is found bears no relationship to the first failure and if there is little, if any, chance that the technician somehow caused the second failure during the troubleshooting procedure, efforts should be made to identify a possible traumatic failure and additional damage. (These problems were discussed earlier in this chapter.)

2.12 MICROPHONICS

A microphonic circuit is one that varies its output in response to being touched or struck because one of the circuit components is acting like a microphone and modulating the output. Microphonics were quite common in the days of the vacuum tube. The elements of a tube were subject to vibration, which would modulate the electron stream on its way through. Special tubes were manufactured to reduce this effect.

The inductors used in some modern radio frequency applications can be microphonic under certain conditions. One such case may occur when an inductor is used in some LC oscillators. This effect can be minimized by firmly anchoring each turn of the coil with an adhesive such as RTV™. Phase-locked radio frequency oscillators may be particularly susceptible to microphonics generated by microscopic physical movement of the inductor.

2.13 NOISY CONTROLS

Noisy controls are probably most noticeable in an audio volume control circuit. Moving the shaft or slider of a volume control can sometimes cause a loud scratching sound in the speakers. The temporary cure for a noisy control is quite easy: using an aerosol product made for this purpose. See Figure 2–11.

Spray the liquid *sparingly* through the tiny tube provided, into the con-

Figure 2–11 This aerosol product will quiet most noisy volume control problems.

trol, onto the inside carbon track against which the slider operates. The best and most permanent cure, however, is to replace the noisy control.

2.14 OPERATOR-INDUCED PROBLEMS

Electronic equipment operators do not always understand equipment controls as well as they should. Wrong assumptions or simple ignorance of how to operate the equipment may play a part in a reported failure. Indeed, the more complicated the equipment, the more likely the operator will mess it up. When equipment works for the technician but the operator is still dissatisfied, it may be time for some tactful schooling in the operation of the controls. Be careful, however, that the problem is not an erratic intermittent which may have the same appearance as an operator's improper adjustment of a control.

The probability of operator error increases by an order of magnitude for computer operators. There are few hardware mistakes to be made on a computer system, but the errors to be made in the use of software are limitless. Chapter 16 addresses this problem in detail.

Examples of operator-induced problems include:

Improper operation of controls (e.g., turning down a monitor's brightness control, forgetting this was done, and then complaining that the monitor doesn't work).

Misinterpreting results (e.g., "I thought the meter read out 'watts,' so I thought my CB set was putting out too much power").

Restricting equipment ventilation (e.g., operating equipment while it is placed on a blanket, thus blocking the vent holes in the bottom).

Physical abuse of equipment (e.g., dropping a microphone on the floor).

Spilling liquids into equipment (e.g., spilling cocoa onto a keyboard).

Tampering with equipment (e.g., adjusting internal variable components).

2.15 THE TOUGH PROBLEMS

Every technician occasionally encounters a problem that defies all efforts to correct it. Nothing seems to go right, and none of the usual procedures help at all. What to do then? Consult this checklist and you may find the solution:

1. Have the batteries of either the equipment under test or the test instruments gone dead? Are the battery connectors clean and making positive contact with the batteries?
2. Check the test equipment test leads and/or RF cables for intermittents or opens that may have occurred since you started troubleshooting.
3. Did you change ranges on some of the equipment under test or the test instruments and forget to change them back?
4. Try substituting known good test instruments for the instruments in current use. A test instrument may have failed. Try the same with the equipment under test: remove the suspected unit and substitute a known good piece of equipment to verify the symptoms you are getting.
5. If you have access to known good equipment of the same type as the defective piece, try comparing readings between good and bad units to help in isolating the problem in the bad one. Apply power to both units and take comparative readings.
6. The problem you are looking for in a circuit with a DC instrument such as a voltmeter or ohmmeter may not be evident from DC readings. It may be a totally unexpected RF problem that will not be indicated by a DC instrument. This principle can apply to low-frequency or audio problems when unintentional RF is present.
7. Get away from the problem for a while. Sometimes you can get become too involved and begin making foolish mistakes.
8. When you go back to a job, consider jotting down notes as you go to assist you in keeping things straight in your mind. This is particularly helpful when you are taking many readings and having trouble trying to remember them.
9. Consider asking the help of another technician. None of us has all the answers, no matter how experienced we may be. You might be overlooking something very simple that another technician could recognize and identify. Describe and talk out your problem with a colleague.
10. Restart your troubleshooting from the beginning. Something may

have changed as you were working that could scramble any logical approach that you are trying to maintain to the problem.

11. Could your manual be wrong? Does it make sense in light of what you know are the basic facts of electronics?
12. Be sure you are using the correct instruction book: Do the listed make, model, year, serial and revisions numbers match the faulty equipment?

CHAPTER SUMMARY

- There are some electronic failures that fit into convenient, easily identified categories: intermittent problems, motorboating, overheated parts, hum, and distortion are examples.
- The competent technician is able to identify these common problems and go directly to their solution.
- Intermittents come in three variations: the mechanical, the thermal, and the erratic.
- The erratic intermittent may respond to over- and undervoltage or to overly high or low temperature.
- The key to troubleshooting an intermittent is to get the trouble symptoms to appear long enough to find the cause of the problem.
- Multiple problems presented by traumatic failures due to fire or water immersion begin with an assessment of the damage.
- Metal oxide varistors (MOVs) protect equipment from power-line voltage transients.
- Distortion problems can be traced with an oscilloscope or a distortion analyzer.
- The solution of operator-induced problems will require that the technician know how to operate the equipment.

REVIEW QUESTIONS

1. If a piece of equipment is inoperative yet plugged into a known good wall outlet with the power switch on, what part of the equipment should be checked?
2. What is the significance of a patch of disturbed paint on an internal adjustment?
3. What is the key to repairing an intermittent?
4. What are the three types of intermittents?
5. What kind of intermittent comes and goes with flexing or bending of the PC board?
6. What kind of intermittent often occurs after equipment is turned on for a few minutes?
7. What two tools or products help locate the problem in question 6?

8. If the intermittent does not occur with flexing of the PC board or after operation for a short while, what type intermittent is present?
9. Name two of the several techniques that might make the intermittent of question 8 occur, thus making a repair possible.
10. What causes motorboating?
11. What is a good indicator of the amount of heat that a piece of equipment has been subjected to during a fire?
12. You notice that there is a high-current diode from the +12–V DC input line to a citizen's band (CB) radio directly to ground. What is the purpose of this diode?
13. Name four kinds of components that are likely to be damaged by the accidental application of reversed DC to the power bus.
14. What must be done first—and quickly—to prevent continuing damage to a portable electronic unit that has been dropped into salt water?
15. Why should a technician always use small-diameter test probe tips, and why should they be sharp?
16. Why should vehicular electronic equipment be turned off while the engine is being cranked by the starter?
17. What is the purpose of an MOV?
18. How many possible causes for unwanted hum are given in the text?
19. How is an audio distortion analyzer used?
20. You find that an inexpensive communications receiver seems to "wobble" in frequency when the case is tapped. This means that one of the internal components is _______.
21. The volume control on your television is very scratchy-sounding when you change its setting. What is a good temporary cure?
22. An old friend of yours, perhaps 70 years old, says he cannot seem to get proper operation from the new ham radio he just purchased. What is the likely problem?
23. You just cannot seem to find the problem you have been working on for the last three hours. The readings you have taken do not seem consistent with the problem at hand. What can you do to try to get back on track?

3

System Troubleshooting

CHAPTER OBJECTIVES

An electronic system is loosely defined, for the purpose of this chapter, as one that is made up of individual, interconnected equipments. One example of a system is shown in Figure 3–1; a radar system, it includes a transmitter, an antenna, a receiver, and an indicator unit. This chapter provides a generic summary of the things to watch for, methods to use, and guidance in finding the bad equipment within any electronic system. It covers the actions required of a technician to respond to a trouble report involving a large electronic system, whatever the system might be. Step-by-step procedures are explained to effectively:

- Learn the overall electronic system.
- Get all the details on the reported failure.
- Use installed indicators in a system to localize a problem.
- Use system signal levels as a troubleshooting method.
- Look first for a simple cure.
- Use substitution as a troubleshooting method at the system level.
- Test wire bundles and coaxial cables.
- Test for normal operation after the system has been repaired.

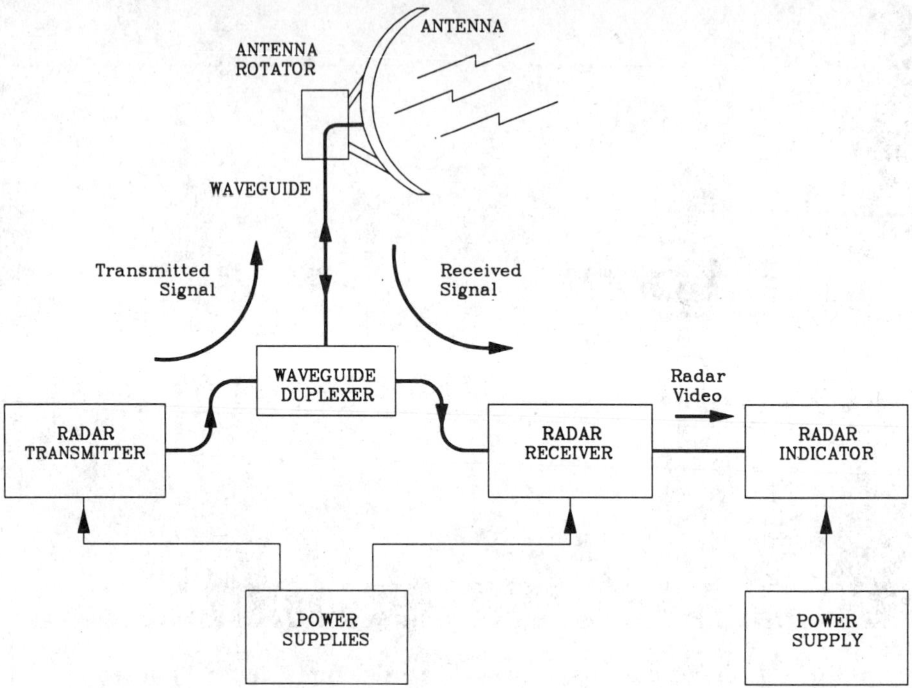

Figure 3–1 Sample block diagram of a radar system.

3.1 THE LOGICAL STEPS OF SYSTEM TROUBLESHOOTING

SYSTEM ORIENTATION

The servicing technician cannot be expected to troubleshoot a system without an overall knowledge of what the system does and how it works. It is putting the cart before the horse to accept a trouble report and only then have to learn how the system works on a panic basis. Knowledge of the system should be acquired before attempting any troubleshooting. Realizing this, most businesses allow a break-in period before putting new technicians on their own. This period of training should be spent studying the system fundamentals, with particular emphasis on learning the system block diagram.

INTEGRATED TEST SYSTEMS

A computer can continuously look for, identify, and locate problems. When a computer is built into a system for troubleshooting purposes it is

Figure 3–2 This telephone switching station uses a computer to automatically and continually test the equipment. (Photo courtesy of GTE.)

called an integrated test system. An example of this kind of troubleshooting is the computer integrated test system used at some telephone exchanges. The computer scans the telephone lines for problems such as shorts and excessive leakage, and then identifies the problem and the affected line. A summary of problems is then printed out on a printer so maintenance personnel can be dispatched.

Integrated test systems can efficiently "patrol" multitudes of complex circuitry such as that shown in Figure 3–2.

The cards within the racks of Figure 3–2 can be individually tested by commands entered at a maintenance and administrative position using a computer and keyboard. An operator trained in the equipment and with a knowledge of how telephone circuits work can make many tests and inquiries about the system status using only the keyboard. Audio levels can be checked, either in the switching station or to the outside world. Direct readout in decibels is available for any circuit that the operator chooses. Defective cards are simply removed from the system, a substitute card is inserted, and the system is back in normal operation. The defective card is sent to the factory, where automated test equipment quickly zeros in on the bad component.

THE SYSTEM BLOCK DIAGRAM

The block diagram of a system shows how signals are handled and indicates their route through the system. Finding where the good signals go into equipments within the system and where they fail to come out properly identifies the bad equipment within the system. In order to understand the symptoms that a particular problem might exhibit with a given failure, the block diagram of the system must be understood and analyzed. Block diagrams should be included in the system documentation. Such diagrams should be committed to memory for the technician to efficiently troubleshoot with a minimum of wasted time during a failure situation. Block diagrams usually do not show the presence or interconnection of power supplies. The servicing technician must keep in mind that the power supplies are connected to the various blocks of the system and that failure of an equipment is often a failure of the power supply circuitry feeding it.

TROUBLESHOOTING CHARTS

Some instruction manuals feature troubleshooting charts of either the tabular or the flowchart type. The tabular type is shown in Figure 3–3.

In either case, these charts are intended to help the technician who is new to the system or equipment in question. Troubleshooting charts cannot cover all of the possible problems that might occur, of course, but in some cases, they can help track down a problem to a smaller area of consideration. The use of the troubleshooting charts can also confuse a technician, however, particularly if the block diagram of the system is not understood. Add to this the fact that some manufacturers invent new names for various special circuits or parts used in the system, and the confusion increases. In summary, the troubleshooting charts have limited use, and then only for new technicians. A thorough knowledge of the system and how it works will quickly eliminate the need for these charts.

GET ALL THE DETAILS

It is a very good idea to speak with the person making the initial trouble report, whether it was verbal or written. Additional facts about the failure may come to light, which can save a great deal of time.

To illustrate this point, consider the example of an aircraft that uses the microphone both for the communications transmitter and for intercommunication with the copilot. The initial report may have indicated that "the transmitter wasn't modulating." Without interviewing the pilot making the report, it might be assumed that the transmitter was defective. Upon closer questioning, however, it might be revealed that the microphone does not work on the intercom circuit either, and therefore, the technician would direct efforts to the likelihood that the microphone or the mike cord was the problem, rather than searching within the transmitter. Note that although the initial report was honest, it was potentially misleading.

VERIFY THE PROBLEM

With an overall block diagram of how the system works, the technician will be ready to begin eliminating the various blocks within the system as probable causes of a system malfunction.

POWER

SYMPTOMS	PROPOSED CHECKS
1. Printer is completely inactive when the power switch is set to the ON position.	a. Check line voltage and power cord for proper connection. b. Check for blown fuse (F1). c. Check for defective power switch. d. Test for defective components in +5VDC power circuit (BR1, VR4, capacitors).
2. Power LED on front panel illuminates, but printhead does not move to home position. (This symptom can also indicate a problem with logic or hardware; refer to CARRIAGE MOTION of this section.	a. Check for +24VDC at the output of transistor Q3 in power supply.
3. Printer operates in self test, serial interface will not function.	a. Check for +12VDC at the output of VR2.

CARRIAGE MOTION

1. Power LED on front panel comes on, carriage does not move to home position.	a. +24VDC not enabled via 24EN by microprocessor (defect on PCB).
2. Power LED on front panel illuminates, carriage does not move to home position and fault LED blinks.	a. Carriage drive cable disconnected. b. Obstruction in carriage path. c. Carriage motor winding open. d. Defective carriage motor drive components on PCB.
3. Carriage stops during print operations or: Carriage slews to home and re-initializes during print operations or: Unusual or excessive noise during print operations. including print head hitting sides of print mech with excessive force. or: Characters not vertically aligned (every other line offset).	a. Duty Cycle on phasing circuits out of adjustment. b. Excessive slack in carriage drive cable.

Figure 3–3 An example of a tabular troubleshooting chart. (Figure courtesy of Mannesmann Talley.)

There are two ways to observe the problem: by watching the operator demonstrate it or by the technician personally operating the equipment. Depending upon the results of testing, the technician should get an indication of where the problem lies and which direction to go to further identify it.

As an example, using Figure 3–1, assume that a radar operator has reported that there are no targets on the radar indicator scope. Finding that the operator has several years of experience, this pretty well rules out the possibility of operator error. Since the report says that no targets are present at all, it cannot be a simple matter of faulty judgment on the operator's part. It would be logical at this point for the technician to be sure that primary power is applied to the entire system, and then to verify the symptoms personally. After verifying that the indicator scope has been operated properly since the front panel controls of the scope were properly set, the technician would next, logically, check the radar receiver unit.

OPERATOR PROBLEMS

Once the details of the report have been filled in, the next step in investigating the problem is to see if the operator manipulated the equipment in the correct manner. Unless he or she is thoroughly familiar with the equipment, the possibility of operator error should be considered. This possibility increases along with the complexity of the system. If practical, the technician should ask the operator to demonstrate the problem. The technician should then allow the operator to manipulate all of the controls while watching for errors or missed steps. To do this effectively, the technician must, therefore, be very familiar with the system, its controls, and how it operates.

A related problem that may confuse the technician occurs when the operator reports a failure that is a matter of judgment rather than a definite problem. Technicians often see trouble reports based on subjective, personal opinions rather than a concrete failure. An example of this is a report that the communications receiver audio output is weak. What is meant by weak? It is a matter of judgment? Perhaps the operator is comparing the present level of audio output with previous levels or with the operation of similar equipment somewhere else. The technician should attempt to verify the reported problem before dismantling the equipment or making any other rash moves.

Another example of a subjective report is one involving a reportedly inoperative aircraft radio transmitter. It is a good idea to quiz the operator as to the frequency that was used, the transmitter location at the time of the supposed failure (airplanes cannot communicate beyond the horizon on very high frequencies (VHF), for instance) and to whom the transmission was directed. It may be entirely possible that there is nothing at all wrong with the transmitter. Some of the reasons why a transmission was not heard are that the receiving equipment was turned off or is defective, the receiving operator stepped out for a minute, or the receiver was set to the wrong frequency. Radio-wave propagation characteristics and the locations of the transmitter and the receiver may be such that communication was unlikely or simply not possible. (There is also the possibility that the receiving operator did not want to hear the transmission.)

USING SYSTEM INDICATORS

Often a system, and sometimes individual equipments, will have system indicators that are of primary importance when tracking problems. On the system level, indicators such as indicator lights or LEDs, installed meters, or cathode-ray tube (CRT) displays provide information that is valuable when troubleshooting. For example, the audio level meters located throughout a broadcasting station provide immediate readout of the presence or absence of audio, which is very useful when time is important in finding an amplifier that has failed. Television stations accomplish a similar purpose when they install TV monitors at selected points in the signal path to the transmitter.

On the equipment level, a single meter may be used, along with a selector switch installed in the equipment, so that one of several key locations in the equipment can be monitored. As an alternative, the meter may be replaced with a metering jack, a connection for an external meter to be attached during troubleshooting.

SIGNAL LEVELS AS SYSTEM OPERATION INDICATORS

Audio voltages in large systems such as those of a telephone company are checked by comparing audio power *levels* to a standard level. Rather than stating the absolute amplitude of signals in average or RMS voltages, it is customary to refer to them as power levels. A level is a reading of power expressed in decibels (dBm) up or down from (more or less than) an understood reference level. The standard power level used in telephone systems is 1 milliwatt dissipated from a 600 Ω resistor. All levels of power are expressed in dBm from this level. The *m* in dBm signifies the 1 milliwatt of reference power and the 600 Ω circuit impedance as the standard level.

If a VOM is calibrated in dBm, it will be calibrated based upon this standard level. When measuring the voltage across a normal 600 Ω load, the scale may be read directly in decibels. Higher voltages may require switching to a higher AC voltage range, in which a specific number of decibels must be added to the indicated decibels under the needle. The factor to add to the meter reading is usually printed on the face of the VOM as a small table.

At least one meter is available in digital format to display dBm levels

Figure 3–4 This meter reads decibels directly, over a range of +59 dBm to –50 dBm. (Reproduced with permission from the John Fluke Mfg. Co., Inc.)

directly. Fluke Instruments offers the model 8060A (Figure 3–4). This instrument will read audio voltages and show their power levels relative to the 600 Ω one-milliwatt standard reference. It has a range of from –50 dBm to +59 dBm. It can also be programmed for different impedances and can be used to perform comparisons between power levels.

Audio levels in a system using a standard impedance will require that the technician give due consideration to the impedance connected at the point of measurement. If the audio line is properly terminated, there will be a resistor connected as a load on the audio line. The technician simply applies the leads of the meter and reads the audio level across that load. The readings taken in this manner will be accurate. If, on the other hand, there is no terminating resistance, one must be provided or the voltage reading will be too high. In the case of a terminating resistor that has already been installed, the voltage would be too low if a second terminating resistance were to be connected to the audio line. Whether to use a terminating resistor on a line is a matter of great importance in obtaining a valid level reading. See Figure 3–5.

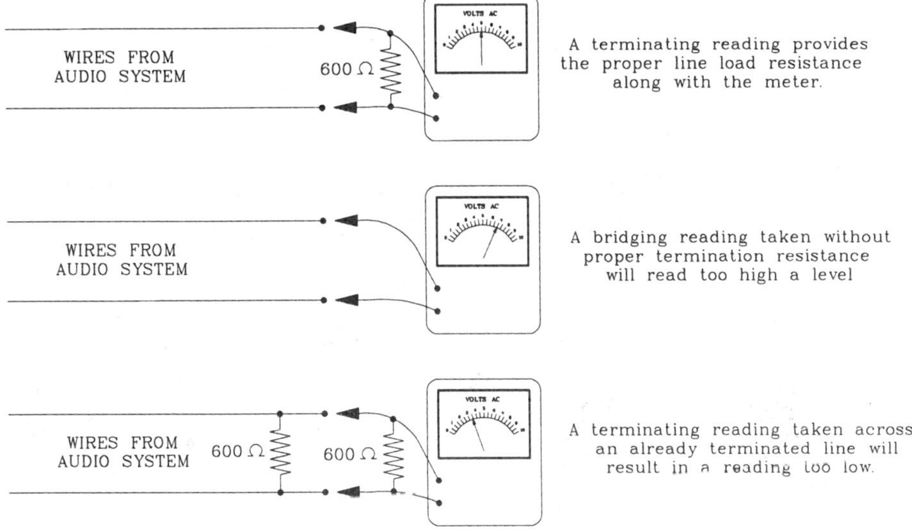

Figure 3–5 Bridging and terminating audio level tests.

3.2 LOOK FOR THE EASY CURES FIRST

It is embarrassing and a waste of time to jump into a problem by dismantling equipment, tracing the signal, or performing other involved troubleshooting, only to find that the fuse on the unit was blown, a cable came disconnected, or a switch was moved to a wrong position. Check these hardware items carefully before assuming that a major problem exists:

Are all fuses good and properly seated?

Are all cables and connectors firmly seated?

Is power actually available at the outlet or batteries?

Are all controls at the right settings?

Are all interlocked doors or panels firmly closed?

An interlock is a special switch used to remove dangerous power when a cabinet door or panel is opened. See Figure 3–6.

3.3 SUBSTITUTION: THE MOST POWERFUL TROUBLESHOOTING TOOL OF ALL

The substitution of known good, working equipment into a malfunctioning system is a quick, relatively easy, and very effective method of troubleshooting. Substitution as a troubleshooting method is more

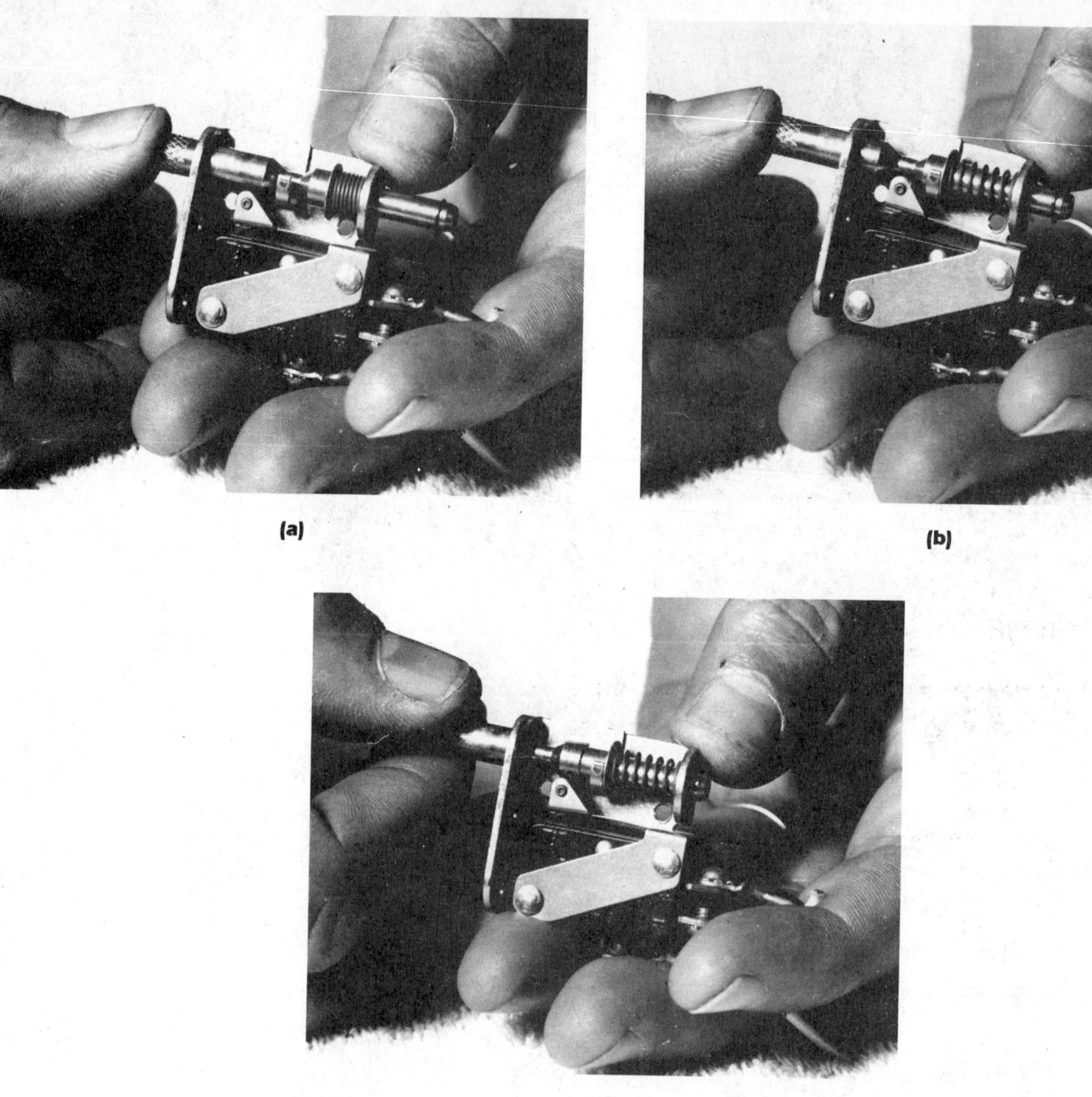

Figure 3–6 One kind of interlock that provides a bypass condition for maintenance.

effective than any other method of finding problems, with the possible exception of automated troubleshooting. Substitution is the only troubleshooting method that is almost always conclusive and effective, all the way from system troubleshooting down to the component level. In this attempt to get the system back up and working, there are some things to watch for.

Generally speaking, substitute equipment must be exactly the same as the suspected equipment that is being replaced. Items that might be checked include input line voltage or power supply voltages, the correct amplifier gains, frequencies used, and so on. Without the same parameters involved, good equipment may function no better than a bad unit. In extreme cases, the good equipment could be damaged or cause damage to the system.

REPLACING SUSPECTED EQUIPMENTS IN THE SYSTEM

The actual replacement of any equipment in a system can involve many different tasks, among them, the removal and replacement of screws, the disconnection of cable connectors, the removal and insertion of printed circuit cards into card edge connectors, and so forth. The most important caution to observe is be gentle. Do not force the hardware. Look for a hidden screw holding the unit together, make sure the connector locks are released before pulling them apart, and, equally important, don't pull cables by the wiring. Grasp the connector to remove connections, and not the wires, as it is very easy to damage cables by pulling on the wires.

Keep in mind also that it is rare, but quite possible, that replacing a bad unit of a system with a known good one may damage the good one. If your good unit suddenly quits working, *don't put in another* until you determine for sure that the system is not "blowing" the good ones.

There is also a potential for damage if the manufacturer changes cabling, color coding, or a hundred other possible "little things" that could make equipment substitution invalid or dangerous to the good units. Be careful and double-check before installing and powering up good units.

3.4 WIRING PROBLEMS

TESTING WIRE BUNDLES WITH AN OHMMETER

If the replacement of "black boxes" (units whose contents are unknown) or circuit cards does not cure the problem in the system, it is quite possible that the interunit wiring or coaxial cables may be the cause.

Wire-bundle problems can be traced using the system blueprints to locate both ends of the cable along with a continuity tester or ohmmeter. The digital multimeter with a continuity "beeper" is a valuable instrument to use when checking wire continuity. There is no need to watch this meter to verify continuity of the wiring.

Wiring extending long distances can be continuity-checked in one of two ways. With some assistance, the far end of the cable in question can be grounded to the vehicle, aircraft, or the equipment grounded framework, if the ground is continuous throughout the system. Then, the near end can be tested for continuity using this common point as a return line. An alternative way to handle the need for a return line for an ohmmeter is to use a

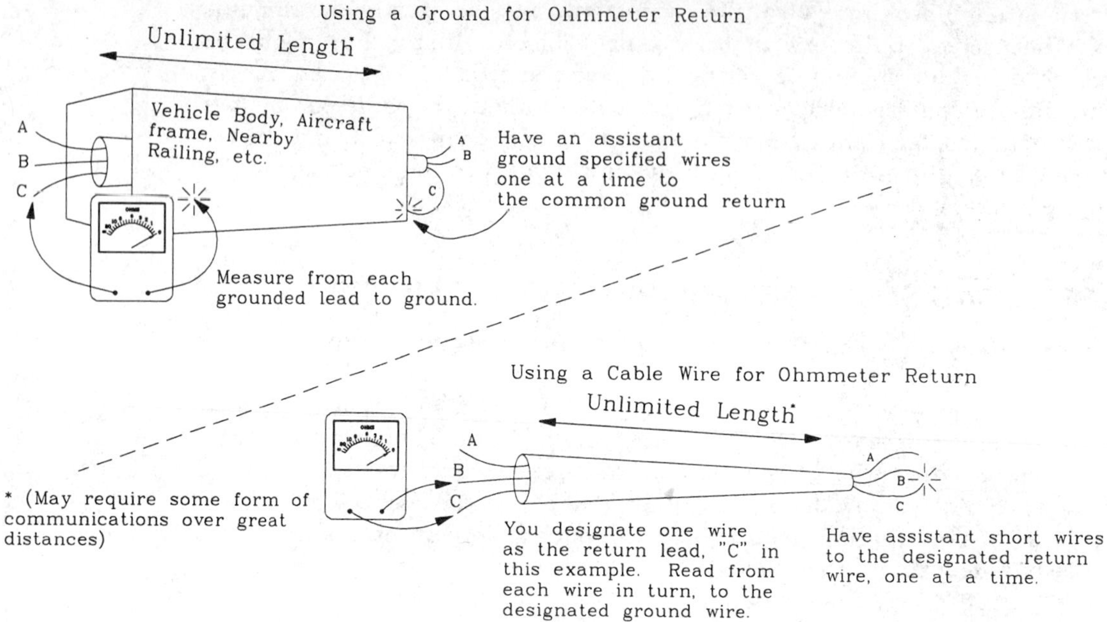

Figure 3–7 Methods of obtaining a return for an ohmmeter during cable continuity testing.

BASIC INFORMATION

single, designated conductor of the cable itself as a return lead. Make all continuity checks using that one lead for the return. See Figure 3–7.

Besides testing for continuity of the wires in a cable, it is also wise to test for possible shorts from wire to wire and from each wire to ground. Testing for shorts to ground is very important when the cable might have developed a chafed portion and one or more of the wires may be contacting the metal frame of the aircraft or other vehicle.

Testing for all possible combinations of shorting or grounding paths can be done efficiently by a series of tests. See Figure 3–8 for the method to use.

Testing for shorts between all of the wires in a bundle is done by putting one ohmmeter test lead on the first wire. Taking the second lead of the meter, touch it to each of the following wires in the cable in some logical order, one by one. After all of the wires have been considered, move the first lead down one wire, using the same sequence, and again touch each of the following leads, one at a time, with the remaining ohmmeter lead. On the third round, again come down one wire with the first ohmmeter lead and continue to look for continuity with the second lead on all following leads. Note that the second ohmmeter lead never has to go to a wire *prior* to the first ohmmeter lead. This method checks for all possible combinations of wires with no wasted motion or needlessly checking for reversed combinations such as from wire B to wire A. Each combination is tested once (e.g., from A to B), and only once.

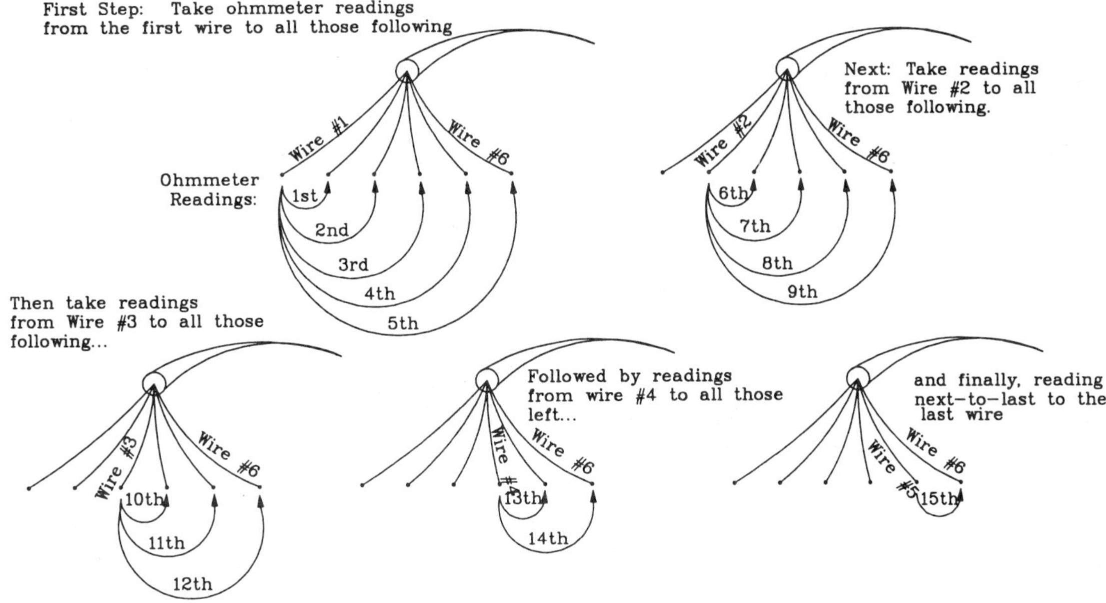

Figure 3–8 Testing a multiple-wire cable for shorts.

Since two people may be required to make end-to-end checks of a cable for continuity, at great distances, some sort of communications may be necessary by either radio or telephone.

TESTING COAXIAL CABLES

Coaxial cables may be checked for simple opens or shorts with an ohmmeter. Other problems, such as damaged shielding and crushed sections, cannot be detected with the ohmmeter and will require either of two more sophisticated methods, either using an RF source (a low-powered transmitter will do), a wattmeter, and a resistive RF load, or by the use of a time-domain reflectometer (explained later in this chapter). Consider first the use of an ohmmeter.

Coaxial Cable Testing Using an Ohmmeter

Testing a coaxial cable with an ohmmeter will reveal only two kinds of failures, the open cable and the shorted one. See Figure 3–9 for an explanation.

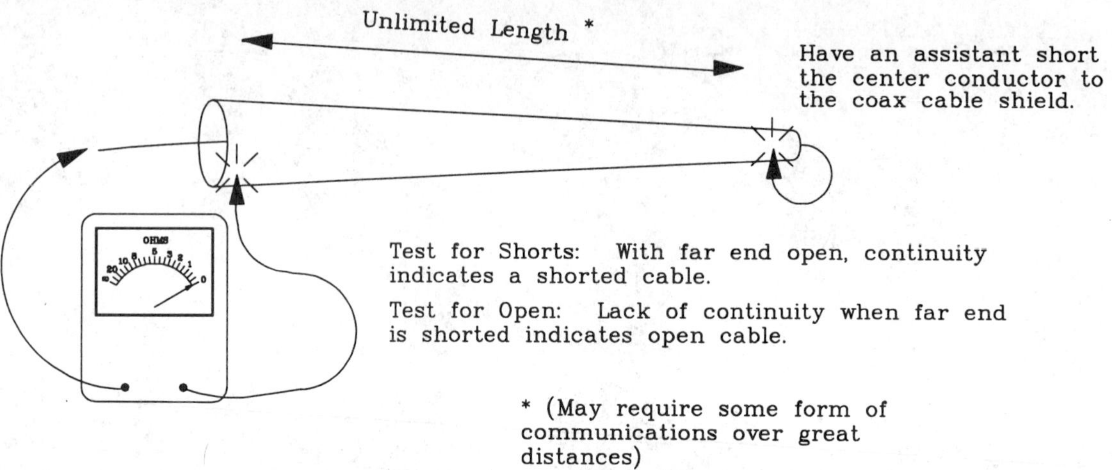

Unlimited Length *
Have an assistant short the center conductor to the coax cable shield.
OHMS
Test for Shorts: With far end open, continuity indicates a shorted cable.
Test for Open: Lack of continuity when far end is shorted indicates open cable.
* (May require some form of communications over great distances)

Figure 3–9 Simple ohmmeter testing of a coaxial cable for shorts and opens.

Coaxial Cable Testing Using an RF Source, Wattmeter, and Load

Partial failures of a coaxial cable, such as impedance changes caused by crushing the cable that are not quite bad enough to short it or damage to cable shield, can be detected with a relatively inexpensive directional RF wattmeter, when used with a radio frequency source capable of a few watts of output. This will be sufficient to get a reasonable reading on the wattmeter. A resistive load equal to the characteristic impedance of the coaxial cable is the last item needed. For instance, a wattmeter with a 10-watt full-scale reading, a 5-watt walkie-talkie, and an RF load resistor of 52 Ω would work very nicely to test lengths of 52-ohm coaxial cable. Antennas can also be tested by the substitution of the resistive load in place of the antenna, noting the changes in RF power indications. Figure 3–10 shows how to read the indications.

Coaxial Cable Testing Using Time-Domain Reflectometry

Crushing a coaxial cable or damaging its outer shielding can make the cable inefficient, particularly at higher RF frequencies. These faults will not show on an ohmmeter if the inner and outer conductors are not shorted together and if there is still DC continuity through a few remaining strands of the outer shield. Worse yet, if there is a long run of this cable through many clamps, such as are used on ships, the *location* of the problem along the length of the cable will not be evident, even when using the wattmeter method just mentioned. One method remains that will indicate the kind of

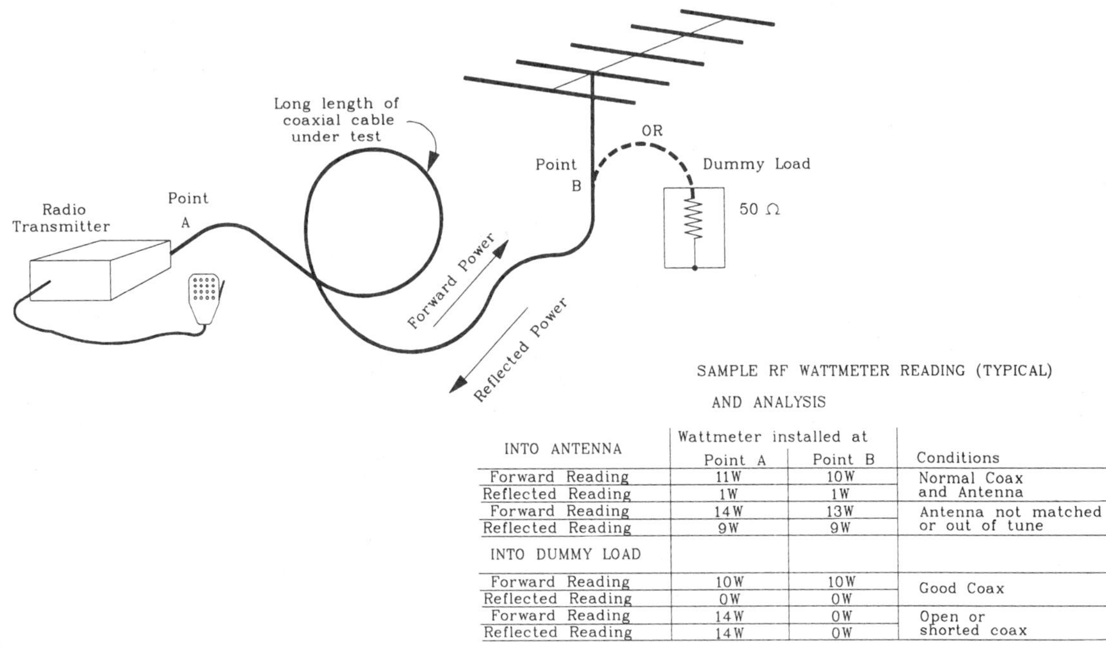

INTO ANTENNA	Wattmeter installed at Point A	Wattmeter installed at Point B	Conditions
Forward Reading	11W	10W	Normal Coax and Antenna
Reflected Reading	1W	1W	
Forward Reading	14W	13W	Antenna not matched or out of tune
Reflected Reading	9W	9W	
INTO DUMMY LOAD			
Forward Reading	10W	10W	Good Coax
Reflected Reading	0W	0W	
Forward Reading	14W	0W	Open or shorted coax
Reflected Reading	14W	0W	

Figure 3–10 Using a wattmeter and dummy load to test coaxial cables and antennas.

problem, its magnitude, and *where the problem is located* on the cable. This method is called time-domain reflectometry or TDR.

TDR, simply stated, pulses a cable and registers any reflections caused by discontinuities in the cable. Discontinuities may be caused by crushed cable, damaged shielding, or, in a very sensitive instrument, even a normal cable connector. Figure 3–11 shows what might be expected on good and bad cables. Note that the distance of the reflected echo along the horizontal axis is proportional to the length of cable from the TDR instrument.

Figure 3–12 shows a TDR instrument that is used to generate the TDR waveform and receive the reflections caused by coaxial cable problems.

3.5 VERIFY PROPER SYSTEM OPERATION AFTER THE REPLACEMENT

Once the suspected equipment or unit has been replaced with a good one, it is important to verify that the whole system is back to normal operation. It is possible to get a bad unit from stock. For example, a good unit may have accidently been marked for repair and a bad one kept for a spare. This

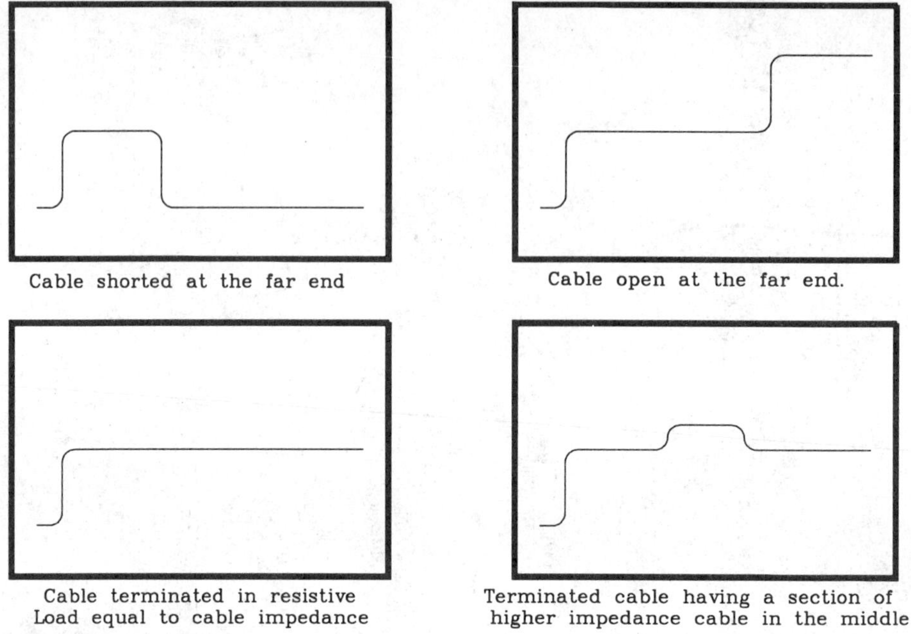

Cable shorted at the far end
Cable open at the far end.
Cable terminated in resistive Load equal to cable impedance
Terminated cable having a section of higher impedance cable in the middle

Figure 3–11 Samplc TDR presentations of good and bad coaxial cables.

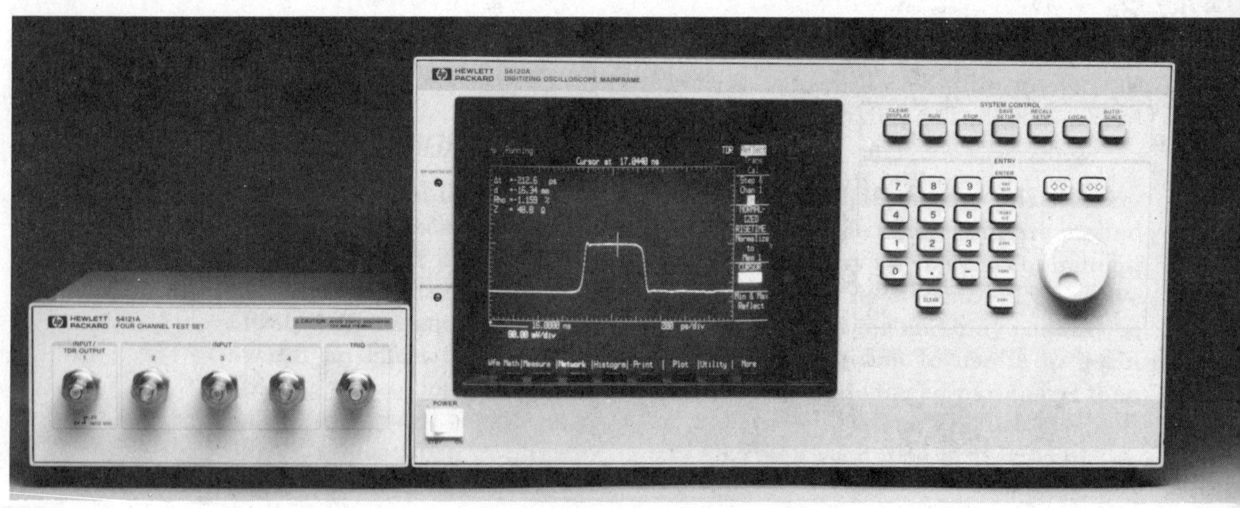

Figure 3–12 A time-domain reflcctometry (TDR) generator for testing coaxial cables. (Photo courtesy of Hewlett-Packard Co.)

can happen very easily when several units are brought from spares storage, unwrapped, and left lying about while a problem is being traced. When the technician finds a bad unit, it may accidentally be shuffled in among the good ones. This is a mistake that technicians should be very careful to prevent.

CHAPTER SUMMARY

- Identifying the bad equipment within a system may be the first—and last step—in effecting a system repair.
- If individual equipment repair is done at another location, the problem is considered solved once the defective equipment has been shipped away.
- In other cases, a repair may be required beyond the equipment level.
- Troubleshooting charts may or may not be useful, depending on the technician's level of familiarity with the system.
- Substitution is the most powerful method of troubleshooting available, and is applicable from the system down to the component level.
- Additional chapters in this book deal with techniques when troubleshooting to deeper levels: to the card, stage, and, finally, the component levels.

REVIEW QUESTIONS

1. What is the greatest help in the system manuals to help the beginning technician understand how the whole system works?
2. What is an integrated test system?
3. When are troubleshooting charts most valuable?
4. Why is it a good idea to speak to the person turning in a problem report?
5. What does a reading of 10 dBm mean?
6. Should a 600Ω resistor be used across an audio system line before measuring the decibel level?
7. Basically, a Db meter is a/an _______.
8. When does an interlock perform its intended function?
9. What is the most powerful troubleshooting technique of all?
10. Can the technique of question 9 be used all the way from the equipment level to the component level?
11. What is the general rule when substituting one equipment for another?
12. How many resistance readings are necessary to completely check a multiple-wire cable for shorts if it has 16 wires?

13. How many methods were given for testing coaxial cables?
14. What instrument will test a coaxial cable only for shorts or opens?
15. The use of an RF transmitter and dummy load will allow the measurement of the _______ of a problem, including shorts and opens.
16. The TDR instrument will add another dimension to the testing of coaxial cables, that of precisely _______ing a particular problem.
17. After the system is supposedly repaired, what must be done before leaving the site?

Getting into the Equipment

4

CHAPTER OBJECTIVES

No matter what sort of circuitry is involved, it is usually necessary to open equipment in order to repair it. This chapter points out some of the things to keep in mind, regardless of what kind of equipment is involved. Included are topics on:

- Avoiding danger to yourself and your equipment.
- Using a mockup or automated testing equipment (ATE) for high-volume troubleshooting.
- Opening equipment for repair.
- Applying time-saving shortcuts to apply after equipment covers are off.
- Using circuit-card extenders during test procedures.
- Using block, functional block, and wiring diagrams as troubleshooting information.
- Making your schematic diagrams more useful.
- Identifying alternatives to consider if no schematic is available.

4.1 SAFETY AND CAUTIONARY NOTES

Electrical shock is an occupational hazard for electronics technicians, just like getting burned is for a welder or falling is for a steel worker. With proper precautions, there is no reason for a technician to ever receive a shock. Receiving an electrical shock is a forceful warning that the proper safety measures have not been followed. Some of the most important safety rules to protect yourself include:

Do not reach into equipment while it is operating. This is particularly important in the high-voltage, high-power stages of equipment, such as radio transmitters. Make your tests on such equipment either while it is turned off or by going through the steps of turning off the power, discharging the filter capacitors, attaching test leads as needed, and then reapplying power to get a reading. Do not handle a meter while it is connected to high-voltage sources.

Discharge high-voltage (over about 24-V DC) or high-capacitance (over about 1,000 μFd) capacitors. This is done by shorting them. A special lead can be made for this purpose, using a clip at one end for connecting to ground and a probe or other suitable terminal at the other. Such a lead is very useful for shorting most of the physically large power-supply capacitors since they are usually grounded at one end. Capacitors that are not grounded (floating) must be shorted by using an insulated tool, such as a screwdriver, placed across the terminals. Discharging a capacitor sometimes produces a loud bang, but it is nonetheless necessary to avoid electrical shocks and/or damage to test instruments. Very high-voltage, high-capacitance capacitors should be discharged through a resistor to limit the high instantaneous current to a reasonable value.

Use only one hand, if at all possible, when working on live equipment containing voltages over about 24 volts. Keep the unused hand in a back pocket, out of the way. Figure 4–1 shows the technique. This reduces the possibility of accidentally passing a current through the chest. A current of only about 40 milliamperes passing through the chest can be fatal. Sweating reduces the resistance of the skin and thus reduces the voltage that can be safely touched.

Another way to avoid accidents is to use a special feature of the meter shown in Figure 5–4, the Fluke 87. This and other Fluke meters have a feature called Touch Hold™. When using this feature, all you have to do is set up the meter for it by pressing a single button, and then concentrate solely on safely taking the reading. This means that a technician can keep an eye only on the probe and the area it is contacting. When the meter beeps, a stable voltage reading has been obtained. After disconnecting the probe and removing it from the circuit, the meter can be read. The voltage reading is held on the digital multimeter (DMM) display until another reading is taken or the instrument is manually cleared.

Remove metal jewelry before working on live circuits. Large metal jewelry can make an excellent electrode to pass current directly into the body

Figure 4-1 Work on high-voltage circuits with one hand behind your back. No metal jewelry, please.

with low resistance. It is also important to remove jewelry when working on low-voltage circuits that are capable of very high currents. High-current circuits may produce enough current flow through metal jewelry to cause it to become red hot.

It is a very good idea to use an isolation transformer when servicing equipment that does not use a transformer in the power supply in order to isolate the chassis from the incoming power line. This isolation transformer will greatly reduce the hazard of working on a chassis that may be electrically hot. Incidently, the use of an autotransformer (e.g., Variac™) does not provide the required power-line isolation.

Cathode-ray tubes (CRTs) use very high voltages for acceleration of the electron beam. One might assume that while the anode of the tube is highly positive, the cathode will be near ground potential and, consequently, harmless. Quite the opposite is often the case, however. The anode may be grounded and the cathode may be very highly negative. Do not assume any electrode of a CRT is safe to touch! Some CRTs are operated between these extremes with the anode fairly high positive and the cathode fairly high negative, all with respect to the chassis. These circuits are all dangerous.

Look at and understand the schematic, and do not assume anything. See Chapter 23 for an explanation of the grounding schemes used in typical CRT circuits.

Innocent-looking coaxial cable connectors can present a shock hazard, too. Coaxial cables are often used to interconnect two equipments, both of which are operating on 120-V AC. If either of the units has a defective chassis ground, a technician may be at risk when separating coaxial connectors between the two. When separating coaxial cables at a connector, make it a habit to never grasp both of the metal connectors when releasing them. It could cause current to flow from the ungrounded chassis of the bad equipment through both arms to the properly grounded unit. As a matter of habit, release the connectors and then slide at least one hand up onto insulation before actually separating them.

Similarly, don't hold on to a ground such as a metal cabinet door while troubleshooting or even pointing at high-voltage circuits.

Always connect the ground lead of instruments first and disconnect it last. This prevents holding an unexpectedly "hot" test lead in your hand.

The following cautionary notes will help protect your test instruments and the equipment under test:

Be especially careful when using your multimeter, whatever the type. The two very common ways to damage or ruin your meter are to use a multimeter on a live circuit while the meter is switched either to the ohms or to the current (milliampere) scale.

A solid-state tester is similar to an ohmmeter in that it, too, must be used *only* on de-energized (dead) circuits. This instrument is covered in Chapter 17.

4.2 THE MOCKUP AND THE AUTOMATED TESTING EQUIPMENT (ATE) STATION

If the technician is expected to work with many equipments of the same type, it is best to provide a quick-connecting array of necessary power supplies and cabling to put the equipment into as near a normal working status as possible. An example might be when a technician is expected to work on numerous CB transceivers. It would be beneficial to have antenna and dummy antenna coaxial cables ready to connect, plus the required 120-V AC or 12-V DC power connectors also at hand. Additional test equipment should be ready to connect, such as an RF wattmeter and an RF signal generator.

Some technicians, particularly those working in a manufacturing area, may require mockups for individual circuit cards. Such mockups allow the technician to quickly plug a card into a "normal" operating situation. Problems on the cards can be more effectively traced under plug-in conditions than would be the case if each card required wiring every connection individually.

Figure 4-2 This automated testing station is able to run detailed tests at high speed on a single kind of card. (Courtesy Hewlett-Packard Company)

Some manufacturers have the facilities to provide more than a simple mockup for the technician to use in determining problems and tracing them down. Automated test equipment (ATE) is computer-driven, and can be programmed to run many tests on a specific card, reporting deviations from normal operation. Testing programs are written to test specific cards. The computer will run a test and analyze the outcome. If it is out of normal parameters, the computer can provide a printout of the test that failed and the results obtained. It is also possible for such programs to list the probable failed components for a given problem. See Figure 4–2 for a photograph of an automated test station.

4.3 OPENING THE EQUIPMENT

Always unplug equipment before removing the cabinet or case. It may be possible for the case to contact dangerous voltages while being removed. Taking equipment out of its case should be done slowly, watching for wiring that can get caught and damaged by pulling. Wires leading to speakers mounted to the case are an example of components that can be torn loose in this process. Some equipment comes with small plugs on these items to allow parts to be disconnected during servicing, while other equipment may require the use of a soldering iron to separate them.

Keep in mind when disconnecting wiring that if the parts needed for repair are not immediately available, it may be some time before the equipment is reassembled. If there is any chance that wires might not be replaced on the terminals from which they came, write down the layout of the wiring and where it connects, and keep these notes with the equipment.

When removing screws from equipment, be careful to note the length of each as it is removed. Some screws may need to be shorter than others to prevent them from going too far into the equipment and possibly damaging or shorting something. Another problem is that some equipment uses two or more different kinds of screws, some sheet-metal–type screws to thread into plastic and others with fine threads to go into threaded nuts. Take note of the threads of the screws as you remove them.

The best way to save the bolts and be sure they are returned to the proper holes is to take off the covers and immediately put the screws back into the holes from which they came. This is a very good idea if the equipment may not be reassembled for some time or if another person may have to do the reassembly. A second-best alternative is to put the bolts into a small container that can be kept with the equipment. A 35mm film canister is a favorite for this use. The worst thing that can be done with loose screws is to lay them somewhere on the workbench. At least one is guaranteed to find its way onto the floor and become lost.

4.4 TIME-SAVING SHORTCUTS

Once the cover is off the equipment, it is quite possible that the problem can be found by a very close visual inspection. Look for burned or broken components, loose or broken wiring, and poorly soldered joints. If there are plastic integrated circuits on the boards, look closely at the center of each for raised dimples, indicating overheated and shorted ICs.

Circuit boards with surface-mounted devices warrant special care in visual inspection. Look for cracked or chipped SMD components, including the terminations, bad solder joints on the ends of the SMDs, and solder bridges anywhere on the board.

Besides visual inspection of the board, the smell of burned components may give a clue to the problem. Resistors and transformers have their own characteristic smell when burned, which the technician will come to recognize.

Figure 4-3 Use a circuit board extender card to get a board up where it can be reached with the test instrument. (Photo courtesy of Vector Electronics Company Inc.)

4.5 USE OF CIRCUIT CARD EXTENDERS

Circuit card extenders allow access to the components of a circuit card under test. Without an extender, it may be difficult or impossible to make even routine voltage checks because other cards or the chassis are in the way. See Figure 4–3.

4.6 USING THE BLOCK DIAGRAM

The use of the block diagram of the equipment under test is often overlooked. The block diagram provides an overall look at how the equipment is supposed to operate; how it handles various inputs and provides the necessary outputs. Without understanding the block diagram, it is very difficult to understand the more detailed information of the schematic diagram. The bottom line is: *understand the block diagram before consulting the schematic.* The block diagram will usually include the operating controls, thus explaining what they do and where within the circuitry they are located. Get the lay of the land, the broad overview, and study the block diagram first. For some unidentified reason, it is a natural inclination for a technician to open an instruction book and go directly to the schematic. Resist this temptation; review the block diagram first, and the schematic will be easier to understand from the start.

4.7 USING THE FUNCTIONAL BLOCK DIAGRAM

A functional block diagram is very similar to a block diagram. The major signal flows are shown, along with the important components or important details in each box. The emphasis of a functional block diagram is to show the important input and output elements of a block, and it commonly uses schematic symbols to show these relationships. See Figure 4–4 for examples of a block diagram, a functional block diagram, and a schematic.

4.8 USING THE PRACTICAL WIRING DIAGRAM

A diagram of the physical layout along with the wiring from point to point is called a practical wiring diagram. Any attempt to make a schematic appear as it is physically laid out will produce too many crossing lines and result in a diagram that is all but useless for troubleshooting purposes. Such a diagram might prove useful to help trace a specific wire from one point to another, but the operation of the circuit will *not* be understandable from an inspection of a practical wiring diagram. A practical wiring diagram is identifiable in that IC chips and other multiple-pin components have all the pin numbers in order, whereas a schematic would not. See Figure 4–5 for an example of a practical wiring diagram.

4.9 USING THE THEORY OF OPERATION

The theory of operation for an equipment or circuit card is the most detailed information available on the operation of that particular circuit. More information could only be available from the engineer who originally designed the circuit: someone who may have long ago left the company. Tracing signals through the various blocks of the schematic while reading the theory of operation is the quickest way possible of understanding the circuit at the pin-for-pin, wire-for-wire level. When large companies send their employees to special schools on specific equipment, the theory of operation for that equipment is the basis for the course curriculum. Look for the section on the theory of operation in the instruction manual whenever you need to know the exact way in which a particular circuit operates.

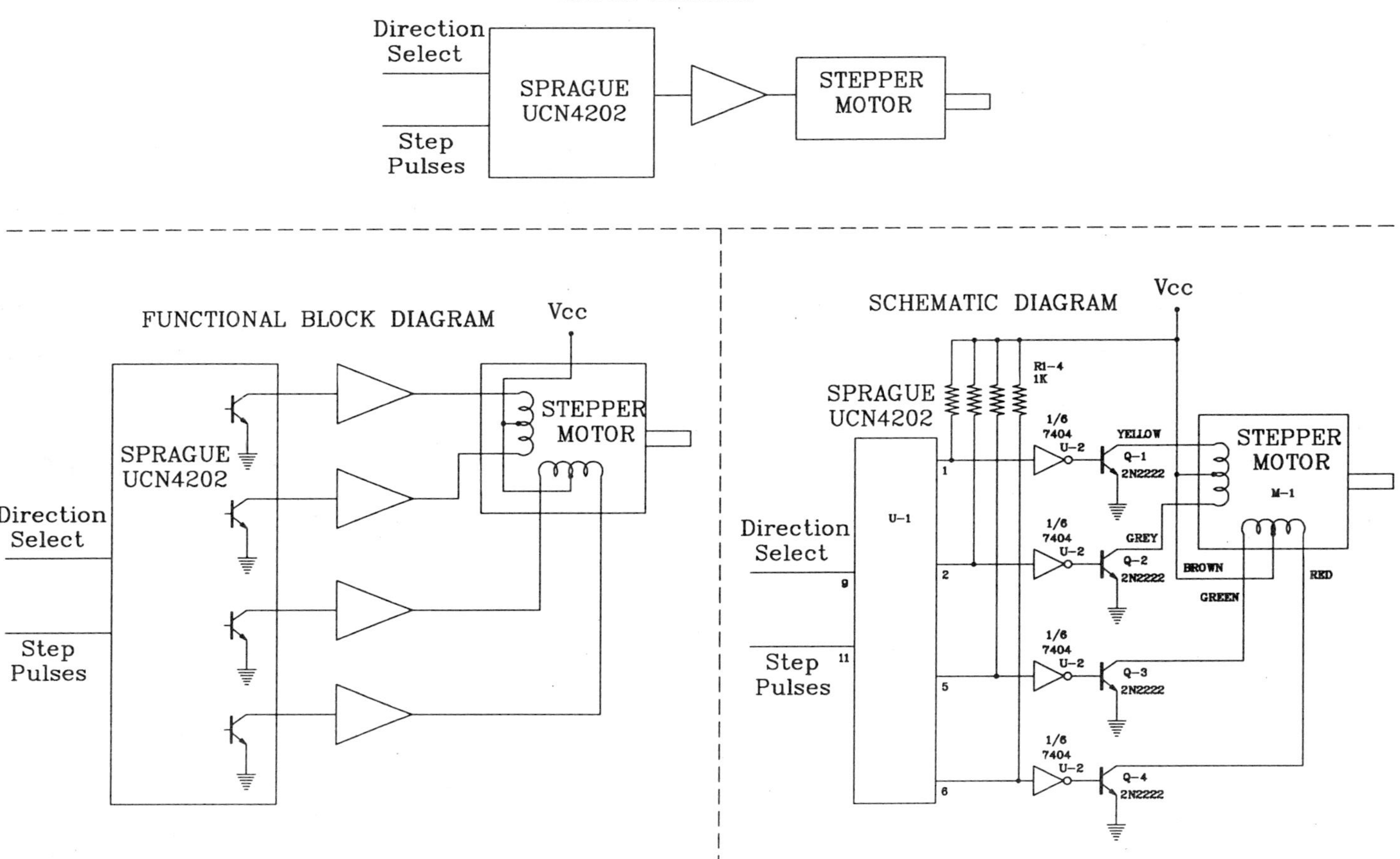

Figure 4-4 Examples of a block diagram, a functional block diagram, and a schematic, all for the same circuit.

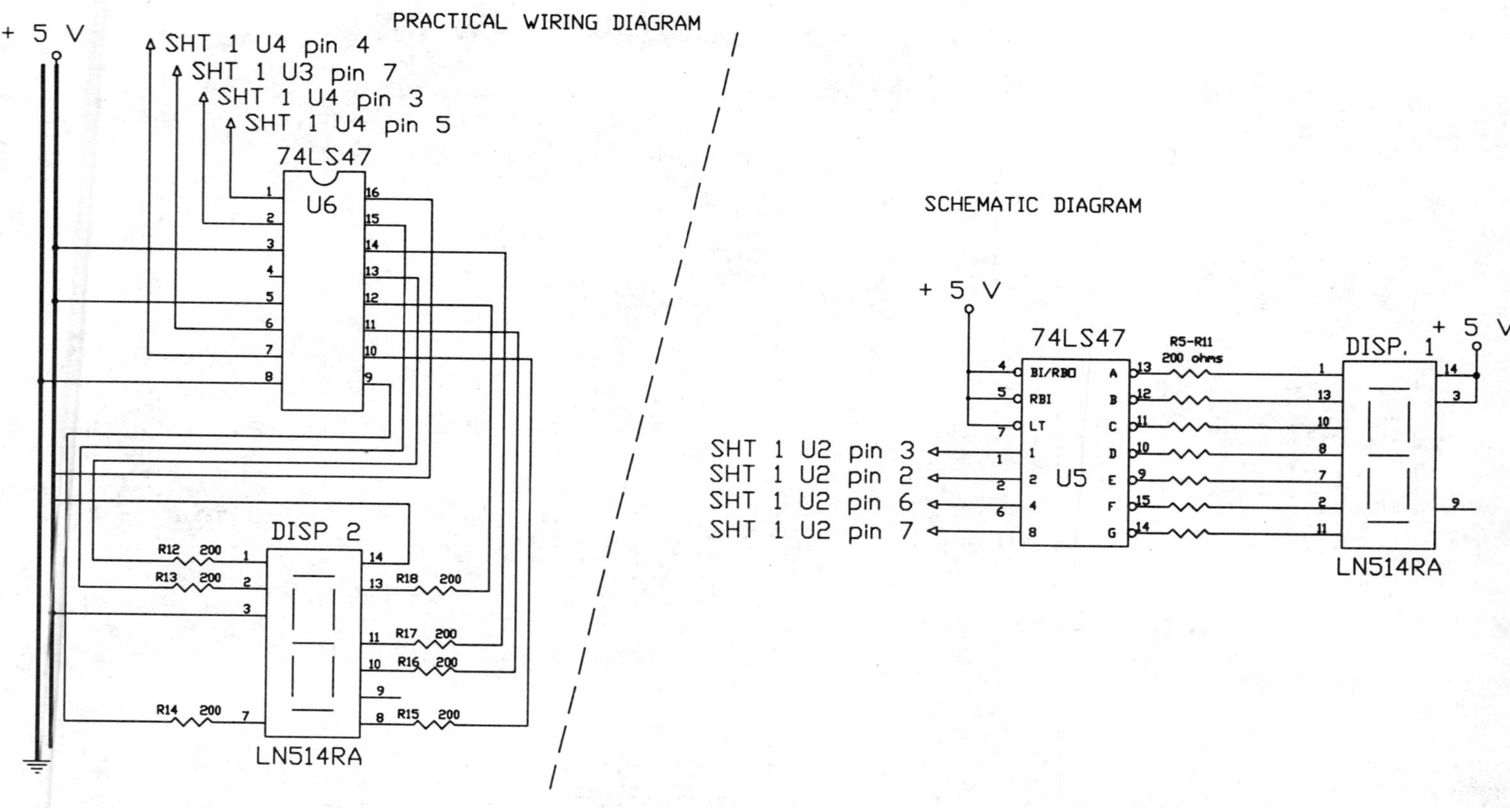

Figure 4-5 Comparison of schematic and practical wiring diagrams for clarity.

4.10 USING THE SCHEMATIC DIAGRAM

The schematic diagram gives the technician the detailed information necessary to troubleshoot and repair equipment to the component level. There is little point in trying to repair equipment without a schematic, particularly if the circuitry is large or complex. Working without one is much like trying to find a specific address in a strange city without the benefit of a road map. Street signs help, and eventually, by checking every address in the city, the address could be found, but is it worth the effort? It is better to have a map. A technician without a schematic can read part values and transistor numbers, but a great deal more information is needed to do detailed troubleshooting efficiently. It may take more than 10 times the man-hours to repair equipment without a proper schematic than with one.

A SCHEMATIC DISPLAY SUGGESTION

Technicians often try to work on a piece of equipment and read a schematic on the same working surface. The circuit of interest invariably ends up underneath various tools, wiring, and even the equipment itself. Of course, the schematic then becomes torn and dirty.

The schematic should be fully visible while a job is under way. It is a simple matter to construct a small easel that holds a large flat backing at a slanted angle, upon which the schematic can be clamped. A piece of quarter-inch plywood measuring 3 feet by 2 feet makes a good backing. It is also helpful if the top of the plywood is fitted with a couple of large spring clamps to hold piles of paper together. It may also be of benefit to preserve important schematics in plastic, especially if they are used often.

CUSTOMIZE YOUR ANALOG SCHEMATICS

Here are some tips that will make your use of schematic diagrams most efficient:

1. It is a big help to color-code your schematics. Make copies of the originals, and then you can mark up the copies all you wish. At first glance, a schematic is confusing to anyone. However, a little color coding can help reduce this visual pollution a great dcal. Tracing over the schematic lines with see-through, alcohol-based colored markers with the following or similar color codes is recommended:

Ground or chassis connection in heavy black lines.

Voltage supply lines in red. If more than one voltage is used, shades of red, orange, or pink may be used for the other supply lines.

Primary signal flows may be marked with broader markers and colors such as blue or green.

Be sure to provide a key to your code somewhere convenient on the diagram.

2. It is very useful to record *normal* DC or AC voltage readings throughout the circuitry in appropriate places. The power supplies should be well labeled this way. Circuits with signals other than DC can be marked to include a sketch of the waveform as seen on an oscilloscope. Be sure to include the vertical sensitivity setting and the sweep time-per-division of the oscilloscope to enable duplication of the pattern in the future.

3. If a solid-state tester is available and if there are a great many identical circuits coming through the repair facility, it may be a good idea to make sketches of the tester's CRT patterns of a *normal* board. Be sure at least to log the patterns obtained at each of the edge connector pins. Include the instrument range in use, too. This will enable a quick initial check of the boards as they enter the shop.

4. A schematic will make more sense if the block diagram is used as a guide to functional areas of the schematic; then divide these areas with dotted lines.

HOW TO READ SCHEMATICS

There are some tips that may help you read schematics. Expect the schematic to flow from left to right, with the input on the left and the output on the right. Though this is not always true, it does make the information easier to read. A radio receiver schematic, for instance, should show the antenna input connection at the left side. The signal would be processed through the receiver from left to right, ending in the speaker output on the right side of the diagram.

Although the lines in the schematic represent the circuit, the circuit's physical appearance is likely to be entirely different. See Figure 4–6.

Consider each end of a line on the schematic as sharing exactly the same voltage at each end and everywhere between.

Components are usually referenced by the use of a letter-number combination in order to save space on the schematic. The parts can be found listed in a separate parts listing, where values, tolerances, dimensions, and other details regarding the part are given. The letter portion of the reference designation is coded as follows:

B	Blower	J	Jack
C	Capacitor	K	Relay
CR or D	Diode	L	Inductor
F or X	Fuse	M	Meter
FB	Ferrite bead (inductor)	P	Plug
IC	Integrated circuit	Q	Transistor
I	Indicator	R	Resistor
JP	Jumper	RFC	Radio frequency choke

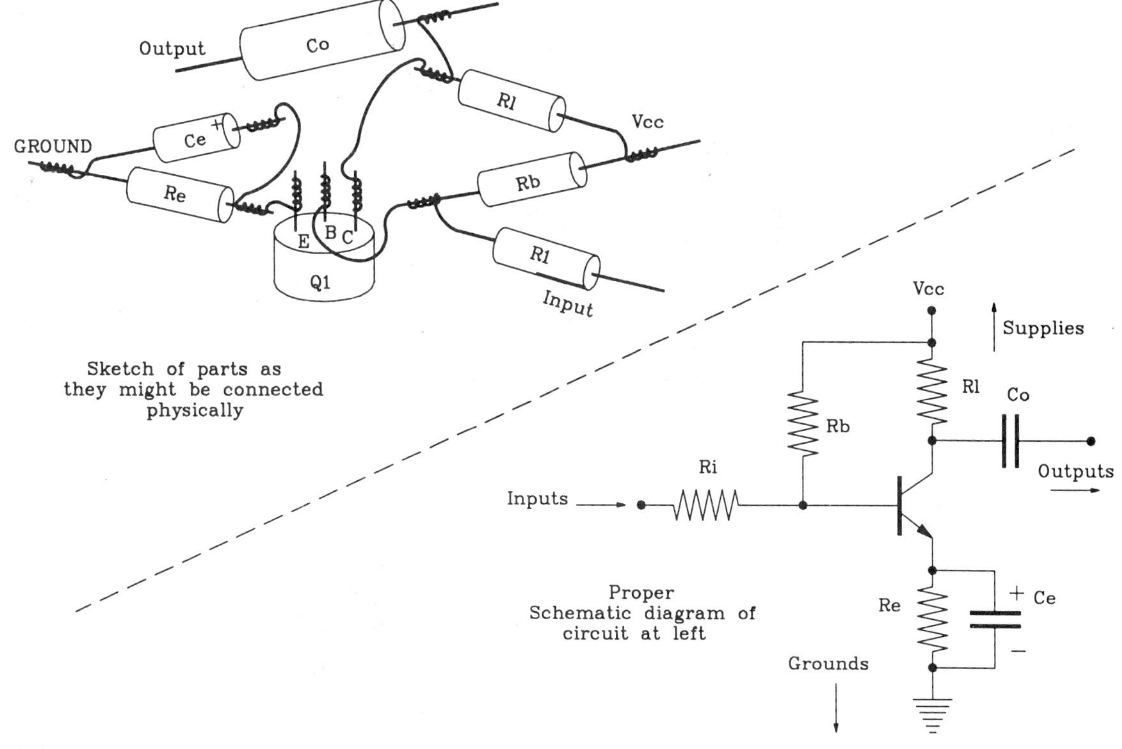

Figure 4-6 Comparison of physical and schematic appearances of a circuit.

S	Switch	U	Integrated circuit
SG	Spark gap	V	Vacuum tube
SW	Switch	VR	Variable resistor (pot)
T	Transformer	TB	Terminal board
TP or JT	Test point	Z or ZD	Zener diode

Only a minimum of component information is given on the schematic, as there is room on the drawing for only the most important notations. Resistors are shown with their resistance value and, in the case of larger resistors, their power rating. Capacitors are given with their capacitance values and possibly the voltage ratings. Transistors and ICs are given only their identification number, and inductors are given their inductance values only.

The use of dotted lines on a schematic is an indication that the enclosed components are not located physically near those drawn around them. An example is the volume control, which is often shown on the schematic deep within the receiver schematic. A dotted box around this control will tell the technician that it cannot be found by looking for nearby components, as the control itself is not located on the same board with the other parts, even though that is where it has been drawn.

Some equipment is made up of several interconnected boards. These boards usually have a different numbering system for each board so that the technician will have an indication of where to find a given component. For instance (and there is no standardization in this matter), the power supply might be assigned all of the numbers between 100 and 199. A resistor called R127 on the schematic would therefore be identified as part of the power supply assembly. Another board in the same equipment might number all the components with the series of 200 to 299, while still another board could use the series 300 to 399. When the technician encounters a component of interest, the identifying number will indicate the right board via the number series, wherever it may be encountered on the diagram.

Advanced practice in reading a schematic diagram is given in Chapter 7, under the heading, "Predicting DC Voltages in Various Configurations."

4.11 IF NO SCHEMATIC IS AVAILABLE

There are several things that may be done if a repair is needed on equipment for which no schematic is on hand.

1. The defective component may be identified quickly by passive testing with a solid-state tester without benefit of a schematic. See Chapter 17.
2. It may be practical to use a schematic that is similar to the proper schematic. For instance, a CB transistorized 27 MHz transmitter is pretty universal in principle and design, so the schematic for another transistorized CB transmitter might be close enough to use in finding some problems. This is particularly true if the same manufacturer is involved and the model number is only slightly different. Of course, circuit details would differ, and this would have to be taken into account during servicing.
3. If another, identical unit in good working order is available, cross-checking of voltages and signals at critical points during operation can often show differences that can lead to finding the problem. In this case, the better the technician knows the general layout (block diagram) of the equipment, the faster the troubleshooting will occur. For example, if the problem is in the modulator section of a transceiver, it makes the job much easier if the technician knows which transistor stage is the modulator. Time can be saved by bypassing the stages that are not involved in the problem.
4. Another possibility is that a schematic might be available from the equipment manufacturer. In such a case it is probably best to put the equipment aside until the diagram has been received.
5. One last possibility, and the one that is the most time-consuming, is

to hand-draw a schematic of the equipment by meticulously examining the actual circuit hardware.

HOW TO DRAW YOUR OWN SCHEMATIC

To draw an entire schematic would be impractical for complex equipment, but for simple units and small areas of direct concern, it is an alternative to consider. This is a particularly applicable choice if the equipment is a unit upon which the technician will often be called to work and if no amount of effort will serve to produce an instruction manual. Knowing color code is a big help in identifying components. Semiconductor reference books giving transistor and IC pinouts and specifications are necessary for this job. If the printed circuit board under consideration is double-sided, the job becomes about four times more difficult than with a single-sided board.

The ability to draw a schematic quickly is largely a matter of practice. Start by drawing schematics of simple circuits involving only a dozen or so components. Then progress to more complicated circuits as you gain experience and confidence. Drawing a schematic is a matter of several steps:

1. The first step is to identify each of the semiconductors and integrated circuits on the board. Pay particular attention to the pinouts. A semiconductor cross-reference guide is often a help in this regard. Do not assume what a component is until the information has been verified. For instance, some regulator ICs look just like power transistors. Verify each component before proceeding.
2. The second step in drawing a schematic is to be sure you can identify all of the components with a unique identifying number, called a *reference designation.* If there is no marking of the components on the board already, draw a somewhat scaled-up picture of the components on the board. Arbitrarily label the components with terms such as, for resistors, R1, R2, and so on, and for capacitors, C1, C2, and so forth. See Figure 4–7.
3. The third step is to identify the power input (the Vcc or B+ lines), the ground bus, and, if possible, the input to the circuit. An input to a power supply circuit would be the power input leads, and for an amplifier, the signal input line. See Figure 4–8.
4. The fourth step is to use the input line as a starting point and trace through the circuit. Mark each component you meet that connects *directly* to this point. Don't try to draw several circuits at once, but rather just identify all of the components connected to this first trace or wire. Remember that if a wire goes between two points, those two points connect to each other on the schematic in any way you choose, especially for a first try. At this point you may have two or more components that each has a single lead connected to the common

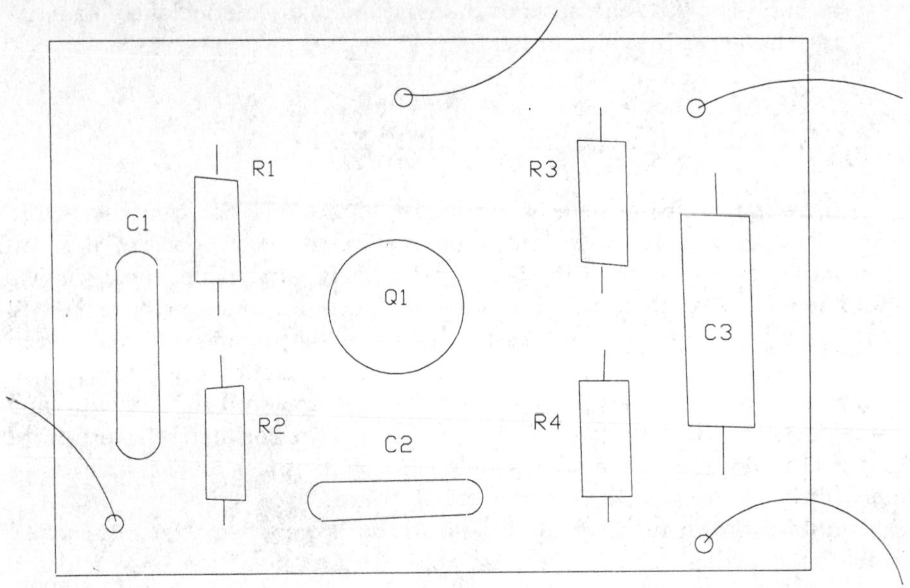

Figure 4-7 The second step in drawing a schematic is to identify each part with a unique number, if these are not already printed on the PC board.

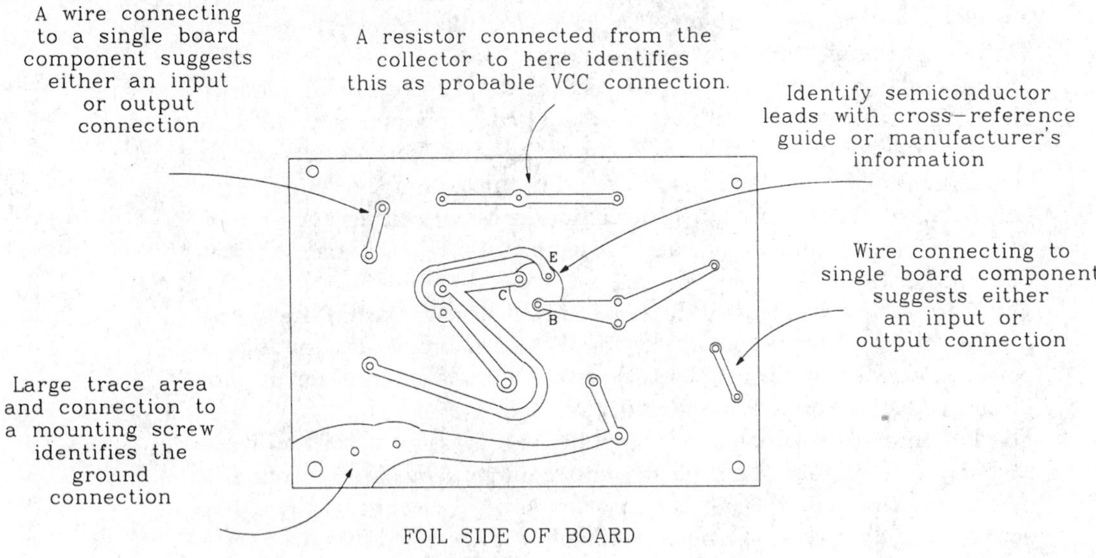

Figure 4-8 The third step is to identify the input, output, ground, and Vcc leads.

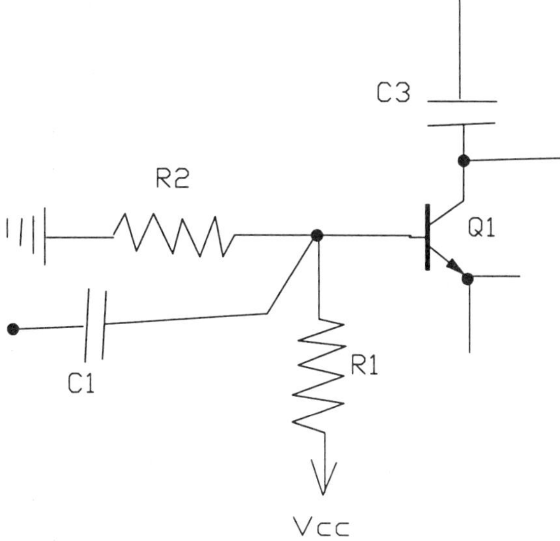

Figure 4-9 The fourth step is to begin drawing the circuit, stepping through the components one at a time.

point. Label the schematic with each of these components, using the identifying codes of R1, C1, or whatever you have assigned on the layout drawing. See Figure 4–9.

5. The fifth step is to select one of the components and "go through" it to the lead on the other end. At this new point, again draw all of the components that connect to it. You may find that this end of a component connects to an unused end of one of the components that you drew in step 3.
6. The sixth step is to continue step 5, going through one at a time until all of the components of the diagram are interconnected. To avoid forgetting a branch wire, make a large black dot at each node (each intersection) of the wiring. Make a short line pointing out of the dot at each node for the paths you see but cannot pursue at the moment. Come back to each dot as soon as you have finished drawing all of the components. Then check to be sure that all of the components that are connected there are accounted for in your drawing and that all of the short lines have been completed to their respective components. Be sure to label the components in each case with the reference designation numbers of step 1. See Figure 4–10.
7. The seventh step is a check for accuracy. Check the first complete drawing against the actual circuit once more, to be sure you haven't missed a part or a connection.
8. The eighth step is to clean up your drawing. As you straighten it out, the goal is to get the inputs on the left, the outputs on the right, Vcc leads from the top, and grounds (use as many different grounds as

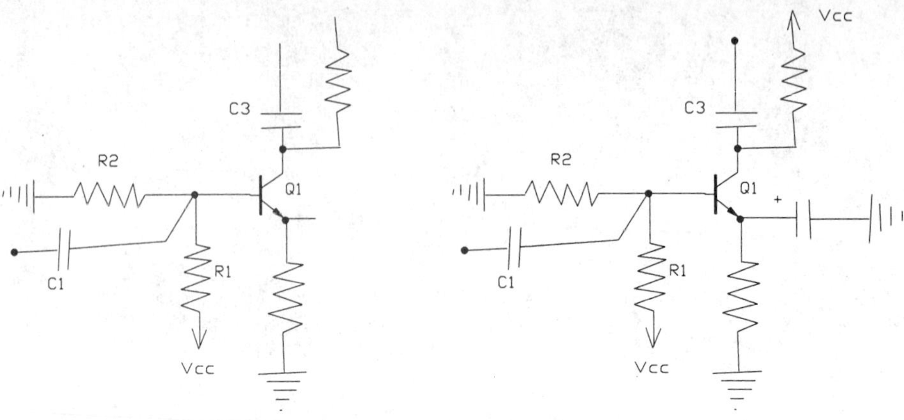

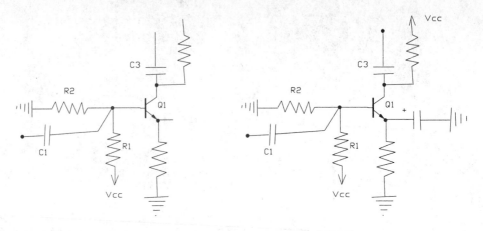

Figure 4-10 The sixth step is to continue drawing until no loose ends are left.

you wish) going downward. This redrawing process may require several drawings, with each representing an improvement over the last. By the time you finish, you might have something like Figure 4–11.

Once the circuit begins to look like something familiar, you may be able to draw the final circuit more easily if you have handy a similar schematic, or you may draw it according to more-or-less standard circuits, such as an amplifier stage. These typical circuits may be available in the reference books that you already own. Reference books for linear circuits, digital integrated circuits, and transistors often have circuits that you can use as models.

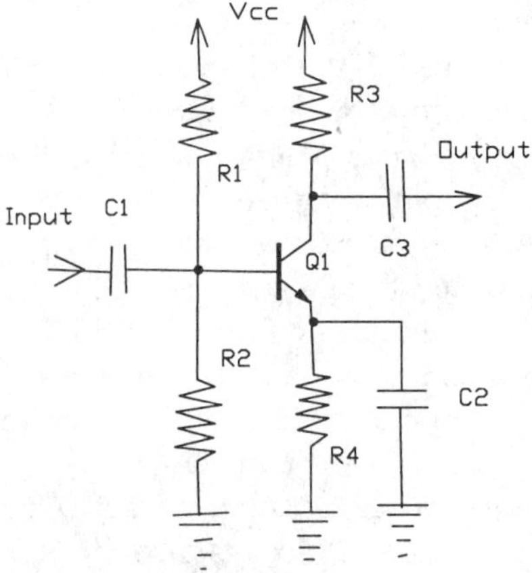

Figure 4-11 The eighth and last step is to clean up the drawing, with inputs on the left, outputs on the right, Vcc from the top, and grounds all going down.

CHAPTER SUMMARY

- Safety rules must be learned and practiced until they become habits.
- Avoid high-voltage circuits while energized, discharge capacitors before touching or measuring resistance, remove metal jewelry while troubleshooting, use an isolation transformer when appropriate, don't assume low voltage, have one hand in a back pocket or on insulation at all times, and connect the test ground lead first, disconnecting it last.
- Besides a schematic, it is also of great value to have the block diagram, theory of operation, and parts list for a given piece of equipment.
- Schematics can be customized and displayed to your advantage with a little effort.
- Standard schematic-circuit letter designations show the kind of component referenced.
- Drawing a schematic from the physical circuitry is time-consuming but may be the only way to obtain one.

REVIEW QUESTIONS

1. Most instruments, such as a multimeter, have two test leads. Which should be connected first and disconnected last, and why?
2. You are asked to repair a television set. Upon removing the cabinet, you see that there is no power transformer. What can you use to help prevent electrical shock while working on this TV? Use a/an _______.
3. You are about to disconnect one coaxial cable from another. What should you remember about this simple act of disconnecting them?
4. Very-large-value capacitors can produce heavy discharge currents if shorted during troubleshooting procedures. What can be done to prevent possible damage due to these large currents?
5. Name the two different dangers of wearing metal jewelry while troubleshooting live circuits.
6. Name the two most common ways of damaging a multimeter.
7. What should you note when removing screws from equipment?
8. What is the worst thing to do with cabinet screws that have been removed from good equipment?
9. When first beginning the study of a new piece of equipment, what graphics aid in the instruction book gives an overall picture of how the equipment works?
10. What kind of diagram uses features of both block diagrams and schematics?
11. What kind of diagram is always drawn with pin numbers in order?

12. What approximate current is considered potentially fatal if passed through the chest?
13. What two parts of the instruction book would be of most value to understand the smallest electronic detail of a piece of equipment?
14. How many alternatives are there to consider if you need a schematic but do not have one?
15. Approximately how much more difficult is a given troubleshooting project if you have no schematic diagram?
16. Your schematic shows a symbol that is unfamiliar, beside which is the code "TP." What is it?
17. You must repair each one of several identical units. You have no solid-state tester and no schematic, not even a similar one. The equipment manufacturer has gone out of business, and you do not wish to draw your own schematic. What alternative is still open?

Troubleshooting with a Voltmeter

5

CHAPTER OBJECTIVES

This chapter covers the details of using a DC voltmeter to find a problem in any electronic circuit. When a component fails in an analog circuit, the DC voltages usually shift considerably from normal values. The reason for most malfunctions can be found by the analytical use of a DC voltmeter. At the conclusion of this chapter, the student should be able to:

- Choose proper test leads.
- *Effectively* use either an analog volt-ohm-milliammeter (VOM) or digital multimeter (DMM) for voltage troubleshooting.
- Properly use an oscilloscope for DC voltage measurement.
- Estimate DC voltages within a DC circuit with a minimum of actually listed voltages.
- Recite the five steps necessary to localize the problem of either a lower- or a higher-than-normal voltage.
- Use an ammeter properly and understand how it may adversely affect certain circuits.

VOLTMETER TEST PROBES

The probes used with any voltmeter should be sharp and should either be of small diameter or have a long, narrow taper with insulation down to the tip. The sharp tip is necessary to pierce any contaminants, solder-mask, or residue of soldering flux on a PC board. The sharp tip is also very good for preventing the probe from slipping from one trace to another, or worse, shorting two traces together. Ordinary test probes may be improved by fitting them with heat-shrink plastic tubing to cover the ends of the probes, leaving only the tips (perhaps 1/16th of an inch) exposed. See Figure 5–1.

Surface-mounted devices (SMDs) require special care when using test leads on them. Scraping some SMDs will change their value, permanently damaging them. The pressure applied with a test probe near the end of some of these components can break the bond to the termination or the solder joint. Whenever test leads are used on SMD circuits, the probe tip should always be pressed against the circuit traces or pads, and never to the SMD itself. To make it easier to attach

Figure 5–1 These test leads have sharp, long tips to avoid shorting traces or pins on printed circuit boards. (Photo courtesy of Huntron Instruments Inc.)

test equipment, some SMD circuits have small loops of wire already provided for test points. These test points are sometimes identified with a "JT" marking ("Jumper, Test").

Test leads are subject to considerable punishment in normal use. An intermittent test lead can produce strange readings that can very easily mislead the technician into thinking the equipment under test is causing the problem. Test leads should be checked frequently for continuity using the lowest resistance scale. Short the leads together and gently pull on the wires, especially where they enter the terminations on each end. A reading of more than a few tenths of an ohm indicates bad leads.

It may be convenient to provide the black (negative) voltmeter test lead with a small alligator clip. This is more convenient than a test probe to attach the lead to the circuit common point. It leaves one hand free to leaf through schematics while the other hand is occupied in taking voltage readings with the red (positive) lead. In the tests that follow it will be assumed that the voltmeter in use has the negative lead connected to the circuit common.

Make it a habit to always avoid touching the exposed tips of the test probes when taking voltage measurements. The reasoning behind this is obvious: carelessly touching the test lead tips is exactly the same as touching the circuit itself. If dangerous voltage is present in the circuit, a shock will result.

At the other extreme are very low-voltage and high-impedance circuits like FET input circuits. While they would not be dangerous to touch, the voltages in these circuits can be seriously affected by touching the meter leads, which can provide a relatively low resistance path in parallel with the circuit.

USING THE ANALOG VOLTMETER FOR VOLTAGE READINGS

The volt-ohm-milliammeter (VOM) is an instrument that is still in common use. This relatively simple and inexpensive tool can detect *most* failures, especially in DC and low-frequency audio circuits. It is based on the d'Arsonval meter movement. This is a mechanism that consists of a tiny coil which is free to move within a fixed magnetic field. A pointer is attached to the moving coil, and as current flowing through the coil is increased, the coil and the pointer are deflected by the interaction of the two resulting magnetic fields. This kind of meter is current-operated and draws its operating current from the circuit under test. Since the coil has a relatively low resistance, resistors are used in series to limit the current at higher voltage inputs. Changing these resistors (called multiplier resistors) results in making the meter indicate different voltages at full-scale readings. A series of multipliers with a switching arrangement is shown in Figure 5–2.

Since the VOM uses current from the circuit under test, this instrument

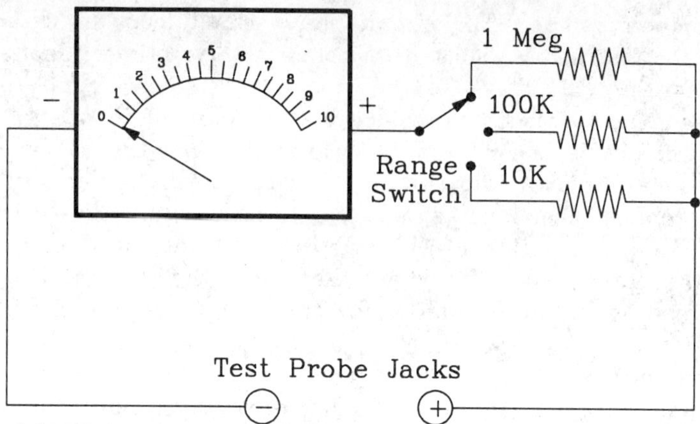

Figure 5–2 Simplified voltmeter with range switching.

can load a high-impedance circuit and give a voltage reading that is incorrect, indicating a voltage lower than is actually present when the voltmeter is not connected. There is a quick way to tell if a multiple-range voltmeter is loading the circuit under test: take a voltage reading on two different voltage ranges. *If the indicated voltage changes appreciably downward on the lower of the two ranges, the meter is loading the circuit excessively.* This loading effect can be a serious disadvantage when measuring voltages in low voltage, high-impedance circuits.

The amount of loading that a VOM will present to a circuit can be easily calculated. On the face of the instrument or in its specifications, a specification of "ohms-per-volt" will be found. Inexpensive meters may have a specification of perhaps 1,000Ω/volt, where a higher-quality meter often has 20,000Ω/volt. Calculating the loading effect for a given range (remember that different resistances are switched into the circuit for each range) is a matter of multiplying this ohms-per-volt figure by the range selected. As an example, if one has a 20,000Ω/volt meter, the 50-volt scale will have a loading effect of

$$20{,}000 \times 50 = 1{,}000{,}000\ \Omega$$

Several instruments were designed to minimize this loading effect while continuing to use the same meter movement. An amplifier circuit with a high-impedance input was placed ahead of the meter. The first of these instruments was the vacuum-tube voltmeter (VTVM). By using the input circuit of a vacuum tube to sample a circuit under test, it was possible to drive the meter movement with the plate circuit of the tube. This instrument was usually operated from 120-V AC because of the relatively high power demand of the vacuum tube.

Later, the transistorized voltmeter (TVM) and the field-effect transis-

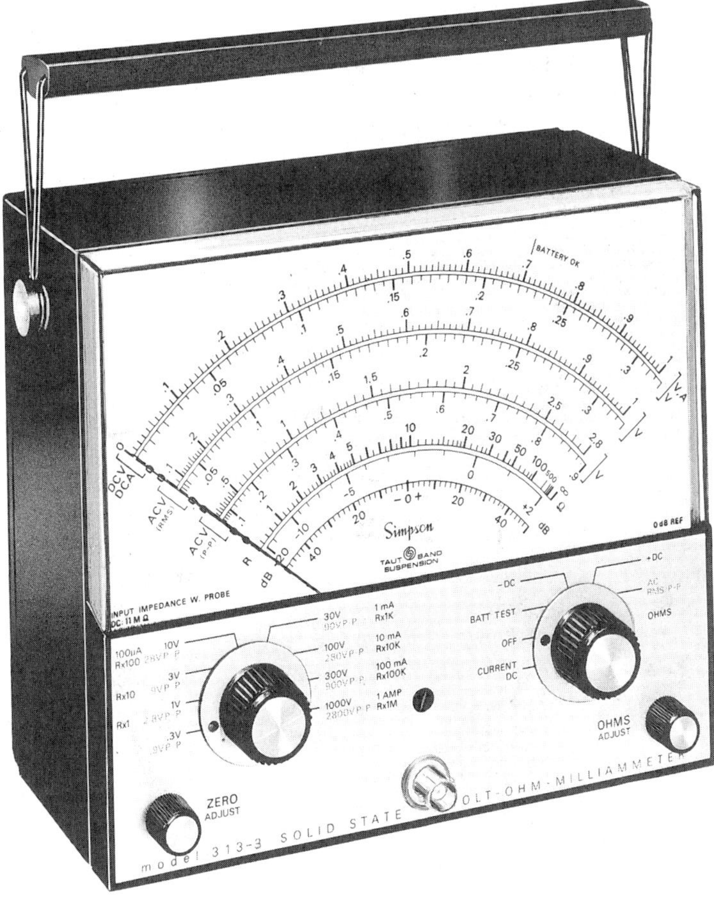

Figure 5–3 A transistorized TVM, which minimized the loading effects of a conventional VOM. (Courtesy of Simpson Electric Co.)

torized voltmeters were developed, using more modern components. These instruments were portable, a big advantage over the VTVM. See Figure 5–3.

The accuracy required of a VOM *for routine troubleshooting* seems to be an overemphasized specification. A simple, inexpensive VOM that measures within 5 percent would be quite sufficient for most voltage troubleshooting, particularly when the symptoms indicate a complete failure and when only DC and low-frequency audio circuits are the subject of the job. Voltage accuracy becomes important when troubleshooting equipment that is almost at normal working specifications or when designing and developing new circuits.

When using a VOM for precision readings, select a range that puts the needle somewhere in the upper two-thirds of the scale. Look at the meter straight on. If there is a mirror behind the needle, aligning the needle with its reflection, which greatly reduces parallax error. The presence of a mirror behind the needle implies a precision meter.

Whenever a VOM is handled a great deal, such as when taking it to a new job site or into the field for servicing, it should be switched to a specified range setting that will afford the best protection for the fragile meter movement. The coil of the meter movement can be shorted out on this scale, which puts a magnetic brake on the meter needle. This helps prevent the needle from banging on the end pegs. Some meters call this special range "Transit" or "Off." Another caution to keep in mind is to handle the instrument by the handle rather than picking it up with your fingers on the glass. The pressure of gripping it on the glass can sometimes cause the glass to come loose from its mounting in the case, forcing it into the needle and risking severe damage to the needle.

An analog meter movement has an advantage over a digital meter with no analog bar graph: slow changes in voltages are more easily interpreted when using an analog indicator. Some circuits require monitoring of voltages that change with adjustments that are made during alignment procedures, for instance. These slow changes are easier to see and interpret when viewed on an analog display than they are to interpret in the changing digits of a digital meter.

USING THE DIGITAL MULTIMETER FOR VOLTAGE READINGS

The digital multimeter is the latest and best all-around meter to use. On the voltage ranges, it has very little loading effect regardless of range, which is typically 10 million ohms (see Figure 5–4). A good-quality 20,000 ohms-per-volt VOM, by comparison, has an input resistance of only 60,000 Ω on the 3-volt range.

In addition to this major advantage, the digital meter has the following additional advantages over a VOM:

- The DMM is better for measuring precision voltage sources since the accuracy of a DMM is commonly 1 percent and sometimes as good as 0.03 percent.
- A constant source of voltage will yield the same reading, no matter who may be operating the DMM. Operator interpolation is not a factor in the accuracy of a reading as it is with the analog meter movement.
- DMMs commonly will give voltage readings regardless of the polarity of the input DC voltage. The polarity is shown as positive (+) when the input voltage is positive on the meter's red lead and as negative (–) when reversed from this condition. This avoids the frequent reversal of the test leads necessary when using a VOM on circuits having both positive and negative power supplies.

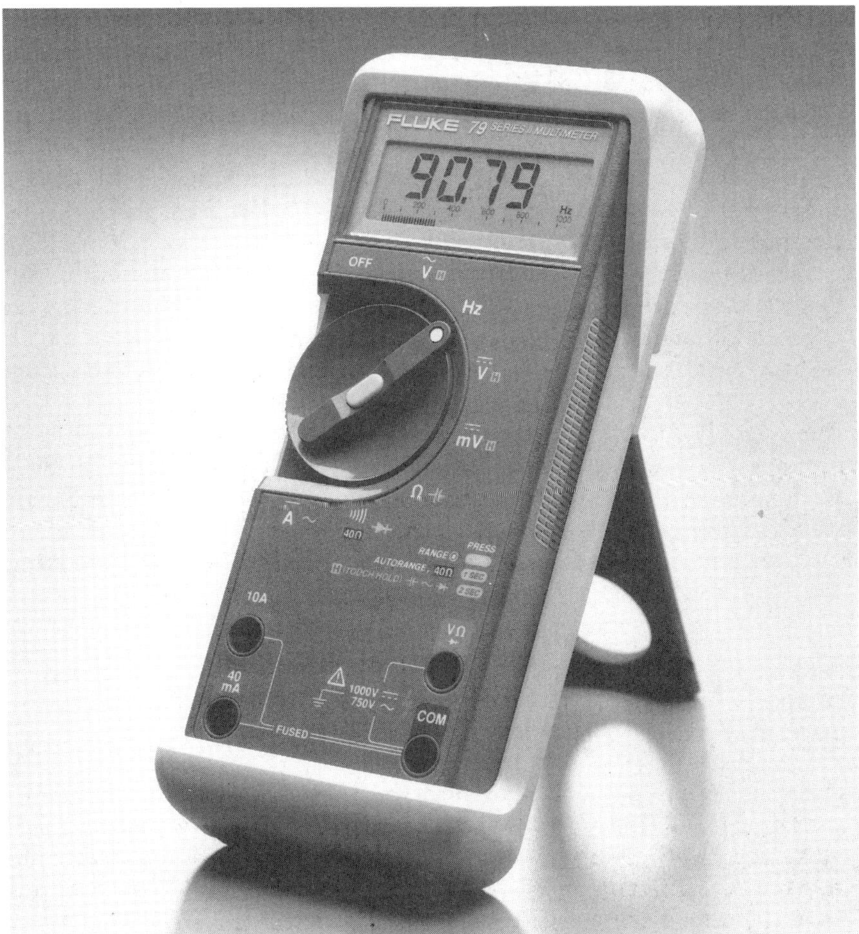

Figure 5–4 This Fluke meter is an excellent value in a digital multimeter. (Reproduced with permission from the John Fluke Mfg. Co., Inc.)

- The DMM amplifies and measures small voltages with accuracy. For example, reading a voltage of 155 millivolts is very difficult and inaccurate with an ordinary VOM, but simple and precise with a DMM.
- Some DMMs have the autoranging feature. This is an attractive feature when troubleshooting. The technician does not have to manually change the voltage range switch while holding a probe with the other hand. Manual range changing can be a real problem at times. Because of the light weight of most meters, when you turn the switch, the whole meter tends to twist around, while the range-change switch fails to move at all. Autoranging eliminates this annoyance. The feature may also be disabled, if desired.
- A feature called Touch Hold™, which is available in the Fluke line of meters, enables the device to hold a reading once it is taken, even with

the probes removed from the circuit. This allows a technician to give full attention to the placement of the test probes without the need to watch for a reading on the DMM. When the DMM has recorded a constant voltage for a half-second, it locks the display on the DMM and sounds a beep. The test leads may then be disconnected and the reading on the DMM may be taken at leisure. To take another reading, the technician simply applies the probes to a new voltage. The DMM will sense a new reading and lock it into the display as before.

- A bar graph display is a useful feature on the 70 and 80 series of Fluke meters. This graph is much like the needle of an analog display but offers additional advantages over a meter movement. The graph will respond faster to changes than a meter needle and will also autorange.

There is only one minor disadvantage to a DMM: the battery required by this meter will eventually wear out. A DMM battery may last from 200 to 2,000 hours, depending on the manufacturer and model. (Remember that the VOM draws power from the circuit under test and requires no battery for voltage readings.) Battery life is a major consideration when selecting a DMM. The Fluke model 77 claims in excess of 2,000 hours of operation; almost 3 months of continuous use or a year of normal workdays.

USING AN OSCILLOSCOPE FOR VOLTAGE READINGS

The oscilloscope can be used to measure DC voltages if its vertical amplifier is DC-coupled. Inexpensive oscilloscopes cannot be used to measure DC because their vertical amplifiers are capacitor-coupled and are thus only usable on AC signals. A look at the front panel of an oscilloscope will tell if it is suitable for DC measurements. If it is, it will have a switch labeled "DC/AC." This switch will be located near the vertical input connector. The same switch may also have "Gnd" as a third position. The absence of such a switch indicates an instrument that is good only for measuring signals of about 60 Hz or more. The application of DC to the input of this kind of scope will result in the upward or downward deflection of the sweep for only a moment, after which the sweep will return to the original position.

Whenever an oscilloscope is operated, the spot on the screen should not be allowed to remain stationary, particularly at high intensities. A bright, stationary spot will burn the phosphor on the screen, resulting in permanent damage at that point. Keep the spot moving or turn down the intensity to a very low degree of brightness.

Using an oscilloscope to routinely measure DC voltages during troubleshooting is not very efficient. It is usually faster and more convenient to use a DMM or VOM for DC troubleshooting. However, if the oscilloscope is the only instrument available, it can be used.

A digital storage oscilloscope (DSO) is a convenient instrument to *permanently record* slowly changing DC voltages. A DSO can have extremely slow sweep rates, as slow as 50 seconds per centimeter. At this rate, the sweep takes 500 seconds (8 minutes) to cross the display. Recording slow DC changes becomes very easy when slow sweeps are coupled with the ability of this instrument to print out (on a dot matrix printer) a hard copy of the screen display. The roll mode of a DSO is very much like that of a paper strip-recorder.

Notes on Oscilloscope Setup

The basic oscilloscope should be a familiar instrument to a technician. Like it or not, however, it is a fairly complicated instrument to learn to use well. Here are some points to remember when using one of these instruments, particularly if this is an instrument that the technician has not used before, such as one taken from the company storeroom. Certain checks need to be made, particularly if someone else used it last.

The vertical positioning control should usually be adjusted so that the center of the screen represents ground. If the circuit under test has no negative voltages to measure, it will produce pictures of twice the size if you set the ground level at the bottom of the graticule (gridwork) of the screen rather than at the middle. If the beam cannot be found, look for the push button labeled "Beam finder" to get an idea of in which direction the spot or sweep has been deflected off the screen.

A test should occasionally be made to see if the trace position remains stable when changing the vertical amplifier attenuator (range switch). This avoids having to constantly adjust the vertical positioning each time the attenuator position is changed. Set the input switch to "Gnd." This prevents outside signals from affecting the vertical amplifier. Put the trace near the center of the screen by using the vertical positioning control. Now move the vertical attenuator switch through all its settings. The center position should not change appreciably. If it does, find the adjustment labeled "DC Bal" ("DC Balance"). Sometimes the trace will even leave the screen because of a gross misadjustment of this control. The proper adjustment of the DC Bal control will minimize the shifting of the trace as the range switch is changed. This adjustment should be made whenever a shift of the DC level with range changes is noticed.

When using an oscilloscope to measure DC voltages, it is usually best to set the sweep speed-range switch once and then leave it alone. Since there is no vertical variation of the trace due to an AC signal, changing the sweep speed affects only the flicker of the horizontal line. Any sweep speed fast enough to avoid flicker is suitable, such as 1 millisecond per division or 100 Hz, depending on how the horizontal range switch is labeled.

The oscilloscope should be used with an appropriate probe for measuring DC voltages. The full gain of the vertical channel can be used without the pickup of hum and noise if a proper probe is used. If a probe is not available, two wires may be used, but the hum pickup and noise may be excessive at high gain settings. Under these conditions, the technician may not be able to tell which signals are coming from the circuit and which are attributable to stray signal pickup.

It is seldom necessary to change the vertical position (the zero voltage reference line) when measuring DC voltages. The vertical reference level should be set at the center or the bottom of the screen and left there; to change it often invites confusion. Changing the vertical sensitivity of the oscilloscope during testing can also be confusing. Once the sensitivity has been adjusted so that the maximum possible circuit voltage is at the top of the screen, the range-switch setting should be noted. This is the "basic setting." If lower settings are used when observing small voltages, the switch should be immediately returned to the basic setting. This will help keep the relative amplitudes of the signals more clearly in mind.

The input circuit of an oscilloscope usually connects the grounded side of the probe to the power-line ground. In some circuits this could create a danger to the circuit or even, possibly, to the technician. Before connecting the ground side of a probe to the circuit common, be absolutely sure that the circuit will not be damaged by connection to an earth ground. In some cases it may be necessary to use an isolation transformer on the circuit under test or to supply power to the oscilloscope itself. Generally, however, this is not a problem since most electronic circuits use a power transformer which provides the isolation needed.

The oscilloscope has an advantage over a DC voltmeter for measuring voltages during troubleshooting: it will show AC signals and DC levels at the same time. In some cases the unexpected AC signal shown on an oscilloscope can lead the technician directly to the cause of a problem. This situation otherwise might escape attention for some time if using only a voltmeter. The oscilloscope will also amplify very small DC voltages that a VOM would not show. Figure 5–5 illustrates this point.

5.2 USING VOLTAGES TO FIND ANALOG PROBLEMS

DC voltage measurements are a primary means of locating electronic problems. In the majority of cases, a defect in circuitry will also shift the circuit voltages out of the ordinary, thus making it possible to find the defects by comparing normal and abnormal voltages.

In the course of troubleshooting with a voltmeter, it is first necessary to *visualize a schematic diagram as DC would "see" it.* Figure 5–6 illustrates this concept. Note that the capacitors in the figure are not drawn in the equivalent circuit. This is because a good capacitor is an open circuit to DC: it simply is not there. The inductors are shown as low resistances because the DC sees them only as their equivalent low values of DC resistance, the resistance of the wire within them.

By this visualization, the technician must be able to estimate the DC voltage to be expected at any point within the diagram. This is necessary

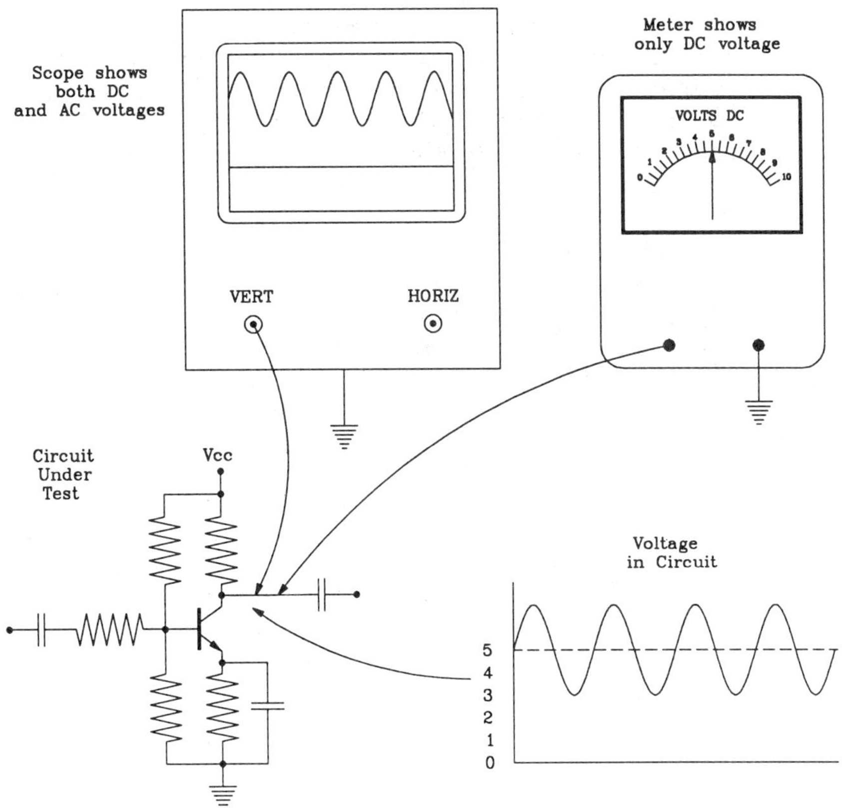

Figure 5–5 A DC meter cannot show an AC signal superimposed upon it.

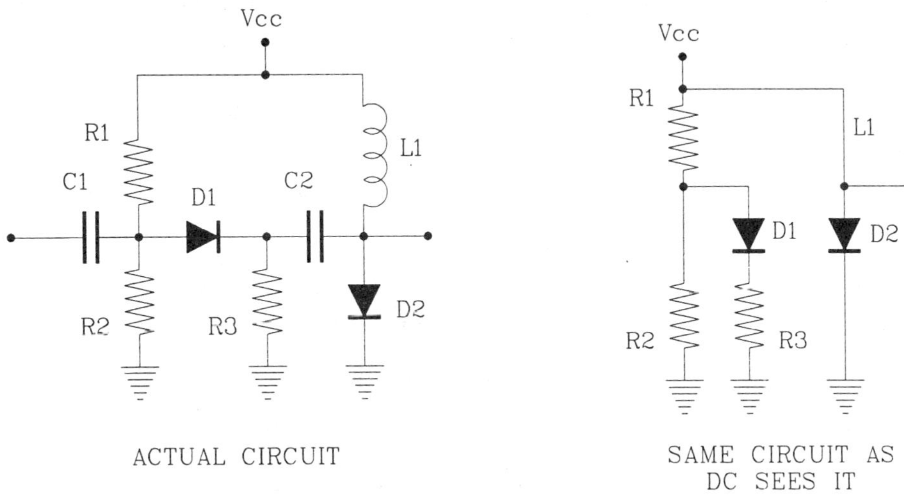

Figure 5–6 Schematic of a circuit, and the same circuit as DC would see it.

because in the real world, very few voltages are given on a schematic; thus, many voltage values must be estimated. When a voltage far from what was expected is encountered, the technician can then recheck the estimate of the proper voltage to be confident of the reading. If there is still a large discrepancy, the cause of that abnormal reading must then be determined.

If circuits were made up of only resistors, estimation would be easier, but real circuits also involve diodes (which may or may not be conducting), transistors, and other nonlinear devices. The estimation of DC voltages in any given circuit requires a bit of both practice and thought.

Understanding the division of a DC voltage across series and parallel loads is essential to the ability to roughly estimate expected voltages. In the words of the mathematician, the voltage will divide in proportion to the ratio of resistances in series. Put more simply, if the resistors are equal, there should be an equal split of voltage between them. If they are not equal, the higher resistance will have proportionately more voltage across it than the other. In any parallel situation, all of the parallel components must have an identical voltage across them. It is very important to grasp the concept involved here: The feel for proper voltage division must become intuitive, like "second nature," when using voltages to troubleshoot circuitry.

How can one estimate the voltages to expect at a particular point in a circuit? This involves the preceding concepts of series and parallel components and how the voltages behave, along with some judgment. Consider the circuit of Figure 5–7.

Note point A in Figure 5–7. This voltage has already been provided. It may have been on the schematic or obtained from a voltage table in the instruction manual. If only a table of voltages is provided, it is a good practice to put the table values directly on the schematic for quicker reference. However, the voltage at point B will have to be estimated by the technician.

The ability to estimate unlisted voltages in a normal circuit speeds the troubleshooting process. The voltage at point B of Figure 5–7 should be approximately 16 volts above the circuit common. This value is arrived at by applying the principle of ratio and proportion. If the ratio of the resistance values is two to one (in our example, an approximation of 47:22), the voltage ratio will also be two to one, with the total being 24 (the value of the supply voltage). If 47:22 is roughly equivalent to 2:1, then the ratio of the voltage input to voltage output (E1:E2) will be about 2:1, and the total must be 24. Therefore, an estimate of the voltages would be 16:8 (total of 24), the circuit total voltage. The larger voltage will be dropped across the larger resistor.

The voltages in a linear circuit vary in direct proportion with variations in the supply voltage. For example, if the 24-V DC supply was a few percentage points higher in voltage than normal, the voltage at point B would also be that same percentage higher than the estimated voltage, as it was based on 24 volts.

Keep in mind that the actual resistors do not have the precise resistance

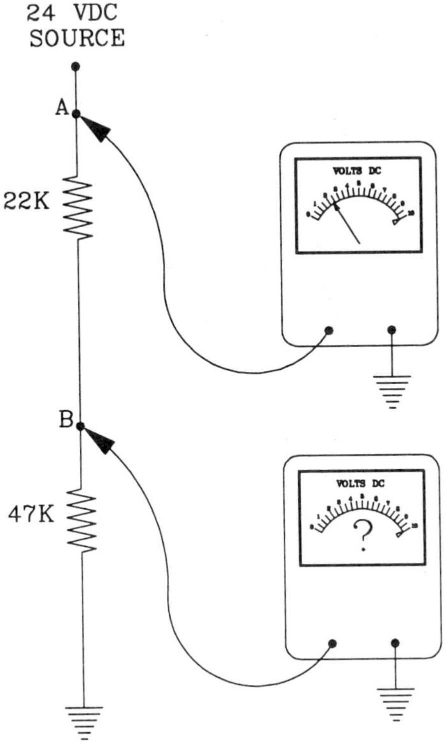

Figure 5–7 Estimating voltages not listed on the schematic.

that is marked on them. Carbon composition resistors have a tolerance rating that allows them to be off as much as 5, 10, or even 20 percent from their marked values. Metal-film resistors will be closer to their marked value (commonly within less than 1 percent). Considering that resistor values might be off by as much as 10 percent (as an example), a technician troubleshooting according to the estimated voltage at point B of Figure 5–7 would probably accept voltages from 14 to 18 volts before suspecting that something was wrong. As a matter of practicality, technicians seldom take the time to actually calculate the possible voltage limits in view of the maximum and minimum possible resistances and the percentages of source voltage variation. This ability to estimate voltages can be developed by experience, a bit of intuition, and a good feel for Ohm's law.

If the circuit under repair is highly calibrated and precise, the technician should accept less deviation in all readings. For example, if the circuit of Figure 5–7 were in the input attenuator circuit of a precision circuit such as an analog meter, the voltage at point B would be very critical. A percentage point deviating in either way from the calculated value could determine whether or not the instrument was in calibration.

Another clue that an experienced technician will take into account while troubleshooting with voltage readings is the type of failure for which the equipment is under repair. For instance, if the equipment is defective because it simply quit working, there is no reason to expect that a voltage only 10 percent from normal is the cause of the failure. The same low voltage reading, however, could have a direct bearing in the case of marginal performance.

5.3 THE PEROZZO METHOD: A MOST IMPORTANT CONCEPT

The principles that follow lie at the very heart of troubleshooting. The reader should understand these principles very thoroughly, for they should be applied whenever using a voltmeter and often for an oscilloscope as well.

WHEN THE MEASURED VOLTAGE IS TOO LOW

If the voltmeter in Figure 5–8 reads a voltage that is too low, there are five reasons why this might be the case. *These are the basis of voltage troubleshooting and should be memorized.*

1. The source itself is low in voltage.
2. The resistance across the voltmeter probes (in parallel with the probes) is too low.
3. The resistance back toward the source is too high.
4. The voltmeter is loading the circuit.
5. The voltmeter is defective.

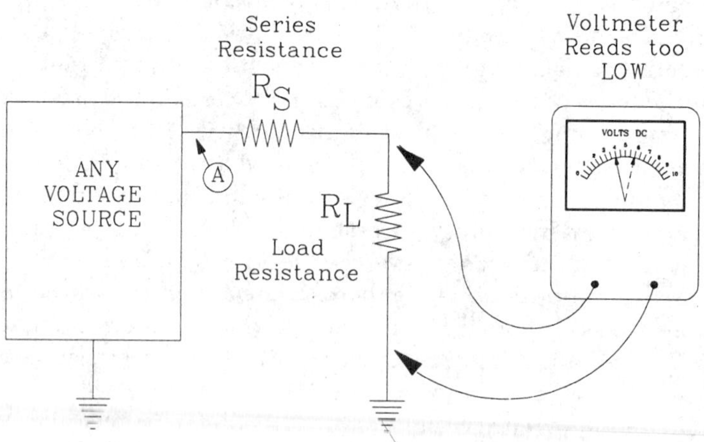

Figure 5–8 Analyzing the cause of a voltage that is too low.

Let's examine each of these possibilities further. Possibilities 1, 2, and 3 warrant particularly careful attention since they are by far the most common causes of low voltage readings in electronic circuits.

Possibility 1 is that the source itself is too low in voltage. Check the source at point A for abnormally low voltages. This may be due to low line voltage, a defective DC power supply, or weak batteries. The internal resistance of the source itself may have increased and be causing the problem. (This is what happens with worn-out batteries.) Note that a good voltage reading at the source eliminates possibilities 1 and 5.

Possibility 2 occurs when the circuit resistance *in parallel* with the meter, R_L (across the meter probes), has *decreased.* This is typically the case when a circuit has an overload of the circuitry or, in the extreme instance, a dead short across it and a resulting zero voltage reading.

Possibility 3 is that a resistance *in series* with the meter, (looking back toward the voltage source) has *increased* in resistance. R_S of the circuit represents any resistance in series, external to the source itself. In extreme cases, this could be a completely open circuit with a resulting zero voltage reading. Don't forget that R_S includes any ground or return path.

Possibility 4 should be considered when using a VOM, with its inherent low resistance, across high-impedance, "weak" circuits. This is particularly a problem on the low voltage ranges of the VOM. Some circuits such as FETs, CMOS, and vacuum tube circuits have very high impedances and are susceptible to this type of error.

NOTE: The Fluke company provides a special function on some of its meters which allows precision voltage measurement in low-voltage, very-high-impedance circuits. Their Models 87 and 8060A, for instance, can be switched to have an input impedance of 40,000,000,000 Ω (40 Gigohms).

Possibility 5 is that the meter has been overloaded (had its needle slammed into either end-peg) or dropped, or is otherwise giving readings that are too low because of problems within the meter. It might also be a case of the meter needle dragging on the meter glass. This drag can be caused by the glass being loose or even by excessive static buildup on the glass, attracting the needle into the glass. The best check for this possibility is to substitute a known good meter for a comparison of readings.

WHEN THE MEASURED VOLTAGE IS TOO HIGH

If the voltmeter in Figure 5–9 reads a voltage that is too high, there are five possible reasons why this might be so (these are mostly commonsense reversals of the reasons for low voltage readings).

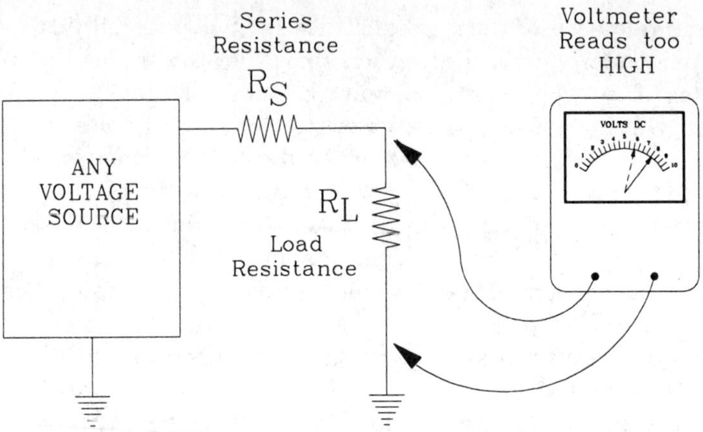

Figure 5–9 Analyzing the cause of a voltage that is too high.

1. The source itself is high in voltage.
2. The resistance across the voltmeter probes (in parallel with the probes) is too high.
3. The resistance back toward the source is too low.
4. The voltmeter is *not* loading the circuit sufficiently.
5. The voltmeter is defective.

Possibilities 1, 2, and 3 deserve careful attention for the same reasons as previously mentioned. Possibility 1 is that the source itself is too high in voltage. Check the source for an abnormally high voltage. A good voltage reading at the source eliminates possibilities 1 and 5.

Possibility 2 occurs when the circuit resistance *in parallel* with the meter, R_L (across the meter probes), has *increased.* This is typically the case when a current path in the load has opened or there is an abnormally reduced load on the voltage source.

Possibility 3 is that a resistance *in series* with the meter (looking back toward the voltage source) has *decreased* in resistance. R_S of the circuit represents any resistance in series external to the voltage source. To be specific, this is often a voltage source–filtering resistor or a voltage regulator pass transistor that has shorted from the collector to the emitter.

Possibility 4 should be considered when using a digital voltmeter or FET-amplifying meter, with its high impedance input, to measure across high-impedance circuits. There are still a few schematics that specify the use of a lower impedance meter for taking voltage readings in fairly high-impedance circuits. In this case, the readings given depend upon a certain amount of loading by the meter. The use of a better meter

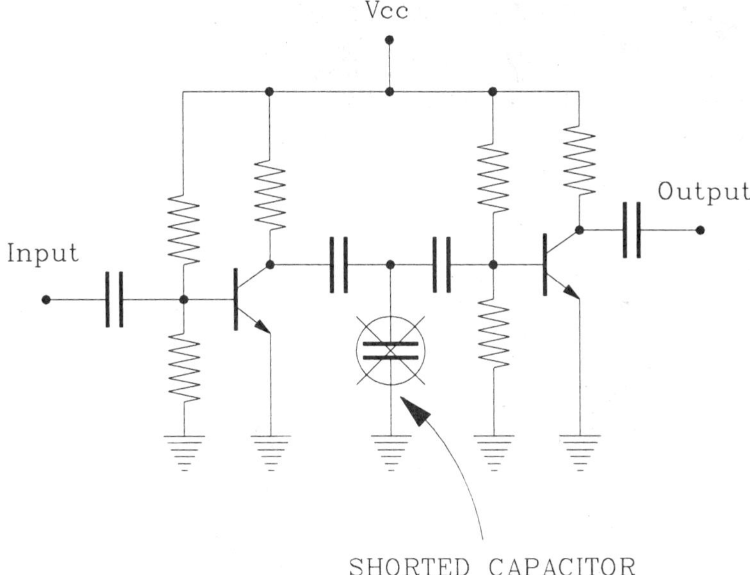

Figure 5–10 Example of a circuit defect that DC voltage readings would not detect. No DC voltages would be affected, but the circuit would not amplify signals.

will result in a truer voltage reading, but it will be higher than specified on the schematic.

Possibility 5 is that the meter is giving readings that are too high because of problems within the meter itself. Again, the best check of this possibility is to substitute a known good meter for a comparison of readings.

Use these five items as a check list, eliminating them one by one for each problem encountered during voltage troubleshooting. Start with possibility 1, jumping to 5 if there is doubt. This leaves 4 to be considered as a remote possibility, and 2 and 3 as the two remaining, most common possibilities.

These principles of voltage troubleshooting apply to AC and other signal tracing methods as well. Missing signals, for instance, may be considered as voltages that are too low: possibly indicating a short to ground where the probe is sampling or an open component back toward the signal source.

Most problems in analog circuits can be located with a voltmeter, but not all. A circuit problem such as that shown in Figure 5–10 will not be evident when using only a DC voltmeter. This sort of problem can be found easily by using an oscilloscope or an AC voltmeter, however.

5.4 USING THE ANALOG OR DIGITAL METER FOR CURRENT MEASUREMENTS

Troubleshooting with an ammeter is like measuring water flow through a pipe. If there is too little current flow, either the source voltage is too low for the normal flow of current or there is too much resistance in the load for the proper flow to occur. Lack of any current flow can be caused by too low or no source voltage or, as is usually the case, an open circuit that prevents any current flow at all. The reverse of each of the above situations is also true; too much current flow results from too high a voltage source or too low a load resistance.

Current measurements are seldom used in troubleshooting. Over 95 percent of troubleshooting is done with a voltage-based instrument such as a voltmeter or oscilloscope. Two possible exceptions are the use of the current tracer instrument (covered in Chapters 6 and 15), and the clamp-on ammeter (discussed later in this chapter). The reason why current troubleshooting is not often used is that it usually requires physically opening the circuit, a procedure that is troublesome and sometimes damaging.

CAUTION: Never Apply A Voltage To An Ammeter!

The internal resistance of an ammeter is near zero. Besides shorting the voltage source, the full current capability of the source is shorted through the instrument.

Measuring current usually means breaking the circuit and putting the meter into the circuit so that all of the current flows through the meter. See Figure 5–11.

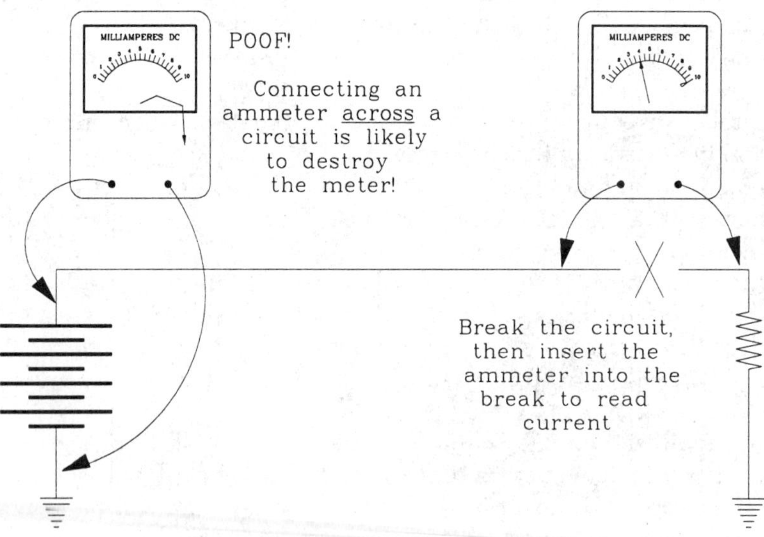

Figure 5–11 How to ruin an ammeter and how to connect one properly.

Figure 5–12 A normal-through phone jack commonly used for current measurement.

Breaking a circuit for troubleshooting purposes is very seldom done. Where current measurements are routinely made, there will be a provision for easy insertion of the meter. This is often a normal-through jack. A normal-through jack will allow the normal circuit current to flow through itself via contacts built into the jack. When an ammeter is plugged in the switch contacts open and the current flows through the ammeter. See Figure 5–12.

When you insert an ammeter into a circuit, you are also inserting a certain amount of resistance. Although this resistance is low, the voltage drop across it can cause a disturbance of low-voltage, low-resistance circuits and, thereby, cause inaccurate current readings. Such a voltage drop introduced into a circuit is called *burden voltage*. If a circuit behaves differently after an ammeter has been inserted, the meter is causing a change in the circuit in this way. A high-quality instrument such as a Fluke model 87 will insert about .03 Ω into a circuit on its 10-ampere scale, 1.5 Ω on the milliampere scale, and 100 Ω on the microampere scale. Other meters may insert 10 times this resistance, which would, of course, cause much more severe circuit changes because of putting the meter into the circuit.

An alternative way of measuring current that does not involve opening the circuit is to use a resistor of known low resistance value which is permanently installed in the circuit. This resistor is called an *ammeter shunt* or *current-sensing resistor* and may be installed in the circuit by the manufacturer or even inserted by a technician for temporary use. It should have a resistance low enough that it does not affect normal circuit operation. Its only purpose is to provide a small output voltage for an indirect current measurement. The digital multimeter is preferred for this method of current measurement because of its ability to measure small voltage.

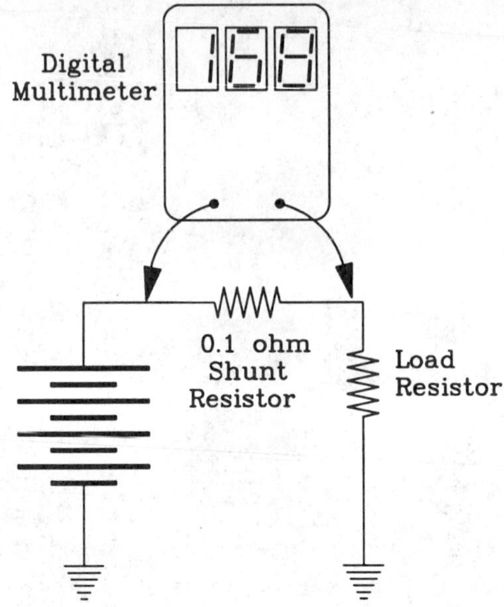

Figure 5–13 Using a low-value shunt resistor to monitor current without having to break the circuit.

Using a DMM allows the use of a much lower resistance, which disturbs the circuit operation less. See Figure 5–13.

Commercial shunts are available to install in very-high-current circuits. Then, using two small wires to operate a meter, which can be located some distance away, the current can be read remotely. These shunts also typically produce 1 millivolt for each ampere measured.

The amount of current measured by a shunt is calculated by Ohm's law (I = E/R or current equals voltage divided by resistance). Divide the voltage read by the value of the resistance. As an example, assume that a resistor of 0.1 Ω had a measured voltage of 168 millivolts across it. This would result in 0.168/0.1 (1.68) amperes of current flow in the circuit. Note that the circuit did not have to be opened for an ammeter to be inserted. Note also that voltage rather than current was indicated. The DC current flow through any resistance can be calculated using this method. It is a very practical way of measuring current in circuits quickly and without the physical damage that might result by inserting an ammeter.

Clamp-on ammeters are also available for high-current troubleshooting. These are often AC ammeters, however, and will not respond to DC currents. The AC ammeter is shown in Figure 5–14.

The AC clamp-on ammeter is actually a winding of an AC transformer, which is constructed to be able to clamp around an active

Figure 5–14 This clamp-on ammeter is particularly useful for electricians measuring AC or DC currents. (Reproduced with permission from the John Fluke Mfg. Co., Inc.)

current-carrying conductor. The clamp produces an AC voltage proportional to the current flowing in the sampled wire, providing a voltage that is directly proportional to the current flowing in the circuit. Through the use of an appropriate range and scale, current is read on the meter attached. It is interesting to note that multiple passes of a wire through the clamp-on ammeter will result in the reading being that many times greater than the actual current flowing. For instance, passing the current-carrying conductor twice through the clamp will show 2 amperes flowing when actually only 1 ampere is present. This is handy to remember when trying to measure very small currents on a large-scale instrument.

A small AC clamp-on device is also available for oscilloscopes, converting AC circuit current flow into small voltages that are usable with the oscilloscope. This small clamp can measure current as low as 2 milliamperes AC, but it is very seldom used for troubleshooting. The oscilloscope clamp-on "current probe" is used mostly in the development of prototype analog circuits.

DC current flow through an individual wire may also be measured, if it is above about 1 ampere, by the use of a special DC clamp-on ammeter or a similar accessory for a DMM. These instruments or accessories are very seldom used in troubleshooting, partly because they require a single, isolated wire to monitor, while most modern circuits are printed on an insulated backing. Also, their lower limit of about 1 ampere is a restriction when circuit currents are well below this level.

The DC clamp-on ammeter uses a Hall effect transistor and requires a battery to power its circuitry. A Hall effect current probe typically produces an output of 1 millivolt of signal for each ampere measured. Such a probe can respond to either DC or AC currents.

CHAPTER SUMMARY

- The intelligent use of a voltmeter of any type to find a problem is one of the basic skills involved in electronic and electrical troubleshooting.
- The loading effects and the limitations of the volt-ohm-milliammeter (VOM) and the digital multimeter (DMM) must be understood to properly interpret the readings that these instruments provide.
- Whether a given voltage is too high or low suggests one of five reasons and the possible location of the problem using the Perozzo Method of voltage troubleshooting.
- Although not often used, current measurements are an alternative method that may be used to localize a problem in a circuit.

REVIEW QUESTIONS

1. A small-value resistor permanently installed in a circuit for the measurement of current is called a/an _______ or _______.
2. You are working on a circuit involving low voltages and very small currents. You decide to break the circuit and insert a milliammeter to read current. The circuit operates differently after the meter is connected. Why?
3. What is the basic caution to keep in mind when using an ammeter?
4. What caution must be remembered when using a voltmeter to troubleshoot a circuit using surface-mounted devices?
5. What is a VTVM?
6. What is a TVM?
7. What is the quick and easy method to determine if an analog VOM is causing the loading of a circuit?
8. Is accuracy of better than 3 percent required for *routine* troubleshooting?
9. The trace of your oscilloscope shifts up or down with changes in the range switch. What adjustment would you use to correct this problem?
10. What must a technician always remember about the ground connection on the probe of an AC line-operated oscilloscope?
11. What five items should be mentally checked off when troubleshoot-

ing a problem with a voltmeter, assuming a voltage is found that is too low?

12. What circuit clue can help the technician in determining if a given voltage reading is "close enough"?
13. Keep in mind that R_S also includes _______.

Fixing the Power Supply

6

CHAPTER OBJECTIVES

Loosely defined, a power supply is the circuitry necessary to convert the available electrical energy into the kind of electrical energy required by the circuits at hand. Power supplies may be involved in over half of electronic failures. Failures involving a power supply fall into two general categories, depending upon whether the power supply fuse blew. This chapter details the troubleshooting methods to find the problems within the power supply and in external load circuits. At the conclusion of this chapter, the student should be able to:

- Analyze the reason why the fuse blew.
- Replace the fuse, if appropriate, with a proper replacement.
- Identify the three basic kinds of power supply.
- Apply power to a shorted power supply with minimum stress on the equipment, for troubleshooting purposes.
- Effectively troubleshoot a shorted power supply.
- Categorize the kind of short within a load connected to a power supply.
- Use one of five methods to locate a short on a PC board.
- Effectively troubleshoot an inoperative power supply.

6.1 FUSES: THE INTENTIONAL WEAK LINK

Fuses are very much like a weak link. They are designed to open the circuit when the current exceeds a specified value. Short-duration overloads might exceed the fuse rating for a short time without blowing the fuse, particularly if the fuse is a slow-blowing type. Sustained current at exactly the fuse rating will eventually cause the fuse to blow because of normal short-term overloads during power-up of the equipment. A fuse is actually a very-low-value resistor, which is specially designed to heat up and melt at a given current value.

A blown fuse is an indicator: read it! It generally indicates a problem *and its severity.*

FINDING THE OPEN FUSE

If there are only a few fuses in the equipment being repaired, checking them visually or with an ohmmeter may be the quickest way to test them. Keep in mind that an open (blown) fuse may not appear bad. If there are many fuses involved, it may be quite a chore to find the open one. Depending upon whether power is available to the equipment, there are two methods that can be used.

First, if the main power can be applied, an open fuse may be revealed by a built-in indicator. In AC-powered circuits, this is usually a neon lamp in series with a resistor, across the fuse. A lit lamp means voltage across the fuse. Since the fuse should be a short, a lit lamp means the fuse is open. If there are no indicators provided, an open fuse may be detected quite readily by using a voltmeter (*not an ohmmeter*) across the fuses while power is applied. The meter must be set to the proper voltage scale for the voltages involved with the fuses. The load normally fed by the fuse *must* be connected, and the circuit switches turned on. See Figure 6–1 for an explanation of this method of finding a bad fuse.

This voltmeter method of finding an open fuse is particularly useful for vehicular installations where the power is not easily turned off without disconnecting the battery. To find the bad fuse in an automobile with a 12-volt system, just turn on the device that has no power and measure the voltage across each fuse until you see an indication of about 12-V DC. Either the fuse with 12-V DC across it is open or the holder is not making good contact with the fuse.

Second, if power cannot be applied for one reason or another, the open fuse may be located by removing each fuse and testing it using an ohmmeter or a solid-state tester. When using either of these instruments, *be sure the power is turned completely off.* Use the lowest ohmmeter range, "R×1" or "Low," of either instrument.

Although fuses can normally be tested with an ohmmeter or solid-state tester, instrument fuses having very low current values (not the usual power-supply fuses) require special attention because of their extremely

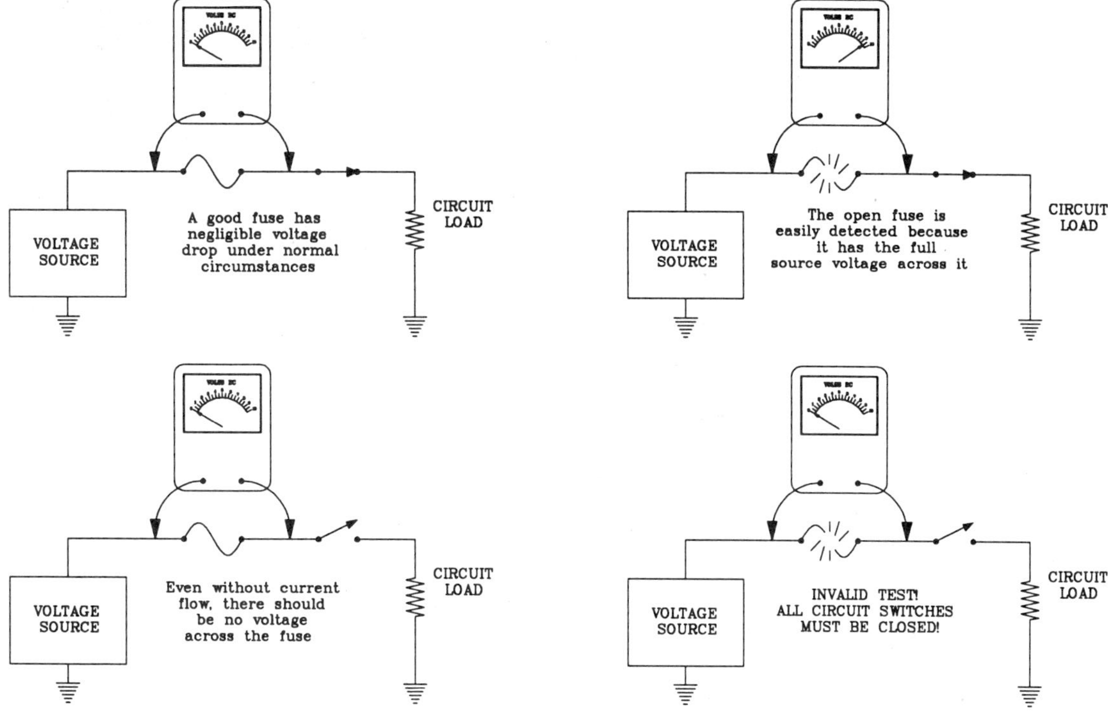

Figure 6–1 The proper method and conditions necessary to use a voltmeter to test for a blown fuse.

low current ratings. A volt-ohm-milliammeter may have up to one-third of an ampere available when using the R×1 scale, possibly enough to blow an instrument fuse during testing. The tracker, too, may cause the same problem. A digital multimeter uses very small currents during testing and should, therefore, be safe to use in testing any fuse.

BASIC INFORMATION

READING THE FUSE

Fuses can open in normal operation. Current surges can progressively weaken them, particularly when turning on equipment. The inrush of current each time the equipment is turned on may weaken a fuse to the point that it eventually fails, which is usually when the equipment is turned on. This kind of failure is more or less normal and is corrected by putting in another fuse of the *correct rating.* This means checking the book or panel markings, and not assuming that the old fuse is the proper type.

Look at the fuse that has been removed. If it is enclosed in clear glass, you can get a clue as to why it failed by close examination. If the fuse element (the tiny wire inside) is simply broken or has been melted into tiny

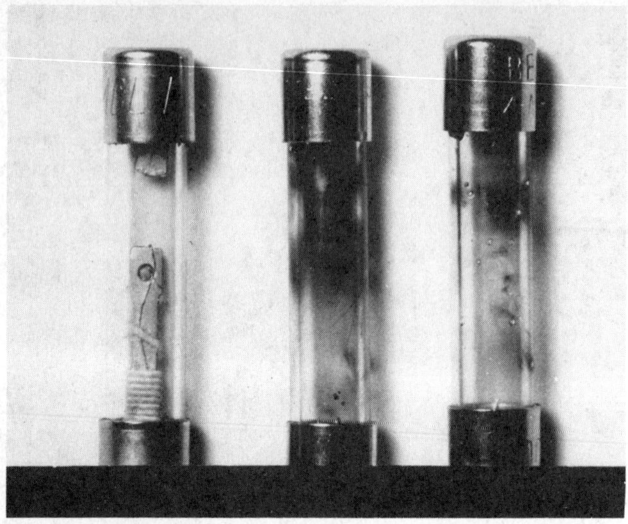

Figure 6–2 Photograph of a soft-blown and two hard-blown fuses.

globules, then the chances are good that the fuse simply became worn (as explained above). This may be called a "soft" blow. If, on the other hand, the fuse has vaporized and coated the inside of the glass with a silvery, mirror-like deposit, then there has been a gross overload. This may be called a "hard" blow of the fuse. Replacing such a fuse without finding the cause is wasteful. See Figure 6–2.

If the fuse has blown violently, there is a good chance that the problem can be found with the use of an ohmmeter and without the application of power. Using an ohmmeter or solid-state tester (if you have access to one), check the power-supply filter capacitors for shorts. Test also for shorts across the output and load terminals, and test each of the rectifiers for shorts. If you have no success with this method, proceed to sections 6.3 and 6.4.

Do not install a fuse of higher current rating unless you are willing to gamble on the probability of burning up some component for the lack of proper fuse protection. In addition, use only a fuse of the same type. The slow-blowing fuses are made to absorb current surges. A fast-blow fuse will likely burn open immediately in a slow-blow fuse circuit. On the other hand, a slow-blow fuse installed in a fast-blow circuit will allow very high, short-term current surges and may allow circuit damage. *As a general rule, replace fuses with the identical type and current rating as recommended by the equipment manufacturer.*

The voltage rating of a fuse is an indication of the voltage under which it can open a circuit without exploding if there is a short-circuit current flow. It is also an indicator of the insulation that will be available end-to-end after the fuse blows.

A small possibility exists that the fuse holder itself may be causing the fuse to open. This can happen in high-current applications if the fuse holder does not make solid contact with the fuse. The passage of sufficient current can cause the holder-to-fuse resistance to heat. This heat can be conducted into the fuse and, in combination with the small amount of normal heat within the fuse, it can cause the fuse to melt open. Be sure the holder makes good contact, especially in a high-current application. Keep the fuse clips clean and tight on the ends of the fuse. If the holder is loose it can sometimes be resprung for a better fit by removing the fuse and squeezing the clips together a bit, and then reinstalling the fuse.

6.2 THE THREE TYPES OF POWER SUPPLIES

There are three common types of power supplies used today, the transformer-rectifier, the switching, and the phasing power supplies. The transformer-rectifier is the oldest and simplest power supply. The switching power supply is a newer, more efficient, voltage-regulated supply that is commonly used in computers. The phasing supply is particularly efficient at producing very heavy output currents at regulated voltage levels. Each of these types will be covered in more detail.

THE TRANSFORMER-RECTIFIER POWER SUPPLY

The transformer-rectifier power supply is sometimes called the linear rectifier. Its basic purpose is to provide a reasonably stable output voltage for a given input voltage. Voltage variations of the input voltage will produce output fluctuations by roughly the same percentage. Output voltages of this basic power supply can be further regulated if necessary by one of the four regulator circuits covered later in this chapter.

Block Diagrams

The block diagram and schematic for a typical transformer-rectifier power supply is shown in Figure 6–3.

Input Circuits

There are several variations of the input circuits of this power supply. This involves the wiring necessary to operate a given transformer on the 120- or 240-V AC power lines. Relatively larger power supplies will be more likely to have this optional feature. These input circuits are shown in Figure 6–4.

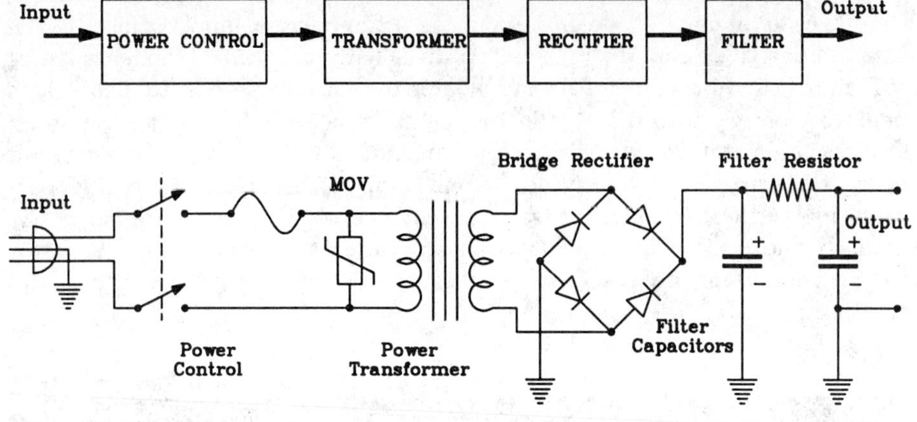

Figure 6–3 The block diagram and a schematic of a transformer-rectifier power supply.

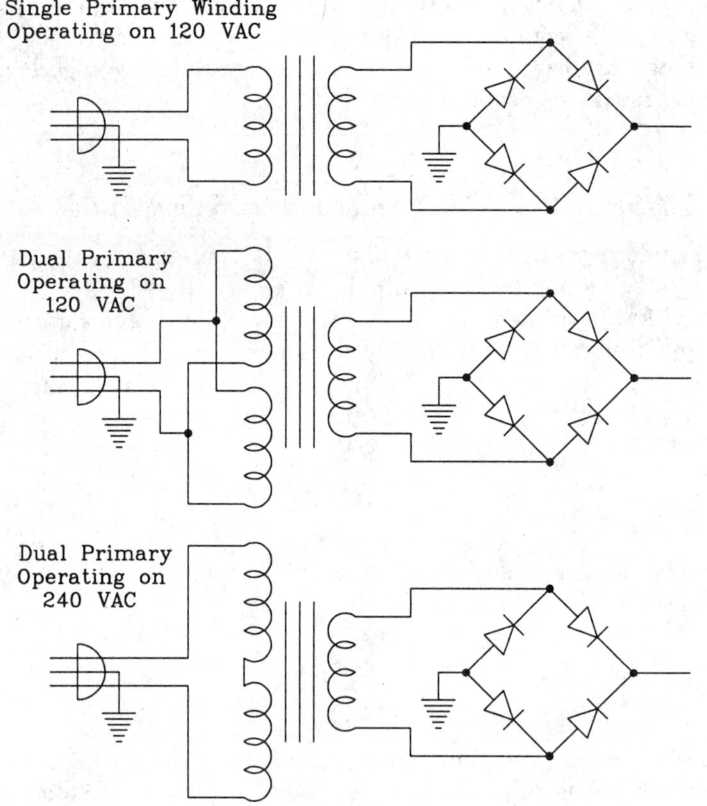

Figure 6–4 Input circuit variations for a transformer-rectifier power supply.

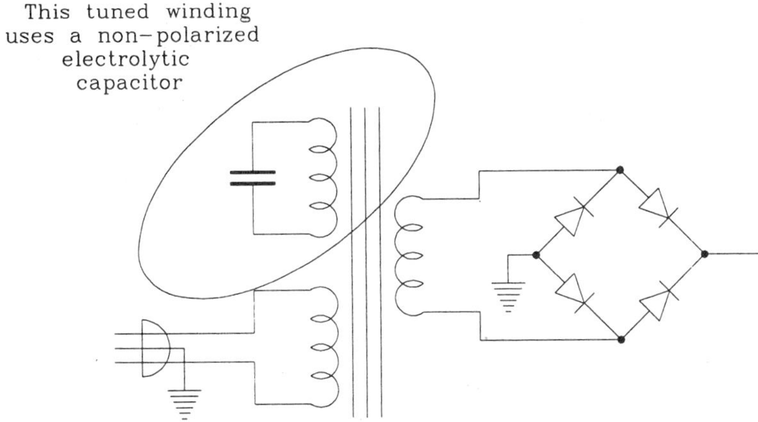
This tuned winding
uses a non-polarized
electrolytic
capacitor

Figure 6–5 The tuned primary winding sometimes used in power supplies helps in keeping the power input free of short interruptions and voltage spikes.

Although it would be rare to have the situation occur, the technician should be very careful not to connect such a power supply wired (or "strapped," as it is sometimes called) for 120-V AC to a 240-V AC source. It should do no harm, however, to connect a power supply strapped for 240-V AC to a 120-V AC source. The outputs will be about half of normal voltages under these conditions.

Another variation of the input circuitry for this power supply is to provide an electronic "flywhccl" to help free the transformer from voltage spikes and short-term power interruptions. See Figure 6–5.

The low-impedance flywheel circuit does not respond well to short-lived transients, and therefore tends to load them down severely, limiting their amplitude. A partially missing cycle from the power line will result in the flywheel circuit giving up some of its energy to the circuit, thus maintaining the energy input to the transformer for a few milliseconds until the power line is back to normal.

Transformers

The transformer of the modern transformer-rectifier power supply usually steps the input AC down to usable levels such as will provide 5-, 12-, and 24–V DC at the output of the power supply after rectifying and filtering. A few applications will involve stepping up the line voltage to higher voltages, sometimes to several thousand volts. Typical applications for higher voltages include the power supplies for magnetrons, which are used in microwave ovens and radars. Oscilloscopes sometimes use very high DC voltages from this kind of power supply for the operating voltages necessary for cathode-ray tubes. Voltage higher than about 24-V, whether AC or DC, should be treated with respect. Any voltage greater than about 48 volts may be lethal under certain extreme conditions, and safety measures must be taken. A transformer with a high voltage winding can deliver lethal currents very easily.

It is common for a power supply to be required to deliver several output voltages. In this case, a single power transformer is usually used, and is provided with the necessary number of windings to fill the requirements of the circuitry.

When compared to the transformer used in a switching power supply, the transformer-rectifier and the phasing power supplies use a physically large transformer because of the necessity of operating at the relatively low frequency of 60 hertz. The size of the transformer is one aid in identifying the transformer-rectifier type of power supply.

Transformer Output and Rectifier Configurations

Please note that the following output circuits are also used with the switching and the phasing power supplies (to be covered later in this section).

The rectifiers used on the output windings of a power supply can be used in several basic configurations. See Figure 6–6. Using these basic configurations, the actual circuits in equipment can either be simple or they can be subtle variations of them. See Figure 6–7, which shows some of the variations possible when wiring rectifiers to the output windings of a transformer.

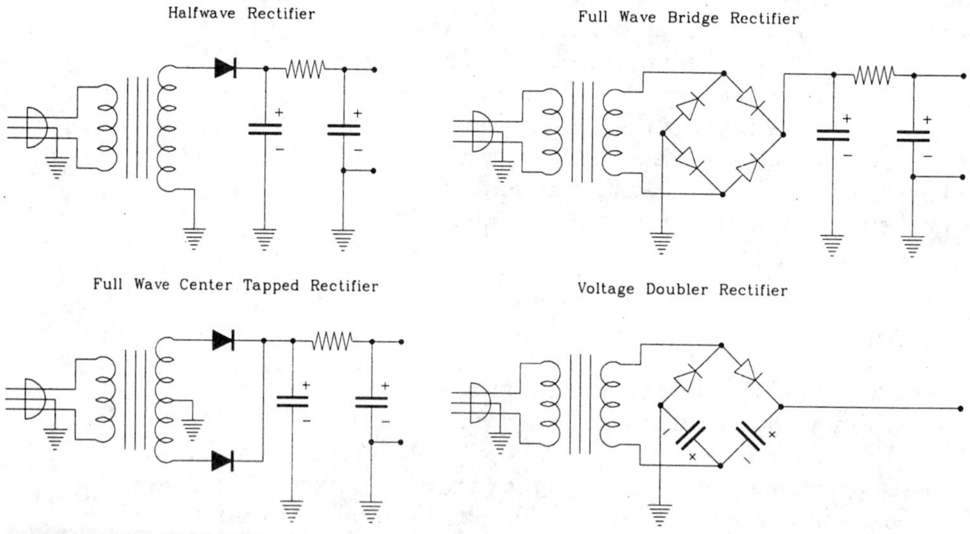

Figure 6–6 The basic power supply output circuits.

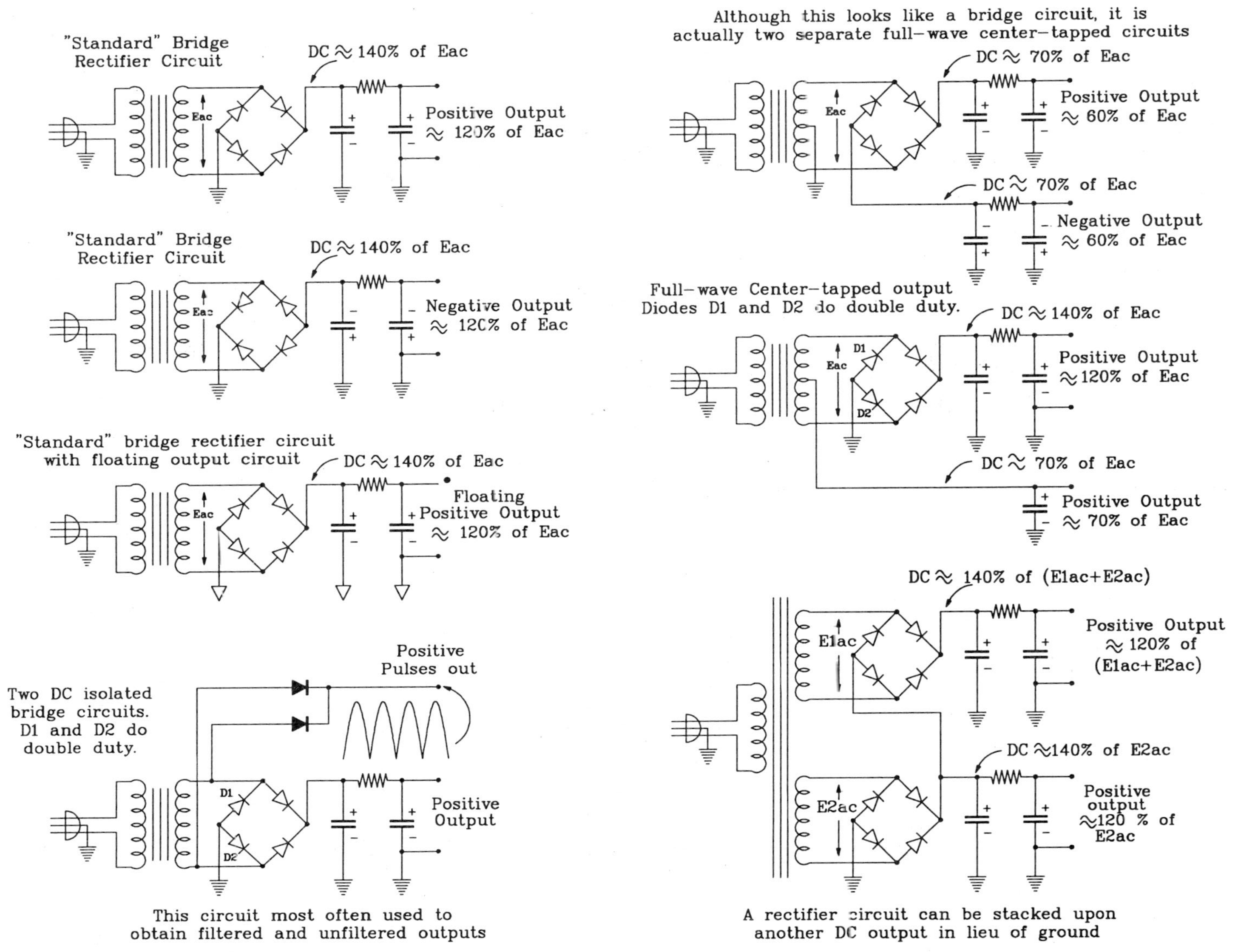

Figure 6–7 Variations of the "standard" bridge-rectifier output circuit.

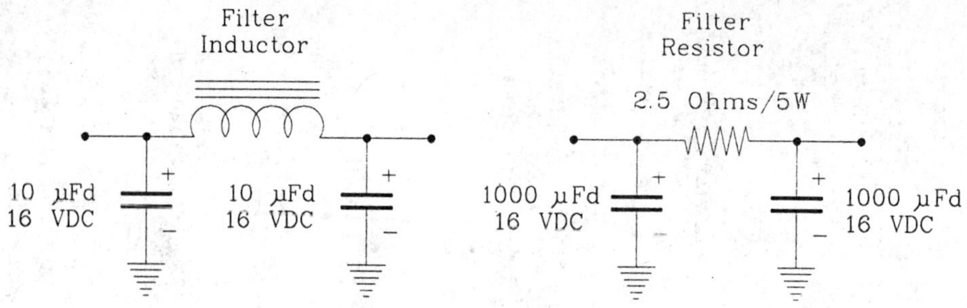

Figure 6–8 An example of two ways to filter rectifier output voltage.

BASIC INFORMATION

Filter Capacitors

The output of the rectifiers is a pulsating voltage of either full or half waves. Either waveform must be filtered to produce the relatively constant voltage required for most circuitry. This can be done in two ways, by using either an inductor or a resistor. See Figure 6–8.

Sometimes electrolytic filter capacitors are placed in series to increase the voltage rating of the filter. Two capacitors rated at 200–V DC, for instance, can filter the output of a 340–V DC power supply. While placing these capacitors in series reduces the overall capacitance of the filter (resulting in half the capacitance of a single capacitor), the voltage ratings add. See Figure 6–9.

Common Failure Patterns

The most common failures of the transformer-rectifier power supply are listed below, along with suggested troubleshooting tips:

1. Overload of the power supply caused by a shorted load: This usually first burns up the series resistor in the filter and then may cause the rectifiers to open or short. Failure of the transformer may occur unless the fuse protects it by blowing first.
2. An open filter resistor in the power supply filter will result in no output voltage, yet the first of the two filter capacitors shows a higher-than-normal DC voltage. Before replacing the resistor, check to be sure that there is no overload or short on the power supply output that originally caused the resistor to fail.
3. An open diode in a bridge rectifier or in a full-wave center-tapped circuit will result in slightly less than the normal output voltage. Again, be sure that there is no overload before replacing the open diode.
4. A lower-than-normal output voltage can be caused by a dried-out,

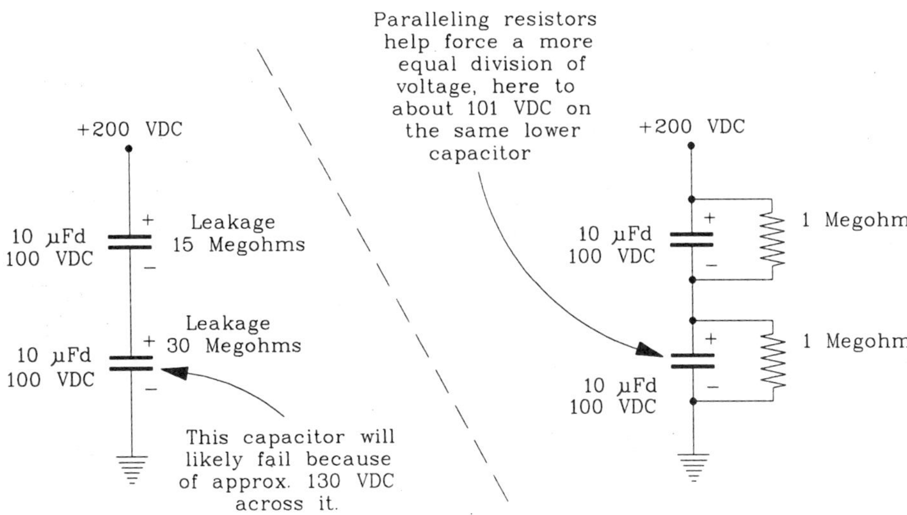

Figure 6–9 High-value resistors across series-connected electrolytic capacitors force the DC voltage to divide more equally.

ineffective filter capacitor. This is especially likely to be true for equipment that has not recently been turned on or has been in storage for long periods of time.

THE SWITCHING POWER SUPPLY

The switching power supply is the latest development in power supplies, and is an improvement over the transformer-rectifier power supply in terms of both weight and size. Since the switching power supply operates at much higher frequencies, the power transformer can be made with considerably less core material (the magnetic laminations inside the transformer). This results in smaller transformer size and weight for a given power output when compared to a power supply operating at 60 Hz.

CAUTION: Always provide a load on a switching supply!

One caution is very appropriate at this point: *whenever a switching supply is being operated, for test or otherwise, it must have a reasonable load placed upon it.* The failure to have a load can easily result in the voltage spikes produced by the transformer puncturing the junctions within the driving transistors. This will, of course, short the transistors permanently. A normal load on the supply will also load down the voltage spikes, helping greatly to prevent this damage. Incandescent lamps make good loads because they also serve as indicators, showing when voltage is present. An automotive store can provide three loads for 12-volt supplies: a tail lamp

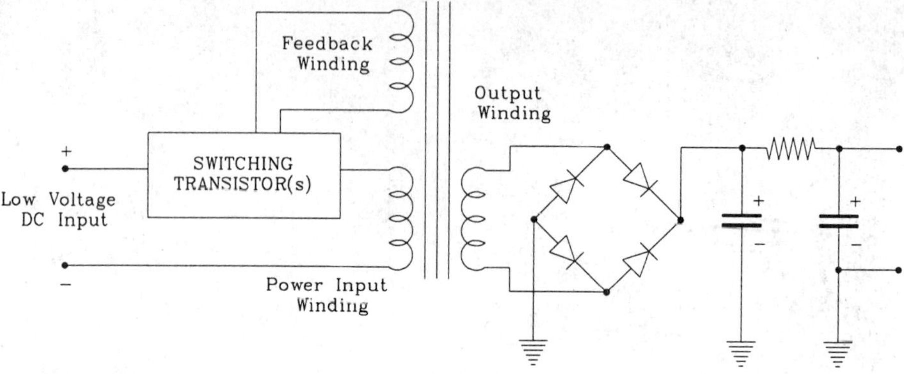

Figure 6–10 Block diagram of low-voltage DC-to-DC conversion which uses an additional feedback winding to produce powerful oscillations in the transformer.

(light load), a brake light (a medium load, it may be within the same bulb as the taillight), and a headlight (heavy load.)

A switching power supply takes one of two general forms. The first is the type that uses 120- or 240-V AC as an input, providing at least one regulated output voltage. The second form of the switching supply is that operating from relatively low DC input voltages as shown in Figure 6–10.

Input Circuits

The EMI Filter. Any form of input, whether DC or AC, applied to the input of a switching power supply is likely to be affected by the sudden changes of current normally produced by this power supply. These electrical jolts should be restricted to the power supply and not be allowed to radiate back into the input source. For instance, the switching power supply can cause large voltage transients (*voltage spikes*) that may be sent back down the power line to other equipment operating from the same source. This is unacceptable. Other equipment may very sensitive to this *conducted* electrical interference.

Short-duration spikes can be prevented from entering the power lines by the use of an electromagnetic interference (EMI) filter, as shown schematically in Figure 6–11.

DC Input (Inverter)

Block Diagram. This circuit was mostly used to produce high DC voltage from low DC sources. It is still used to produce high DC voltages for

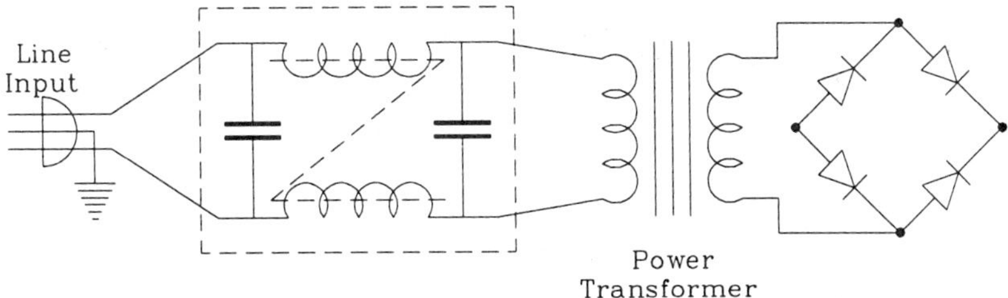

Figure 6–11 Schematic of a typical electromagnetic interference (EMI) filter.

vacuum tubes or other applications when operating from relatively low voltages, such as 12 volts. It is also efficient in stepping down a DC voltage from one level to a lower one, which is more efficient than simply dropping the voltage through resistances. See Figure 6–10 for an example of a DC-to-DC inverter circuit.

AC Input

Block Diagram. Figure 6–12 shows that the AC input to a switching power supply adds another block or two to that of the basic inverter of Figure 6–10.

Single Voltage, Bridge Input. A switching power can be designed to run directly from the 120-V AC line by first converting the AC to DC and filtering it with large capacitors. It is also easy to operate such a rectifier from either of two AC input voltages by changing the input circuit.

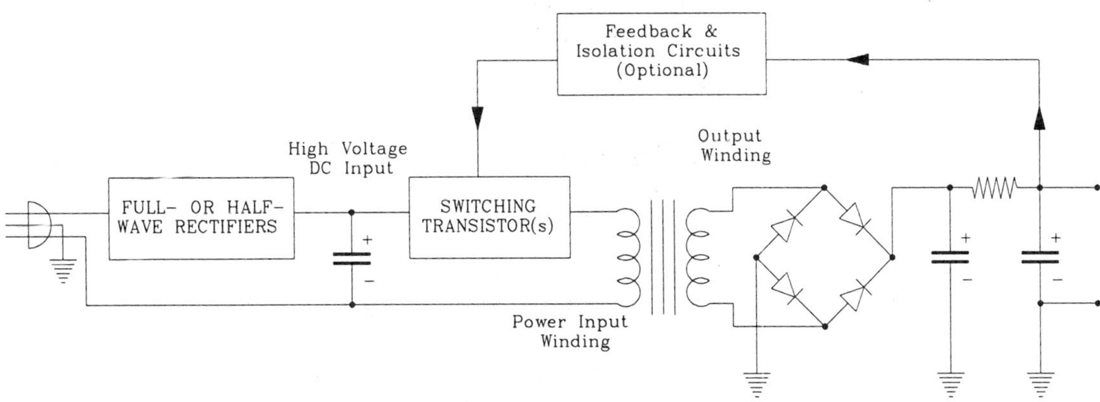

Figure 6–12 Block diagram of a line-operated switching power supply.

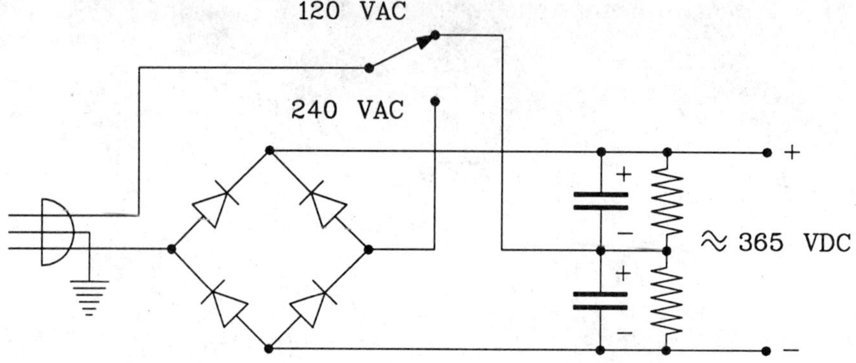

Figure 6–13 The switching power supply will sometimes use this input circuit because of its ability to operate on either 120-V AC or 240-V AC.

Special Dual-Voltage AC Input. Converting incoming 60 Hz to pure DC for further use of the switching power supply may provide an extra option: being able to simply and easily switch between two input AC voltages. When operating on 120-V AC, the AC can be voltage-doubled to produce about 340-V DC. When operating on 240-V AC, the full-wave bridge configuration can be used, which will also produce the same 340-V DC. Thus, by changing the circuit with a single wire, the same output voltage can be supplied by either input voltage. See Figure 6–13.

Often Regulated by Pulse-Width Modulation. One of the big advantages to using a switching power supply is that the output voltage can be held to close tolerances by varying the duty cycle (pulse-width modulation) of the square-wave produced by the switching transistor. The higher the duty cycle, the higher the output voltage produced by the rectifiers. This means that the switching power supply can be very easily modified to produce regulated output voltage.

The Switching Transformer and Output Circuits

The transformer used in a switching power supply is much smaller than one used in a transformer-rectifier power supply. The switching transformer is operating at a much higher frequency than 60 Hz (typically 25 kHz or more). The higher frequencies allow the use of less core material, resulting in a smaller transformer for a given total power output from the secondaries. This transformer often has more than one output winding, allowing the generation of multiple, electrically isolated, outputs. The frequencies selected for operation are usually above the limit of hearing so that normal operation is not heard as an irritating squeal.

The output circuits of the switching power supply are the same kinds of circuits used in the transformer-rectifier power supply.

Rectifiers

The switching power supply requires the use of higher-speed rectifier diodes than those used at 60-Hz power-line frequencies. Except for this requirement, the rectifiers operate in the same manner as those in the transformer-rectifier power supply.

Common Failure Patterns

The switching power supply has several common failure patterns. If the power supply input fuse blows, it is most likely that:

1. One or both input high-voltage filter capacitors are shorted, or
2. The switching power transistor is shorted.

If the power supply input fuse does not blow, expect that:

1. The switching power transistor is open, or
2. There is a short somewhere *in or following the transformer, including the load.*

NOTE: Although this may seem counterintuitive (the presence of a short *not* blowing a fuse), this is a special characteristic of most switching power supplies, and is a great advantage in some applications. The short in the load on the supply merely places the power supply in an "idling" condition, in which it consumes little power, until the short is cleared. This idling condition can sometimes be heard as a chirping sound coming from the switching transformer.

THE PHASING POWER SUPPLY

The phasing power supply is very similar to a transformer-rectifier power supply. It is normally fed with 120-V AC or 240-V AC from the power lines. The output, however, is regulated by using only part of the full sine wave available from the power lines. See Figure 6–14.

The phasing power supply is used mostly to provide high-current DC output such as that required for commercial battery chargers. It is always a voltage-regulated supply. The block diagram of a phasing power supply is shown in Figure 6–15.

Input Circuits

The EMI Filter. The phasing power supply generates some very rapidly changing voltages during the switching of the SCR or TRIAC used within the transformer primary circuit. These rapid changes could do harm if

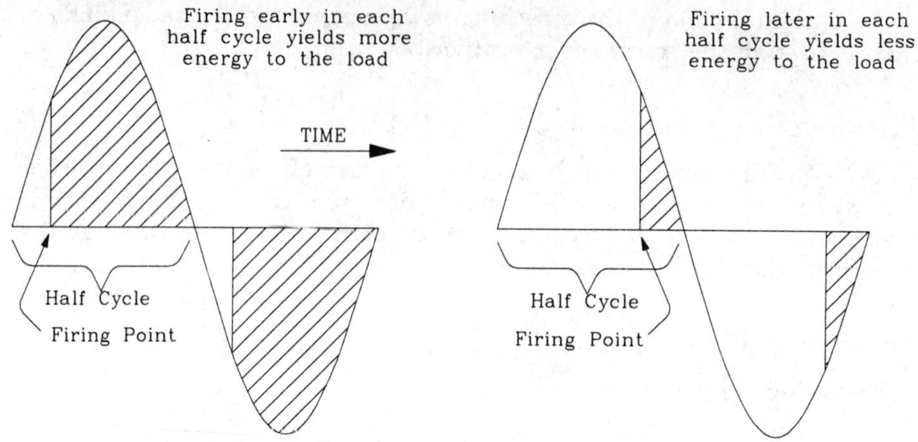

Figure 6–14 How varying the time of firing during each AC half-cycle can vary the total energy coupled through the SCR or TRIAC (three-layer AC device) of the phasing power supply.

allowed to reenter the power line, thus possibly affecting other sensitive equipment. As used with the switching power supply, the phasing power supply also needs an EMI filter to isolate the noise from the power line.

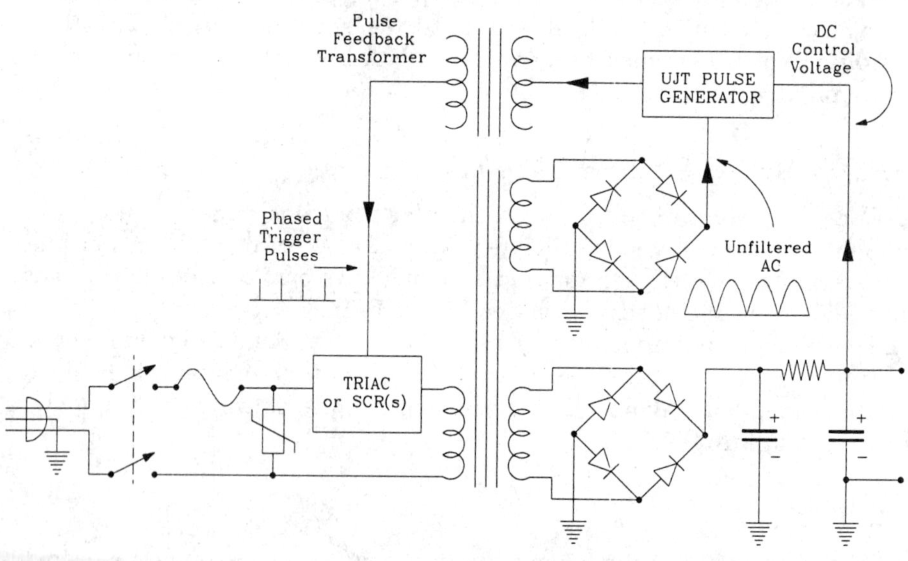

Figure 6–15 Block diagram of the phasing power supply.

These filters were covered in the discussion of input circuits in the section titled "Switching Power Supplies."

The Phasing Power Supply Transformer. Comparing the block diagrams of the phasing and transformer-rectifier power supplies will show that the only difference is that the input to the transformer is controlled by an SCR or a TRIAC in the case of the phasing power supply. Both kinds operate at the power-line frequency of 60 Hz, with a transformer designed for use at this frequency.

The SCR/TRIAC and Unijunction Transistor (UJT) Feedback Circuit. Once an SCR or TRIAC used in a phasing power supply has been triggered into the conducting state by a trigger pulse, the device will continue to conduct heavy current until the line voltage goes through zero voltage. All that must be done is to trigger the device into conduction at an appropriate time within each cycle of line voltage to get the desired output from the transformer. This is usually done by using a special discrete component, the unijunction transistor (UJT). This transistor will (similar to the SCR) trigger into a "shorted" condition between the base 1 and base 2 terminals, until the voltage at its emitter falls below a certain voltage, at which time it "opens" between base 1 and base 2 terminals. If the base number 2 is supplied with an *unfiltered* full-wave supply voltage and the emitter resistor and capacitor values are chosen properly, the UJT will trigger reliably at some point within each cycle of the 60-Hz line voltage.

An alternative to using a UJT is to use a programmable unijunction transistor (PUT). This device acts similarly to a UJT in that it suddenly conducts and produces an output pulse, as shown in Figure 6–16. (Note that the PUT elements are called anode, cathode, and gate).

The exact time of firing within each cycle is influenced by the addition of a small DC voltage applied, as shown in Figure 6–16.

Rectifiers

The rectifiers used in a phasing power supply are typically high-current diodes which are suitable for a particular application, such as battery charging.

Filter Capacitors

The filter capacitors of a phasing power supply may not be as large in value as expected, since the output of the supply is used for battery charging in most cases, an application that does not need well-filtered DC. The circuit that samples the output voltage for the feedback circuit, however, may be separately and well filtered.

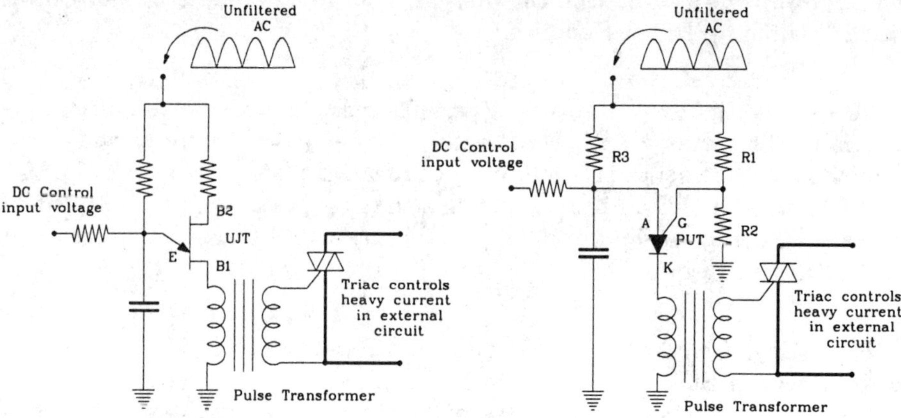

Figure 6–16 When the UJT or PUT circuit is powered by an unfiltered ripple voltage, the time of the first firing on each pulse of the ripple supply is greatly influenced by a DC applied to the input element.

Common Failure Patterns

The most common failure patterns for the phasing supply are:

1. Output voltage is too high and cannot be controlled by normal adjustments. This is caused by a shorted SCR or TRIAC, which allows maximum input power without control.
2. Output voltage is zero. This is caused most often by an open SCR or TRIAC.

6.3 APPLYING POWER TO A SHORTED POWER SUPPLY

If a load on a power supply (of any type) is overloading that supply, the problem cannot be repaired by the usual methods of voltage troubleshooting. The short, whatever it may be, must be removed before normal operating voltages will be present.

THE "SOFT FUSE" METHOD

The "soft fuse" method of applying power to a shorted power supply is effective for any kind of supply. A suitable series resistance must be used for the voltage level used. A 12-volt lamp (an automobile headlight, for

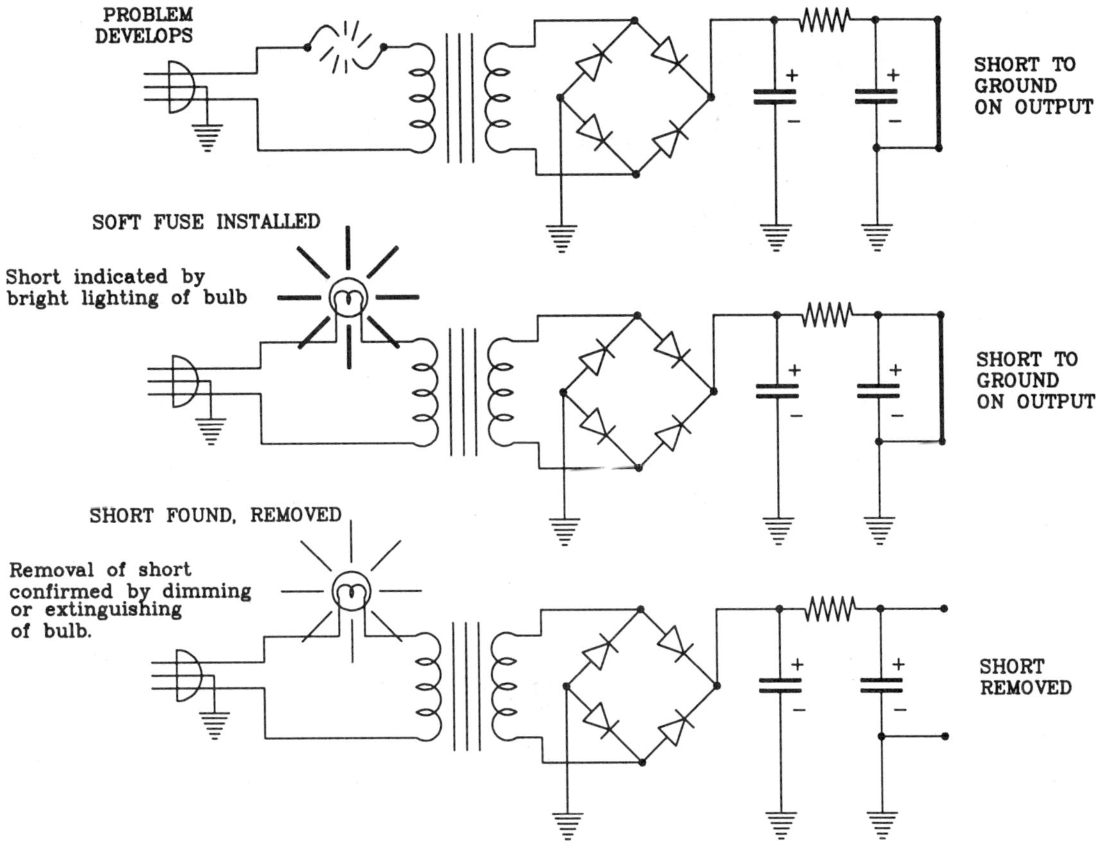

Figure 6–17 The principle of the soft fuse in schematic form.

instance) is appropriate for 12-volt equipment, while a 120-volt bulb is often used for 120-V AC operated equipment.

With AC Input Circuits

The best method of troubleshooting a shorted power supply that operates from 120-V AC power lines is to place a current-limiting resistance in series with the shorted supply-input line. The resistor can also perform the important function of an indicator if an incandescent lamp is used. An ordinary 100-watt (W) light bulb, for instance, will limit the possible current into the shorted supply to about 1 ampere. See Figure 6–17.

With DC Input Circuits

The same principle can also be used for shorted equipment, such as automobile radios, that operates directly on low-voltage DC inputs. Put a 12-V lamp (about 12-watt rating), in series with the input line. The stop-light filament (the brighter, heavier filament of the two) of a dual-filament, automobile taillight will do this job nicely. The lamp will light brightly until the short is cleared.

THE VARIABLE INPUT VOLTAGE AND AMMETER METHOD

With AC Input Circuits

If the equipment in question operates from 120-V AC, an alternative way to apply power to a shorted supply without causing damage is to monitor the AC current input to the supply while bringing the applied voltage up *slowly and carefully* until the power supply is drawing no more than normal *current,* as it would if operating properly. For instance, if the supply normally provides 250 watts of output power, approximately 2 amperes of current would normally be flowing in the primary circuit (2 amperes times 120 volts produces 240 watts). An alternate way of determining the safe current flow in the primary circuit is to look at the fuse current rating. If the fuse normally used in the equipment primary circuit is rated at 1.5 amperes, you should stay below this value of current as the input voltage is increased. One method of providing a variable AC input voltage is to use a variable transformer. See Figure 6–18.

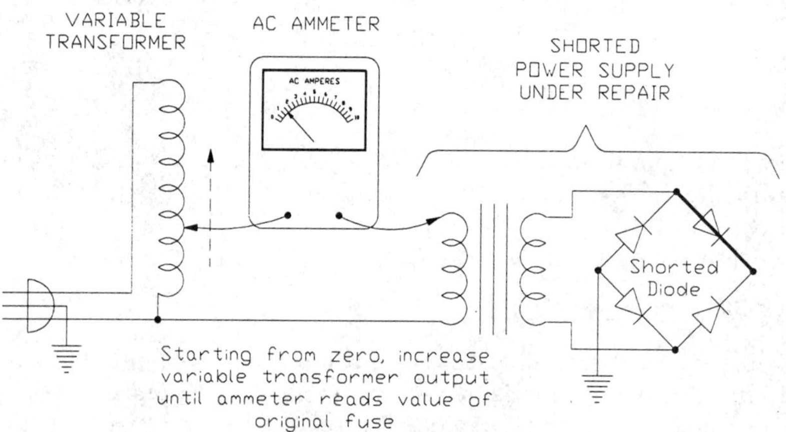

Figure 6–18 Using a variable transformer and an ammeter to keep current flow into a shorted power supply to a safe value.

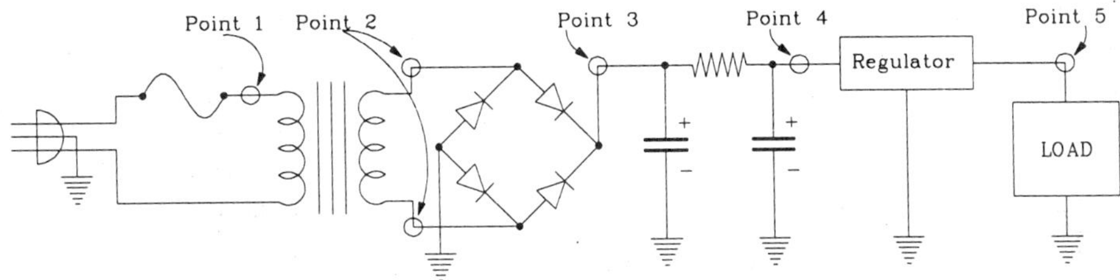

Figure 6–19 Break points to be used to locate a short within a power supply.

With DC Input Circuits

If the equipment used low-voltage DC input, such as 12-V, it will be necessary to use a variable-voltage, DC power supply capable of providing the current that is normally required of the power supply in question. Using the same basic idea as in Figure 6–19 above, substitute the DC power supply for the input and a DC ammeter as a monitoring indicator.

THE "FEED IT FUSES" METHOD

This method of applying power to a shorted power supply is applicable to power supplies of either AC or DC input. You simply put in a fuse and see if it blows. If it does, the short is still present.

6.4 TROUBLESHOOTING THE SHORTED POWER SUPPLY

Using the transformer-rectifier power supply as an example, consider where the circuit should first be opened when troubleshooting a shorted power supply with the "Soft Fuse" or Variable Input Voltage and Ammeter methods. See Figure 6–19.

THE HALF-SPLIT TECHNIQUE OF TROUBLESHOOTING

It is usually faster to start troubleshooting in the middle when attempting to identify where a problem lies within several cascaded stages. At this halfway point in the circuitry, determine whether the problem lies before or after this point. This method has also been called the "divide and conquer" method of finding a problem. By successively reducing the possibilities by half, the problem can be localized quickly. Finding the short in a power supply is a particularly appropriate application of this technique.

Without power applied, break the chain of stages approximately in the middle, such as point 3 in Figure 6–19. Turn on the power at the reduced voltage and see if the current, as indicated on the ammeter, falls drastically. If it does, the short is in circuitry that is no longer connected, and lies to the right of point 3. In this case, it will be necessary to turn off the power, reconnect the break at point 3, and then break the circuit at point 5. Then reapply power to determine if the overload is prior to or after point 5. On the other hand, if the break at point 3 did not reduce the current being drawn, the short is to the left of point 3 in the block diagram. Again, turn off the power, reconnect point 3, and make a new break (perhaps at point 1 or 2); then rerun the test.

A SPECIAL TECHNIQUE FOR THE "FEED IT FUSES" METHOD

A point to remember about using this method is that it will impose the least stress on the equipment if the short is isolated by breaking the power supply circuitry *at the input end of the circuit*, moving progressively further into the equipment. In this way, only one fuse need be sacrificed. This is a deliberate departure from the half-split method explained above.

The first step when using the "Feed It Fuses" method is to open the circuit of Figure 6–19 at point 1, insert a fuse, and apply power. If the fuse blows, the short is to the left of point 1 in the block diagram. If it does not blow, turn off the power to the circuit and reconnect the circuit, breaking it next at point 2. Again, apply power. If the fuse blows, the problem lies between points 1 and 2. If it does not blow, turn off the power, reconnect point 2, and break the circuit at point 3. Repeat this procedure until the location of the short is identified.

6.5 ANALYZING THE SHORTED LOAD ON A POWER SUPPLY

CONFIRM THE PRESENCE OF THE OVERLOAD

A power supply is designed to provide one or more voltages to specified loads. If an overload condition occurs within the load (the internal resistance of the load decreases drastically), it will make the power supply appear defective, often blowing the line fuse.

If you are in doubt as to whether the load placed on a power supply is causing a problem, disconnect the load. If the power supply is a transformer-rectifier or phasing type, turn it on and check for normal output voltage without blowing the power supply fuse. If it is a switching type, however, a reasonable dummy load must be placed on the power supply before applying power. After connecting such a load (anywhere from about half to full normal load is ideal), the switching power supply can be turned on and its output can be checked for proper voltage.

If the power supply runs normally under these test conditions, it confirms that there is an overload or short in the load that was connected before the test.

MEASURE THE OVERLOAD RESISTANCE

The next step in identifying the location of the short is to measure the resistance that the power supply "sees" in the load circuitry. Be sure to use the proper polarity of the ohmmeter leads, applying the positive ohmmeter lead to the normally positive lead of the circuit under test. This resistance can tell a great deal about the kind of short that is present. There are three possibilities:

1. Short of less than about 2 Ω.
2. An overload resistance of from 2 Ω to perhaps 50 Ω.
3. A nearly normal resistance

Shorts of Less Than about 2 Ω

This indication means that either there is a hard-wire short (such as one trace shorted to another) or there a shorted bypass capacitor. A bypass capacitor is one of perhaps many capacitors, within the range of from about .1 to .0001 pfd, connected directly across the input voltage of the card. Their purpose is to absorb very-short-term pulses that are typically caused by the normal operation of the circuit, particularly TTL digital integrated circuits. This kind of short can be called a *direct short.*

An Overload Resistance from 2 Ω to Perhaps 50 Ω

A resistance within this range, typically from 2Ω to 15Ω, is a strong indication that one of the semiconductors on the board has shorted. This might be called a *Semishort*. Note that when a semiconductor shorts, its internal resistance does not go to a complete, absolute short of zero ohms. The term *semiconductor* includes all types, including integrated circuits and all kinds of transistors.

A Nearly Normal Resistance

A relatively high resistance measured when testing the supply leads of a circuit should be compared to that obtained when measuring a known good circuit of the identical type. This case is somewhat rare, but it may occur. The ohmmeter seems to indicate that the circuit is functioning properly yet the circuit loads the power supply badly. This kind of overload can be called a *pseudo-zener* overload. It is caused by one of the semiconductors breaking down internally in such a manner as to cause it to now perform like a Zener diode. This Zener diode breaks down *only at a specific voltage*, making the application of higher voltages appear as an overload.

6.6 METHODS FOR LOCATING THE SHORT IN THE LOAD

There are five methods available to find the exact location of a short. The choice will be determined mostly by the kind of short, as identified above, and secondly, by the convenience of the method. These methods are:

1. "Smoke-out" method
2. SHORTRACK™ method
3. Removal of most likely components
4. Cut-trace-and-try method
5. Freezer method

THE "SMOKE-OUT" METHOD

The "Smoke-Out" method should *not* be used for finding direct shorts because circuit board damage could occur if the current supplied is too high.

If the short is a semishort or a pseudo-zener short, the failure is due to a defective semiconductor. The easiest and quickest method for finding the offending component is the "smoke-out" method. This involves applying a voltage-regulated supply to the circuit under test. After a few moments of operation, the offending semiconductor will heat up abnormally, making it quite easy to identify the component by carefully touching the semiconductors. The bad part may become very hot, so be careful when using this method.

An overheated resistor is almost always an indication that something in series with it is shorted (usually a capacitor) and that the resistor itself is not the bad component.

A voltage-regulated supply must be used to "smoke-out" bad parts. If the offending part should suddenly open during this test, a regulated supply voltage will remain steady at the proper value, thus avoiding possible damage to other components. An unregulated supply would increase in output voltage if the load suddenly becomes less.

THE SHORTRACK™ METHOD

This method is most effective when looking for the cause of a direct short. It is especially valuable when faced with the problem of determining the shorted bypass capacitor or shorted trace on a large circuit board involving dozens of bypasses and many traces to consider. The SHORTRACK™ is particularly useful in finding short circuits on PC boards without damage to the board or the removal of many parts.

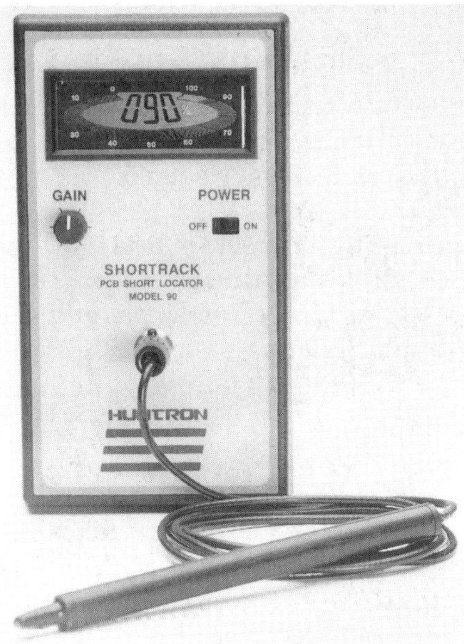

Figure 6–20 The SHORTRACK™ is designed to find short circuits on PC boards. (Courtesy of Huntron Instruments, Inc.)

The procedure is to supply a low-voltage current from a Huntron Tracker™ directly into the shorted supply line and ground connections. Using the SHORTRACK™, follow the path of heavy current flow. Refer to Figure 6–20.

Current is traced by first adjusting this small instrument for approximately full-scale indication on the indicator, an elliptical liquid crystal display (LCD). Position the probe of the instrument near either of the input leads of the Tracker™ to make the adjustment. This sets the basic sensitivity of the instrument. Further use seldom requires a readjustment of the sensitivity. Once this level has been set, the indicator will display current intensity as you "sniff" for the current along the various traces on the PC board. The LCD display shows the relative current strengths. It is sensitive to the current flowing directly beneath the sensing coil at its tip. Keep in mind that current density changes as the trace width varies, increasing where the trace narrows and decreasing where it widens. The LCD display will show an apparent increase of current flow for a narrowed trace and less current flow where the trace widens.

When the Shortrack™ is used, it should be constantly rotated back and forth for maximum response to the current flow. If the current turns a corner, it will be necessary to reorient the probe for maximum sensitivity.

Watch for the display of the Shortrack™ to show a decrease in response as the current is traced. This is usually an indication that you have left the main current flow and taken a smaller, incorrect side branch. Double back until the instrument shows the same intensity as that shown at the beginning, allowing for wider or narrower traces.

Another thing to watch for is current flow that goes through the board and continues on the opposite side. Multilayer boards also may confuse troubleshooting by a similar feature, having current flow within the board. Trace the fault current using the side of the board that keeps the trace closest to the Shortrack™ probe. This will help you narrow in on the proper trace, even though the instrument is quite capable of tracing current through the thickness of a board.

Look for a bypass capacitor or a solder bridge as the most likely components to be causing the problem. Although using the Shortrack™ requires a bit of skill to operate it properly, it only takes a few minutes to get the feel of this valuable troubleshooting instrument.

REMOVAL OF MOST LIKELY COMPONENTS

This method is most effective for finding semishorts and pseudo-zener shorts. A careful analysis of the schematic of the defective circuit will show that some of the components in the circuit *cannot* cause a major current flow, even if they short completely, because of other resistances that are in series with them. The most likely components will be semiconductors of any kind, and particularly power transistors and SCRs. Electrolytic capacitors are also good possibilities. Using this fact, together with a careful study of the schematic, will reveal the most likely components that could cause the problem. For an example, see Figure 6–21.

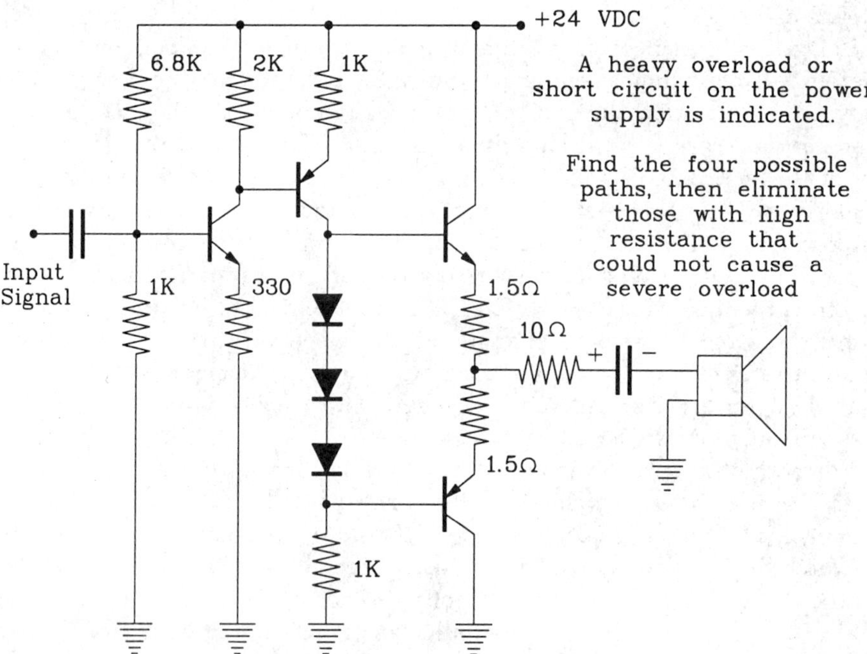

Figure 6–21 Use circuit resistances to eliminate those components that cannot be the cause of a high-current short.

In Figure 6–21, the four paths of possible overcurrent are those beginning at the top with the 6.8 K, 2 K, and 1 K resistors, along with the path through the complementary-symmetry stage. *A direct short from ground in any of the first three paths cannot overload the power supply* because of the current limiting of the resistors themselves. Only the fourth path, the two transistors in the output stage itself, can cause a "dead short" on the power supply. (However, the two low-value resistors will limit the current to about 8 amperes or less.)

Remove the most likely components and test them for shorts. Continue to remove components until the offending component has been identified.

THE FREEZER METHOD

This method is dependent upon the nearby availability of a freezer to chill the PC board well below freezing temperature. For this reason, it is probably the least used method for finding a short on a PC board. It will be necessary to be able to bring the chilled PC board to the bench and very quickly connect normal operating voltage to it. This may require a mockup for maximum speed.

Place the shorted board in a very cold freezer for perhaps an hour. Upon its removal from the freezer, the board will quickly accumulate a light covering of frost. This frost is the indicator that you need. Quickly put the board into operation so that a heavy current will flow through the short in the board. *The board will show the heavy current flow path as the first place that melts the frost.* Follow both the supply and ground traces, and they will point to the shorted component or solder bridge.

THE CUT-TRACE-AND-TRY METHOD

This method involves physically cutting the PC board traces at selected points and testing for whether the short has cleared. This is the most damaging method to use in finding a short in a circuit.

Using this method will make it necessary to physically trace the supply-line on the board. This may take considerable time, and there may be many branches. There are five different physical structures for the Vcc and ground buses on a PC board:

1. Parallel bus structure
2. Tree structure
3. Loop structure
4. Random structure
5. Power plane structure

Figure 6–22 shows examples of the first three types of bus structures.

The tree structure branches off into major and then minor branches of current. The parallel bus structure has independent loads, with each going

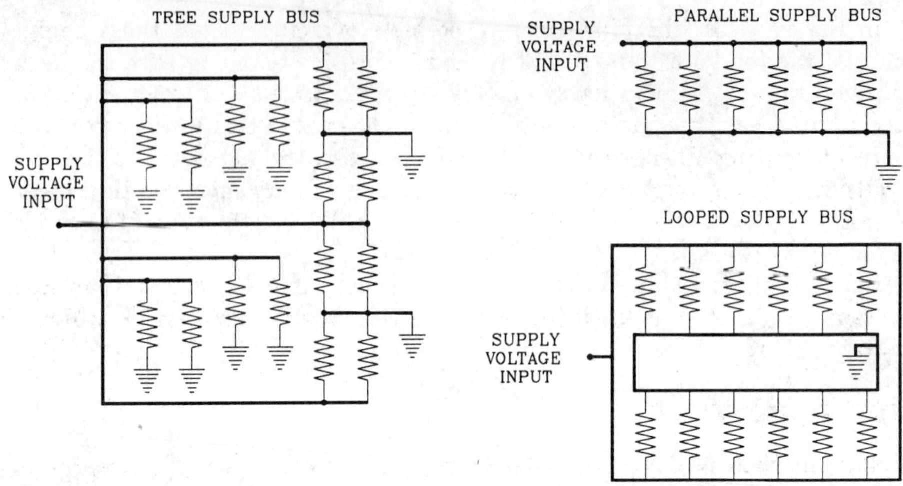

Figure 6–22 Representations of three power bus types: the tree, parallel, and looped structures.

from a main power line to a main grounded line. The looped power bus structure is similar to the paralleled structure, except that the power and ground lines are connected to the power supply by several routes rather than a single one.

Location of the short using this method consists of a division of the circuitry in half (again using the half-splitting technique) and determining at each cut where the short must be. When presented with a parallel bus or tree structure board, pick the point at which the first division into two branches occurs, breaking one of these two branches. Determine if the short is still present. If not, the short lies in the branch that was cut; if not, it is in the branch remaining connected. Then move to the next major branch containing the short, again cutting the board to determine the location. Keep up this cutting and mending of the breaks until the short has been located.

The looped structure is a bit different to troubleshoot, in that the loop must first be broken with a cut, and then another cut must be made at an appropriate location to determine where the short lies. A single cut in a looped structure must be left open, or the short will always appear to be there, regardless of further cuts.

The random power structure will require careful study to determine the best points at which to cut and test for the short. Such power structures may even trade sides of the circuit board several times.

The power plane structure cannot be troubleshot using the cut-trace-and-try method, since the Vcc is a flat conductor sandwiched within the structure of the circuit board.

6.7 TROUBLESHOOTING AN INOPERATIVE POWER SUPPLY

VOLTAGE TROUBLESHOOTING IS THE FIRST METHOD TO USE

The multimeter is the instrument of choice when troubleshooting a power supply that does not blow fuses and provides little or no output voltage. Both the AC and DC voltmeter scales may be of use. Figure 6–19 will again be used as an example of the half-split technique which should be used.

TROUBLESHOOTING INOPERATIVE TRANSFORMER-RECTIFIER OR PHASING POWER SUPPLIES

First, check for normal AC voltages at the outputs of the power transformer. In the case of multiple output windings, check each one for the proper AC voltage value. The parts list description for the transformer may have to be consulted to obtain the correct voltages. If only one winding is missing an output AC voltage, the secondary winding is open. If all of the windings have normal AC voltage output, the problem lies to the right of these points. DC voltage readings become appropriate at this point as the problem is successively narrowed down.

If none of the windings has AC voltage output, the problem lies to the left on the diagram. In this case, check for proper AC voltage to the input winding right at the transformer. If there is voltage here, the primary winding is open. If AC voltage is not available at the primary, however, one must progress toward the left in the diagram, toward the line input.

The exact location of an open circuit within a power supply, whether in the AC or DC portions of the circuit, can be determined as lying between those points where voltage is normal or nearly so and those where voltage is zero or almost zero.

Partial output voltage from any type of power supply can be caused by an ineffective filter capacitor. Electrolytic capacitors can dry out and cease to have capacitance at all, becoming little more than a high-resistance component. Partial output voltage can also be caused by failure of one or more diodes, with remaining diodes providing some output.

TROUBLESHOOTING THE INOPERATIVE SWITCHING POWER SUPPLY

The first thing to check in an inoperative switching supply is the presence of DC voltage for the switching transistor. Without DC voltage (which can be as high as 340-V DC in some switchers), the problem lies to the left of the switching transistor, in the input rectifier circuitry or earlier. See Figure 6–12.

If the DC input voltage is normal, the switching transistor is probably open. If there are two switching transistors in the transformer primary, the supply may not work if only one is defective. This is the most common failure of a switching power supply because the transistors are subjected to voltage spikes of hundreds of volts, and they must also dissipate a substantial amount of heat. The replacement transistor must be properly installed, including the "grease" for the heat sink.

If there is normal DC at the output rectifiers, the open lies to the right of this point in the diagram, toward the load. If not, the problem is either a defective switching transformer or lies in the feedback circuits.

The switching power supply may have a shorted output circuit or load on the supply yet still not blow the input fuse. This characteristic will make it necessary to modify the methods of troubleshooting as used with the other two types of power supplies. A clue to this possibility can sometimes be heard as a chirping sound coming from the switching transformer and a small current being drawn from the source voltage that is supplied to the switching power supply. The absence of any current being drawn at all indicates a simple open circuit within the power supply. This is usually caused by an open switching transistor. A second possibility involves open diodes in the AC-to-DC conversion stage, the stage that feeds the switching transistor.

To determine if a short in the output circuitry of a switching power supply is causing the problem, break the circuit at the output of the switching transformer and *provide a load* for the power supply. It may be necessary to calculate a suitable resistor for the dummy-load resistor value and power dissipation to be used. See Figure 6–23.

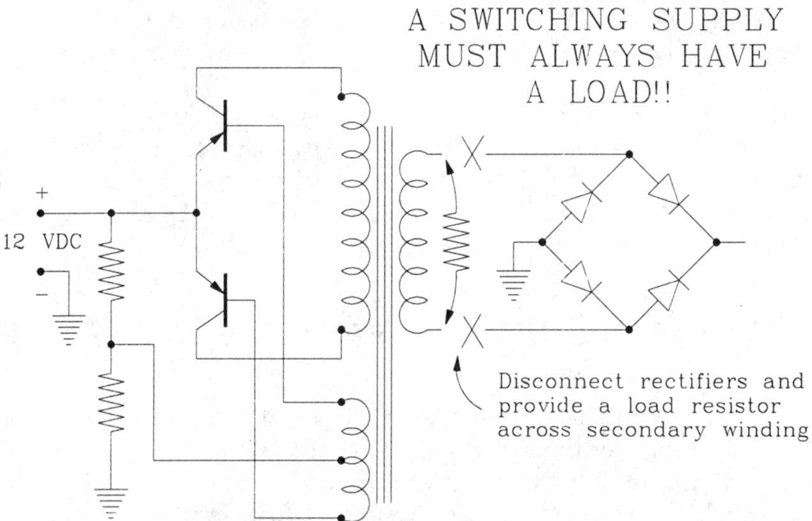
A SWITCHING SUPPLY
MUST ALWAYS HAVE
A LOAD!!
+
12 VDC
−
Disconnect rectifiers and
provide a load resistor
across secondary winding

Figure 6–23 Method to determine if a problem is in the transistor oscillator section of a DC-to-DC inverter.

Apply power to the supply and see if the output voltages from the AC windings are now approximately normal. If they are, the supply was connected to an overload. Whatever has been disconnected during this test should be investigated as having an overload.

CHAPTER SUMMARY

- The analysis of the fuse supplying power to a defective power supply is a valuable indication of the kind of problem that the power supply has and the approach that must be used to find the problem.
- An analysis of the transformer-rectifier, switching, and phasing power supplies revealed their details, similarities, and peculiarities from a troubleshooter's viewpoint.
- Methods of applying power to a shorted power supply and how to find the problem were given.
- Determination of the types of external circuit problems that may cause a power supply to be overloaded and methods to find the cause of the problem conclude this chapter.
- Troubleshooting an open, inoperative power supply was covered in detail as a basic exercise in the use of an AC and a DC voltmeter in finding a problem.

REVIEW QUESTIONS

1. You wish to locate the bad fuse out of a bank of 24 fuses, using a voltmeter. What must you first do before the testing will be valid?
2. Using the above method, the first fuse you test shows no voltage across it. This means that the fuse is _______.
3. You find a power transformer with two identical primary windings. How should these windings most likely be connected to operate on 120-V AC?
4. What does the schematic symbol of an open triangle pointing downward mean?
5. What is the approximate maximum voltage obtainable from a half-wave rectifier?
6. Is it permissible to "stack" bridge rectifiers in order to get higher output voltages than either one can produce alone?
7. Why are resistors used across each of series-connected electrolytic capacitors in high-voltage DC applications?
8. What component in a power supply with a capacitor-resistor filter is most likely to be damaged by a severe overload?

9. What kind of circuit connects one side of the AC voltage into two capacitors, with the other side going into two rectifiers?
10. What is the general rule for the replacement of fuses?
11. Why should you not use a VOM on the R×1 scale to test an instrument fuse?
12. What are the three common types of power supply?
13. What voltage would you expect across a fuse if the power is on, the circuit switches are closed, and the fuse is good?
14. What are two purposes for a power transformer winding to be connected only to an AC electrolytic capacitor?
15. Which type fuse—fast- or slow-blowing—should be used to protect a strictly resistive load?
16. What is the basic caution to observe when troubleshooting a switching power supply?
17. What does the EMI filter do?
18. AC line-operated switching power supplies commonly use a special line-voltage–switching input circuit. What kind of a circuit is used for 120-V AC operation? What kind is used for 240-V AC operation?
19. Approximately what is the highest DC voltage that can be expected within a switching power supply operating from 120-V AC?
20. Name two reasons why switching power supplies operate at frequencies above about 25 kHz.
21. If a switching power supply blows fuses, what two causes are most common?
22. What are the two most likely causes of an inoperative switching power supply that does *not* blow fuses?
23. What often happens when the output of a switching power supply is shorted?
24. Name two kinds of power supplies that usually have an EMI filter to reduce the electrical noise they produce.
25. What two semiconductor devices are commonly used to generate line voltage–synchronized trigger pulses?
26. What is the likely cause of a phasing power supply that has abnormally high voltage output that cannot be adjusted downward?
27. What is the likely cause of a phasing power supply that has no output voltage?
28. Name two of the three methods to apply power to a shorted or overloaded power supply.
29. What three reading ranges might you expect when disconnecting and measuring the input resistance of a PC board that overloads its power supply when turned on?
30. Referring to question 29, what are likely causes for a resistance reading of 1 Ω?
31. Referring to question 29, what is the likely cause of a resistance reading of 30 Ω?
32. Again referring to question 29, what does the presence of a nearly normal resistance suggest that the problem might be?

33. When, and only when, is the "smoke-out" method recommended?
34. What kind of power supply must be used for question 33, and why?
35. What are the five methods for finding a Vcc-to-ground short on a PC board?
36. What is the best, least damaging method to find a shorted bypass capacitor on a large board?

7

Troubleshooting DC Voltage Regulators

CHAPTER OBJECTIVES

DC voltage regulators are used in most electronic equipment. The voltage regulator is the link between the production of raw DC power and the voltage stability requirements of the circuitry it drives. Because of the importance, the technician should be very familiar with these circuits. The electronics technician must be familiar with the different types of regulators and their characteristics, including some of the newest switching regulators. At the conclusion of this chapter, the student will:

- Understand the basic concept of voltage regulation.
- Know how the basic Zener diode regulator works.
- Know how the linear regulator IC works, including some subtle but important features often incorporated within these components.
- Understand the basic operation of a discrete voltage regulator, including remote voltage sensing and current overload protection.
- Recognize and understand the use of a crowbar circuit.
- Recognize and be able to troubleshoot the switching regulator in any of its three configurations: step-up, step-down, and polarity reversing.

7.1 HOW A VOLTAGE SOURCE CAN BE REGULATED

There are two basic ways in which the output voltage of a power supply can be regulated. The first to be discussed is the series regulator. See Figure 7–1.

If the series resistance between an unregulated source and a load resistance is variable, the voltage reaching the load can be held constant. This is done electronically, replacing the variable series resistance with a transistor. The less the transistor conducts, the higher will be its effective series resistance, thus compensating for an increasing voltage input or a load that is demanding less current.

The second method of providing a regulated output voltage is through the use of a variable resistance across the power supply, which is fed through a resistor in series. See Figure 7–2.

7.2 THE ZENER-DIODE SHUNT VOLTAGE REGULATOR

OPERATION

The simplest voltage regulator, the shunt regulator, finds frequent use as a voltage reference for more complex regulators. As the voltage across a zener tends to drop because of an increasing load in parallel with itself, the zener itself *decreases* in resistance. The overall current from the power supply is about the same. The opposite also occurs: when the output voltage tends to rise due to a decreasing load, the Zener drops its internal resistance and conducts more current, thus keeping the voltage across itself relatively constant.

The Zener diode passes maximum current when the load across it is at a

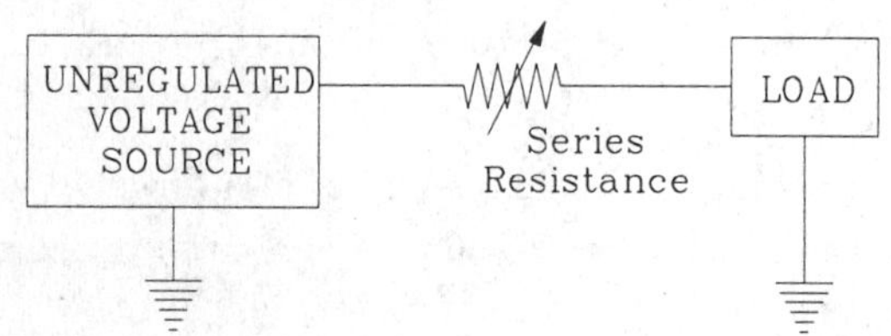
Varying the series resistance results in the loss of a variable amount of voltage
UNREGULATED VOLTAGE SOURCE
Series Resistance
LOAD
Series resistance may be varied to compensate for variations of the source or for changes in load requirements.

Figure 7–1 The principle of operation of the series regulator.

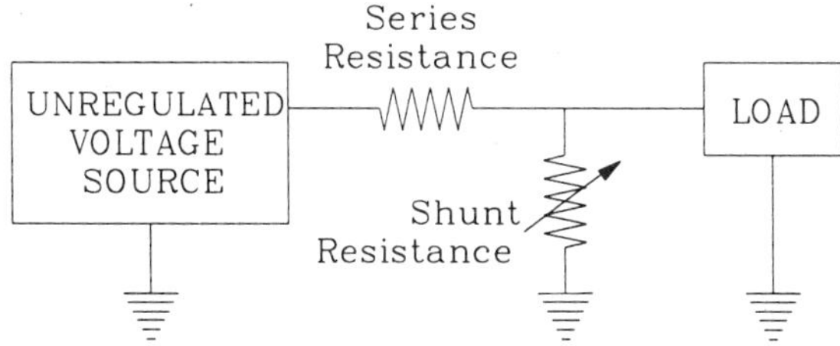
Varying the shunt resistance causes a variable voltage loss across the series resistance
Series Resistance
UNREGULATED VOLTAGE SOURCE
LOAD
Shunt Resistance
The shunt resistance may be varied to compensate for variations of the source or for changes in the load requirements

Figure 7–2 The principle of operation of a shunt regulator.

minimum, and vice versa. If the load across the Zener diode should short, the current through the Zener will cease, thus preventing any damage to the Zener. See Figure 7–3.

FAILURE PATTERNS

The Zener diode is best analyzed for failures by measuring the voltage directly across the Zener itself. The Zener should show the DC voltage as stated by the specifications for that diode. In other words, a 12-V Zener should have 12.0 volts across it, with perhaps a 0.1-volt variation due to temperature and tolerance. A deviation of more or less than roughly this amount indicates a problem, as suggested in Figure 7–4.

7.3 THE LINEAR VOLTAGE REGULATOR IC

Regulators are available in a convenient package with current capabilities up to several amperes, depending upon the physical size of the regulator ICs and their ability to throw off wasted energy in the form of heat. These regulators are sometimes called three-terminal regulators because of the number of pins. See Figure 7–5.

These regulators come in many different packages. The more common ones are the 7805 +5-V DC and 7812 +12-V DC regulators. Negative regulators are also available with designations of 7905 and 7912. An improvement over these is the LM340, which may be resistor-divider programmed over a wide range of positive output voltages. The LM320 regulator can be used for negative voltage regulation.

Some of these small regulators may have additional features which the technician should understand. One such feature is built-in temperature

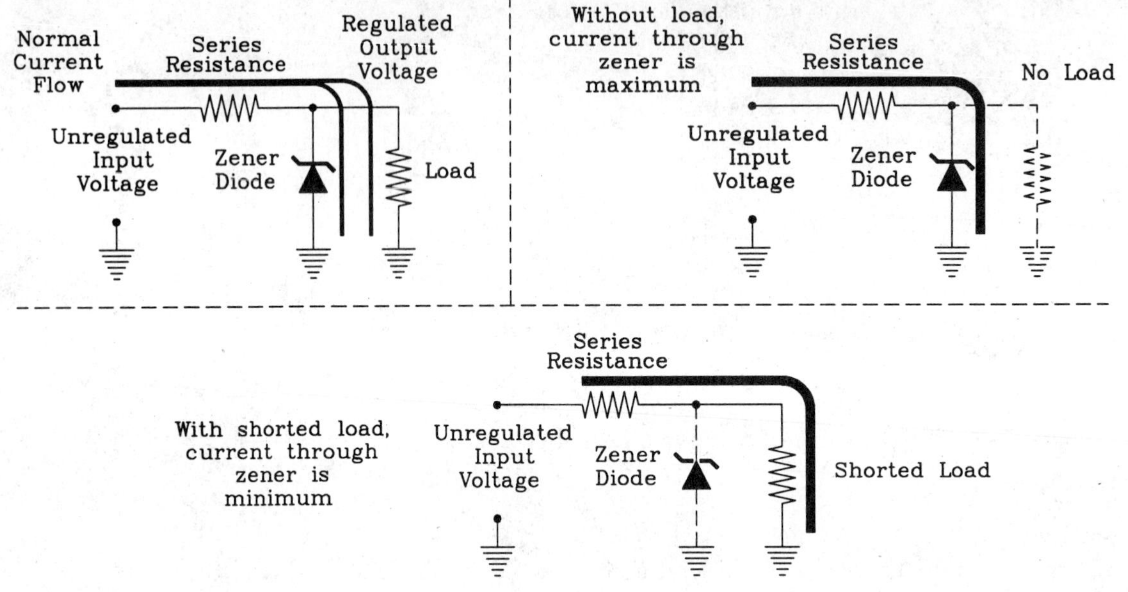

Figure 7–3 Current flow through the Zener regulator under various conditions.

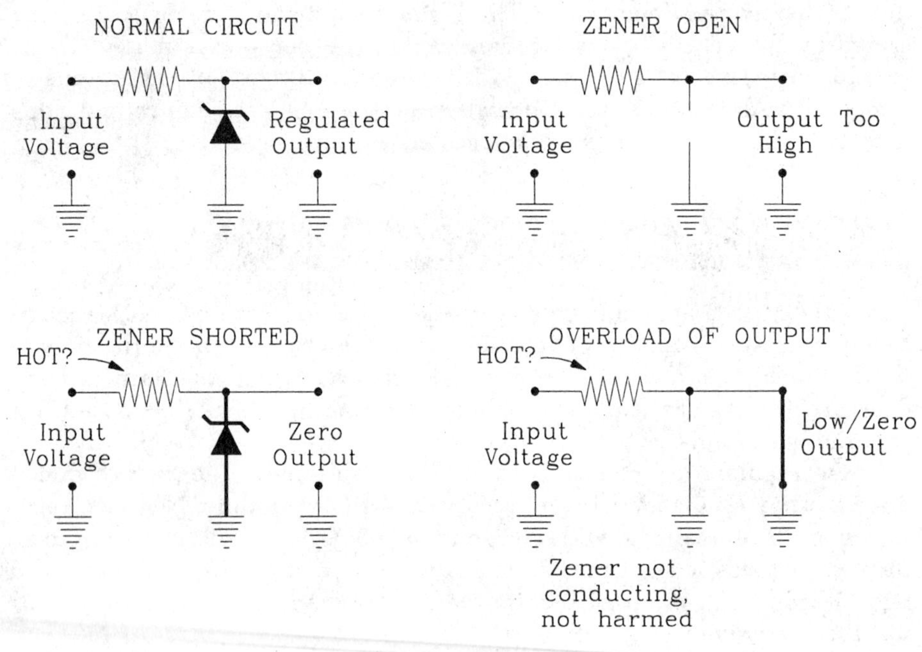

Figure 7–4 Problems of the Zener diode regulator.

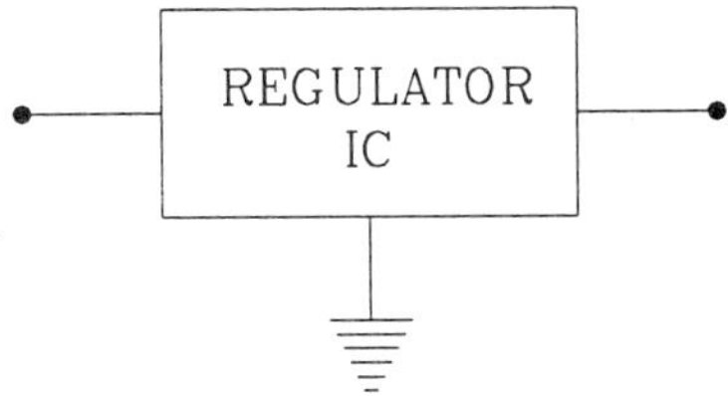

Figure 7–5 The three-terminal regulator integrated circuit.

overload protection. If the IC should overheat for any reason, the output voltage falls to a lower—hopefully, safe—value. Allowing the regulator to cool restores its normal operation. Current overload may also be provided for, again reducing the output voltage to a safe value. Even a direct short of the output won't damage the regulator, and reducing the load current to a normal value will restore the rated output voltage.

BASIC INFORMATION

FAILURE PATTERNS

The failure of a regulator IC is indicated when there is a lack of output voltage with normal load and an adequate input voltage. The simplest thing is usually to replace the regulator. If this is not convenient or if a replacement is not readily available, disconnect the load and again measure the output voltage from the IC. If the output voltage is normal under these conditions, try connecting a resistive load that draws between 75 and 100 percent of normal current. Correct output voltage across the load resistor indicates there was an overload in the load that was normally connected to the IC. There is no fault within the regulator.

It is possible for some regulator ICs to provide a good voltage output only until a load is applied, at which time the output voltage falls below normal. This is caused by the malfunction of the internal current-overload circuitry, making the entire regulator defective.

A technician should also be aware that these regulators require an adequate heat sink if they are to be operated at anywhere near their maximum current ratings. If the regulator has an internal thermal-overload protection circuit, the IC will produce decreased output voltage when it gets too hot. Without such internal protection, the IC could destroy itself for lack of proper heat sinking.

7.4 THE DISCRETE LINEAR-SERIES VOLTAGE REGULATOR

The discrete linear-series voltage regulator is made up of individual components connected together to reduce and regulate a given input voltage to a specified output voltage. This output voltage will be held

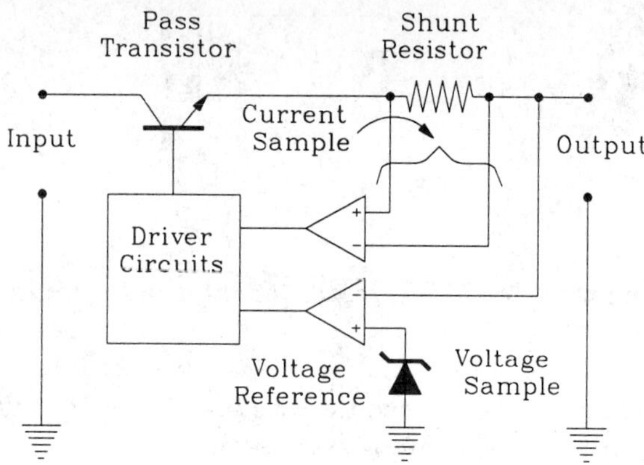

Figure 7–6 Block diagram of a discrete regulator.

within a specified range for variations in the input voltage and for variations in the load placed on the regulator, from open circuit to full load conditions. In order for a regulator to respond both upward and downward in voltage, the amplifiers within the regulator must be operated as Class A amplifiers. In addition to voltage regulation, most discrete regulators also include the circuits necessary for current monitoring and limiting. See Figure 7–6.

OPERATION

Referring to Figure 7–6, it can be seen that the discrete linear regulator performs a simple job. The output voltage is maintained at a specified level by changing the emitter-to-collector resistance of one or more paralleled power transistors. These are located between the input voltage and the output voltage.

If more than one transistor must be used to pass the heavy current demanded of the supply, low-value resistors should be used to help divide the current more equally between the transistors. See Figure 7–7.

It is interesting to note that if power FETs (field effect transistors) are used as pass transistors, the resistors shown in Figure 7–7 are not required. This is because FETs are not subject to thermal runaway; they have a positive rather than a negative temperature characteristic, and thus will automatically divide the current equally between paralleled transistors.

If the output voltage to the load tends to rise for any reason, the series transistor(s) are caused to develop more internal resistance, thus tending to drop the output voltage back to normal. This is a looped circuit, in which part of the output is fed back into the input circuitry.

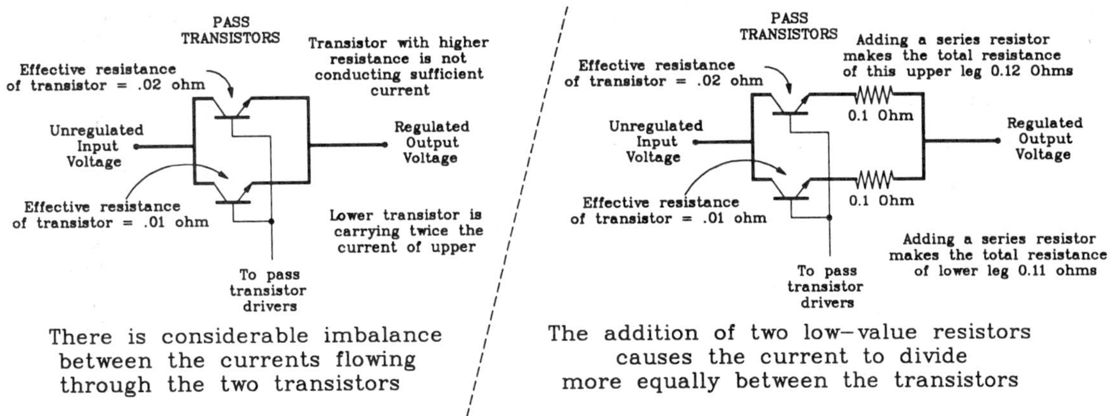

Figure 7–7 Low-value resistors are used to help divide current equally between two or more paralleled transistors.

REMOTE VOLTAGE SENSING

Most regulators do a very good job of regulating their output by sampling the output voltage *at the output terminals*. A problem will arise, however, if the power supply produces relatively low voltage and high currents and if there is also a long run of wire between the regulator output and the load. When the load changes current requirements under these conditions, the voltage drop in the high-current lines can change substantially. This makes the voltage variations *at the load* unacceptable, even though the regulator is doing its job by holding the output voltage *at the regulator output* well within limits.

If the regulator is modified to sample the output voltage at the load rather than at the regulator output, this problem can be solved. When the current requirements of the load change, the change of voltage at the load due to line loss is detected and the regulator compensates for the change. The LM723 is an IC that incorporates this feature. See Figure 7–8.

Regulators with remote sensing can, if operated improperly, cause excessive voltage at the load. On a typical remote-sensing power supply there will be a pair of small jumpers or straps to disconnect when running it in the remote sensing mode. If these jumpers become disconnected and if there are no resistors installed (as described in the following paragraph), the regulator can detect no output voltage at the sensing leads. This can result in the output voltage rising to the maximum and possibly damaging the circuitry of the load.

Resistors may already be installed inside the regulator to connect the output-sensing leads to the voltage output leads. These resistors will sense the regulator output voltage if one or both sensing leads are disconnected,

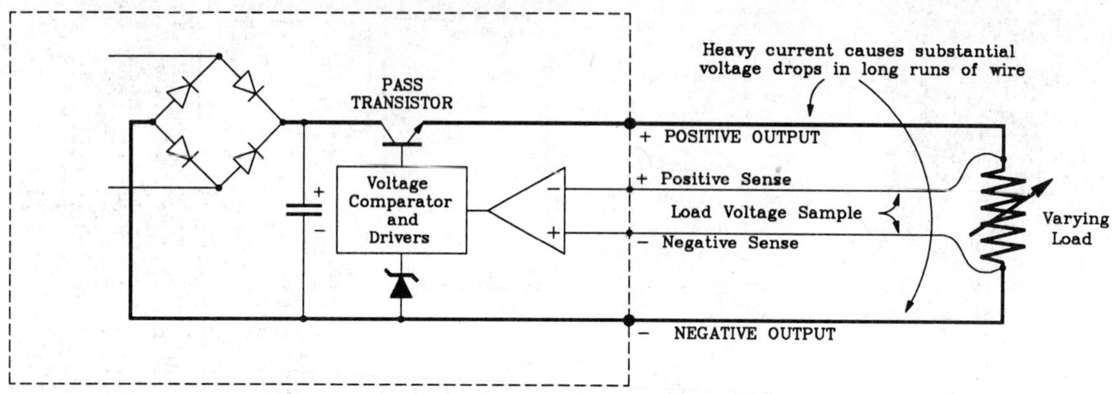

Figure 7–8 Sensing leads are used to "feel" the voltage at a remote load and compensate for voltage loss on long runs.

which may prevent the output voltage from going to an excessively high voltage. See Figure 7–9.

OVERLOAD PROTECTION

Many discrete regulators have an added feature intended to protect the regulator in the event of an overload. By reducing the output voltage, the current requirement is also reduced. Regulators perform this function in

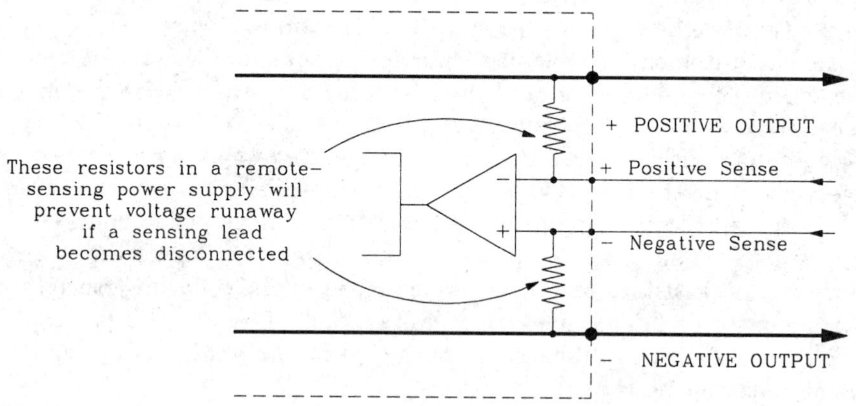

Figure 7–9 The addition of internal resistors prevents extreme overvoltage if the sensing leads open.

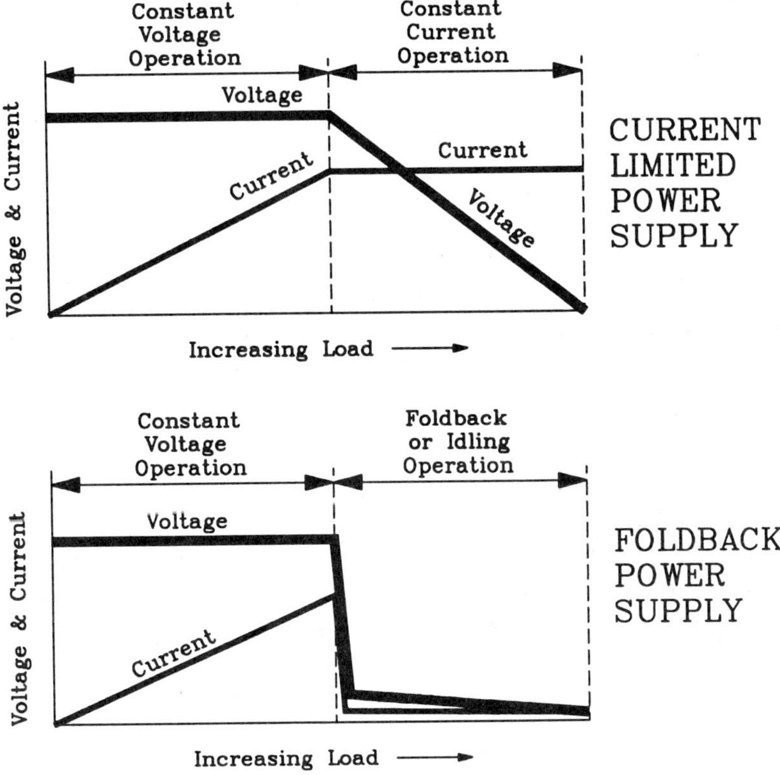

Figure 7–10 Graphs of voltage and current for the current-limited and the foldback types of power supplies.

either of two ways: by limiting of the current of the output or by using the foldback technique. When an overload occurs, the power supply can either reduce the output voltage so that the rated output current is not exceeded, or it can simply reduce the output voltage to a very low value. This low voltage value will be maintained until the power supply is electrically reset (whether automatically or manually) or, in more sophisticated supplies, until the overload is removed. Figure 7–10 shows the graphical difference in the constant-current and foldback protection schemes.

THE CROWBAR CIRCUIT

The crowbar circuit is a safety circuit that prevents the accidental application of too much voltage from the power supply to the load that it protects. It is often used to protect TTL circuitry, which is important due to the sensitivity of TTL to overvoltages above 7–V DC. If the voltage tends to go too high (usually because of a series regulator failure), the crowbar circuit

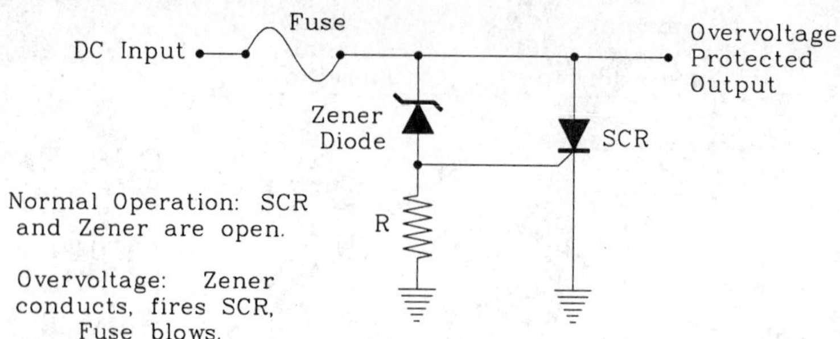

Figure 7–11 The crowbar circuit is designed to blow the nearby fuse to protect circuitry further down the line from abnormally high voltages.

is supposed to actually short the power supply. A fuse between the power supply and the circuitry it feeds should then open. See Figure 7–11.

If a crowbar circuit has blown its associated fuse, it is an indication that the output voltage of the power supply has gone too high. The first component to suspect would be the series-pass transistor of a discrete regulator circuit.

STATIC DC TROUBLESHOOTING

Troubleshooting a DC regulator requires techniques that are typically used when tracing problems in any DC amplifier. Since it is appropriate here, static DC troubleshooting will be discussed in detail.

Transistor Amplifier Configurations

BASIC INFORMATION

There are three basic amplifier configurations. Each has advantages, and the technician must know what to expect when encountering them in working circuits.

The common emitter circuit is the most common circuit configuration for the bipolar transistor. It is characterized by high gain, in both voltage and current. The output is reversed in phase from the input. In other words, a positive-going input results in a negative-going output voltage, and vice versa. The common emitter circuit also has a relatively high input impedance. See Figure 7–12.

The common collector circuit (often called an emitter follower) is used to obtain an increase of current from input to output. It does not provide any voltage gain at all. The circuit also does not produce a phase shift. It features relatively high input impedance and very low output impedance. One common use is in voltage regulators as a constant-voltage source, since the voltage at the emitter is dependent upon the base voltage, and not upon the voltage available at the collector.

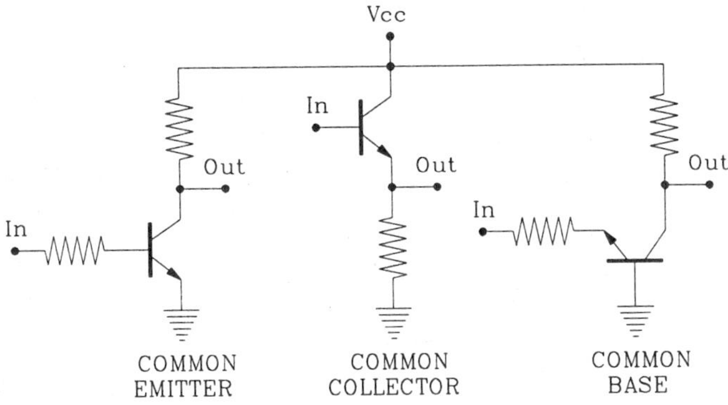

Figure 7–12 The three transistor amplifier configurations.

The common base configuration provides a large power gain. The input impedance is low, requiring considerable power to drive it. Voltage gain is very good, but the input current is not amplified. This circuit is sometimes used as a constant-current source, since the output current depends upon the bias current, not the supply voltage available at the collector.

All of these transistor configurations can be used with the biasing schemes of the various classes of operation, A, B, or C.

To determine the configuration of a circuit, identify the input and output elements of the transistor. These elements cannot be located in common with each other, so this identifies the third, remaining element as the common element. For example, if the input is on the base and the output is from the emitter, you are examining a common collector configuration.

Bipolar Transistor Inputs and Outputs

Regardless of whether the transistor is an NPN (negative-positive-negative) or a PNP (positive-negative-positive) type, the following three rules will always hold true. These are important facts to keep in mind when troubleshooting based upon static DC voltages. They are also important ground rules to use when analyzing the detailed operation of DC amplifiers. Refer back to Figure 7–12 during the following discussions. Class A amplification is assumed for this discussion because virtually all DC amplifiers operate as Class A.

In the Common Emitter Configuration. If the voltage between the base and the emitter increases, the emitter-collector circuit will decrease in resistance. This may be accomplished by changing the base voltage *more toward the collector*. The reverse situation, with the base voltage going toward the emitter, will cause the emitter-collector circuit to increase in resistance.

An increase of the base-emitter voltage can be caused by changing the base input voltage of a common emitter stage (at the input of any series resistor) more toward the collector voltage. Thus, if you are using an NPN transistor with positive supply and a grounded emitter, and you are driving the base from a quiescent value of 4.0 volts to 4.3 volts at the input of the series base resistor, the output collector voltage will *drop* in amplitude. (Remember the phase reversal of a common emitter circuit.)

NOTE: The common emitter circuit usually has a resistor in series with the base. The purpose of this resistor is to allow the voltage input to vary, which at the same time varies the *current* into the transistor. The resistor drops any excessive voltage above the 0.7 volts normally required for forward bias. Without this series resistor, the input voltage could possibly drive excessive current through the base, distorting the output waveform and possibly destroying the transistor.

In the Common Base Configuration. As explained above, if the voltage between the base and the emitter increases, the emitter-collector circuit will decrease in resistance. This may be accomplished changing the *emitter voltage away from the base.* The reverse, of course, also holds true.

The common base configuration holds the base voltage constant. The input signal is applied to the emitter, usually through a resistor which serves the same purpose as the base resistor discussed above. It "converts" the input voltage to a change of current without forcing the emitter voltage beyond the 0.7 volts required for operation.

In the Common Collector Configuration (Also Known as a Voltage Follower or Buffer). If the base voltage changes, *the emitter voltage follows* by the same amount.

If the base of a common collector circuit increases from 1.8 volts to a new value of 2.5 volts with reference to ground, the emitter circuit will change from about 1.1 volts to 1.8 volts. (Remember the initial 0.7 volts of forward bias required for operation of a silicon transistor.) The reverse situation is also true.

Predicting DC Voltages in Various Configurations

There are, in any given circuit, certain voltages that are normally present on the elements of a transistor in the absence of any signal. These voltages and currents determine the quiescent bias of the transistor and are the voltages given on the "voltage troubleshooting" charts. When the bias is changed, the transistor will either conduct more or less current through the emitter-collector circuit. It is often a great help during troubleshooting to be able to predict, and to thoroughly understand, the relationships that exist between a changing input and the resulting change in the emitter-collector circuit. This ability is particularly helpful when troubleshooting DC-coupled amplifiers, such as voltage regulators.

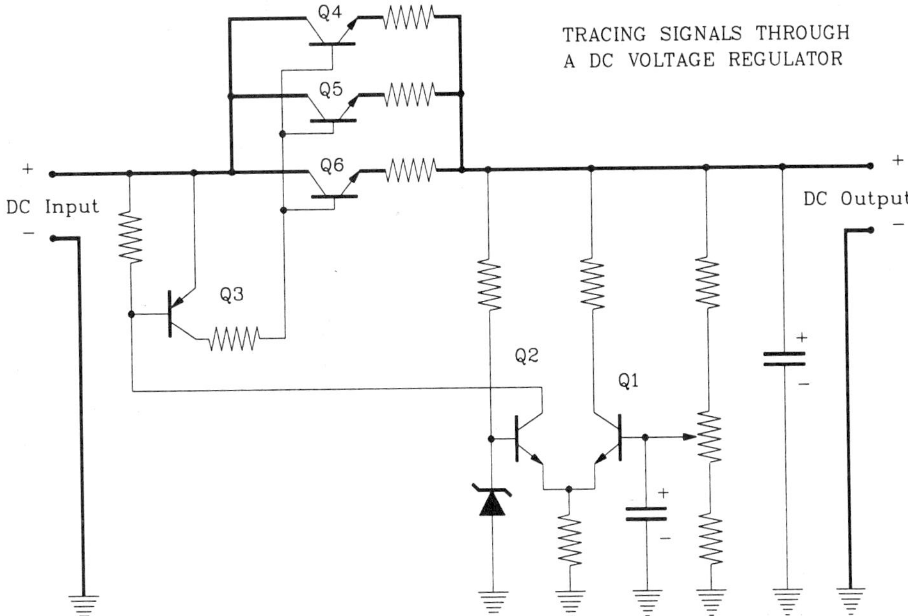

Figure 7–13 This sample circuit has all three configurations of transistor amplifiers for signal-tracing practice.

Examining a discrete voltage regulator provides an extra check of your understanding of the circuit. If you can "walk through" a regulator circuit, the end result should be predictable. Let us *assume* that the output voltage of the regulator goes slightly lower than it should be (for example, an increased load would cause this). The result of our going entirely through the circuit should be an *increase* in the output voltage. This is because the regulator normally does just that: it counteracts any tendency of the output voltage to change. If each stage of the regulator is thoroughly understood, we should be able to predict how the voltages will change throughout the circuit, assuming only that the output is going to be abnormally low.

Refer to Figure 7–13 for an example of how this might be done. This regulator has all three configurations of transistor within it, which can assist us in understanding how the input-versus-output relationship operates in all three types.

Analysis of a Sample Circuit

Let us assume that the DC output of the regulator in Figure 7–13 had an increased load placed upon it, causing the voltage to be less than it should be. After correctly going through all of the stages, you should produce a corresponding reaction that will *raise* the output voltage.

Q1 is set up as an emitter follower, since the input is on the base and the output on the emitter. The DC voltage feeding the base of Q1 will also decrease. The base will be dropped more toward its emitter, increasing the emitter-collector resistance, and the emitter voltage will also fall.

Q2 is a common base amplifier, with the base held at a constant voltage by the zener diode and the resistor above it. When the voltage input decreases across the emitter resistor, the emitter is pulled away from the base. This causes the emitter-collector to decrease in resistance, conducting more.

Q3 is a common emitter configuration. The voltage at its base is being pulled more toward its collector, reducing the resistance of the emitter-collector circuit.

The output transistors (called pass transistors) are connected in a common collector circuit. The decrease in resistance of the emitter-collector of Q3 causes the bases of Q4, Q5, and Q6 to be pulled more toward their collectors, decreasing their emitter-collector circuit resistance.

The decrease of emitter-collector resistance of the pass transistors causes the output voltage to increase, back to where it belongs.

Short Base to Emitter to Shut-Off Stage

Here is a trick that can be used to test a specific transistor as a simple go or no-go check. This check applies only to Class A stages, which normally conduct halfway. *This trick should never be used with a DC-coupled (direct-coupled) audio amplifier* because damage to the amplifier can result. Use only on AC-coupled (capacitor-coupled) amplifiers.

Identify the emitter, base, and collector of the transistor in question. With power applied, monitor the DC voltage from the collector to the emitter. This voltage should be about half of the available voltage. While watching the collector-emitter voltage, short the base lead to the emitter. The voltage across the transistor should increase to the maximum voltage available for the stage. *It is important to be absolutely sure of the connections to the transistor, as accidentally shorting its base to the collector can instantly destroy it.*

FAILURE PATTERNS

Perhaps the most common failure of a discrete regulator is the failure of a series pass transistor, the transistor that passes the full current of the regulator to the external circuits. This transistor is required to dissipate a substantial amount of heat, and heat contributes to failures. Two failures are common, those of the shorted and the open pass transistors. When the pass transistor shorts, the output voltage increases dramatically, nearly to the level of the available input voltage from the power supply. When the pass transistor opens, there is almost no voltage at the regulator's output.

Other common failures include failures of the intermediate amplifiers which feed the error signal to the base of the pass transistor. The reference voltage should also be checked, as reference diodes (Zeners) are a likely cause of regulator problems.

7.5 THE SWITCHING REGULATOR

The switching regulator represents a major advance in regulator design. We can probably expect to see more of these used in electronic equipment in the years to come. Where the linear regulator discards excessive voltage and current (power) in the form of heat, the switching regulator wastes very little power. Consequently, efficiencies of as much as 90 percent are possible. Because of their high efficiency and decreased dissipation of heat, regulators can be made smaller. This is a particularly attractive characteristic when equipment operates from limited power sources such as batteries or solar cells. The switching regulator can also *increase* its output voltage over that of the input voltage or even produce an output of reversed polarity from that of the supplied input voltage. Switching regulators use an inductor as an energy-storing element.

The major components of a switching regulator are available in integrated circuit packages, greatly simplifying regulator design. These chips sample the output voltage and vary the pulse width of the gate signal to the switching transistor in order to maintain a constant output voltage. Examples of such chips are Fairchild's uA78S40 and Signetic's NE5560N.

THE STEP-DOWN SWITCHING REGULATOR

The step-down regulator produces an output voltage that is less than that of the supply voltage. It is sometimes called a *forward converter circuit*. When the transistor is conducting, current flows through the series inductor, building the magnetic field. (See Figure 7–14). When the transistor is not conducting, the inductor's now-reversed polarity discharges current due to the collapsing field and maintains the output voltage to the filter capacitor via the discharge diode.

The on- versus off-time (duty cycle) of the transistor conduction determines the average amount of current flowing into the inductor/capacitor filter. Increasing current demands of the load are compensated for by varying the average amount of energy coupled through the transistor from the input supply voltage source.

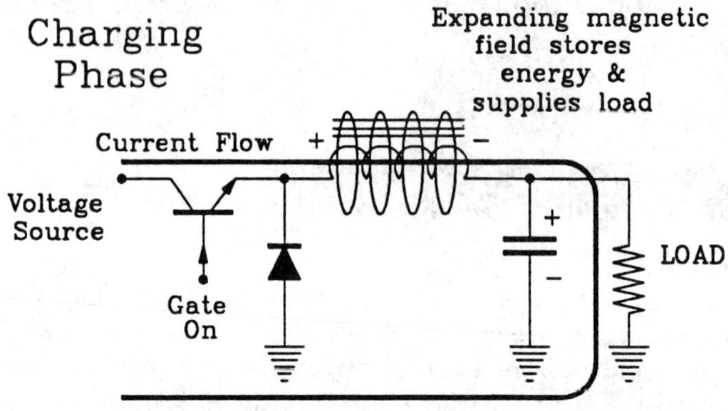

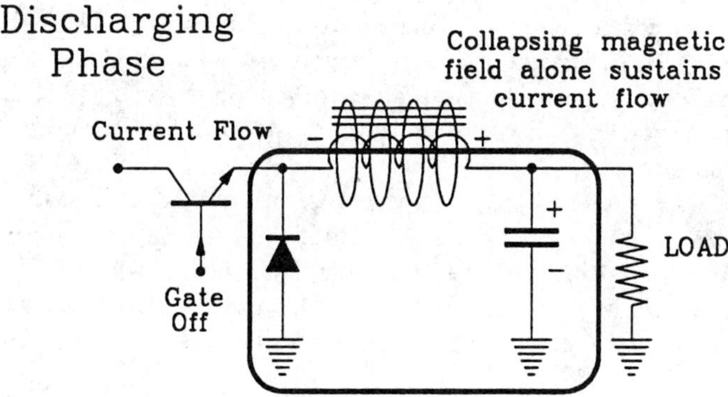

Figure 7–14 Simplified schematic of a switching step-down regulator during the charge and discharge cycles of the inductor.

Failures of the Step-Down Switching Regulator

The normal operation of the discharge diode protects the transistor from potentially damaging voltage spikes during the discharge cycle of the inductor. If this diode fails by opening, it will often cause a failure of the switching transistor as well.

If the output filter capacitor fails by shorting, it will overload the power supply. Since the regulator will attempt to compensate for the increased current demand, large amounts of current will be pulsed into the shorted capacitor.

If the switching transistor shorts, the full DC input of the supply voltage

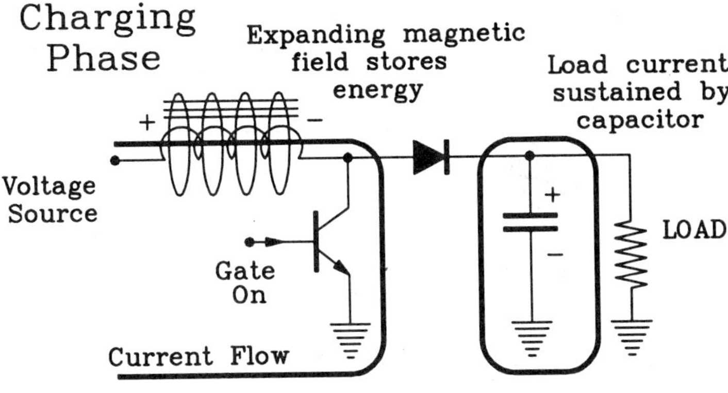

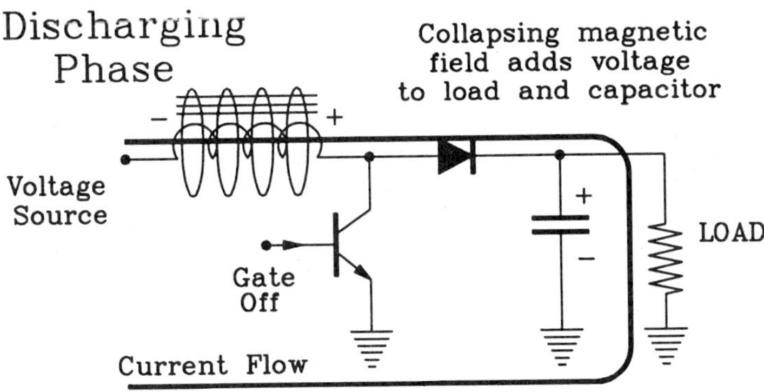

Figure 7–15 Simplified schematic of a switching step-up regulator during the charge and discharge cycles of the inductor.

will be delivered to the load. This is likely to damage the load due to the overvoltage.

THE STEP-UP SWITCHING REGULATOR

The step-up switching regulator provides a higher output voltage than that provided by the input to the circuit. This is possible because of the ability of an inductor to store energy in the magnetic field, which can, through an appropriate circuit, actually add to the voltage of the source. This circuit is sometimes called a *flyback circuit*. All that is needed is a method of causing the inductor to charge and then to discharge in a series-aiding configuration with the input voltage source. See Figure 7–15.

Again, the duty cycle of the on- and off-times of the transistor determine the average energy supplied to the load.

Failures of the Step-Up Switching Regulator

The transistor used in a step-up regulator must be switched to "off" before the inductor saturates. If the inductor is allowed to saturate, the resulting high current may open the transistor. Failures of the transistor should, therefore, be sufficient reason to check the driving circuitry of the transistor base. Opening the series diode to the load will subject the transistor to much higher than normal voltage on the collector, and is also likely to cause the failure of the transistor.

THE POLARITY-INVERTING SWITCHING REGULATOR

By charging an inductor to ground and then allowing the natural polarity reversal of the discharge cycle to feed the load, polarity inversion becomes practical. This circuit may be termed an *inverting flyback circuit*. See Figure 7–16.

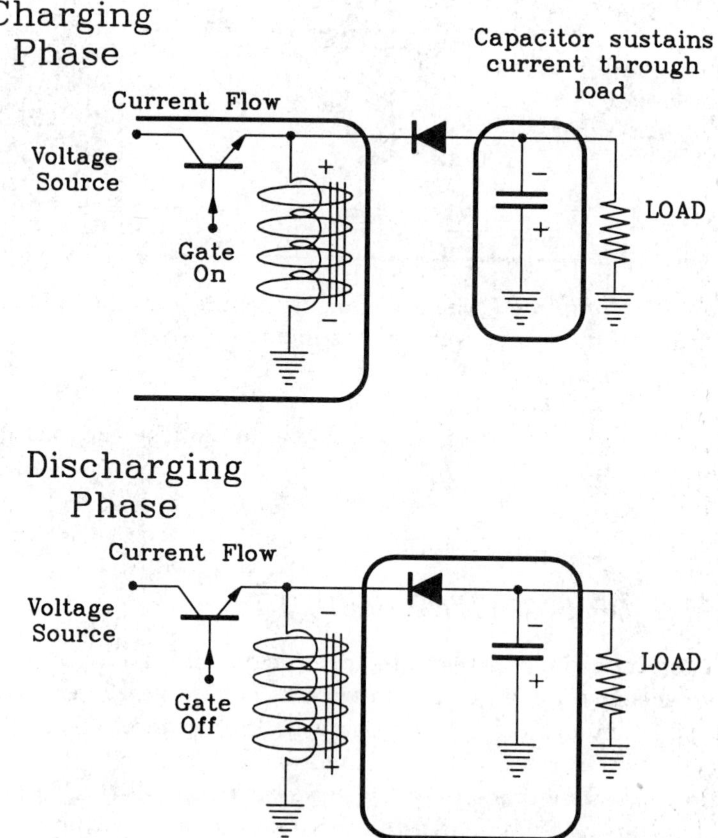

Figure 7–16 Simplified schematic of a polarity-inverting regulator during the charge and discharge cycles of the inductor.

Failures of the Polarity-Inverting Switching Regulator

A failure of the transistor or the diode used in this circuit could cause an overload of the input source if either or both should short. Opening either would simply result in no operation and no damage to the load or the power supply.

CHAPTER SUMMARY

- There are four different types of voltage regulators in common use today, the Zener regulator, the linear regulator integrated circuit, the discrete linear-series voltage regulator, and the switching regulator.
- The principles of tracing a problem within the stages of a discrete regulator were presented: these are techniques used in tracing problems in any DC amplifier circuit.
- The different configurations of transistor amplifiers, common base, collector, and emitter were given, along with the principal characteristics of each.
- The operation of switching regulators for stepping the unregulated input voltage down or up or even inverting the input polarity were explained.

REVIEW QUESTIONS

1. Name the two fundamentally different ways in which a voltage source can be regulated.
2. In what use is the shunt regulator most often found?
3. If the load across a Zener regulator should short, should the Zener diode be replaced as part of the repair?
4. What voltage should be measured across an operating Zener?
5. What is indicated as the probable problem if you measure a voltage across a Zener and find it to be 35 percent more than the voltage specified for the Zener?
6. Name the two internal protection features sometimes found in linear three-terminal voltage regulator ICs.
7. If there is proper voltage into a three-terminal regulator but the output is only 10 percent of what it should be, name the two possible causes that would *not* necessarily mean a failure of the regulator.
8. The voltage amplifiers within a discrete regulator are operating as Class _______.
9. Why do the three pass transistors of a high-current linear discrete regulator have low-resistance resistors connected to their emitters?

10. What is the basic reason for remote voltage sensing on a power supply?
11. Name the two methods of protection incorporated into a power supply that will protect it from current overload.
12. What is the purpose of a crowbar circuit?
13. If the signal comes into a transistor's emitter and leaves by the collector lead, what configuration is this?
14. If the signal comes into a transistor's base and leaves by the collector lead, what configuration is this?
15. If the signal comes into a transistor's base and leaves by the emitter lead, what configuration is this?
16. Can one tell by the configurations of questions 13, 14, and 15 the class of operation expected?
17. After identifying a configuration as being a common collector circuit, one could expect a *change* of 1.5-V DC at the base to appear as a *change* of ______ volts at the emitter output.
18. What can you assume about the voltage supplied to a base circuit if you identify a common base configuration?
19. Why is a resistor usually used in series with the base or emitter of a transistor when using it as the input element?
20. What is a very common failure of discrete voltage regulators, and what causes these failures?
21. What is the basic difference between a linear and a switching regulator in regard to heat?
22. What are the three types of switching regulators?
23. Which one of the three types of switching regulators would benefit from the installation of a crowbar circuit?
24. In any of the switching regulator circuits, and in the simplest terms, what is the switching transistor actually doing while it is gated on?

8

How to Trace Analog Signals

CHAPTER OBJECTIVES

This chapter covers the basic concepts of signal tracing which apply to tracing the signal through DC, audio, and pulse circuits. The technician uses signal-tracing techniques to identify which area or card within the equipment is defective, and then further narrows the problem to the stage that is malfunctioning. At the conclusion of this chapter, the student will:

- Know why experienced technicians repair equipment so quickly, and apparently with little effort.
- Be aware of the possible uses of a Tracker™ to quickly find a problem on a board.
- Be able to identify when signal-tracing techniques are appropriate.
- Use a bench power supply effectively and with an understanding of its capabilities and limitations.
- Be able to identify the general type of analog circuits in terms of their circuit function.
- How to use the block diagram in tracing the signal through equipment.
- Know the techniques to use in narrowing a problem to a stage by the use of front panel controls.

- Identify and use either of two signal-tracing methods.
- Know how to trace an unwanted signal to its source.

8.1 REPAIR BY EXPERIENCE

Just about everyone has watched a technical person of one kind or another make a quick repair. Office workers often see the copy-machine or computer repair technician come in, do a few quick tests, and then go straight to the cause of the problem. These technicians have been trained on specific equipment and, through experience and repetition, they know that certain symptoms mean a specific failure. Only occasionally does a new set of symptoms slow them up.

Repair by experience is relatively easy to do if one goes to the company school and there are only a few different models of equipment with which to deal. This kind of troubleshooting is fast and can make a good profit for the company employing the technician. Many electronics technicians will not have this luxury, however. Dozens of different circuits may have to be repaired by a single technician, without the benefit of formal schooling. Electronics technicians are very often left to their own devices to educate themselves on the intricacies of the circuitry on which they work. Most of the material of this book, including its basic concept, has been written with these technicians in mind.

8.2 A QUICK REPAIR ALTERNATIVE

At this point, it is quite possible to find the problem in a circuit by using an instrument generically referred to as a *solid-state tester*. This alternative is particularly attractive if there are one or more of the following handicaps to doing a more elaborate signal-tracing job:

No schematic or instruction manual.

You've never seen this board before.

The board must be fixed as soon as possible.

You can't connect power to the board for some reason.

Details of the use of this instrument are covered in Chapter 17, "Dead Circuit Troubleshooting and Part Removal."

8.3 WHEN IS THE TRACING OF SIGNALS NECESSARY?

Once the technician is certain that the reported problem is still present (if it is not, see the section on intermittents in Chapter 2), that it is not operator-induced, there is no visual defect, and that the necessary power supply voltages are present and correct (if they are not, see Chapter 6), the next step is to attempt to operate the equipment under repair.

Operating the defective equipment may mean that it will be necessary to operate it with the covers off or cabinet access doors open. In such a case, the interlocking switches must be defeated to provide the necessary voltages. Some interlocks can be defeated by pulling on them. Refer back to Figure 3–6.

Much of the equipment that the technician will be working on will consist of several printed circuit boards or cards. A defect somewhere within the equipment must be localized to progressively smaller areas until the defective component has been identified. From there, it is a relatively simple matter to replace the bad part and get the equipment working again.

While it is occasionally possible to directly detect a bad component based on smoke, burned components, or other visual indications, it will usually be necessary to operate the equipment and observe the symptoms carefully. By comparison to normal operation, the process of narrowing down the problem to one area begins.

Some equipment comes with self-contained power supplies such as batteries or an AC-line-operated power supply. In these cases, you won't need an external power supply. However, if you are asked to service equipment that does not have its own power supply, you will have to provide voltages to the circuit to make it operate. For this you will require at least one appropriate bench power supply. Let us take a look at the subject of bench power supplies.

8.4 USING A BENCH POWER SUPPLY

Some circuits require more than one source of voltage. For instance, analog integrated circuits may require both positive and negative supplies for operational amplifiers. Some digital circuits, such as in microcomputers, require +5, +12, and –12 volt supplies. A separate external supply will be needed for each of the required voltages.

Bench power supplies are available in several different types:

Unregulated fixed or variable voltage with fused output.

Regulated fixed or variable voltage with fused output.

Regulated fixed or variable voltage with fixed overcurrent protection.

Regulated fixed or variable voltage supply with adjustable overcurrent protection.

UNREGULATED POWER SUPPLIES

Unregulated fixed- or variable-voltage power supplies can be used in cases where the current demand is reasonably constant and the power supply is able to supply the required current without overheating. A good example of a fixed-voltage unregulated power supply is the small transformer that is designed to plug into a 120-V AC socket and has a pair of wires to a load, such as a small tape recorder or radio. These small units may put out either AC or DC, depending upon whether the rectifier is contained within the case of the transformer or in the equipment itself. The output voltage of these units is not critical, and the load is relatively constant. Inexpensive automobile battery chargers are also examples of fixed-voltage unregulated power supplies. These usually do not even have a filter, making the battery under charge receive pulses of DC directly from the charger rectifiers.

Protection against an overload on one of these power supplies should be provided in the form of a fuse or circuit breaker. If an overload occurs, the supply will be turned off until an operator corrects the condition and then replaces the fuse or resets the breaker.

REGULATED POWER SUPPLIES

Regulated power supplies are needed when a constant supply of voltage is required. Granted, if a sufficiently heavy-duty power supply is made, its output voltage may not vary much under normal load conditions. In some cases, a volt or two of power supply drop under heavy current loading will pose no problem. A typical small automotive battery charger is an example of an unregulated power supply. When a heavy current is demanded of it, its output voltage drops considerably, rising only when the load becomes less severe.

In other cases, however, a drop of a volt or two cannot be tolerated. When working on TTL circuits, for instance, the supply voltage must not vary from 5.00 volts more than plus or minus 0.25 volt, even if the supply current changes considerably during normal operation. This is only one example of cases in which a voltage-regulated supply is required.

If a power supply is referred to as a *regulated* power supply, it is assumed that it is the voltage that is regulated, or held constant. A regulated fixed- or variable-voltage power supply is an improvement over the unregulated supply because the output voltage is held relatively constant as the load increases—but only to a point. This point of heavy current is the maximum current capability of the supply. If the current demand exceeds the designed rating of the supply, there should be a fuse or circuit breaker to protect the supply (as discussed in the previous paragraph).

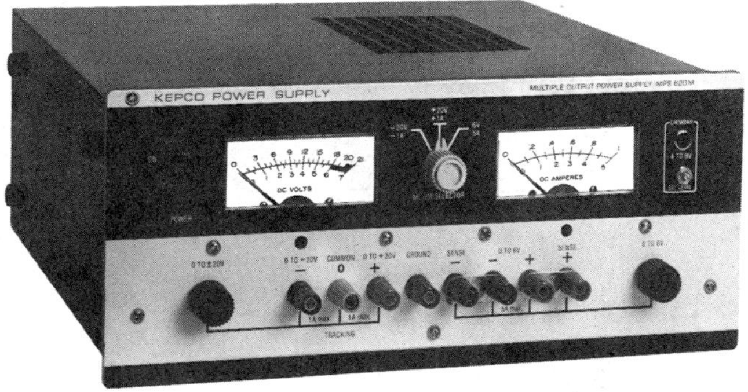

Figure 8–1 An example of a variable-voltage, variable-overcurrent protected power supply. (Courtesy Kepco, Inc., Flushing, NY)

FIXED OVERCURRENT PROTECTION

A fixed or variable voltage power supply can be provided with additional circuitry that will protect the supply against current overloads without requiring the replacement of a fuse or the manual resetting of a circuit breaker. There are two methods of protecting such a supply when an overload occurs: to simply cause the supply to quickly reduce its output to a minimum until the load is gone (this type may require manual resetting) or to reduce the voltage to what is necessary to permit only the rated current to flow. A graph of the voltage and current outputs of these two methods was given in Figure 7–10.

ADJUSTABLE OVERCURRENT PROTECTION

A power supply such as the one in Figure 8–1 has the added feature of adjustable overcurrent protection.

Variable overcurrent protection is an advantage when testing a variety of loads with different current demands. As each is operated by this kind of supply, the maximum current demanded by a normal load can be set into the power supply. If there happens to be a shorted board in the lot, it will merely limit the power supply in current, causing the power supply voltage to drop drastically. This would be an easily detected indication of a short from the Vcc bus of the board to ground. Note that an excessive current cannot flow into the PC board under these conditions, which protects the board.

SETTING UP A BENCH POWER SUPPLY FOR USE

The details of setting up a variable-voltage regulated power supply with variable current overload may vary in detail but generally include the following steps.

Setting Up for Resistive Loads

1. Determine the operating voltage and the normal maximum current demanded by the circuit under test.
2. With the output terminals of the supply unconnected, adjust the open-circuit voltage from the supply to only a few volts. This step is necessary to have a voltage to cause a current flow for the next step.
3. Short the output terminals of the supply. Set the maximum current adjustment to a few percent more than the normal current to be supplied to the circuit under test.
4. Remove the output short and adjust the voltage control to the full voltage value required for the circuit under test.
5. Turn off the power supply.
6. Connect the power supply to the circuit under test.
7. Turn on the supply. The circuit under test now has the proper amount of voltage applied. If there is a malfunction, the current-limiting feature of the power supply will protect the circuit from possible further damage.

Setting Up for Charging Batteries

A bench power supply can be put to use in many different applications, including individual component test procedures. Charging batteries, however, requires particular care. *Even a momentarily reversed connection of an apparently discharged battery to a regulated power supply can severely damage the supply.* The electronic regulating circuits of the supply will not tolerate a reversal in polarity of the output terminals. Connect batteries for charging by connecting positive (+) to positive and negative (–) to negative. The color codes do match (red to red and black to black).

There are two ways to charge batteries: with constant current or constant voltage. Nickel-cadmium batteries (Ni-Cads) are best charged from a fully exhausted state by applying a charging current through them of 1/10th their ampere-hour rating for a period of 14 hours. Lead-acid batteries, on the other hand, should be charged with a fixed voltage. The setup procedure when using a regulated variable-voltage supply with adjustable overcurrent protection varies for the two types of charging methods.

Set up for Constant-Current Ni-Cad Charging

1. Determine the fully charged battery voltage and the maximum charging current to be allowed.
2. With the output of the supply open, turn the voltage control to a few volts. This step is necessary to have a voltage to cause a current flow for the next step.
3. Short the output terminals of the supply. Set the current adjustment to the value of current required for charging. Ni-Cads require a charging rate of 1/10th their ampere-hour rating.

4. Remove the output short and adjust the voltage control to a value of a few volts over that of the fully charged battery. By doing so, you ensure that the current will continue to flow even after the battery reaches normal terminal voltage.
5. Turn off the power supply.
6. Connect the power supply to the battery to be charged. *Be certain of correct battery polarity!*
7. Turn on the supply. The battery will charge at the amount of current set by the current control. It is up to the operator to turn off the supply in about 14 hours.

Setting Up for Constant-Voltage Lead-Acid Charging

1. Determine the fully charged battery voltage and the maximum charging current to be allowed.
2. With the output of the supply open, turn the voltage control to a few volts. This step is necessary to have a voltage to cause a current flow for the next step.
3. Short the output terminals of the supply. Set the current adjustment to the maximum current to be delivered during charge. A value of 1/4 the ampere-hour rating of the battery is a heavy charging current.
4. Remove the output short and adjust the voltage control to a value a few tenths of a volt over that of the fully charged battery. By doing so, you ensure that the battery will continue to receive a trickle charge to hold the battery at maximum charge. A fully charged 12-volt automobile battery has a fully charged terminal voltage of about 13.8 volts. Set the battery charge voltage to about 14.2 volts.
5. Turn off the power supply.
6. Connect the power supply to the battery to be charged. *Be certain of correct battery polarity!*
7. Turn on the supply. The maximum charging current will be supplied until the battery voltage reaches the final charged voltage, at which time the current will decrease to a trickle.

Now that the bench power supply is understood, the equipment to be repaired can be powered up and further analyzed.

8.5 GENERAL TYPES OF ANALOG CIRCUITS

Before using the block diagram of a circuit to get the initial bearings concerning what is happening and how it is accomplished, it is appropriate now to review the six basic building blocks of analog circuits. When each of these are understood, the block diagram can be examined to see in what category each block fits. Figure 8–2 shows the basic circuits.

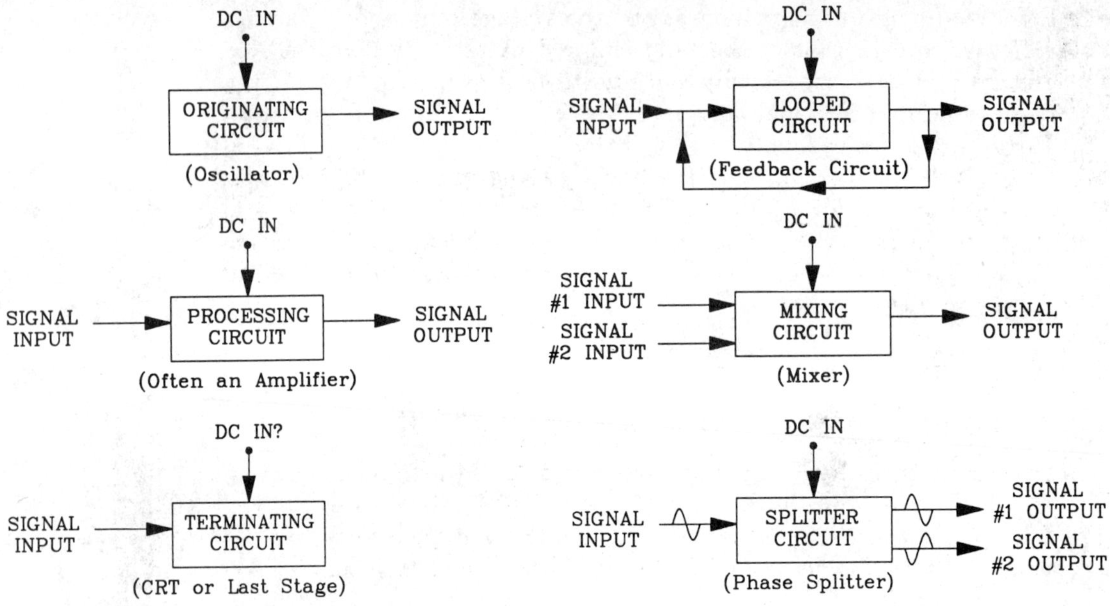

Figure 8–2 General types of analog circuits.

BASIC INFORMATION

THE ORIGINATING CIRCUIT

Originating stages produce an output when provided only with normal DC voltages to power the stage. They are usually oscillators that produce analog or digital signals as an output. The oscillator operates by virtue of positive feedback, which causes it to repeatedly swing from one extreme output voltage to the other. While the feedback path may be obvious, it is sometimes obscure, using the internal capacitance of the amplifying device to provide the feedback.

Testing an oscillator consists of checking its output for the proper frequency, waveform, and amplitude, as necessary. The oscilloscope is the instrument of choice for this purpose. The major consideration in this case is to be sure that the oscilloscope has sufficient high-frequency capability for the job.

THE PROCESSING CIRCUIT

The processing stage takes a single input signal and produces either a voltage or a current gain, and sometimes both. The output of a processing stage will depend upon the configuration in which it is used. Refer back to Figure 7–12.

Testing the processing amplifier amounts to providing a suitable input and then looking, usually with an oscilloscope, at the output. If the proper amplitude and waveform are present, the stage is operating normally. Remember that the common collector (or common drain, if using an FET) provides no voltage gain. The phase reversal of a common emitter (common source) amplifier will not be evident unless the special triggering of an oscilloscope is used. The output voltage of either the common emitter (source) or common base (gate) amplifiers should almost always be larger in amplitude than the input voltage.

THE SIGNAL OR PHASE SPLITTER

Signal-splitting stages take a single input and generate two signals from it. This is most often done in audio circuits. An example is the audio phase splitter used to take an audio input voltage and from it produce two similar signals at the outputs, each 180 degrees apart in phase from one another. See Figure 8–3.

Testing the phase splitter usually means providing a proper input and using an oscilloscope on the outputs of the stage. A dual channel instrument is nice to use, looking at each of the output waveforms with a different probe. There should be two outputs, but *the oscilloscope should be triggered on only one of the input waveforms (e.g., Channel A). This is necessary to observe the 180-degree difference in phase* between them. There should be no visible distortion of either of the waveforms.

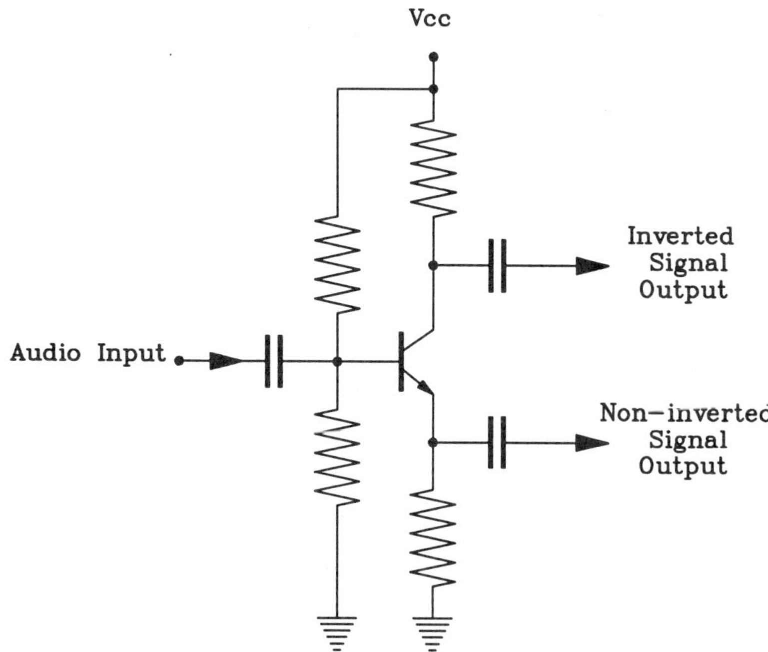

Figure 8–3 A typical signal-splitting stage.

BASIC INFORMATION

THE MIXING OR CONVERGING CIRCUIT

Mixing stages combine two or more inputs to produce a third output signal. Mixing is most often done in radio frequency circuits. In this case, the frequency of the output is the difference between the two incoming radio frequencies, although the output also has components of the two original inputs and their sum frequency. See Figure 8–4.

RF mixing circuits use two inputs, one of which is much larger than the other. The large signal comes from the local oscillator and can be several volts in amplitude. The operation of a mixer depends upon a sufficiently high amplitude of one of the signals to make the mixing action occur. The second input is usually a signal being received via an antenna; it may be in the microvolt region of amplitude and therefore not directly visible with an oscilloscope.

Troubleshoot a mixing circuit by verifying that the large signal is present, using an oscilloscope. Troubleshooting of RF circuits beyond this point is detailed in Chapter 13.

THE TERMINATING CIRCUIT

The terminating circuit is the last, end-effect stage: for example, a TV cathode-ray tube or an audio-output amplifier. This is the end result of all the previous processing. With a proper input test signal, you will usually

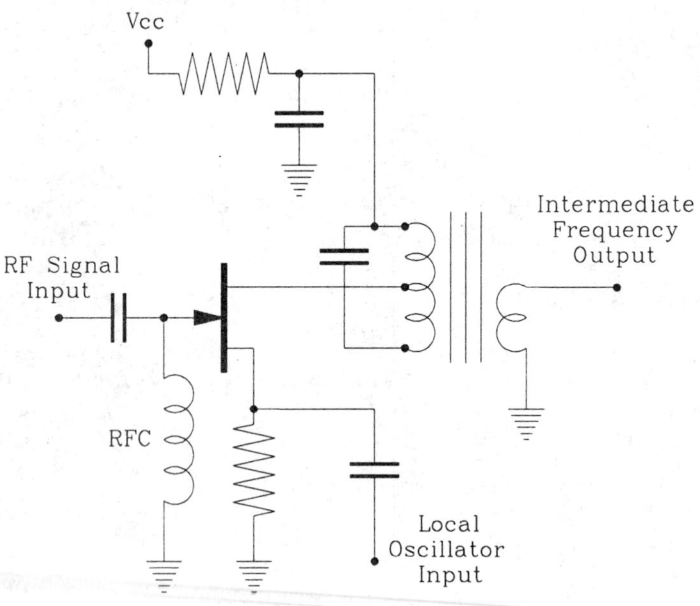

Figure 8–4 A typical radio frequency-mixing stage.

see or hear the proper output, without connecting any special load instrument as an indicator.

THE LOOPED OR FEEDBACK CIRCUIT

The technician should be aware of the unique problems of troubleshooting closed-loop circuits. Such circuits are called closed-loop because they depend at least in part upon their outputs for an input. A problem anywhere within this loop will cause an apparent malfunction of all of the stages within the loop. *The key to troubleshooting a closed-loop circuit is to break the loop at an appropriate point, thus causing it to become just another series of cascaded stages.* Under these new conditions the circuit will not do what it is supposed to, but by varying a *dummy input* to the loop, each stage should be operating sufficiently close to normal to allow troubleshooting as an independent stage. See Figure 8–5 for an example of one closed-loop DC circuit, a DC voltage regulator.

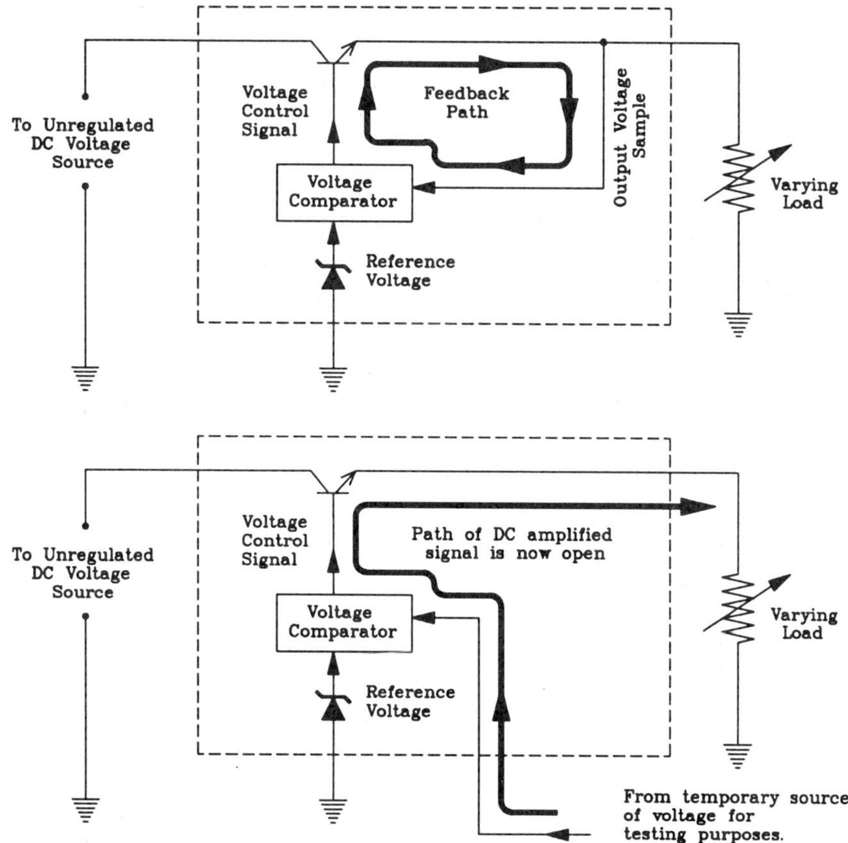

Figure 8–5 Break a looped circuit to troubleshoot it as a series of cascaded stages.

The regulator varies the resistance of the series transistor to maintain a specified DC output voltage. If there is any change in the output voltage, the feedback loop counteracts the change at the output.

A problem in this particular closed-loop circuit will be easier to trace if the feedback voltage were supplied, not by the output voltage but by a separate voltage input from a variable voltage supply. Then, by varying this external input voltage, the circuit will become a series of ordinary DC amplifiers.

The specific closed-loop circuit under test will have to be carefully examined for the signals normally present in various portions of the circuit. Break the loop at a point where external dummy signals can be introduced with the greatest ease and simplicity. Keep in mind that DC levels and AC signals are often simultaneously present in a normal working circuit and that breaking the circuit at such a point will require similarly superimposed signals to operate it as an open-loop circuit. In the previous figure, note that the break point chosen had only a simple DC voltage input requirement with reference to ground.

There are some limitations to this technique of breaking a closed-loop circuit. The overall gain of many looped circuits is much higher than needed for the job. The voltage regulator in the previous example will be extremely sensitive to variations of the dummy voltage input. In this case, it may be better to temporarily use a battery instead of a variable power supply for the DC input signal. The output voltage of the regulator can go from one extreme to the other with a very small adjustment of the dummy input voltage. This is normal, but even with this behavior, the circuit can be analyzed for a malfunction.

Another use of feedback in a looped circuit is to reduce signal distortion produced in the stages within the loop. This feedback is out of phase with the input signal and has a canceling effect on the input signal. See Figure 8–6.

Breaking a distortion feedback path will not only cause the circuit to produce more distortion, the lack of negative feedback may cause the gain to increase dramatically, producing positive and negative clipping of the output signal.

8.6 USE OF THE BLOCK DIAGRAM IN SIGNAL TRACING

Before a technician can get to more detailed troubleshooting, the block diagram must be understood. The path of signals through the equipment should be reviewed, and the effect of each block of the diagram analyzed. Omitting a review of the block diagram can cause confusion later in the troubleshooting process because signal processing within the blocks may not be fully understood.

The equipment operator uses the *operating manual* for instructions on

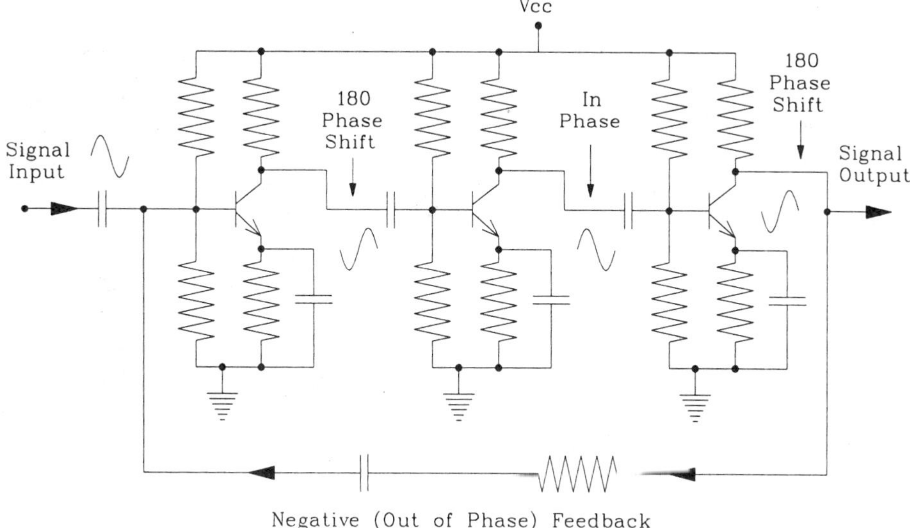

Figure 8–6 A sample discrete amplifier circuit using negative feedback to reduce distortion produced within the loop.

how to operate the controls of the equipment. A *maintenance* or *repair manual* should be provided for the technician's use. This manual is meant for technical personnel, and not the equipment operator. The technician must have information that goes much deeper into the hardware of the equipment in order to repair it.

The block diagram will usually be provided near the back of the manual, near the schematic diagrams. It is often helpful to place the schematic alongside the block diagram in order to understand the block diagram more easily.

In the absence of a block diagram for the particular model of equipment under repair, it is sometimes helpful to have a block diagram of a similar equipment, preferably by the same manufacturer. Be sure to allow for differences in the equipments involved if this approach is used.

8.7 NARROWING THE PROBLEM TO AN AREA

An area, for our immediate purpose, can be defined as one particular printed circuit card out of many within the equipment, or a specific area, determined by function, on a very large PC board.

The next step is to apply normal power to the equipment or circuit board to be repaired. Now is the time to do the following technique of manipulating the knobs.

MILKING THE FRONT PANEL

After the block diagram has been reviewed, the operation of front-panel controls can provide valuable information as to which stages appear to be operating normally. Take careful note of the blocks into which each of the front panel controls connect. Varying these controls should, along with some thought, provide clues as to where the problem lies. Carefully note which controls are operating normally and which are not. Keeping in mind that signals flow from one end of the block diagram through the blocks to the other, *find the first malfunctioning control* in the flow of the signals. The problem will lie just prior to this control. Another way of describing this process is: locate the last normally functioning control in the flow of the signals, and then look just after that point in the circuit for the problem.

As an example, consider a series of blocks that amplify a signal, designated as shown in Figure 8–7.

Be sure to use any built-in indicators as well. These are connected to specific points within the circuits and can tell the technician a great deal about what is happening at that particular point in response to the various front panel controls. Examples of indicators are LEDs, meters, cathode-ray tubes, and status indicator lights. Relays should also be carefully inspected to see if their position (open or closed) can be seen.

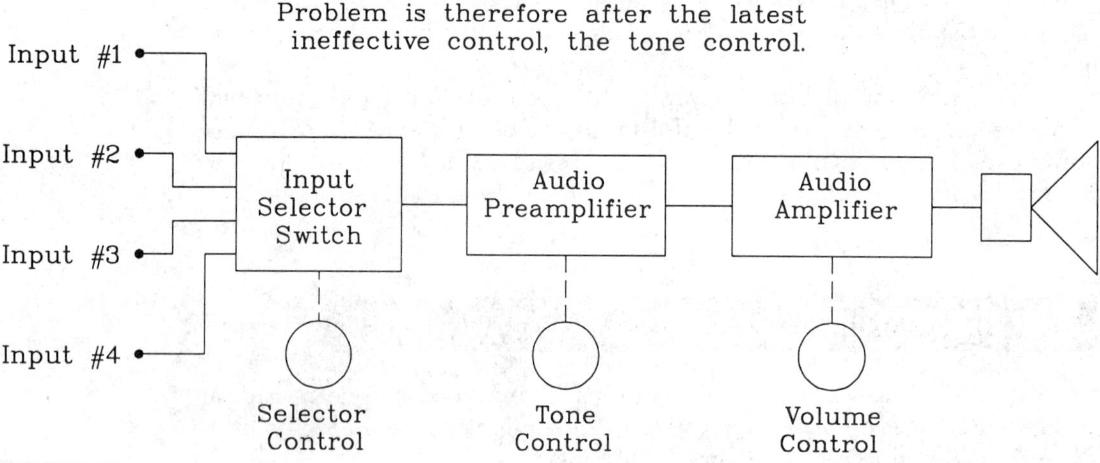

Figure 8–7 Demonstration of the principle, "The problem is near the latest malfunctioning control."

8.8 NARROWING THE PROBLEM TO A STAGE

SIGNAL-TRACING CONSIDERATIONS

Now that you know the approximate area in which to concentrate your efforts, the next step is to verify your assumptions and then find the defective stage within the suspected area. For these purposes, you will need to apply signals into the circuitry and/or verify that signals generated with the circuits are being processed through the equipment as they should. This procedure is called signal tracing and can be accomplished in one of two slightly different methods.

One method of signal tracing is to apply an input to the beginning of the circuitry under test and then trace the signal through successive stages with a signal-detecting instrument. This could probably be called the *signal detection method,* since the signal detector is the instrument being handled. The second method is to apply a signal-detecting instrument at the output of the circuitry, and then change the point of signal injection backward through preceding stages. This can be called the *signal injection method.* The method used will depend upon what is most convenient for the technician and what is available in the way of instruments. Figure 8–8 shows both methods.

The idea in tracing a signal is to determine where the problem lies. A bit of logical deduction is necessary, depending somewhat upon which method is used, signal detection or signal injection. If there is normal operation of the circuits between the signal source and the detecting instrument, then the problem does *not* lie between the two. Include more stages one at a time between the signal source and the detecting instrument until the signal ceases to be normal. The last stage to be included between them is the defective stage. See Figure 8–9.

8.9 TRACING THE UNWANTED SIGNAL

Unwanted signals such as 60- or 120-Hz hum or squeals in audio amplifiers can be traced to their sources by *shorting out the signals* at the input to the various stages. In discrete AC-coupled transistor amplifiers, shorting the transistor bases to their emitters does no harm and will quickly eliminate the signal from passing through that transistor. If the unwanted signal ceases when an input is shorted, you have identified one stage in the path required for the signal to be amplified along the way. Work backward through the various stages from output to input until shorting an input has no effect. The signal must be originating within the last stage that *did* eliminate the signal.

Integrated-circuit audio input circuits should be shorted to ground using a capacitor rather than a dead short to ground. Use a capacitor of about 0.1 to 1 μfd. This will prevent shorting any required DC voltage present on the chip input, yet will load any incoming AC signal

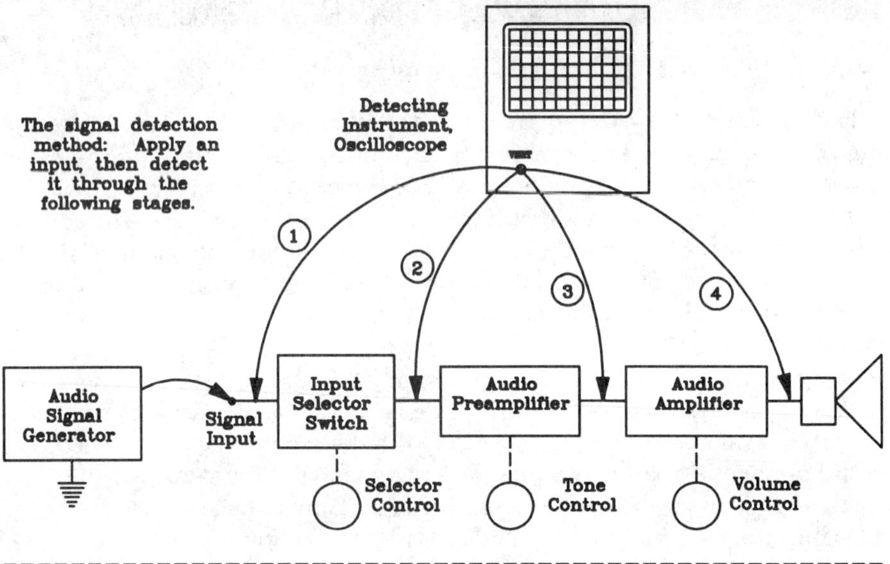

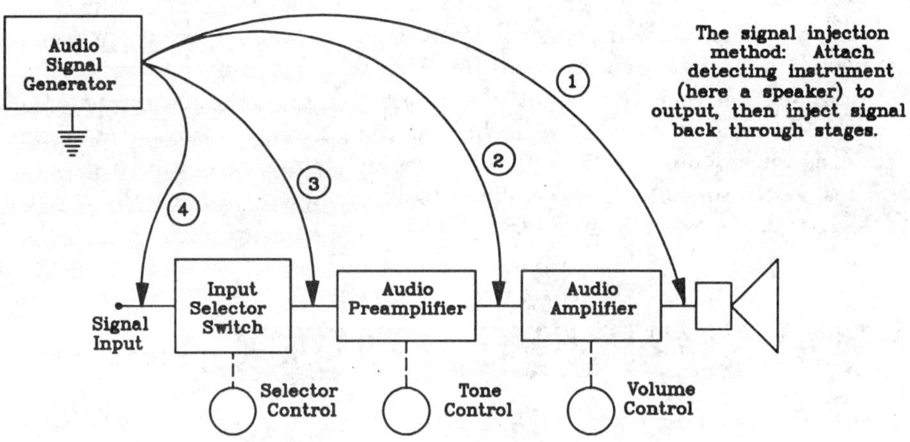

Figure 8–8 Illustrations of the detection and injection methods of signal tracing.

almost as severely as a short circuit. A capacitor of 0.01 μfd works well in radio frequency amplifiers.

This method of applying a dead short should *not* be used in a DC-coupled amplifier. To do so could cause succeeded stages to be damaged by the excessive bias upset that would occur. Rather than apply a dead short, use the method recommended for integrated circuits, using a large-value capacitor (approximately 1,000 μfd) from base to emitter

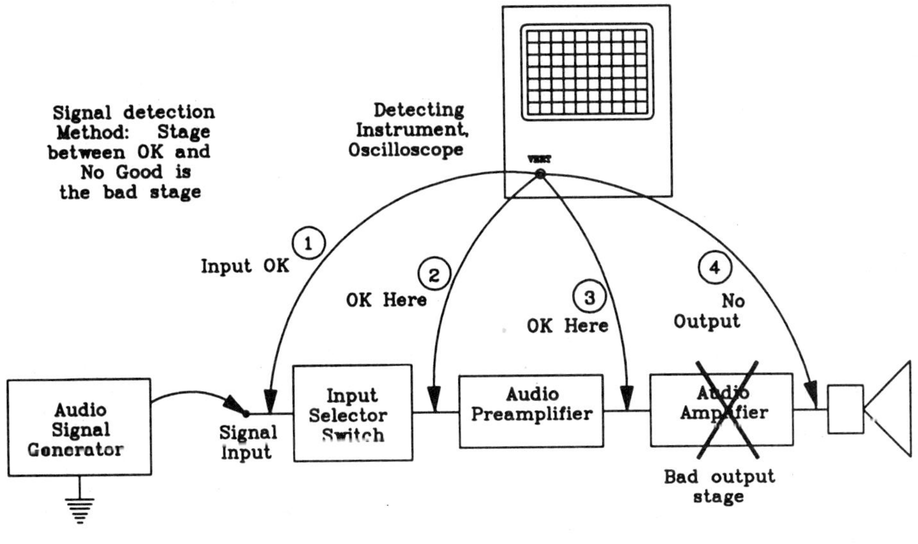

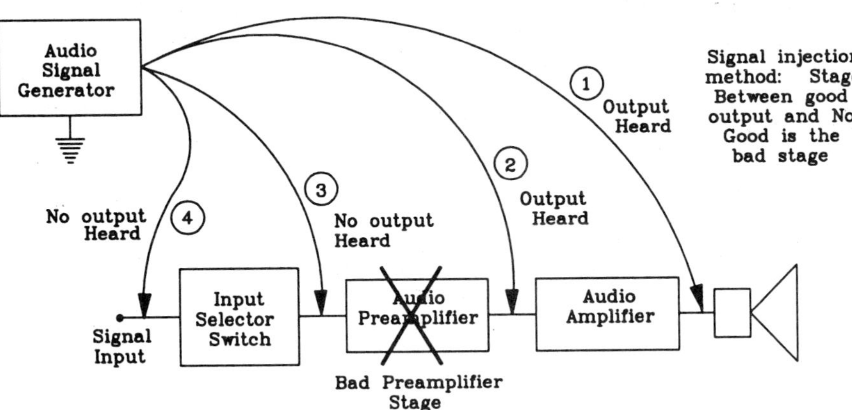

Figure 8–9 How to identify the bad stage—the one between good and bad signals.

CHAPTER SUMMARY

- Signal tracing is sometimes necessary to locate which stage of a piece of equipment is malfunctioning.
- The six general types of stages were explained: the originating, processing, signal-splitting, mixing, terminating, and looped stages.

- Tips were given on the use of the block diagram in locating a problem, including the technique of "milking the front panel."
- The bench power supply must sometimes be used to apply power to a circuit for testing purposes.
- Cautions and tips are given in regard to the bench power supply to prevent damage to the circuit and the supply itself.
- The signal detection and signal injection methods of signal tracing are shown to be similar. Which to use is a matter of available equipment and convenience.
- Tracing the cause of an unwanted signal such as a squeal or thumping sound requires a special technique of troubleshooting, involving shorting the signal to ground along the signal path.

REVIEW QUESTIONS

1. What alternative may be used if you have no schematic, no instruction manual, have never before worked with the particular board, and can't even connect power to the equipment yet must fix it quickly?
2. What two desirable features would you like in a bench power supply (not considering the cost)?
3. What is the definition of a looped circuit?
4. What is the key to troubleshooting a looped circuit?
5. Why would an audio amplifier be designed to feed back part of the output into the input?
6. What is meant by "milking the front panel"?
7. What are the two methods of signal tracing?
8. What determines the method of signal tracing to use?
9. What is the basic concept of tracing unwanted signals?

Audio and Low-Frequency Troubleshooting

9

CHAPTER OBJECTIVES

Amplifiers covering the audio range of 20 to 20000 Hz are all around us, in the telephone equipment we use, background music systems, video camera-recorders, televisions, and public address systems, to name only a very few examples. This chapter will introduce the troubleshooting instruments most commonly used to service audio equipment and additional tips to keep in mind when servicing low-frequency equipment. At the conclusion of this chapter, the student will know:

- The importance of reference material for troubleshooting.
- Input signal sources.
- Output indicators.
- Basic amplifier types: single-ended, balanced, and push-pull balanced.
- How to trace audio distortion problems.
- How to troubleshoot consumer equipment involving complex, multiple-purpose linear integrated circuits.
- How to troubleshoot commercial audio systems, including resistive audio pads.

9.1 GET ALL POSSIBLE REFERENCE MATERIALS

A simple replacement of audio equipment seldom requires reference material. With reasonable care, almost anyone can replace an audio amplifier within a stereo system. Specific repairs to the board or component level will require much more technical ability, however, and, if at all possible, should be assisted by additional documentation for the equipment in question.

One of the principal suppliers of full documentation for electronic equipment is the Howard Sams Co. This company publishes all the necessary technical information, including parts lists, block diagrams, alignment information, and schematics. The schematics are reasonably well marked with pertinent voltages and signal waveforms. Some of the better-equipped libraries may have a section devoted to these information folders.

Another source for technical information on equipment is to insist upon its inclusion as part of the purchase price. Be forewarned, though, that much of the equipment sold these days simply does not have technical information available, even to the dealer who sells the products. Be particularly cautious about buying equipment for which technical information is available "only through recognized service centers." Such information will probably be all but impossible for you to obtain, regardless of the personal inconvenience that it may cause you later in the event of an equipment failure.

Whether or not the manufacturer's service information is available, it may be a big advantage to have available guides for generic parts interchange. These guides are produced by the major producers of generic replacement parts. Using them, it is possible to get at least an approximate indication as to the ratings of solid-state devices such as diodes, transistors, and some integrated circuits. Chapter 24 deals with this subject in detail.

9.2 GENERIC LOW-FREQUENCY TROUBLESHOOTING INPUTS

INPUT SOURCES

Some kind of input signal may be required to trace through the stages of the equipment. These signals can come from three principal sources: the normal signal inputs, externally generated signals from an instrument designed for that purpose, and a "quick-and-simple" source of signal—simply touching sensitive circuits with a finger.

Installed Inputs

Whatever the actual use of the low-frequency equipment, there is a good chance that the signals normally used with the equipment will be available to trace through the equipment. As an example, the audio amplifier of a home stereo system can be easily supplied with a variety of inputs: for example, the radio tuner, a tape deck, a compact disc (CD) player, or a phonograph. Using one of these inputs is not only easy, it is already the proper amplitude for the input circuits of the amplifier. Keep in mind that the tape, CD, and auxiliary inputs to a stereo amplifier require a relatively large audio signal, whereas the phono input is a very small amplitude signal. The phono input jack of a stereo has additional amplification over that of the other inputs.

Audio Signal Generators

Audio signal generators are a second choice when selecting a signal source for application to defective equipment. The signal generator is less convenient to set up than an installed signal source, but it can be used when no other source is available. When setting up a signal generator for signal tracing, remember to use only the minimum amount of amplitude necessary to accomplish the job. Overdriving the input circuits by applying too high an amplitude can cause them to produce large amounts of distortion and even, possibly, to damage your ears or the speakers that are connected to the equipment, if the equipment should for some reason suddenly begin to work during troubleshooting.

Another point to keep in mind is to connect the signal generator to the normal input connectors whenever possible. Applying a signal into the middle of the circuitry can be hazardous to the signal generator if there is substantial DC present at the point where the signal generator is to be connected. Such DC could damage the output attenuator of the signal generator. See Figure 9–1.

A capacitor in series with an AF or RF signal generator will prevent the flow of DC back into the attenuator of the signal generator. The size of the capacitor chosen to block the DC should be suitable for the frequencies involved. See the following list for recommended capacitor sizes and types for various frequencies:

Low-frequency audio, 1 to 10 μfd electrolytic with appropriate polarity.

General audio, 0.1 to 1 μfd electrolytic with appropriate polarity.

Low-frequency RF (to about 1 MHz), .01 to .1 μfd disk.

High-frequency RF (to about 100 Mhz) 0.001 to 0.01 μfd ceramic or mylar.

Touch the Circuit

Sometimes simply touching a sensitive input line will produce enough output for signal-tracing purposes if the equipment in question has sufficient gain. *(Be sure to keep the volume control at a low setting to prevent speaker damage when working with high-powered amplifiers!)* This is often the case when troubleshooting stereo amplifier equipment using the phono

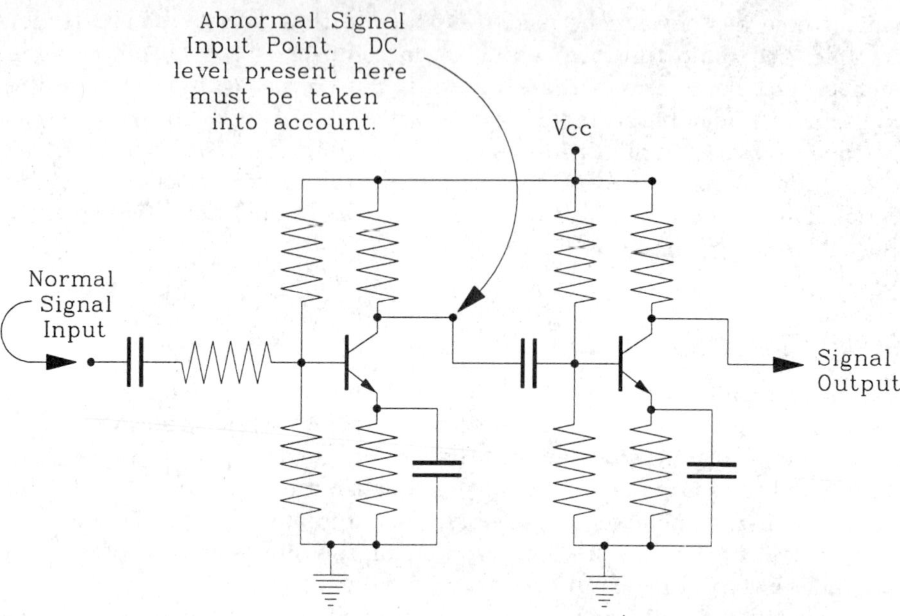

Figure 9–1 Examples of normal and abnormal signal injection points.

input. The phono input to an amplifier has the most overall gain. Of course, one must be very sure that the circuit, and nearby points as well, are operating at a safe enough voltage level to be touched without personal danger. Any voltage over about 48 volts should be considered dangerous.

9.3 OUTPUT DEVICES AND INSTRUMENTS

INSTALLED OUTPUT DEVICES

Speakers

Most amplifiers in the 20 Hz to 20 kHz range are audio amplifiers whose output devices are a speaker. Troubleshooting this equipment is easy in that the output of the device can be heard, without the use of an indicating instrument to tell if the output voltage is there and if it is correct. Thus, most troubleshooting of low-frequency amplifiers depends upon listening to the results of the procedures used.

Listening to a speaker during testing, particularly if you are using a single audio tone, can become irritating if the level must be turned up. A cure for this problem is to use a 4- or 8-ohm dummy load resistor instead of a speaker. The output can still be monitored if a speaker is placed in

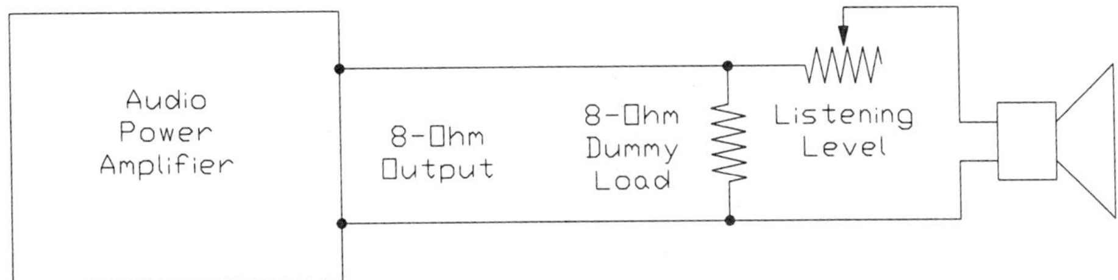

Figure 9–2 This circuit provides a good load on the amplifier at high volume settings, yet operates the speaker at a comfortable level.

parallel with the dummy load resistor, using a series resistor to keep the listening level reasonable. See Figure 9–2.

BASIC INFORMATION

Video Amplifiers

Video amplifiers are designed to provide voltage amplification over a very wide range of frequencies, from perhaps less than 100 Hz to several megahertz. These amplifiers are generally used to feed digital or analog signals into a cathode-ray tube. When troubleshooting these video amplifier circuits, the CRT itself is often used to detect the presence of video. If for some reason the CRT cannot be used, an oscilloscope will be needed.

ANALOG OSCILLOSCOPE

A common use of the oscilloscope is to detect signals as they pass through the various stages of equipment. These include audio and radio frequencies, up to the frequency limitations of the oscilloscope.

The usual way to trace signals through a series of amplifiers is to place a signal into an input of the equipment and then use the oscilloscope to find which stage has an input but no output (the defective stage). This is the case when there is apparently a dead amplifier somewhere along the way. Tracing distortion is done in a similar manner, but the signals between stages are observed for distortion rather than looking for the absence of a signal.

Cautions in Grounding the Oscillocope Probe

The technician must be careful when selecting the common or ground point within equipment to which is connected the ground of the oscilloscope. Selection of such a ground point is particularly hazardous when dealing with amplifiers that do not have a power transformer to provide isolation between the power line and earth ground. See Figure 9–3.

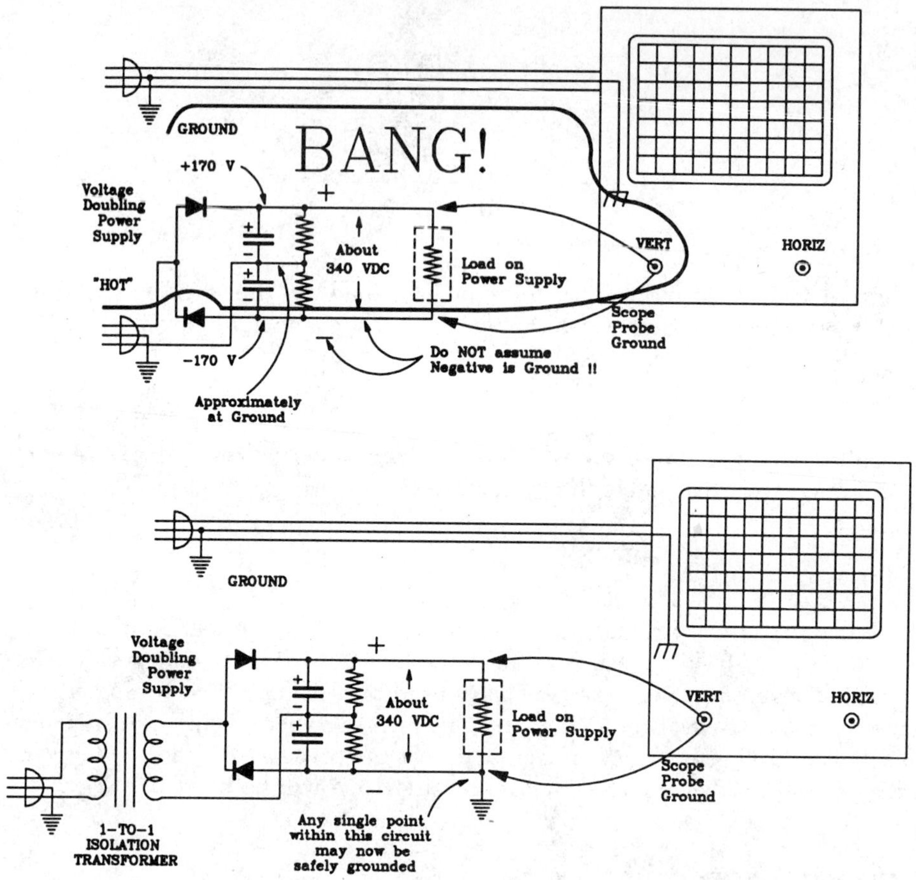

Figure 9–3 Unthinkingly connecting an oscilloscope ground lead to a negative point, assuming it is grounded, can cause serious circuit damage.

Although the oscilloscope ('scope) is the instrument of choice for most analog troubleshooting, its use may present some problems. As the 'scope is used to take signal measurements through equipment, the question arises, "What is the proper signal at this point?" Intermediate signal levels are seldom given on schematics, partly because the amount of input to the circuit can vary greatly. In an effort to prevent the same problem from happening repeatedly with a specific piece of equipment, settle on a fixed "standard" input signal amplitude setting for your purpose, and then mark on your schematic the proper signal voltages at given points throughout the equipment for future use. An alternative is to apply the same input to two amplifiers (in a stereo, to both channels) and then compare signal levels between the good and the bad channels. This technique of using one stereo amplifier channel to fix the other is particularly useful if no information is available for the unit.

Be sure to operate your oscilloscope in a basic manner, dispensing with the dual sweeps, special triggering, and any other exotic settings of the instrument controls. Most oscilloscopes have an overabundance of controls for simple troubleshooting, which often simply involves looking for a missing signal.

AC VOLTMETER

True Root Mean Square (RMS) versus RMS-Scaled AC Voltmeters

An analog AC voltmeter (VOM) will have a certain amount of loading effect on the circuit under test, just as a DC meter does. The AC loading may be quite a bit more than DC loading. A popular high-quality VOM has a 20KΩ/volt DC loading and a 5KΩ/volt AC loading factor. Such a meter would have only 15K of internal resistance when used on a 3-V AC scale. Check the meter you use to determine the loading factor on AC.

The RMS (root mean square) value of a sine-wave alternating voltage is equal to 70.7 percent of the peak voltage value. Using this value, one can calculate a sine wave's true power, or *heating value as compared to a DC voltage*. For example, an AC sine-wave voltage with a peak value of 170-V AC has an RMS value close to 120-V AC. This means that both the AC voltage of 170-V peak and a DC voltage of 120-V will produce the *same amount of heat* when applied to a given resistor.

It is fairly easy to take a basic DC meter and, with a rectifying circuit, make it produce a reading of an AC input voltage. Such a circuit will cause the meter to respond to the *average value* of the applied voltage waveform, *not its RMS value*. The meter can then be recalibrated to, in effect, "lie": the scale *indicates* RMS, even though the meter is actually responding to the average value. Such a meter is called an *RMS-scaled* meter. The readings obtained from such a meter are accurate *as long as the input waveform is a sine wave.*

Using an RMS-scaled meter on nonsinusoidal waveforms may produce a reading on the meter, but the indicated amount can be as much as 30 percent lower than the true RMS value of the waveform. See Figure 9–4 for examples of the relationships between average, RMS, and peak voltages for various waveforms.

Although the RMS-scaled meter is accurate when measuring the voltage of sine waves, its inaccuracy on other waveforms still does not mean that it cannot be used to troubleshoot them. AC voltmeter readings taken on nonsinusoidal waveforms can still be meaningful if used for comparison. For example, assume that the meter normally reads a voltage of 23.5-V AC in a circuit that uses a triangular waveform. If there is a problem in the circuit, a reading of 12.6-V AC is significant: you have a problem. In this case, the actual reading of half normal is the important fact, and not the actual value obtained. An RMS-scaled meter is adequate for almost all electronic troubleshooting. Unless otherwise labeled, an AC voltmeter may be assumed to be an RMS-scaled meter.

	Peak to Peak	Zero to Peak	Root Mean Square*	Average
SINE WAVE 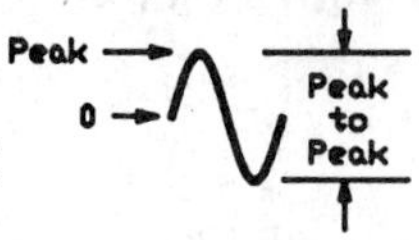	2.828	1.414	1.000 / 1.000	0.900
RECTIFIED FULL WAVE 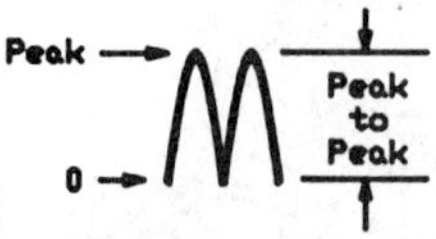	1.414	1.414	1.000 / 1.000	0.900
RECTIFIED HALF WAVE 	2.828	2.828	1.414 / 0.707	0.900
SQUARE WAVE 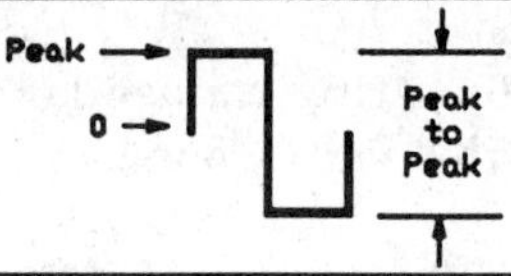	1.800	0.900	0.900 / 1.11	0.900
RECTIFIED SQUARE WAVE 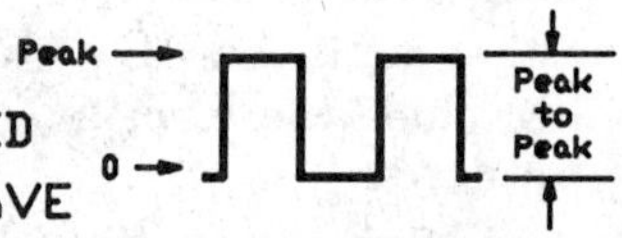	1.800	1.800	1.272 / 0.786	0.900
RECTANGULAR PULSE 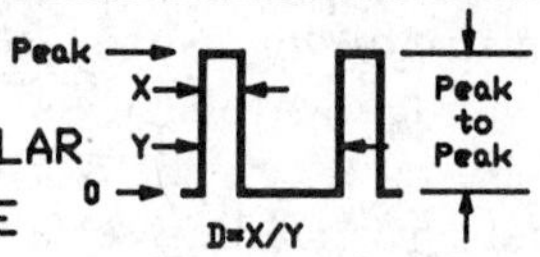 (D=X/Y)	0.9/D	0.9/D	$0.9/D^{1/2}$ / $1.11\sqrt{D}$	0.9D
TRIANGLE WAVE 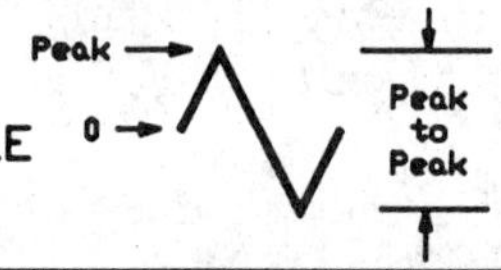	3.600	1.800	1.038 / 0.963	0.900

Multiply an RMS-scaled meter reading by the upper left factor to obtain true RMS.
Multiply a true RMS meter reading by the lower right factor to obtain what an RMS-scaled meter would read.

Figure 9–4 Relationship between average, RMS, and peak voltages for a variety of common waveforms.

For general troubleshooting, there is infrequently a need for an accurate voltage reading on nonsinusoidal waveforms. When there is a need, the best solution is to obtain an instrument that responds to the true RMS value of the waveform, almost regardless of its shape. See Figure 9–5 for an example of such an instrument.

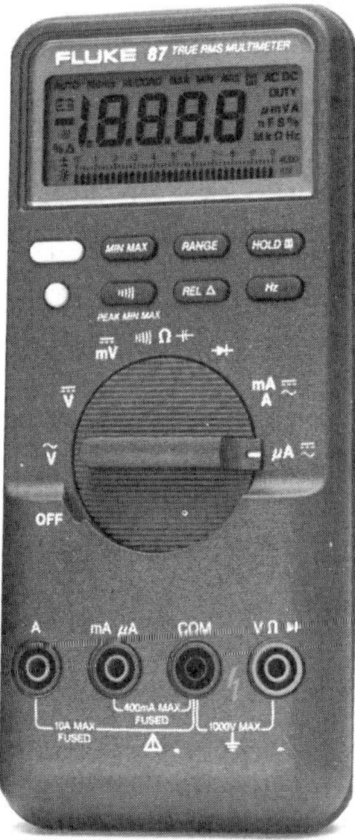

Figure 9–5 This digital multimeter responds to the true RMS value of a waveform. (Reproduced with permission from the John Fluke Mfg. Co., Inc.)

An instrument like this will give accurate readings on pulsed waveforms such as those found in high-powered AC motor speed controllers. A true RMS-responding meter requires special circuitry to respond to the actual RMS value of a waveform, and you can be sure that there will be a label on the face of the instrument if it is of this type.

Limited Usefulness of an AC Meter in Signal Tracing

An oscilloscope is the best instrument to use to trace signals through low-frequency amplifiers. While an AC voltmeter can be used if it is the only instrument available, the meter's limitations must be kept in mind as signals are traced through the equipment. These limitations depend on the kind of instrument being used, the volt-ohm-milliammeter (VOM) or the more modern digital multimeter (DMM).

Using a Volt-Ohm-Milliammeter on AC Signals

The VOM has some severe limitations when used to measure AC signals of less than a few volts. There is no amplification of input signals when using a VOM. The signal is simply rectified with a few diodes to operate the meter. The inability to indicate small signals linearly is due to the characteristics of the diodes used in the meter to rectify the AC into DC, which is then used to drive the meter directly. Remember that it takes about 0.7 volt to make a diode begin to conduct. This makes it necessary to have a special scale to measure low-voltage AC signals.

Even if the AC voltage to be measured is relatively large in amplitude (over a few volts), there is another limitation to keep in mind if using a VOM to read signal levels. Because DC will flow through a rectifier, a VOM will respond to any DC present in the circuit, along with the AC voltage reading. The meter reading could be very misleading because of this sensitivity.

The problem of DC affecting an AC reading when using a VOM is solved by using a DC blocking capacitor in series with the meter. Some meters have this capacitor located internally. In such a case, it can be used by changing the negative test lead from its normal jack to a jack marked "output."

Using a Digital Multimeter on AC Signals

The digital voltmeter has the ability to *amplify* and measure signals well below the capabilities of a VOM. Signal levels in the millivolt range can be measured reliably with a DMM. The DMM is also not affected by DC levels superimposed on the AC signal because of a DC-blocking capacitor within the instrument.

It should be kept in mind that the typical AC voltmeter cannot respond in the same way to any AC frequency that might be applied to the test leads. It is common for an AC voltmeter meter of any type to be calibrated only at a frequency of 60 Hz, with many meters being capable of responding with reasonable accuracy up through 1000 Hz and even to the top of the audible range, about 20 kHz. If the voltmeter is to be used above 1000 Hz, the specifications for the instrument should be consulted for any corrections that might be necessary.

There are audio applications that require the use of voltmeters that respond accurately to signals varying in frequency throughout the audio spectrum. Telephone companies and the audio amplifiers used in the broadcasting transmitters of radio and television are examples of these applications. An example of such a meter was shown previously in Figure 3–4.

9.4 BASIC LOW-FREQUENCY AMPLIFIER CIRCUITS

AC- VERSUS DC-COUPLED AMPLIFIERS

AC-coupled amplifiers for low frequencies can be inexpensively designed to amplify frequencies of as low as 30 Hz. Designing an AC-coupled amplifier for lower frequencies would require the use of unreasonably large coupling capacitors and transformers. Instead, the amplifier can be designed as a DC-coupled amplifier. No coupling capacitors or transformers are used. Rather, each stage is directly coupled through resistors to the following stage.

Although the DC-coupled amplifier has a big advantage in being able to amplify very-low-frequency signals, it suffers a disadvantage of being capable of dramatic failures as well. It is quite possible for a DC-coupled amplifier to have a defective transistor in the earlier stages cause the failure of all the transistors following it. This is caused by the drastic changes in bias that a failure can cause by holding an improper bias on the following stage until it, too, fails. The effect is that the failure exerts a "domino effect" through the following stages. When servicing DC-coupled amplifiers, the technician should look carefully for associated transistor failures if a single bad transistor is initially found. It would be unfortunate to simply replace a bad transistor and then apply power, only to find that the new transistor was again blown because of an earlier problem still in the circuit.

UNBALANCED (SINGLE-ENDED) AMPLIFIERS

An unbalanced amplifier uses a single supply voltage. The output of an unbalanced amplifier is a voltage somewhere between the supply voltage of the final amplifier stage and ground. See Figure 9–6.

If the unbalanced amplifier is DC-coupled, a small DC input can be applied through a potentiometer and the voltage changes caused by changing the potentiometer can be traced through the amplifier with a DC voltmeter. If the amplifier is AC-coupled, the input signal can best be traced through the following stages with an oscilloscope.

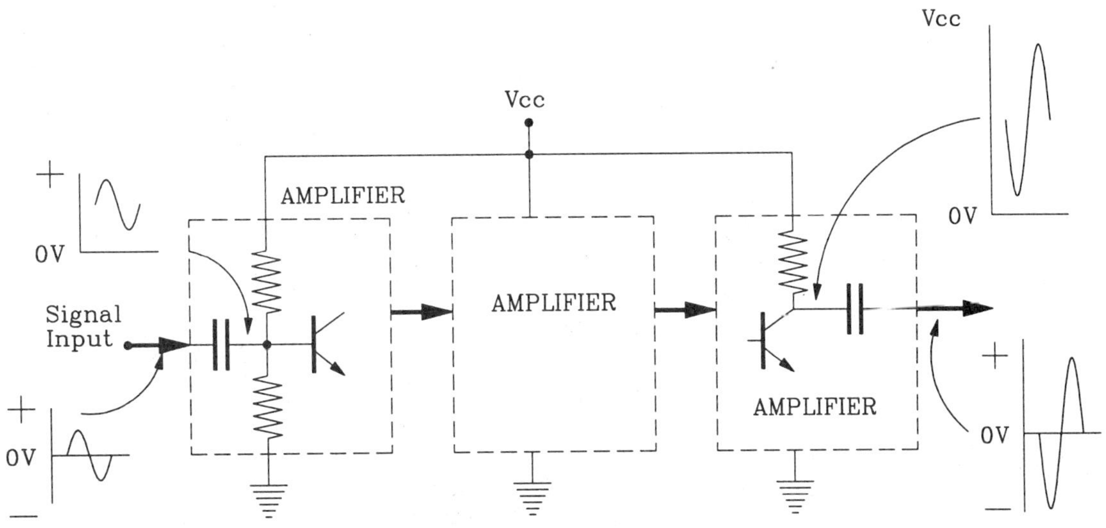

Figure 9–6 Tracing a signal through an unbalanced (single-ended) amplifier.

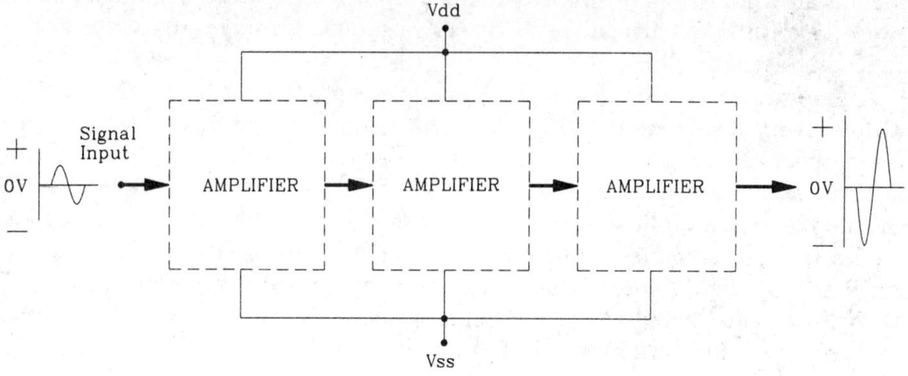

Figure 9–7 Operating and troubleshooting principles of the balanced amplifier.

BALANCED AMPLIFIERS

The balanced amplifier is so called because it is "balanced" around zero volts (ground) as a neutral or quiescent condition and uses two supply voltages, one positive and the other negative. Whereas the input to an unbalanced amplifier must ride upon a DC component, the input voltage to a balanced amplifier is referenced to the circuit ground. The input voltage goes both above (positive) and below (negative) from that point.

The balanced amplifier uses two similar power supply voltages, one above ground (positive supply) and the other below (negative supply.) The output voltage of the balanced amplifier will also vary above and below ground, following the input signal with amplification of the input voltage level. There may or may not be an overall 180-degree phase shift from input to output. See Figure 9–7.

Troubleshooting a balanced amplifier is relatively easy. Simply short the input to ground, and the output should then measure very near zero volts. Some balanced amplifiers have an internal adjustment to ensure that under grounded input conditions, the output is exactly zero volts. This adjustment is usually called a DC balance adjustment.

If the output voltage is not near the required zero volts, signal trace through the stages while the input is shorted to ground.

PUSH-PULL BALANCED AMPLIFIERS

With the addition of a phase splitter, two balanced amplifiers can be operated in such a manner that the two instantaneous output voltages are balanced with respect to ground, with one being negative and the

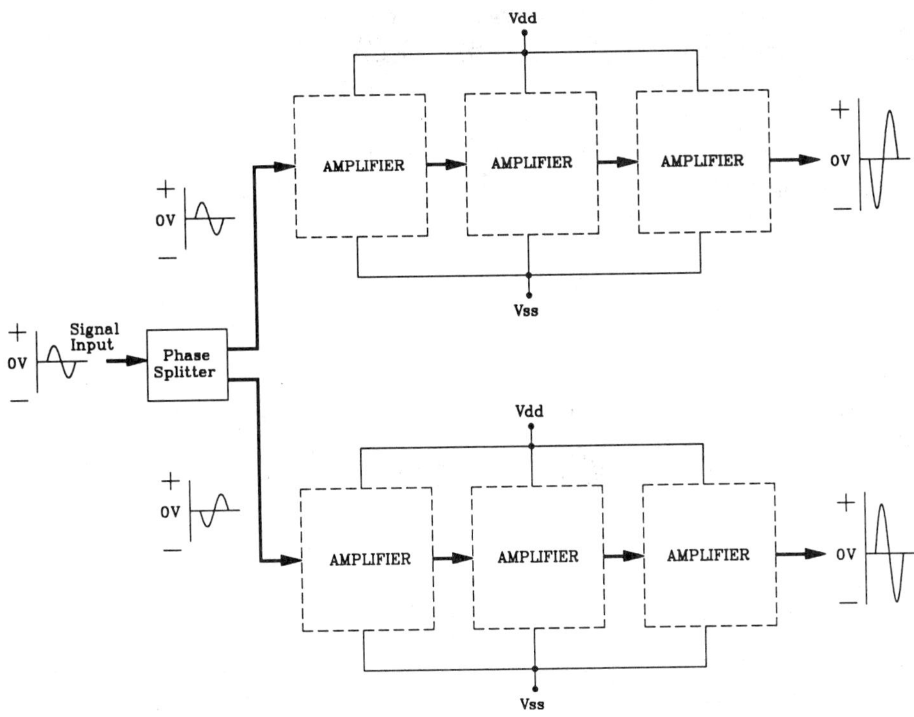

Figure 9–8 Operating and troubleshooting principles for push-pull balanced amplifiers.

other positive. Amplifiers of this type are used in oscilloscopes to drive the deflection plates for both the vertical and horizontal axes. See Figure 9–8.

Each of these amplifiers may be troubleshot separately by using the procedure given above for the balanced amplifier.

STEREO AMPLIFIERS

Stereo amplifiers are paired audio amplifiers. The main advantage of troubleshooting these circuits is that there are two identical circuits available. A problem in one channel can be efficiently located by simply comparing the good channel to the bad one, stage by stage. Voltage readings in the bad channel will be different from those of the good channel, all the way from the defect to the output of the amplifier. The ability to compare two identical channels makes the troubleshooting of stereo amplifiers considerably easier than troubleshooting a single-channel amplifier such as a public-address amplifier.

9.5 AUDIO DISTORTION PROBLEMS

CAUSES OF DISTORTION

There are two principal causes of distortion: (1) improper biasing and (2) signal input overdriving. Improper biasing of an audio amplifier stage can include too much forward biasing of the Class A stage, as shown in Figure 9–9.

The opposite problem can also occur: operation of a stage with insufficient forward biasing current will cause the symptoms shown in Figure 9–10.

Another case of improper biasing can cause a push-pull or a complementary-symmetry power amplifier to produce distortion of the signal near zero crossover. Logically, this is called cross-over distortion. See Figure 9–11.

Distortion would be easily detected if one transistor of a pair in a push-pull or complementary-symmetry circuit should open. Under these conditions, all of either the positive or negative part of the waveform will be missing.

Operational amplifiers are often used to provide high gain in amplifier circuits and can also produce distortion problems. A frequent cause of distortion in an operational amplifier (op-amp) is caused by the equipment itself or by the same circuit problems as in the bipolar transistor. Improper biasing voltages and overdriving an amplifier with an input that is too high

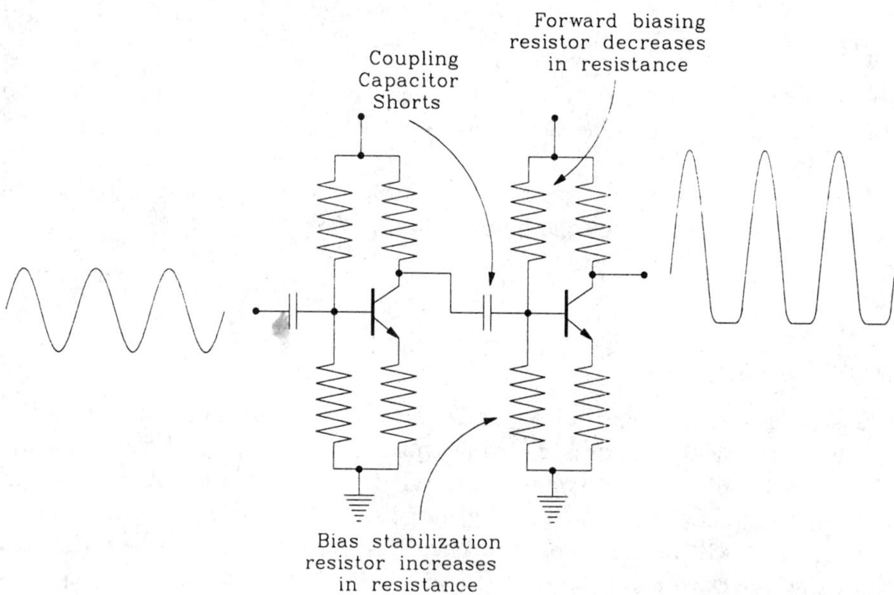

Figure 9–9 Three of the possible causes of an amplifier stage being driven too deeply into the operating curve, resulting in negative output clipping.

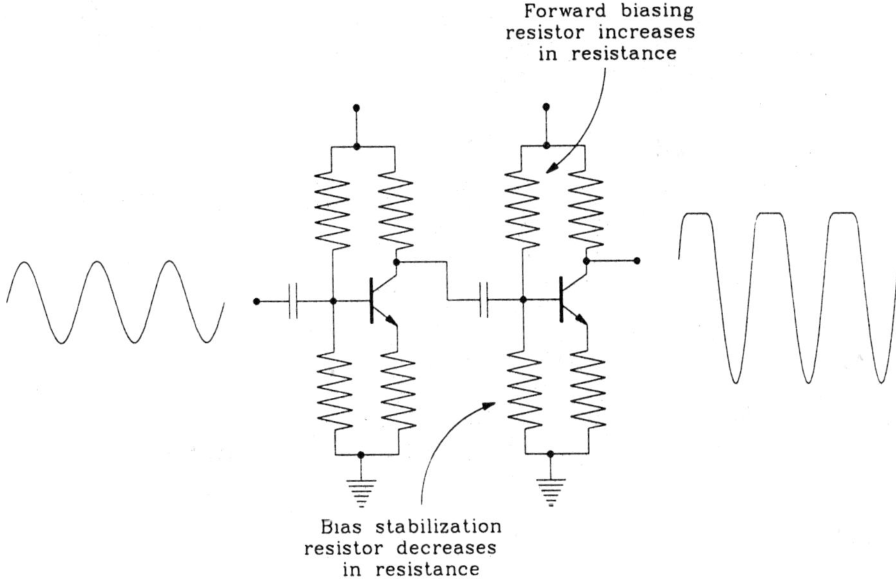

Figure 9–10 Two possible causes of an amplifier stage being driven too lightly into the operating curve, resulting in positive output clipping.

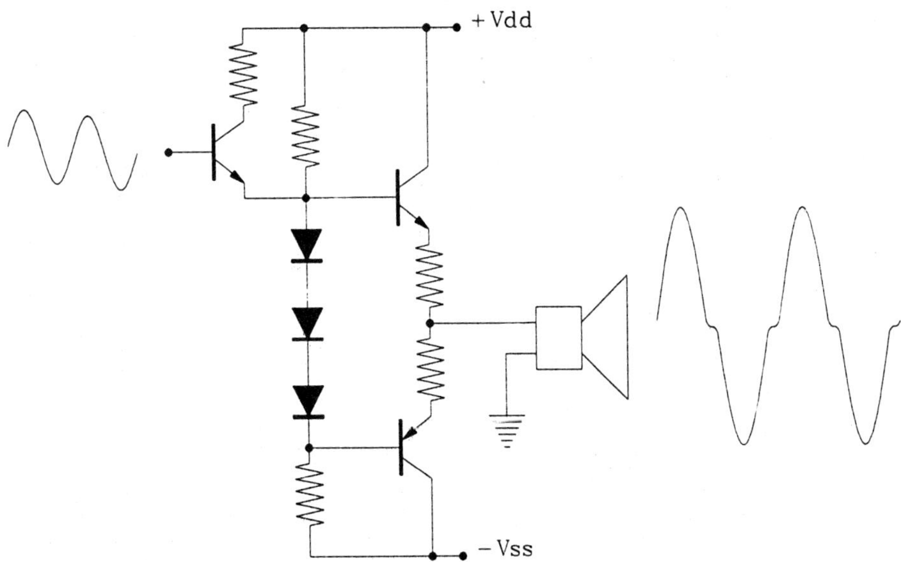

Figure 9–11 Exaggerated effect on the output waveform of too little forward bias in a complementary-symmetry Class B amplifier stage.

in amplitude causes the same distortion problems. Figure 12–8 in Chapter 12 shows common causes of distortion in operational amplifiers.

Distortion in a DC-Coupled Amplifier

A DC-coupled amplifier has no interstage transformers or coupling capacitors. Instead, the signal is superimposed upon the normal quiescent (static) DC voltages throughout the amplifier. Distortion in one of these amplifiers is difficult to troubleshoot because of the interdependence of the DC voltages in the circuit. One of the best ways to troubleshoot such a problem is to disconnect all external AC input signals and troubleshoot the circuitry with a DC voltmeter. The stage with a biasing problem, and thus causing the distortion, should be evident by carefully comparing the proper DC voltages, particularly biasing voltages, through the stages.

DETECTING AUDIO DISTORTION

The Distortion Analyzer

Some audio systems such as broadcasting studios must routinely check for excessive distortion in their systems. The minimal amount of distortion that a distortion analyzer can detect is very low, less than 1 percent. The human ear, on the other hand, can easily tolerate distortion to 10 percent before it becomes objectionable to the casual listener. Thus, the use of a distortion analyzer is generally restricted to critical applications and it is not usually used in troubleshooting. Its principal use is to detect problems before they are noticeable and to isolate the amplifier that is causing the problem. The distortion of an amplifier is determined by measuring a test sine wave signal's residual distortion going into an amplifier. Then, a similar reading is taken on the same signal's distortion at the output of the amplifier. The difference in distortion readings between the input and output is a measure of the distortion produced within the amplifier. See Figure 9–12.

An example of one use for a distortion analyzer is shown later in Figure 13–27, during an evaluation test of a communications receiver.

Using Lissajous Patterns

A distortion analyzer may not available for troubleshooting, and an oscilloscope may not show distortion sufficiently well by using the normal horizontal time-base sweep. In such a case, a Lissajous pattern can be used to identify the source of a distortion problem. The basic principle of the Lissajous pattern is that voltages are compared, point for point, between a known good audio tone (a sine wave is best to use) and a tone having an unknown amount of distortion. See Figure 9–13.

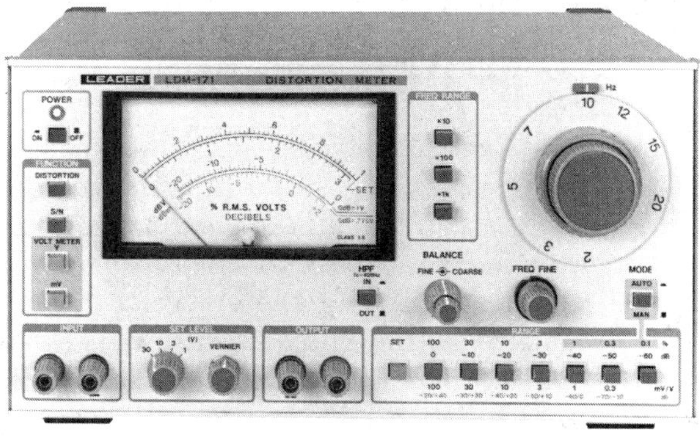

Figure 9–12 Commercial audio distortion analyzer used in sound studios. (Courtesy Leader Instruments Corp., Hauppauge, NY)

When using a Lissajous pattern, be sure not to overdrive the amplifier under test with an excessive input voltage. Doing so will result in hooks at both ends of the oscilloscope pattern, indicating distortion at both the top and bottom of the output waveform.

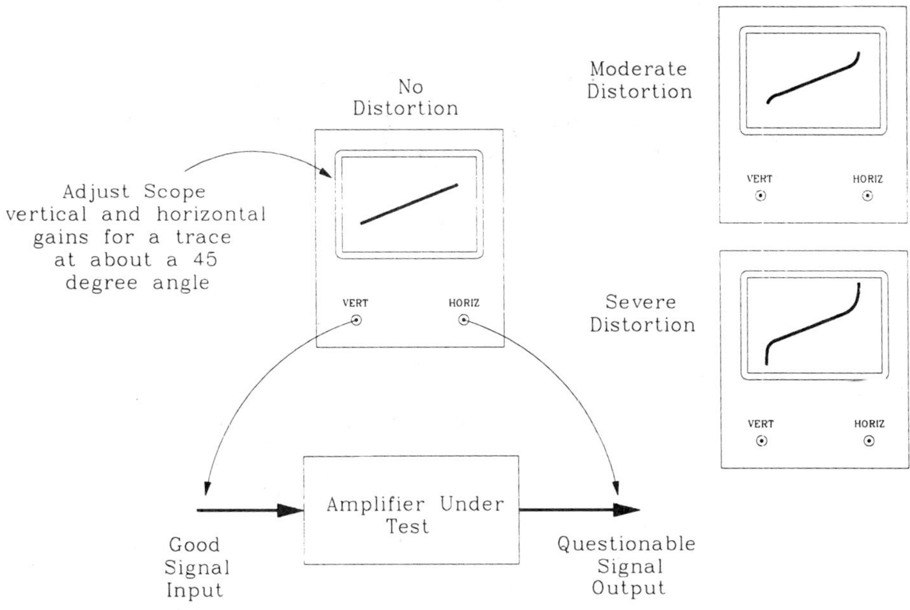

Figure 9–13 Setting up a Lissajous pattern to show distortion.

9.6 TROUBLESHOOTING AUDIO AMPLIFIER CONSUMER CHIPS

Modern electronic equipment makes extensive use of integrated circuits. These circuits take the place of many discrete transistor stages, simplifying assembly and making the equipment cheaper to manufacture and, thus, more competitive in the marketplace.

Troubleshooting circuits containing these special-purpose chips will require specific information on the chips themselves. Failures within the chips will usually result in not only the lack of a signal coming out when a good input is present, but also in a shift in the DC output voltages.

The first action to take is to be sure that the input signal to the chip is correct. This will mean that not only will the chip require a specified voltage amplitude, but any DC component that is required must also be present. On the other hand, the chip may require a signal input without a DC offset voltage. Variations of the DC input level along with the signal can make the chip inoperative.

Some consumer chips also require more than a single supply voltage. Each DC input must be checked for the proper voltage and, in some cases, must also be checked for the absence of any substantial ripple voltage superimposed on the DC voltage. The most conclusive test for a consumer chip is to replace it with a known good chip. Be cautious, however, that the circuitry around the chip is normal before replacing the chip. It would be a shame to replace a bad chip with a good one, only to have the good one destroyed by a failure lurking elsewhere in the circuitry.

9.7 TROUBLESHOOTING COMMERCIAL AUDIO SYSTEMS

SPECIFYING AUDIO LEVELS: THE DECIBEL

Audio systems like those of the telephone companies and the audio systems of broadcasting stations routinely require the measurement of audio signal amplitudes in many locations throughout the system. The measurement of signal amplitudes, or *levels,* as they are called, is used as the primary troubleshooting indicator in tracing problems.

Rather than keeping track of the amplification factor of an audio amplifier, it is more convenient to express the output signal amplitude in reference to a fixed amplitude. This fixed amount, the reference against which to compare audio levels, is 0.775 volts across a 600 Ω resistor. This causes a dissipation of 1 milliwatt. This level is called zero dBm, with the *m* referring to the 1-milliwatt dissipation.

The use of a fixed impedance (600 Ω for audio) allows inputs and outputs of equipment to be built to a standard. With this standard, equipment from different manufacturers will match and operate properly when connected together.

To review, the Bel is a measurement of sound energy. In practice, the Bel is too large, so we use a more convenient unit, a decibel (1/10th of a Bel) to measure the intensity of sounds. To a human ear, a difference of a single decibel is a barely perceivable change in intensity, either up or down. Three decibel changes result in an apparent doubling of the perceived sound intensity.

Because the response of the human hearing mechanism is logarithmic, power levels of sound must also increase in a logarithmic curve for the resulting sound intensity to *seem* linear. In other words, a linear potentiometer used in an audio system would seem too sensitive at low volume settings and almost unchanging at higher settings. This is why audio applications use variable attenuators and potentiometers with a logarithmic taper of actual resistance value from one end of rotation to the other. The greatest change of resistance per unit of shaft rotation occurs at the "loud" end of rotation.

The intensity of steady-state audio levels can be read on special portable digital multimeters with a scale that reads directly in decibels. Such an instrument must be used across a load of 600 Ω in order to accurately read out in decibels. A failure to have the proper terminating resistance (reading across an open 600 Ω system line) will render the readout invalid. If a dB meter is connected to a 600 Ω circuit that is not terminated in 600 Ω, it will read close to 6 dB too high. On the other hand, if a bridging reading is made on a circuit that is already terminated in 600 Ω, the effective load resistance will be 300 Ω, and the reading will be almost 4 dB too low. An explanation of bridging and terminated readings was shown in Figure 3–5.

Audio levels are often read out on audio meters installed within equipment. These meters are most accurate when the signal being measured is constant in amplitude. Because of the inertia of the needle, a meter cannot provide accurate instantaneous readings of rapidly changing levels such as those encountered when measuring speech or music. A special meter called a VU (volume unit) meter is constructed to better keep up with the rapidly changing signal amplitudes of speech and music. These meters respond faster and have less overshoot, and are calibrated in VUs or a combination of VUs and dBs.

AUDIO PADS

It is often an advantage to simply reduce the amplitude of a signal in the processing of audio signals. Radio broadcasting stations and sound studios have many such applications. When the output of several amplifiers are fed into a single master amplifier input, for instance, each of the amplifier signals must be reduced to a standardized output level for delivery to the input of the final master amplifier. Using pads in this manner also offers a

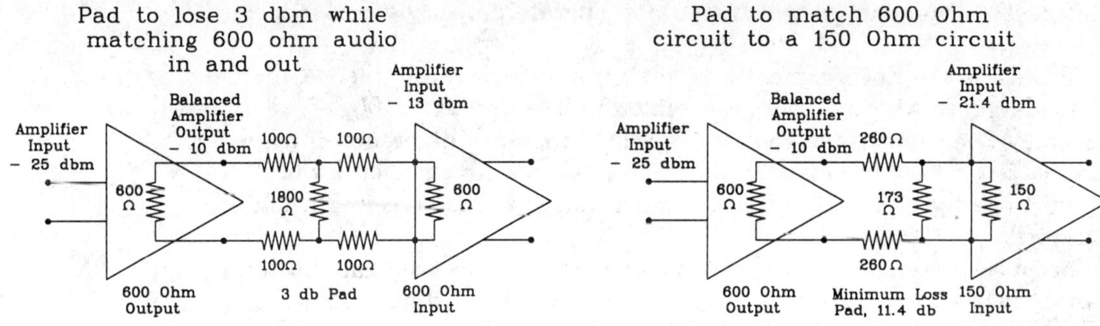

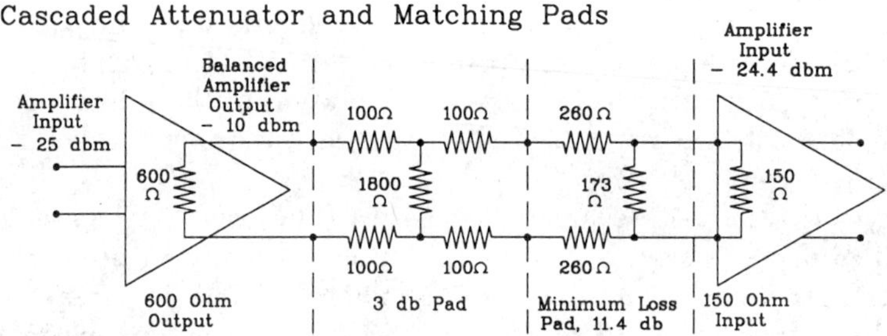

Figure 9–14 Examples of audio attenuation, impedance matching, and a combination of both.

considerable amount of isolation between signal sources when they are connected to a common bus, avoiding much of the problem of signal change when paralleling two or more sources onto a common output bus. The combination of resistors used to reduce the amplitude of a signal is called a *resistive attenuator pad.*

It is also possible to provide a match between two different impedances using nothing but resistors. When a combination of resistors is used to match impedances with a minimum of attenuation, it is called a *minimum loss pad.* Attenuators and matching pads can be cascaded to provide both functions. For examples, see Figure 9–14.

Appendix VI provides tables of decibels versus voltages and resistor values for attenuator and minimum loss pads.

Audio levels can be read with a special audio voltmeter calibrated to read decibels directly. The standard VOM cannot reliably measure audio levels less than about –4 dB because it has no way to amplify the smaller signals. A better choice of instrument for measuring audio levels is one that has amplification capability. Such AC voltmeters may read decibel levels down to as little as –50 decibels.

AUDIO DISTRIBUTION SYSTEMS

Public address systems that feed many speakers located throughout a large area will require special installation and equipment. This is necessary in order to get the audio signals to remote locations without excessive line losses due to the resistance of the wiring and also to provide for independent audio adjustment at various locations without affecting sound intensity in other areas.

Speakers are low-impedance devices. This means simply that it requires relatively high current and low voltage to operate them. The high current requirements of the speaker make it impractical to operate directly at great distances because the resistance of the wiring would dissipate much of the audio signal, thus losing signal intensity at the speaker. Adding more speakers to such a system at other locations would make the problem of line losses much worse.

The solution to line losses is to change the audio power voltage and current at the source and then run it through distribution lines at relatively high voltage and low current. Transformers are used to step up the voltage and reduce the line current at the source. Another transformer at the end of the line changes the voltage and current back to low voltage and high current, as required by the speakers. Transmitting AC signals at five times the voltage necessary at the far end results in transmitting 1/5th the required current. The reduction of line current to 1/5th results in line losses of only 1/25th of what they would have been if connected directly.

An audio signal line amplitude of 70.7 volts is a common distribution standard. An audio distribution system is based upon this voltage and is limited by the power capability of the audio power amplifier. Thus, a 100-watt audio amplifier could be used to drive twenty 5-watt speakers at various remote locations.

One problem remains: some of the speakers may need to be adjustable in volume. Changing the volume of a single speaker by simply inserting resistance in the speaker circuit would result in loading down the distribution line at high volume settings and cause overvoltage on the line when the speaker has a high resistance in series for minimum volume. Varying the loading on the line in this direct manner is an unsatisfactory solution.

A tapped transformer is often used to couple audio power from the distribution lines to a speaker. A tapped transformer is wired for a given volume. If the volume of the speaker must be variable, a special audio pad is used to maintain a constant load on the distribution line, regardless of the setting of any of the individual volume controls. This pad is called an *L-pad,* because of its schematic configuration. It is constructed to dissipate a specific amount of power, as necessary to maintain a constant load on the distribution line. See Figure 9–15 for examples of both these methods of controlling volume from an audio transmission line.

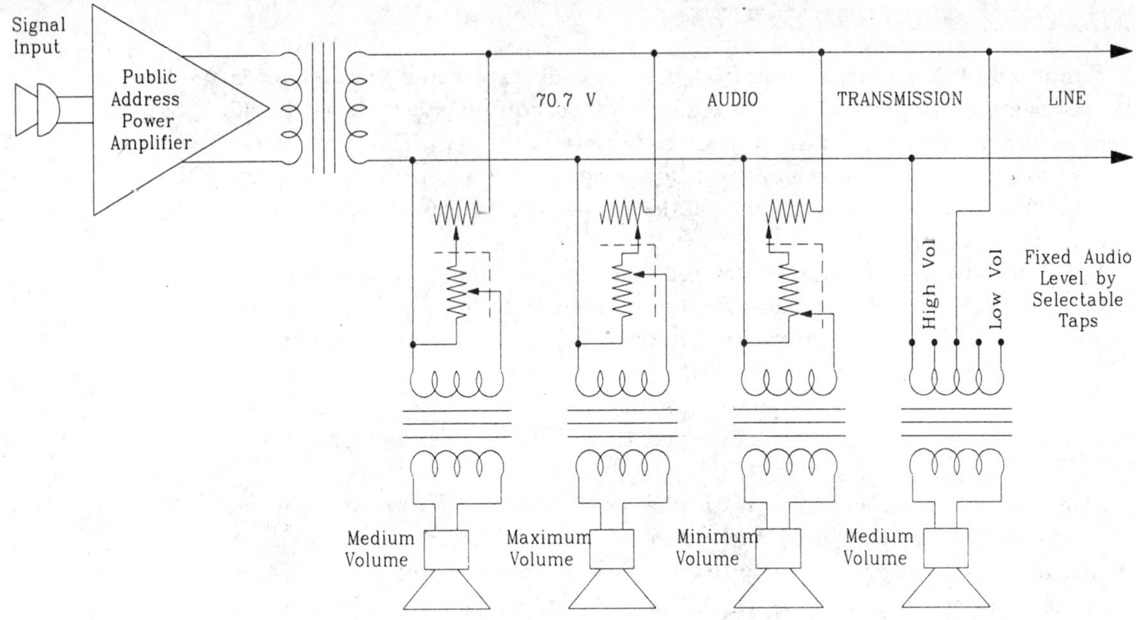

Figure 9–15 Schematic of 70.7 audio distribution system using "L-pads" for local volume control.

CHAPTER SUMMARY

- Efficient repair of audio and other low-frequency AC equipment requires proper information, maintenance manuals, and reference material on individual parts.
- Input signals needed for signal tracing through these equipments include the normal signals, a signal generator, and even the touch of a finger.
- The oscilloscope is a good signal indicator.
- In the absence of an oscilloscope, a digital or analog meter can also sometimes be used, keeping in mind their limitations.
- The DC-coupled amplifier is ideally suited for amplifying very low frequencies, but when failure occurs, many stages can fail together.
- Amplifiers can be built as single-ended (unbalanced) amplifiers, balanced amplifiers, or push-pull balanced amplifiers.
- Stereo amplifiers are two identical equipments, which is a great

troubleshooting advantage because of the ability to compare readings between channels.

- Audio distortion is usually caused by improper biasing of an amplifier or overdriving an amplifier with an excessive amplitude input signal.
- Detecting distortion can be done by ear for large amounts, with an oscilloscope for moderate amounts, with a Lissajous pattern for small amounts, and with a distortion analyzer for very small amounts.
- Consumer chips must have proper DC and AC inputs for proper operation.
- Substitution is the final criterion for determining a faulty consumer chip.
- Audio pads are resistive networks that are used to reduce the amplitude of audio signals while keeping the input and output impedances equal, match differing impedances with a minimum loss of signal, or both attenuate and match impedances.
- Commercial audio distribution systems often use a 70.7-volt distribution voltage and "L-pads" at each speaker location to distribute audio with minimum line loss and to enable the adjustment of local speaker volume without changing the loading on the distribution line.

REVIEW QUESTIONS

1. What is the purpose of a blocking capacitor when using a signal generator?
2. What should you remember to do when applying a signal into the collector circuit of an amplifier?
3. An RMS-scaled AC voltmeter is one that responds to the _______ value of the applied waveform but reads out in _______ voltage.
4. Can an RMS-scaled meter be used for most troubleshooting purposes on nonsinusoidal waveforms?
5. Your RMS-scaled meter reads a value of 10-V AC on a sinusoidal waveform. What is the average value of this voltage?
6. How can you tell if you are using a true RMS AC voltmeter?
7. What is the purpose of the "output" jack of a VOM?
8. Why is there no "output" jack on a digital multimeter?
9. Why can a DMM measure much smaller AC voltages than a VOM?
10. The terms *unbalanced, balanced,* and *push-pull balanced* refer to amplifiers with a balance on either side of _______.
11. What are the two causes of waveform distortion as it goes through an amplifier?
12. What instrument will measure audio waveform distortion in percentages?

13. How can the oscilloscope be used to indicate distortion?
14. What is the standard audio impedance for commercial sound and audio systems?
15. What are three uses for an audio pad?
16. An audio transformer can be used to match impedances in audio circuits. Where can you find information to use resistors for the same purpose?
17. What is an "L-pad" volume control?

How Passive Components Affect DC and AC Signals

10

CHAPTER OBJECTIVES

This chapter reviews the fundamental ways in which resistors, capacitors, and inductors behave with a variety of input signals. To effectively troubleshoot DC, low-frequency AC, radio frequencies, or pulse and square-wave circuits, a technician must be aware of how passive components affect the circuit waveforms. The ability to estimate the current or voltage waveforms that result when a given input is applied to a passive network will provide a comparison of what the waveforms should be, which is then compared to the actual measurement. If the result is not as expected, the cause of the problem can then be quickly determined and corrected. At the conclusion of this chapter, the student should understand:

- The effect of resistors, capacitors, and inductors (including relays and solenoids) on a DC circuit.
- How resistors, capacitors, inductors, and transformers interact with sine waves and complex audio waveforms.
- How ordinary components take on modified behavior when used at radio frequencies (RF).
- The effects of resonance and ringing of LC circuits.

- How a coaxial cable can be used as a reactive element (either capacitive or inductive) when used at radio frequencies.
- What helical resonators and cavity resonators are and how they are used.
- How a pulse or square-wave waveform is affected by a resistor-capacitor or resistor-inductor configuration.
- The meaning and significance of time constant (TC).
- The use of pulse transformers.
- The operation and use of a flyback transformer.
- The concepts of parallel and series electronic dominance and its use for fine adjustment of circuits.

BASIC INFORMATION

10.1 PASSIVE COMPONENTS IN DC CIRCUITS

RESISTORS IN DC CIRCUITS

When resistors are used in DC circuits, the distribution of voltage and current is based on the application of Ohm's law. Briefly, in a series resistor circuit, the voltage will divide due to the flow of the same current through each element. In a parallel circuit, the voltage is applied to all branches and the current divides according to individual resistance paths. See Figure 10–1.

The voltages to expect at any given point in a circuit can be calculated. The three most common forms of Ohm's law are as follows:

$$I = E/R \qquad E = I \times R \qquad R = E/I$$

Since this chapter is a review of electronic fundamentals rather than a basic text in electronics, further information on Ohm's law should be obtained from an elementary electronics text.

RESISTOR FAILURE PATTERNS

Resistors are made to throw off heat. The larger the resistor is physically, the more heat it can dissipate without damage to itself. If a circuit is properly engineered, the resistors that are used will be operated well within their power ratings. Marginal circuits may have resistors that get very hot, sometimes scorching the circuit boards, other components, or

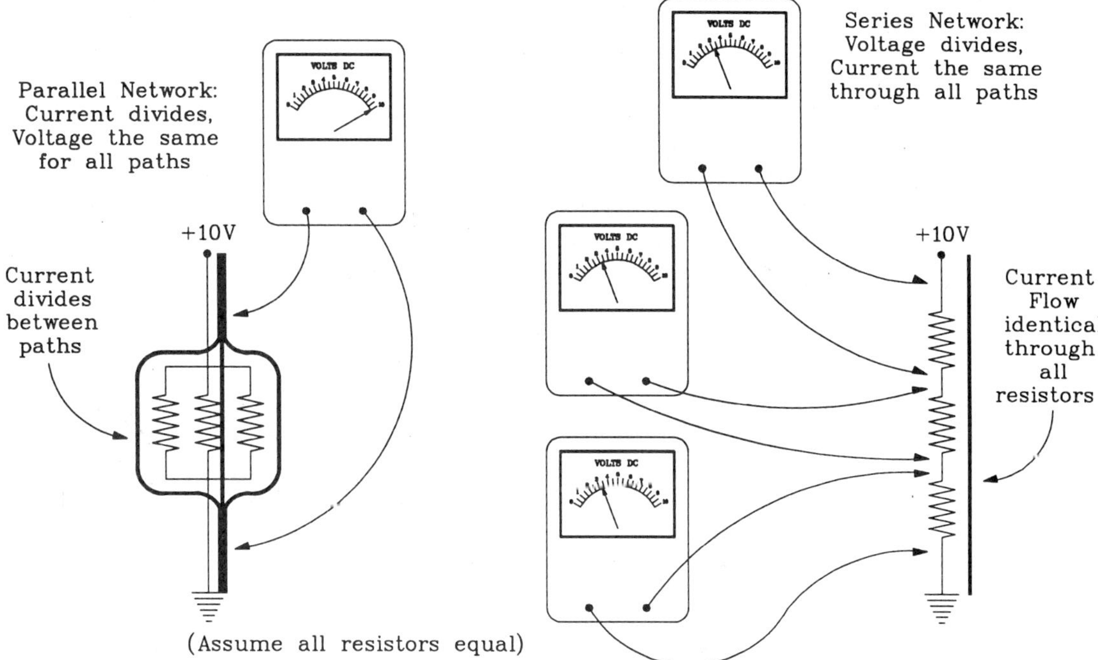
Parallel Network:
Current divides,
Voltage the same
for all paths
VOLTS DC
+10V
Current
divides
between
paths
(Assume all resistors equal)
Series Network:
Voltage divides,
Current the same
through all paths
VOLTS DC
VOLTS DC
VOLTS DC
+10V
Current
Flow
identical
through
all
resistors

Figure 10–1 The voltage and current distribution within parallel and series circuits must be thoroughly understood in order to quickly estimate normal DC voltage and current values.

nearby wiring. Resistors very seldom fail of their own accord. Rather, they are generally caused by the failure of another component that causes too much voltage drop across the resistor, increasing the current and power dissipation beyond the ratings. Under these conditions, resistors will simply burn open. Such a failure is usually obvious during a visual inspection. It is, therefore, very important for a technician encountering a burned resistor to check for the cause of such a failure. An inspection of the circuit schematic will usually reveal the most likely candidate for the original failure.

Metal film resistors have another method of failing: If cracked, they may open. However, the failure may not be obvious during a visual inspection because such cracks are often microscopic.

CAPACITORS IN DC CIRCUITS

How the Capacitor Works in DC Circuits

Capacitors in a DC circuit should be open circuits. This is the case for all types of capacitors except the electrolytic and tantalum varieties. Electrolytic capacitors may have some very high values of resistance leakage. As a general rule, the greater the capacitance of the electrolytic, the lower the leakage resistance. This resistance is usually so high that in practical circuit design, it is ignored. When a capacitor is placed across a DC voltage, it will tend to hold that voltage constant. If the DC voltage rises, the capacitor will charge, providing a path for the current flow caused by the voltage increase. On the other hand, if the DC voltage falls, the capacitor will discharge into the circuit, tending to hold the DC voltage at the original value. The larger the capacitance of the capacitor, the more effective the capacitor will be at holding the DC value constant.

The Paralleled Capacitor and Resistor

The capacitor is sometimes used in parallel with a resistor. In this configuration the capacitor is called a *bypass* or *stabilizing capacitor,* since it bypasses changes yet allows a constant DC across its terminals. Its purpose is to hold the average DC voltage produced across the resistor at a constant or nearly constant value. A good example is the emitter bypass capacitor shown in Figure 10–2.

The DC-Isolating Capacitor

The capacitor is often used to isolate DC voltages from one stage to the next allowing changes (the interstage signals) to pass in a relatively undiminished state. A capacitor can be used to remove a DC component, add it,

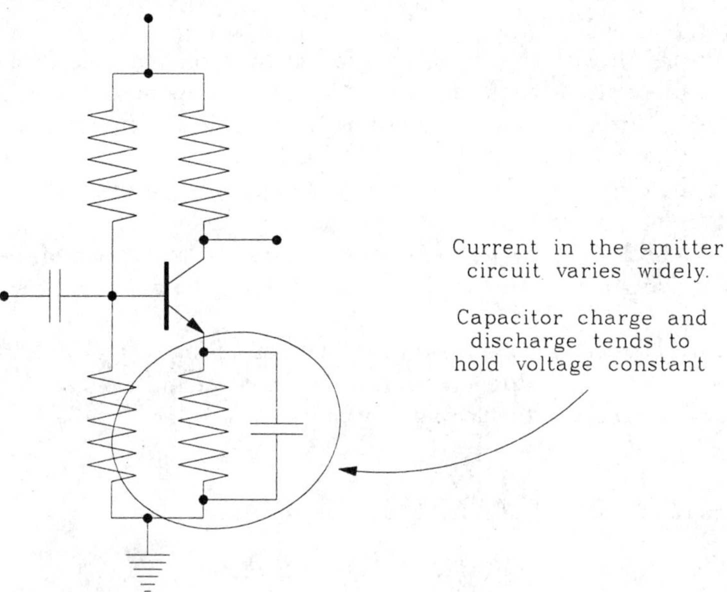
Current in the emitter circuit varies widely.
Capacitor charge and discharge tends to hold voltage constant

Figure 10–2 Example of a capacitor used to hold the DC voltage value constant across a resistor.

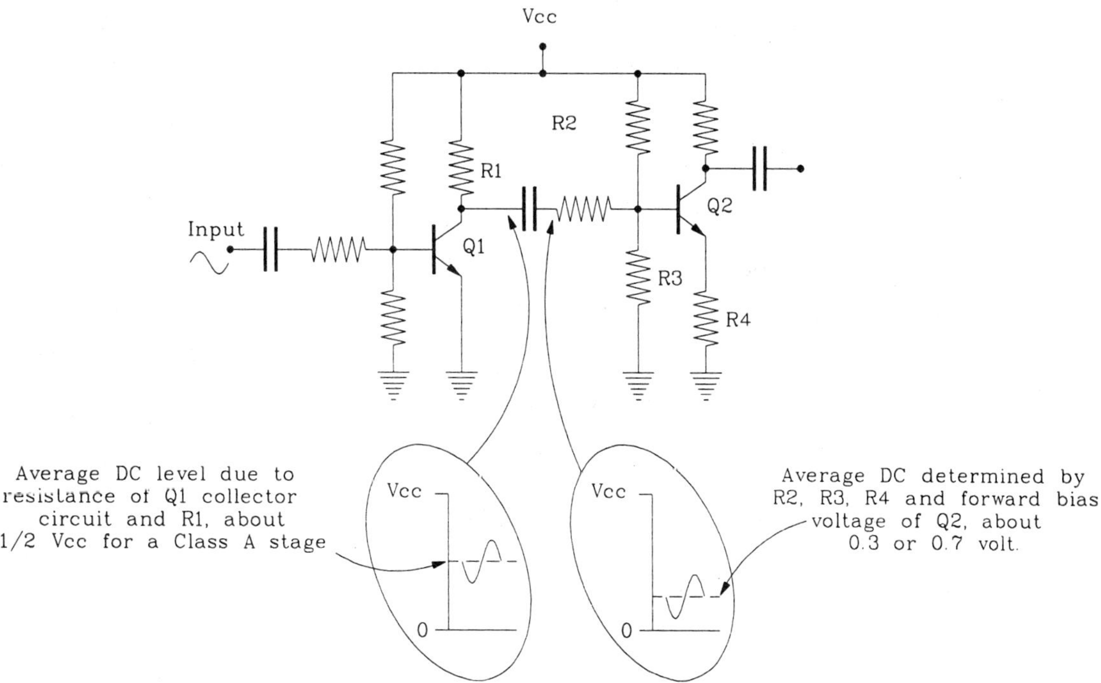

Figure 10–3 A capacitor can remove DC levels of applied waveforms.

or change it. A common example is the output stage of an RC-coupled transistor amplifier. The capacitor is used to remove the DC component of the signal, which otherwise would upset the normal functioning of the following stage. See Figure 10–3.

A capacitor can be used to insert a DC level into a circuit, too. See Figure 10–4.

Predicting the DC levels that will be found after a series-connected capacitor is quite easily done. See Figure 10–5.

Capacitor Failure Patterns in DC Circuits

The great majority of capacitor failures, perhaps 90 percent, involve the simple shorting of the capacitor internally. Once shorted, an overload of the power supply frequently occurs, which often causes the power supply to blow a fuse or otherwise fail as well. Troubleshooting of this kind of failure is covered in Chapter 7. In less drastic failures, the capacitor will no longer perform the function of isolating DC voltages from one circuit to another. This kind of failure can be easily determined with a DC voltmeter if power

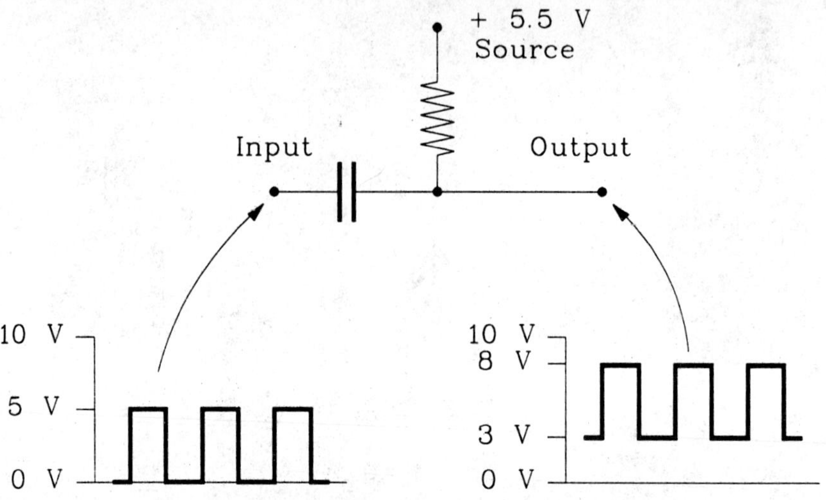

Figure 10–4 A capacitor can add DC voltage to an AC signal.

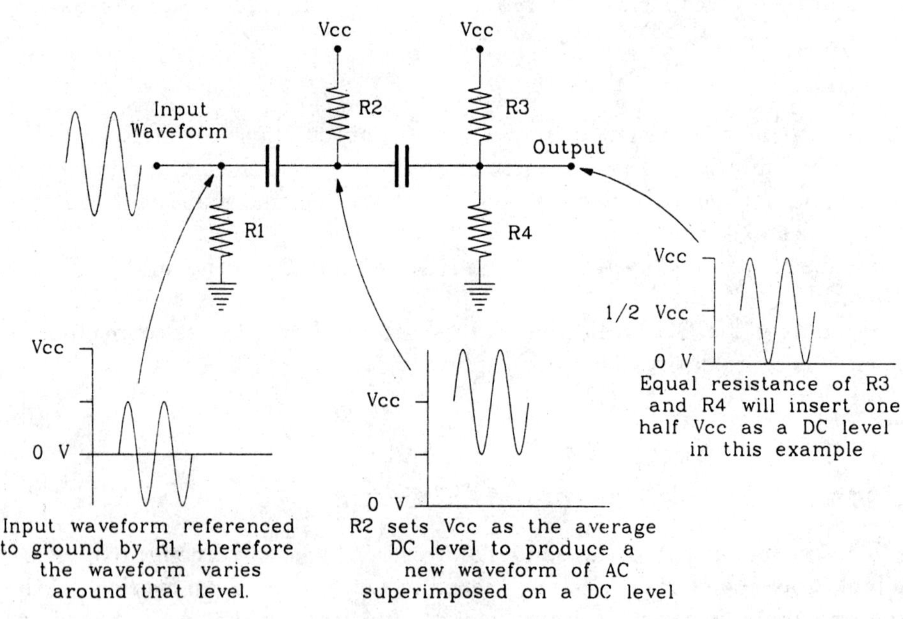

Figure 10–5 Predicting DC levels after a series capacitor.

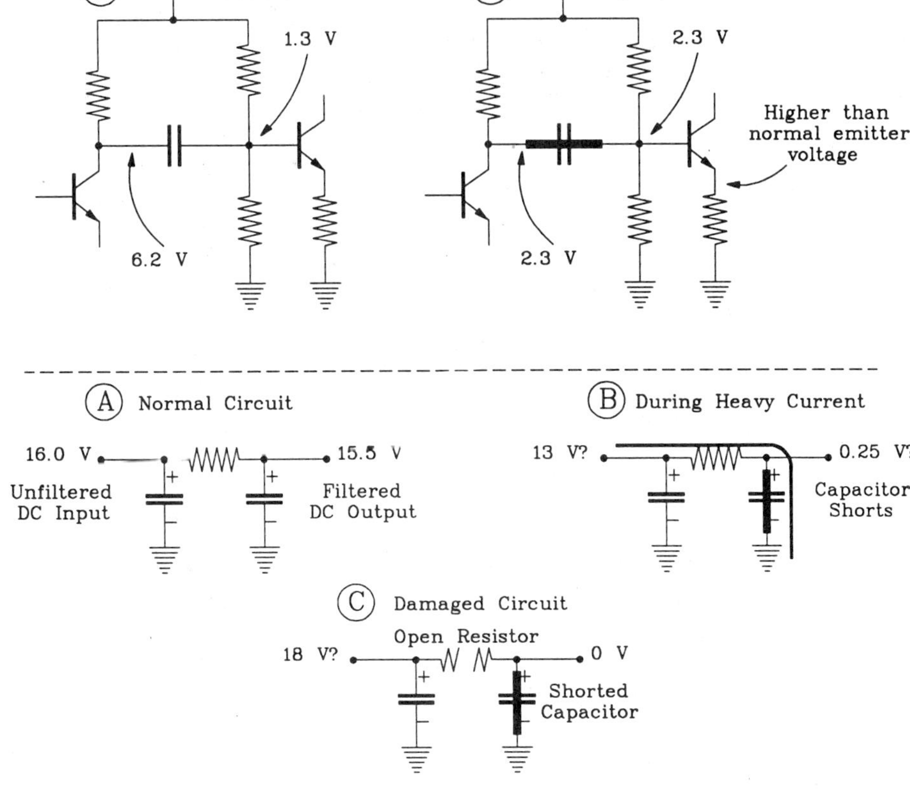

Figure 10–6 Two examples of how a shorted capacitor changes the circuit voltages when it fails by shorting.

is still applied: there will be zero volts across a shorted coupling capacitor. See Figure 10–6.

INDUCTORS IN DC CIRCUITS

How the Inductor Works in DC Circuits

Inductors basically consist of many turns of wire. This wire will have some resistance, but it will often be very low when compared to the other resistances within a given circuit. For the purpose of estimating DC voltages, inductors can usually be replaced with a short circuit.

When used in a DC circuit, the inductor merely passes DC current, with the current flow limited by external resistances. In this case, there is no change of the current and thus, no expansion or collapsing of the magnetic field. Consequently no *counter-electromotive force* will build up. The inductor will tend to hold the circuit current constant. If the current increases, the inductor will counter the increase by storing more energy in its magnetic field. This action of increasing the magnetic field results in an opposing, or canceling, voltage being temporarily developed across the winding due to the expansion of the field. Counter EMF can continue only while the magnetic field is increasing, until the core material becomes saturated with the magnetism. At that point, further current increase will no longer be opposed, and the inductor thus becomes, effectively, a low-value resistor. See Figure 10–7.

The opposite phenomenon also occurs: when current flow begins to decrease, the coil will produce a voltage that aids the source voltage, which, in turn, will tend to keep the original current flowing.

In summary, the inductor looks like a very low resistance when used in DC circuits, except when the current through the inductor begins to change, whereupon the inductor will attempt to maintain the original current value.

Inductor Failure Patterns

The inductor often fails in much the same way as the resistor: by excessive current flow due to the failure of some other component. An inductor that is overloaded by excessive current flow may overheat, burning the

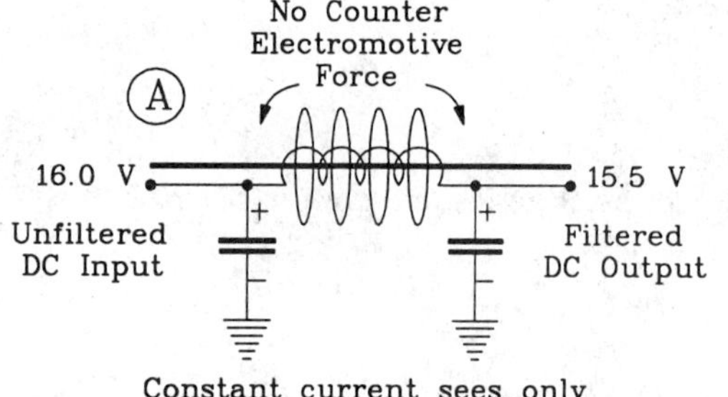

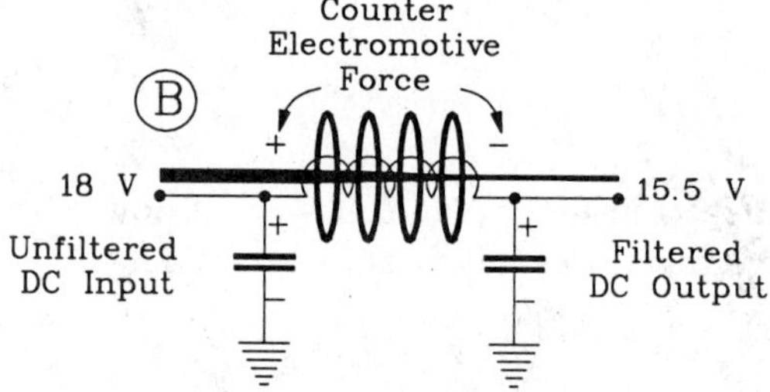

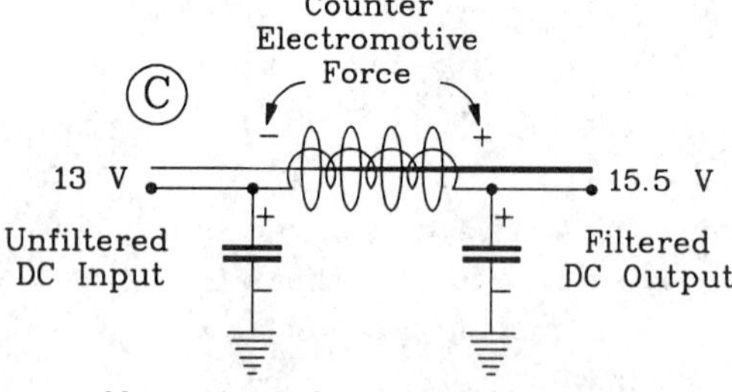

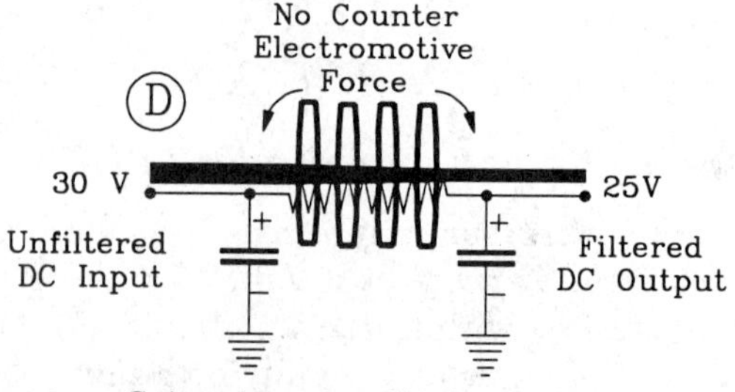

Figure 10–7 How an inductor reacts to a changing current.

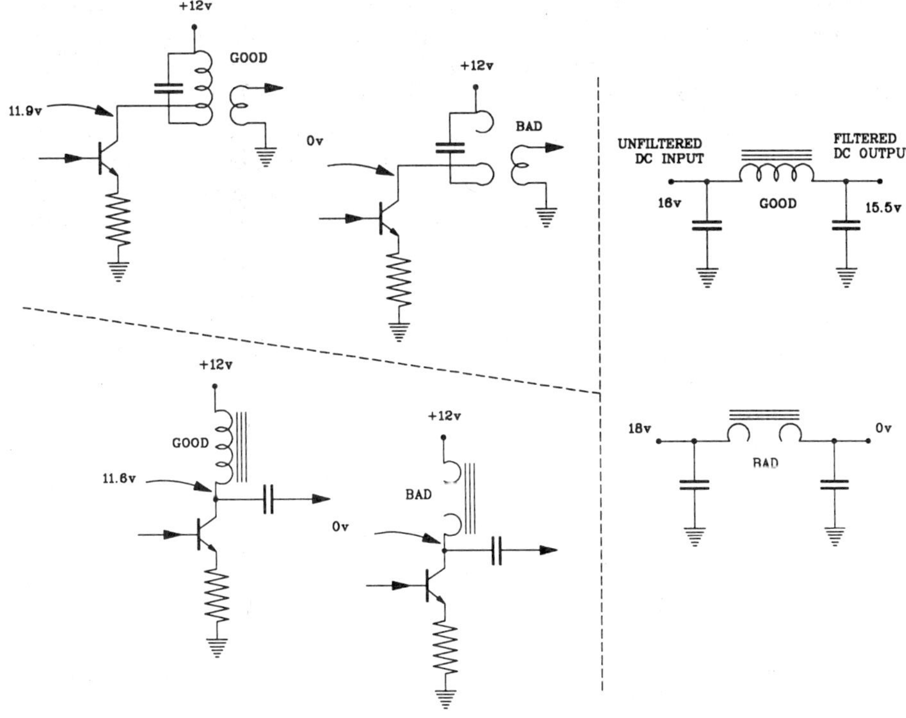

Figure 10–8 Detecting the open inductor is usually easy since it will no longer pass DC current.

insulation varnish and a special, paper-like insulation called *fish paper,* which is used inside the inductor. Once this happens, the inductor may simply open, as shown in Figure 10–8.

An inductor may also short from one winding to others, or to the metal case of the inductor, if it has one. Failures of this kind are hard to detect with an ohmmeter because of the initially low resistance of the windings, which often falls below the reliable measurement capability of an ohmmeter. However, shorts from the windings to the metal case are easily detected with an ohmmeter. The best test of an inductor with suspected shorts of its windings is the substitution test: if a new inductor works well and the old one did not, chances are very good that there were shorted turns. Shorted turns prevent the buildup of a CEMF, making the inductor operate much like a simple piece of wire.

RELAYS AND SOLENOID COILS

The coils within relays and solenoids are there for a single purpose, to produce a magnetic field. A solenoid exerts a pull on a plunger for mechanical purposes, and the relay exerts a pull on an armature with attached switching contacts. Once the rated voltage has been applied to one of these coils, the magnetic field will quickly build to a maximum and the pulling action will occur. The coil can then be left energized on DC for as long as necessary, provided it is designed for continous use. In such a case, the resistance of the wire in the windings will be sufficient to limit the current through the coil to a safe value. Intermittent-duty solenoids and relays are meant to be operated for only a few moments, as the resistance of the windings is insufficient to limit the coil current to a safe value for continuous dissipation. Solenoids, too, are frequently rated only for intermittent use, particularly the stronger ones.

When the DC voltage applied to a coil such as a relay or solenoid is suddenly removed, the coil will be left with a strong magnetic field, which represents energy. Without a current flow to sustain it, the field must collapse. In collapsing, the magnetic field will again cut the wires, producing a high-voltage pulse that is opposite in polarity to the pulse that established the original field. In practical circuits, this voltage pulse can often be 10 or 20 times the strength of the original applied voltage.

This development of very high voltages can be destructive, breaking down the insulation of the coil windings to other turns or to the metal parts of the relay or solenoid frame. If they are driven by semiconductors, the voltages can destroy the associated junctions by arcing through them. Thus, it is important to prevent these large voltage spikes. This can be easily done by installing a small diode across the coil winding. See Figure 10–9.

Relay and Solenoid Coil Failure Patterns

Relays and solenoids usually fail by opening. In this case, testing for energizing voltage *right at the coil terminals* is the best tactic. If the voltage is available at the coil connections and yet there is no magnetic field, then the coil is open. This can be verified after its removal with an ohmmeter. Sometimes it is possible to repair such a coil if you find the break where the coil wires come out of the coil itself. A few shorted turns in a DC coil can go unnoticed and produce no undesirable effects, other than a slightly higher-than-normal current flow.

10.2 PASSIVE COMPONENTS IN 60 HZ AND AUDIO SINE-WAVE CIRCUITS

The range of audio is commonly accepted as being from about 20 to 20000 Hz. Audio amplifiers such as stereo and automobile audio equipment uses sine waves and complex sound waves, both speech and music, over these ranges. There is also a predominance of equipment that uses 60-Hz sine waves, power supplies being the most common. All these frequencies will

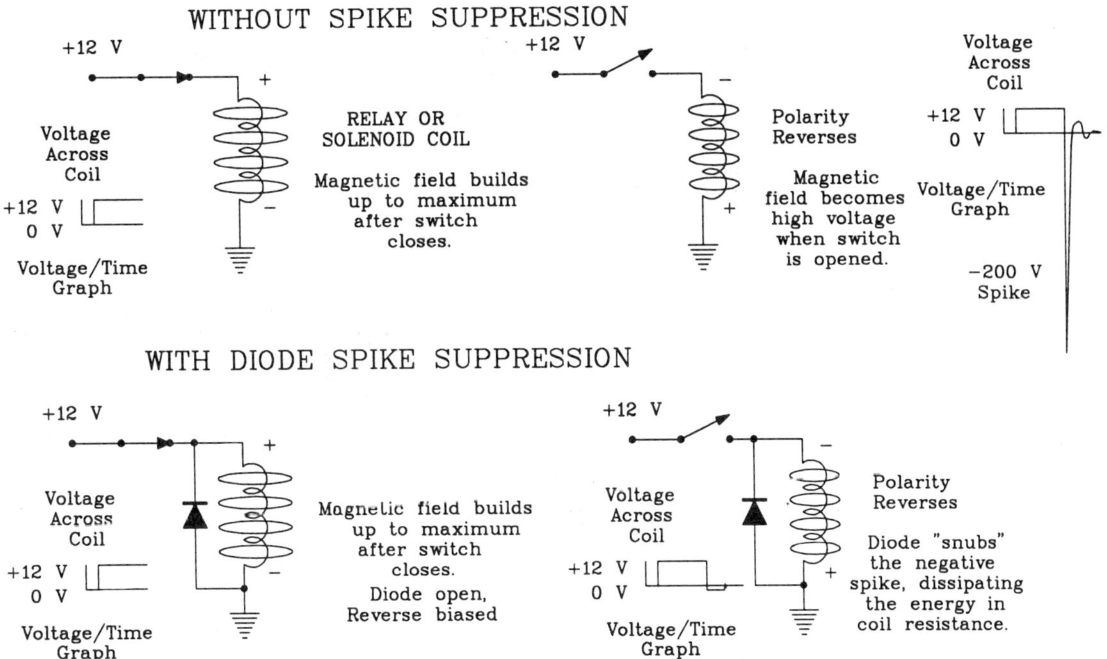

Figure 10–9 Using a diode to prevent a large voltage spike across a relay or solenoid coil when operating from a DC source.

be considered together simply as low-frequency circuits for the purposes of this chapter.

RESISTORS

At the relatively low AC frequencies of the power line (60 Hz) and up through the audio frequencies to about 20000 Hz, resistors still look like standard resistors. When using only resistors, they may be calculated using the RMS value of the AC voltage and current waveforms. In real circuits, resistors often have both DC and AC currents flowing in them. This is frequently referred to as having a signal voltage along with a DC offset. The AC and DC current flows are often considered separately, being conveniently measured with an AC meter having a series, a DC-blocking capacitor, or a DC meter that averages any AC to its zero overall average. Placing components such as capacitors or inductors into the circuitry will change the overall effect drastically, however.

CAPACITORS IN LOW-FREQUENCY CIRCUITS

Capacitors have to be relatively large to be effective at power-line frequencies and up through the audio spectrum. Capacitors of 1 to several thousand μfds are common in these kinds of circuits. The lower the frequency that must be handled by the circuit, the larger the capacitor values must be.

How the Capacitor Works

The capacitor, as used in these low-frequency circuits, operates by providing a reservoir of electrons stressing a dielectric material, which forces electrons off the opposite plate. Electrons do not go through the capacitor, but in the process of charging and discharging, the effect is similar to that of a flow directly through the device. During this process, there is a certain amount of "resistance" to the apparent current flow (a quantity called *reactance*). Reactance is a function of both frequency and the capacitance of the component, according to the following formula:

$$Xc = \frac{1}{6.28 \times F \times C}$$

A technician should know the two facts that follow almost by instinct or intuition:

1. The higher the frequency applied, the more a given capacitor will approach a low short, or a low reactance.
2. The lower the frequency applied, the more a capacitor will appear to be an open, or a high reactance.

The Shunt (Paralleling) Capacitor: Bypassing

The most common use for a capacitor is as a filter, across a source of power from the "hot" side to ground. The capacitor is a reservoir of voltage energy. A mechanical analogy of a capacitor is a shock absorber. Both resist quick changes yet allow gradual changes to occur with little opposition. Another way to look at this is that the capacitor allows fast changes to be transferred directly to ground. In other words, high frequencies are passed directly to ground, bypassing other circuitry. The capacitor used in this way is often called a *bypass capacitor*. See Figure 10–10.

A rule of thumb for using a capacitor for bypassing is that the reactance of the capacitor should be less than one-tenth of the resistance of the load at the lowest frequency to be bypassed.

The electrolytic capacitor exhibits a small amount of internal, series inductance. At low and audio frequencies, this presents no problem, but for radio frequencies, this series inductance prevents the electrolytic from being effective. To provide proper filtering at low and high frequencies at the same time, it is standard practice to provide two bypass capacitors, one electrolytic and the other, a smaller mica or disk ceramic capacitor, from the power bus to ground.

The power supply filter is also a bypass capacitor. Each filter capacitor

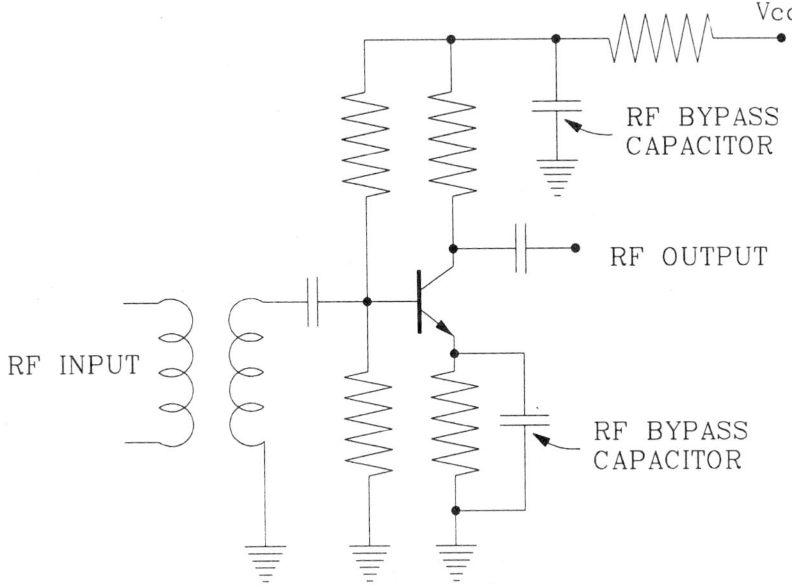

Figure 10–10 Typical application for a bypass capacitor, which is used to bypass high frequencies to ground rather than allowing them to enter other circuitry.

bypasses the ripple waveform to ground rather than allowing it to pass on into the load circuitry.

The Series (Coupling) Capacitor

The series, or signal coupling, capacitor is used to pass a changing (AC, audio, RF, or pulse) signal from one stage to the next, yet allow the DC levels of the output of one stage to differ from that required for the following stage. See Figure 10–11.

A rule of thumb for using a capacitor for signal coupling is that the reactance of the capacitor should be less than one-tenth that of the resistance of the load at the lowest frequency to be coupled.

Capacitor Failure Patterns in Low-Frequency Circuits

The capacitors used in low-frequency circuits are, of necessity, of relatively large in size. The internal plate-to-plate spacing of some of these capacitors is very close, with separations maintained by an insulating layer of some sort. Associated circuit malfunctions can cause these capacitors to have voltages that are higher than the rated voltages applied. An overvoltage of more than 10 percent of the rated voltage may be sufficient to cause an electrolytic capacitor to fail by shorting.

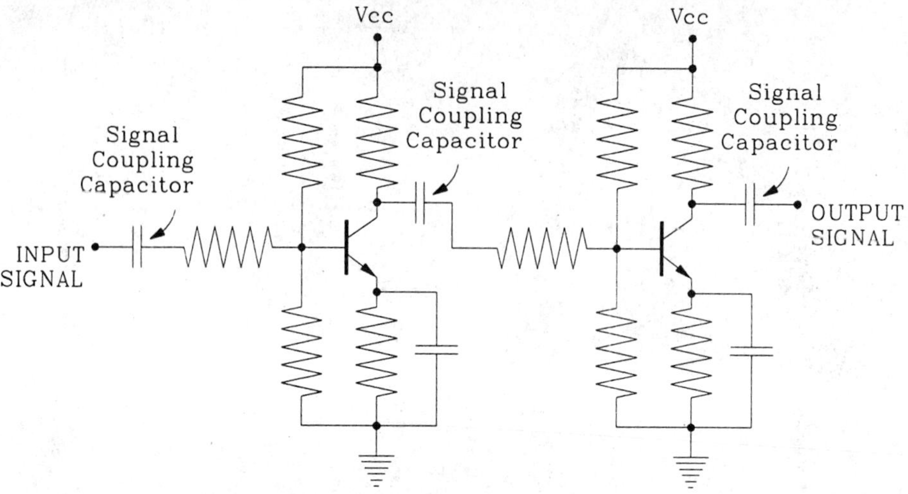

Figure 10–11 The interstage-coupling capacitor passes the signal yet isolates DC voltages from one stage to the next.

In the process, considerable heat may be developed, and, in the case of metal-cased capacitors, there can be a violent explosion if the overvoltage continues for too long. Capacitors other than electrolytics often short as well. In such cases, if the capacitor is connected to the main power bus, there may be a heavy overload placed on the power supply. The shorting of coupling capacitors, on the other hand, will seldom cause an overload on the power supply. In this case, the coupling capacitor will often apply an overly high DC voltage from the preceding stage on the input of the following stage. This will often result in the destruction of the semiconductor device in the following stage.

Older electrolytic capacitors did not have the benefit of the improved case seals that we have today. This leads to a common failure of equipment of more than perhaps 20 years of age: the electrolytic capacitors may dry out, losing capacitance and, in severe cases, simply opening. This condition can be often be verified by observing that leakage has taken place, as shown by the depositing of white salts from the end of the capacitor.

Although it is rare, capacitors can develop an internal open circuit, becoming disconnected from the input wire at either end. An even rarer problem is the capacitor that changes value. While most will change value a small amount with changes in temperature, a sudden, drastic drop in capacitance is very rare, but nonetheless, it can happen.

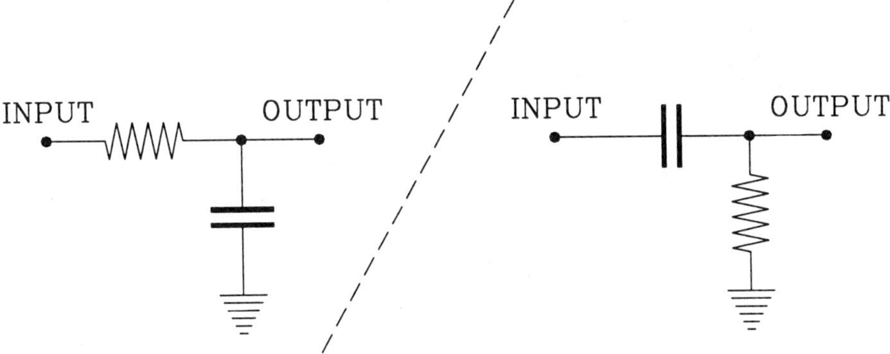

Figure 10–12 The capacitor and resistor in two different configurations.

USING CAPACITORS WITH RESISTORS IN LOW-FREQUENCY CIRCUITS

There are two basic ways of connecting a resistor and a capacitor, as shown in Figure 10–12.

When the resistance and the reactance values are comparable *at a stated frequency,* a phenomenon called *phase shift* will occur. This means that the voltages across the two components are not in step with one another. The voltage across the capacitor will lag behind the source voltage, since it takes time to charge a capacitor through a resistance. See Figure 10–13.

If a capacitor and a resistor are connected, the phase shift will change greatly along with changes in the frequency applied. Such changes normally appear in audio amplifiers, and they are one cause of audio distortion that is built into the amplifier. In other words, some frequencies pass through the amplifier with either more or less of a timing shift than others due to phase shifting within the amplifier.

INDUCTORS IN AC AND AUDIO CIRCUITS

Inductors perform the opposite function to that of capacitors. (Inductors are sometimes called chokes.) The technician should be completely familiar with the following facts when dealing with inductors:

1. The higher the frequency applied, the more an inductor will look like an open, or a high reactance.
2. The lower the frequency applied, the more an inductor will look like a short, or a low reactance.

The inductor is—as determined by its construction—an expensive component. Using a capacitor in a complementary circuit is preferable to using an inductor because even a large capacitor is cheaper. The use of inductors is a mark of quality in low- and audio-frequency amplifiers.

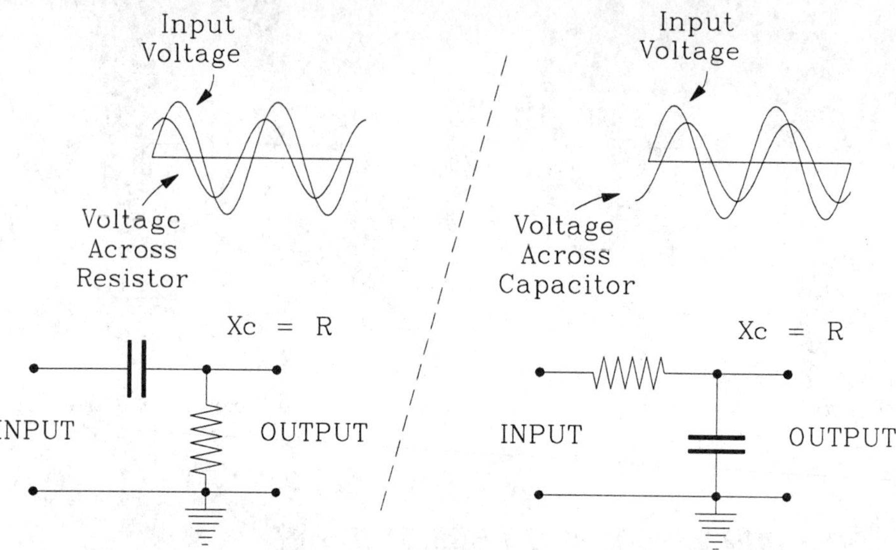

Figure 10–13 At the frequency at which the capacitive reactance equals the resistance, the voltage between the resistor and the capacitor will be shifted in phase by 45 degrees.

The most common use for an inductor is within a power supply filter. The presence of a filter inductor is a mark of quality in power supplies. The inductor provides smoother power flow than the more familiar capacitor-resistor filter of Figure 10–14.

Another use for inductors in low-frequency circuits is to provide operating current to an amplifier stage in a more efficient manner than a resistor can. This method of coupling a signal from one stage to another is called

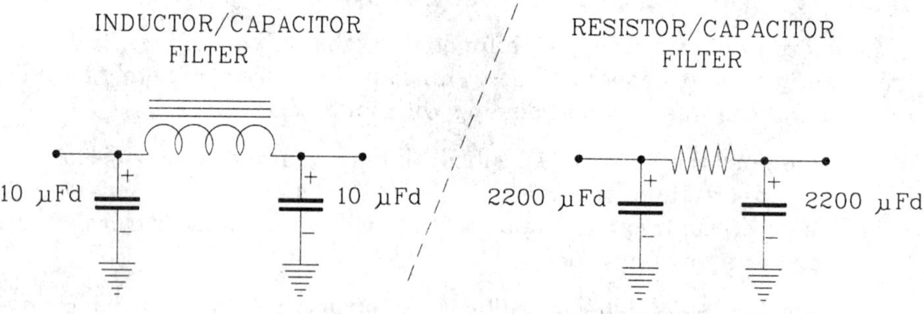

Figure 10–14 How the capacitor can do the job of the inductor for less money.

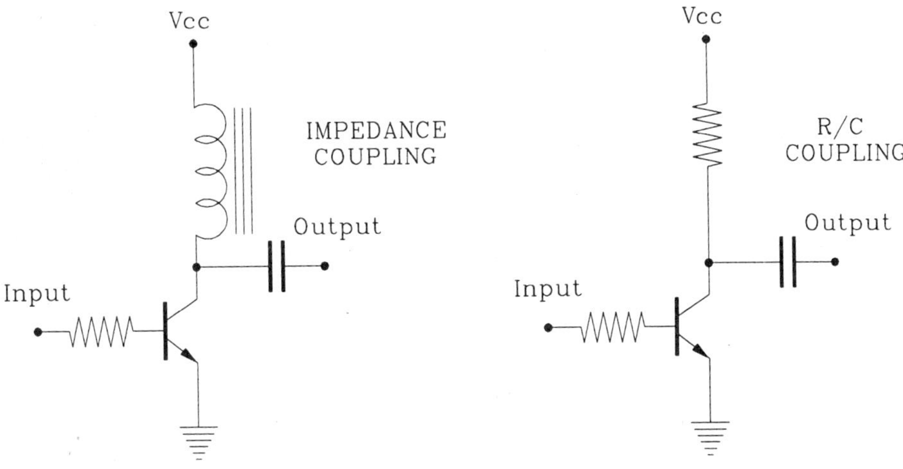

Figure 10–15 The impedance-coupled circuit uses an inductor instead of a resistor to provide operating current for the amplifier stage.

impedance coupling. It is nowadays rarely used in low-frequency equipment due to its cost. See Figure 10–15.

TRANSFORMERS

Power-Supply Transformers

Power-supply transformers used at 60 Hz are usually just windings of copper wire around a common magnetizable core, which usually consists of laminations (layers) of soft iron. The basic idea usually involves at least two windings, an input and an output. However, there are several other ways to accomplish the purposes of a transformer, as shown in Figure 10–16.

The autotransformer can provide a reduction in voltage with an accompanying increase in current capability, but it fails to provide one of the greatest advantages of using a multiple-winding transformer in the first place: isolation between grounded systems. See Figure 10–17.

How Transformers Work

When a transformer has no load connected to it, the expanding current in the primary causes a counter-electromotive force across the winding. This CEMF balances the incoming voltage nearly exactly, so the resulting current will be very small in the primary winding. The small amount of current flow is due mainly to the internal core losses within the transformer.

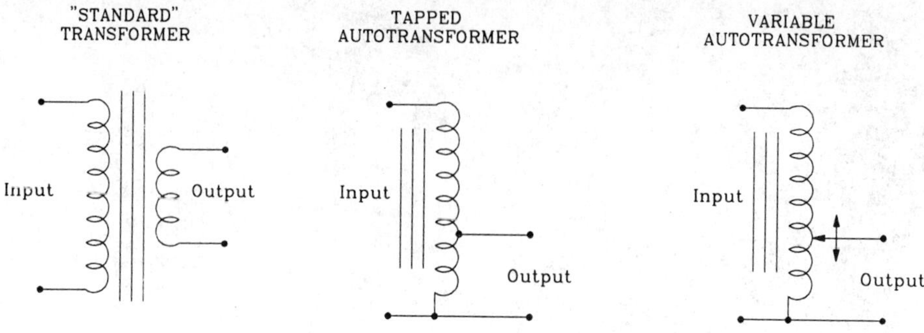

Figure 10–16 Power transformer variations.

The loading of a secondary winding will cause the CEMF of the primary to be reduced. This, in turn, will cause a correspondingly greater current flow in the primary. Thus, the input power increases as a function of the loading on the secondary. It is said that the load in the secondary is "reflected" into the primary.

The losses of a transformer are relatively small, often 5 percent or less in larger transformers. Transformers transform energy, losing very little to internal heating. With this in mind, it is easier to visualize

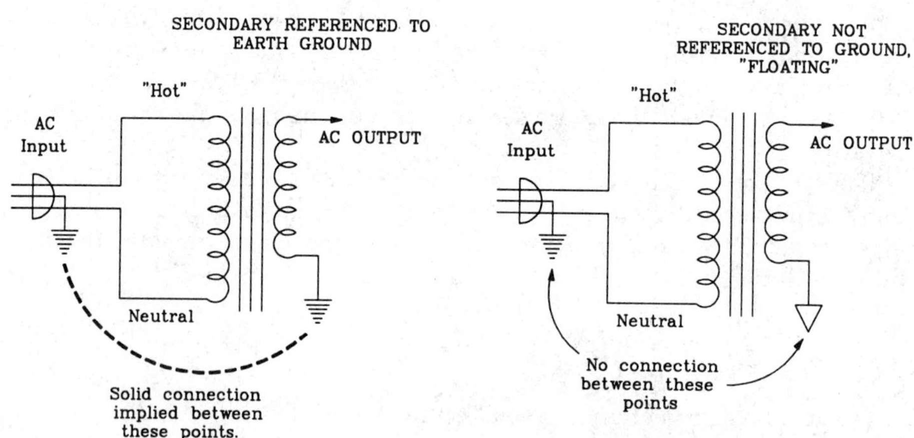

Figure 10–17 Using a transformer with a separate output winding allows the secondary winding to be either grounded or ungrounded, as the designer chooses.

the current and voltage ratios of a transformer. Transformer losses are often ignored when considering the practical aspects of transformers.

To review how transformers operate, start with a given voltage—120-V AC, for example—into the primary winding of a transformer. If the turns ratio between the primary and the secondary is 10:1, the secondary winding will have one-tenth of the primary voltage, or 12-V AC. The primary current multiplied by the primary voltage equals the input power in volt-amperes (VAs). Since the secondary circuit must have the same power output as the primary (ignoring losses), the current flowing in the secondary will have to increase as the voltage decreases to maintain the same power. For example, a transformer with a 10:1 turns ratio would have to produce 10 amps in the secondary to have a 1-ampere flow in the primary. Both the input and the output would equal to 120 VA. (In an actual circuit, the output voltage might well be 12-V AC under full load, but the current will be slightly less than theoretical due to the small transformer losses.)

A ferrite core is a ceramic-like material that is often used for small inductors and transformers operating at audio and low radio frequencies. This type of core will sustain a heavy magnetizing force and sustain fewer internal losses than the solid or laminated iron core of the common power transformer. The ferrite material will easily fracture, however, and it must therefore be handled with care or it will crack due to excessive prying, pressure, or dropping.

Audio Transformers

Audio transformers are designed for use on higher and lower frequencies than the fixed 60 Hz of power transformers. (Audio frequencies are generally understood to extend from 20 Hz to 20000 Hz.) In addition to pure sine waves, these transformers can also handle the complex waveforms of music and speech. Instead of considering audio transformers as voltage- and current-modifying components, they are usually described as *impedance matching* devices.

To explain this different description of what is the power transformer that was explained earlier in this chapter, consider an example that might be used in a telephone application, where the incoming line is known to be a 600 Ω line. See Figure 10–18.

The turns ratio necessary within an audio transformer to match two impedances is expressed as the square root of the ratio of the two impedances involved.

$$\frac{Turns_{primary}}{Turns_{secondary}} = \sqrt{\frac{Z_{primary}}{Z_{secondary}}}$$

As an example, a transformer matching a 600 Ω line to a 4 Ω speaker would need a ratio of:

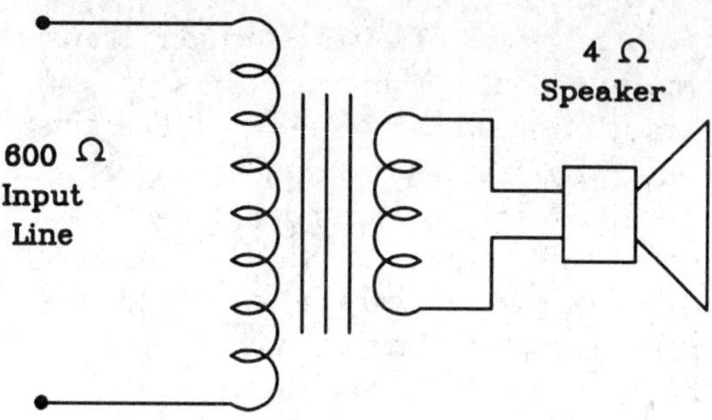

Figure 10–18 Telephone 600-ohm line-matching transformer driving a 4-ohm speaker.

$$\sqrt{\frac{600}{4}} = \sqrt{150} = 12.25:1$$

In matching impedances, the transformer must also be designed to handle the maximum power levels involved.

Common audio impedances for speakers are 4, 8, and 16 Ω . Microphones are often of 50 Ω impedance, and they may contain a transformer to increase the impedance to 600 Ω for connecting through long, shielded cables to remote amplifiers. Using a higher impedance means using a higher voltage and lower current, thus reducing losses in line resistance.

Power transformers and impedance matching transformer failures were covered earlier in this chapter under "Inductors in DC Circuits."

10.3 PASSIVE COMPONENTS IN RF CIRCUITS

Resistors

Carbon-composition and metal-film resistors act basically the same with DC and audio and at low radio frequencies. A wire-wound resistor will act like an inductor at higher frequencies. In winding a resistor of resistance wire, some inductance will be introduced along with the resistance. Because of this fact, high-powered resistors intended for RF use will be made of a conductive, ceramic-like material or else will be wound in a special manner for high-frequency use. The inductance of the winding can be almost completely canceled if the resistor is bifilar-wound. Bifilar winding results in the winding going in a clockwise direction around the core, and then reversing and winding counterclockwise for the remaining half. In the process, the magnetic field of half the winding cancels the field of the other half.

CAPACITORS IN RF CIRCUITS

Capacitors are often used in RF equipment to bypass any possible RF signals to the circuit ground. The kind of capacitor that is most often used for this purpose is the disk ceramic capacitor, whose use was discussed earlier in this chapter under the topic of using the shunt (paralleling) capacitor for bypassing.

Capacitors used in radio frequency tuning applications and precision balancing adjustments are designed for very low internal losses and low resistance. Common dielectrics for RF circuits include air, vacuum, mica, ceramic, or glass. Variable RF capacitors are also available using all five of these dielectrics. See Figure 10–19.

While fixed-value RF capacitors seldom give any trouble, the adjustable capacitors usually fail mechanically. The most common problems with screwdriver-adjusted capacitors are that the capacitor cracks and breaks or the screw slot tears out. In either case, one can only replace the capacitor. The replacement of such a capacitor will almost always require realignment of that particular adjustment, following the procedures in the instruction manual.

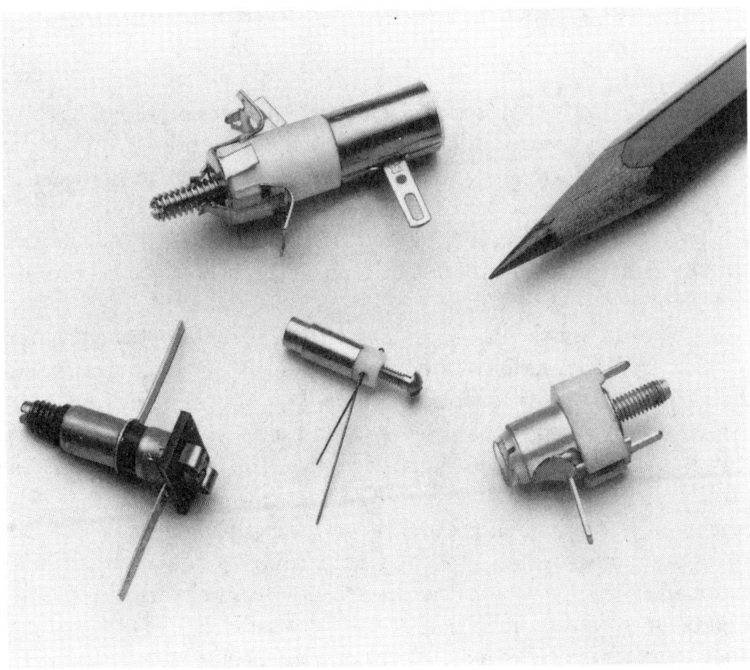

Figure 10–19 Several different kinds of variable capacitors for adjusting radio frequency tuned circuits. (Courtesy Sprague-Goodman Electronics, Inc.)

Stray Capacitance

Radio frequency circuits sometimes, in the course of being designed, become subject to an undesirable capacitive coupling of signals from one circuit to another. It is a major concern to the designing engineer, but seldom a problem for the technician.

Stray capacitance in RF circuits can cause amplifiers to suddenly become oscillators, generating interference to other services and preventing their normal operation.

Undesirable capacitive coupling between two components or circuits can often be eliminated by the installation of a grounded element, such as a shield or screen, between them. A shield installed between two windings of an RF transformer in order to allow only magnetic coupling is called a Faraday shield. The technician must be aware of the need to replace the internal shields provided within and around equipment before the circuitry is tested and declared ready for service.

Some kinds of capacitors, especially disk ceramic capacitors, have a substantial series-internal inductance. As a result, these capacitors can exhibit self-resonance at high frequencies. At frequencies higher than resonance, these capacitors resemble inductors!

INDUCTORS IN RF CIRCUITS

Skin Effect

Inductors at RF frequencies are often small and made of relatively heavy wire. The use of heavy wire reduces *skin effect,* the tendency of RF currents to flow near the surface of conductors where there is less inductance to impede progress. It also provides adequate stiffness to prevent any inductance change with vibration. A current through the center of a wire is subject to the reactance of magnetic lines of force cutting through all the wire up to its surface.

Inductors include fewer windings as the frequency of operation increases. A very effective RF transformer can be made of half a dozen turns at a frequency of 150 MHz, for instance. Air is the core material on almost all RF transformers. Ferrite cores are the exception; they are sometimes used on the lowest RF frequencies, such as with the AM broadcast band of 500–1600 kHz.

Inductors will have a certain amount of distributed capacitance from one end to the other, due to the windings' proximity to each other. This effect can be reduced by constructing the inductance from several lumps of windings rather than a single one. The lumps of windings break up the overall capacitance into several distinct capacitors, each of which is in series with the others. Since capacitors in series produce a capacitance that is less than that of any one capacitor, the total capacitance will be greatly reduced.

Stray Inductances

The use of wires to carry RF currents from one place to another must be kept to a minimum for two reasons. First, a wire, even a short one, will exhibit a substantial amount of inductance, particularly at the higher RF frequencies. This inductance, in combination with existing or stray capacitances, may resonate at unsuspecting frequencies and generate harmonic signals. These can cause problems further on in the system, even, in extreme cases, causing interference to other signals. Second, if the length of a wire is a substantial part of a quarter wavelength at the frequency of operation, it will act like a short antenna, transforming voltage and current levels along its length. For instance, a quater-wavelength line left open at its far end will appear as an RF short if fed a signal at its near end. If it is shorted at the far end, the near end will seem to be an open.

In summary, if RF currents are to be carried for any significant distance, this must be done with a properly driven and terminated coaxial cable to prevent reflections, the introduction of external noise signals into the line, and impedance changes due to the physical length of the cable.

THE RESONANCE PHENOMENON: TUNED CIRCUITS

The principal use of capacitors and inductors at radio frequencies is to select a specific RF frequency or a band of frequencies. When a properly designed L and C are used in series, there will be very little loss through the circuit; almost all the input signal will pass along to the following circuits. The parallel inductance (L) and capacitance (C) circuit, on the other hand, will have an extremely high loss (approaching an open) and will keep signals from flowing through it. See Figure 10–20.

The same circuits can be used *across* a given circuit rather than in line with it, producing the opposite effect. See Figure 10–21.

Resonance occurs when the capacitive reactance equals the inductive reactance. When this happens, the circuit is selective for the frequency at which this reactance occurs, as shown:

$$F = \frac{1}{2\pi\sqrt{LC}}$$

In practical RF circuits, the capacitor is usually adjustable and is used with a fixed-value inductor for tuning purposes. The capacitor is adjusted for the exact frequency of operation desired.

Lower frequencies such as AM broadcast sometimes use a fixed capacitor with an inductor that can be adjusted. Adjusting an RF inductor is usually done by changing the position of a ferrite tuning "slug" within the core.

These ferrite-adjusted coils are often used in intermediate-frequency interstage-tuned transformers.

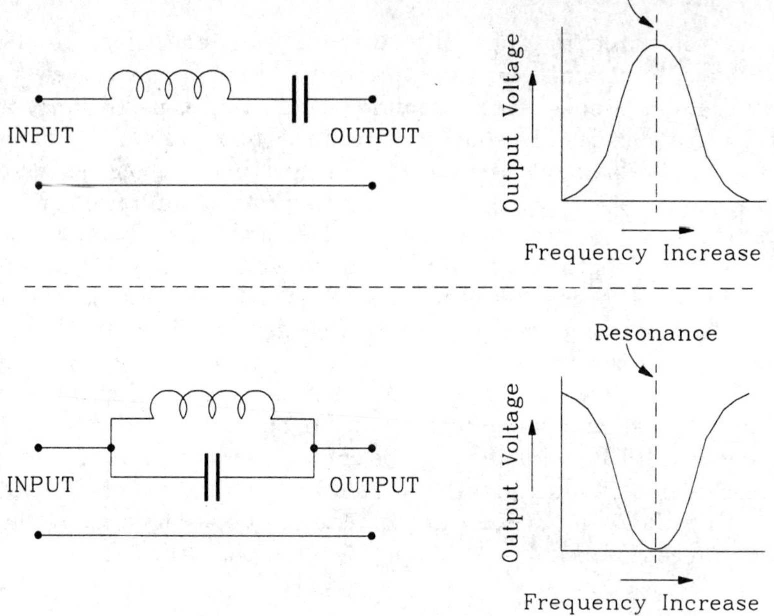

Figure 10–20 L and C circuits in series with the signal path.

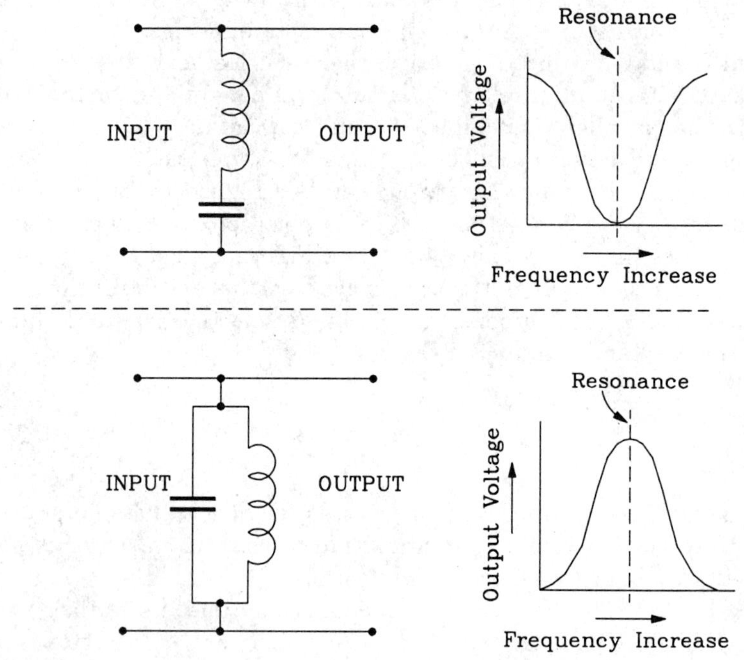

Figure 10–21 L and C circuits and their effects when placed in parallel with the signal path.

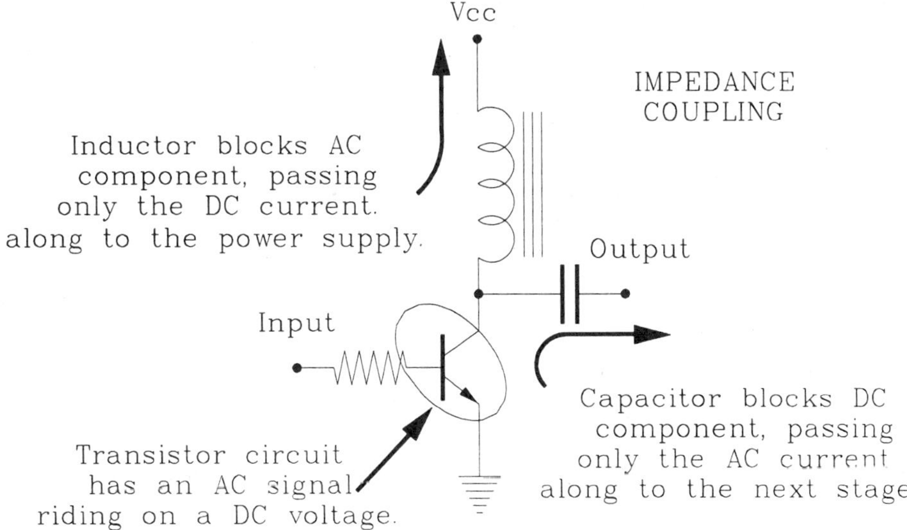

Figure 10–22 Schematic of a power amplifier stage using an inductor and a capacitor to separate the AC and DC components that are present in the amplifier output circuit.

The inductor is sometimes used in quality radio frequency filters, preventing strong RF high-frequency signals from later stages from getting back into earlier stages. This action prevents the oscillations that would otherwise occur. In this application, the filter inductor is sometimes called a radio-frequency choke (RFC).

RF inductors are sometimes used to provide high-efficiency DC power to amplifier output stages. In this application, which is called *impedance coupling*, the DC and RF components which are combined within the amplifier are separated by an inductor and a capacitor. See Figure 10–22.

Tuned Circuit-Response Modification

The bandwidth of an LC circuit is normally only a few percentage points of the applied frequency in most RF applications. In other words, applying the resonant frequency plus or minus a few percent will still result in an output response. The farther an input signal is from resonance, the less response will result.

An overall improvement of amplification over a wider band of frequencies can be obtained by three methods: stagger-tuning several stages, overcoupling two stages, or using swamping resistors across resonant circuits.

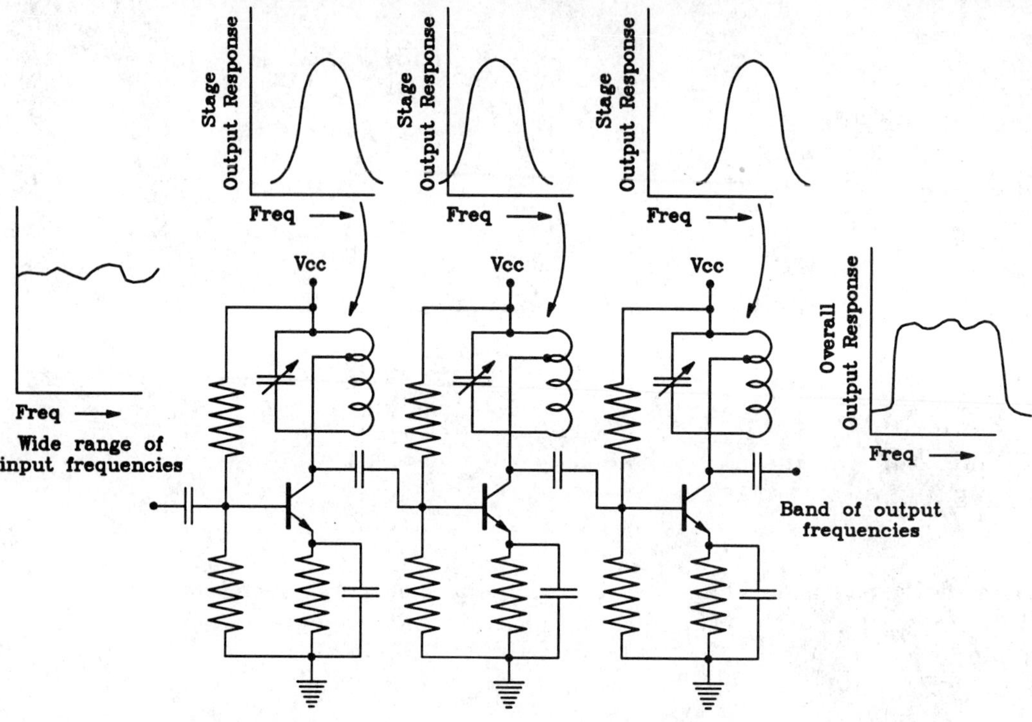

Figure 10–23 The effect of cascading several stagger-tuned stages is a broader overall frequency response curve than that of a single stage.

Stagger-Tuning

Stagger-tuning is the alignment of several stages to the desired center frequency as well as a frequency above and below. See Figure 10–23.

Overcoupling

A second method of broadening overall frequency response is to overcouple the interstage-coupling RF transformer in an intermediate-frequency amplifier. See Figure 10–24.

Swamping Resistor

The swamping resistor is often used to make the bandwidth of a single stage wider that it would be otherwise. Compare the output responses of Figure 10–25 to those of Figure 10–20.

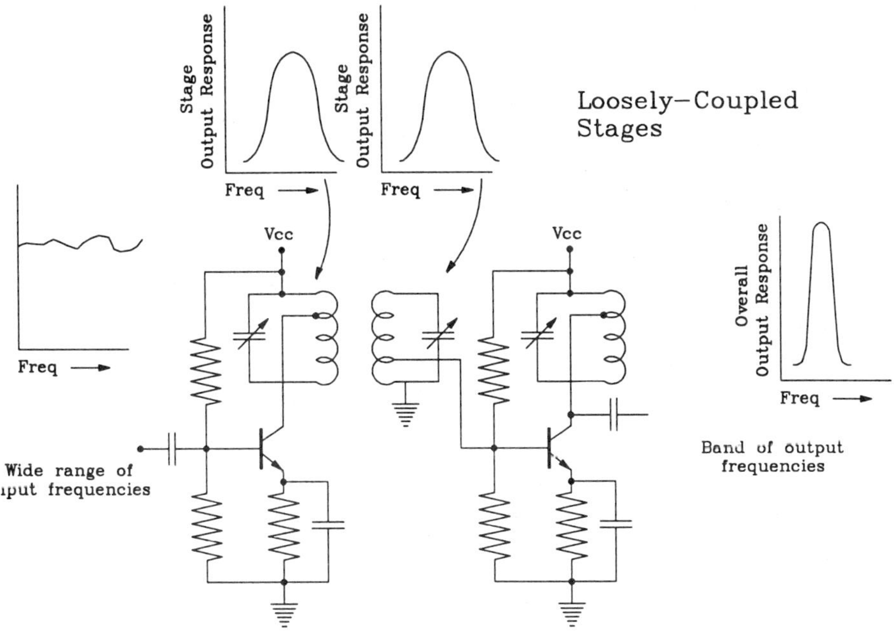

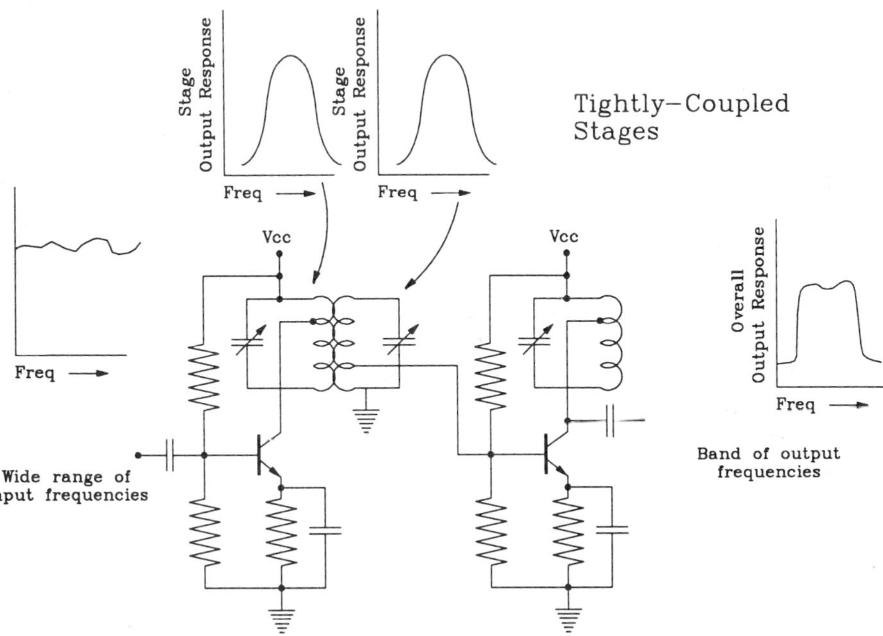

Figure 10–24 The effect on frequency response of using loose and tight coupling within the interstage transformer.

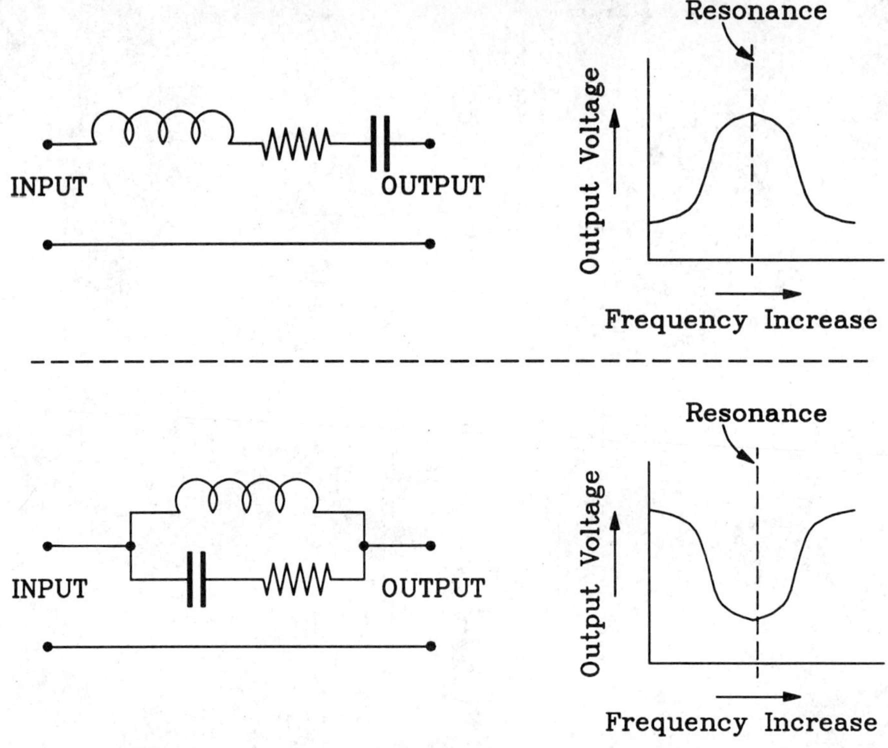

Figure 10–25 Adding resistance to an LC circuit broadens its response.

RESONANT CIRCUIT–RINGING

If an LC resonant circuit is excited by a pulse of current that lasts a very short time, the LC circuit will "ring." This is analogous to the striking of a bell with a mallet. Simply pushing on the bell with the mallet will not make it ring, but a short, hard rap will do the job. A short pulse (short in duration, as compared to the period of oscillation of the LC circuit) can be timed to occur at just the right intervals to repeatedly "kick" the LC circuit once each cycle, producing a constant sine wave. See Figure 10–26.

The arrival of only a single pulse will cause the circuit sine-wave amplitude to rapidly die out. The waveform thus produced is called a *damped oscillation.*

The Frequency Multiplier

Crystal oscillators are the modern means of producing very stable radio frequency oscillations. Crystals cannot be ground for direct use at VHF and higher frequencies because they would be too thin and fragile. Using the principle of resonant circuit–ringing (explained above), lower-frequency RF

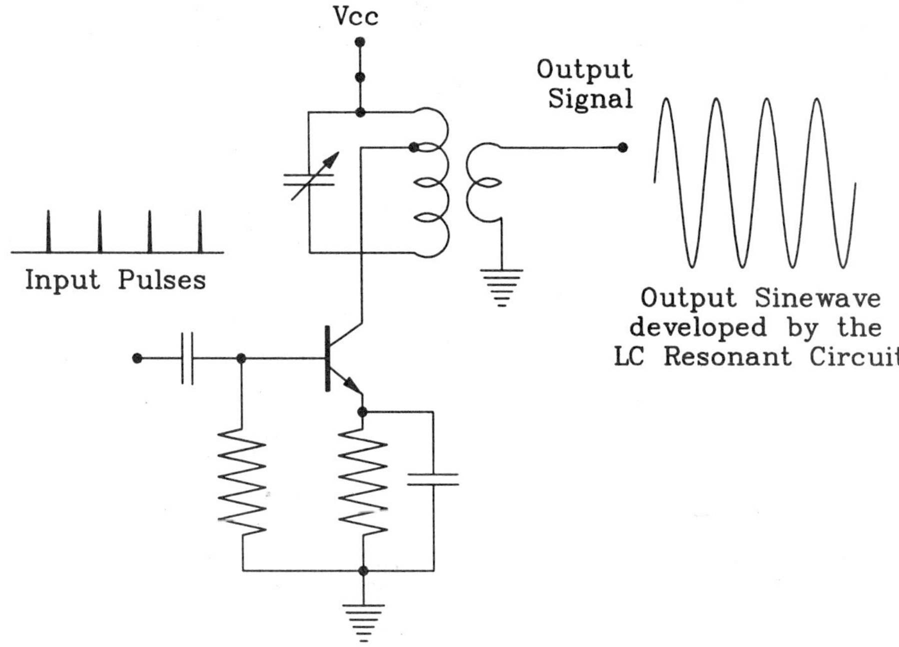

Figure 10–26 How timed pulses of energy into an LC circuit can produce a sine-wave output.

signals can be multiplied up to the desired radio frequencies. Frequency doublers and triplers are the most common multiplier stages. The input radio frequency signal to a Class C amplifier will produce pulses of current in the output circuit of the stage. If the output contains an LC circuit that is carefully tuned to an even multiple (usually ×2 or ×3) of the input frequency, the output frequency will be exactly that amount times the input frequency (in the usual case, double or triple). Several stages can be cascaded to produce a final frequency that is the *product* of the individual stage-multiplication factors. See Figure 10–27.

This process of multiplying radio frequencies is often used within very-high-frequency (VHF) and ultra-high-frequency (UHF) receivers and transmitters.

THE COAXIAL LINE AS A REACTIVE COMPONENT

A complete study of the coaxial line and its uses is subject enough for an entire book. In this volume, the topic will be treated only at a review level for orientation within the overall subject of inductance and capacitance as used at radio frequencies.

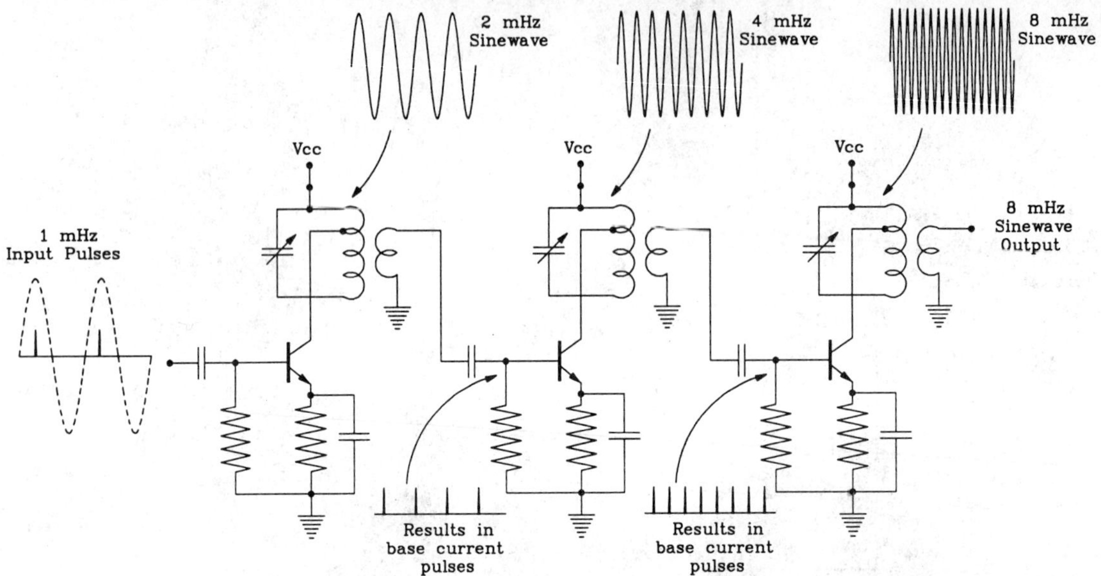

Figure 10–27 Simplified-frequency multiplier stages (doublers) and how they can be cascaded to produce an overall frequency multiplication from a low-frequency RF input signal.

The Terminated Coaxial Line

A coaxial line can best be analyzed as a series of inductances charging capacitors to ground, as shown in Figure 10–28.

Applying a DC voltage to the end of a coaxial cable will cause the first capacitor to begin to charge, but it does not charge instantly because of the series inductor. An instant later, the second capacitor will begin to charge through the second inductor. This process then continues, and the wave-

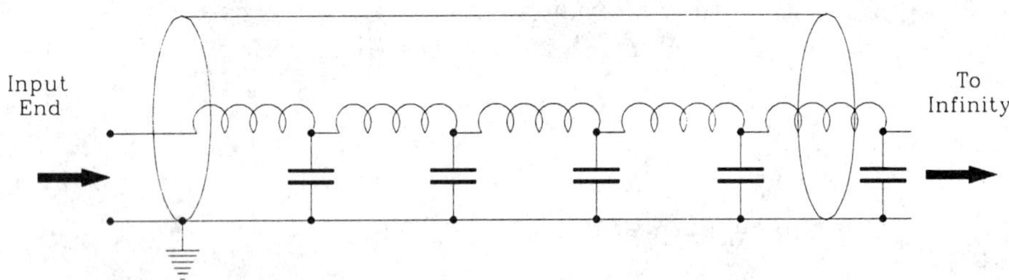

Figure 10–28 A coaxial line may be more easily understood if it is viewed as a series of series inductors charging successive capacitors to ground.

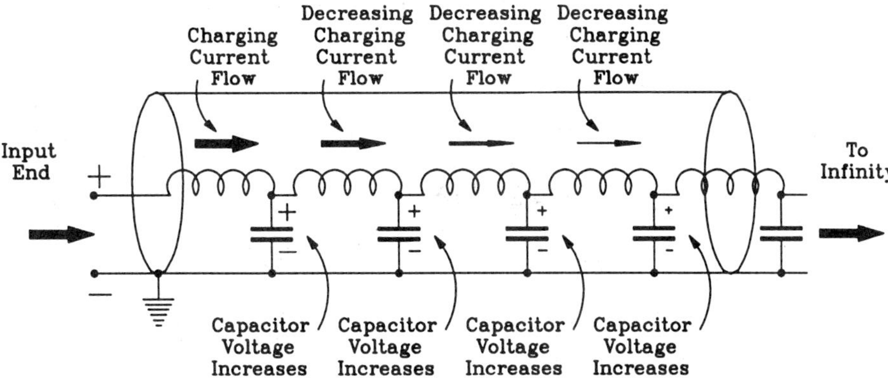

Figure 10–29 Application of a DC voltage to a coaxial cable and how the charging progresses down the cable's length.

front of charging progresses down the cable. The result is a current flow into the coaxial cable. See Figure 10–29.

If this coaxial line were infinitely long, there would be a continuous DC current into the cable under the influence of the applied voltage. Using these figures of voltage and current, we could calculate the value of a resistor that would act exactly like the coaxial cable. The value of this theoretical resistor is called its *characteristic impedance*. The value of impedance is determined by the diameter of the inner conductor and the diameter of the inside of the shield, along with, to a lesser extent, the dielectric material separating them. The most popular impedance for communications coaxial cables is 52 ohms. Other coaxial cable impedances are 75 and 93 ohms. These cables may be either small or large physically. The larger sizes are preferred for high-power applications and when efficiency (low loss) is important.

As long as the RF impedance at the load end of a coaxial cable is the same as that of the cable itself (under these conditions, the cable is said to be "properly matched"), there will be maximum transfer of power from the source to the load. This is the purpose of coaxial cables; transferring radio frequency energy from one point to another with minimal loss enroute.

Quarter- and Half-Wave Coaxial Lines

The full wavelength (in feet) of a radio frequency in free space is determined by the formula:

$$\frac{982}{F_{MHz}} = Wavelength_{Feet}$$

This formula can be used to calculate the approximate full wavelength of antennas. Half- and quarter-wavelength antennas may be calculated by using this formula and dividing the answer by 2 or 4, respectively.

Coaxial cable is used to carry radio frequencies from one end to the other, but the speed at which the wavefront travels within the cable is much less than it would be in free space. A typical *velocity of propagation* for 52-ohm coaxial cable is 0.68.

A piece of "coax," as it is often called, can show unusual properties when fed a radio frequency that is *improperly terminated* in its characteristic impedance. If the line is quarter-wavelength in length and the far end is an open circuit, the cable will appear as a short. This is caused by the wavefront reflecting off the open circuit at the far end and returning back along the coax toward the input end. When it returns, it meets a voltage that has had time to change to the opposite polarity, half a cycle later. The result is similar to connecting two cells together in a plus-to-minus order: the maximum current will flow in the circuit.

A half-wavelength piece of coax will repeat the far end. If the far end is open, the source voltage will match the reflections (plus-for-plus and minus-for-minus), resulting in negligible current flow into the cable. Each of these examples is shown in Figure 10–30.

Improperly terminated coaxial lines that are less than quarter-wavelength or somewhere between the exact quarter-wavelength multiples will appear to be either capacitively or inductively reactive. For this reason, *coaxial cables should always be terminated in their characteristic impedance unless there is a need for the reactive effect that will result.*

HELICAL RESONATORS

The helical resonator is a low-loss tuned circuit. Since the losses are low, the resonator is sharply tuned and highly selective. The helical resonator finds use as a first filter in VHF and UHF radio receivers, where it largely eliminates out-of-band signals and images. See Figures 10–31 and 10–32.

The helical resonator consists of a few turns of heavy wire inside a metallic enclosure. This inductance is tuned, by distributed capacitance, to the sides of the enclosure and to an adjustable capacitive disk at one end. Signals are coupled magnetically through ports between the enclosures. See Figure 10–33.

There are two ways to tune a series of helical resonators. One method is to simply adjust them for maximum signal for the center frequency of a narrow band of frequencies. Incoming signals outside this band will be greatly attenuated. The second method of tuning is to stagger-tune each of the stages so that there is an acceptable sensitivity across a wider band of frequencies. The method to be used in tuning resonators should be covered in the maintenance manual for the equipment under repair.

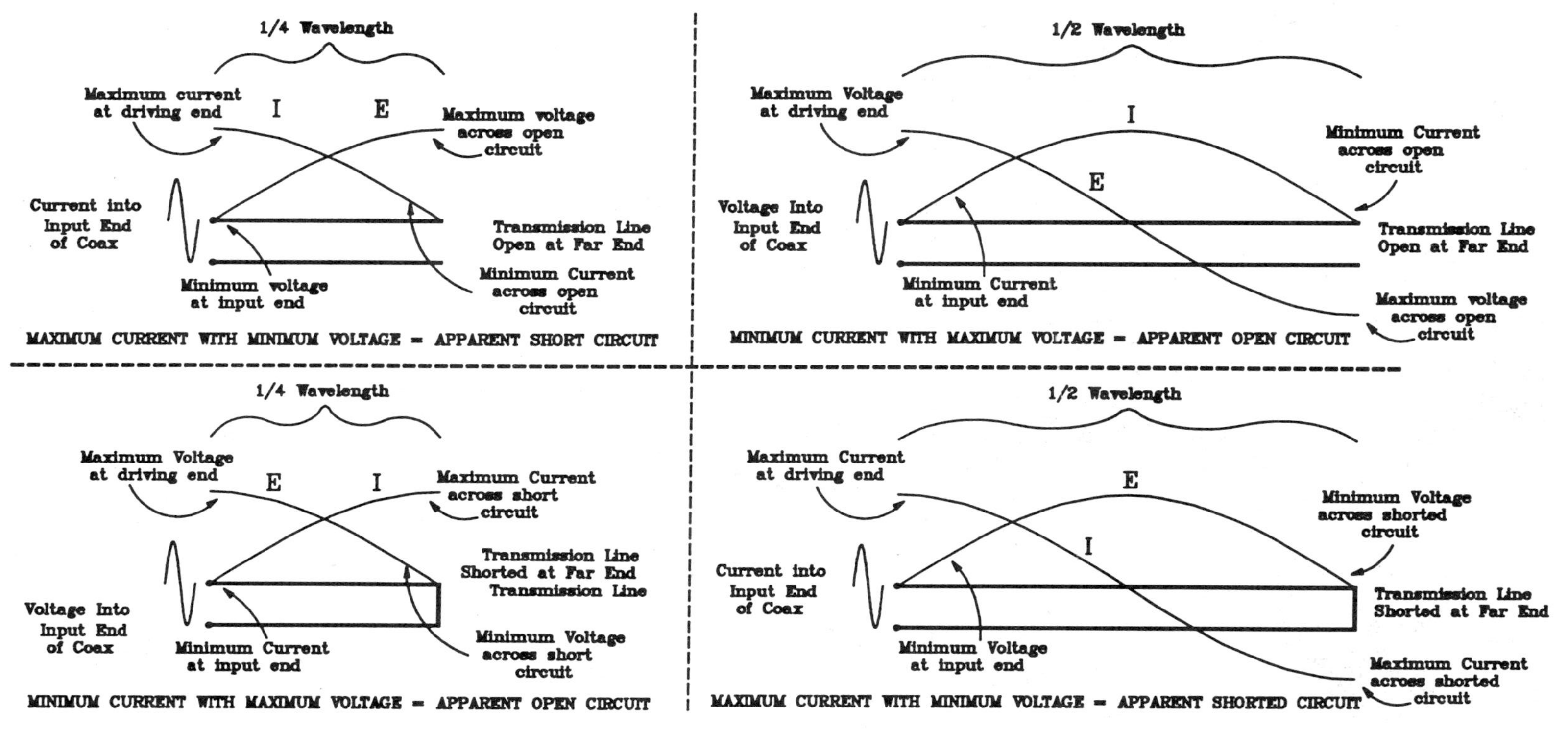

Figure 10–30 The results of exciting quarter- and half-wavelength sections of coaxial lines terminated in a short or an open.

Figure 10–31 The helical resonator is used as a front-end bandpass filter in VHF and UHF radio communication receivers.

TUNED CAVITIES

Operating VHF and UHF communications systems sometimes requires the use of adjacent transmitting and receiving frequencies on a single equipment site. Simultaneously transmitting and receiving on closely

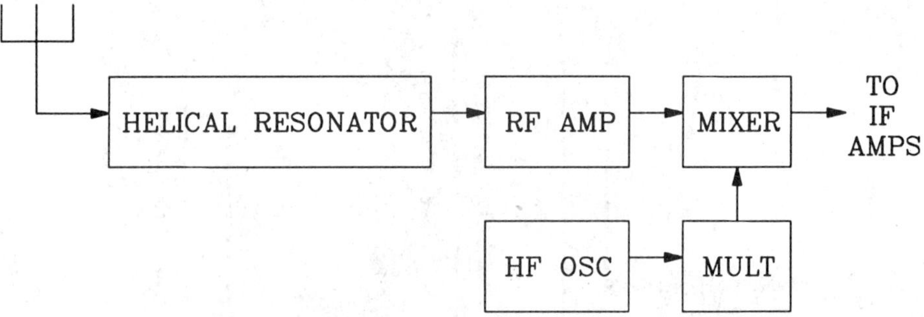

Figure 10–32 Block diagram of the location for a helical resonator in a typical VHF communications receiver.

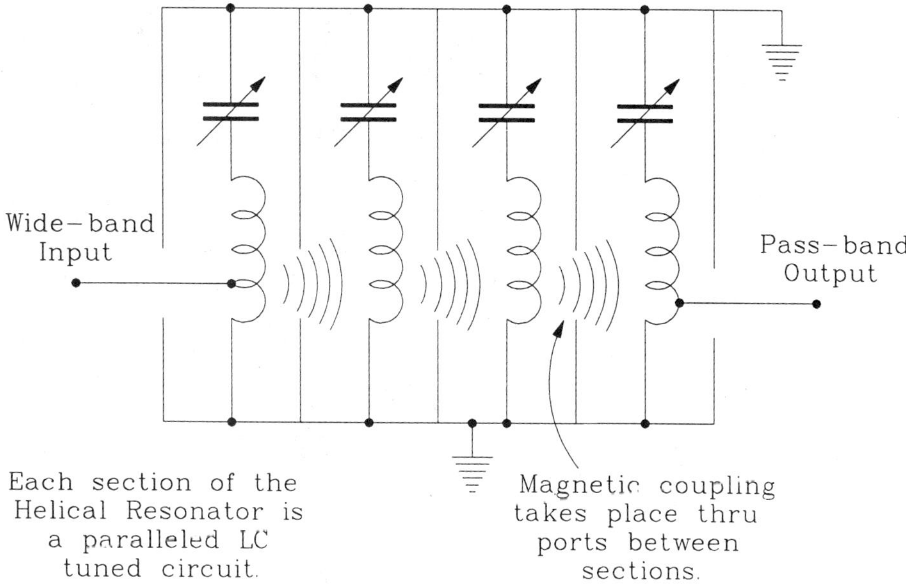
Wide-band Input
Pass-band Output
Each section of the Helical Resonator is a paralleled LC tuned circuit.
Magnetic coupling takes place thru ports between sections.

Figure 10–33 Side view of the operation of a helical resonator showing how signals are coupled into, between, and out of a series of resonators.

spaced radio frequencies in one location will lead to interference and desensitizing of the receivers. The tuned cavity is used to overcome these problems.

Tuned cavities are resonant to specific frequencies by virtue of their dimensions. The higher a frequency, the smaller the tuned cavity will be. Tuned cavities can be designed either to pass a specific frequency and reject all others or to reject a frequency and pass all others. See Figure 10–34.

The tuned cavity is a reliable component used at VHF and UHF frequencies. A servicing technician must remember that they are very critical to tune and thus should not be adjusted unless proper test equipment is available.

10.4 PASSIVE COMPONENTS IN PULSE AND SQUARE-WAVE CIRCUITS

Overview of Effects

This chapter has, to this point, discussed the behavior of resistors, capacitors, and inductors when operated by DC, low- and audio frequencies and by radio-frequency sine waves. Resistors used in combination with capaci-

Figure 10–34 These tuned cavities are used to prevent interference between transmitters and receivers installed at a single equipment site.

tors or inductors have completely different effects when operated with simple on-off waveforms or in circuits that use pulses. If the voltage applied to a resistor-and-capacitor combination changes, it will cause the capacitor to charge or discharge electrostatically. If the current applied to a resistor-and-inductor combination changes, the inductor will charge or discharge electromagnetically under the influence of the new current. The charging or discharging of the capacitor or inductor from a non-sinusoidal voltage source is expressed as a *time constant.*

The Time Constant

If a voltage is applied to a capacitor and a resistance, the time constant of the circuit is shown by:

TC = RC where R is in ohms and C is in farads.

The capacitor will continue to store voltage until the capacitor reaches the voltage of the source. It will hold that voltage until a discharge path is provided.

If a current is applied through an inductor and a resistance, the time constant of the circuit is shown by:

TC = L/R where R is in ohms and L is in henries.

The inductor will store energy in its magnetic field when the current flowing through it increases. The magnetic field will be stable when the current stabilizes. When the current decreases, the collapsing magnetic field will tend to keep the current flowing.

Time constants can be described as long, medium, or short. This relative evaluation of a time constant infers a comparison, which is based on the period of the applied waveform. If the period of a waveform is approximately equal to the time constant of a circuit, the time constant is considered medium. If the time constant is very short compared to the waveform period, it is considered short, and similarly, a time constant that is much longer than the applied waveform is termed a long time constant.

RESISTORS AND CAPACITORS

The Resistor-Capacitor Combination

A resistor and a capacitor form a natural timing circuit. It takes time for a capacitor to charge or discharge to a new voltage level through a resistor. Figure 10–35 shows a basic timing circuit to illustrate this point.

If the DC source voltage does not change, the capacitor will reach 63.2 percent of the source voltage in a length of time determined by the simple formula:

$$\text{Time Constant}_{\text{Secs}} = \text{Resistance}_{\text{ohms}} \times \text{Capacitance}_{\text{farads}}$$

or

$$TC = RC$$

Thus, the capacitor of Figure 10–35 will reach 6.32 volts of charge in:

$$10{,}000 \times .0001 = 1 \text{ second}$$

After charging to 63.2 percent of the source voltage, the next second of time will see the voltage rise to an additional 63.2 percent of the remaining 3.7 volts left, or 8.65 volts of capacitor charge. The third second will take

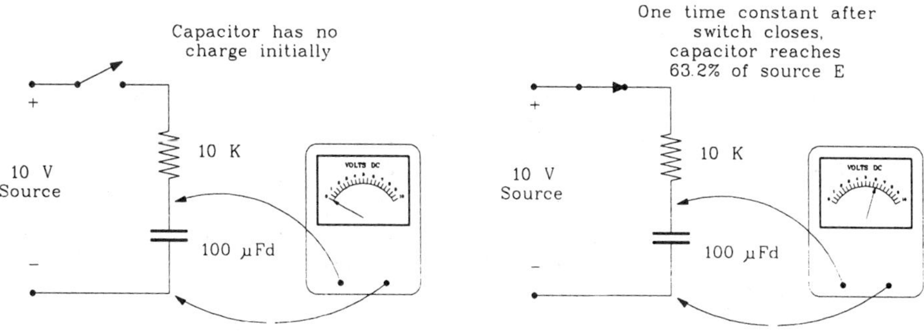

Figure 10–35 Basic RC timing circuit.

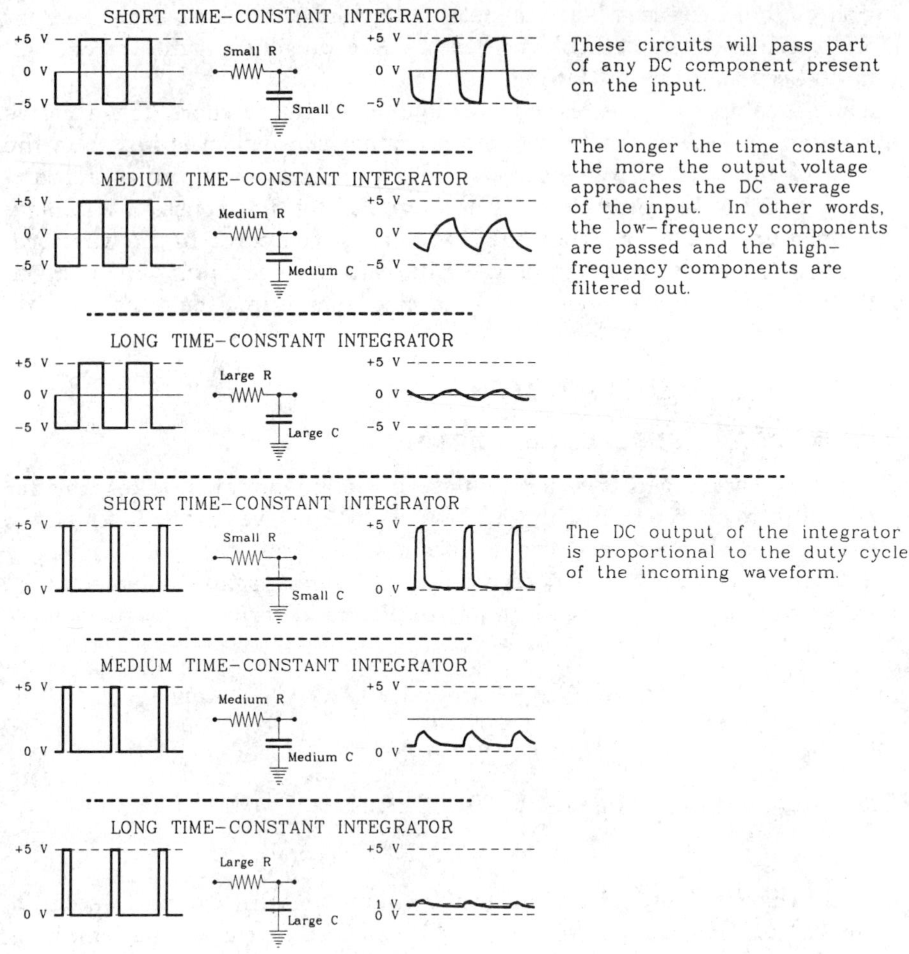
SHORT TIME–CONSTANT INTEGRATOR
+5 V
0 V
-5 V
Small R
Small C
These circuits will pass part of any DC component present on the input.
MEDIUM TIME–CONSTANT INTEGRATOR
Medium R
Medium C
The longer the time constant, the more the output voltage approaches the DC average of the input. In other words, the low–frequency components are passed and the high–frequency components are filtered out.
LONG TIME–CONSTANT INTEGRATOR
Large R
Large C
SHORT TIME–CONSTANT INTEGRATOR
The DC output of the integrator is proportional to the duty cycle of the incoming waveform.
MEDIUM TIME–CONSTANT INTEGRATOR
LONG TIME–CONSTANT INTEGRATOR
1 V

Figure 10–36 RC integrator circuits.

the capacitor to a charge of 9.5-V. After five time-constant intervals, the capacitor is considered to have achieved full charge.

To examine how the time constant relates to the period of the incoming signal, consider the circuit of Figure 10–36.

With this circuit, which is sometimes called an *integrator*, the output waveform increasingly approaches the average value of the incoming waveform as the time constant increases. Averaging waveforms is a principal use for this circuit. Note also that the output circuit will retain any DC signal present in the input signal and superimpose the average value of the AC signal on it.

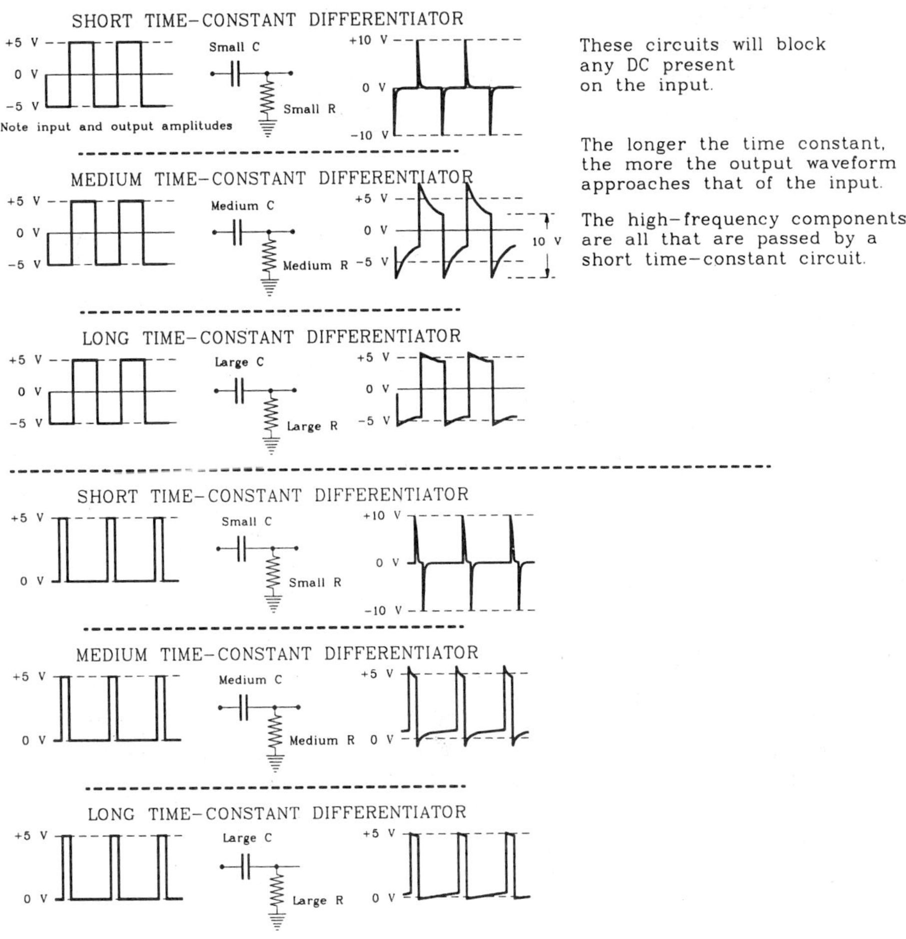

Figure 10–37 RC differentiator circuits.

Now consider the effect of the reversing the position of the components and the effect of time constant on the output waveform. See Figure 10–37.

The technical name for this capacitor-resistor combination, when used in pulse applications, is a *differentiator*. Notice that as the time constant becomes *shorter,* rapid changes come through the circuit, but the incoming DC levels and low frequencies do not. The more rapidly the input voltage changes, the higher the voltage output of the stage. A major use for this circuit is to make voltage spikes from square waves. Note that this circuit also blocks any DC present on the input from appearing in the output signal.

As the time constant becomes shorter compared to the period of the incoming signal, notice also that the capacitor has more time to reach a full charge. Because this capacitor charge adds to the voltage of a suddenly reversing input, the output voltage from the differentiator results in output pulses that momentarily may peak at up to *twice the maximum input voltage.*

Capacitive Energy Storage Circuits

A large-value capacitor can be charged over a relatively long period of time under the influence of a high-voltage charging source, and then suddenly discharged to produce a very high current pulse. The high voltage and high current flow during the discharge can be used to produce high-energy pulses for special applications. Photographic flash guns use this principle, for instance.

An electromagnet can be made to produce an extremely powerful magnetic pulse for a brief time by discharging a capacitor through a coil.

By controlling the capacitor-discharging current with an inductor, a high-energy, flat-topped pulse can be produced. A radar modulator is an example of a circuit that charges several capacitors over time and then discharges them into a load for a high-energy pulse. See Figure 10–38.

RESISTORS AND INDUCTORS

A resistor and an inductor also form a natural timing circuit. Note that it takes time for an inductor to build up or decay a magnetic field to a new level through a resistor. Figure 10–39 shows a basic timing circuit to illustrate this point.

From the instant the switch is closed, the inductor will reach 63.2 percent of the maximum magnetic field strength in accordance with another simple relationship:

$$\text{Time Constant}_{\text{Secs}} = \frac{\text{Inductance}_{\text{Henries}}}{\text{Resistance}_{\text{ohms}}}$$

Thus, the inductor of Figure 10–39 will reach its first time constant in:

$$\frac{1}{1} = 1 \text{ Second}$$

After one second, the inductor will have reached 63.2 percent of the full field strength possible with the voltage applied. This process repeats until after five time constants, at which point the inductor is considered to be fully magnetized. The current at that time is the maximum that the resistance of the circuit will allow.

Note that *as the resistance decreases, the time* to reach full magnetization *increases.* In other words, if the resistor of Figure 10–39 were changed to a 0.1-ohm resistor instead of a 1-ohm component, the inductor would take 10 seconds to reach full magnetization. This is the opposite effect of changing the resistor in a resistor-capacitor combination.

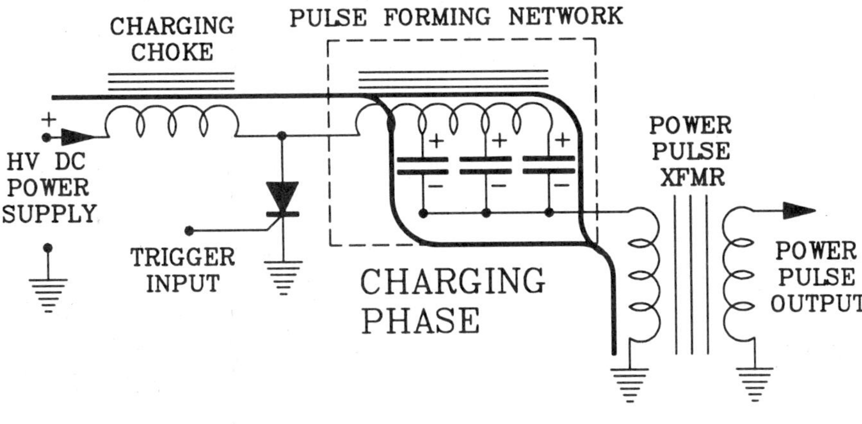

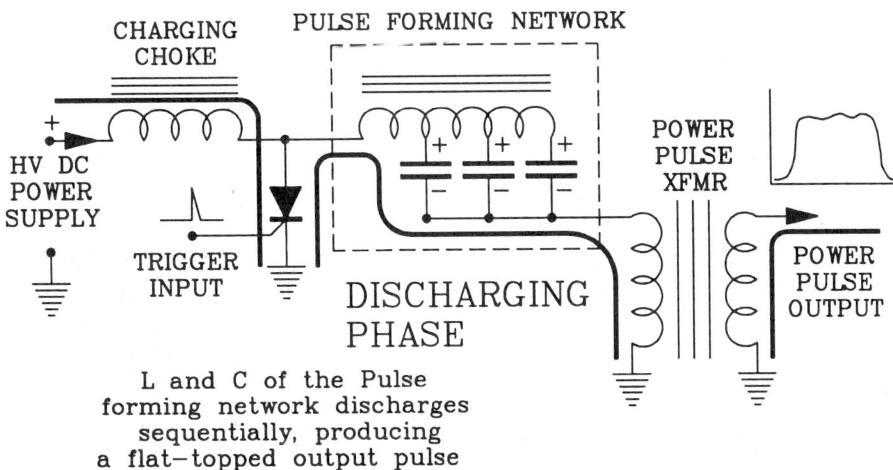

Figure 10–38 Simplified schematic of a radar pulse modulator.

To examine how the time constant of an RL circuit relates to the period of the incoming signal, see Figure 10–40.

With this circuit, which is also called an *integrator,* the output waveform increasingly resembles the average value of the incoming waveform as the time constant decreases. Averaging waveforms is a common use for this circuit. Note that the relative positions of the inductance (L) and resistance (R) are reversed from those of the capacitor-and-resistor integrator. This circuit will pass along any DC present in the input signal to the output waveform due to the low DC resistance of the inductor winding. In addition, any changes in current flow through the inductor will be opposed by the inductance. Thus, this circuit is also commonly used to smooth out DC power sources, such as the pulsating output of an AC rectifier.

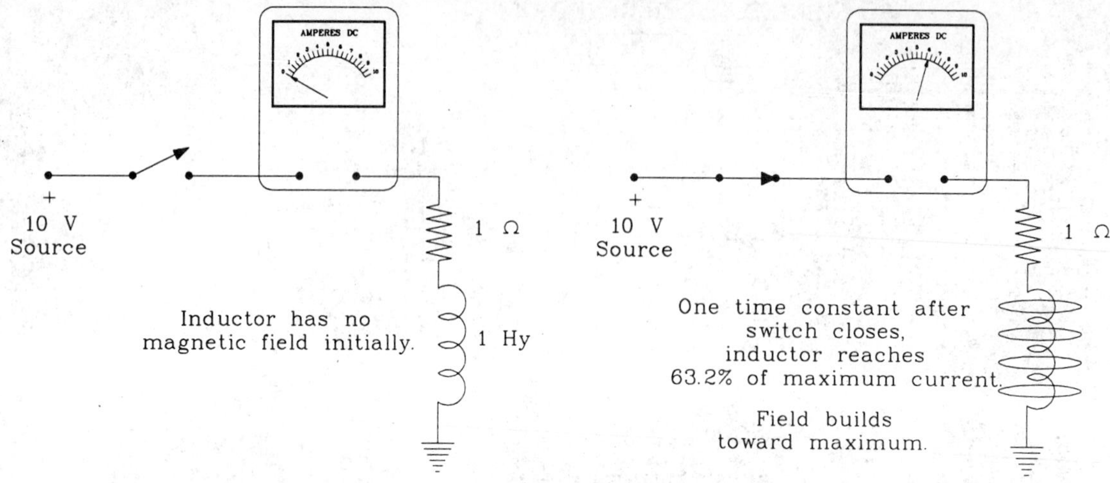

Figure 10–39 Basic LR timing circuit.

Now consider the effect of reversing the positions of the R and L components from the last example and also the effect of the time constant on the output waveform. See Figure 10–41.

This inductor-and-resistor combination is also called a *differentiator.* Notice that *as the time constant decreases,* the more rapid changes can get through the circuit but the incoming DC levels and low frequencies cannot. A major use for this circuit is to make spikes out of square waves. Note also that any DC present in the input signal will be shorted to ground by the relatively low resistance of the inductor winding. As the time constant decreases, the inductor has time to reach full magnetic field strength. Because the inductor opposes any change in current flow through itself, the output from the differentiator circuit results in output voltage pulses that momentarily may have up to *twice the maximum input voltage.*

Inductive-Energy Storage Circuits

The inductor, like the capacitor, can also be used to store energy. When an increasing amount of current is passed through an inductor over a period of time, energy is stored in the magnetic field. The collapse of this field can then be used to produce a high-voltage pulse into a load.

Besides the filtering action of an inductor (as explained earlier in this chapter), this magnetic energy can also be used for one of two special purposes. One typical application is producing a very-high-voltage pulse. This is the principle of operation of the flyback transformer which is used in power supplies for cathode-ray tubes and is the means of producing the high voltage for automobile spark plugs. The second common use is to

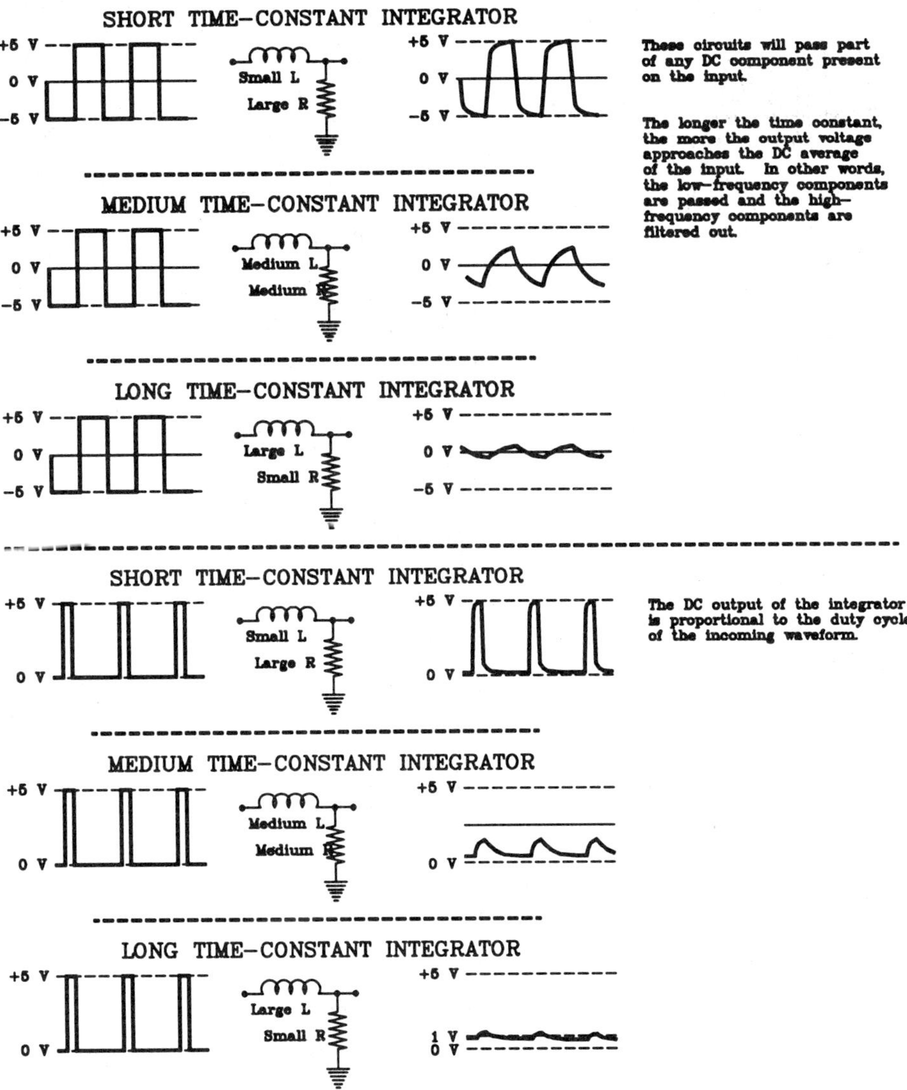
SHORT TIME–CONSTANT INTEGRATOR
+5 V
0 V
-5 V
Small L
Large R
These circuits will pass part of any DC component present on the input.
The longer the time constant, the more the output voltage approaches the DC average of the input. In other words, the low-frequency components are passed and the high-frequency components are filtered out.
MEDIUM TIME–CONSTANT INTEGRATOR
Medium L
Medium R
LONG TIME–CONSTANT INTEGRATOR
Large L
Small R
SHORT TIME–CONSTANT INTEGRATOR
The DC output of the integrator is proportional to the duty cycle of the incoming waveform.
MEDIUM TIME–CONSTANT INTEGRATOR
LONG TIME–CONSTANT INTEGRATOR
1 V

Figure 10–40 L and R integrator circuits. Compare to Figure 10–36.

produce a voltage pulse opposite to the polarity that originally produced the magnetism. This principle (as explained in Chapter 7) is used in the polarity-inverting switching regulator.

PULSE TRANSFORMERS

Pulse transformers are small transformers, usually with an iron or ferrite core. They are not required to pass any appreciable power from one

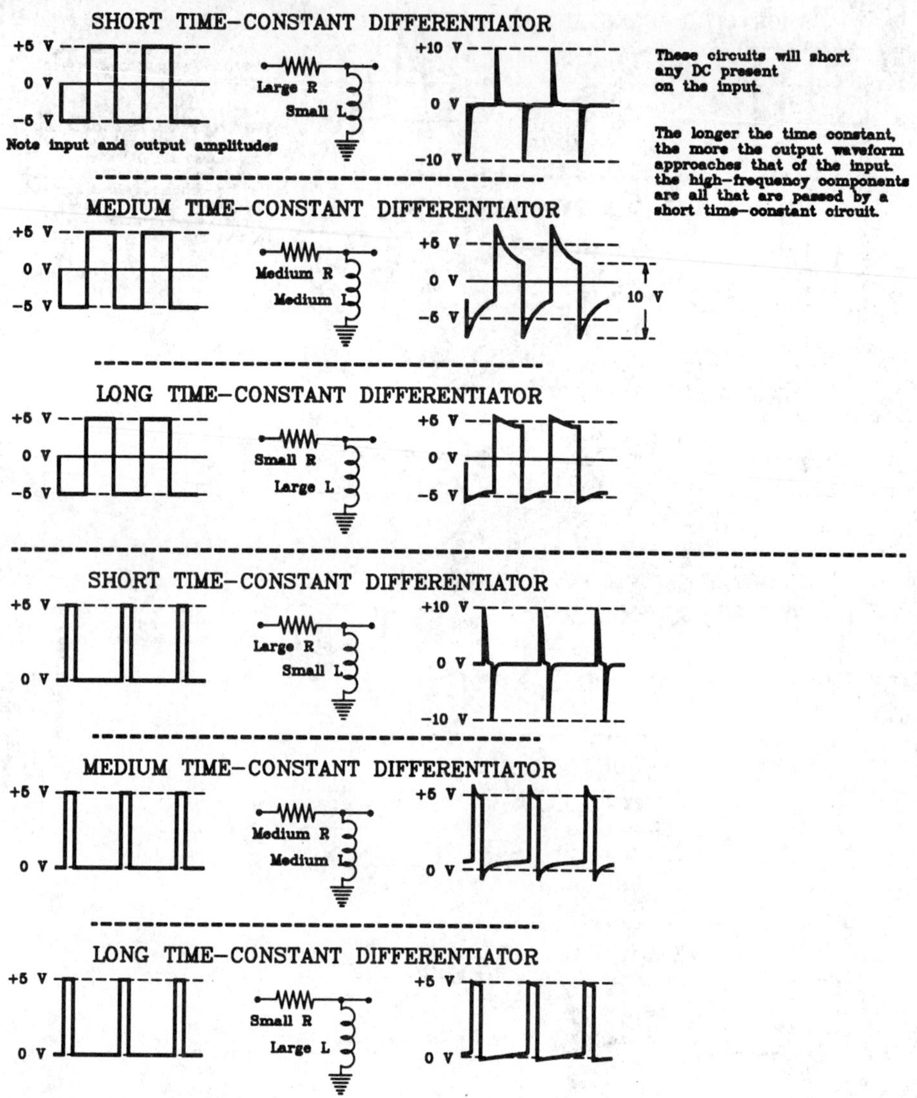

Figure 10–41 An L and R differentiator. Compare with Figure 10–37.

winding to another, which explains their small size. There are three purposes that a pulse transformer may accomplish.

1. It may provide isolation between two or more circuits, while still passing a timing pulse between them.
2. It can convert a high-current, low-impedance pulse to one with high impedance and high voltage, or vice versa.
3. A pulse transformer can be used to invert the polarity of a pulse,

making a negative pulse from a positive one or going in the opposite direction.

A very common use for a pulse transformer is to pass a pulse from one circuit to another circuit with a different common or ground point, while in the process providing isolation between the two common points. See Figure 14–29. The transformer may have a step-up or step-down ratio, depending on the application.

Pulse transformers can be operated with a current that is high enough to saturate their cores. This is acceptable, since a circuit designed for this operation will have a current-limiting feature provided within the circuit. Only the timing of the pulse from the transformer is of importance in pulse circuits, provided the pulse is of sufficient amplitude to trigger the next stage. These transformers are covered in more detail in Chapter 14.

The Ignition Coil

An automobile ignition coil is an excellent example of the use of a collapsing magnetic field to produce a very high voltage. The name is a misuse of the electronic term *coil,* since it is actually a transformer having two windings. One winding is meant to carry a large current that builds up the magnetic field around the transformer core. This current is controlled by the "points" (actually just a switch). When it is closed, the magnetic field builds up to maximum strength. When the switch opens, the magnetic field collapses, producing about 20,000 volts to fire the spark plugs. The schematic for a simple ignition system is shown in Figure 10–42.

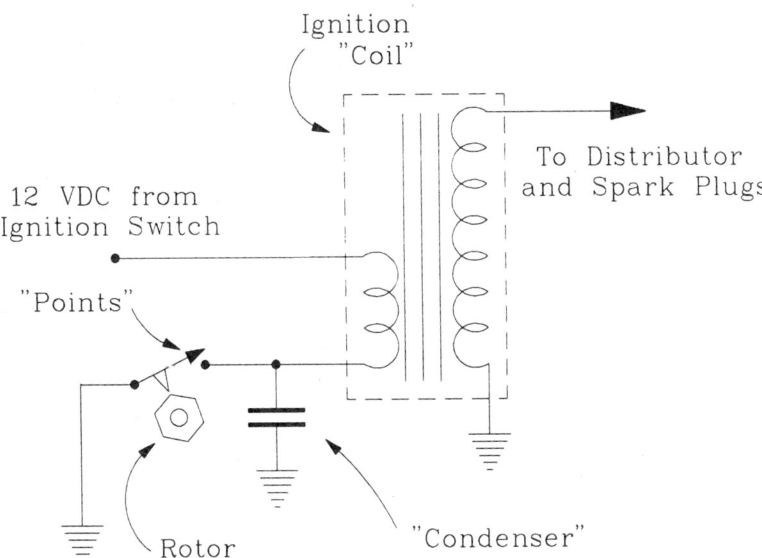

Figure 10–42 Circuit of a simple ignition system for a six-cylinder engine.

The Flyback Transformer

The flyback transformer is used to build up a magnetic field within its core when a power transistor passes current through its primary winding. The current is then abruptly cut off and the collapsing magnetic field is transformed to several other voltages. One of these windings has many turns in order to produce a much higher voltage. This voltage is rectified and used to supply thousands of volts for the CRT high-voltage anode. This voltage can be as high as 26,000 volts for a large television CRT. See Figure 10–43.

Very high voltages are produced by the collapsing field. Since an oscilloscope probe can commonly tolerate only a maximum voltage input of 500 volts without damage, flyback circuits should not be investigated with an oscilloscope. If the high voltage must be tested, a special meter and/or probe should be used that is designed to measure these voltages. See Figure 10–44.

Flyback Failure Patterns

Flyback transformers and associated circuitry are a common cause of cathode-ray-tube equipment failure. This circuit operates with relatively

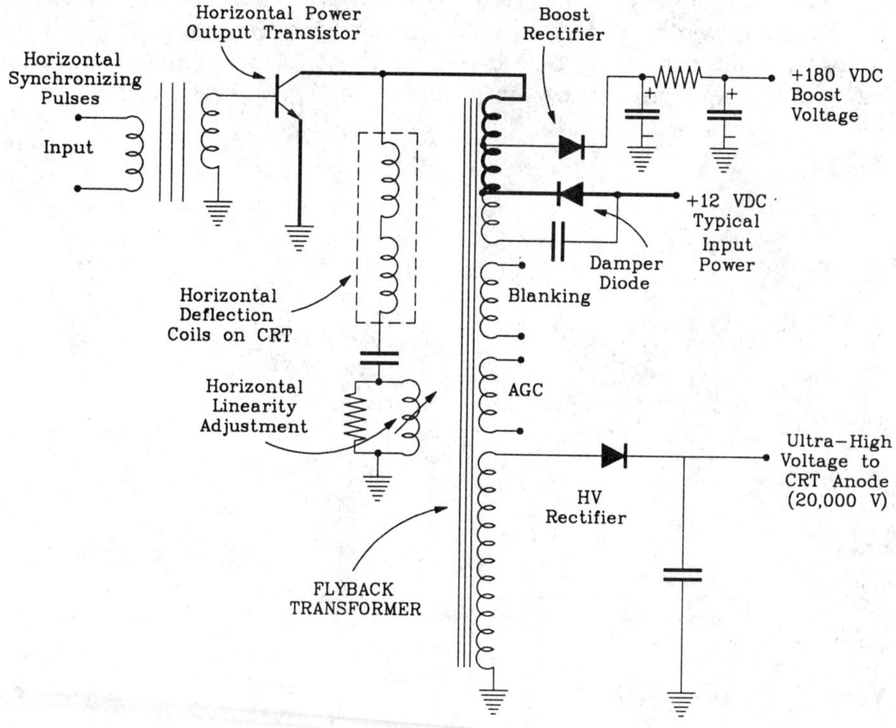

Figure 10–43 Simplified cathode-ray-tube horizontal-output circuitry.

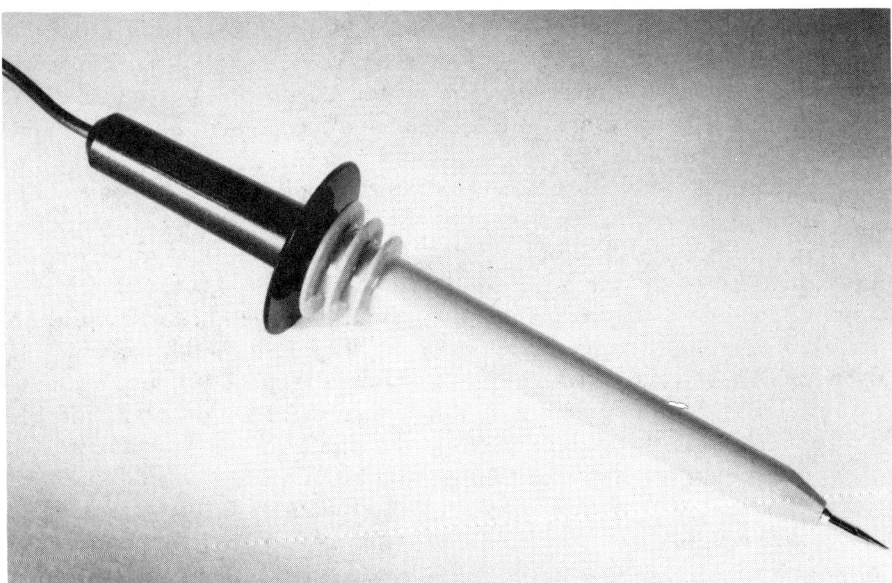

Figure 10–44 Probe for measuring the very high DC voltages encountered in flyback transformer circuits. (Reprinted with pemission from the John Fluke Mfg. Co., Inc.)

high currents and power levels on the primary side and with very high voltages on the secondary side. Both high-power and high-voltage circuits are prone to failure, due to heat, on the one hand, and arc-over and shorting on the other. When possible, it is best to change the entire module as a first troubleshooting method. Lacking this as an option, the transistor supplying the flyback transformer is the first component to suspect.

There may or may not be a fuse feeding current to this stage. If one is present, it should be checked first, of course. When a flyback transformer draws so much current that the fuse blows, the power transistor feeding it is likely to be shorted.

Arcing can sometimes be identified by its sound. A hissing or buzzing noise can often be tracked to its source to find where the high voltage is shorting to chassis ground. Cleaning or repair is the usual cure for this kind of problem.

10.5 THE MATTER OF DOMINANCE AND FINE ADJUSTMENT

Resistors and capacitors are often connected in circuits in parallel or series configurations. Equal-value resistors are sometimes operated in this way to increase the power dissipation of the circuit rather than using a single resistor of larger physical size. Capacitors are connected in parallel for a similar reason: to obtain more capacitance without a large capacitor. However, when these components are connected in series or parallel and the values differ greatly, one of the components will have a greater effect in the circuit than the other.

The best way to explain this concept is to consider unequal resistors in series and how they their combination will influence a circuit. If two potentiometers of, for instance, 1,000 Ω and 100 Ω, are connected in series, the total resistance of the circuit is 1,100 Ω. Now, if the 1,000 Ω resistor is adjusted to increase 10 percent in value, the total resistance will change to 1,200 Ω. The overall change in resistance of the circuit is 9.2 percent.

Now consider a case in which only the 100 Ω resistor is changed, again by 10 percent. If the two pots (potentiometers) were both linear, this percentage change would require turning the shaft the same amount. The lower-value potentiometer will change to a value of 110 Ω, and the total circuit resistance will change from the initial value of 1,100 Ω to 1,110 Ω. The overall resistance will change to just slightly less than 1.0 percent. See Figure 10–45.

We can summarize this concept by stating that *when components are*

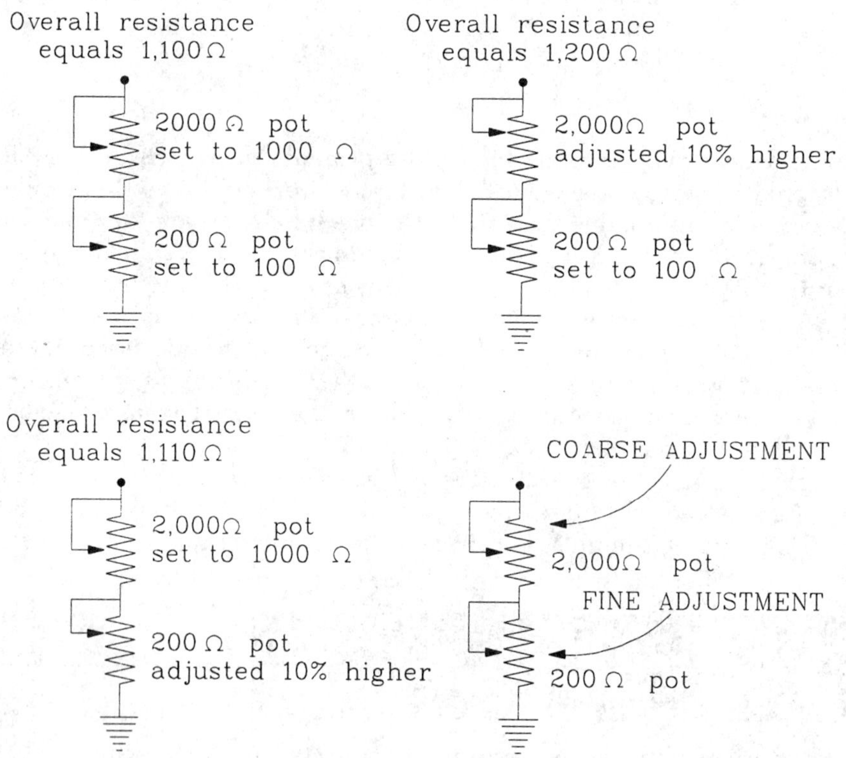

Figure 10–45 Two resistors in series offer the possibility of using both coarse and vernier control by varying one of the resistors.

connected in series, the larger value (resistance or reactance) will be dominant (coarse control) and the smaller will be a final precise adjustment, called a vernier control. This principle is sometimes used to obtain a precise resistance. If one needs a resistor of exactly 1,010.0 ohms, for instance, a resistor of about 1,000 ohms can be selected for the dominant resistance, and then small resistors of about 10 ohms can be individually selected and connected in series to get the precise overall value that is desired.

Precision circuits sometimes take advantage of dominance when it is necessary to adjust precisely to a final overall resistance value. A large value resistor of slightly less than the required resistance is used with an adjustable potentiometer of lesser value placed in series. Then, the potentiometer is adjusted for the final circuit value required. A bit of thought will show that *adjusting the smaller value pot in series with a large, fixed resistance is much less critical in adjusting to an exact value than it would be when using a single potentiometer for the entire resistance.* End-to-end manual adjustment of the small, series potentiometer will change the overall resistance of the circuit by 5 percent or less in a practical circuit, since the higher resistance in series with it is dominant. See Figure 10–46.

Components can also be paralleled to obtain precise overall values. Now let us consider what happens when resistors are connected in parallel. Assume a resistor of 1,000 Ω and one of 100 Ω are connected in parallel. The total resistance of the circuit would be very close to 91 Ω. Changing the value of the 1,000 Ω resistor upward by 10 percent will have very little effect, only about a 1 percent change in the overall resistance of the circuit. This also results in a trimming or vernier effect. Increasing the value of the 100 Ω resistor by 10 percent, however,

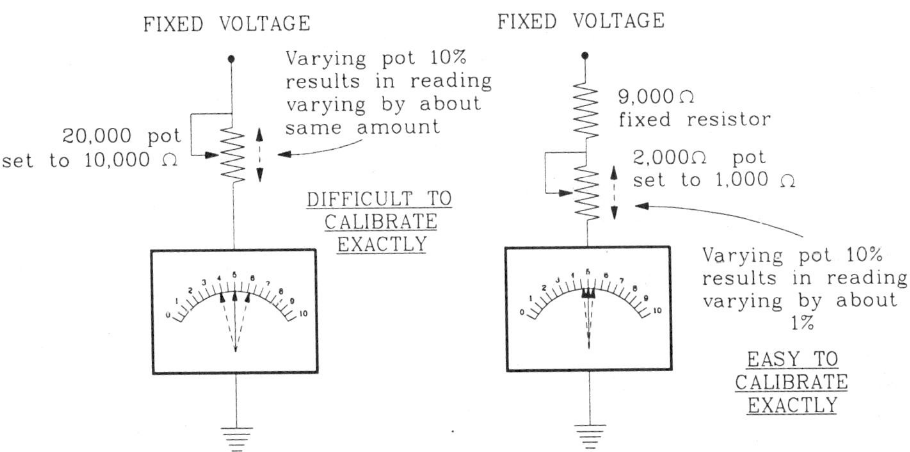

Figure 10–46 Using the principle of series vernier control, meter calibration is less critical to adjust.

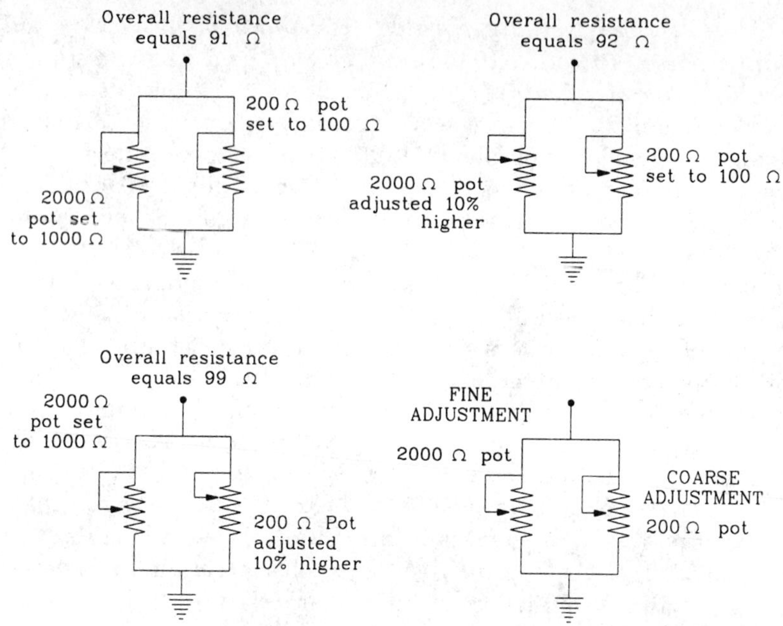

Figure 10–47 Vernier control can also be produced by connecting components in parallel.

will have a large effect, changing the total resistance about 10 percent. See Figure 10–47.

From the above discussion, we can see that *when connected in parallel, the resistor of lower resistance value will be dominant, making the larger resistance a fine adjustment, or vernier.* This principle could be used to obtain a precise adjustment in a circuit, with a resistor of slightly too much resistance being paralleled by another resistor of high value. Changing the value of the higher resistance provides a fine adjustment for calibration of the total resistance.

Capacitors are often used in series or parallel for tuning purposes in radio frequency transmitters. Remember that a smaller capacitance has a higher reactance value at a given frequency of operation. Variable capacitors of high capacitance values, which are capable of high voltage operation, are also difficult and expensive to manufacture. It is much cheaper to use a fixed capacitor of high, nearly sufficient capacitance and voltage capability, and then use a smaller, high-voltage variable capacitor in parallel with it to get the exact final capacitance required. See Figure 10–48.

Besides being less expensive, the smaller variable capacitor has less critical adjustment when tuning (a vernier control), since the large fixed capacitor is dominant in the parallel circuit.

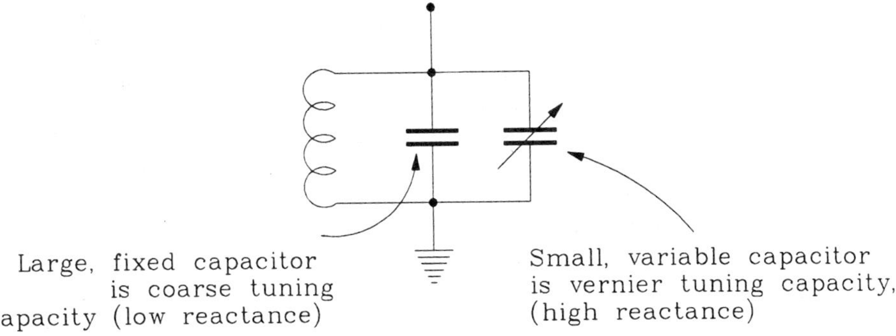
LC TUNED CIRCUIT
WITH TUNING VERNIER
Large, fixed capacitor
is coarse tuning
capacity (low reactance)
Small, variable capacitor
is vernier tuning capacity,
(high reactance)

Figure 10–48 Tuned circuits used at low frequencies often use paralleled capacitors for vernier tuning.

CHAPTER SUMMARY

- Resistors in DC circuits act predictably in accordance with Ohm's law.
- Capacitors in DC applications should be open circuits and inductors should be nearly zero ohms (a short).
- Low-frequency sinusoidal (AC) circuits use the properties of capacitive and inductive reactance.
- The reactances of these circuits are sometimes used in conjunction with resistances to produce a composite property called *impedance*.
- Radio frequencies use capacitive and inductive reactances together to produce the effect called *resonance*.
- Resonance is used to select or deselect specific frequencies or bands of frequencies.
- Applying pulses or square waves to passive components makes it necessary to apply the time constant of the combination, together with the applied waveform period, to determine the expected output waveform.
- Capacitors can be used to store voltage for high-current pulses.
- Inductors can be used to store magnetic energy for the production of high-voltage pulses.
- Pulse transformers provide isolation, impedance matching, pulse-polarity reversal, or combinations of these effects.
- The flyback transformer converts a collapsing magnetic field to several high-voltage pulses which can then be rectified to become high-voltage sources.

- Flyback circuits produce very high voltages that require a special probe to measure them.
- Components such as resistors or capacitors are sometimes used in series or parallel combinations with one of them variable in order to obtain a vernier or fine-adjustment capability that is easy to adjust to precise criteria.

REVIEW QUESTIONS

1. Resistors act predictably in DC circuits according to _______ law.
2. Why are some resistors physically much larger than others?
3. In a DC circuit, a capacitor should "look like" a/an _______.
4. What does a bypass capacitor do?
5. What does an isolating capacitor do?
6. What is the quick check to see if a coupling capacitor is shorted?
7. What is a frequent result of a capacitor shorting?
8. DC voltages and currents will react to an inductor as a/an _______.
9. What is fish paper and where is it used?
10. Where is the winding of a transformer or relay coil most likely to open?
11. What limits the current flow through a solenoid or relay coil when operated on DC?
12. The higher an applied frequency, the more a capacitor looks like a/an _______.
13. What is the generally accepted ratio between the reactance of a bypass or coupling capacitor and the resistance associated with it?
14. What prevents an electrolytic capacitor from being an effective capacitor at high frequencies?
15. What can be done to compensate for the problem in question 14?
16. What is the most common failure of a capacitor?
17. When inductors and capacitors are used with resistors on sine waves, the voltage across the components is not in step. This is called _______ _______.
18. The lower the applied frequency, the more an inductor looks like a/an _______.
19. What does an autotransformer *not* provide that a multiple winding transformer does?
20. As the magnetic field of an unloaded transformer increases and cuts the windings of the primary, the inductance produces a/an _______ which limits current flow.
21. When transformers are used at audio frequencies, they are often referred to as _______ matching devices.
22. What is the output impedance of an audio transformer having 1,000 turns on the primary and 200 turns on the secondary, if it is fed with a 600–ohm line?

23. Unintended capacitance within an actual circuit is often called _______ capacitance.
24. RF inductors used at high frequencies are often made of heavy wire to reduce the _______ effect.
25. A circuit trace that is an appreciable part of a _______ wavelength can cause impedance-matching problems.
26. A paralleled LC circuit placed in parallel with (across) an input signal will cause a/an _______ (*increase* or *decrease*) of signal amplitude in the output when *off* the resonant frequency. (Hint: Draw out the circuit.)
27. If an inductor alone is used in the collector circuit of an audio or RF amplifier, this is called _______ coupling.
28. The three methods of widening the bandwidth of an LC circuit or string of amplifiers are: (a) Using a _______ resistor, (b) _______ tuning a series of amplifiers, or (c) use of an _______ interstage transformer.
29. Pulses of collector current applied to the base of a transistor are smoothed out to a sine-wave form by the _______ and the _______ in the collector circuit.
30. What frequency input is necessary to a frequency tripler to produce 30 MHz in the output circuit?
31. Under normal circumstances, it is desirable to terminate a coaxial cable in its _______ _______ in order to obtain maximum _______ transfer from source to load.
32. A shorted quarter-coaxial line will look like it is a/an _______ at the generator end.
33. A helical resonator is used as a _______ _______ in a VHF receiver.
34. When square waves are used on resistors and capacitors or inductors, the _______ constant becomes of primary important.
35. The integrator circuit will convert an AC waveform into its _______ DC voltage.
36. What is the time constant of a 10–μFd capacitor when used with a 10-K resistor?
37. If the resistance in an LR time constant is reduced to half, the time constant will _______ (*increase* or *decrease*).
38. A switching regulator is an example of an _______ energy storage circuit.
39. Give the three reasons for using a pulse transformer.
40. Name two common examples in which the collapse of a magnetic field is used to produce extremely high voltages.
41. What is the most likely component to cause the failure of a flyback transformer circuit?

Troubleshooting Discrete Semiconductor Circuits

11

CHAPTER OBJECTIVES

Troubleshooting techniques at the component level are usually centered around the active components in the circuitry; the diodes, transistors, and FETs. Understanding the normal operation of these discrete components will enable the technician to quickly and efficiently troubleshoot circuitry by noting differences between the normal and actual operation of the circuits in which they are installed. This chapter will acquaint the technician with the most commonly used active components and how they work in real-world circuits. At its conclusion, the student will be able to:

- Understand the three basic diode circuits according to the percentage of time during which the diode conducts.
- Be familiar with the bipolar amplifier in circuits using the three classes of operation, A, B, and C.
- Know the troubleshooting tips appropriate to the three classes of operation.
- Identify the three circuit configurations for an amplifer, common base, emitter, or collector (gate, source, or drain, respectively, for an FET.)

- Identify the special biasing circuit for a junction field effect transistor (JFET) and describe how it works.
- Identify and troubleshoot insulated-gate field effect transistor (IGFET) circuits of either enhanced or depletion types.
- Identify and troubleshoot circuits using analog switches.
- Troubleshoot in circuits using transistor and resistor arrays.

It is often helpful in studying a new component to look at the operating curves, which will give a much clearer picture of what the device does in a circuit. Appendix II provides these operating curves.

11.1 TROUBLESHOOTING DIODE CIRCUITS

SPECIAL RADIO FREQUENCY DIODES

Diodes for use at radio frequencies are discussed in Chapter 13. These include detectors, mixers, and varactor and PIN (positive-intrinsic-negative) diodes.

POWER DIODES

The power semiconductor diode used in today's circuits is usually made of silicon, although sometimes one may encounter a germanium device. The only practical difference between the two for troubleshooting purposes is that the silicon diode will have about 0.7-V DC across itself while conducting, whereas the germanium diode will have close to 0.3-V DC. Since the silicon diode is the more common type, any quote of a 0.7-V DC drop of a diode will also imply that the circuit has a silicon diode. If a germanium diode is used, of course, the voltage will be 0.3-V DC instead.

Power diodes carry relatively heavy currents while conducting. They are used mostly in power supplies to rectify AC voltages into DC. This use of a rectifying diode means that it will be conducting when the cathode is negative with respect to the anode and will be an open circuit when the cathode is positive with respect to the anode. When used in a circuit with a large filter capacitor, the diode only conducts during a very small portion of the AC cycle, in order to bring the filter capacitor back to a topped-off charge after it discharges slightly between cycles. In a power supply with positive DC output, the diode's cathode will be held at a relatively high DC voltage and the anode must exceed this voltage in order for the diode to conduct.

Signal Tracing in Power Supplies

When a rectifier diode shorts in a power supply, the fuse generally blows and the power supply is shut down. A shorted power supply is repaired using the techniques explained in Chapter 6. An AC voltmeter can be used to locate an open diode in a power supply. (An open diode will not blow the fuse.) Figure 11–1 shows the results of open diodes in half- and full-wave power supplies and the indications to be found when using an AC or DC voltmeter to find and verify the problem.

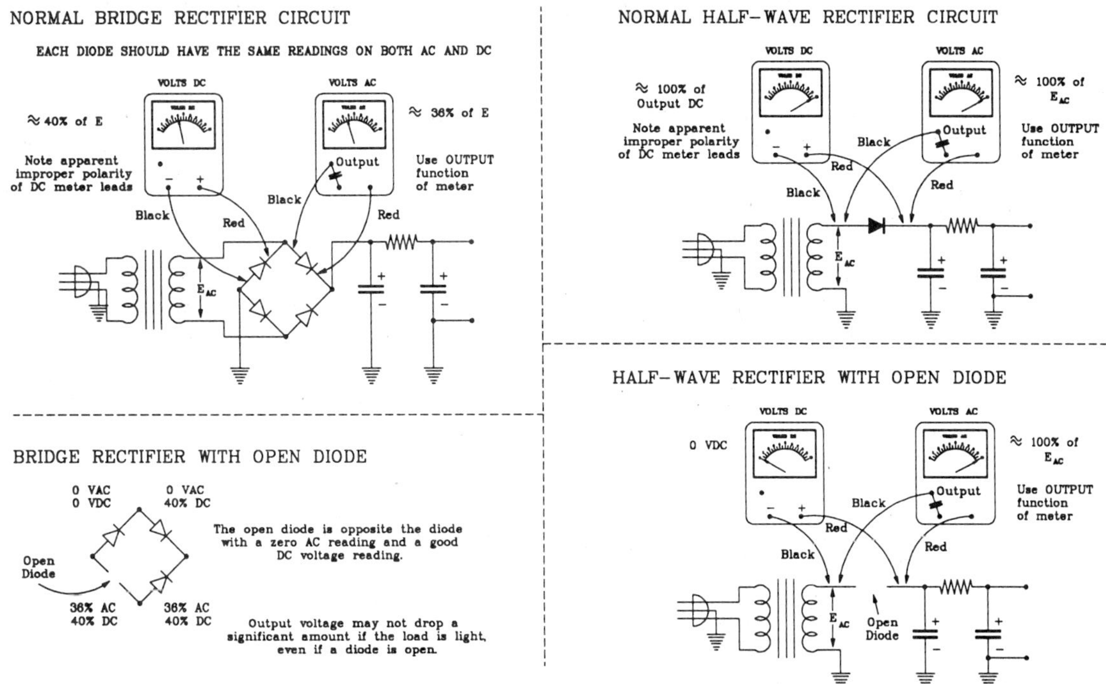

The internal forward voltage drop of a rectifier diode becomes more significant as the design voltage of the power supply decreases, causing the approximate readings above to change accordingly.

Figure 11–1 AC and DC voltage readings for bridge and half-wave rectifiers, with good circuits and circuits with an open rectifier diode.

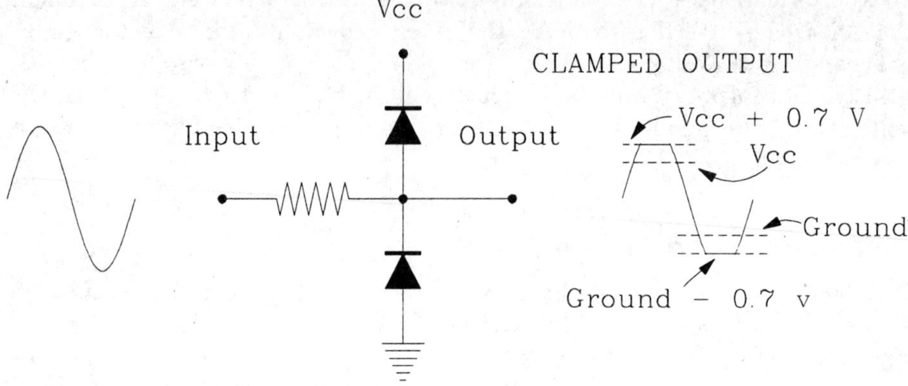

Figure 11–2 These transient-protection diodes do not normally conduct, but they prevent static pulses or signal inputs from exceeding Vcc or going below ground by more than 0.7 volts.

Circuits Using a Diode That Does Not Normally Conduct

Transient-Protection Diodes. There are a few circuits that employ diodes that, in normal operation, do not conduct at all. Instead, they are included for unusual circumstances. An example of such diode use is shown in Figure 11–2.

Using a Diode for Spike Suppression. The circuit of Figure 11–3 shows an important application for a diode: shorting out the spike of voltage that would otherwise occur when the coil is suddenly deenergized by the removal of DC current.

When the normal driving current is suddenly interrupted, a reverse polarity pulse of more than 10 times the original exciting voltage may appear across the coil. For example, a 12-V DC relay coil can produce a pulse reaching as much as 200 volts. Left unattentuated, this spike can puncture the junctions of the driving transistor or cause other mischief within the circuit.

Reversed-Polarity Protection. Another application for a diode that does not normally conduct is the reverse-polarity protection diode, which is sometimes used in equipment that runs a definite risk of being connected to DC power with the wrong polarity. Such circuits are common on consumer equipment such as mobile radios and clocks. See the middle example in Figure 2–5.

Circuits Using a Diode That Always Conducts

Another use for this type of diode is to provide an essentially constant voltage difference of 0.7 volts (0.3 volts for a germanium diode) across its terminals while passing a signal through without affecting it (see Figure 6–21). The three diodes used between the transistor bases allow each base to receive the same AC signal voltage yet operate at about 2.1-V DC apart from each other.

From the examples given thus far in this chapter, it should be evident that understanding the use of diodes in operating circuitry will depend upon what the diode is expected to do: conduct all the time, part of the time, or almost never.

Voltage Clipper Diodes

One more use for a diode (often a pair of them) is to clip, or limit, voltages in a circuit. See Figure 11–4.

A diode can be used to clip a voltage near another voltage source (including the zero voltage of ground) within 0.7 or 0.3 volts, respectively. Clipping may also be done by putting diodes in series, which results in clipping to within 1.4 or 0.7 volts (or multiples, depending on the number of diodes used in series). An alternate way to get clipping at voltage over about 1.4 volts is to use a zener diode of the proper voltage rating.

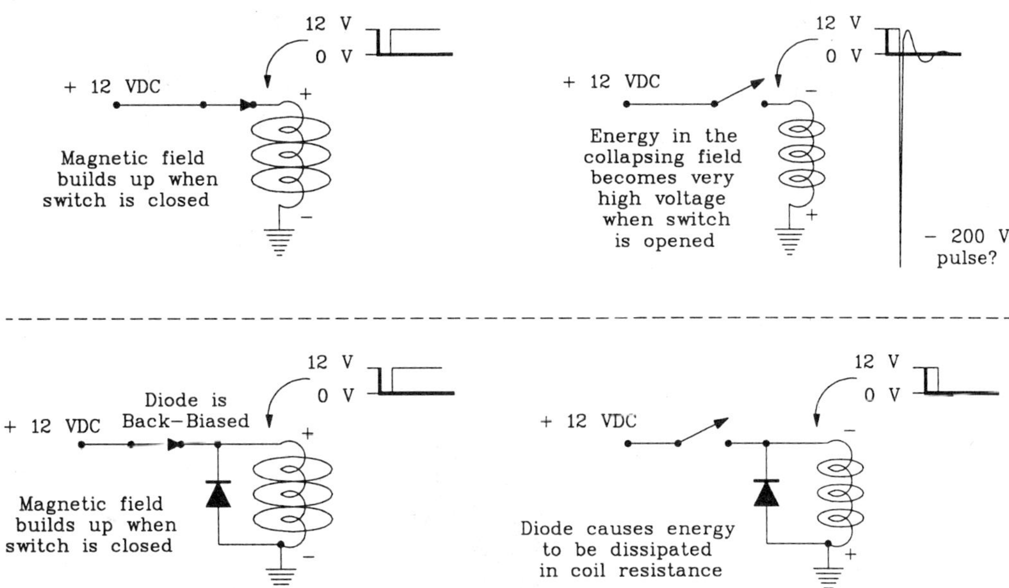

Figure 11–3 Circuit using a diode to prevent a high voltage pulse when the DC current through a coil (solenoid, relay, or inductor) is suddenly interrupted.

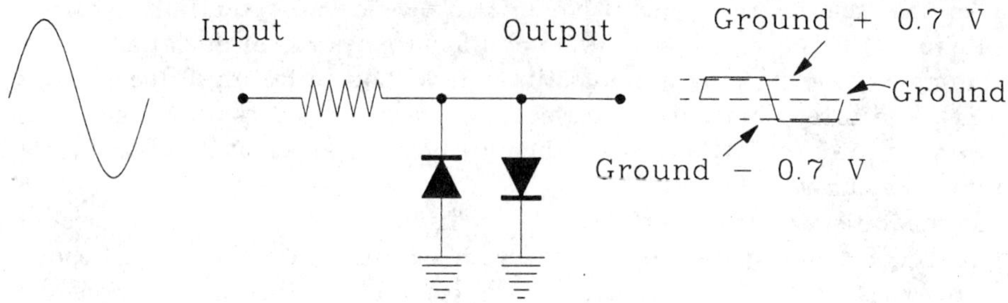

Figure 11–4 The clipper circuit prevents a signal from exceeding specified voltage limits, in this case, ground.

LIGHT EMITTING DIODE (LED) CIRCUITS

The LED provides a visual indication of the presence of voltage or current flow. LEDs are a very common type of semiconductor. Standard colors for LEDs are red, green, and yellow. Troubleshooting the LED circuit is simple: Test the voltage across the device with a DC meter while the diode should be lighted. If there is a proper voltage drop, the LED must be lighted. If the voltage is excessive, the LED is open; if too little, the LED is shorted, and if it is reversed in polarity, the LED may be installed backward or the circuit may have failed in such a manner as to cause the reversal of polarity. Refer back to Figure 1–4 to identify the cathode and anode leads of an LED.

The voltage drops expected across a forward-conducting LED vary with the type:

LED Type	*Forward Conduction Voltage*
RED	1.6
YELLOW	2.0
GREEN	2.0
Infrared	1.0

Troubleshooting an infrared (IR) LED circuit is a bit more difficult, since the LED will emit no visible light at all. A simple way to test an IR LED is to procure an IRED (infrared) detector card from some RCA distributors, or from Edmund Scientific (101 E. Gloucester Pike, Barrington, NJ 08007–1380). These cards are a little larger than a business card and have a small piece of specially treated paper fixed in the center. When viewed in normal light (hold the IRED LED touching the indicator), the application of strong IRED will cause a faint red glow on the paper.

There is another LED available, which is called a three-color LED. This is nothing more than two diodes, a red and a green, placed in parallel within a single plastic indicator. When current flows in one direction, the LED glows red; when the direction is reversed, it glows green. The application of AC causes both diodes to light, resulting in a yellow light.

DIODE FAILURE PATTERNS

Diodes almost always fail by shorting or opening internally. They can usually be easily found using a DC voltmeter as shown in Figure 11–5.

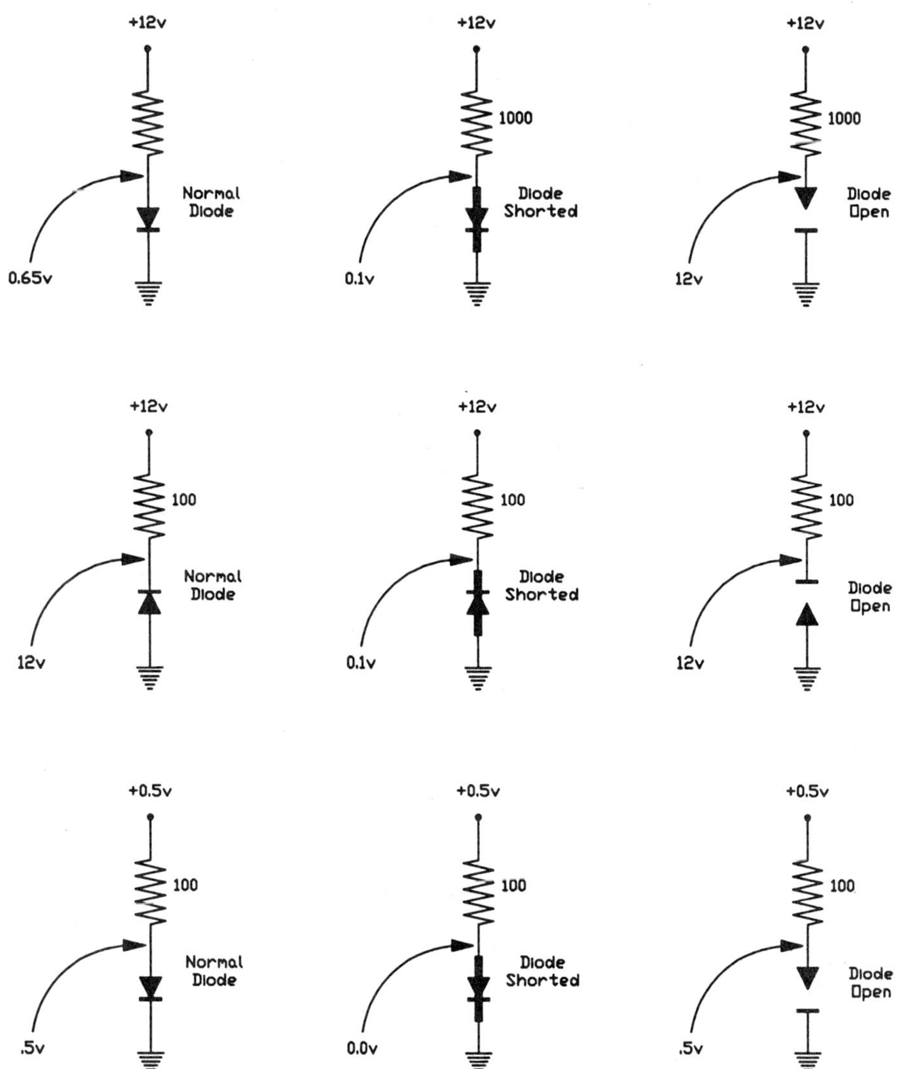

Figure 11–5 Failure modes of the junction diode. Note the use of a voltmeter to find the defective diode.

11.2 TROUBLESHOOTING BIPOLAR TRANSISTOR AMPLIFIER CIRCUITS

It is important for troubleshooting purposes to be aware of the class of operation under which an amplifier is operating. Class A is the most common operating configuration. The Class A amplifier is used to amplify very small amplitude signals and is usable to amplify signals from DC up through high-frequency RF. The classes of operation were covered in Chapter 1.

FIRST CHECKS

In any bipolar circuit, two items bear checking first: bias and collector voltage. Then, depending on the class of operation and the configuration of the circuit (common emitter, collector, or base), further tests should be made.

Check the Transistor Bias

The reference element of a bipolar transistor (the device lead from which voltage measurements are made for troubleshooting purposes) is the *emitter lead.* Bias voltage is the voltage from the emitter to the base, and the collector voltage under specified conditions is the voltage from the emitter to the collector.

The first voltage to check is the forward biasing voltage applied to the transistor. This forward bias is what determines the class of operation, and therefore, it is of great importance. See Figure 11–6.

If the biasing of the stage is incorrect, it is often due to the transistor itself being defective. The base can and often does short to the emitter, and it may sometimes short to the collector. In either case, the voltage read between the emitter and the base will not be the expected 0.7 (for a silicon transistor) or 0.3 (for a germanium transistor) volts.

If the circuitry is DC coupled (it amplifies DC and has no series-coupling capacitors), there is a very good possibility that one or more previous stages are defective. A DC-coupled amplifier will sometimes fail with a domino effect: the failure of an early stage causes later stages to fail as well. Check for this possibility and replacing defective transistors before reapplying operating power to the circuits.

If the biasing for a transistor is incorrect, the problem may be the transistor or it may be a fault in the biasing circuit itself. Since it is more likely that the transistor is causing the wrong bias voltage to appear, the transistor should be removed and out-of-circuit transistor tests should be done to determine if the transistor or the circuitry is at fault.

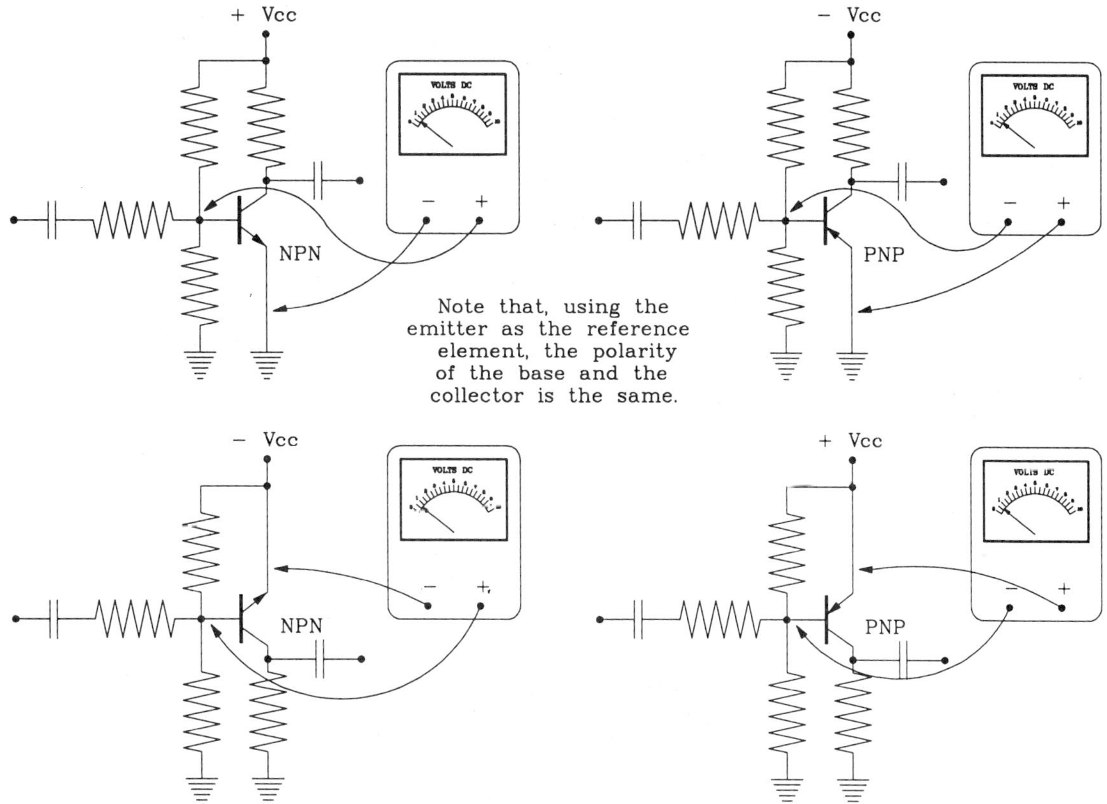

Figure 11–6 Checking for normal bias voltage and polarity in Class A bipolar amplifier stages.

Check Collector Voltage Compared to Available Voltage

Once the biasing of the stage has been determined to be correct, the collector circuit should be tested next. In a Class A amplifier, the collector voltage with respect to the emitter should be within the range of about 50 to 60 percent of the available collector-supply voltage at the end of the collector resistor. See Figure 11–7.

Failure of the collector voltage to be within the approximate values of 50 to 60 percent of thc available voltage indicates a problem within the transistor or a biasing problem in the base circuit. See Figure 11–8.

A quick test for the Class A amplifier consists of shorting from base to emitter while watching the collector voltage. The collector voltage should go to full supply voltage if the base is shorted to the emitter. Be very careful to properly identify the emitter and base, however, as even a momentary short from the base to the collector will likely destroy the transistor in most circuits (see Figure 11–9). This test is also not recommended for an amplifier that is DC-coupled. To do so may damage *all* the following stages!

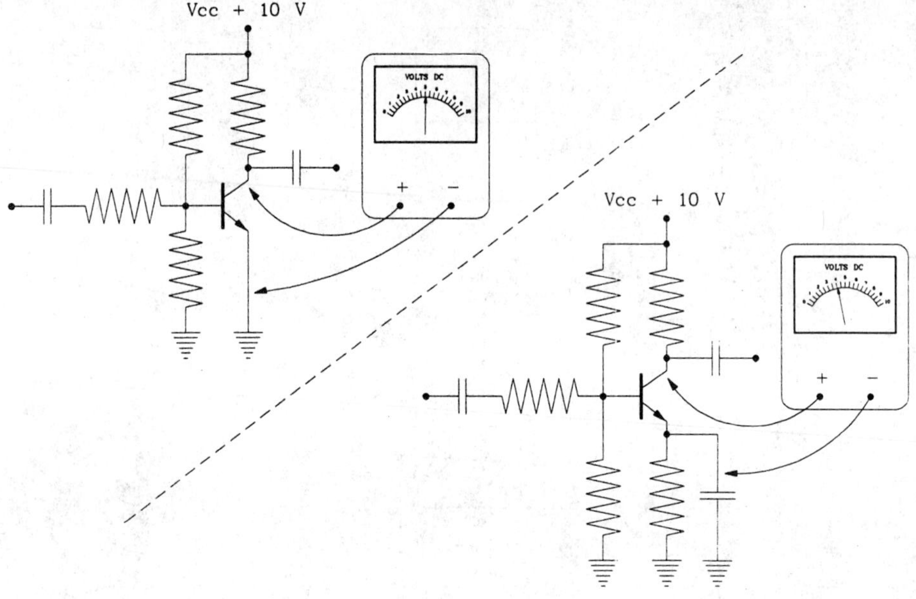

Figure 11–7 The collector voltage of a Class A amplifier should be about half that of the supply voltage.

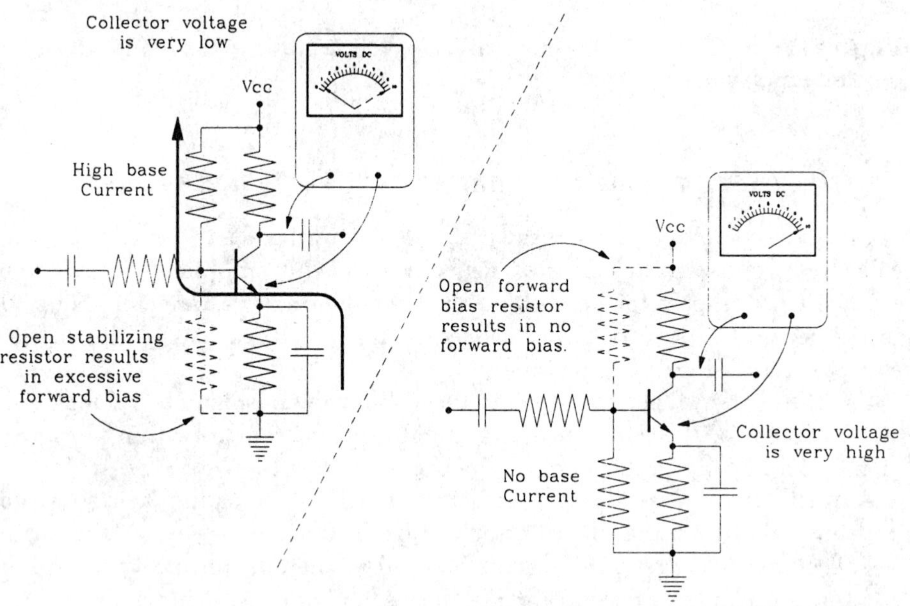

Figure 11–8 Effects that may be expected in a common-emitter bipolar transistor amplifier circuit if either of the biasing resistors opens.

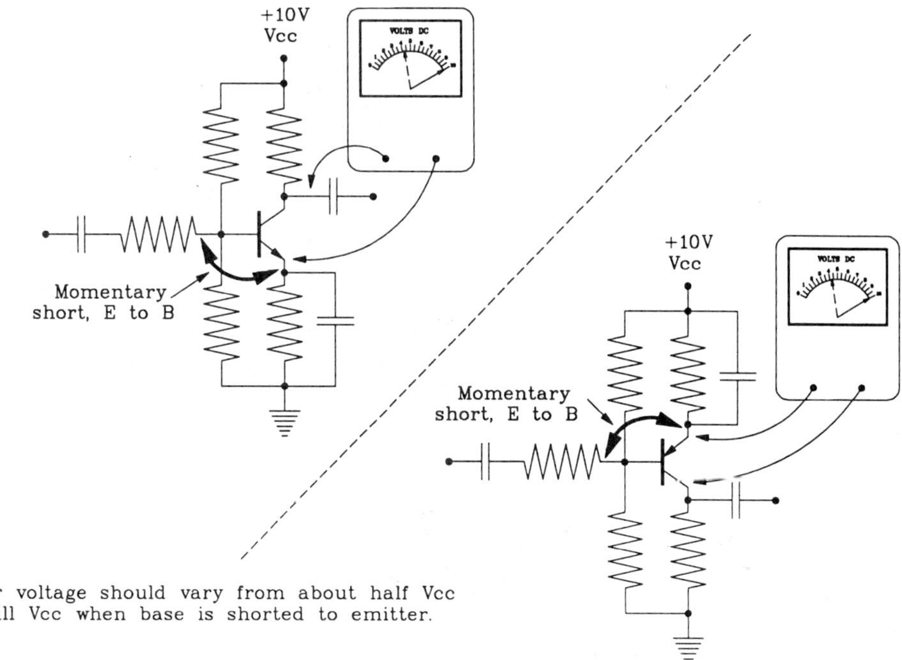

+10V
Vcc
Momentary
short, E to B
+10V
Vcc
Momentary
short, E to B
Collector voltage should vary from about half Vcc
to full Vcc when base is shorted to emitter.

Note: This test applies only to class A resistor–capacitor coupled stages, NOT to DC coupled stages. Also, do NOT accidentally short base to collector, as probable damage to the transistor will result.

Figure 11–9 An in-circuit transistor test for Class A resistance-coupled amplifier stages.

Figure 7–12 may be reviewed at this point for the definitions of the three configurations of transistor circuits.

TROUBLESHOOTING A COMMON-EMITTER AMPLIFIER CONFIGURATION

Most troubleshooting of a Class A amplifier can be effectively accomplished by using a DC voltmeter. No signals should be applied to the amplifier stage in this case. The static distribution of DC voltages will tell most of what needs to be known about an individual stage. To get a better feel for the bipolar, common-emitter, Class A amplifier, *study* Figure 11–10.

The common-emitter configuration is the usual way of connecting a bipolar transistor into circuitry. This configuration results in both current and voltage gain. Although there is a 180-degree phase reversal from input to output (a positive-going signal results in a negative-going output), the entire cycle of input voltage is seen in the output. Refer to Figure 11–8 and identify the forward-biasing resistor in each circuit.

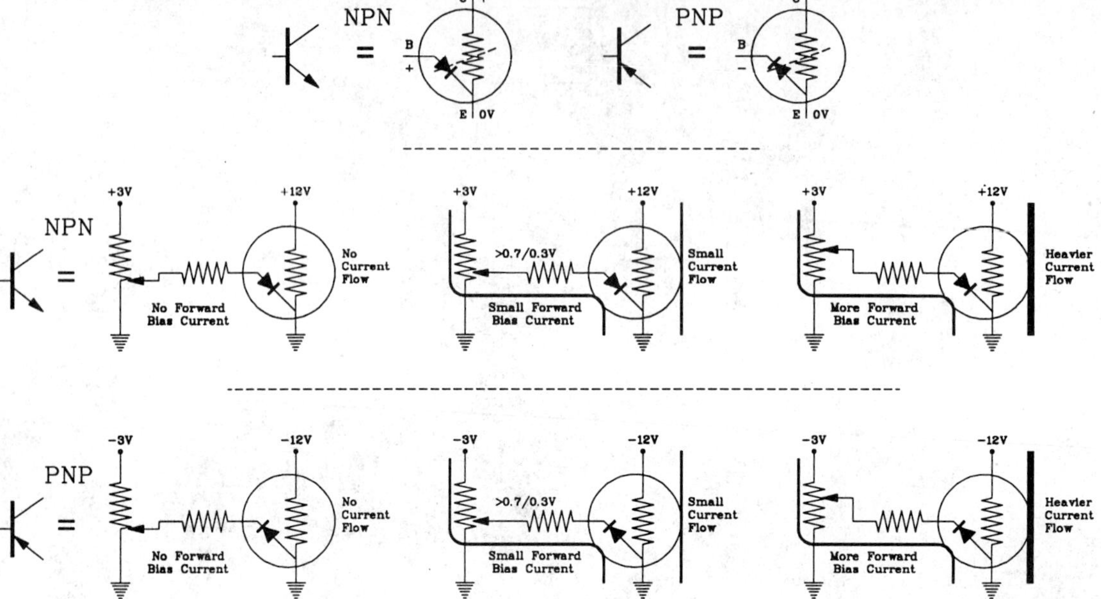

Figure 11–10 The bipolar transistor can be considered a diode and a current-controlled resistor for the purpose of estimating DC voltages within a circuit.

A Source of Constant Current

There is an occasional use for a source of current that does not vary, within reasonable limits, even with variations in the voltage across the load. The constant current source is based on the fact that the collector current flowing through a transistor is dependent on the base current multiplied by the amplification of the transistor. Note that the available voltage at the collector is not a controlling factor. Thus, the transistor will deliver essentially the same current to either light or heavy loads in the collector circuit. See Figure 11–11.

The constant current source is particularly useful in developing a linear ramp of voltage. See Figure 11–12.

TROUBLESHOOTING THE CLASS B PUSH-PULL COMMON-EMITTER POWER AMPLIFIER

The Class B common-emitter amplifier collector circuit will conduct in the absence of an incoming signal, but only very little. The emitter-collector voltage under these conditions is typically high (almost that of the available voltage source). There will be a forward-biasing resistor to the collector circuit, but it will have a relatively high resistance value.

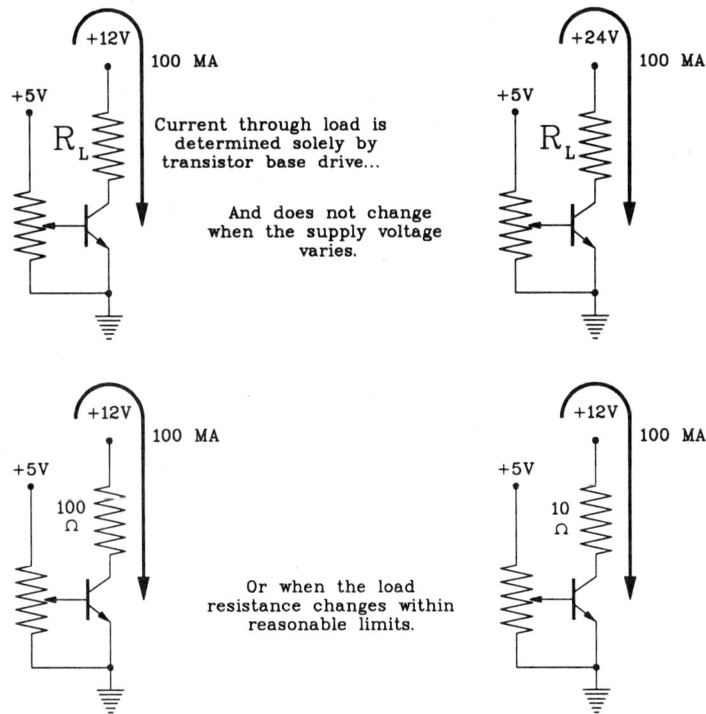

Figure 11–11 The collector circuit of a common emitter amplifier configuration is a source of constant current in spite of supply and load variations.

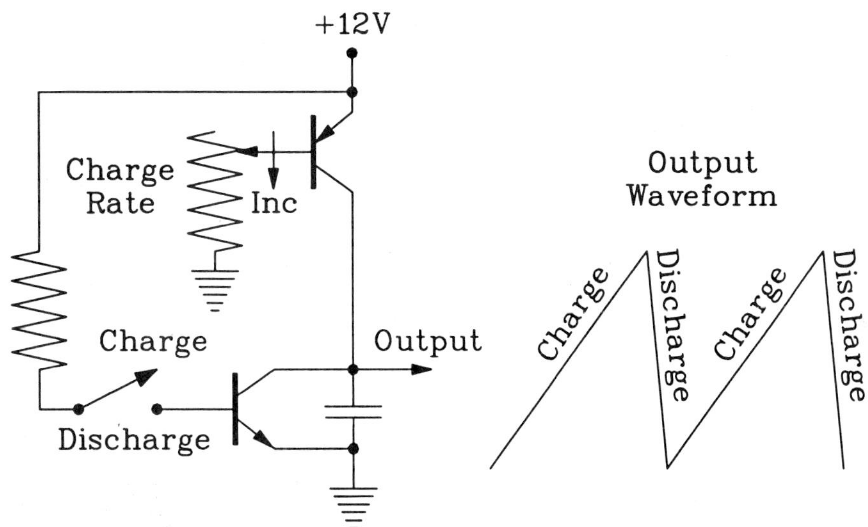

Figure 11–12 The constant current source can be used to charge a capacitor in order to produce a linear voltage ramp.

Class B stages are almost always used with a second, mirror-image amplifier stage to amplify the opposite polarity of the input waveform.

The Class B amplifier is used mostly in high-powered audio stages in which one of two transistors amplifies one polarity of the incoming signal, and a second transistor, placed in the circuit "upside down," supplies the opposite polarity. The Class B stage can be identified when the stage amplifies linear signals (audio frequencies, for instancc), if there are two transistors in the stage (one is often drawn upside down), and if there is a transformer in the output circuit. When two transistors share the amplification in this manner, it is called a *push-pull stage*. See Figure 11–13.

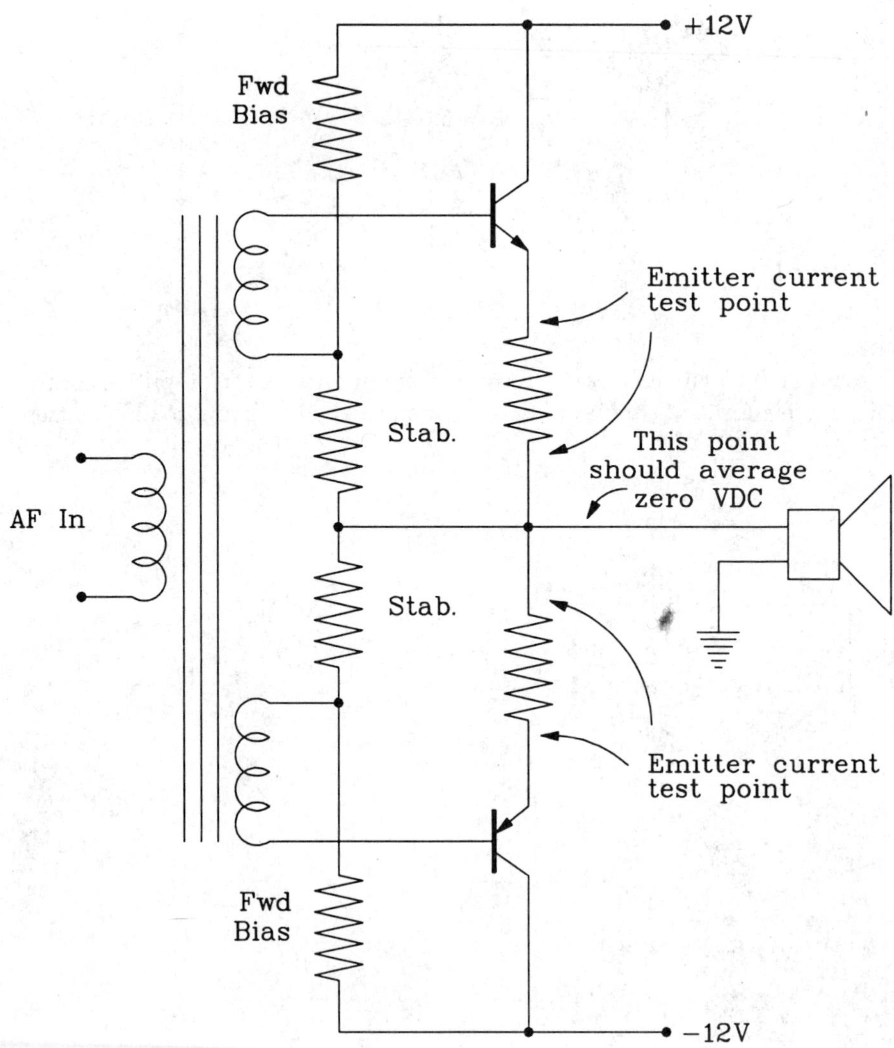

Figure 11–13 Troubleshooting test points of the push-pull Class B audio amplifier.

The push-pull audio amplifier stage can also be analyzed by checking the bias voltage. The bias should be such that the transistors are turned on a little bit, thus avoiding distortion problems with very small signals. A "little bit" means that the base junction will have the familiar 0.7 or 0.3 volt drop without an incoming signal. The current flowing into the base, however, will not be as much as it would be if the transistor were operating Class A.

Emitter resistors, if provided, give the technician a very good place to monitor the current flowing into each of the transistors. Measure the voltage drop across each of the two emitter resistors to get a comparison of the current flow between the two transistors, which should be nearly equal. An emitter resistor with no voltage drop indicates either that a transistor has an open collector or base junction or that a power supply has failed.

TROUBLESHOOTING THE CLASS B COMPLEMENTARY-SYMMETRY AMPLIFIER

The expensive interstage and output transformers sometimes used with push-pull Class B amplifiers can be eliminated, with a substantial reduction in cost, by using a complementary-symmetry output stage. See Figure 11–14.

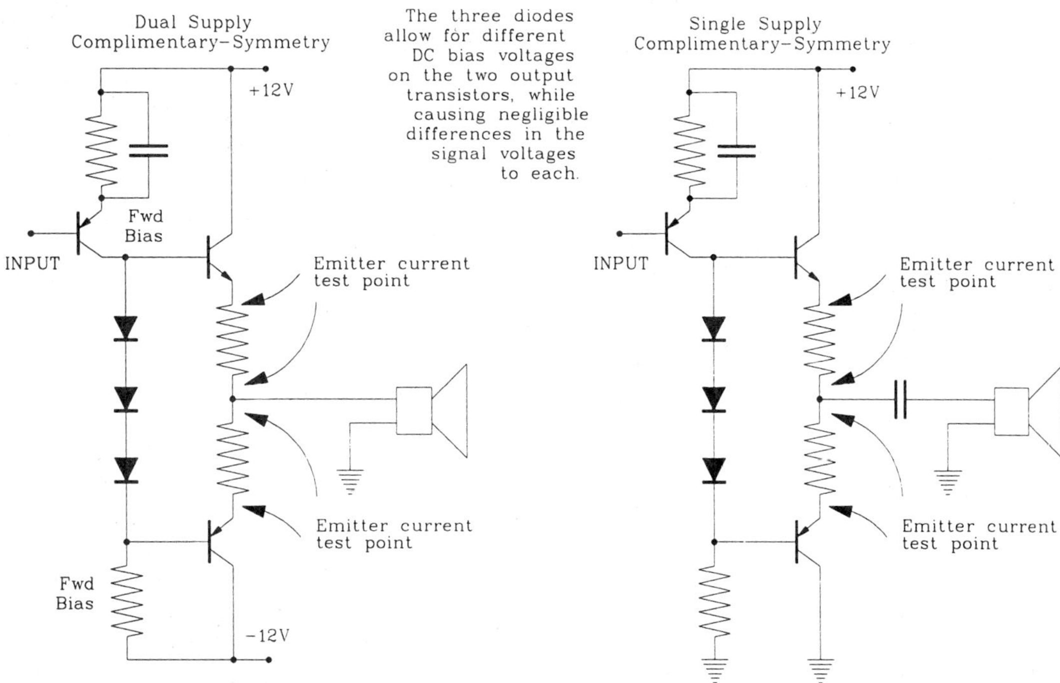

Figure 11–14 Important test points for the Class B complementary-symmetry amplifier stage.

This amplifier is easily recognizable because it has two different transistors connected to the output speaker, one PNP and the other an NPN. There will also be a large coupling capacitor going from between the transistors to the output (usually a speaker) if the stage is operated from a single supply voltage. This capacitor can be eliminated if there are two separate supply voltages, one negative and the other positive, for the stage.

The capacitor coupling the audio to the speaker is a common source of problems. It often shorts, causing a pronounced "thump" in the speaker when power is first applied. If the speaker baffle is removed, the bass speaker will be seen to press outward or inward and remain there under the influence of the unwanted DC component to the speaker because of the defective capacitor.

Individual transistor currents can be monitored in the complementary-symmetry circuit by noting the voltage drop across each of the emitter resistors, if they are provided. These voltages should be very close to one another. The bias voltages should also be either the familiar 0.7 or 0.3 volt forward bias.

One disadvantage of the complementary-symmetry circuit is that if one of the transistors shorts, the opposite transistor will often fail as well. This results in a short on the power supply, with blown fuses or other failures.

TROUBLESHOOTING THE CLASS C COMMON-EMITTER AMPLIFIER

The Class C amplifier is used in only two applications, for large-signal (power) amplification of radio frequency signals, such as in transmitter stages, and as a pulse amplifier in cases where the transistor is normally cut off and saturates completely when conducting.

The servicing technician can look for the lack of a forward biasing resistor, as described for Class A amplifiers. (This is the resistor connected between the base of a transistor and the collector circuit.) The absence of this resistor aids in identifying the Class C amplifier. See Figure 11–15.

Troubleshooting the Class C RF Power Amplifier

The bipolar transistor Class C amplifier stage has no biasing circuitry to bring the transistor into an idling condition of forward bias. The incoming signal to be amplified is the only means of turning the transistor on. It drives the base from zero forward bias voltage to the point of conducting (the 0.7 or 0.3-V point) and then higher, causing a pulse of current in the output circuit. This class of operation is used in large-signal radio-frequency amplifier circuits where the pulses of collector current are smoothed into a sine wave by the flywheel effect of inductance and capacitance.

A more detailed analysis of troubleshooting the RF Class C amplifier may be found in Chapter 13.

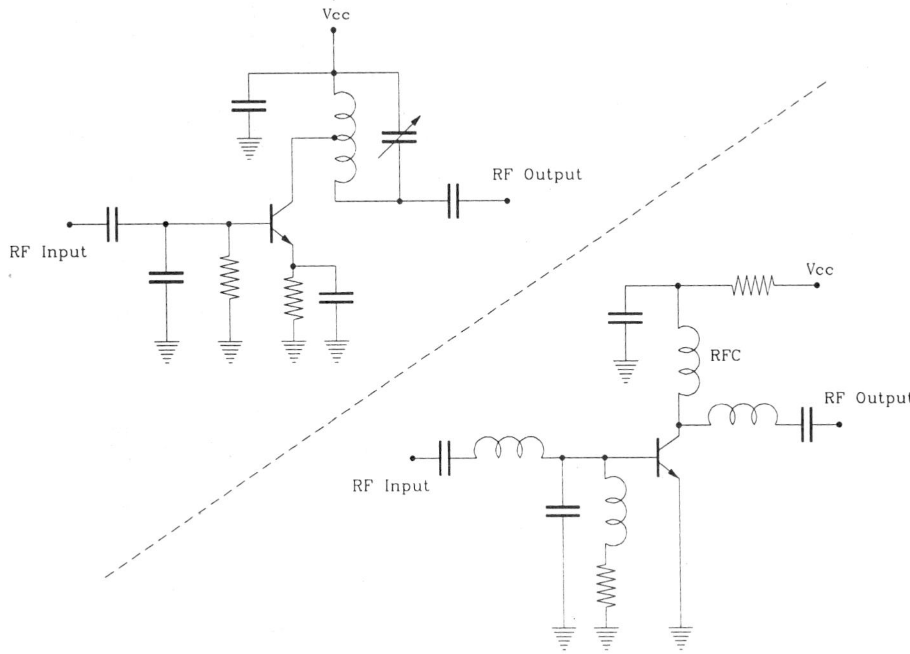

Figure 11–15 Identifying the Class C stage by the lack of a forward-biasing resistor (base to collector). See also Figure 13–2.

Troubleshooting the Switching Amplifier

Switching applications involve the transistor as a simple switch, either conducting heavily (saturated) or not at all (cut off). A switching circuit makes use of the amplification of the transistor, controlling a higher collector current with the small current of the base circuit. Switching applications may involve anything from high-speed switching all the way to DC switching, in which the circuit may be energized for hours or days at a time. See Figure 11–16 for examples of bipolar transistors and insulated-gate field effect transistors (IGFETS; sometimes called metal-oxide-semiconductor field effect transmitters or MOSFETs), which are used in switching applications.

The bipolar switching circuit is commonly used when interfacing digital circuits and microprocessors to analog devices. IGFETs are widely used in applications to provide switching of relatively large DC currents with the mere presence of a DC voltage at the gate.

Failure Patterns of Switching Circuits

The Bipolar Switching Transistor. Troubleshooting a bipolar common-emitter switching circuit is easy. First, look for the proper driving voltage

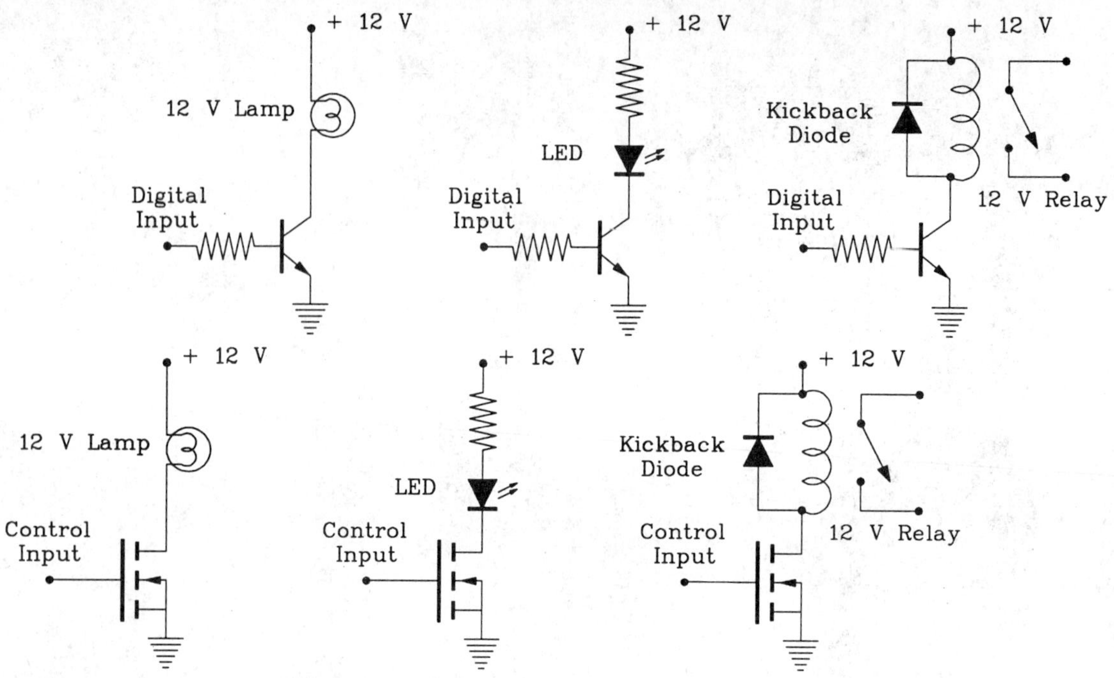

Figure 11–16 Switching transistor interface circuits.

ahead of the current limiting resistor that is in series with the transistor's base. A normal voltage (typically greater than 3 volts or more from digital outputs) indicates a proper drive into the transistor base. The base of the transistor will have near zero volts when gated off and either 0.7 or 0.3 volts when gated on, regardless of the amplitude of the driving voltage. The presence of near-zero voltage at the base when the driving voltage is 3 volts or more indicates either a shorted junction between the base and the emitter or an open resistance between the resistor and the base.

If the base of a switching transistor is receiving a normal signal in a malfunctioning circuit, either the transistor or the load is at fault. Be sure, of course, to check for the presence of normal supply voltage to the load. If the collector voltage remains low at all times, causing the load to constantly receive current and be energized, the collector is shorted to the emitter. If the collector is low at all times and the load never energizes, the load is open. On the other hand, if the load is never energized and the collector voltage is always high, the transistor collector is open.

The Enhancement IGFET Switching Transistor. The IGFET requires a relatively large voltage to control the current through the drain/source circuit. Several volts are required to properly saturate the FET in a switching application. The exact voltage required for saturation will vary with the specific device used, but 4 or 5 volts is typical.

If the proper driving voltage is present and the device is not saturated, check for drain voltage. If none is apparent, the load may be open or the power supply for the load may have failed. If the transistor is not saturated sufficiently with a large enough input voltage, look for unsuspected oscillation in the input signal, which can effectively turn the device off and on at a high rate of speed, giving the appearance of partial operation. Erratic or partial operation is also an indication of a defective device leaking from gate to source.

Troubleshooting the Class C Pulse Amplifier

When transistors are used in pulse amplifiers, they are operated Class C because the stage absorbs no power unless it is needed for the actual amplification operation. The input waveform is seldom of importance as far as distortion is concerned, so linearity of the amplification process is not a major consideration. Only an increase in power is important. Pulse transformers are also commonly found in pulse amplifiers (also see Chapter 14).

Many pulse applications use thyristor semiconductors such as SCRs and TRIACs, whose method of operation involves the timing of sudden saturation and self-latching. This is a separate subject, and is also covered in Chapter 14.

The wave shape of a pulsed waveform may or may not be critical, depending on the application. Television circuits use many nonsinusoidal waveforms whose wave shape is critical. On the other hand, the pulse used to initiate the firing of the horizontal or vertical sweep circuits can be a simple, short pulse needing only a steep wavefront to trip the circuit. The schematics that are used frequently by a technician should include wave shapes for those applications for which the wave shape is critical. If the manufacturer shows a wave shape, it is probably critical to the proper operation of the circuit.

Pulsed circuits are sensitive to the polarity of signals. For example, if it takes a positive pulse to turn on a transistor, a negative pulse will not affect the circuit at all. *Be conscious of signal polarity as you troubleshoot in pulsed circuits.*

Pulsed circuits often use the charge and discharge of capacitors and inductors to accomplish the purposes of the circuit. The capacitive and inductive charge and discharge curves will determine the circuit timing and waveform generation. Switching regulators are a good example of this kind of operation, as discussed in Chapter 7. Chapter 10 covers the subject of passive components and how they affect signals.

Pulse Amplifier Failure Patterns

Finding the bad stage in a string of pulse amplifiers should be easy. The interstage voltage levels are sufficiently high to use an oscilloscope. Just look for any deviation from the normal waveforms in the circuit. Watch for sufficient pulse amplitude and wave shape very close to that in the docu-

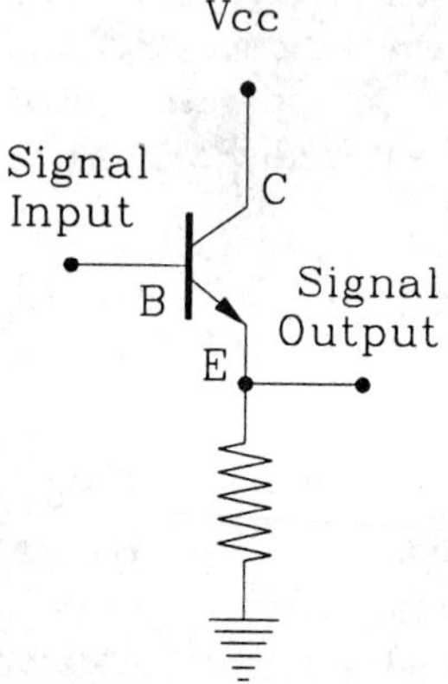

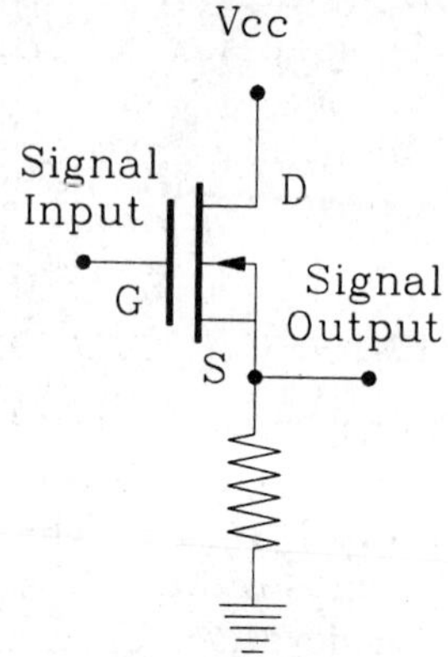

Figure 11–17 The common-collector or common-drain configuration, operating Class A, is sometimes called an emitter or source follower.

mentation for each specific point in the circuit. When a pulse amplifier causes a problem, it usually stops working: the input pulse may be correct but the output will be missing entirely.

THE COMMON-COLLECTOR CLASS A AMPLIFIER

The common-collector or common-drain Class A amplifier is sometimes called an emitter or source follower, depending on the type of semiconductor involved. See Figure 11–17.

This configuration for an amplifier provides a voltage gain of only 1, but it does provide current gain and, therefore, a power gain. Thus, this circuit is often used as a driver when the voltage level from a circuit is sufficient but its current capability is not

A Source of Constant Voltage

The basic operation of a transistor as a constant voltage source is as follows: the voltage at the base circuit alone determines the voltage at the emitter. Based on this fact, the emitter of a transistor becomes a constant source of voltage regardless of the voltage available at the collector (within reasonable limits). The constant voltage source is based on the fact that a bipolar transistor's emitter will be 0.7 volts (for a silicon transistor, or 0.3

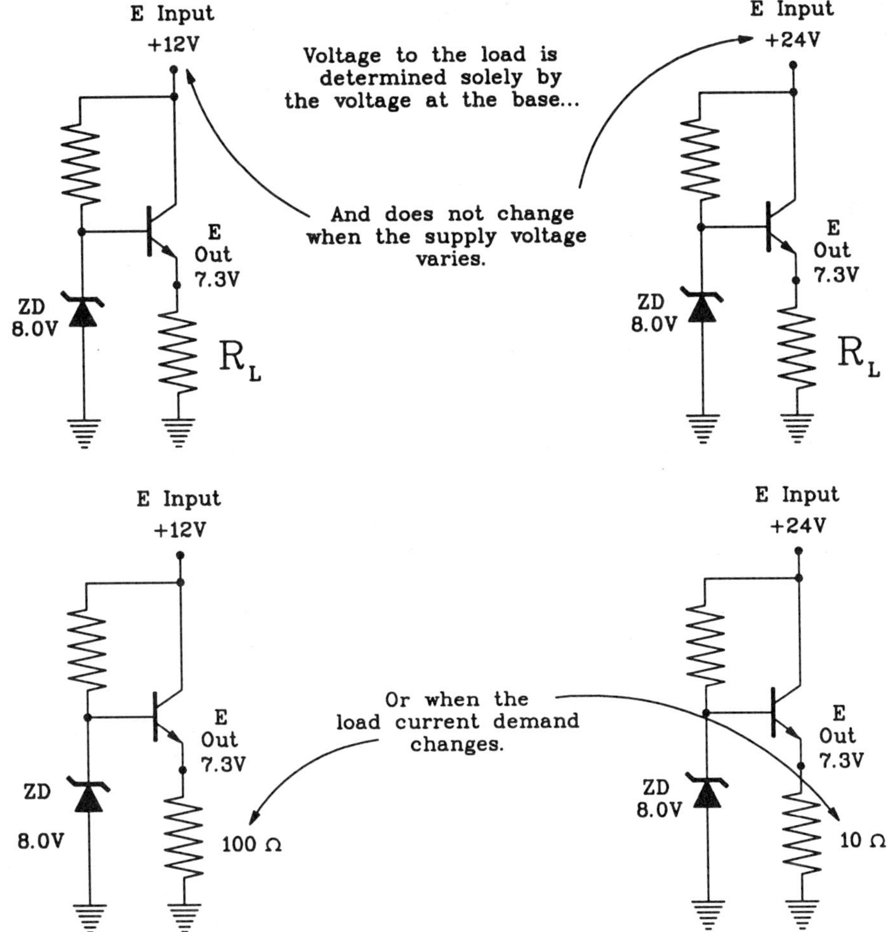

Figure 11–18 The emitter circuit of a common-collector configuration is also a source of constant voltage, which is determined only by the base voltage.

volts for a germanium transistor) less than the base voltage, regardless of the emitter circuit current demand. Thus, if the base of a transistor is held constant with a voltage reference, the emitter of the transistor will provide an output voltage of about 0.7 (or 0.3 volts) less. See Figure 11–18.

Because the common-collector circuit is a source for fixed voltage, it is most commonly used as an amplifier for a voltage regulator. In this circuit, the transistor is most often a large transistor that is able to dissipate a considerable amount of power; it is called a *pass transistor* in this application.

THE COMMON-BASE AMPLIFIER

Although the common-base amplifier provides no current gain, there is voltage gain and, therefore, power gain. This type of amplifier is only occasionally used, in cases where its low input impedance is an advantage. The common-base configuration is mostly used as a radio-frequency linear power amplifier because of the isolation between the emitter and the collector and also the ease of matching its low input impedance to transmission lines. Troubleshooting the RF amplifier is covered in Chapter 13.

BIPOLAR TRANSISTOR FAILURE PATTERNS

Bipolar transistors fail most often by shorting between elements internally or by opening one or both junctions. Transistors that are operated in high-power applications are more prone to failure due to heat than transistors operated at relatively cool temperatures. As the temperature of a bipolar transistor increases, so does the leakage of the junctions, which can contribute to the device failure.

Overheating is probably the most common cause of transistor failure. Whenever a transistor is required to dissipate appreciable amounts of heat, it should be provided with some means to do so. A heat sink can be used to pull heat from the device and keep it much cooler than if no heat sink were provided. A poor mechanical and thermal bond between a transistor and its heat sink will cause the transistor to overheat. When a power transistor fails, be very sure that the new replacement transistor is well bonded to the heat sink. Additional heat transfer can be accomplished through the use of special heat-conducting pastes made for the purpose.

Another reason for some transistor failures is the application of more than the rated voltage across a junction when that junction is open. The voltage from base to emitter in the reverse-biased condition and the collector-to-emitter voltage when not conducting must be kept within the specifications for the transistor. Excessive voltages will arc across inside the transistor, destroying it. Transistors that drive inductive loads, such as the output transistor for the horizontal deflection circuit of a television or computer monitor, often fail for this reason.

Improper bias is another reason for a bipolar transistor to fail. Even momentarily shorting the base of a transistor to its collector will usually destroy it, particularly if there is no current-limiting resistor in the circuit. This is a common reason for transistor failures while wiring new circuits. If a transistor fails in an otherwise working circuit, be sure there is no failure of the biasing circuit before installing a new transistor.

11.3 TROUBLESHOOTING JFET TRANSISTOR AMPLIFIER CIRCUITS

The junction field effect transistor (JFET) is quite different in its operation from the bipolar transistor. Where the bipolar transistor is a current-operated device, the JFET is a voltage-operated device. See Figure 11–19.

The reference element of a JFET (the device lead from which voltage measurements are made for troubleshooting purposes) is the *source lead.* Bias voltage is the voltage from the source lead to the gate input lead, and output or drain voltage is the voltage from the source to the drain.

While there is no reason why the JFET cannot be used in other classes of operation, Class A is by far the most common use and will be the only class that is covered here.

The JFET is available in two varieties, N-channel and P-channel. The N-channel uses a negative ground and a positive source voltage, and the P-channel is the opposite, using a positive ground and a negative supply voltage.

The principal advantage of using a JFET is that it has an extremely high input impedance. The connection of a voltmeter (even a digital voltmeter with an input impedance of 10 megohms) may completely upset the operation of a JFET amplifier. A clue as to the susceptibility of a circuit to the loading effects of a voltmeter can be obtained by looking at the value of the

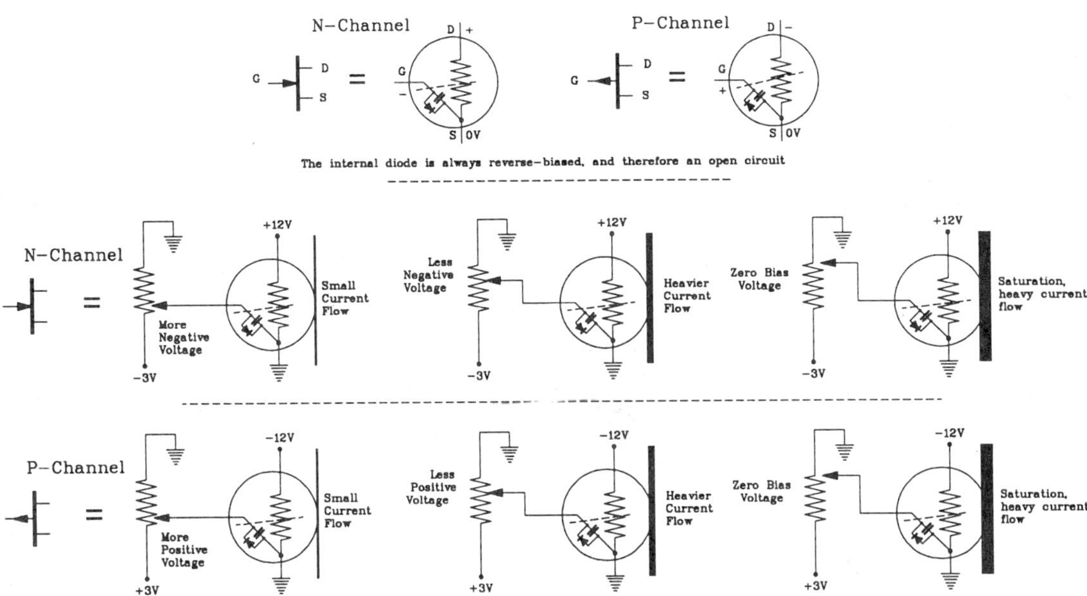

Figure 11–19 The JFET can be visualized as an open circuit input and a voltage-controlled resistor.

resistors used in the input circuit. Any resistor used in the circuit with a resistance of more than a few megohms will indicate that a voltmeter will have a substantial loading effect. The output circuit is a much lower impedance circuit, and it should be safe to use a voltmeter anywhere in the output circuit without loading effects.

Since the JFET is most often used as a Class A amplifier in DC circuits, any disturbance of the input circuit should be reflected as a change in the resistance of the component from source to drain. Because of the high resistance of the JFET input circuit, sometimes simply placing a finger on the input circuitry is sufficient to make a substantial change in the output voltage of the JFET. If no change occurs, this is a good indication of a defective JFET.

JFET BIASING

Biasing the JFET amplifier requires that, using the source lead as the reference, the input gate be of opposite polarity to that of the drain. Although this voltage can be supplied by a separate source (opposite to the drain source), it is more common to elevate the source in voltage by using the current through the device. See Figure 11–20.

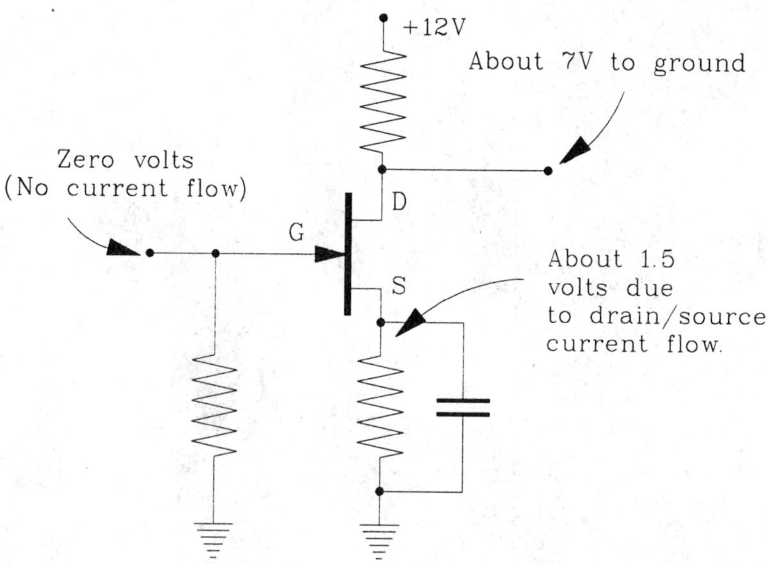

Figure 11–20 A common method for obtaining bias for an N-channel JFET.

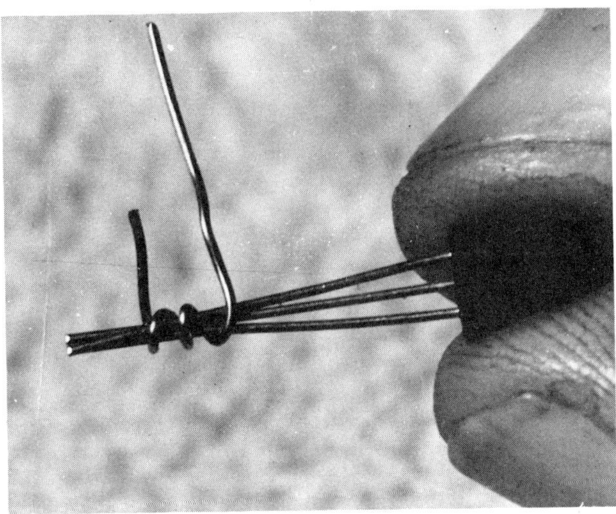

Figure 11–21 Keep the leads of all FETs shorted together until installed.

JFET FAILURES

The most common failure of a JFET occurs when the input diode shorts, which is often due to excessive input voltages or static damage to the device. For this reason, you should work on JFET circuits in a static-free environment and leave new devices in their original containers, with the leads shorted together, until you are actually ready for installation. See Figure 11–21.

11.4 TROUBLESHOOTING MOSFET/IGFET TRANSISTOR AMPLIFIER CIRCUITS

A MOSFET is a metal-oxide-semiconductor field effect transistor. A more accurate acronym for this device is insulated-gate field effect transistor (IGFET). An IGFET is similar to a JFET in that the input resistance to the device is extremely high. It is also subject to the same cautions concerning static damage prevention as given above: keep the leads shorted together until the device is installed and work in a static-free environment.

The reference element of an insulated-gate field effect transistor (the device lead from which voltage measurements are made for troubleshooting purposes) is the *source lead.* See Figure 11–22.

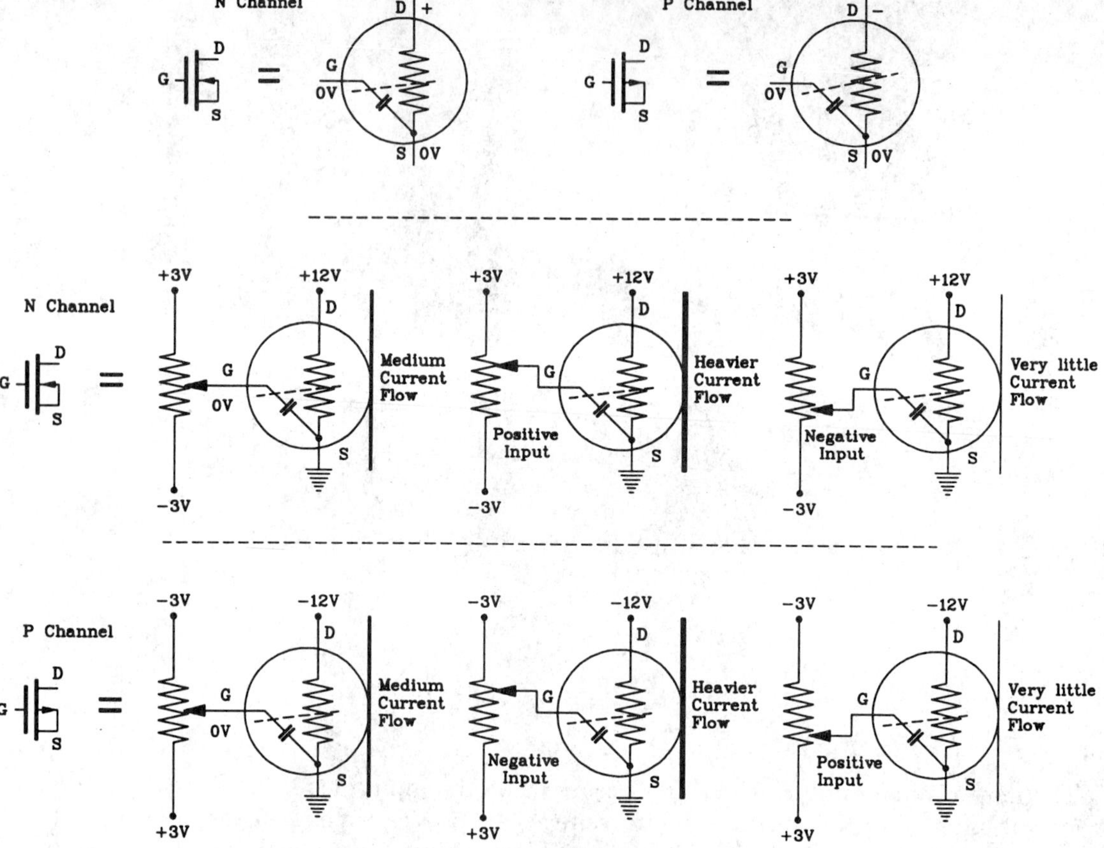

Figure 11–22 The depletion-channel insulated-gate FET varies the resistance of the source-to-drain channel in response to a voltage change between the gate and the source.

The depletion-channel IGFET is a natural Class A amplifier since there is current flow without any bias provided for it. Consequently, the depletion-channel IGFET is often used as an audio and radio-frequency small-signal amplifier.

The enhancement-channel IGFET amplifier is a natural Class C amplifying device since it requires an input voltage before it will conduct between the source and the drain. For use in Class A or B, this device requires a bias voltage of the same polarity as that provided for the drain circuit. See Figure 11–24.

Note the difference in the symbols between the depletion- and enhancement-mode circuit symbols. One has a solid line from source to the drain, and the other has a broken line. This prompts the technician concerning what current flows in the output circuit *without a bias*. The solid line from

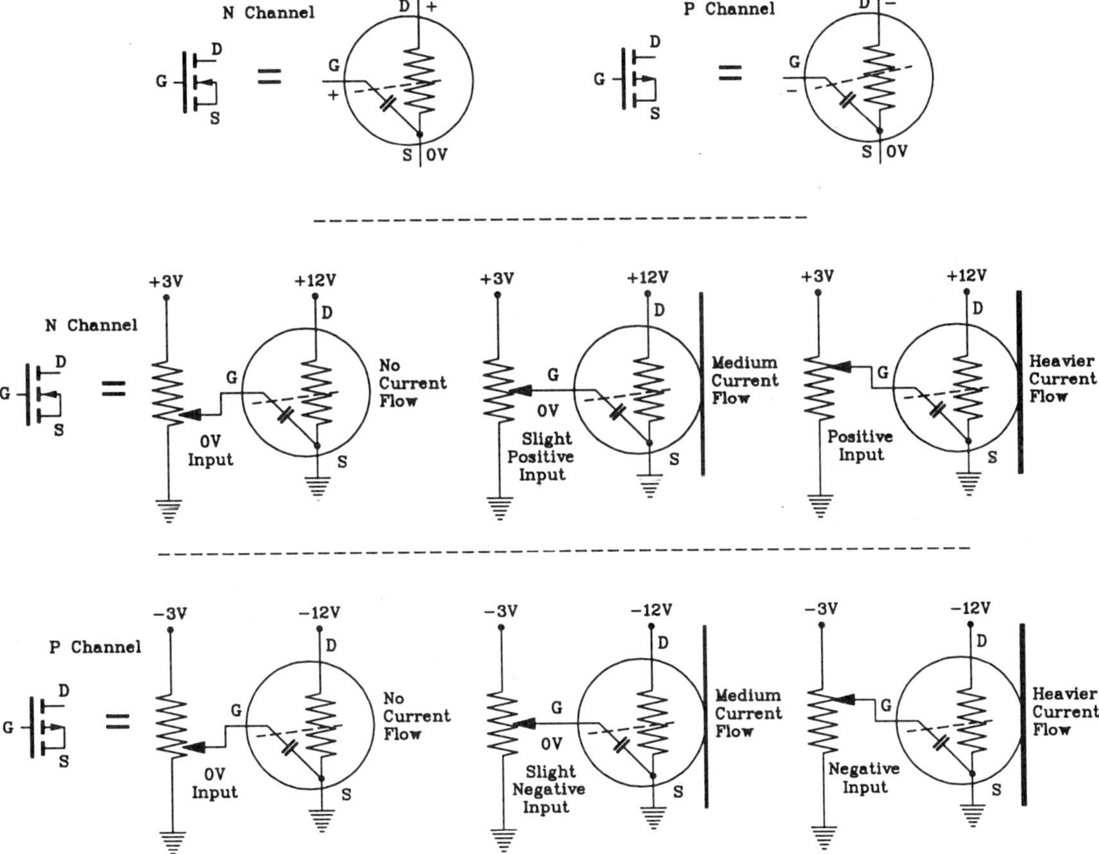

Figure 11–23 The enhancement-channel insulated-gate FET also varies the resistance of the source-to-drain channel in response to a voltage change between the gate and the source.

source to drain of the depletion-mode IGFET indicates that *there will be output circuit current flow if there is no input bias.*

The N-channel IGFET requires a positive voltage applied to the drain connection and a negative connected to the source. This is similar to the N-channel JFET polarity. The P-channel, of course, has all polarities reversed from those required for the N-channel device.

THE DUAL-GATE IGFET

The IGFET can be obtained with two input elements. This makes the device very suitable for mixing circuits, such as radio-frequency mixers.

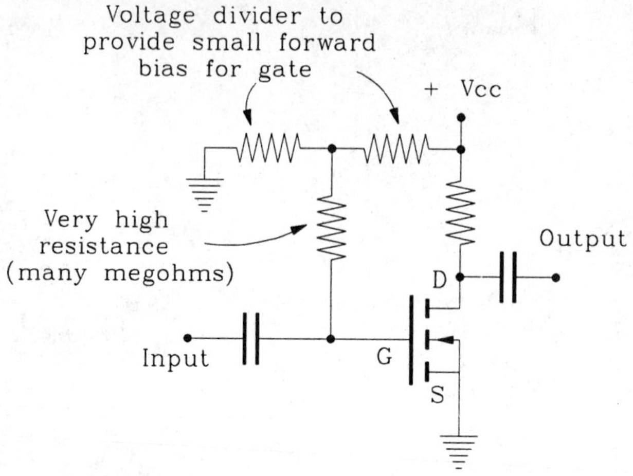

Figure 11–24 Biasing the enhancement IGFET

Radio-frequency IGFETs, including gallium arsenide field effect transistors (GAsFETs), are covered in more detail in Chapter 13.

The gate shown nearest the source is the primary signal input. The second gate can be used to establish the gain of the device or as a second signal-input element.

THE ANALOG SWITCH

The IGFET functions very well as an analog switch, passing signals such as DC and audio frequencies or turning them off in response to other DC control signals. This ability to control signals with other signals is being used in increasing numbers of applications, particularly when signals are to be controlled by digital means.

A common control circuit using the IGFET as an analog switch involves the use of an operational amplifier (op-amp). The op-amp is used because it has a virtual ground at the input of a negative-feedback, controlled-gain amplifier. The source lead of an IGFET is held constant, and the input gate is fed the controlling signal in order to pass the analog signals into the op-amp. See Figure 11–25 for a typical application of the analog switch.

IGFET FAILURE PATTERNS

Failures of IGFET circuits most often involve a failure of the insulated gate. This gate is insulated from the source and drain with an extremely thin insulator which is easily punctured by electrostatic discharges due to careless handling. Any leakage from the gate element to the semiconductor itself will result in unpredictable voltage drops across the device when it is

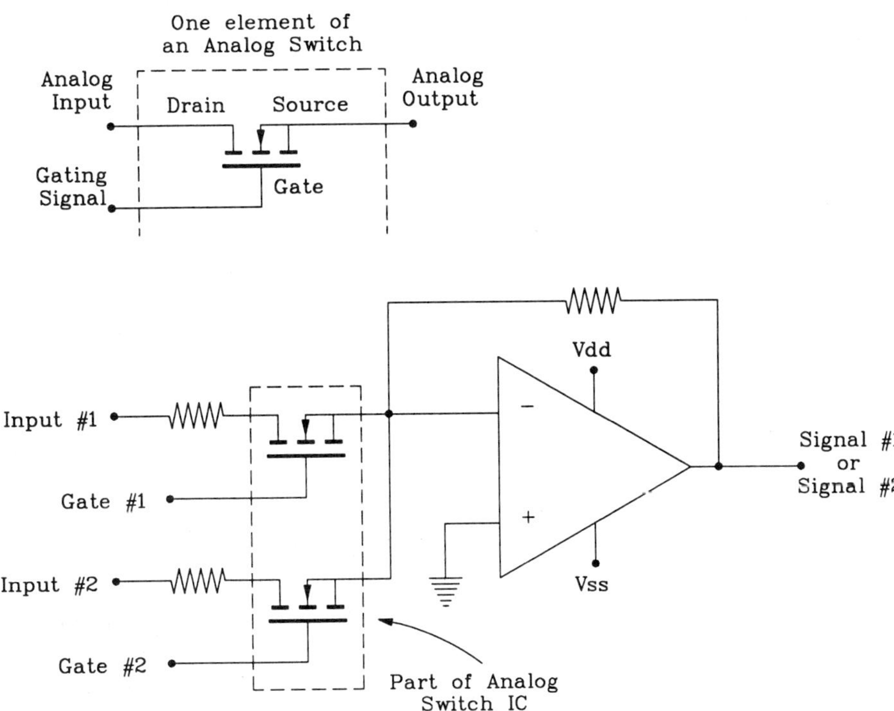

Figure 11–25 A typical circuit using the IGFET as an analog switch.

installed in a circuit. Replacement of the device is indicated if an out-of-circuit ohmmeter check shows any leakage at all from the gate lead to either of the two remaining leads. These devices will be discussed further in Chapter 12.

IGFET circuits all have some amount of resistance in the circuit to tie the gate to a known voltage potential. This resistance will make an IGFET gate seem defective if it is tested in-circuit. If an in-circuit check with an ohmmeter shows a resistance that is substantially less than the value of this resistance, the reading will indicate a damaged transistor. For instance, if a 10-megohm resistor was installed between the gate and the source of an IGFET, and if an ohmmeter shows a resistance of 5 megohms, there is most likely a bad IGFET.

TROUBLESHOOTING THYRISTOR CIRCUITS

Thyristors are semiconductors that are operated in either a cutoff or a saturated mode. These include silicon-controlled rectifiers (SCRs), TRIACS, DIACS (two-layer AC devices), SBSs (silicon bilateral switches), UJTs, and PUTs. They are commonly used in 60-Hz power circuits and are covered in detail in Chapter 14.

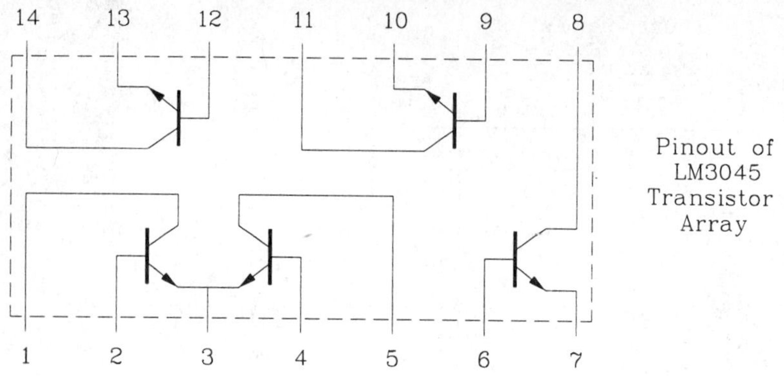

Figure 11–26 Schematic of a transistor-array integrated circuit chip.

11.5 TRANSISTOR AND RESISTOR ARRAYS

Rather than mounting many separate transistors on a board, a manufacturer may opt to use a *transistor array,* which consists of several transistors in an IC-like package. Such packaging of transistors can save space and speed the automatic assembly of the PC board.

The internal structure of a transistor array will not be evident by an inspection of the part. Instead, references will be necessary to determine the quantity and wiring of the internal devices. An example of such an IC is shown in Figure 11–26.

Resistors can also be made and packaged in an IC configuration. These resistors are often used to obtain a better match between resistors for special purposes, and, of course, to save space. It is also easier to insert one IC rather than seven or eight individual resistors. Figure 11–27 shows two common means of internally wiring these resistors.

Resistor packs are also made in small IC packages with only one row of

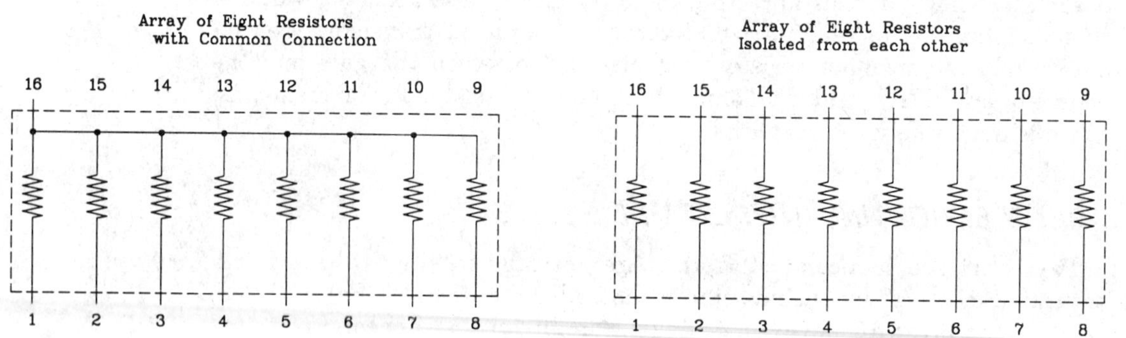

Figure 11–27 Sample resistor-array internal connections.

pins. These are called SIPs (single in-line plastic carriers). These packages are spaced with the common 0.1-inch spacing and can be inserted into a row of an IC socket.

Troubleshooting these resistor packs is quite simple. Keeping in mind the internal connections of the IC, check for resistance or voltage drops as though working with individual resistors.

CHAPTER SUMMARY

- Power diodes conduct only part of the time.
- Power diodes are generally made of silicon and pass heavy currents.
- Signal diodes deal with very small currents and voltages.
- Light emitting diodes have different voltage drops than power diodes.
- The biasing of a transistor amplifier determines how it will conduct both at rest and when given an input signal.
- The common-emitter circuit is the most common for a bipolar amplifier.
- The common-collector circuit is a constant voltage source, while the common-base circuit is a constant current source.
- A junction field effect transistor has a very high input impedance and is a voltage-operated device, as opposed to the current-operated bipolar transistor.
- The insulated-gate field effect transistor is also a voltage-operated device and is available in two versions.
- The depletion-mode IGFET requires no special biasing, being a natural Class A amplifier.
- The enhancement-mode IGFET requires circuitry to make it conduct.
- The analog switch, a special application of the IGFET, is often used with operational amplifiers.
- Transistors and resistors are sometimes made into IC-like packages to simplify the assembly of printed circuit boards.

REVIEW QUESTIONS

1. You are troubleshooting a diode bridge rectifier of an inoperative power supply and find zero-V AC as well as zero-V DC across one of the diodes. Is the diode bad?
2. A transient-protection diode prevents input pulses from going more than 0.7 volts from what voltage levels?
3. Why is a diode often connected across a DC-operated relay coil?
4. What DC voltage should you expect across a lighted green LED?

5. What is the reference element of a bipolar transistor?
6. What is a frequent cause of an incorrect bias voltage reading?
7. What is the normal approximate collector voltage in a Class A amplifier connected to a source of 20-V DC?
8. If a Class A amplifier has a bias problem that results in too little forward bias current, the collector-to-emitter voltage will be substantially _______ (*more* or *less*) than normal.
9. The bipolar transistor can be thought of as a _______-controlled _______ for the purposes of troubleshooting with a DC voltmeter.
10. The collector circuit of a bipolar transistor is a constant _______ source.
11. The constant source of question 10 is often used to charge a capacitor to produce a _______ voltage ramp.
12. Evaluating the operation of a Class B audio amplifier can be most effectively done by measuring the voltage across the _______ resistors, if they are provided.
13. You have found that one of the transistors in a complementary-symmetry amplifier has shorted. What should you also look for?
14. What can be looked for as an aid in identifying a Class C amplifier?
15. The voltage at the base of a common-emitter bipolar-switching amplifier will be driven as high as _______ volt(s) when saturated.
16. A switching transistor should be driven into _______ or _______, and not between.
17. You read 0.13-V DC between the emitter and base of a saturated bipolar-switching amplifier. The load is receiving normal "on" current. Is the voltage reading correct for this circuit?
18. You must troubleshoot a series of pulse amplifiers. To what should you pay particular attention, besides signal amplitude, as you signal-trace through the circuit with an oscilloscope?
19. What are the input and output elements of a source follower?
20. What element of a bipolar transistor is a good source for a constant voltage, regardless of load or Vcc variations?
21. A JFET transistor may be thought of as a _______-controlled _______ for the purposes of troubleshooting.
22. The principal advantage of using a JFET instead of a bipolar amplifier is its much higher _______ _______.
23. You wish to monitor the gate circuit of a JFET with a voltmeter: What must be kept in mind is the _______ effect of the meter.
24. The JFET most often fails by _______ of the _______.
25. The reference element of a JFET is the _______.
26. The IGFET reference element is the _______.
27. Which IGFET is a natural Class A amplifier?
28. With zero bias, a JFET will have _______ (*maximum, medium,* or *minimum*) drain current flow.
29. With zero bias, a depletion IGFET will have (*maximum, medium,* or *minimum*) drain current flow.

30. With zero bias, an enhancement IGFET will have _______ (*maximum, medium*, or *minimum*) drain current flow.
31. Which kind of IGFET is a natural Class C or switching amplifier?
32. What is the common purpose of a second input gate of an IGFET, which is usually shown above the primary signal input gate?
33. An analog switch is just a series of _______.
34. Failures of an IGFET usually involve the _______ lead.
35. An IC chip containing several transistor drivers is called a transistor _______.
36. What is the meaning of the acronym *SIP*?

Troubleshooting Analog IC Circuits

12

CHAPTER OBJECTIVES

This chapter will acquaint the technician with a few of the most popular kinds of analog integrated circuits. The operational amplifier is one of the most widely used analog integrated circuits in use today. The analog switch, the 555 timer chip, optical isolators and a short summary of special consumer ICs round out the chips discussed. At the conclusion of this chapter the student will:

- Realize the importance of having proper reference material.
- Be able to categorize the use of an operational amplifier by inspection of the associated circuit.
- Be able to predict to a certain extent the output of an operational amplifier, depending upon its use in the circuit.
- Recognize the analog switch and how it is used to switch analog inputs into operational amplifiers.
- Become familiar with the configurations in which the 555 timer chip is used, as determined by the associated circuitry.
- Understand and recognize the various types of optical isolators and why they are used.

- Know the troubleshooting methods to use for complex consumer chips.
- Become familiar with the troubleshooting tips for working on circuits with Surface Mounted Devices (SMDs.)

12.1 THE NEED FOR REFERENCE BOOKS

When working with any integrated circuit, it will be necessary to have the technical information for that chip on hand. Besides identifying the power and signal inputs and outputs, other pins may have special purposes such as serving as a bypass to ground through an external capacitor in order for the chip to act in a stable manner. An excellent reference, the *Linear Databook,* may be obtained from National Semiconductors (through CMC Publications, 408–945–1557) or get Motorola's *Linear and Interface Integrated Circuits Manual* (no. DL128, available through the Semiconductor Division of your local Motorola sales office).

Remember that all *inputs* to a chip should almost always be used or tied high or low. A floating input can act erratically, particularly on CMOS (Complementary Metal Oxide Semiconductor), PMOS (Positive Metal Oxide Semiconductor), or NMOS (Negative Metal Oxide Semiconductor) chips. Unused *outputs* should be left floating and should *not* be tied either high or low.

12.2 THE OPERATIONAL AMPLIFIER

The operational amplifier is an extremely versatile chip which provides both current and voltage gain. It can produce a specific gain by properly selecting a pair of resistors. The output voltage can be inverted or inverted from that of the input waveform. "Op-amps," as they are often called, are small and require very little power. They are available in specialized packages for very low power, extra high gain, low noise, and power applications. The following pages will feature some of the more generic properties and circuits and prepare the technician for troubleshooting operational amplifiers.

Basically, the operational amplifier has at least two inputs, (inverting and noninverting), an output pin, and two pins to connect to the supply source (Vcc (Positive Supply Source) or Vdd (Positive Drain Supply Voltage) and either a ground connection or a Negative Supply Source (Vss). See Figure 12–1.

An operational amplifier circuit may or may not have a feedback path from the output back into one of the inputs. The presence or absence of this

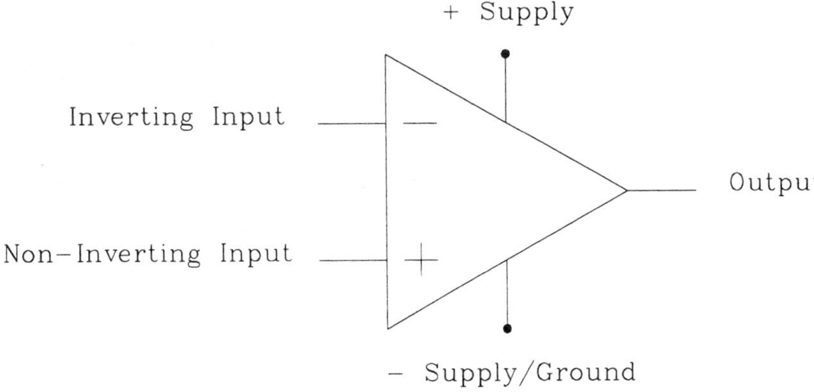

Figure 12–1 Schematic symbol for the operational amplifier.

feedback path is a very important clue to how the operational amplifier circuit is operated. The following is a list of the major uses for an operational amplifier:

1. Single input with feedback to the (–) inverting pin: used as a programmed-gain amplifier.
2. Single input with feedback to the (+) noninverting pin: used to develop a snap-action, variable-input voltage, but output can only be at one of the two possible rails.
3. Single input with the output tied to the (–) input: used as a voltage follower to provide current gain only.
4. Two inputs and no feedback: used as a high-gain voltage comparator.
5. Two inputs and negative feedback: a differential amplifier.

SINGLE-INPUT CIRCUITS

The operational amplifier is often operated with a single input. These circuits will be explained first. (Dual inputs are discussed later under "Dual-Input Circuits.")

The Operational Amplifier with Negative Feedback (Programmed Gain)

The basic circuits for a programmed-gain operational amplifier using the inverting input are shown in Figure 12–2.

The voltage gain of the negative feedback circuit is determined simply by the ratio between the feedback resistor (R_{fb}) and the input resistor (R_{in}). This gain is, of course, limited to the maximum gain the operational amplifier might be capable of achieving if the feedback resistor were completely eliminated.

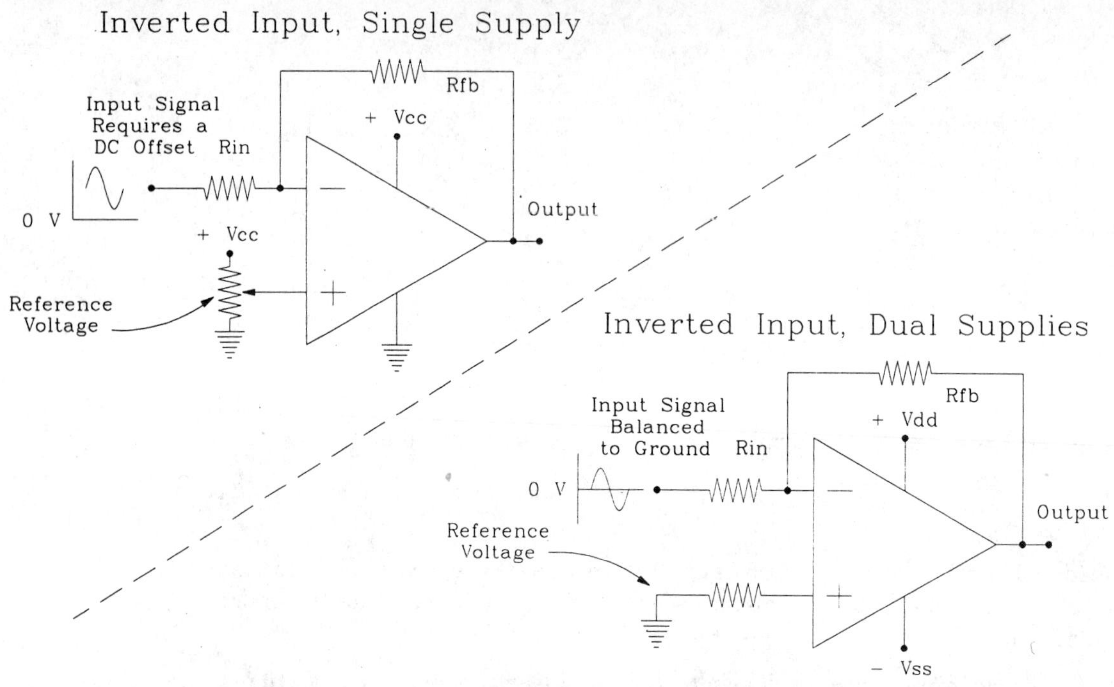

Figure 12–2 Basic circuits for programmable gain (negative feedback) with input to the inverting pin.

There are several facts about the operational amplifier when used in this configuration that bear careful note. First, if the input voltage to this circuit is less than that required to drive the output voltage to either rail (the most positive and most negative supply voltages connected to the chip), *an oscilloscope connected to the inverting pin of the chip will register no signal.* This is due to the presence of a *virtual ground* at this pin, which is the result of the complete cancellation of the input signal by the opposing voltage of the output through the feedback resistor. See Figure 12–3 for an explanation of virtual ground.

The operational amplifier with programmed gain may also have its input applied to the noninverting input. See Figure 12–4.

Some feedback circuits of an operational amplifier may use the three-resistor attenuator feedback arrangement shown in Figure 12–5 rather than a single resistor. This circuit uses lower values of resistors for a given gain of the circuit, which behaves as though a single resistor had been used.

Offset and Gain Calibration Adjustments

Either the input resistor (R_{in}) or the feedback resistor (R_{fb}) may be varied to change the gain of the operational amplifier. If the calibration range is

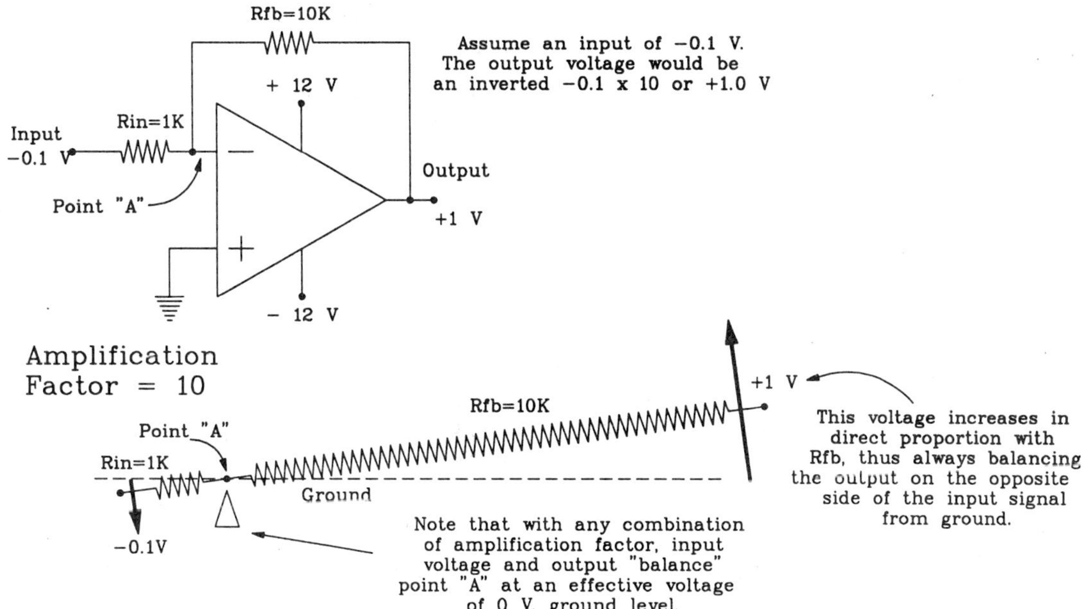

Figure 12–3 An explanation of *virtual ground.*

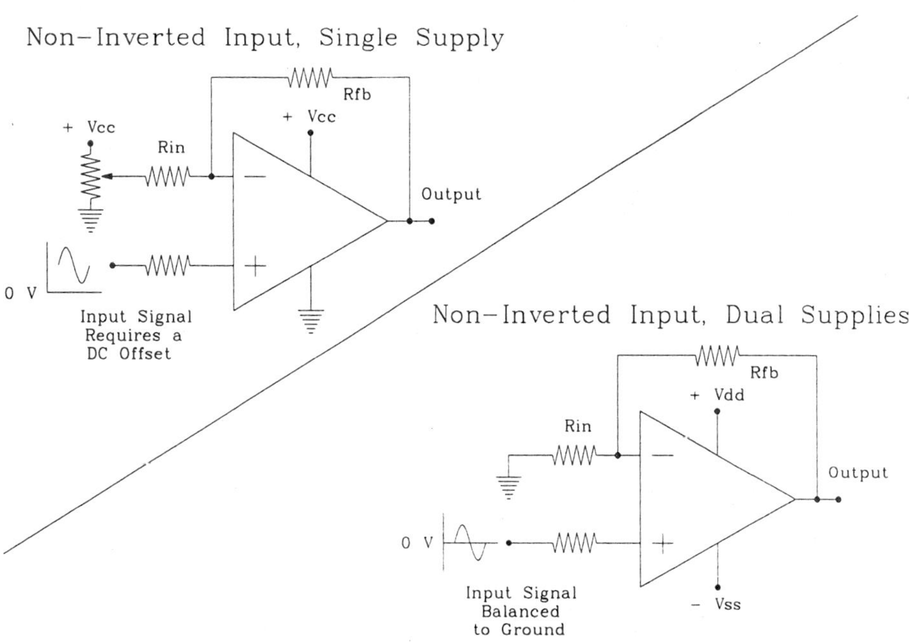

Figure 12–4 Basic circuits for programmable gain (negative feedback) with input to the noninverting pin.

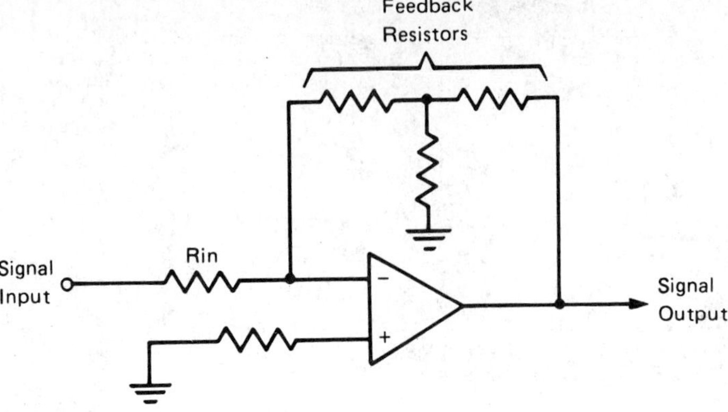

Figure 12–5 A variation of the feedback resistor for programmable gain.

to be restricted to a small percentage, a pair of resistors is often used; a larger resistance, which determines the "coarse" gain, and a smaller variable resistor to adjust the gain factor with a finer adjustment. This variable resistor might be called a *calibrate adjustment* or *vernier gain.* See Figure 12–6 and paragraph 10.5.

Another adjustment that may be present alters the DC offset. This adjustment is intended to ensure that at rest, the operational amplifier output is centered at the proper quiescent operating point in the absence of an

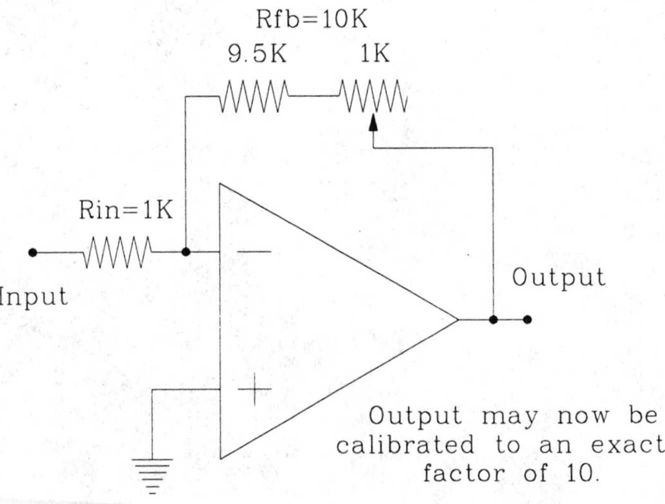

Figure 12–6 Using two resistors (one variable) for setting gain to an exact amount.

input signal. Variations in manufacturing will result in slight imbalances within the chips. These will cause the chip output to be other than zeroed to the proper quiescent point, even when the inputs are shorted together. An adjustment may be provided to make the chip produce the correct output when the input is shorted. This is a common calibration procedure for precision-gain operational amplifiers. To accomplish this adjustment, short the inputs together by whatever method is prescribed by the equipment manufacturer, and then adjust the offset control until the proper DC output voltage from the operational amplifier has been obtained. See Figure 12–7.

Failure Patterns of the Programmed-Gain Operational Amplifier

Many of the apparent failures of the operational amplifier are actually failures of the circuitry before the stage in question. Since these amplifiers deal easily with DC voltages, a bit of leakage of a capacitor feeding them will add a DC component that is amplified along with the signal. The output will, of course, have the same DC influence, but it will be multiplied by the amplification factor of the stage. Consequently, any apparent failure of an operational amplifier should be first investigated to be sure there is

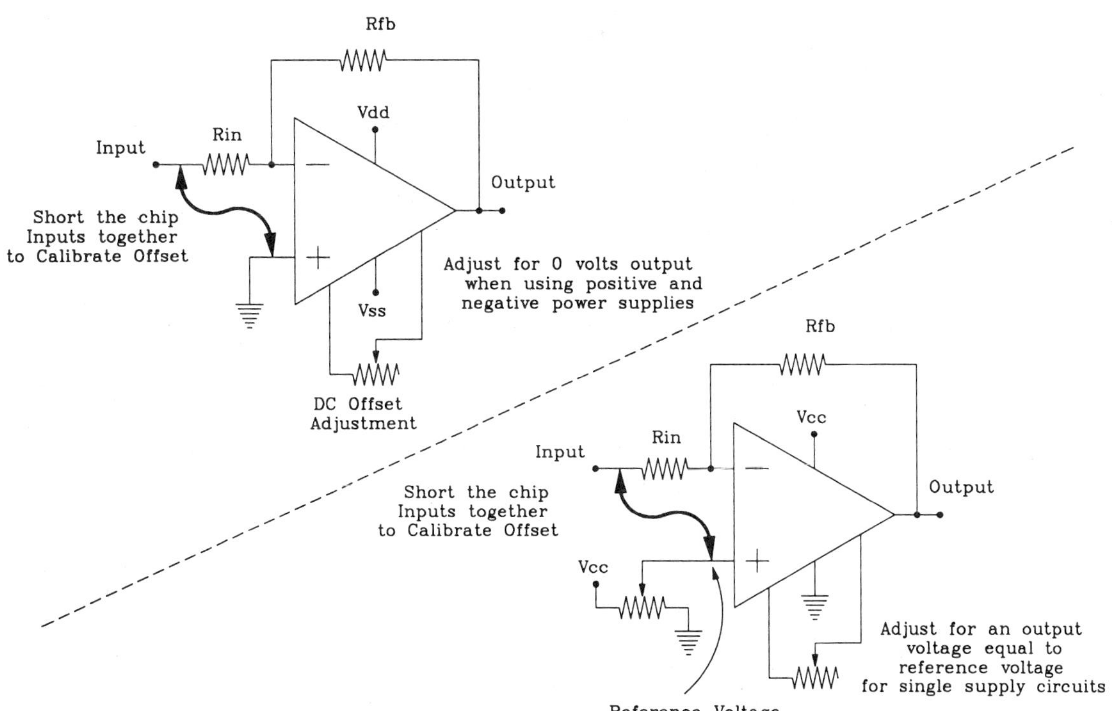

Figure 12–7 How to adjust the DC offset.

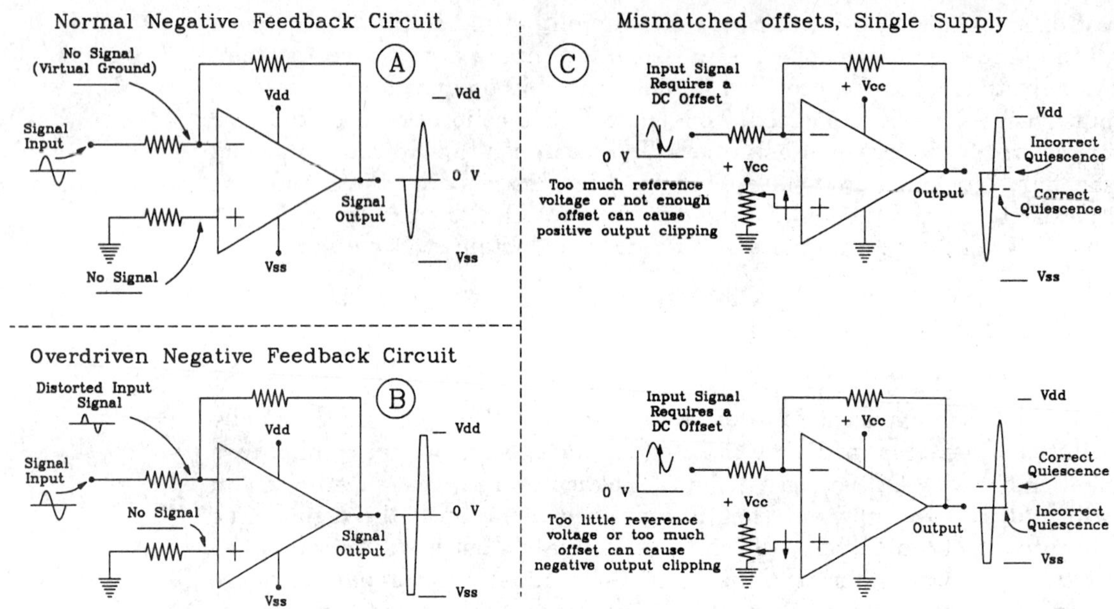

Figure 12–8 Troubleshooting the programmed-gain operational amplifier.

no stray DC component present on either input. Also be sure to check for the proper supply voltages, positive and ground, or a negative supply (if applicable) before determining that the operational amplifier is defective.

The negative-feedback operational amplifier offers a valuable checkpoint for troubleshooting. Check the signal present at the virtual ground: the inverted input pin, right at the IC. A linearly operated IC with an inverted input will have no signal here. See part A of Figure 12–8.

The presence or absence of a signal at the inverting input can tell much about the operation of the circuit. If an AC signal at the inverting pin is a series of positive and negative pulses, the operational amplifier may be driven into the rails, both positive and negative, by an excessive input. This symptom can also be caused by selecting R_{in} and R_{fb} resistors that result in excessive gain. See part B of Figure 12–8.

The presence of clipped positive pulses may mean that the reference input has too much positive DC offset voltage or the signal-input DC offset voltage is too low. The opposite case is true if clipped negative pulses are seen at the inverting input pin: in that case, the reference input is experiencing application of an excessive negative DC offset voltage applied or the signal input DC offset is too high. See part C of Figure 12–8.

If the input signal is the same on both ends of the input resistor, the operational amplifier may not be amplifying at all because of an internal

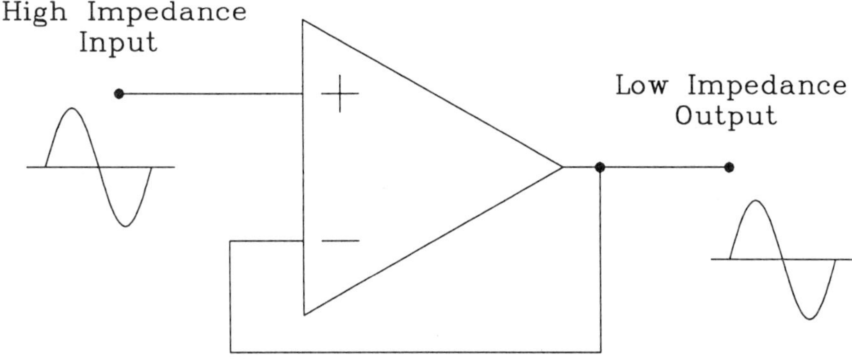

Figure 12–9 The voltage follower circuit.

failure, and will consequently have no output signal voltage. This symptom can also be caused by a shorted load on the output of the IC.

The Voltage Follower Circuit

Sometimes it is required that the current capability of a signal be amplified in its ability to drive a load, without the necessity of increasing the voltage available (a voltage amplification factor of 1). This can be done by using an operational amplifier as shown in Figure 12–9.

A defective voltage follower can be identified simply by checking the input versus the output. The lack of an output when the input is normal can also be due to the *following* stage having an internal short to ground or to the Vcc supply.

The Operational Amplifier with Positive Feedback (Snap-Action Output)

The operational amplifier with positive feedback will produce an output voltage that will snap high when the input voltage exceeds a certain voltage. When the input then drops to a *lower* voltage value, the output voltage will suddenly snap to the opposite rail.

As a way of explaining the operation of a positive-feedback circuit, consider this: If there were no positive feedback, the input could swing the output voltage from one rail to the other with only microvolts of difference from the reference voltage. Providing feedback resistance makes the output voltage hold at either rail. When the output is high, the feedback resistance will tend to hold the input voltage high. If the output voltage is low, the feedback switches low too, thus holding the input low. Any input voltage must overcome the tendency of the feedback resistor to keep the input at its present location. The less resistance there is in the feedback path, the

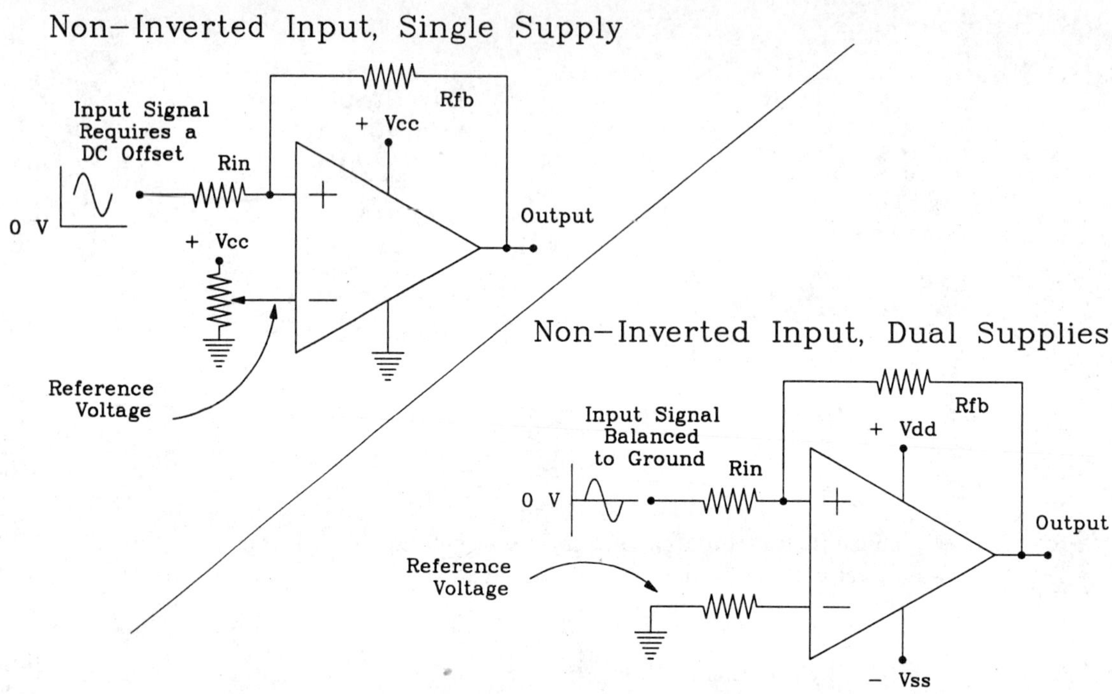

Figure 12–10 Basic circuits for snap action (positive feedback), with input to the noninverting pin.

greater the input voltage must be to overcome this "holding" voltage which originates from the output circuit. Once an input voltage overcomes the feedback voltage, the feedback will suddenly assist the input, resulting in a very fast snap action at the op-amp output.

The actual voltages required to toggle the output back and forth are determined by the amount of positive feedback, which is a function of the ratio of the input and feedback resistances. The lower the ratio, the wider the input voltage range required to snap the circuit output voltage to the opposite rail. Figure 12–10 shows typical circuits for this configuration.

The presence of positive feedback results in an amplifier that cannot maintain an output between the rails of the highest and lowest possible voltages. In other words, the output will be either high or low, and never in between. The high and low values will approach those of the supply voltages, Vcc and ground, or, in the case of dual supplies, Vdd and Vss. Since there will be small internal voltage drops within the transistors inside the chip, the output voltage will not go exactly to the rails, but will closely approach them.

The static operational amplifier with positive feedback will produce a constant output voltage near one rail. This output voltage will apply a very small current back into the input circuit that will, at first, oppose a changing input signal. When the input signal begins to overpower the feedback

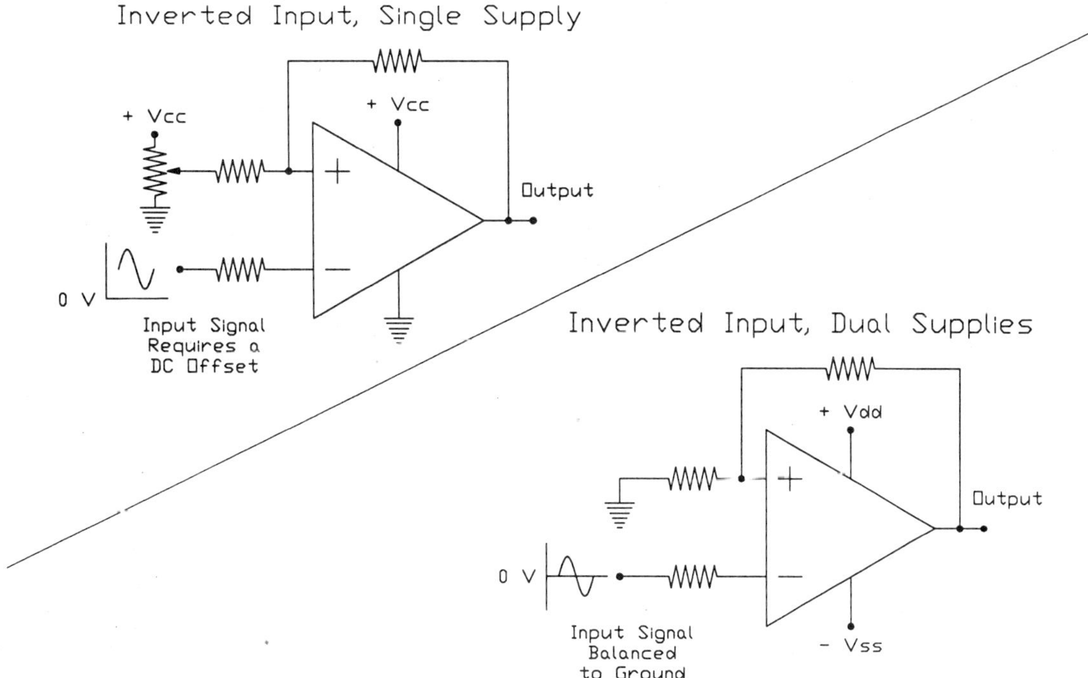

Figure 12–11 Basic circuits for snap action (positive feedback), with input to inverting pin.

signal, the output will suddenly change, suddenly producing an aiding signal which will force the operational amplifier output voltage to the opposite rail.

The operational amplifier with positive feedback may also have an input signal applied to the inverting input. See Figure 12–11.

DUAL-INPUT CIRCUITS

The operational amplifier basically provides an output voltage that amounts to the algebraic difference between its inputs. In other words, when two voltages are applied to the inputs of an operational amplifier, the amplifier output will depend on the relative values of both. The operational amplifier is operated with two inputs and negative feedback as a *programmed-gain amplifier*. If it is operated with no feedback at all, the circuit is known as a *voltage comparator*.

The Differential Amplifier Circuit

The differential amplifier will have an output voltage that is determined by two factors: the difference between the two input voltages and the ratio of the feedback and input resistors. As an example, if the ratio of the two

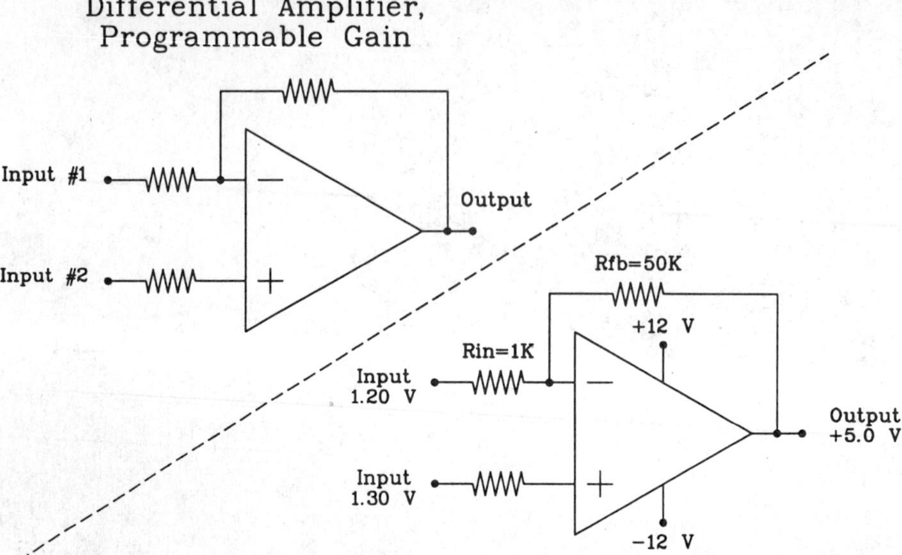

Figure 12–12 An example of how a differential amplifier operates.

resistors is 50:1 and the inputs signals are 1.20 and 1.30 volts at a given instant, the output voltage should be as shown in Figure 12–12. Notice that it is the *difference* between the input voltages that is amplified, and not the absolute value of either.

The Voltage Comparator Circuit

The voltage comparator is similar to the differential amplifier circuit except that there is no feedback. The high open-loop gain makes the output seek either the maximum or the minimum possible voltages of the supply. This circuit is used to provide a yes-or-no output signal indicating which of the two input voltages is greater in voltage. See Figure 12–13.

The output voltage expected from the voltage comparator can best be predicted by mentally "standing" on the voltage of the inverting pin. Compare the voltage at the noninverting pin. If the voltage at the noninverting input pin is higher than where you are located, then the output voltage should be near the high rail. The opposite is equally possible: if the noninverting pin is lower in voltage, the output will be near the low rail.

OPEN-COLLECTOR OUTPUTS

Some operational amplifiers require a pull-up resistor on the output to provide the "high," with an internal transistor to provide the "low" output

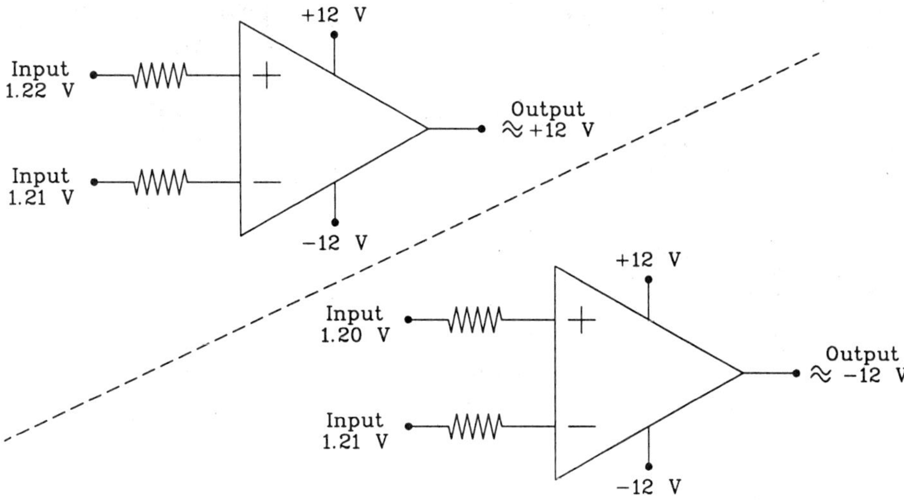

Figure 12–13 Two examples of how a voltage comparator operates.

level. This type of output circuit is called an open-collector output. It is used in circuits that require only a high or low output voltage, such as voltage comparators. See Figure 12–14.

Troubleshooting an open-collector chip should begin with a check that both the chip operating voltage (Vcc) and the secondary voltage source are

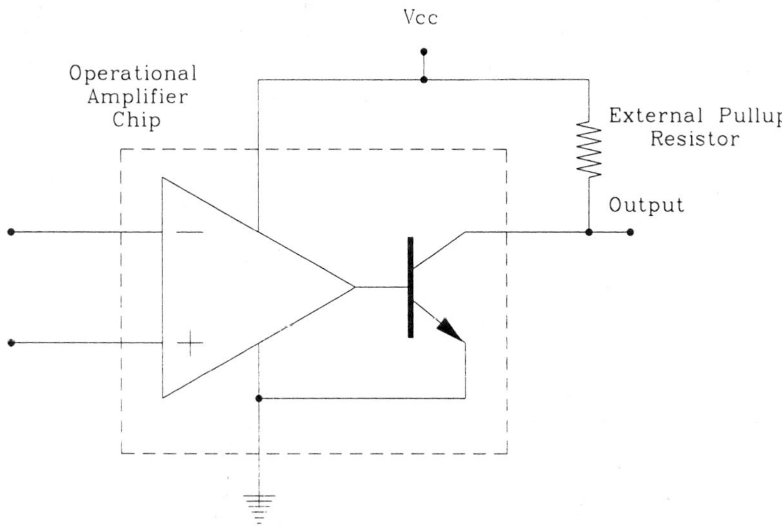

Figure 12–14 The open-collector output stage which is sometimes used within operational amplifiers.

supplying the proper voltages for operation. For instance, such a chip might require +5-V DC for the chip and the output stage might use +12-V DC for its operation. These stages are often operated in parallel, too. This results in a "wired-NOR" logic function and is most often used in digital circuits. Remember that all paralleled stages can seem defective if a single output is either bad or unexpectedly conducting.

ANALYSIS OF OPERATIONAL AMPLIFIER CIRCUITS

A summary of the above material might reduce to the following information. Upon inspecting an operational amplifier circuit, ask yourself the following question:

1. Is there positive feedback, negative feedback, or none at all?
2. How many *signal* inputs are there, one or two?
3. Are one or two power supplies provided?

Analyzing operational amplifier circuits is made easier by knowing what to expect. Depending on the answers to the above questions, here is what you may expect:

Type of Feedback

First, determine whether there is positive feedback, negative feedback, or none at all. (Refer to Figures 12–2 and 12–10 for examples.) If there is positive feedback, you should expect the output of the amplifier to be either at the positive or the negative rail. Because of this kind of feedback, a normally operating amplifier *cannot* have an output voltage between these two possible values. In the case of a single power supply, the output will be either near the value of the supply or nearly at ground potential. Internal voltage drops within the IC prevent the attainment of the actual supply or ground voltages.

The use of negative feedback makes an output voltage possible anywhere between the rails (in the case of a DC input voltage). This is the programmed-gain method of operating an operational amplifier. The exact voltage at the output will depend mostly on the programmed gain and the voltage difference between the two input pins of the IC.

If there is no feedback at all, the amplifier is operating at maximum gain. Operational amplifiers are capable of very high gain, as much as 100,000. Without feedback, all it takes is a microvolt or two of voltage difference between the two inputs to swing the output to either rail. If, by chance, the input voltages are very close to one another, circuit noise may be amplified, causing the output of the amplifier to switch from one rail to the other and giving the test instrument indications of what may appear to be noise or oscillations.

Number of Signal Inputs

Next, determine whether there are one or two signal inputs. (Refer to Figures 12–12 and 12–13 for an examples.)

There are two inputs to an operational amplifier. Even when it is operating with a one-signal input, the remaining input must be tied to a specific voltage. We shall call this the *reference pin.* When the reference pin is held at a constant voltage, the signal input is always compared to the voltage at that pin.

One Input, Negative Feedback. If the signal is applied to the inverting pin, watch for the virtual ground. Expect signal voltages at the input to the input resistor and at the output pin, but not at the input pin of the amplifier. If the signal is applied to the noninverting input, expect to see the signal at *both* inputs, even though the negative feedback point may seem a surprising place to find it. The signal appears here because of the voltage-divider action of the input and feedback resistors on the inverting pin. See Figure 12–15.

One Input, Positive Feedback. If the signal is applied to the noninverting pin, expect to see the signal at the input to the input resistor and

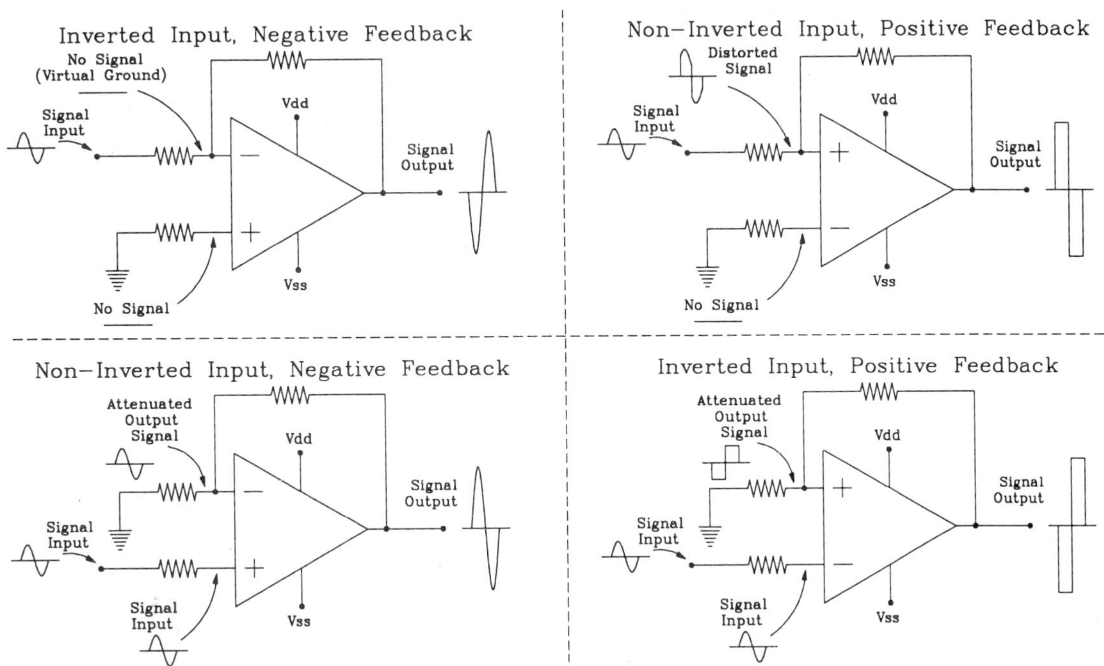

Figure 12–15 Troubleshooting criteria for various operational amplifier circuits.

to see the signal amplified with square-wave distortion at the input to the amplifier. The output should be at either rail with a DC input, or should go from one rail to the other with an AC input to the amplifier. When the input is applied to the inverting pin, the same signal will be seen at either end of the input resistor. The noninverting input will have an attenuated version of the output waveform, a square wave with an AC input. Again, see Figure 12–15.

Two Inputs. There are two principal uses for a circuit with double inputs: (1) to provide amplification of their *difference* (a differential amplifier) or (2) to provide a voltage output that is high or low, depending on the *relative amplitudes* of the two inputs (a voltage comparator). Refer back to Figure 12–12.

The use of programmed gain (feedback to the inverting pin) will indicate a differential amplifier. Only the voltage *difference* between the two input pins will be amplified by the gain of the stage. By measuring the DC voltages at the two inputs, the output of the circuit can be estimated. Keep in mind when troubleshooting that it is quite possible for a circuit defect to cause a small voltage difference to be amplified to a point where the output of the amplifier is held at one of the two rails.

The lack of feedback signifies that the circuit is being used as a voltage comparator as shown in Figure 12–13. In this use, the operational amplifier's output is determined by which of the two inputs is greater than the other. This application is similar to that of the differential amplifier just described, but the output of the voltage comparator is expected to be at one rail or the other because of the very high gain of the amplifier.

Number of Power Supplies

Dual Power Supplies. If two power supplies are available to operate the circuitry, this simplifies the use of operational amplifiers. The operational amplifier is, by its nature, a balanced amplifier. Using two supplies, one positive and the other negative, allows for placement of the quiescent operating point at ground. Both the input and the output voltages rest at zero, or ground voltage. When an incoming signal swings the input, the output varies above and below ground.

Single Power Supply. If only a single power supply is available, the operational amplifier is usually operated so that it is operated halfway between ground and the power supply voltage. This is accomplished with the use of some sort of voltage divider on the reference input. Figures 12–2, 12–4, and 12–8 show simplified circuits of this type. It is important to remember during troubleshooting that the output of the operational amplifier in the negative-feedback circuit (programmed gain) will be driven to match the reference input voltage in the absence of any external signal. Review Figure 12–7 for examples of this concept.

Another important point to remember is that the signal input to a single-power-supply operational amplifier circuit will need some DC offset to

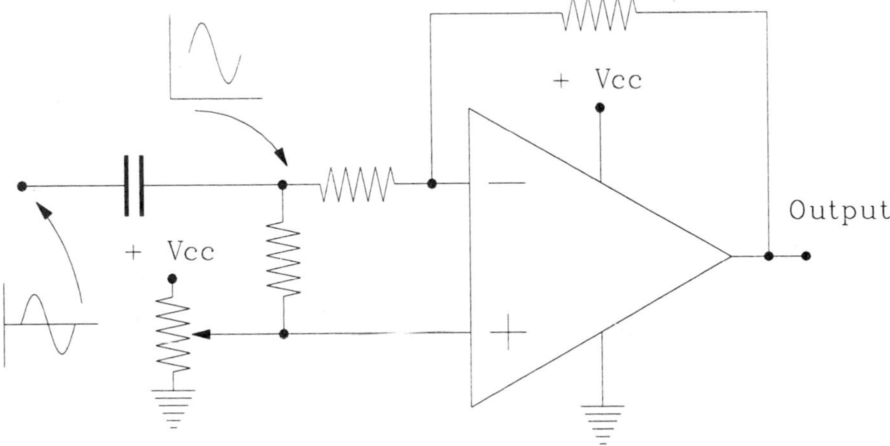

Figure 12–16 Use of a resistor and a capacitor to provide the DC offset voltage required for linear operation of an operational amplifier with a single power supply.

match that of the reference voltage. Failure to do this will result in the distortions shown in section C of Figure 12–8.

A simple way of providing the required DC offset is to use a capacitor and another resistor. The capacitor is used to change the DC level of the incoming signal to that of the reference voltage itself. See Figure 12–16.

12.3 THE ANALOG SWITCH

It is sometimes advantageous to switch an analog signal into an operational amplifier under the control of a gating signal. This makes it possible for a single operational amplifier to amplify one of several different possible inputs, only one of which will be enabled at a time. The gating signal is usually a digital control signal. See Figure 12–17.

The analog switch conducts (turns on) when the gating signal is of the proper polarity with respect to the internal source lead of the enhancement field effect transistor (FET). Consequently, it is best to keep the source lead at a constant voltage. The virtual ground of the programmed-gain operational amplifier provides this type of stable potential. Thus, the analog switch is most often used on the input of a programmed-gain operational amplifier.

The enhancement field effect transistor makes a pretty good switch. All one has to do is to drive the gate lead of an N-channel FET positive with respect to its source, and the device will change to a low resistance (typi-

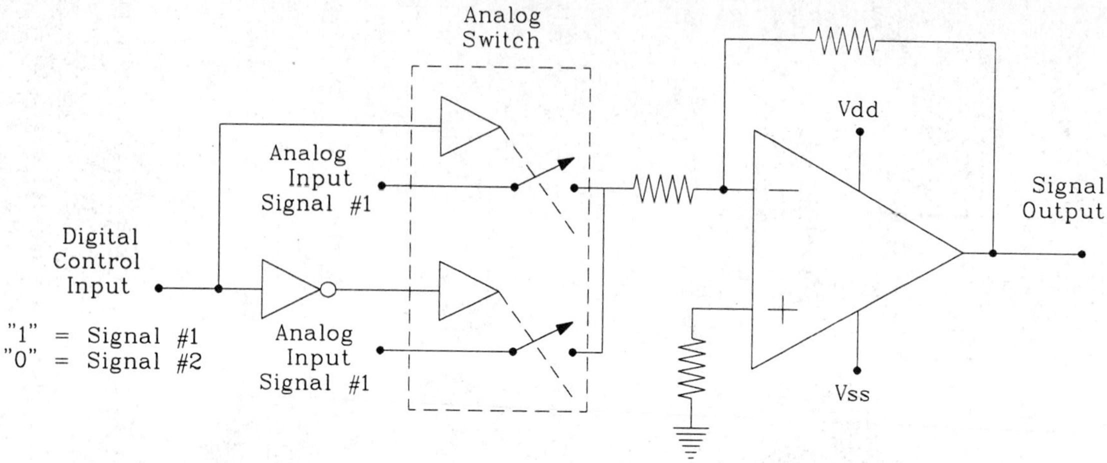

Figure 12–17 Example of switching analog inputs into a single operational amplifier.

cally, 10 to 400 Ω) between the source and drain connections. When gated open, the FET becomes many megohms of resistance.

An analog switch is an IC that contains several insulated-gate FETs. These FETs may be ganged together so that there is a common input or a common output line. Each FET within the IC is called a *channel.* One or more pins are then provided to control the conduction of the internal FETs, either individually or in sets. See Figure 12–18.

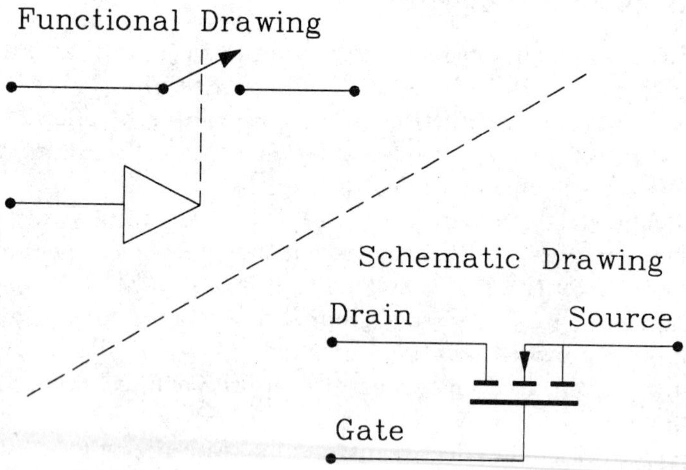

Figure 12–18 The internal workings of an analog switch.

TROUBLESHOOTING AN ANALOG SWITCH

The analog switch may be tested while in the circuit, using either AC or DC signal inputs. Monitor the input signal voltage from the input to the output pin of the switch, using a DMM for DC and low audio or an oscilloscope for higher frequencies. (Since the oscilloscope will probably be earth-grounded, a comparison of input to output will be necessary rather than a direct measurement across the device.) See Figure 12–19.

Most circuits using an analog switch will have high impedance, so an oscilloscope or DMM is recommended for testing them. If there is only negligible signal voltage drop between the input and output pins (less than a half volt or so), that channel is switched "on." If all of the signal voltage is found across the switch, the channel is switched "off." Changing the actuation voltage should reverse these indications if the channel is good. Continue testing any remaining channels in the same way. A voltage that does not change with the actuation voltage indicates a bad channel.

Analog switches that are designed to operate from TTL signals will, by definition of the TTL switching levels, turn "on" above a gate voltage of 2.4 V and turn "off" below a gate level of 0.8 V. This is important to keep in mind when troubleshooting any chips controlled by TTL digital logic chips. Remember, too, that a shorted load on any kind of chip output may make that chip seem defective when actually it is not. TTL chips are explained in Chapter 15.

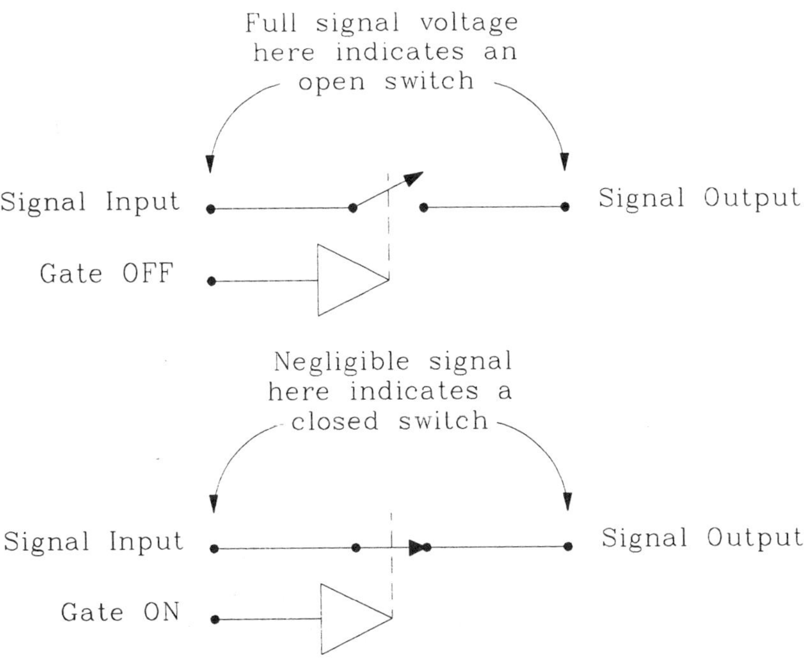

Figure 12–19 Troubleshooting the analog switch.

12.4 THE 555 TIMER CHIP

The 555 timer chip is a relatively simple chip that, like the basic operational amplifier, has been put to a great many uses in both analog and digital applications. While whole books have been written on this chip and its uses, for our purposes, the technician should simply be aware of the more common uses and typical circuits.

The 555 is used in two principal ways:

1. As a triggered time delay (monostable multivibrator), and
2. As a free-running oscillator, with or without pulse width considerations.

THE 555 BLOCK DIAGRAM

The operation of the 555 can best be understood by a careful study of the chip's internal block diagram. Basically, the chip consists of a 1/3–2/3 voltage divider and several voltage comparators, a flip-flop and output power amplifier, and a timing capacitor discharge transistor.

The heart of the chip is its three-resistor voltage divider. The basic function of the 555 chip is to compare external voltages to the voltages at the junctions of these resistors. Operational amplifiers monitor the differences between external voltages. These op-amps then control a flip-flop. The output of the flip-flop is used to allow an external capacitor to charge through an external resistor. When the voltage of the capacitor reaches two-thirds of the applied Vcc voltage, the charge is stopped. *The time required for the capacitor to charge from one-third to two-thirds of Vcc is the basic timing factor for the chip.* The output pin, no. 3, goes active low during this charging time. The discharge transistor is then used to discharge the capacitor, sometimes through an external resistance, back to the one-third voltage level. The chip is then ready to recycle. See Figure 12–20 for an internal block diagram of the 555 timer chip.

THE 555 CHIP AS A MONOSTABLE MULTIVIBRATOR (TIMER)

When pin no. 2 (Trigger) is pulled down to less than one-third of Vcc, the monostable operation of the 555 chip will result. This produces a single, positive output waveform of a duration determined by the formula:

$$\text{Time high} = 1.1\ R_{\text{charge}} \times C$$

Figure 12–21 shows a typical circuit using a 555 chip as a monostable multivibrator. This circuit can be recognized in that *pin no. 2 is a separate input* that initiates the timing cycle, and is not tied to the timing capacitor.

Pin no. 4 of the monostable circuit may be connected as an additional active low input to abort the charging time of the capacitor. This results in the output going negative to the original (high) condition earlier than it

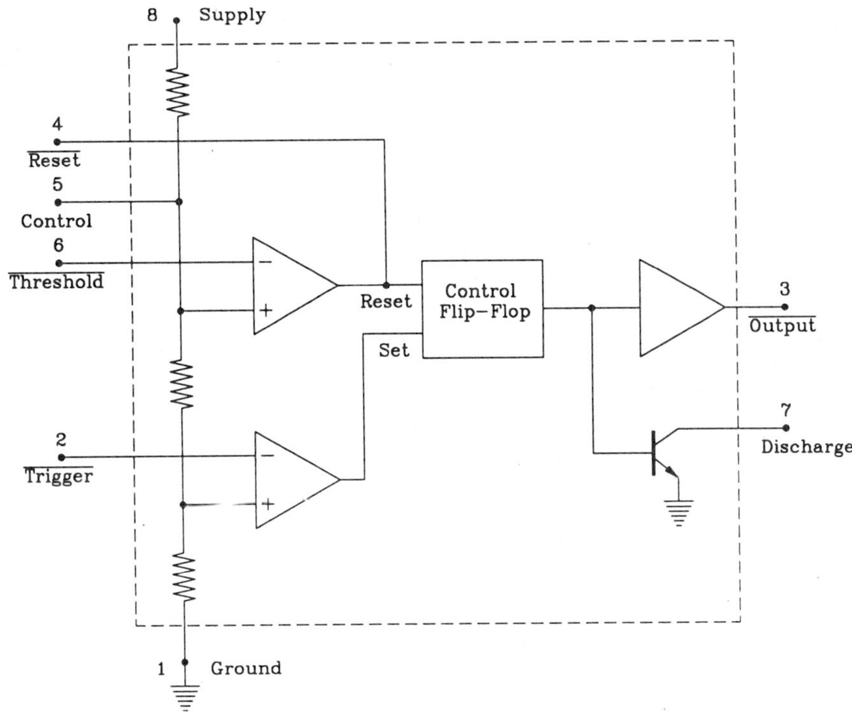

Figure 12–20 Block diagram of the 555 timer chip.

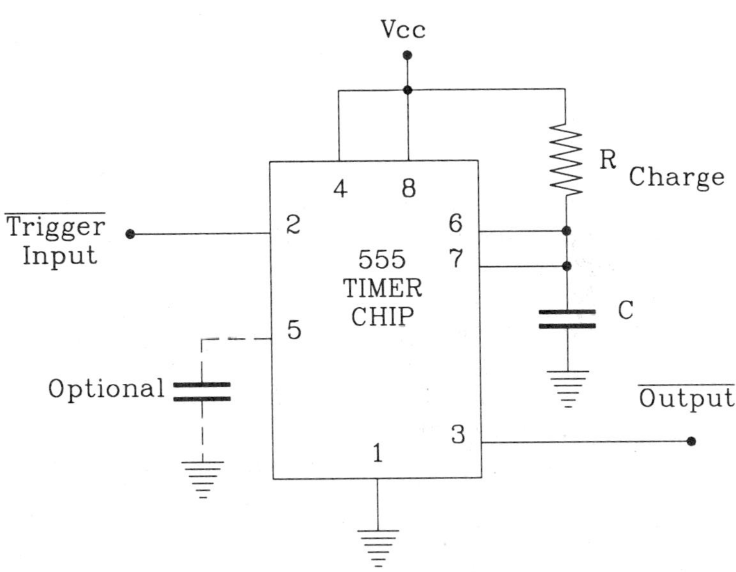

Figure 12–21 Typical 555 monostable multivibrator circuit.

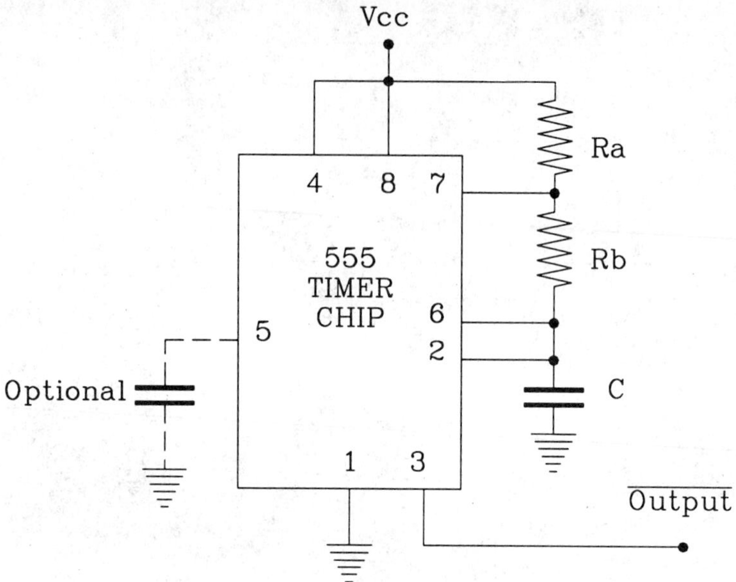

Figure 12–22 Typical 555 free-running oscillator circuit.

normally would if the capacitor were allowed to charge all the way to two-thirds of the Vcc voltage.

THE 555 CHIP AS AN ASTABLE MULTIVIBRATOR (OSCILLATOR)

The 555 finds frequent application as a simple, one-chip oscillator that is easily programmed from very low- to high-frequency operation. Fractional cycle frequencies (less than 1 Hz) to frequencies as high as a megahertz are possible merely by changing the values of the resistor and capacitor used in the timing circuit. See Figure 12–22.

The use of a 555 as a free-running oscillator is recognizable by the use of two resistors and the fact that pin no. 2 is connected to the timing capacitor. Because of the charging and discharging paths used in the circuit, the duty cycle cannot be less than 50 percent without the addition of several more components, including diodes to separate the charge and discharge paths. The duty cycle can be as high as 99.9 percent with this basic circuit, however.

In case it is necessary to estimate the period of the output waveform, use the formula:

$$\text{Period (secs.)} = .693\ (\text{Ra} + 2\text{Rb}) \times \text{C}$$

The duty cycle of the waveform generated by a given circuit can be calculated by this formula:

$$\text{Duty Cycle} = \frac{R_a + R_b}{R_a + 2R_b} \times 100$$

FAILURE PATTERNS

Failures of the 555, *when used as an oscillator,* can often be traced to the failure of pin no. 4 to be held high or a defective timing resistor or capacitor. The 555 itself can be defective as well, simply failing to oscillate. If the 555 is installed in a socket, replace it with a known good chip to see if this was the problem.

When the 555 is used as a monostable multivibrator, be sure that the trigger signal applied to pin no. 2 reaches a negative value of less than one-third Vcc. This is necessary for the trigger to bc effective. Also be sure that pin no. 4 is held high to enable the internal flip-flop.

The 555 can fail in a manner that will provide an output that is inverted from normal. In pulse circuits, this failure can disable later stages from operating, yet signal activity will continue to come from the chip.

12.5 OPTICAL ISOLATORS

The optical isolator provides two valuable benefits: isolating one circuit from another against electrical noise and also isolating circuits from each other's voltage and/or grounding potential.

When used to isolate voltage sources, the optical isolator often has very high (and very dangerous) voltages on one or both sides of the isolator. Consequently, the servicing technician must be aware of the possible dangers. Check the schematic diagram for the circuit in question to locate potential electrical shock hazards. Also keep in mind that an oscilloscope, if used, will introduce a direct connection to earth ground into the circuit when the scope probe ground is connected. Be sure that grounding the circuit will not cause damage before using a grounded oscilloscope on optical isolator circuits.

To troubleshoot these chips efficiently, find out what type of output device is used within the optical isolator chip. The output device might be a transistor, an SCR, or a TRIAC. See Figure 12–23.

Use of a reference book will be necessary to determine the details and pinout of a given chip. Depending on the design of the circuitry at hand, the optical isolator may be used in a linear manner (passing analog signals) or it may be operated as a simple on-off switch (switching applications.) For troubleshooting purposes, the technician must determine exactly how the isolator is being used, whether linearly or in a switching mode. Since a schematic diagram may not give sufficient information about how the circuit works, detailed information must be found in the theory of operation

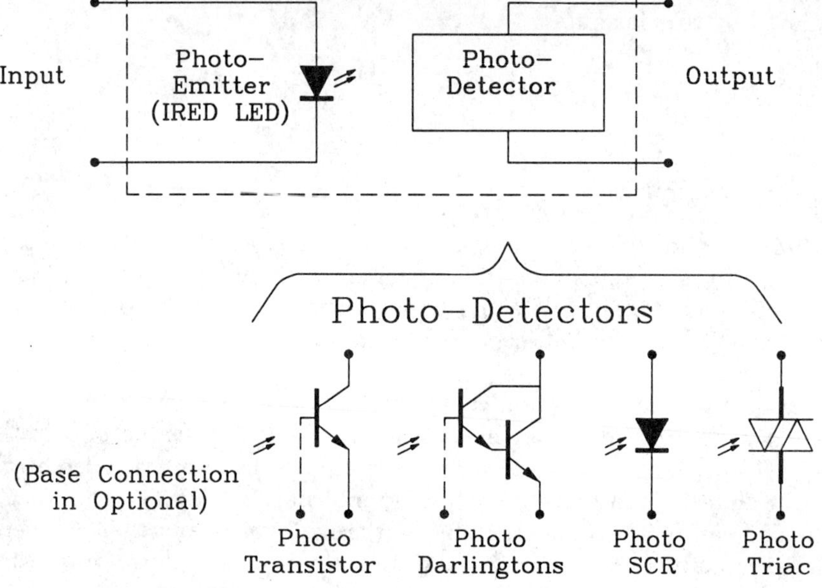

Figure 12–23 Schematic symbols for several kinds of infrared optical isolators.

for the circuit. Even when the theory of operation is available, linear or switching operation must often be obtained through deduction of how the isolator works rather than a direct statement.

FAILURE PATTERNS

Failures of optical isolators will most often be evident in that the isolator no longer passes signals from input to output. The output device inside an optical isolator may open or short, producing a constant output in spite of a normal signal input. When troubleshooting these devices, remember that the input LED is usually an infrared unit. This should result in a constant voltage drop of about 1.0 V across the input leads when the isolator is conducting. Substantially more than this voltage indicates an open LED, while less indicates a shorted LED.

12.6 CONSUMER IC CHIPS

Consumer chips are those that combine several stages of related circuitry in a single chip. For instance, Motorola produces the MC1357, which combines the intermediate frequency (IF) amplifier and detector circuits of a television receiver in a single chip. See Figure 12–24.

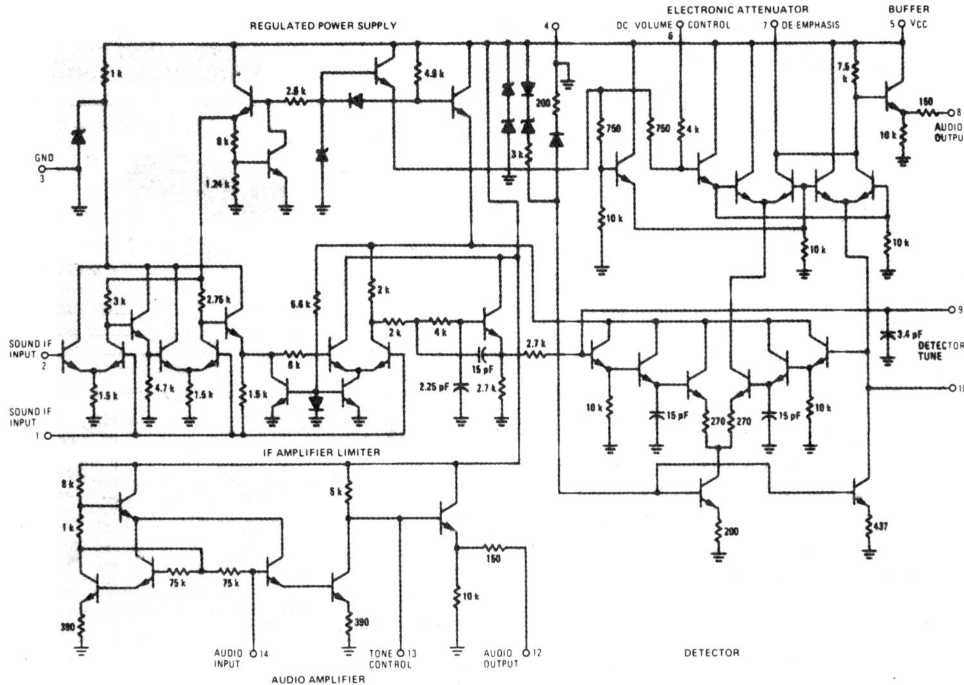

Figure 12–24 Internal schematic of a consumer IC chip illustrating the many functions available on a single chip. (Reproduced with permission from Motorola).

There is often a need for external voltage dividers to provide biasing and normal operating voltages to the various stages within a given IC. Because of this need, as well as the fact that capacitors are generally too large to place inside an IC, the connection of multiple external resistances and capacitors to consumer ICs is very common.

The consumer IC chip should be viewed as a "black box." A black box represents an unknown circuit that has a given input or inputs and from which we may expect a given output or outputs. The primary troubleshooting objective when dealing with these chips is to be sure, according to any documentation available, that the input signals, whatever kind they may be, are actually present and that they are of sufficient amplitude. All the inputs must also be checked to be sure that there is proper DC applied along with the signals (called *DC offset*), if applicable, or that there is no DC if none is required at that particular pin.

External circuit defects often make a chip seem defective when it is not. This is something to check when replacing the power output chips of an audio system. Be sure that the output lines are not shorted, which could cause excessive heat buildup in the output chips.

It is next to useless to try to troubleshoot a soldered-in consumer IC circuit without detailed information for that particular circuit. Without documentation for the circuit, an alternative is to compare the bad circuit with an identical, known good circuit. It may also be a good idea to simply replace the chip if it is installed in a socket, keeping in mind the cost of the chip, its availability, and the implications of a circuit failure that could ruin the good IC.

Since many of the consumer IC chips are used in DC-coupled amplifier stages which are prone to cascading-failure problems, it is wise to be sure that all the proper voltages are correct before installing a new chip.

FAILURE PATTERNS

Because of the wide range of consumer ICs, about the only generalization that can be made is that reliability will vary inversely with the power required of the chip. In other words, the power output ICs, some of which are quite large and provided with large heat sinks, are more likely to fail simply because they normally produce heat. These are the components that fail first.

12.7 TROUBLESHOOTING SURFACE-MOUNTED DEVICES (SMDs)

As mentioned in Chapter 18 and Appendix V, SMDs are very small, discrete components such as resistors and capacitors that require special care when troubleshooting. Press test leads to the traces of the PC board, and not on the ends of these tiny components. These fragile components can be changed in value or permanently damaged by scraping or gouging them with the sharp tip of a probe. Appendix V lists the common methods of identifying SMDs and reading their values. Remember also to avoid bending the PC board itself, since such action could break the components or their soldered bonds. Look for permanent test points installed as small wire loops on the circuit board. These may be marked on the board or on the schematic as "JT" ("Jumper, Test").

CHAPTER SUMMARY

- The operational amplifier is a very important analog device.
- The op-amp is used in two basic circuits, either negative or with positive feedback.
- A negative feedback results in a gain that is programmed according to the ratio given by dividing the resistance of the input resistor into that of the feedback resistor.
- Positive feedback in an operational amplifier results in the input "snapping" the output from one rail to the other.
- Using both inputs to an operational amplifier results in what is

known as a differential amplifier, which amplifies only the voltage difference between the two inputs.

- The analog switch is just an IGFET, which is used to switch analog signals under the control of a digital yes-no gating signal.
- The 555 chip is used as an oscillator or monostable multivibrator.
- Optical isolators use an infrared LED to drive various output devices, providing noise isolation and isolation of voltage or ground between two different circuits.
- Troubleshooting tips for repairing circuits having consumer chips include checking for proper input voltages, both AC and DC.
- Surface-mounted devices require special care to avoid component damage during troubleshooting.

REVIEW QUESTIONS

1. What are the five basic uses for an operational amplifier?
2. How is the gain of a negative-feedback amplifier determined?
3. How can the virtual ground be shown using an oscilloscope?
4. Will the input signal to a programmable-gain op-amp circuit always be inverted at the output?
5. Generically speaking, how is the DC offset control of an op-amp circuit adjusted in order to "zero" the chip?
6. What two factors should be checked before assuming an op-amp is defective?
7. You find that a small input signal is the same amplitude on both ends of an op-amp input resistor. Name the two common causes of this symptom.
8. The output voltage waveform of a negative-feedback op-amp circuit is clipped on both the positive and negative peaks. What is the probable cause?
9. Analysis of an op-amp circuit shows an input to the positive (noninverting) pin and also shows that the output of a stage is wired directly back to the inverting input. What kind of a circuit is this, and what is its gain?
10. What is the basic input/output characteristic of an op-amp with positive feedback?
11. Can a positive-feedback op-amp circuit have programmable gain?
12. What is the expected output voltage of a positive-feedback op-amp?
13. Why can't the output voltage of a positive-feedback op-amp ever reach the exact voltage of either rail?
14. Can a signal input be applied to the inverting pin of a positive-feedback op-amp circuit?
15. If no feedback path is provided for an op-amp, the circuit is called a ________.

16. What two factors determine the given output voltage of a differential amplifier?
17. You wish to determine the output voltage expected of a voltage comparator. If you use the _______ pin of the op-amp as a reference, the relative voltage at the _______ pin (higher or lower) will determine if the output should be high or low.
18. What would be indicated if you see a resistor from the output lead of an op-amp that leads to the positive supply?
19. An analog switch is basically a series of _______-type _______s.
20. Each controlled switch of an analog switch is called a/an _______.
21. Where can a technician measure an analog input voltage to see if an analog switch is operating properly?
22. What are the two basic ways in which a 555 timer chip is used?
23. How can one tell, when inspecting a schematic, in which of two ways a 555 time chip is being operated (see question 22)?
24. What is the peak negative trigger voltage required of the signal to pin no. 2 of the 555 timer chip to properly trip the multivibrator?
25. What are the two reasons to use an optical isolator?
26. You intend to use an oscilloscope in a circuit that uses an optical isolator. What must you keep in mind?
27. What is the normal voltage drop across an infrared LED when it is operated from a DC source?
28. Defective equipment containing consumer chip stages should first be checked for correct supply voltages, and then for proper _______ and _______ at appropriate pins.
29. What must be remembered when probing around in SMD circuits?

Radio Frequency Components and Troubleshooting

13

CHAPTER OBJECTIVES

This chapter will acquaint the technician with some of the unique instruments, components, and generic problems likely to be encountered in servicing radio frequency equipment. A basic understanding of communications fundamentals must be assumed (this is available through other radio texts). An explanation or expansion of those basic principles will be given where applicable to the topic of troubleshooting. At the conclusion of this chapter, the student will:

- Be familiar with the variations of rules and regulations governing the maintenance of transmitting equipment.
- Know what to look for and what to do on an RF equipment service call.
- Be familiar with generic RF test instruments, including internal operation, where appropriate.
- Have been exposed to the unique components used only at RF frequencies, such as quartz crystals, VVCDs, frequency mixers, and PIN diodes.
- Have been introduced to generic methods of RF equipment testing, using specialized RF instruments.

- Become familiar with the use and capabilities of a service monitor.
- Know the reason for using special RF adjustment tools.
- Know how to adjust an RF receiver and transmitter, using generic methods.
- Know the cautions of RF component replacement.
- Be familiar with the special components and techniques used at microwave frequencies.

13.1 A BRIEF OF FCC COMMUNICATIONS REGULATIONS

Radio communications require, at the most basic level, a transmitter and a receiver. It is legal to work on any receiver without a license of any kind. Misadjusting or tampering with a receiver cannot do much damage to other communications. Such is not the case, however, when working on transmitting equipment. A misadjusted transmitter can actually endanger lives and property by producing unintentional interference. Consider what might happen if a police or ambulance radio transmission is not received in a timely manner due to interference and you can see why the law requires that anyone working on a transmitter must be licensed. Almost all the laws of the Federal Communications Commission (FCC) in regard to maintenance are concerned with the proper operation, maintenance, and repair of transmitting equipment.

BASIC FCC LAW

The basis of most FCC laws is a reasonable assertion: it is illegal for anyone to interfere with radio transmissions. If the interference was unintentional, a notice of violation may be issued by the FCC, *which must be answered in writing.* Intentional violation may easily result in more severe penalties, including fines and/or imprisonment.

Another law is that, regardless of the licenses required, anyone may, in a true emergency (such as imminent danger to life or property), use any means available to summon help.

The intentional destruction of transmitting equipment is also illegal and carries heavy penalties. This law is aimed at those who would destroy radio equipment with the effect of placing human life in danger, particularly on the high seas.

Besides these laws, additional regulations address the matter of licensing those who use radio equipment as a matter of ensuring some minimal knowledge on the part of the operators (this is the operator's license). Other regulations provide for the licensing of the transmitting equipment (a station license) to minimize interference on common and adjacent frequencies.

SPECIFIC LAWS VARY WITH SERVICE

Commercial Broadcasting

Commercial broadcasting stations require both operator and station licenses. The station license is the authorization by the FCC for the use of the frequency at a specific level of power. Routine operators require at least an FCC restricted operator's license. The station licensee is responsible for the technical operation of the station, and must hire qualified personnel as necessary for the purpose.

An AM station operates on one of 107 specified frequencies between 535 and 1605 kHz. Each channel is 10 kHz wide. All stations are required to keep modulation below 100 percent and RF power at a level within a few percentage points of that authorized on the station license. The station licensee is responsible to ensure that the antenna current is correct, particularly if multiple towers (a directional antenna array) are involved.

An FM commercial broadcasting station will be operated on one of 100 channels from 88 to 108 MHz. The maximum deviation allowed is +/– 75 kHz from the carrier frequency. With an additional 25 kHz guard band on both ends of a channel, each channel will have a total width of 200 kHz. The power output to the antenna (which usually has considerable gain due to the use of stacked elements) must again be within a few percentage points of what is authorized on the station license.

Television stations operate on one of the 12 TV channels allocated in the ranges of 75–86 MHz (low band) or 174–216 MHz (High band), or else on one of the 55 UHF channels available, between 470 and 806 MHz. Each of these channels has a picture carrier with a sound carrier located close to it, occupying a total channel width of 6 MHz. The picture carrier is amplitude-modulated, while the sound carrier is frequency-modulated.

Citizens Band (CB)

No operator license is currently required to operate a citizens band (CB) radio. Infractions of rules of common sense or of the interference rules can, and likely will, result in a notice of violation from the FCC.

Tinkering with a CB transmitter can easily cause interference to other radio services and lead to an FCC Notice of Violation, or "ticket." *Modulation must be less than 100 percent and the power input to the final amplifier must be no more than 5 watts.*

The information of Appendix IX will be useful when working with CB transceivers. It includes a listing of the CB channels and their frequencies.

Amateur Radio Service (Hams)

The amateur operator must pass comprehensive tests on radio theory, FCC regulations, and sometimes even Morse code to earn a license. There are five levels of licensing, each with greater difficulty of testing but more privileges than the previous level. These licenses are a combination operator and station license. The classes available are Novice, Technician, General, Advanced, and Extra Class. A new, "codeless" license is now available that offers all amateur privileges above 30 MHz.

Amateur radio operators can repair their own equipment, and they are actually encouraged by the FCC to do research and development of communications projects and ideas, within the limitations of their licenses. They use blocks of frequencies from just above the broadcast band (1800 kHz) to far up into the microwave frequencies. The low-end frequencies of each of the common amateur bands are 3.5 MHz, 7 MHz, 14 MHz, 21 MHz, 28 MHz, 50 MHz, 144 MHz, and 220 MHz. Other additional bands are available at even higher frequencies.

The methods of communication within the amateur bands cover most types of modulation: single sideband (SSB), FM, CW (continuous wave, "Morse code"), television, and packet. Up to 1000 watts of power into the antenna is authorized in most cases, although there is a stipulation that the minimum amount of power necessary be used for communications.

NABER and CET Licenses

Electronics technician certificates are available from the National Association of Business and Education Radio (NABER). This certificate is earned by paying a fee and passing a standardized test.

A similar apprentice certification, Certificated Electronics Technician, may be obtained by contacting a local representative. This program is managed by the National Electronic Associations, Inc. The location of the nearest test adminstrator may be obtained by contacting:

ETA, I Director of Certification
P.O. Box 1258
ISU Station
Ames, Iowa 50011

While neither of these certificates is required by law, they are recognized in some fields and may be required for employment as a consumer electronics technician working on entertainment radios, TVs, videocassette recorders (VCRs), and the like.

Marine Radio

Every vessel equipped with a radio must have an authorization from the FCC in the form of a station license. Each operator must have at least a Restricted Radiotelephone Permit. An FCC Form 753 is used to apply for this permit.

In addition to communications, each vessel must be licensed by the FCC before using radar and, if installed, a high-seas radio installation. The radar authorization is an endorsement on the basic station license, which, by itself, authorizes a VHF-FM radiotelephone. A high-seas radio is necessary only when operating the vessel off-shore, beyond about 50 miles out. Beyond this range, VHF-FM communications are not reliable. High-seas radios use blocks of frequencies from 2 to 23 MHz. They make use of ionospheric skip to cover great distances with little power.

VHF-FM is the primary communications media for vessels in and near port. It is used to listen to channel 16 marine party line, for initial radio contacts and for distress calls. Marinas and bridges may be contacted to open, if necessary, using this service on appropriate channels. Communications to other vessels for traffic safety reasons and for placing telephone calls (via the marine operator) are all possible using a VHF-FM marine set. Marine equipment may be maintained only by the holder of an FCC General Class license, with radar endorsement, if appropriate.

Appendix IX will prove useful when working with VHF marine frequencies. This appendix lists the frequencies of the most important channels.

Aviation

Because of the importance of communications in the operation of aircraft, it is easy to see why only qualified, experienced persons are allowed to give the final inspection and certification of avionics equipment. This requires two major accomplishments: a proper, appropriately equipped shop and experienced repair personnel who have demonstrated their competence.

The first step, the shop, is made available by an employer. During an 18-month training period, the shop supervisor is responsible for certifying the new repair technician's work. After having repaired avionics equipment or been in training for repairing such equipment for 18 months or more, a repair person may qualify for an Federal Aviation Administration (FAA) Repairman's Certification. The recommendation required for this certificate must be supplied to the FAA by the shop supervisor. Once certificated, the repair technician may inspect his or her own work.

Working in aviation with a certificate is unique. Once a technician leaves a particular shop, the certification expires. After finding employment at a different shop, recertification must done, but it will not require another 18-month training period.

Government/Military

The U.S. government, including the military services, the Federal Aviation Administration, the National Space and Aeronautics Administration (NASA), and others, do not require FCC licensing for stations or individual operators. Possession of a General Class FCC license is, however, a good license to have in hand when applying for jobs with the U.S. government, since it shows formal evidence of endorsement by the government itself.

Public Safety

Public safety organizations such as police, fire, and ambulance companies must have their transmitting equipment repaired and maintained by a holder of an FCC General Class License. Sometimes the larger of these organizations will have one or more persons employed part- or full-time to handle such tasks.

Business

Businesses such as taxis and towing companies, including paging companies and the telephone company, have need for General Class licensees to maintain transmitting equipment that is located in vehicles, carried by hand, or installed in permanent locations. Both the transmitting equipment and the operators must be licensed, with operators required to have at least a Restricted Permit.

13.2 WHEN A PROBLEM IS REPORTED

There are two things that a service technician should consider before removing equipment or making checks on it:

1. Is there a possibility that the operator may have caused the problem?
2. Should communications really occur under the given circumstances?

POSSIBLITY OF AN OPERATOR PROBLEM

If the equipment operator is new to the position, there is a chance that a switch is not in the right position or that the correct button was not pressed. With the options available on some of today's sophisticated equipment, this is a very real possibility. Modern amateur radio equipment, for example, often requires hours of studying the instruction book before it can be intelligently operated—and even then it is easy to hit the wrong button or the right buttons in the wrong sequence. On the other hand, if there are only a few controls or if the operator has used the equipment for a long time (possibly every day for months), then the chance of operator error is remote.

ASSESSING THE COMMUNICATIONS CONDITIONS

Communications systems rely on the transmission of information from a transmitter and the reception of that signal into a receiver. Anything that can interfere with the path of the transmission can make the transmitter and/or the receiver appear defective when this is really not the case. An example of this might be a small VHF transceiver that reportedly will not transmit a mile to another transceiver. An interview of the operator might reveal that communications were attempted while one was within an office building, which is, effectively, a metal shield entirely surrounding the operator and the transceiver. Had the operator stepped to a window favoring the line-of-sight required for VHF communications, good communications might have occurred after all.

13.3 SOME UNIQUE RADIO FREQUENCY COMPONENTS

THE RADIO FREQUENCY CRYSTAL

A radio frequency crystal is used to provide very stable oscillations at radio frequencies. It is relatively insensitive to voltage variations and temperature and humidity. It can be ground to hold a tolerance of +/– .0005 percent of the marked frequency for months at a time without adjustment. It is this component that ensures that all of the communications of today are on-channel and stable.

A crystal is ground for operation at only one frequency. In equipment operating on one to perhaps a half-dozen channels, each channel for transmit and each channel for receive will use its own specially ground crystal for frequency stability. On equipment operating on more channels than this, the phase-locked loop (PLL) is the logical choice for generating many frequencies without the expense of crystals for each channel. (The PLL is covered later in this chapter.)

Crystals can be ground so that they operate on a harmonic of their fundamental frequency, with the third-overtone type being the most common. Such a crystal will be physically thicker and more rugged than one ground to operate directly at the higher frequency. These crystals are often used to generate frequencies beginning at about the citizens band (27 MHz) and up. They are particularly useful for generating the frequencies required of the local oscillator in receivers. Transmitters more often use fundamental crystals, then use frequency multiplier stages to multiply the frequency up to the channel frequency.

The technician may encounter a unit called a *crystal resonator*. These crystal-like devices have a tolerance of only about 1 percent. Their principal use is as clock sources for microprocessor circuits or as filters in the IF stages of receivers, and their chief advantage is that they are less expensive than a communications crystal. A crystal resonator is never used to determine a transmitter's frequency.

THE VOLTAGE-VARIABLE CAPACITANCE DIODE (VVCD) OR VARACTOR DIODE

Mechanically variable tuning capacitors are made for analog tuning, but they are mechanically unreliable and relatively fragile. Their plates are easily misaligned or bent, causing shorting and failure of the units. In addition, multiple-sectioned, ganged variable tuning capacitors for tuning many stages simultaneously become difficult to use at VHF and UHF frequencies.

The modern solution to ganged tuning of many stages is the use of the tuning diode. This diode is made with a relatively large junction area. As the diode is reverse-biased, the depletion area of the junction becomes a capacitive dielectric and the diode exhibits capacity. Thus, the VVCD is a voltage-variable tuning capacitor. As such, it can be very quickly changed from one frequency to another, and multiple VVCDs can be ganged together under the control of a common tuning voltage to simultaneously tune many stages at once. They are particularly well suited for use with digitally controlled phase-locked loop frequency synthesizers. A single DC voltage can be used to generate the proper frequency and at the same time tune following stages for proper tracking.

Only a small DC voltage is required for tuning, (from 0 to 30-V DC), the VVCD offers the ability to remote-tune a device through a small wire rather than using mechanical means. A sample VVCD tuning circuit for a UHF television tuner is shown in Figure 13–1. This circuit is only a small part of a large schematic, simplified here to show how the VVCD can be used. Three separate LC circuits are tuned with a single tuning voltage.

VVCDs are made with up to about 500 pfd of capacity. They have a wide tuning range and are available in the same capacitance ranges as mechanical variable capacitors. They are replacing air dielectric capacitors in all but high-power applications.

Critical applications for the VVCD may require some temperature compensation for voltage/capacitance stability with changing temperatures.

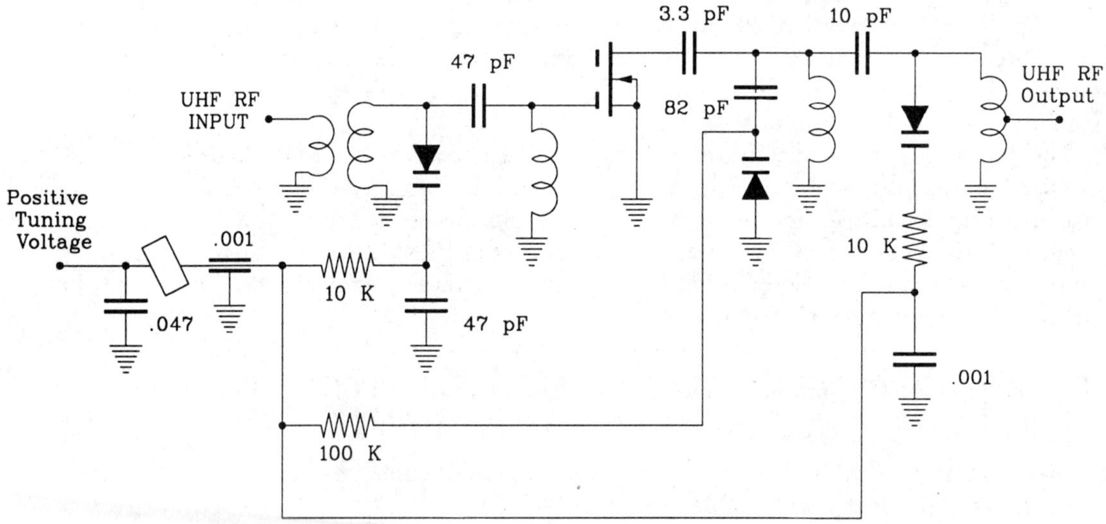

Figure 13–1 Several tuned stages controlled by a single DC tuning line.

Balanced applications and some tracking of multiple tuning circuits may require the use of matched sets of VVCDs, which are also available.

13.4 A REVIEW OF COMMON INSTRUMENTS USED AT RF FREQUENCIES

THE DC VOLTMETER

A normal DC level present at the transistor emitter resistor, if any, is an excellent indication of proper Class C circuit operation and sufficient driving signal amplitude into the circuit. A voltmeter or an oscilloscope with DC coupling may be used to monitor the voltage at the emitter. See Figure 13–2.

The emitter voltage is the principal means of tracing signals through a radio frequency amplifier, even though the signals are radio frequency and the indicating instrument is a DC device. The DC level is approximately the peak value of the voltage resulting from the many pulses of current through the resistor, held at a DC level by the bypass capacitor provided across the emitter resistor.

Common problems detectable by measuring the emitter voltage include:

1. Lack of any DC across the emitter resistor, possibly indicating an open transistor base, too little incoming signal, or a shorted emitter capacitor.

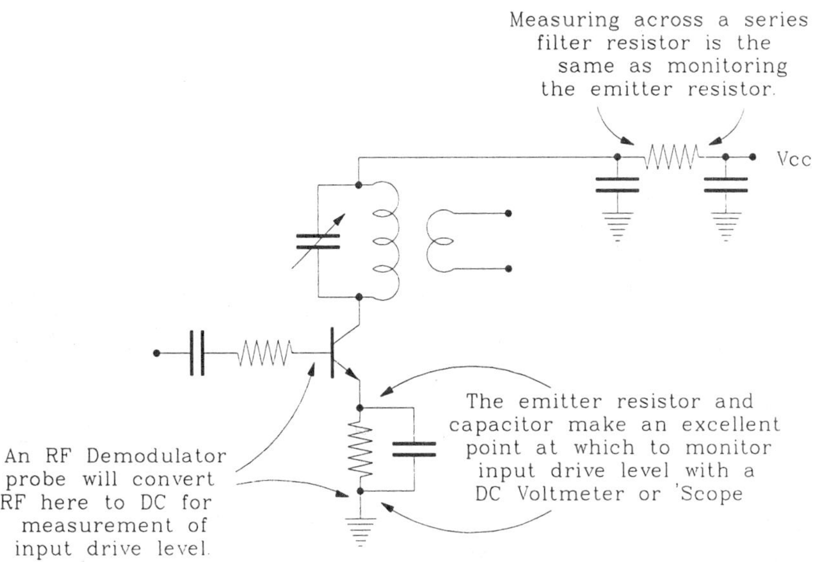
Measuring across a series filter resistor is the same as monitoring the emitter resistor.
Vcc
The emitter resistor and capacitor make an excellent point at which to monitor input drive level with a DC Voltmeter or 'Scope
An RF Demodulator probe will convert RF here to DC for measurement of input drive level.

Figure 13–2 Monitoring the performance of a Class C radio frequency amplifier.

2. Too little DC across the emitter resistor, indicating lack of input drive, a possible open collector circuit, or lack of supply voltage at the collector.
3. Too much voltage across the emitter resistor, indicating a probable shorted transistor (collector-to-emitter).

It is common for manufacturers to provide several test points wired to a connector on VHF and UHF mobile and base transmitters. Connecting the manufacturer's special test set to this connector, one can change the meter selector setting to rapidly monitor a series of these emitter test points.

THE RF WATTMETER

There are basically three different models of radio frequency wattmeters. One is intended to be inserted within an existing coaxial line by disconnecting the line and inserting the meter into it, thus forcing all the RF currents through the meter. Another RF wattmeter reads only the amount of power received, "burning up" that power in a very nearly perfect RF load resistor. The third type reads peak rather than RMS power. See Figure 13–3.

The Thruline™ radio frequency wattmeter is doubly useful because it can be used to evaluate more than just the incident (outgoing) power from a transmitter. By turning the "slug" 180 degrees, the instrument can also

Figure 13–3 These high-quality RF wattmeters are often used for both bench- and fieldwork. (Photo courtesy Bird Corporation)

read the power reflecting from the load (usually an antenna). A perfect load would reflect zero power. Practical antennas commonly measure reflected powers of less than approximately 10 percent of the incident power. If it is necessary to read very small amounts of reflected power, a more sensitive slug may be inserted. The Bird Thruline™ meter has been extremely popular among communications field and bench service technicians for the past 30 years. It is exceptionally rugged and stable, and it retains its original +/– 5 percent accuracy very well for years at a time. A modern slug will fit a 30-year-old Bird Thruline ™ and still produce readings within the accuracy specifications.

An RF wattmeter must provide accurate readings. Due to the many variables involved, the slugs used with these RF wattmeters have a range of frequencies within which it is accurate. The servicing technician must be aware of the frequency limitations of the slug in use. If an improper slug is used outside its specified frequency range, the power reading will not be accurate. It may still, however, be useful for *relative* power readings where the absolute accuracy of indicated power is of secondary importance. One such use would be to peak up the stages of a transmitter for maximum output without regard to the actual power delivered.

The second kind of RF wattmeter includes a termination resistor (typically 50 Ω), as part of the meter. The Termaline™ terminating wattmeter in Figure 13–3 reads only power coming into the unit, since there is no reflected power from the internal "perfect" termination.

The first two wattmeters shown in Figure 13–3 actually rectify the sampled RF voltage into a DC voltage, which is then read on the sensitive meter. This method holds well for continuous RF power measurement. However, peak power measurement requires a third model of RF wattmeter.

Single-sideband transmitters do not produce a continuous RF output, making the use of these meters impractical for measuring their power output. An SSB transmitter is rated by its *peak power* rather than its RMS power. The proper way to measure the power output of an SSB transmitter is to first modulate it with a two-tone audio input. This modulation waveform will produce alternating peaks and valleys of RF power from the transmitter. Then, a special peak-holding circuit causes the RF wattmeter to read the RMS power of the peak RF voltage waveform. The meter to the right in Figure 13–3 is an example of this kind of RF wattmeter.

THE RF DUMMY LOAD

A radio transmitter should not be keyed into an active antenna, or into no load at all, for testing purposes. The radiation of RF signals from an antenna while a transmitter is being repaired can result in adjacent channel interference or interference at harmonic frequencies. Connecting a proper resistive termination rather than an antenna can prevent such interference possibilities and make working on the transmitter legally safe.

Figure 13–4 Dummy RF loads prevent RF radiation and protect the RF final amplifier of a transmitter. (Photo courtesy Bird Corporation.)

There is another reason for connecting a resistive load: operating a transmitter without any load at all (antenna or coax line disconnected) can result in abnormally high RF voltages at the output. These high voltages can easily damage the final amplifier stage of a transmitter. Thus, the rule when working on transmitters of any kind is to simply *connect an RF dummy load whenever the transmitter is being serviced or tested.*

If the technician is using a terminating wattmeter, the termination is already provided. A through-line wattmeter will require the use of an external resistive load. Ordinary resistors are not suitable for RF dummy load use since they have considerable inductance. Special materials should be assembled for this specific use. See Figure 13–4 for an example of proper RF load resistors.

THE PRECISION RECEIVER AS A TEST INSTRUMENT

A receiver can also be used as a test instrument for some transmitter testing. A receiver set for AM reception can be used to compare a standard frequency to another, given frequency. See Figure 13–5.

If the receiver is digital and properly calibrated, it can be used as a frequency standard in the CW mode. See Figure 13–6.

An AM or FM receiver in good condition may be used to recover the modulation waveform of a transmitter for analysis. This analysis may be done on an oscilloscope or meter. This testing can show gross distortion on an oscilloscope, and also may show relative modulation signal amplitude.

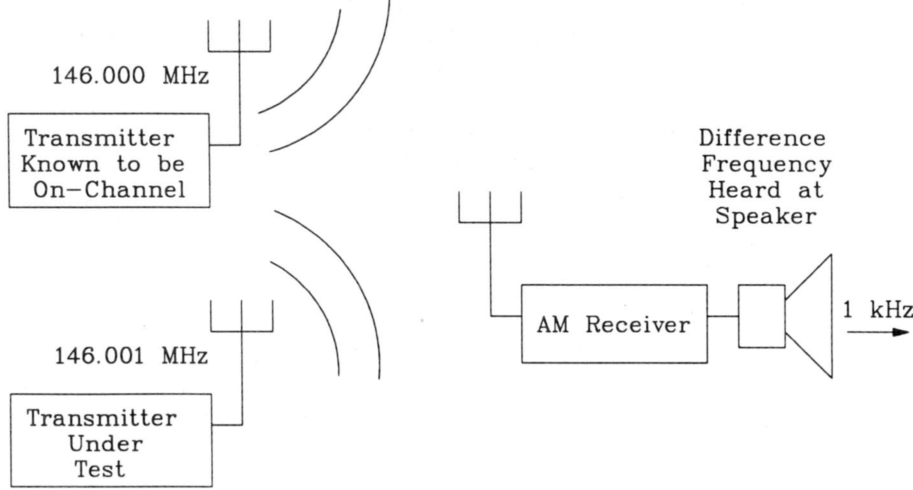
146.000 MHz
Transmitter Known to be On-Channel
146.001 MHz
Transmitter Under Test
Difference Frequency Heard at Speaker
AM Receiver
1 kHz

Figure 13–5 Using an AM receiver to compare two transmitters for on-channel operation.

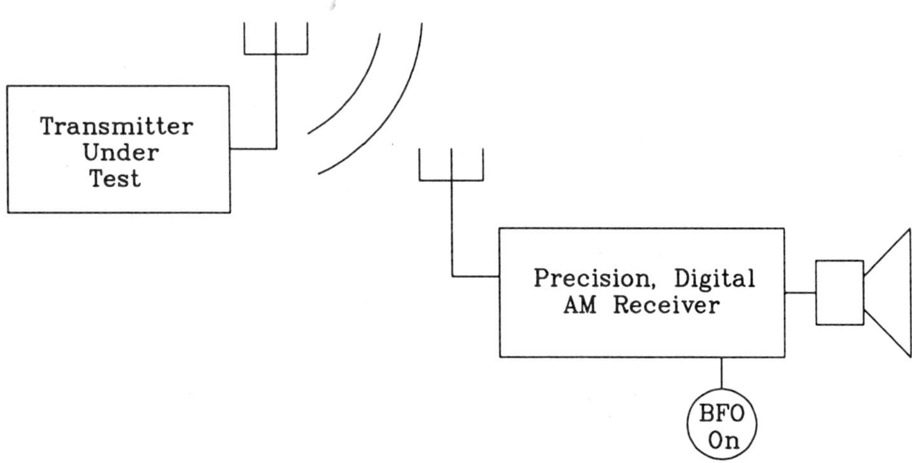
Transmitter Under Test
Precision, Digital AM Receiver
BFO On
If the receiver is tuned exactly to the proper frequency with the BFO centered on the passband of the receiver, a transmitter exactly on-channel will result in a zero-beat from the receiver.

Figure 13–6 A calibrated digital receiver with a beat-frequency oscillator may be used to check transmitter frequency.

A more sophisticated use of a receiver is possible if the receiver can be *swept* in frequency. This results in a basic *spectrum analyzer* (covered later in this chapter).

One of the uses of a receiver is as a microvolt voltmeter. With appropriate output indication, such as provided by an oscilloscope, the strength of microvolt-level signals can be compared. In extreme-precision equipment, the receiver can read directly in microvolts.

One way to think of the whole problem of measuring RF amplitude is to consider the common instruments used for AC measurement. A DMM can measure AC signals in the range of whole volts when the frequency involved is audio or less. An oscilloscope can measure millivolts of RF, limited in frequency by the bandpass of the vertical amplifier. A microvolt-measuring receiver can measure any voltage within its RF range, down to microvolts of amplitude. In addition, the receiver can be made extremely selective, measuring only one of perhaps many different RF voltages that may be present.

THE FREQUENCY COUNTER

Counting Transmitter Frequencies

One of the methods of determining the exact output frequency of a transmitter is to use a frequency counter. The frequency counter must be carefully calibrated to be accurate enough for this measurement. The common method of calibrating a frequency counter is to use a receiver to tune in WWV, the transmitting station of the National Institute of Standards and Technology (previously called the National Bureau of Standards) in Boulder, Colorado. These signals are transmitted on 2.5, 5, 10, 15, and 25 MHz *exactly*. Once WWV is received, the oscillator of the frequency counter is also coupled very loosely to the antenna circuit of the receiver. When properly done (assuming that the frequency counter has a 1-MHz or harmonically related internal frequency standard), there will be a beat-note heard at the receiver output. The frequency counter's internal time base oscillator is "warped" to obtain the zero-beat. See Figure 13–7.

Using a frequency counter with any given transmitter is quite easy, but the typical counter can be easily damaged. The technician must always keep in mind that *the input to a frequency counter may have a voltage limitation of as little as 2 volts*. Thus, one should never couple a transmitter output directly into a counter. Neither should one touch the transmitter antenna to the input of the counter such as when testing hand-held transceivers.

There are two ways of counting the output frequency of a transmitter. One is to briefly transmit (being sure the channel is clear) and couple a signal into the counter by using a small whip antenna on the counter input. This is the usual way to quickly test low-powered, hand-held transceivers for correct output frequency. See Figure 13–8.

The Power Attenuator

The second method of counting a transmitter's frequency is to use a power attenuator. Connect the transmitter directly into the attenuator, where it acts as a dummy load. A very small sample of the transmitter

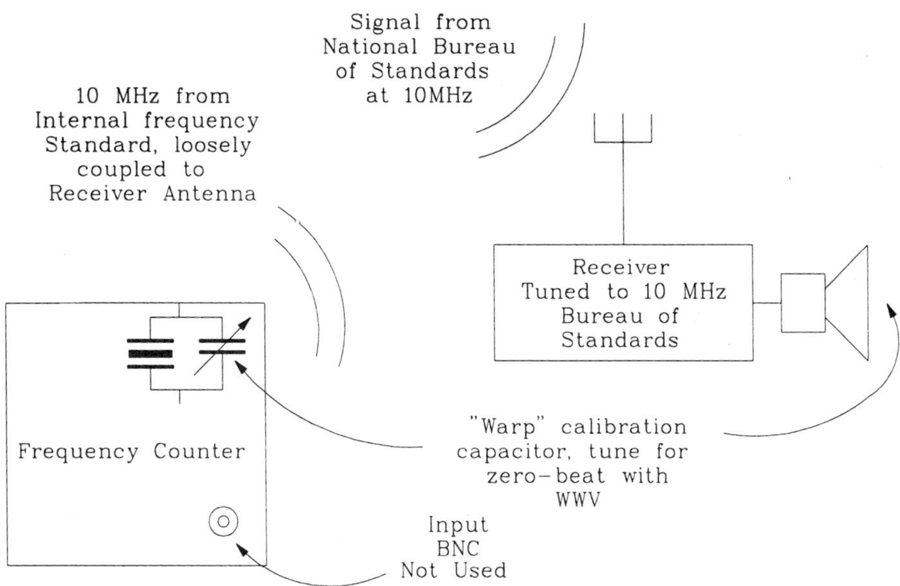

Figure 13–7 Common method of calibrating a frequency counter to the National Institute of Standards and Technology's transmitting station, WWV.

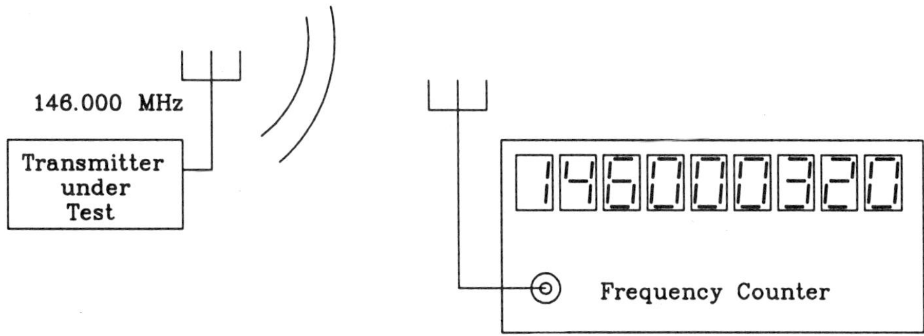

Figure 13–8 Reading transmitter frequency on a frequency counter using two antennas.

Figure 13–9 These power attenuators may be used as a dummy load and to reduce RF energy to safe levels for sensitive instruments. (Photo courtesy Bird Corporation.)

output is available at the other end of the attenuator, where the frequency counter may be directly coupled. See Figures 13–9 and 13–10.

A power attenuator is a good item for the technician to use routinely, since it can be used as a simple RF dummy load, without connecting the opposite end of the attenuator to anything at all.

Counting Voltage Signals

A frequency counter can be used to count the frequency of signals within radio equipment, too. One of the easiest and best ways to avoid overloading the input to a frequency counter is to use a common 10X oscilloscope probe between the counter and the circuit under test. With

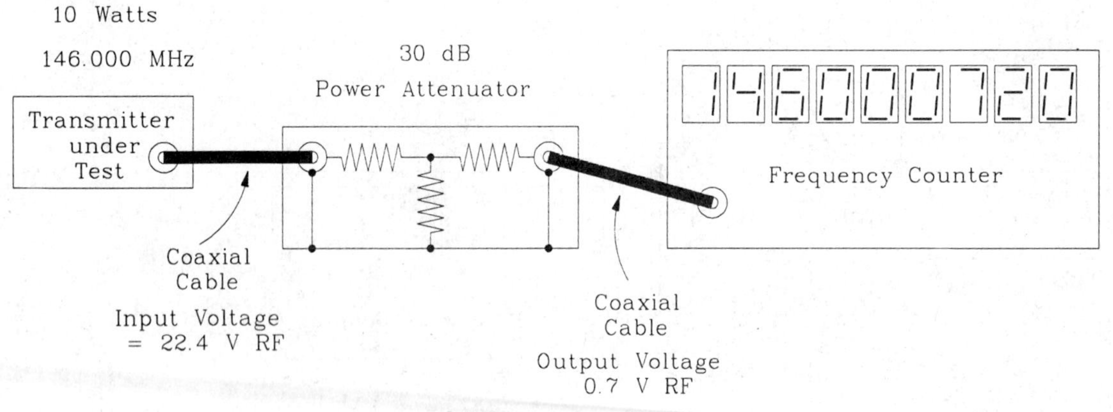

Figure 13–10 Block diagram of one use for a power attenuator.

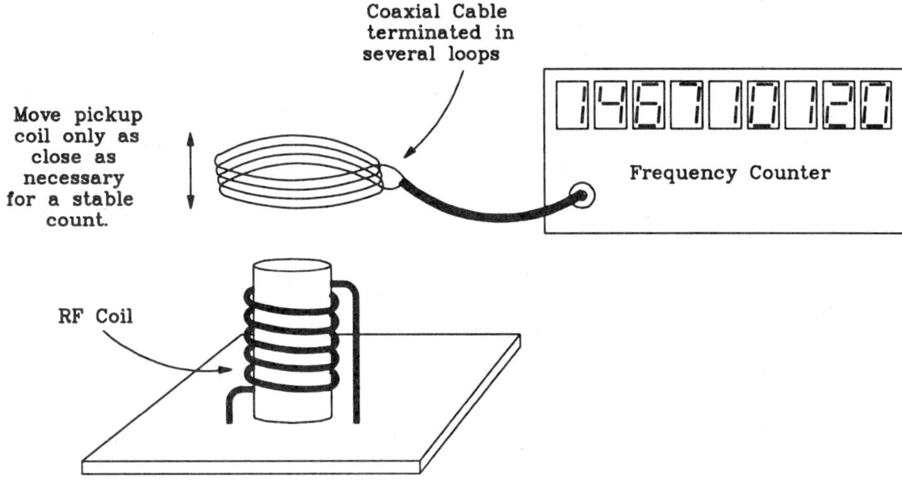

Figure 13–11 Using a magnetic pickup loop with the frequency counter.

this test setup, up to 20-V peak signals can be safely counted out when applied to the probe tip.

Counting RF Signals Magnetically

The frequency of magnetic fields may be counted by using a small coil of wire connected across the input terminals of the frequency counter. By placing this coil near an inductor, sufficient signal can be coupled into the loop to provide a stable count. See Figure 13–11.

RADIO FREQUENCY SIGNAL GENERATORS

The usual signal source for troubleshooting and tracing signals through RF receivers is an RF signal generator. A good RF signal generator will provide both an accurate signal frequency and a calibrated amount of RF voltage at its output. The output of an RF signal generator is relatively small, from about a quarter of a volt down to perhaps .1 of a millionth of a volt (250 mv to 0.1 μv).

Depending on its use, an RF signal generator may use either an analog dial indicator or a set of digital selectors to set the frequency to be generated. While a dial indicator might be acceptable for television servicing, the narrow widths of VHF and UHF communications channels makes the use of a single-channel precision crystal oscillator or a digital signal generator a necessity. When it is necessary for an analog signal generator to be more accurate in output frequency, an internal crystal calibrator may be provided. Its use and the method of calibrating the signal generator to it are a matter of following the specific instructions in the signal generator instruction manual.

Setting the operating frequency of a signal generator must be done with care. An RF signal generator must produce the frequency for which it is set. Errors in the output frequency can very seriously affect the quality of work performed on equipment. When servicing many different kinds of two-way radios, for instance, the selected frequency should be within perhaps 100 cycles out of 150 million in order for receiver alignments to be correct. A critical requirement such as this dictates the use of a digital frequency generator.

The calibrated output attenuator of an RF signal generator is almost always a simple analog dial readout. Some older models of signal generator require an initial manual setting of the amount of RF internally applied to the output attenuator. This is usually done by adjusting a control to bring a meter to a predetermined setting. Once a known amount of RF enters the attenuator, the output of the attenuator is then calibrated. When such a signal generator is used, the technician should perform this calibration whenever sensitivity checks are performed. It should also be rechecked whenever the signal generator is changed more than a few percentage points in frequency. Newer signal generators automatically keep the output amplitude at the proper level.

The output attenuator of most signal generators is subject to damage if a strong burst of RF is accidently applied back into the attenuator from an external source. This mistake is particularly easy to make when servicing transceiver equipment. All it takes is a normal test setup for receiver sensitivity and then unthinkingly keying the transceiver. The transmitter output (which can be from 5 to 100 watts) is immediately applied back into the signal generator attenuator. Preventing such a mistake is easier if the technician remembers to *disconnect the microphone of a transceiver when testing the receiver section*. Then, if the mike is accidentally keyed, it cannot do any damage. Special instrument fuses are available as additional insurance against such mistakes. These fuses are connected as a module between the signal generator output and the coaxial cable going to the unit under test.

Coupling a signal generator to a receiver requires a coaxial cable. For communications equipment, this is usually a 52-ohm coaxial cable. Television and video equipment uses 75-ohm coax cable. A shielded cable must be used to provide the calibrated amount of RF at the end of the cable and to prevent stray noise pickup on the way to the circuit. Using wires rather than coax at radio frequencies destroys any calibration of the amount of RF at the end of the wires.

The PLL Signal Generator

Radio spectrum space is at a premium. With more communications packing into the available space, channel spacing is getting narrower to meet the demands for more channels. With this decrease of channel width, more stable and precise frequencies are necessary for servicing two-way radios. The best way for a signal generator used for servicing to generate the necessary multitude of precise frequencies is to generate them by digital means. Front-panel thumb switches set the output frequency of a phase-locked loop (PLL) oscillator. The accuracy and stability of a PLL signal generator is controlled internally by one or more crystal oscillators.

THE AUDIO SIGNAL GENERATOR

The audio signal generator finds some use when servicing radio frequency equipment. It can be used to modulate the carrier of a signal generator for receiver testing or to modulate a transmitter for transmitter testing. If it has sufficiently low distortion, it can also be used as part of a 12-dB SINAD test (a test of Signal and Noise and Distortion as compared to noise and Distortion; to be covered later in this chapter).

THE SPECTRUM ANALYZER

A spectrum analyzer is basically a frequency-swept receiver with an AM output applied to a cathode-ray tube. See Figure 13–12.

A spectrum analyzer is easier to understand if one keeps in mind that the horizontal dimension is not time, as in an ordinary oscilloscope, but instead represents frequency.

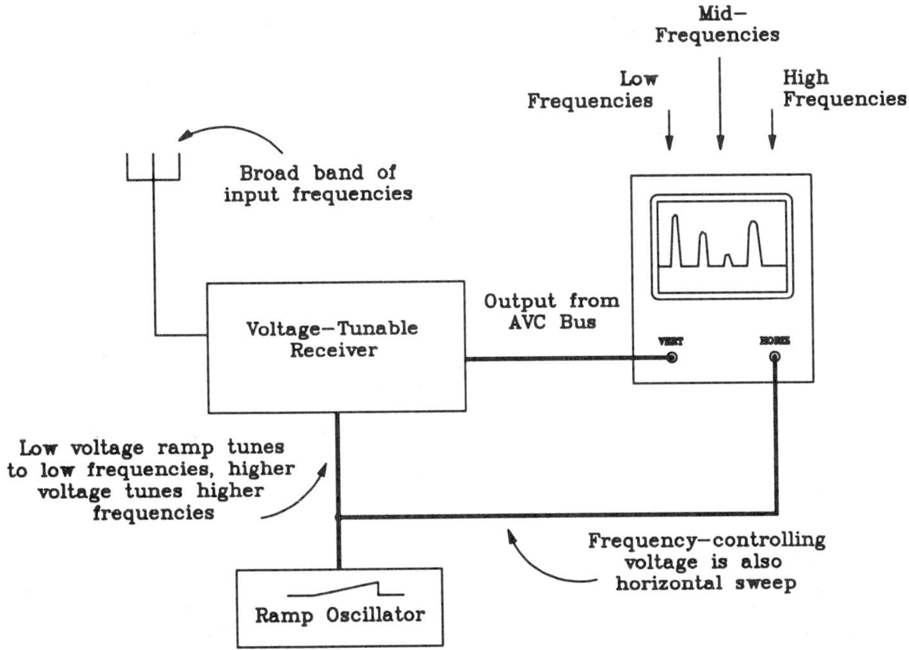

Figure 13–12 Simplified block diagram of a spectrum analyzer.

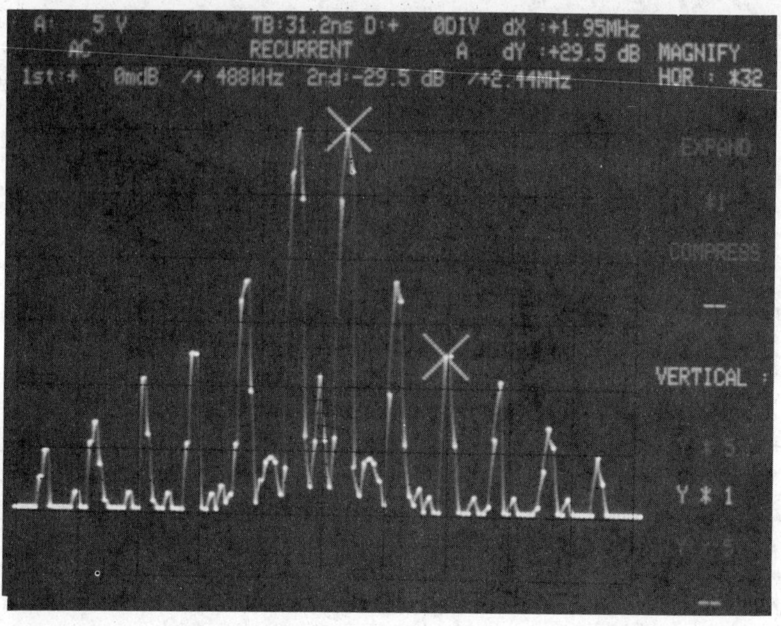

Figure 13–13 Digital oscilloscope calculating RF spectrum. (Reproduced with permission from the John Fluke Mfg. Co., Inc.)

While individual spectrum analyzers are available, Figure 13–13 shows a digital storage oscilloscope (DSO), which can also be used as a spectrum analyzer. It can be used to calculate the spectrum of an input RF signal, thus making it a very versatile instrument.

A spectrum analyzer is particularly useful to ensure that there is no adjacent channel interference from a transmitter.

When the analyzer receiver is sufficiently broad in coverage, it can also be useful in detecting and showing spurious harmonic-related outputs from a given transmitter.

THE MODULATION MONITOR

An oscilloscope can be used to calculate the amount of amplitude modulation of a carrier by measuring the maximum and minimum envelope voltages, as shown in Figure 13–14.

While measuring the amount of AM modulation is relatively simple, the measurement of FM modulation requires considerably more sophisticated means. A special meter is required to show FM modulation. An instrument such as this would be especially useful where a continuous readout of a specific transmitter is desirable.

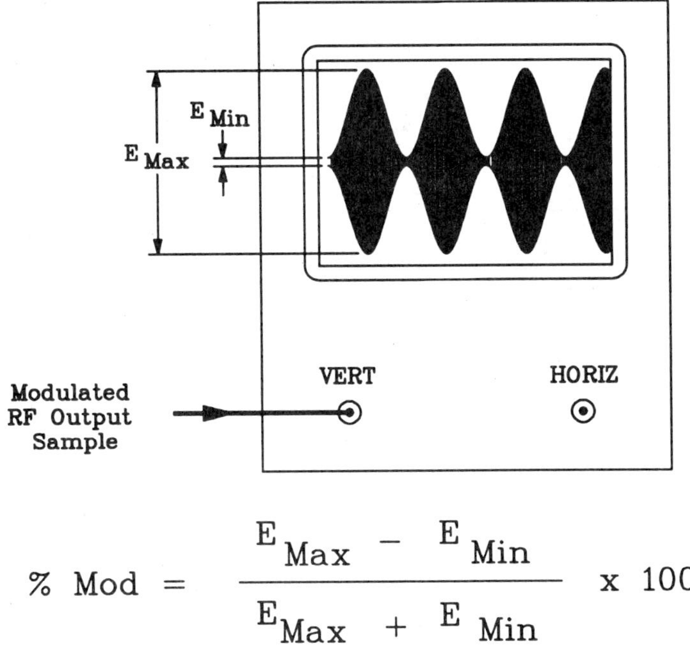

$$\% \text{ Mod} = \frac{E_{Max} - E_{Min}}{E_{Max} + E_{Min}} \times 100$$

Figure 13–14 A relatively simple method of checking AM modulation with only an oscilloscope.

THE SERVICE MONITOR

All of the instruments discussed for servicing to this point could amount to a very considerable investment to service two-way radios. The instruments needed are an RF wattmeter, RF dummy load, precision receiver, frequency counter, RF signal generator, audio signal generator, spectrum analyzer, and modulation monitor. The benefits and use of all of these instruments, optimized for two-way radio servicing, is available in a single instrument called a *service monitor*. See Figure 13–15.

The only other equipment needed to service two-way radios, besides a service monitor, is a DC power supply sufficient to operate DC equipment and a multimeter, preferably of the digital variety. With these three items and a reasonable investment in electronic tools one could go into business servicing two-way radio communications equipment and systems. The application of a service monitor will be covered throughout the rest of this text when applicable.

VOM OR DMM WITH AN RF PROBE

The VOM or DMM with an RF probe can be used for tracing RF signals of more than about a volt through equipment. Without an RF probe, the

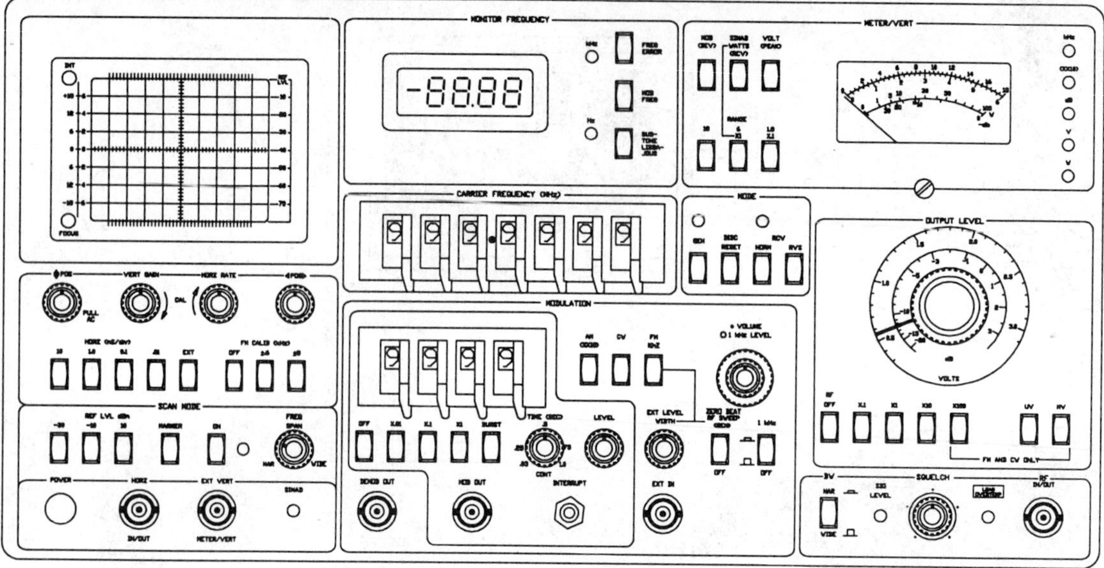

Figure 13–15 A service monitor.

DMM can be used only at audio frequencies at the most. The RF probe rectifies RF into DC, which the meter can then read using the DC scales. The RF probe has been largely replaced by modern oscilloscopes with their high-frequency vertical amplifier response. Today's premium-quality oscilloscopes often have a frequency response of 50 to 100 MHz.

THE ANALOG OSCILLOSCOPE AT RADIO FREQUENCIES

The oscilloscope is a very versatile instrument. It will show RF and can be used to indicate amplitude, frequency, and distortion. It is not a perfect instrument, however, and it must be used with some knowledge of its limitations.

Vertical Amplifier Frequency Response

An oscilloscope can be used to show RF voltages of more than a few millivolts only up to an approximate usable frequency limit, as determined by the bandwidth of the vertical amplifiers of the scope. Frequencies above that limit will show less and less amplitude on the screen until nothing at all will be shown other than the baseline sweep. Some method for determining a useful frequency limit had to be standardized. This is known as the *3 dB point* of vertical frequency response. To find this limit, an input frequency was applied to the scope and increased in frequency slowly while its actual input amplitude was held constant. When the vertical amplitude on the screen decreased to 0.707 of the actual amplitude being applied, the frequency of the input signal was noted. This is the method used to compare the frequency response of an oscilloscope's vertical amplifier. It means that, at this frequency and beyond, the oscilloscope will be more and more deficient in providing calibrated amplitude measurement.

Signal Tracing with the Oscilloscope

The oscilloscope may be used for RF signal tracing purposes as an output indicator at reasonable frequencies. "Reasonable" frequencies are those that are not far above the upper frequency limit of the vertical amplifier of the oscilloscope. An oscilloscope vertical amplifier with a response of 20 MHz, for instance, may be quite usable for signal tracing up to as much as perhaps even 40 MHz, but the amplitude indications will be far less than they should be. Below this frequency of 20 MHz the oscilloscope will provide more accurate voltage readings. The technician is seldom interested in the precise value of an output voltage during RF signal tracing, being concerned more often with the simple presence or absence of a signal.

Limitations of the Oscilloscope

A high-quality oscilloscope probe should not appreciably change the waveform of the input signal as it is presented to the oscilloscope. This means that it should have the precise resistance and capacitance to match the oscilloscope input. In order to accomplish this, the probe should have an adjustment located at either end of the probe cable to properly balance the capacitance of the probe and cable to the input circuit of the oscilloscope. When a probe is used for *any* measurements, it should be checked for a "flat" frequency response. This is easily done by touching the probe tip to the "calibrator" output of the oscilloscope and adjusting the probe for a flat waveform. See Figure 13–16.

Oscilloscope probes are available in standard attenuation factors of 1X, 10X, and 100X. The 1X probe is used because there is no conversion factor to consider when using it: what is seen on the screen is basically what is present at the probe tip. The 1X probe, however, has one serious disadvantage: it will pass on to the circuit under test all of the inherent capacitance to ground of the oscilloscope's input circuit, the connecting coax cable, and the probe tip itself. This can amount to a considerable amount of capacity, as much as 20 picofarads or more. In DC applications, this is of no particular consequence, but in many RF circuits it can completely change circuit operation. A much better solution is to use an attenuator probe. A 10X probe, for instance, will have less than one-tenth of the capacitance loading effect of a 1X probe (perhaps only a single picofarad). A 100X probe will have even less loading, but the attenuation factor may become a problem for viewing low-amplitude signals.

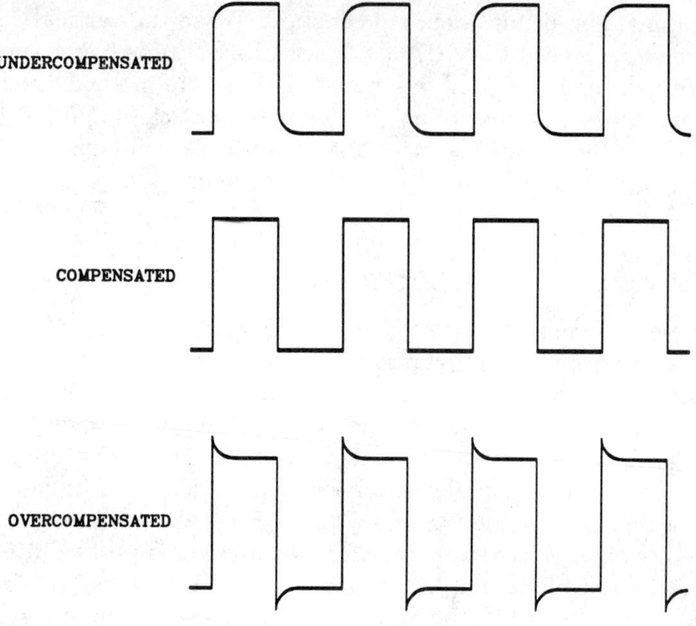

Figure 13–16 Waveforms obtained when compensating the oscilloscope probe.

When dealing with RF signals, always be sure to ground the working end of the probe to the circuit under test with as short a ground clip as possible.

Although the input resistance of the 10X test probe is a high impedance of 10 megohms, the capacitance of the probe to ground is around 1 pfd. This capacitance might be enough to upset the tuning of critical circuits. Even a good 10X probe may have a 1,000-Ω loading effect when used at a frequency of 100 MHz.

If oscilloscope probe loading appears to be a factor during troubleshooting, the loading effect may be verified very easily. Whether minimal or severe, the degree of loading can be determined by simply placing another probe (perhaps the 'scope's channel 2 probe) in parallel with the one in use. If the oscilloscope display decreases in amplitude appreciably, the probes are now *both* loading the circuit.

Frequency Determination with an Analog Oscilloscope

The approximate frequency of unknown signals may be determined by using an oscilloscope. A proper calculation of frequency with a high-quality oscilloscope should be within +/–5 percent.

Count the number of *whole* cycles (counted between the same point on succeeding cycles) in a given number (and fraction) of horizontal divisions. Don't try to estimate portions of cycles to make the measurement come out

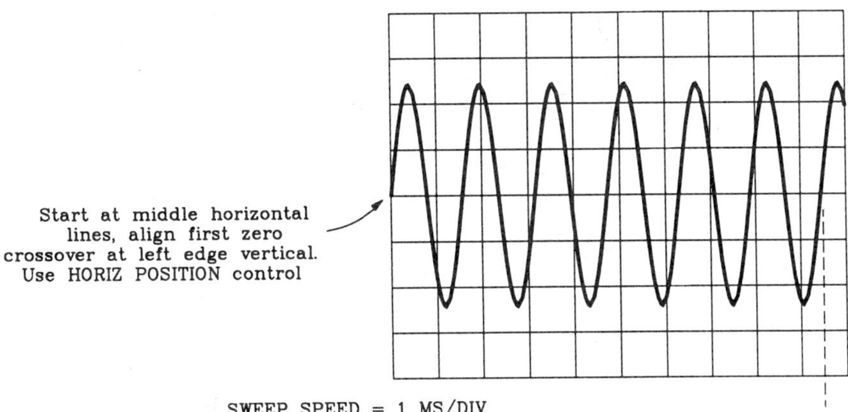

Start at middle horizontal lines, align first zero crossover at left edge vertical. Use HORIZ POSITION control
SWEEP SPEED = 1 MS/DIV

Note that exactly 6 cycles have completed in exactly 9–1/2 horizontal divisions right here

CAUTION: Be sure the horizontal sweep is calibrated. In other words, the sweep vernier is NOT used to obtain coincidence of a cycle completion and a horizontal division mark.

Figure 13–17 Calculating frequency with an analog oscilloscope

an even number of horizontal divisions. The best accuracy is obtained when many divisions and cycles are used. See Figure 13–17.

Use the formula below to determine frequency within about five percent. The accuracy will depend upon the accuracy and linearity of the oscilloscope's horizontal sweep and the skill of the operator in reading the screen.

$$F = \frac{C}{DS}$$

where

F = Frequency in Hertz

C = Whole cycles

D = Horizontal divisions and fractions

S = Sweep speed per division

(Convert to seconds; 1ms = .001; 1 μs = 0.000001)

The frequency of the signal in the figure above would be:

$$F = \frac{6}{9.5 \times .001} = \frac{6}{.0095} = 631.58 \text{ Hz}$$

USING A GRID DIPPER

In years past, the grid dipper was an inexpensive, popular source of RF for RF troubleshooting. It has fallen out of use due to its frequency instability. Merely touching the instrument can change the output frequency; thus grid dippers are seldom used today as signal sources for signal tracing.

A grid dipper can still perform the useful task of determining the approximate resonant frequency of an isolated parallel tuned circuit or an antenna. The meter on the instrument is set to approximate full-scale indication and then the sensing coil of the instrument is loosely, inductively coupled to the tuned circuit in question. The frequency of the dipper is then changed slowly and the meter watched for a sudden dip of the needle. At the bottom of the dip, the frequency knob is read to indicate the resonant frequency of the circuit. Looser coupling provides sharper dips.

13.5 USING COAXIAL CABLE

Coaxial cable must be used with radio frequencies to carry signals from one point to another with minimum loss, and to shield against unwanted external interference. *Improperly or poorly installed coaxial cable connectors account for a large percentage of RF equipment failures*, particularly during the installation of RF equipment.

A properly prepared cable is necessary for the finished job to be acceptable. Proper preparation of the cable will make the final assembly strong, able to stand the normal stresses in operation and handling of the cable.

As a matter of information and interest, Appendix X provides information on the more common coaxial cables. This information will be of value when selecting a coaxial cable for a given job, as it will permit the determination of the approximate attenuation and power-handling capability.

13.6 SPECIAL TOOLS FOR RF USE

Much of the RF circuitry that a technician will be required to work upon will be sensitive to the touch of a screwdriver or a finger. Because of this fact, a whole line of special adjustment tools are available to adjust RF circuits. These tools are often made of plastic or Teflon and are sometimes tipped with a very small piece of metal when absolutely necessary for strength. See Figure 13–18.

The use of a metal screwdriver to adjust some circuits, especially those within high-powered transmitters, can be very dangerous. Some of the adjusting screws can have dangerously high DC potentials, particularly those in vacuum tube circuits. Since the vacuum tube may still be used in some transmitting applications, *only insulated adjusting*

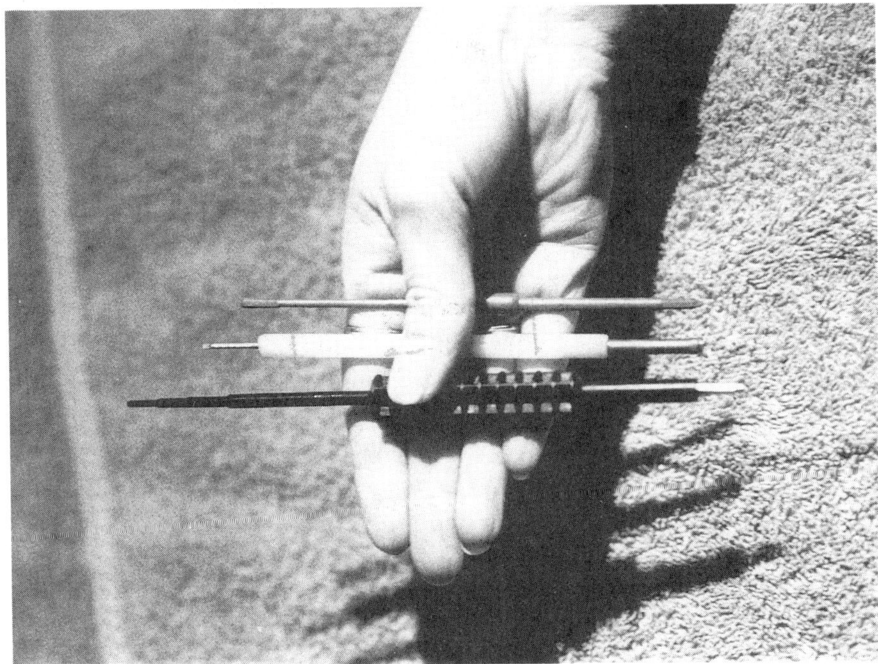

Figure 13–18 These tools should be used for RF work in cases where detuning may be a problem if metal tools are used.

tools should be used when working upon such circuits. In addition, since some adjustments have DC on them, damage to the circuitry can result if accidentally shorted to ground by the use of a metal tool rather than an insulated one.

Another word of caution is appropriate at this point. One kind of adjustable inductor in common use consists of a plastic tube around which a coil is wound. Inside the tube, threads are made to mate with a threaded ferrite core. *These ferrite cores are fragile. Only the proper size of six-sided allen-wrench tool should be used* to adjust them. A smaller tool will slip and may produce a radial crack along one or more sides of the core. See Figure 13–19.

Using a tool that is too large can also crack the core. Once a ferrite core is broken, any attempt to turn it with even a proper tool will cause the core to expand, much like the brake shoe of an automobile. Such breakage is difficult to repair, since the core won't turn. Replacement of the entire coil assembly is the best repair. In noncritical applications (e.g., television repairs) one can sometimes force the core out of the coil, hoping that a replacement core will still grip the damaged threads sufficiently to adjust. Another possible alternative would be to put a *small* amount of super-glue on a toothpick, inserting it gently into the broken core, and waiting for the

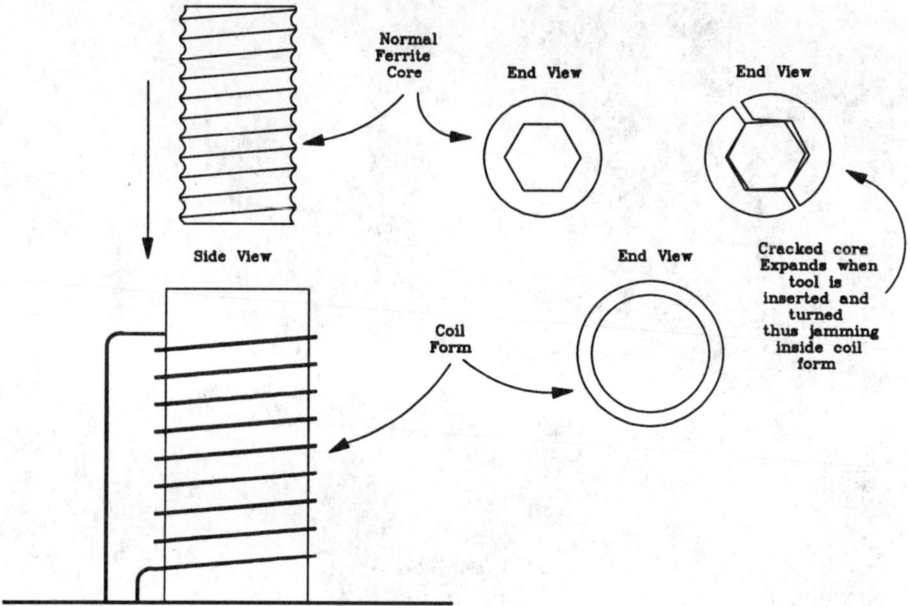

Figure 13–19 Construction of a threaded ferrite core and how it can crack.

glue to set up. Once set, it may be possible to unscrew the core since it can no longer expand and the toothpick does not exert outward force.

13.7 WORKING WITH MICROVOLT SIGNALS IN RECEIVERS

A LITTLE HISTORY

The first radio receivers were the diode detector (the crystal detector, a primitive form of point-contact diode) and the tuned circuit. See Figure 13–20.

There was no amplification in the crystal-set radio, so only strong signals could be received. The crystal set also did not provide adequate separation of incoming signals, often receiving two or more stations at the same time.

The vacuum tube made it possible to amplify the radio frequency signals, thus making it possible to receive much weaker signals. In order to get as much gain as possible, some of these circuits fed part of the tubes' output back into the input, "bootstrapping" itself, providing much more gain than could otherwise be obtained from a single stage. These were called regen-

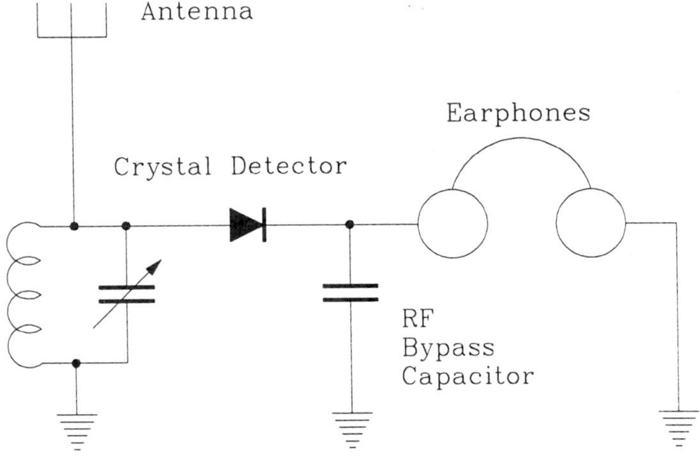

Figure 13–20 Circuit for a crystal set radio receiver.

erative and super-regenerative receivers. A major disadvantage is that they were critical to adjust and could break into oscillation, transmitting signals of their own and causing interference to other receivers in the vicinity.

The next major advance in radio receivers was the tuned-radio-frequency, or TRF, receiver. It consisted of multiple stages cascaded together, one following another, for additional amplification and to give more selectivity. See Figure 13–21.

The transistor then replaced the vacuum tube in most receivers, making it possible to build smaller radios that required much less power than before. Today, vacuum tubes are used only in designing high-powered RF applications where solid-state components cannot yet compete.

The next major step forward in receiver design was the heterodyne receiver. This receiver took advantage of the fact that when two radio frequencies are mixed together, their sum, difference, and the original

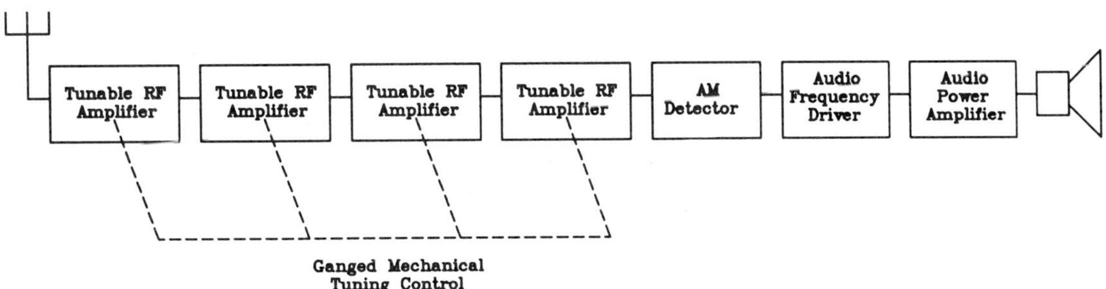

Figure 13–21 The tuned-radio-frequency (TRF) receiver had several gang-tuned RF amplifiers.

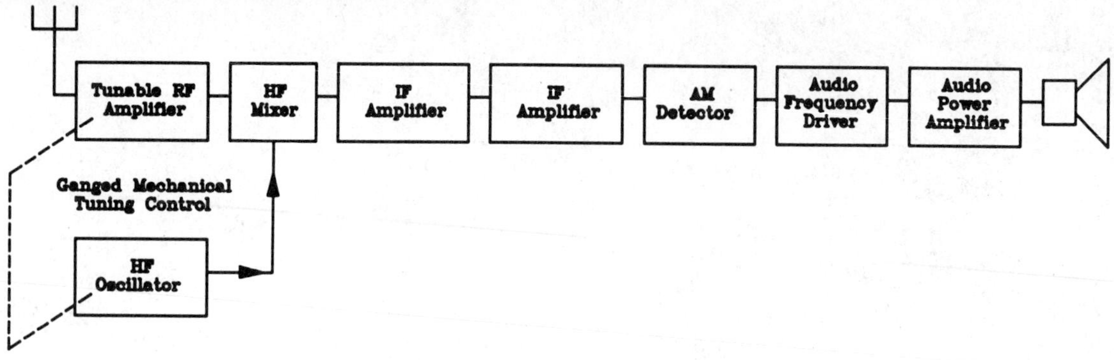

Figure 13–22 The superheterodyne receiver is a big improvement over earlier receiver designs.

frequencies appear at the output of the mixer. By using a local oscillator to mix with incoming frequencies, the receiver could be tuned to another frequency by changing only two or three stages at the most, even for a complex receiver for very high frequencies. All that had to be done to change the incoming frequency is to change the frequency of the local oscillator and the tuning of the RF amplifier stage. Only one channel would be received, the one which produced the proper difference frequency, which is called the *intermediate frequency* (most often abbreviated as IF). See Figure 13–22.

TESTING AND ADJUSTING A SUPERHETERODYNE RECEIVER

Low radio frequency receivers, such as those used for AM commercial broadcast, use a single-conversion design. A receiver designed for any frequency above very roughly 2 MHz will probably use a dual-conversion scheme. The reason for this is that the first conversion to what is known as the high IF provides rejection of the *image frequency*, that frequency which will also give the same difference as the intended frequency of reception, but is *twice the IF frequency* from the intended, *on the opposite side of the local oscillator*. Some VHF and UHF receivers may use two or three IF conversions. See Figure 13–23.

Helical resonators are sharply tuned LC circuits sometimes used in the RF amplifier stages of a receiver to eliminate image frequencies. Due to their cost, their presence is a sign of high quality in receiver design. (Refer back to Figure 10–31 for a photograph of a helical resonator.) They are used as bandpass filters, allowing all the desired channels to enter, while rejecting others outside the selectivity curve, including images.

Once the image frequency has been rejected by the tuned circuits of the RF stage, the high IF has served its purpose and will pass the signal on with some amplification to the second mixer. At the typical high IF fre-

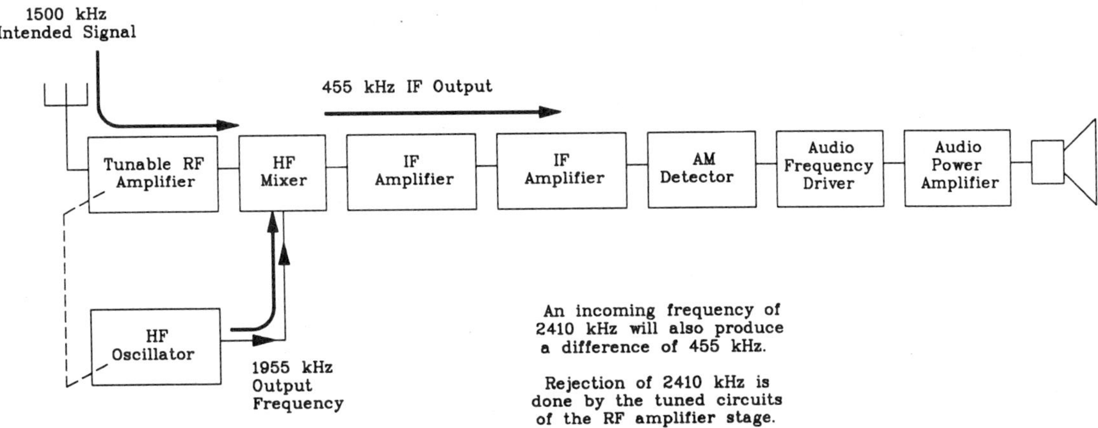

Figure 13–23 The superhetrodyne receiver will receive two frequencies.

quency of 10.7 MHz, amplification is more difficult than at a lower RF frequency, and several adjacent channels can pass through an IF of 10.7 MHz together.

After reconverting the 10.7 MHz down to another intermediate frequency called the low IF, amplification is easily accomplished. In addition, a single channel is easy to select at the low IF, particularly if a crystal bandpass filter (BPF) is used. Adjacent channels are rejected by the skirt selectivity of the 455 IF amplifiers.

Here is an important point to keep in mind: The bandpass filter of the low-intermediate frequency is seldom tunable. It is the fixed-frequency component around which alignment adjustments are made to put the receiver exactly on the proper frequency and to properly tune it for acceptance of the necessary sidebands above and below the center frequency of the channel.

MAKING RECEIVER CHECKS

Basic Receiver Performance Testing

The performance of a communications radio should be tested whenever a receiver is examined by a service technician. The ability to pass the performance tests determines what work, if any, needs to be done to the receiver. There are two basic tests and several optional tests that can also be made. The basic tests are discussed here, with the optional tests to follow. Any tone-controlled squelch circuitry must be disabled for these tests.

The 20-dB Quieting Test

Any receiver in good condition will produce "white" noise at the speaker output when there is no signal applied to the antenna input. When a substantial signal is present, the receiver will quiet, with the amount of noise decreasing as the signal increases in strength. Receiver sensitivity is measured by noting the amount of RF signal that it takes to reduce the no-signal speaker noise level to one-tenth of its no-signal level.

Using a Signal Generator and a Voltmeter

To conduct the 20-dB quieting test, the receiver squelch is turned all the way off so that noise is heard from the speaker. This receiver noise is measured with an AC voltmeter across the speaker terminals, without a signal applied to the input of the receiver. The amount of noise is noted on the voltmeter scale. Then, an on-channel signal is applied to the receiver antenna input and gradually increased in strength until the AC voltmeter reading drops to one-tenth its original noise value. Reducing a voltage to one-tenth constitutes a 20-dB power ratio. This test may be conducted with separate test equipment, as shown in Figure 13–24.

The 20-dB quieting test can be summarized graphically, as shown in Figure 13–25.

"Counting the Popcorn"

If the technician wishes to conduct this test but for some reason does not have an AC voltmeter, a good approximation of the 20-dB quieting point may be determined by increasing the RF signal input just until the popping of the noise slows enough that it can just barely be counted. This method is informally called "counting the popcorn."

While the 20-dB quieting test is useful, it is not the final word in sensitivity performance measurement. A better receiver performance test is the 12 dB SINAD test (to follow).

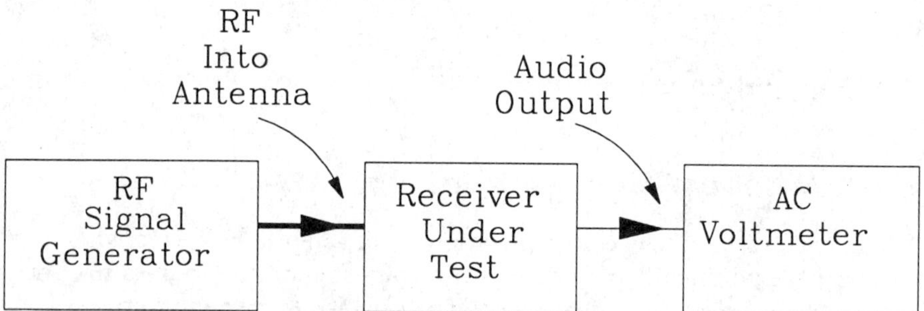

Figure 13–24 Block diagram of the separate instruments necessary to perform a 20-dB quieting test.

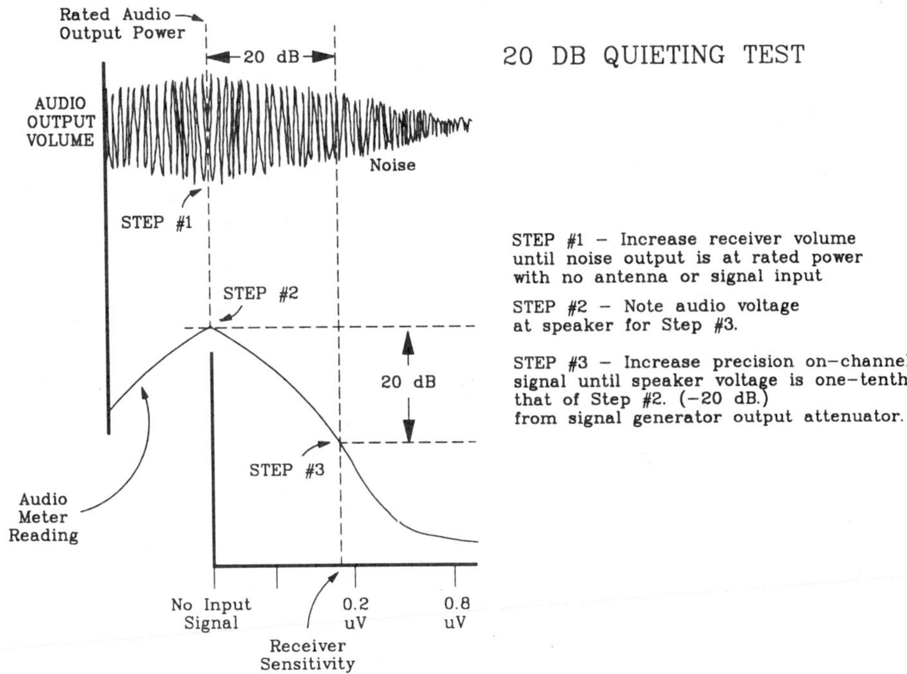
Rated Audio Output Power
20 dB
AUDIO OUTPUT VOLUME
Noise
STEP #1
STEP #2
20 dB
STEP #3
Audio Meter Reading
No Input Signal
0.2 uV
0.8 uV
Receiver Sensitivity
20 DB QUIETING TEST
STEP #1 - Increase receiver volume until noise output is at rated power with no antenna or signal input
STEP #2 - Note audio voltage at speaker for Step #3.
STEP #3 - Increase precision on-channel signal until speaker voltage is one-tenth that of Step #2. (-20 dB.) from signal generator output attenuator.

Figure 13–25 Graphical representation of the 20-dB quieting test.

Using a Service Monitor

If a service monitor is available, the AC voltmeter and/or oscilloscope provided within the instrument is used to measure the audio output of the receiver while also providing the precision signal generator. The same connections are used for the 20-dB quieting test and the 12-dB SINAD test. The internal block diagram and external setup are as shown in Figure 13–26.

Typical receiver sensitivity readings should be from 1.0 microvolts for 20-year-old receivers to as little as 0.15 microvolts for a modern unit. The failure of a receiver to meet the 20-dB quieting specification by a small amount suggests that a simple alignment would correct the problem. A large discrepancy, say 3 microvolts or more, suggests that there is a gross misalignment (perhaps someone else worked on the equipment) or that one of the amplifiers in the receiver is defective. First, try realigning the receiver. If this does not correct the problem, the procedure of stage gain measurements will locate the bad stage (a procedure covered later in this chapter).

The 12-dB SINAD Test

A receiver may be very sensitive and well within its specification yet be unreadable because of distortion created within the circuitry. The discrim-

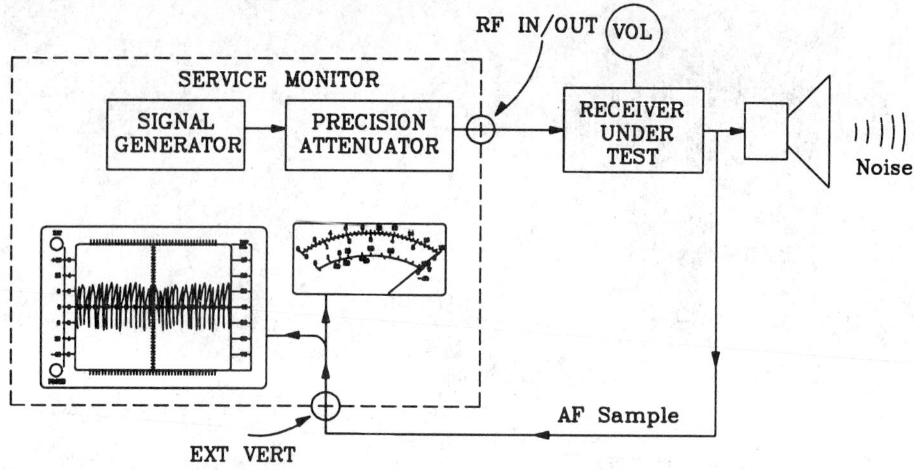

Figure 13–26 Internal block diagram of the 20-dB quieting test using a service monitor.

inator of an FM receiver must be properly centered on the low IF bandpass, and the following audio stages must have low audio distortion for the receiver to sound good and for communications to be easily understood. The 12-dB SINAD test (SINAD stands for Signal and Noise and Distortion as compared to Noise and Distortion) evaluates both the sensitivity and the distortion of a receiver in a single performance figure.

This test involves the use of an audio distortion meter. A distortion meter measures the distortion of an audio tone by comparing the tone with the same tone minus the fundamental frequency. For example, a 1000-Hz tone is analyzed by comparing the input and the output of an efficient 1000-Hz filter. If there is a large difference between the original input tone and what is left after the 1000-Hz tone has been filtered out, there was little distortion within the original waveform. Distortions of the 1000-Hz waveform produce harmonics which remain after filtering the 1000 Hz out. See Figure 13–27.

The 12-dB SINAD test compares a strong signal (of, typically, 1000 Hz modulating 60 percent of the channel width) with the distortion produced by the receiver along with noise. This is done in five distinct steps.

1. Set up a signal generator on-channel and modulate it to 60 percent of channel width with a *pure* 1000-Hz tone.
2. Apply this signal to the receiver input at an input level which will provide a full-quieting signal (about 1 to 10 microvolts typically) and monitor the audio output of the receiver with a voltmeter.
3. Set the receiver audio volume control to a high setting, but well below the point where distortion occurs at maximum gain. Note the voltmeter reading.

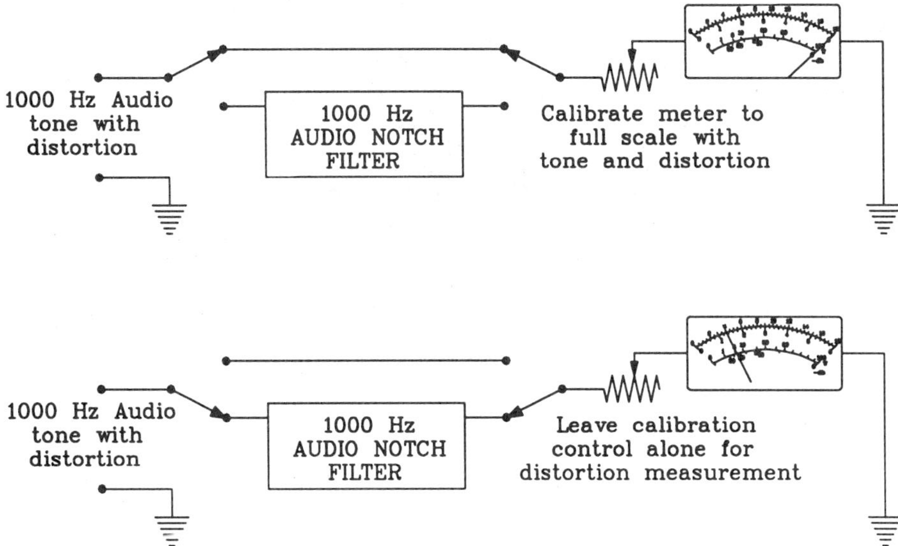

Figure 13–27 Block diagram of a distortion meter and its operation.

4. Cut in the distortion analyzer and note the drop in voltage shown on the meter. A value of at least a 12-dB decrease (1/4 voltage) is required for a usable receiver. A value of –20 dB is much better (1/10 voltage), and –30 dB (1/30) is excellent. Log this value as a measure of the receiver's distortion.
5. Decrease the RF input until the receiver noise increases the meter reading to –12 dB, or one-quarter of the original voltage reading of step 2 above. Read the RF attenuator for the 12-dB SINAD sensitivity. This should be a reading close to that obtained when using a 20 dB quieting test.

The equipment required for a SINAD test and how to connect it are shown in Figure 13–28.

It is much simpler to use a service monitor for this test, since it contains a low-distortion source of 1000-Hz modulation and a special SINAD switch position to eliminate the 1000-Hz fundamental. The connection of a service monitor for SINAD measurement is identical to that used for the 20-dB quieting test. A single push button is pressed to eliminate the 1000-Hz fundamental, and the dB drop is read directly in dB from the meter on the instrument. See Figure 13–29.

The failure of a receiver to pass the SINAD test may be an indication that the discriminator is not centered on the IF bandwidth (noise centering), the received frequency is not coming directly down the center of the passband, or the passband is out of adjustment (usually involving the 455

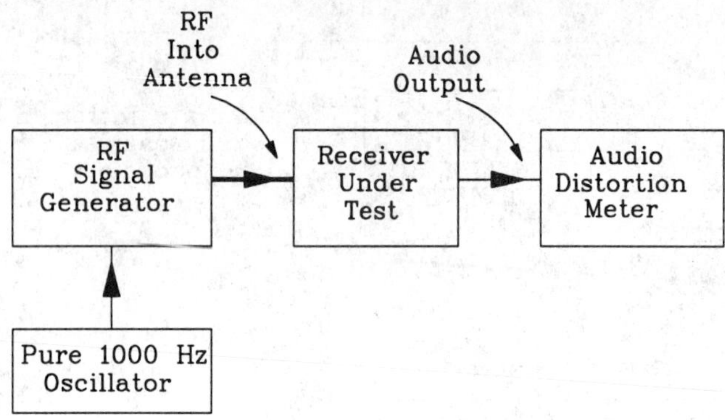

Figure 13–28 Block diagram of the separate equipments necessary for a 12-dB SINAD test.

kHz bandpass filter). The 12-dB Sinad test can be summarized as shown in Figure 13–30.

On-Channel

It would do no good to have a receiver of excellent sensitivity that did not receive the proper channel. With communications channels only 10 kHz wide, a receiver must be exactly on channel to be effective. Off-channel

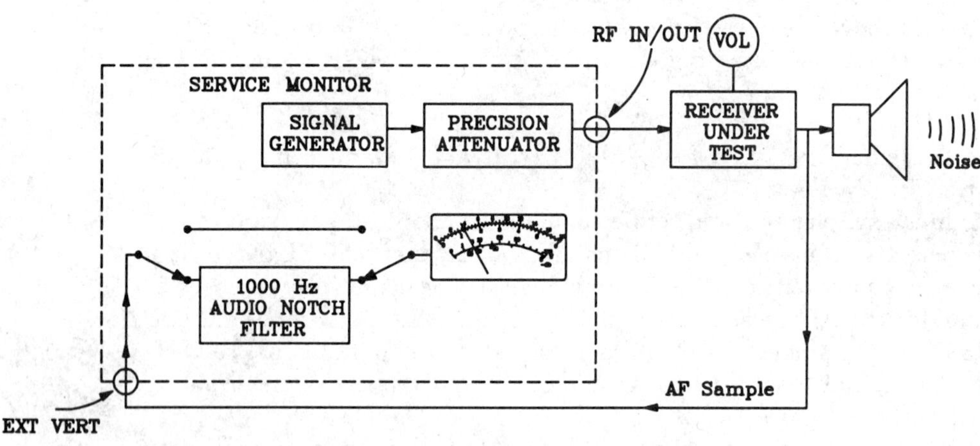

Figure 13–29 Internal block diagram of a service monitor performing a 12-dB SINAD test.

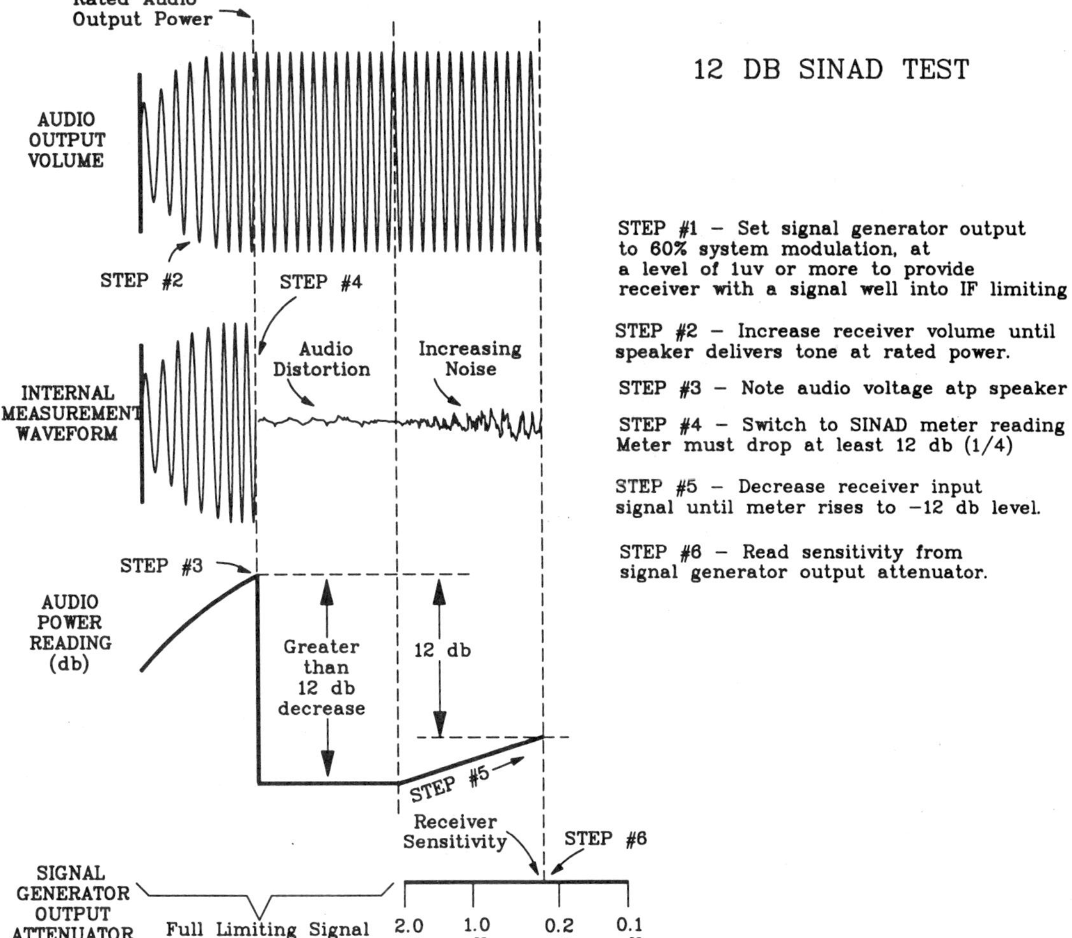

Figure 13–30 Graphical representation of the 12 dB SINAD test.

reception by perhaps 3 kHz or more will result in excessive distortion of the received audio and possible bursts of interference from the next channel.

The on-channel evaluation of a receiver can be done two ways, depending on the availability of a precision, digital-type signal generator or of the availability of a prime signal, such as the transmitter with which the receiver will normal be associated.

On-Channel Checks with Precision Signal Generator. A digital signal generator is the only kind of signal generator that is sufficiently precise in frequency generation to perform this test. An analog generator does not have sufficiently good frequency stability.

Perform a 20-dB quieting test with the proper input frequency. Leave the signal generator output level control at the 20-dB quieting output level. Remove the RF signal, then adjust the squelch for quieting of the receiver noise. Turn on the RF, add 2000 or more kHz to the generated frequency, and note the frequencies at which the receiver's squelch closes and the receiver audio turns off.

Now reset the frequency to the same amount off-channel on the opposite side of the proper frequency. Manipulate the frequency setting slightly up or down in frequency until the receiver audio again squelches and goes quiet. Log this frequency, too.

The frequency about which the receiver is centered may be determined by finding the frequency between the upper-frequency and the lower-frequency settings. Subtract the smaller from the larger frequency, divide the answer by two, then add this figure to the lower of the two frequencies. If the receiver is more than about 300 Hz off the assigned channel frequency, it should be put back on. Procedures for doing this are covered later in this chapter.

On-Channel Checks with Associated Transmitter. Checking for on-channel operation with only a single frequency source such as this will require opening the receiver. Locate the discriminator output test point that is used to test for centering of the discriminator. Three of the most common discriminators and their corresponding on-channel test points are shown in Figure 13–31.

Modern FM receivers, particularly the smaller, hand-held ones, may use an IC chip to perform the demodulation process. If this is the case, the documentation for the receiver should indicate a test point near the chip that serves the purpose of zeroing the discriminator.

Use a DC voltmeter and probe this test point, at first with no antenna or incoming signal. The DC at this point should be very close to zero volts, perhaps within several tenths of a volt. This indicates whether the discriminator is zeroed on the noise coming through the low-IF amplifiers. If not within a few tenths of a volt on noise, the receiver should be aligned (as covered later in this chapter).

If the DC voltage reading of the discriminator is within a few tenths of zero volts, apply the prime signal by attaching the antenna and keying (or having keyed) the main transmitter that will normally be received. The discriminator should again be reading very near zero volts. The significance of either a positive or a negative voltage of more than a few tenths of a volt indicates that although the receiver may be centered on noise, the high-frequency oscillator is not properly trimmed for the exact frequency required. (This adjustment is also covered later in this chapter.)

Optional Receiver Performance Testing

Squelch Threshold. It is a good idea to check the point at which the receiver will "break squelch" and provide an audio output. This point should be about the same as the 20-dB sensitivity level. To check this, leave

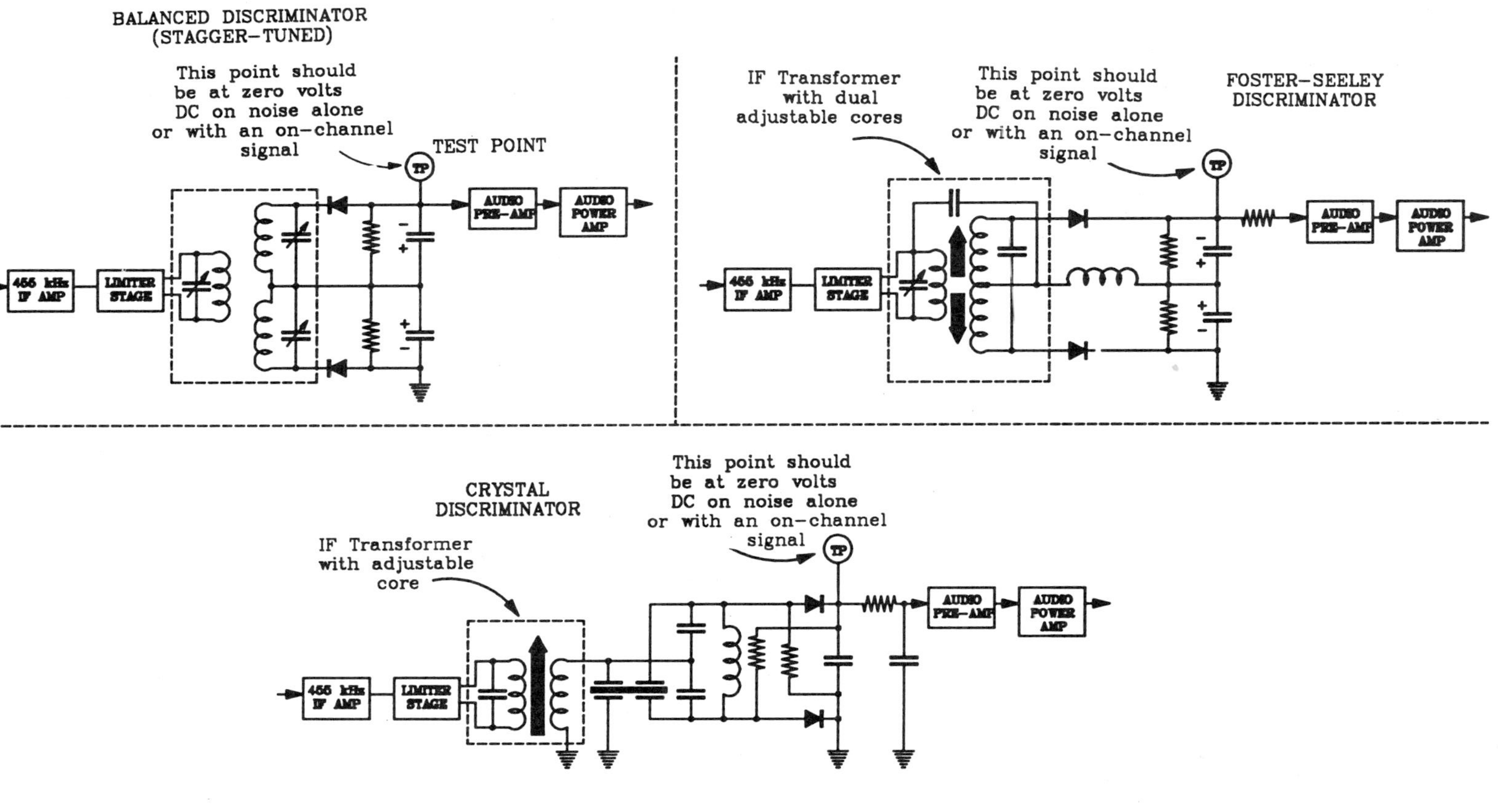

Figure 13–31 Three discriminators and their zero-voltage test points.

the receiver set up as for a 20-dB quieting test. With no signal coming into the receiver, adjust the squelch so that it just kills the noise. Then apply signal from the signal generator, beginning with a voltage too low to open the squelch, well below the 20-dB quieting voltage previously measured. Start below 0.1 microvolt. Slowly increase the RF level until the receiver opens its squelch and noise is heard from the receiver. Stop increasing the RF level, and read the dial. This is the squelch threshold level. Try running this test several times to be sure you get the same reading each time.

Tight Squelch Sensitivity. Tight squelch sensitivity is the RF level required to open the receiver when the squelch control is at its extreme setting, the maximum setting that results in no noise from the receiver without an incoming signal. Run the test as just explained for squelch threshold, but with the squelch control at its maximum setting. This should result in an incoming signal in the approximate range of from 0.5 to 1.5 microvolts. Record both the threshold and tight squelch settings for future use.

Tone-Coded Squelch. Some receivers have additional circuitry that prevents the audio circuits from passing signals until a single or multiple tones of the proper frequencies are received. Some circuits require continuous tones (as provided by the Continuous Tone Coded Squelch System CTCSS), short bursts of tone upon initial transmission (tone burst), or multiple, sequential tones. These circuits are bypassed or made inactive during the above-mentioned tests. To be sure that the receiver is operating properly, the tone circuits must also be tested to be sure they are working properly.

An inspection of Appendix IX, Tone Modulation Standards, shows the standardized audio frequencies used for this purpose.

The signal generator must provide the exact tones for the required duration in order to open the receiver. A continuous tone control requires that the tones be present on the carrier all the time a transmitter is on the air. This is the easiest of tone squelches to test. Simply provide the proper on-channel RF frequency, modulate it with the exact tone frequency. Deviate the carrier only +/–600 Hz with the tone. Once the signal generator is set up this way, adjust the receiver controls to enable the tone-coded squelch. Gradually increase the signal generator output from below 0.1 microvolt, and note the level when the receiver opens. This level must be near the 20-dB quieting sensitivity level.

Receiver Bandwidth Acceptance

Before performing a bandpass acceptance test, be sure that the discriminator is centered on noise and that the incoming signal also gives a DC output from the FM discriminator. These procedures are covered in the following paragraphs, beginning with the section titled, "FM Receiver Oscillator Alignment Procedures." The receiver bandpass should be checked whenever there is excessive distortion of the audio output of a receiver or when there is excessive noise within the receiver. An off-centered IF bandpass filter (usually for low IF) or one that is not symmetrical about the incoming frequency will produce audio distortion that is difficult to find except by performing this test.

The idea of this test is to identify the frequencies which cause the output of the receiver to fall by 3 dB from the mid- or on-channel frequency input. This is done by first applying a signal of a few microvolts and recording the voltage of the AVC (automatic volume control) bus (for AM receivers) or of the limiter (for FM receivers). Reduce the input level at this frequency by exactly 3 dB according to the dB scale, or by 71 percent of the initial voltage setting. *Record the AVC or limiter voltage that results,* as this will be the voltage that will identify the upper and lower frequencies being sought. Now take the input level back to the original setting. Increase the input *frequency* until the AVC/limiter voltage falls to the –3 dB point, then record this frequency as the high bandwidth frequency. Do the same by decreasing the frequency below the channel frequency until the same -3 dB point is reached. Record this as the low frequency. The difference between the two frequencies, the high- and low-frequency 3 dB points, is the bandwidth of the receiver. The requirements of a specific receiver are called out by the manufacturer in the specifications for that receiver.

Generic Alignment of a Superheterodyne Receiver

The alignment of a superheterodyne receiver can be simple or complex, depending on how badly the receiver deviates from specifications. If the sensitivity should be 0.5 microvolt, for instance, but actually measures 0.75 microvolt, there is probably only a small adjustment required. If a radio has been tampered with, or alignment attempted without proper equipment, the realignment can be complex.

The final authority on the alignment steps, and the order in which to perform them, is the manufacturer's maintenance manual for the receiver. In the absence of such information, the technician will usually find that those instructions follow about the same basic format:

1. Monitor the limiter with a DC meter.
2. Provide 455 kHz at the output of the second mixer.
3. Peak the low-IF amplifiers.
4. Center the discriminator on noise with a DC meter.
5. Provide an exact high IF of 10.7 MHz at the output of the first mixer.
6. Peak the high-IF amplifiers.
7. Provide exact on-channel RF signal at antenna input.
8. Warp the high-frequency oscillator to zero discriminator DC voltage output.

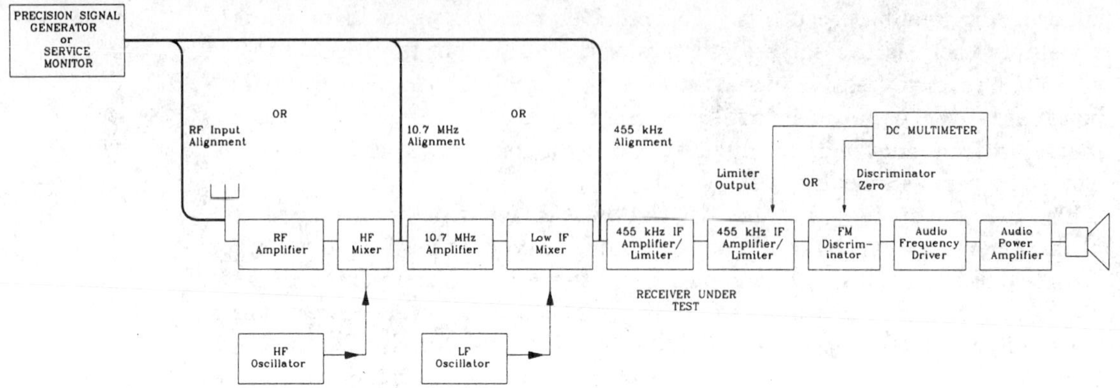

Figure 13–32 Block diagram of the use of instruments for aligning a dual-conversion receiver.

These adjustments may be done using a precision signal generator and DC voltmeter. The signal generator must be precise, as it may be impossible to bring a receiver back on-channel with sufficient sensitivity if either of the intermediate frequency amplifier strips is aligned away from the proper frequency. The instruments necessary for these adjustments are shown in Figure 13–32.

Three things must be kept in mind when doing a major alignment such as this:

1. *Never apply the output of a signal generator into a circuit that has DC present* without first using a series-connected DC blocking capacitor. About .01 μfd is adequate for most RF alignment work.
2. *Use only enough signal from the signal generator to do the job.* Overdriving a signal into a stage has the effect of broadening all the adjustments, making precise adjustment impossible.
3. *Do not force ferrite core adjustments or use an improper tool on these components.* Remember the caution at the beginning of this chapter in this regard, in section 13.6, "Special Tools for RF Use." Don't neglect to use the correct type and size of tool.

IF and RF Stage Alignment Procedures for FM

Step 1: Monitor the Limiter with a DC Meter. The effect of adjusting any of the amplifier stages in an FM receiver is best monitored by watching the DC level of the limiters at the last IF stages in the receiver. It will be necessary to find the limiter test points. There are often two limiters, one following the other. As the amount of signal increases, the voltage of the last limiter stage increases up to a "saturation" point, at which time the first limiter stage starts to go into limiting if the signal input continues to increase. Once the last limiter test point has been located, a DC voltmeter is connected to it as a signal strength indicator. Next, a signal generator must be connected and set to the correct frequency.

Step 2: Provide 455 kHz at the Output of the Second Mixer. Connect a precise 455-kHz signal (This is almost always the frequency used for the lowest IF frequency) into the circuit at the output of the second mixer, the input to the 455-kHz amplifier string. Use a DC-blocking capacitor if necessary.

Step 3: Peak the Low IF Amplifiers. The signal generator 455-kHz output is then varied up and down in large increments a few times to get the "feel" of the limiter output voltage. Leave the signal generator output control at about the halfway point between maximum and minimum limiter DC readings.

If necessary, due to a preliminary near-saturation of the limiter, use the first limiter as a tuning indication instead. Align the 455-kHz stages between the generator and the limiter for maximum output of the limiter. As tuning progresses, the generator output level will probably have to be reduced to prevent saturation of the limiter.

The failure of an adjustment to peak or to significantly affect sensitivity may indicate an amplifier stage that is defective. This is what the technician would watch for when looking for the cause of a receiver falling short of the sensitivity test by many dB. For instance, if the sensitivity of a receiver were 5 microvolts instead of 0.5, an unresponsive stage would be a good indication that the stage is not amplifying.

Step 4: Center the Discriminator on Noise with a DC Meter. Now disconnect the signal generator and turn it off. No incoming signal is desirable at this point. If the receiver is operating normally, it will be receiving a good quantity of RF noise. Turning off the squelch and turning up the volume should make the noise audible. If the 455-kHz amplifier strip is operating normally, this noise will now (after aligning the 455-kHz amplifiers) be centered within the passband of the amplifiers. The discriminator must be centered on this noise.

Connect the DC meter to the discriminator output. If the DC output is not zero, center the reading by adjustment of the discriminator RF transformer. The location of the proper test point for this adjustment will be designated in the instruction book. (Note that a few FM discriminators cannot be adjusted using this procedure. See the instruction book for variances from this "standard" procedure.)

Step 5: Provide a High IF of Exactly 10.7 MHz at the Output of the First Mixer. This step will align the high-IF amplifiers. Although 10.7 MHz is the most common high-IF frequency in use, it is not as "standard" as the 455 kHz of the low IF. The equipment instruction manual should give this high-IF frequency. In some cases, the high-IF frequency can be calculated "backwards." Multiply the receiver crystal frequency by any multiplication factor used. The high-IF frequency is the difference between the channel frequency and the multiplied receiver crystal frequency.

Step 6: Peak the High-IF Amplifiers. As progressively earlier stages are brought into the alignment area by moving the signal generator closer to the antenna input of the receiver, it will probably be necessary to move the DC voltmeter to the first limiter stage, since the second stage may saturate with noise alone once the circuits have been properly peaked up. Again, get the "feel" of the limiter response by turning the signal generator output amplitude up and down, and then set it to about halfway through the limiter range to do the actual aligning of the circuits.

Once a precision RF signal has been coupled into the output circuit of the first mixer, peak the high-IF amplifiers by monitoring the limiters again, as was done to peak the low-IF amplifiers. When the final tuning adjustment has been made on the high-IF amplifiers, recheck the DC output of the discriminator. If it is still on zero DC volts, the alignment is complete thus far. If it is not, it may be necessary to trim ("warp") the low-frequency oscillator that feeds the second mixer until the zero is obtained. If no adjustment is provided for this procedure, compensation can be made for the tiny amount of off-channel operation in the following procedures.

Step 7: Provide an Exact On-Channel RF Signal at Antenna Input. This step is probably the most critical. An *exact* on-channel signal must be provided at the antenna input. Peak the RF amplifier(s) using as low an RF output setting as possible while getting a good limiter response. An alternative method is to provide a signal from a transmitter that is normally used with this receiver as a precision signal source. The transmitter, of course, must be exactly on-channel as well. The RF amplifier and the intermediate amplifiers can be simply tuned for maximum limiter voltage. The multipliers that may be used between the high and low crystal oscillators and the mixers may also be peaked in this manner.

IF and RF Stage Alignment Procedures for AM

An AM receiver is aligned by watching the automatic volume control (AVC) line while adjusting individual stages. As the strength of an exact on-channel RF input increases, the AVC voltage will also increase. By monitoring this DC voltage with a voltmeter, the intervening stages may be aligned, peaking each for the maximum AVC voltage.

The detector of an AM signal is simply a diode rectifier that provides an AVC DC output that is proportional to the amplitude of an applied RF input signal. Since they are used at relatively low voltages, the germanium diode is often seen in this application. This detector is nothing more than a rectifier of the RF, provided with a small filter circuit whose output voltage can still vary at an audio rate. See Figure 13–33.

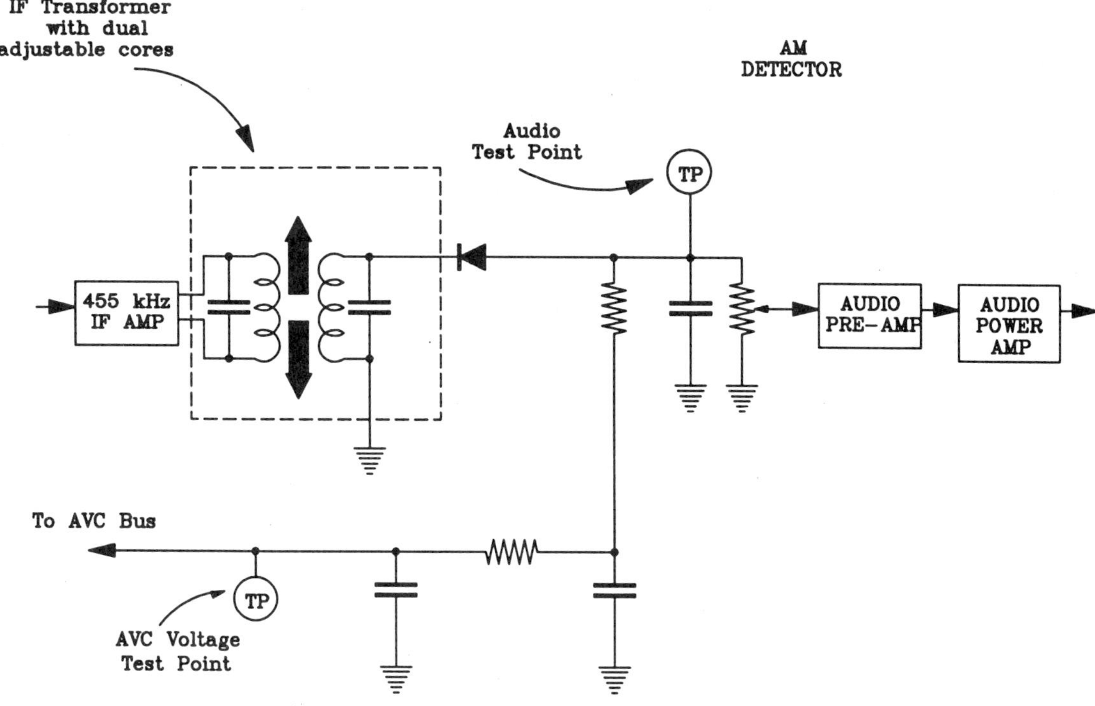

Figure 13–33 A typical AM detector stage with AVC provision.

The audio detector diode and the first stage or two of most modern radios is now often contained in a consumer chip rather than being discrete components. Such a chip will have a pin for AVC output which is used during alignment.

Swept-Frequency Receiver Alignment Procedures

Some receivers are required to respond with the same amplification over a relatively broad range of input frequencies. Radar and television receivers are in this category.

In order to properly shape the response curve of a receiver over a specified range, it is necessary to have a special hook-up of instruments. Figure 13–34 shows such a connection.

Instead of applying a fixed frequency input and peaking all the necessary stages for maximum, the swept-frequency alignment procedure provides an input that varies in frequency over time in a ramped fashion. The input frequency is begun below the lowest frequency that will be amplified, continuing to increase in frequency until above the highest frequency to be amplified. This sweeping is kept at a low audio rate, often near 60 Hz.

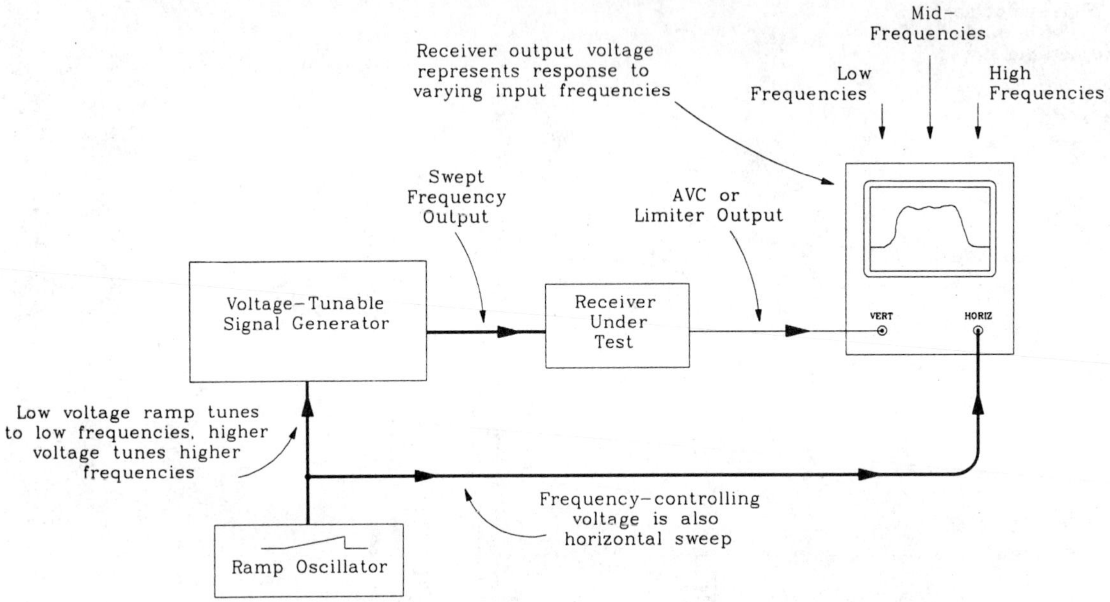

Figure 13–34 Block diagram of separate equipments required to frequency-sweep align a receiver.

The response of the receiver varies according to the frequency applied at that moment. The AVC line of an AM receiver or the limiter of an FM receiver is monitored at the same time to determine the response of the receiver, with more voltage indicating more amplification and more sensitivity at a given input frequency.

Both the ramp voltage controlling the frequency sweep and the output of the receiver are applied to a cathode-ray tube or oscilloscope set up for an X-Y display. The ramp frequency is applied to the horizontal and the receiver output to the vertical.

An elaborate test setup is almost useless unless some means is taken to identify important frequencies on the oscilloscope display. The means of doing this is to mix in one or more precise, fixed frequencies along with the swept frequency. As the swept frequency passes the fixed frequency, an audio difference briefly appears, resulting in a "blip" on the swept waveform. This "blip" is called a *marker*. Figure 13–35 shows typical waveforms that might be obtained during the frequency-swept alignment of a receiver.

The aligning of a receiver using this method is done by noting the effect that each of the appropriate tuning adjustments has on the overall waveform. Many adjustments, going back and forth from one adjustment to another, may be necessary to obtain the proper frequency response waveform as required by the receiver maintenance manual.

Sweep-aligning a receiver with a service monitor is much easier than

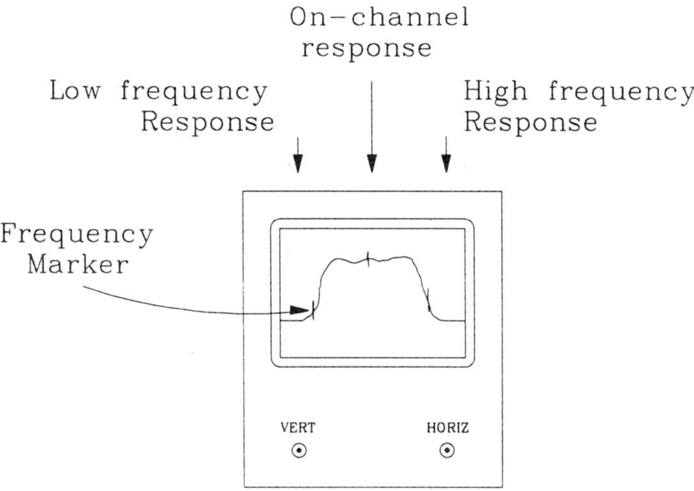

Figure 13–35 Example of a waveform that might be obtained during frequency-sweeping alignment of a receiver.

setting up separate instruments. Only two cables need be used. See Figure 13–36.

FM Receiver Oscillator Alignment Procedures

The oscillators of an FM receiver should be adjusted according to the manufacturer's instructions. Lacking this, it is possible to get good results if the low-frequency oscillator is simply left alone. The discriminator is first

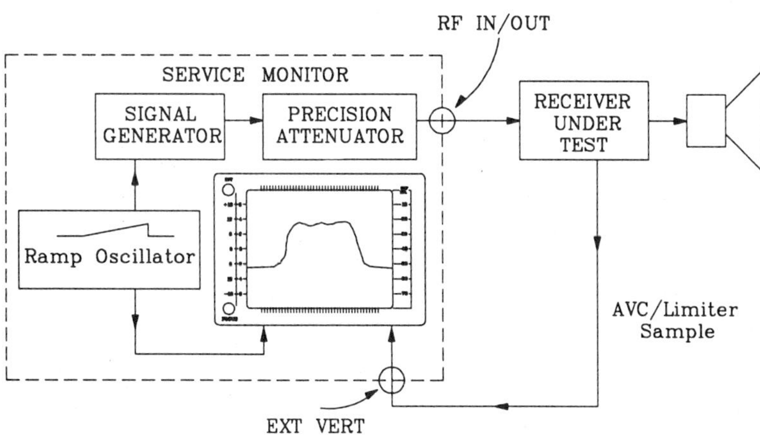

Figure 13–36 Cabling setup for doing a swept-frequency receiver alignment with a service monitor.

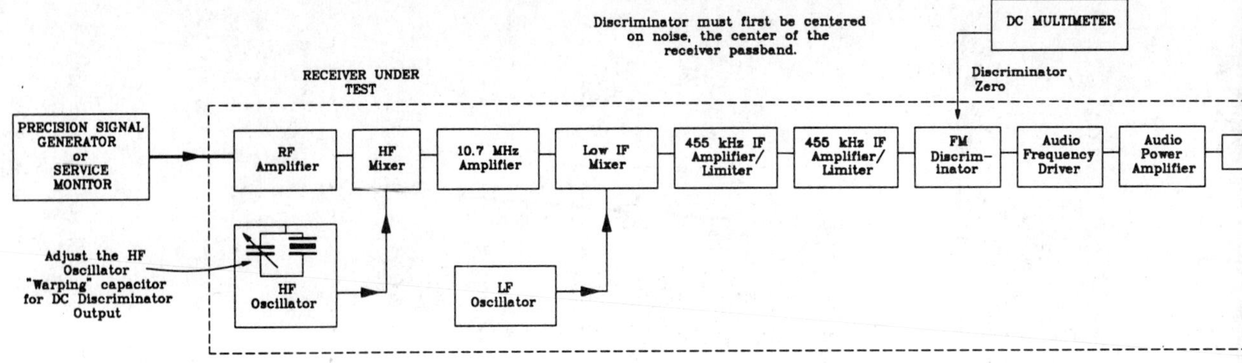

Figure 13–37 Cabling to use a service monitor to zero an FM discriminator on-channel with the warping capacitor of the receiver's HF oscillator.

adjusted for zero DC output without any RF coming into the receiver. This centers the discriminator on noise alone, in the center of the 455-kHz bandpass.

The high-frequency oscillator is then adjusted for the same DC zero, but with a prime signal entering the antenna, by warping the crystal of the oscillator with a small trimmer capacitor. Inability of the crystal to warp to the proper frequency indicates that the crystal must be replaced.

A service monitor is connected as shown in Figure 13–37 to zero the discriminator on-channel by warping the high-frequency oscillator crystal.

AM Receiver Oscillator Alignment Procedures

The oscillators of an AM receiver should be adjusted according to the manufacturer's instructions. The process of aligning an AM receiver's oscillators is not quite as critical as an FM receiver. Generally speaking, the high-frequency oscillator of an AM receiver may be adjusted for maximum on-channel response of a modulated signal. The oscillator should be adjusted for minimum distortion of, and maximum audio response to, the input signal. This will indicate that the received signal is coming directly down the middle of the low-IF amplifier stages and that the signal is not limited by the skirt selectivity of the IF amplifiers. The low-frequency oscillator should usually be left alone and may not even have an adjustment provided.

Adjusting the Phase-Locked Loop Frequency Synthesizer

If a communications receiver will be used on many different channels, it will probably be outfitted with a frequency synthesizer rather than using many crystals. This is a less expensive alternative than buying two crystals per channel when more than about six channels are involved.

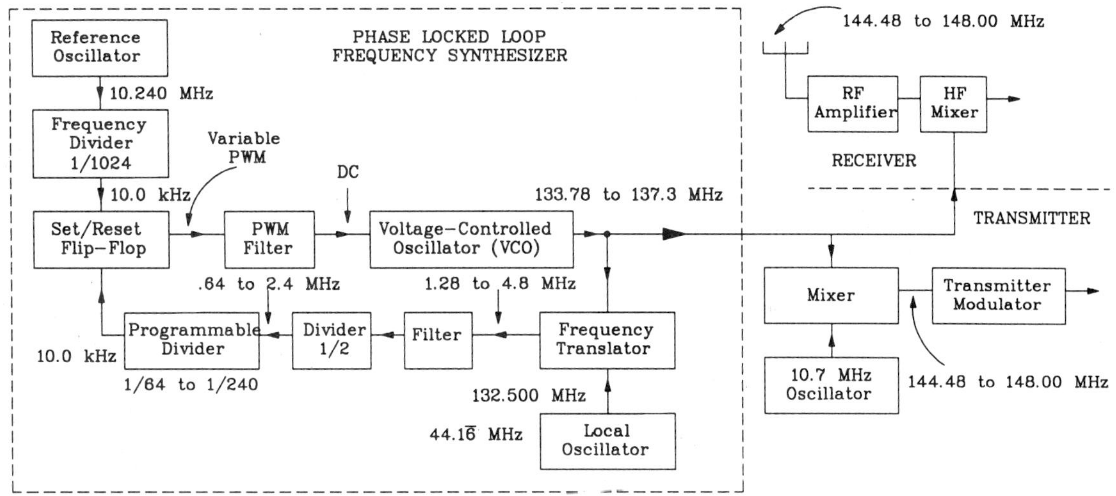

Figure 13–38 The phase-locked loop and how it works to generate both receive and transmit frequencies.

There are many variations on the circuits used to build a phase-locked loop (PLL) frequency synthesizer. Figure 13–38 shows a typical PLL and how the output frequency is divided down and compared to a reference frequency to lock the voltage-controlled oscillator (VCO) to a particular frequency.

Any tendency for the VCO to drift will be immediately compensated for and the VCO will be brought back to proper frequency. New frequencies are selected by changing the division factor of the output, producing a new signal compared in the phase detector, thus driving the output of the VCO to the new frequency.

The PLL generates RF signals over a specified frequency range. The PLL output is often used directly as the HF oscillator of a receiver. As such, it will be off from the desired channel by the intermediate frequency. For instance, an amateur transceiver PLL might produce 135.82 MHz and be used as the local oscillator. This would mix with a carrier frequency of 146.52 MHz to produce an IF of 10.7 MHz. This PLL must have 10.7 MHz added to it in order to produce the proper frequency for transmitting on the same frequency. Thus, this example uses the PLL directly for receiving, and another oscillator of 10.7 MHz must be added to transmit on the same channel. This extra 10.7-MHz mixing crystal is usually provided with a warping adjustment so that the received and transmitted frequencies are identical.

The location and use of each of the adjustments associated with a PLL are largely equipment dependent. Thus, adjustments of the PLL will require the manufacturer's maintenance manual. All of the adjustments must be taken in order, since the outcome of one adjustment may affect all others following. Taking just one in the wrong order could not only undo the accuracy of previous adjustments, it will require the adjustment to be made again, later, after the mistake has been discovered.

Stage Gain Measurements

A few manufacturers provide stage gain figures for the amplifier stages within their receivers. These gain figures are expressed in dBs. Theoretically, the introduction of a signal of the correct frequency will result in the amplification by the amount specified for that stage. Two methods are available for testing stage gain, both of which are useful to positively identify a defective stage within a receiver that results in poor sensitivity. One method involves the use of only a signal generator, and another method is more precise, but requires the use of a separate signal generator and a service monitor.

Signal Generator Alone. Stage gain measurement requires connecting the signal generator into circuitry that often contains a DC component. Be sure to use a series DC blocking capacitor in the signal generator lead as noted earlier in this chapter.

Stage gain measurements are not so simple that one can just connect a signal generator to the input of a stage and expect a given amount of amplification. This is due in part to impedance mismatches between the signal generator and the circuit under test. Another problem is that signals will radiate from the signal generator leads to earlier, more sensitive stages, producing more input signal than intended at the stage under test. Individual stage gain measurements may be performed, keeping in mind these limitations. When in doubt, *compare identical stage gain results* that you obtain against a unit known to be in good operating condition, and then log your readings for future use.

One way to measure stage gain measurements is to record how much signal is required to open the squelch circuit of the receiver with a signal introduced at the output of a given stage. Then move the signal generator to the input of the same stage, again measuring how much signal is required to break the squelch. The dB difference between these two voltage levels may be calculated by reference to the dB scale of the signal generator output control. The dB figure for a given stage should only approximate that given for the stage by the manufacturer due to the limitations already explained above.

Signal Generator and Service Monitor. A service monitor may also be used as a frequency-selective RF micro-voltmeter, which will measure RF voltages down to the microvolt level. It is best to use a standard oscilloscope probe on the input of the service monitor receiver to provide some DC and AC isolation and excessive loading of the RF circuits. Even so, the probe will have some loading effect on the stage under test, particularly at higher frequencies.

The basic procedure is to apply sufficient RF signal input with a separate signal generator to produce a readable signal with the service monitor. Of course, the service monitor must be tuned to the same frequency as the RF stage under test. Once this has been accomplished and verified (by slightly changing the input level from the signal generator and noting a response change at the service monitor), the output of the stage under test should be probed. If there is amplification, the service monitor receiver will show a stronger signal on the built-in oscilloscope. Reduce the input signal generator level until the same amplitude is read on the service monitor. The difference in dB from that applied to the input of the stage and the reduction in the signal generator in dB to produce the same at the stage output is the gain of the stage. See Figure 13–39.

13.8 WORKING WITH RF POWER AND TRANSMITTERS

A Practical Look at Decibels

The decibel provides a very important means of expressing meaningful comparisons when discussing transmitters, receivers, antennas, and transmission lines. Practically speaking, a technician will seldom actually calculate dBs. Knowing that the formula for comparing two power levels is 10 times the logarithm of the power ratios is of little help when neither log tables or a calculator are handy. Far more useful would be a method by which a technician could quickly and simply estimate the dB figure when provided only with the two powers in question.

Power Ratios in dBs

It is really quite simple to work with power ratios and dBs if a few basic facts are kept in mind:

1. A power increase is positive, while a decrease is negative.
2. A power ratio of 2:1 is a matter of about a 3-dB difference.
3. A power ratio of 10:1 is a matter of a 10-dB difference.
4. Decibels always add or subtract.

Using this information, one can easily understand that raising a transmitter's power from 5 watts to 10 watts will raise it by 3 dB. Likewise, raising that power from 10 watts to 100 watts will increase it by 10 dB. A slightly trickier calculation must be made when, raising power from 5 watts to 100 for an increase of 13 dB. The first 3 dB is caused by doubling from 5 W to 10 W, and then 10 dB is added to the 3 dB due to increasing

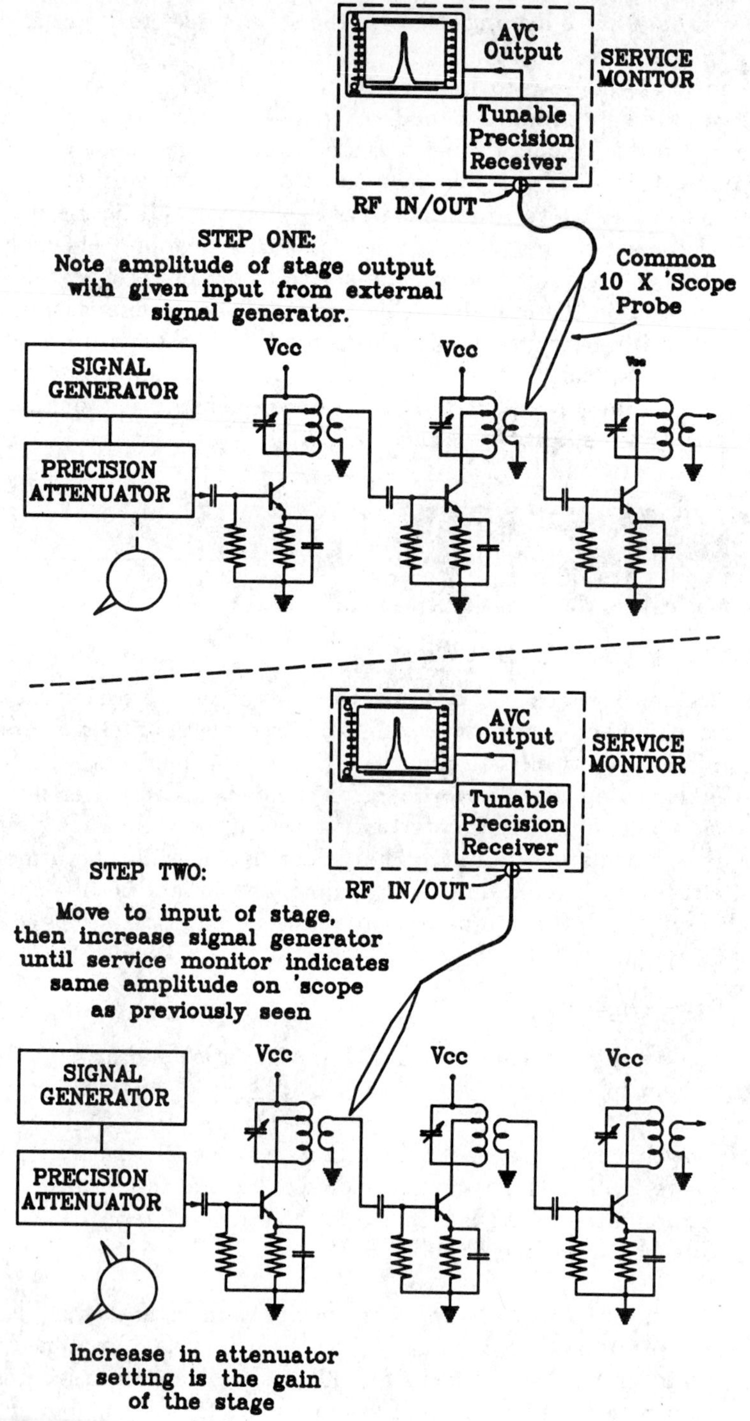

Figure 13–39 Equipment setup to determine stage gain, using a signal generator and a service monitor as a microvoltmeter.

power from 10 W to 100 W. Decreasing power from 100 W to 5 W would be a loss of –13 dB.

Voltage (and Current) Ratios in dBs

Voltage (and current) ratios can be expressed in dBs of change in a similar manner, provided the resistance involved does not change between the two voltage readings. For a 52 Ω coaxial cable, for instance, a voltage of 10 V into the cable and only 5 V coming out the other end would suggest a loss of 3 dB—except that the final answer must be doubled. Thus, 6 dB is the power loss in this cable, as shown by the voltage ratio.

The relationship between dBs and voltage ratios can be verified by looking at the output attenuator scale of an RF signal generator, provided it has both microvolts and dB scales. Note that the dB figure for an output of 2 μv is shown as an arbitrary –1 dB. Reducing the voltage reading to 1 μv lines up with –7 dB, a difference of 6 dB.

Practically speaking, this method of estimating dBs should enable the technician to make dB answers come out to within + or – a single dB, which is quite sufficient for fieldwork.

Decibels comprise the ratio of one power to another. They are most often expressed in reference to a beginning, or understood, reference point. For instance, a milliwatt (0.001 watt) is the most common reference power level for radio frequency use. Once in a while, a reference level of 1 watt is used. The reference in question is verified by the abbreviation used: dBm refers to a reference level of a milliwatt, while a dBw refers to the 1-watt level.

MAKING TRANSMITTER TESTS

Why Transmitter Tests Are Important

Improper transmitter performance can cause illegal and potentially dangerous interference with communications already in progress on other channels. A transmitter that is off its proper channel can interfere with adjacent channels. Moreover, a transmitter that is illegally high in power can cause interference at great distances to communications on the same frequency. A transmitter that is overmodulating will probably cause "splatter" interference to adjacent channels, too. Consider the fact that safety communications on police, ambulance, and emergency rescue services may disrupted by a defective transmitter, and the importance of transmitter operation becomes clear. The Federal Communications Commission takes a dim view of illegal operation, and for good cause. It is up to the servicing technician to be certain that transmitters are not only operating properly, but that they are within the limits of the station license as to power and channel bandwidth.

Checking Power Output with Separate Instruments. Power output is usually the first performance test to be made on a transmitter. The connections to be made when using separate instruments are shown in Figure 13–40.

Never key a transmitter without a dummy load or antenna attached. To do so can cause the final amplifier to be destroyed by the high voltages caused within the amplifier by the lack of a proper load.

If the technician is using an RF power meter, the meter must be capable of accurately measuring the transmitter power at the transmitted frequency. RF wattmeters usually have a specified range within which they will accurately indicate transmitter power. If it is used to read power of frequencies outside this range, the wattmeter will not be accurate, although it may be used for relative RF power readings.

Checking Power Output with a Service Monitor. A service monitor may have a built-in dummy load for measuring transmitter power. If so, this instrument probably has a unique feature: when in the receive mode, a transmitter may be keyed directly into the attenuator of the signal generator output without harm. Internal circuitry detects any incoming RF of more than about 200 milliwatts and automatically switches off the attenuator and onto a dummy load. All the technician needs to do is select the proper power indicator range and read the transmitter power directly from the meter provided. This connection is made as shown in Figure 13–41.

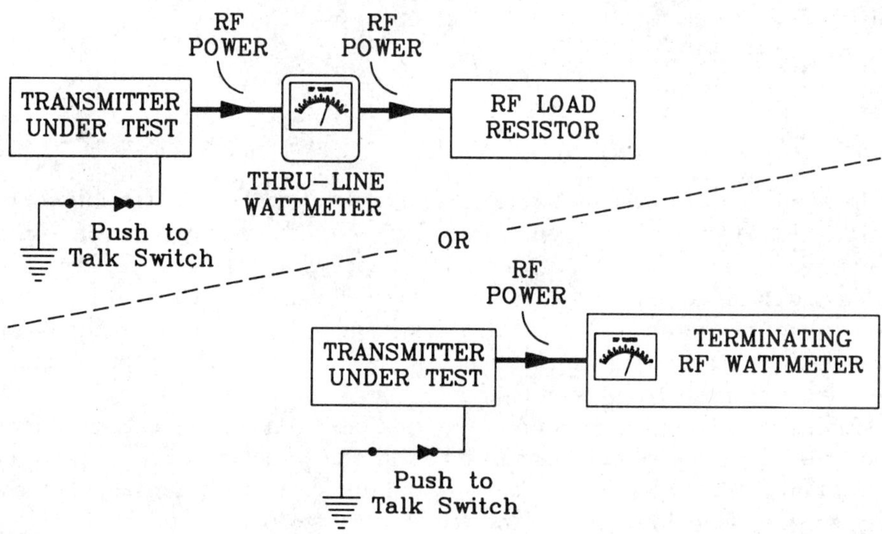

Figure 13–40 Block diagram of the use of separate equipments for measuring RF output power.

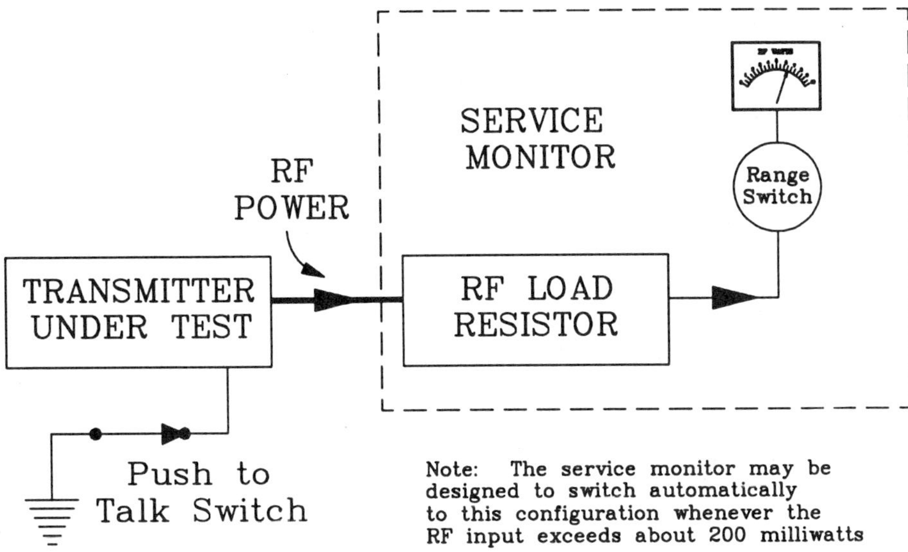
SERVICE
MONITOR
RF
POWER
Range
Switch
TRANSMITTER
UNDER TEST
RF LOAD
RESISTOR
Push to
Talk Switch
Note: The service monitor may be
designed to switch automatically
to this configuration whenever the
RF input exceeds about 200 milliwatts

Figure 13–41 Connecting a service monitor for measuring transmitter power output.

Being Reasonable about Transmitted Power. The servicing technician should keep in mind the significance of the decibel when testing transmitters. For instance, if one can enhance the power output of a given transmitter from a level of 9 watts to a new level of 10 watts with a simple adjustment, that's fine. However, if all the adjustments are correct and the transmitter still fails to produce the advertised 10 watts, the technician should not invest hours of work in replacing components to get the extra watt. The difference between 9 watts and 10 watts is very little in terms of dBs. It would take an increase to 18 watts just to give a power increase of 3 dB. Gaining less than a single dB is not worth the investment of a lot of a technician's time. The additional dB after exhaustive tuning and replacement could not be detected by a listener at a remote receiver, anyway.

Testing Transmitter Frequency

Using a Frequency Counter. Communications transmitters must be on channel to a high degree of precision. Frequency tolerances range from .02 percent to .00015 percent, depending on the carrier frequency and the transmitter power range. These tolerances are set by the FCC and represent maximum limits above or below the assigned frequency. The technician will want to keep the system as close as possible to the channel frequency, however, because operating at the frequency tolerance limits would make communications garbled and unsatisfactory (although legal).

A transmitter may be checked for on-channel operation by the use of a precision frequency counter. (Remember that the input circuitry of a counter may be overloaded by any voltage of more than 2 volts.) Use a power attenuator to reduce the transmitted signal to a safe value for counting. This subject was discussed under "Frequency Counters," earlier in this chapter.

Using a Service Monitor. Testing a transmitter for on-channel operation requires a very precise signal generator, using the signal generator as the frequency standard. To be legally used, the signal generator must be capable of generating a frequency that is ten times the accuracy of the channel-determining circuitry of the transmitter. The internal block diagram of the circuitry necessary to check a transmitter for proper frequency is shown in Figure 13–42.

It should be noted that these are exactly the same connections that are used for testing the transmitter power output. All one need do to check frequency at the same time that transmitter power output is tested is to previously punch up the right combination of push buttons on the service monitor. Small errors of frequency may be read on the LCD display on the service monitor or heard by listening to the zero-beat function that is also provided.

It is easy to misread the transmitter frequency, particularly if multiple-channel equipment is being tested. Attempting to find a frequency error that is more than about 10 kHz from the frequency dialed into the service monitor will give a power output indication, but there will be a reading of 0.00 on the frequency display. In this case, one may suspect a transmitter to be far off-channel, usually as the result of an operator error in setting up the service monitor or the transmitter under test. In extreme cases, it may be necessary to use the spectrum analyzer function of the service monitor to find the frequency actually being produced by the transmitter.

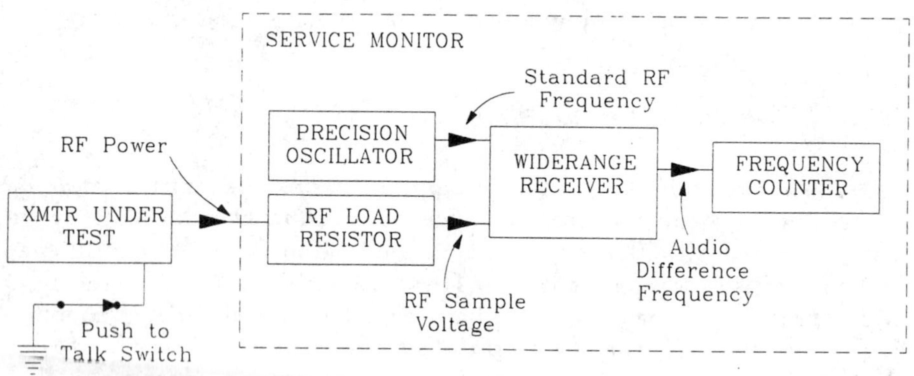

Figure 13–42 How a service monitor measures frequency.

Testing the Percentage of Modulation of AM Transmitters

Amplitude modulation is still used for aircraft communications and in commercial broadcast. Other applications have changed to single-sideband or FM modes of modulation.

The modulated output of an AM transmitter can be observed on an oscilloscope, as shown previously in Figure 13–13, *provided* the oscilloscope is capable of observing the RF frequencies involved. An oscilloscope of 100 MHz could be used to observe the modulation envelope of a 120-MHz signal, although the overall amplitude will not be accurate. It is the relative amplitude of the maximum and minimum modulation envelope that is of importance, not the absolute amplitude.

The real test of modulation concerns the negative portions (valleys) of modulation. Whereas a positive peak overmodulation does not create interference to adjacent channels, negative peak modulation momentarily shuts down the amplifier output and thereby produces splatter interference. The servicing technician should concentrate on the negative portion of the modulated waveform to be sure it does not cut off the RF waveform entirely.

The linearity of AM modulation may be tested by using a Lissajous pattern. Simply feed a sample of the modulating audio into the horizontal input of an oscilloscope and a sample of the output RF from the transmitter into the vertical. See Figure 13–43.

Another method of determining the percentage of amplitude modulation is to use a special instrument made for the purpose. A sample of the transmitted RF is fed to the instrument, which is calibrated. The percentage of modulation is indicated on the instrument meter.

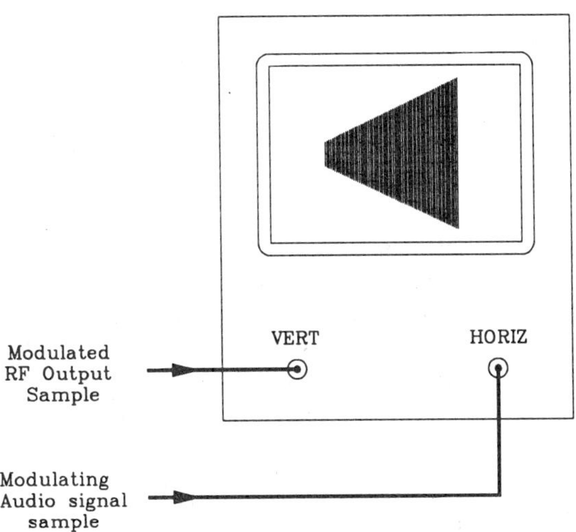

Figure 13–43 Testing an AM transmitter for modulation linearity. The top and bottom of the waveform should be flat.

Testing Frequency Deviation of FM Transmitters

Using a Special Deviation Meter. The deviation of an FM carrier is not as simple as that of an AM transmitters. There is no technical "100 percentage" point when deviating a carrier from center frequency. Only the legal definition of channel width determines the limits of how far the carrier may be deviated from rest frequency. An FM deviation meter must be set for the maximum legal deviation before taking a reading.

Using a Service Monitor. A service monitor can provide two very convenient methods of checking deviation. While keying the transmitter into the service monitor as when testing transmitter power, modulation may be applied by simply whistling past (and not directly into) the microphone of the transmitter. The deviation meter on the service monitor is set for a full-scale reading of 6 kHz, and the peak deviation is read directly on the meter. When using a whistle, the deviation should be about 4.5 kHz peak. when a sinewave-like whistle deviates to this amount, voice peaks may take the deviation just to the edge of 5 kHz deviation. The oscilloscope, if provided, will also show the audio modulating waveform. The service monitor may provide another feature of use for this test: a pair of baselines representing +5 kHz and –5 kHz is simultaneously shown along with the modulation on the oscilloscope face. If the modulation remains between these two lines, even the peaks do not overdeviate the carrier. This feature enables the technician to see whether short spikes of audio will overmodulate the carrier.

The use of an oscilloscope to monitor deviation has two advantages over a meter: its ability to show distortion of the modulating waveform and its depiction of unequal modulation as positive and negative. Either distortion of the modulation or unequal deviation must be corrected for the transmitter to sound properly on the air.

OPTIONAL TRANSMITTER TESTS

Testing Transmitter Tone Generation

The transmission of low-level audio tones can be used to selectively call one or a group of receivers rather than calling all of the receivers on a given channel. This reduces the perceived traffic on the channel, since any receiver will open only for those signals intended for it. Other communications on the same frequency will not open the receiver at all.

The audio tones used may vary from subaudible to high audio frequencies. A listing of the frequencies of these standardized tones is available in Appendix XI.

It is common for FM communications transmitters to deviate the carrier only 600 Hz with these tones. This makes them much lower in amplitude than the normal voice communications on the channel, often all but unnoticeable to the casual listener.

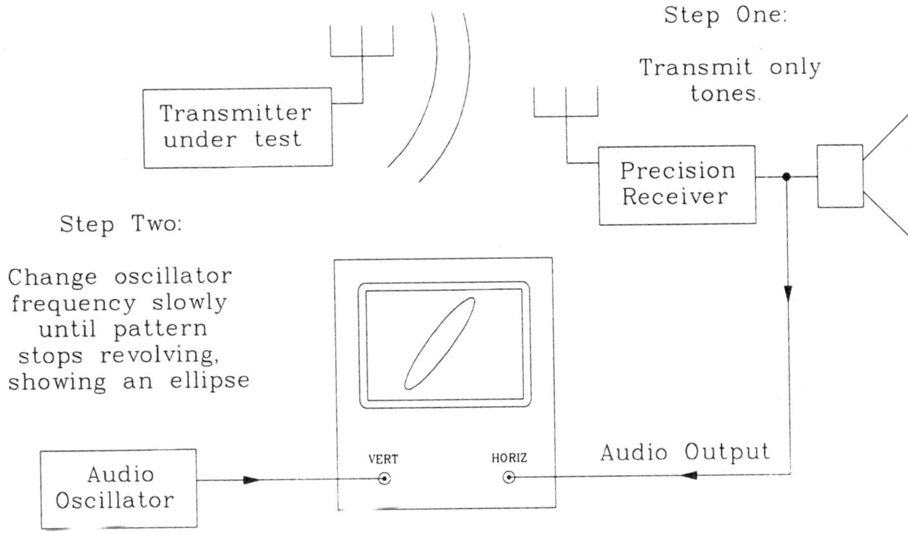

Figure 13–44 Equipment setup to check subtone frequency.

A precise audio signal generator able to duplicate the tones, an oscilloscope, and the transmitter under test make up the instruments necessary to get exact readouts of the frequency of the tones. See Figure 13–44.

As might be expected, the same test is much more easily accomplished with a service monitor. This instrument will show the Lissajous pattern on the CRT of the instrument by simply pressing the correct buttons and connecting the test equipment as shown in Figure 13–45.

Transmitted Spectrum Analysis

If the output of a transmitter contains strong components that are off channel center, adjacent channel interference can occur. Just because a transmitter has a rated power output, do not assume that all that power is contained within the proper channel width. FCC rules, which vary according to the radio service in question, require only a specific percentage of the radiated power to be outside the specified channel width.

The misadjustment of a transmitter, especially in the UHF and higher-frequency bands, can produce major sidebands that are illegal. Whenever a transmitter is placed into service, it is a good idea to run a check of the spectrum that the transmitter is producing.

It is not practical to connect several instruments, such as a narrow-band, sweepable receiver, a ramp generator, and an oscilloscope, in order to perform the function of a spectrum analyzer. Although it is expensive, a spectrum analyzer is a very good investment for technicians who work on

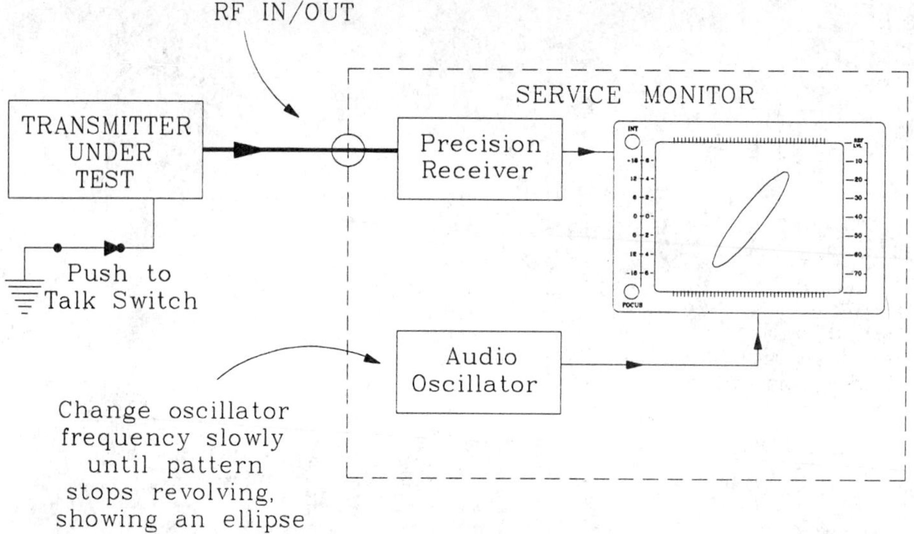

Figure 13–45 Lissajous subtone frequency determination using a service monitor.

numerous transmitters, particularly of the UHF and higher-frequency varieties.

If a service monitor with the capability of functioning as a spectrum analyzer is available, it should be used before clearing a transmitter for use. The internal block diagram of the service monitor, when set for the spectrum analysis of a transmitter, is shown in Figure 13–46.

If any lobes or spikes of radiation exceed the manufacturer's specifications for the transmitter, each of the internal stages, and particularly the frequency multiplier stages, should be retuned carefully while watching the spectrum on the CRT of the monitor and, at the same time, watching to see that the transmitted power output is not seriously affected by the readjustment.

GENERIC ADJUSTMENT OF A RADIO TRANSMITTER

Bringing Transmitter Power Up to Specifications

Amplifiers and Frequency Multipliers. Most of the amplifier stages within a transmitter are amplifier or frequency multiplier stages. These stages usually operate as Class C amplifiers, but in early stages they may operate Class A. The block diagram of the transmitter under test will show these stages. Tuning them is a matter of adjusting each one for maximum signal into the following stage. Often, all that is needed is to watch the transmitter power output while "touching up" the amplifier or multiplier

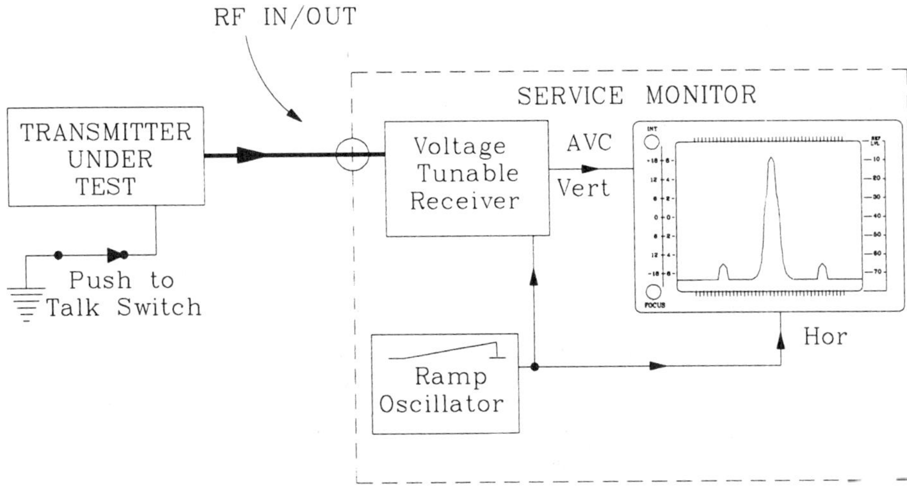

Figure 13–46 Internal block diagram of a service monitor in the spectrum-analysis mode.

stages between the oscillator and the final amplifier stage. Each adjustment is left in the middle of the setting that produces maximum power output. The manufacturer's procedures, of course, are the final authority on the alignment of any given transmitter.

Linear Amplifiers. Remember that the Class C amplifier cannot amplify small input signals because it takes a certain amount of voltage to make the stage begin to conduct. A different kind of amplifier must be used to amplify an amplitude-modulated or a single-sideband input signal, since these signals vary in amplitude from small to large voltages. An RF amplifier that will provide the same fixed gain of a small or a large signal is called a *linear amplifier*. The linear amplifier is usually operated near Class B operation, at a point where the amplifier operates in a fairly linear fashion. At this point, the amplifier may dissipate a considerable amount of power in heat, even when the input signal is idling or at minimum amplitude. This is the price of operating this class. The linear amplifier can amplify AM, SSB, or FM signals. It is more efficient, however, to operate an FM amplifier at Class C because there will be less waste heat, and the input signal does not vary in amplitude.

The RF Power Output Stage

While some low-powered RF amplifiers may be coupled to the antenna in a nonadjustable manner, others may use a special circuit called the *pi-network output*, or *pi-net* for short. This circuit allows the technician to do two

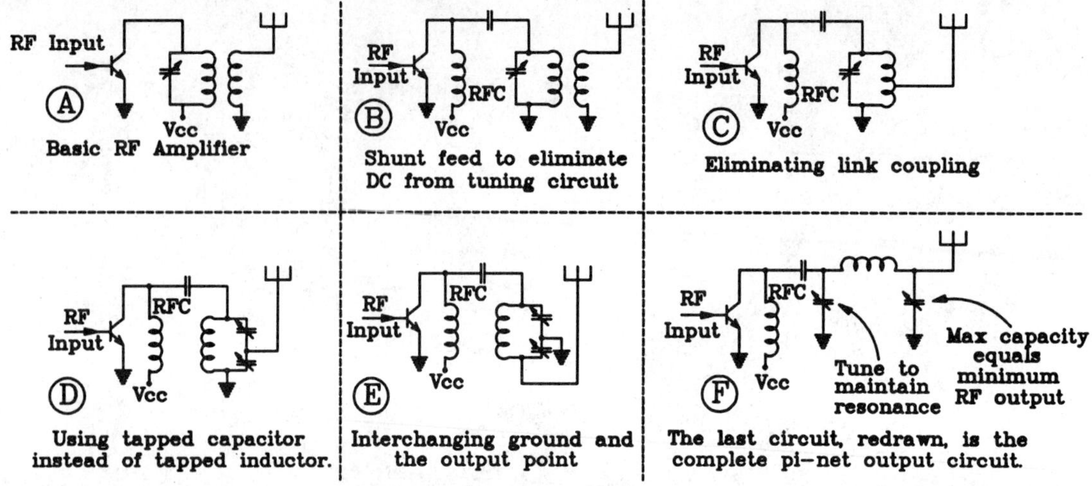

Figure 13–47 Derivation of the pi-net output-coupling circuit.

things: tune the circuit to resonance and also vary the amount of energy coupled out of the LC circuit to the antenna.

The input capacitor of a pi-net circuit is the tuning capacitor, which is smaller in capacitance value than the output capacitor. The output capacitor is used as a variable RF voltage divider, across which the output load (antenna) is connected. As the mount of capacitance is decreased (and the plates disengage), the output energy increases across the resulting higher reactance. Figure 13–47 shows the derivation of the pi-net circuit from a simple LC circuit.

Adjustment of this circuit begins with fully engaging the plates of the output capacitor (the one on the right of F in Figure 13–47). Keep the circuit in tune (tune for minimum amplifier current) with the input capacitor while making output-coupling changes in small increments with the output capacitor. Stop increasing the coupling when the rated current read on the output amplifier stage when the circuit is tuned to resonance indicates full output.

Putting the Transmitter Exactly On-Channel

Transmitter Oscillators. In a crystal-controlled transmitter, there are often one or more frequency multiplying stages following the oscillator. This is particularly true of VHF and UHF transmitters. The overall frequency multiplication that takes place is the result of multiplying the individual stage multiplication factors. For example, two doubler stages plus a tripler results in an overall multiplication factor of 12 of the oscillator frequency. The transmitter oscillator determines the final transmitted frequency, and it must be set accurately, as discussed earlier in this chapter, "Testing Transmitter Frequency."

Crystal-Controlled Oscillators. If the crystal of a transmitter cannot be warped exactly on-channel, it must be replaced. If the crystal is heated in a small oven, however, the failure of the oven heater can cause it to drift off-channel. The oven heater element and the thermostat controlling its temperature should be checked for proper operation before changing the internal crystal in favor of a new one.

The setup for checking transmitter frequency has been covered above under the section, "Testing Transmitter Frequency."

Phase-Locked Loop Frequency Synthesizers. A phase-locked loop frequency synthesizer, as shown in Figure 13–40, is sometimes used to generate the operating frequency for transmitters, especially if there are many possible channels on which the radio may be required to operate. In addition to the PLL output frequency, there is often another crystal oscillator combined with the PLL to generate either the frequency or a submultiple of it. Remember, frequency multipliers are often used in VHF and UHF transmitters. The frequency of this extra crystal (which is often 10.7 MHz) will probably be adjustable so that the transmitter will be on the same frequency as the associated receive channel. The PLL must first be accurately adjusted to be on-channel with the receiver, and then the offset crystal (10.7 MHz) for the transmitter should be trimmed to put the transmitter exactly on-channel as well.

Since PLLs have many different configurations, the method of aligning them and ensuring proper frequencies for both the receive and transmit functions must be found in the maintenance manual for the unit under test.

Adjusting Transmitter Modulation or Deviation

The adjustment of percentage of modulation for an AM transmitter or the deviation of an FM transmitter is an extension of the modulation and deviation tests discussed in this chapter, under "Testing Percentage of Modulation of AM Transmitters" or "Testing Frequency Deviation of FM Transmitters." Leaving the equipment connections as they were for the appropriate test, adjust the appropriate internal potentiometer in the transmitter for the proper amount of modulation. This control will be located in the late audio stages between the microphone and the modulator of the transmitter.

The legal width for voice communications on VHF and UHF transceivers is +/–5 kHz from the carrier frequency. This represents the maximum and minimum amounts by which the carrier can deviate and still be legal, an amount for which the receiver is designed. Exceeding this amount of deviation will produce interference on adjacent channels and may cause the intended receiver to block out parts of the transmission as the carrier swings out of the receiver's passband. The squelch circuit sees this as noise and shuts the receiver audio off.

An AM transmitter that exceeds 100 percent modulation of the carrier in the negative direction will produce splatter on nearby channels and will sound very distorted to a receiver tuned to receive it.

13.9 REPLACEMENT OF RF COMPONENTS

Some of the components within RF equipment deal entirely with DC voltages and currents. Generally speaking, the value tolerance of these components are not critical to the proper operation of the circuit. They can be replaced with new components that may vary 10 percent or more without degrading the circuit operation measurably. Filtering components such as capacitors and resistors used to remove RF from DC circuits are examples of parts that are not critical.

Components that operate directly with RF voltages, on the other hand, can be very critical to the proper operation of the circuit. The inductance or capacitance of a tuned circuit, for instance, must be very carefully matched, or tuned, for the circuit to work at all. The identification of value-critical components is necessary for a proper repair. If a critical part is found defective and replaced, only an identical part should be used for replacement. If very critical, the part will be adjustable. The use of an adjustable component is an indication of a critical circuit.

Once a critical part has been identified as such, its replacement will require a realignment or touch-up of the circuit before the overall equipment may be expected to operate normally. Occasionally, the schematic will identify critical parts with a special symbol. The asterisk (*) is sometimes used for this purpose. A tunable IF transformer, for instance, may have an asterisk appearing at the schematic symbol. The schematic notes will verify if this symbol is used to identify a critical component, one that must be adjusted after replacement.

13.10 WORKING WITH MICROWAVES

Microwave Advantages

Frequencies above approximately 1000 MHz (1 gHz) are referred to as microwaves. The wavelength of a 1 gHz cycle is slightly less than 1 foot. A quarter-wave antenna would need to be only 3 inches long at this frequency.

The use of these higher frequencies makes it possible to construct antennas with a great deal of gain. At 6 gHz, a television satellite receiving dish has a gain of 40 dB. This provides a gain of 10,000 by means of the antenna design alone. The use of small wavelengths also makes it possible to focus radio waves into very narrow beams. Additionally, these frequencies allow the transmission of much wider bandwidth emissions than would be acceptable on lower frequencies.

Another use for microwaves is to multiplex (Mux) many telephone conversations on a single, low-powered transmitter. A demultiplexer (Demuxer) at the receiving end separates each conversation back into individual signals. In this application, the single carrier wave, with all its sidebands, is transmitted via a sharp beam to a remote receiving antenna dish.

Microwave receivers use variations of the basic superheterodyne receiver. These receivers may or may not have an RF amplifier, as some applications apply the incoming signal directly to a mixer for immediate conversion to a lower frequency.

MICROWAVE HARDWARE

Waveguides

The length of wiring at microwave frequencies presents complicated problems. If a wire is a quarter-wavelength long, it will act as a very good antenna. This means that any wire of about 3 inches or less is unacceptable for wiring point-to-point. Special techniques must be employed to generate and process microwave frequencies.

Waveguides replace coaxial lines at microwave frequencies, providing a means of connecting microwave equipment to remotely located antennas. The physical size of waveguide required to transmit a given frequency is such that the wide dimension of the waveguide is half-wavelength and, the narrow dimension, quarter-wavelength.

Stripline Amplifiers

Special circuits are also necessary at microwave frequencies. The length of the wiring in the PC board circuits is carefully adjusted so that the lines act as tuned lines, and their length is used to advantage in coupling signals from one circuit to another. An amplifier with this kind of wiring is called a *stripline amplifier*. See Figure 13–48.

The Stripline Opposed-Emitter (SOE) Package

Special semiconductors must be used at these frequencies as well. Motorola has an example of this, a design for the transistors to be used as amplifiers. This construction is called a stripline opposed-emitter package. See Figure 13–49.

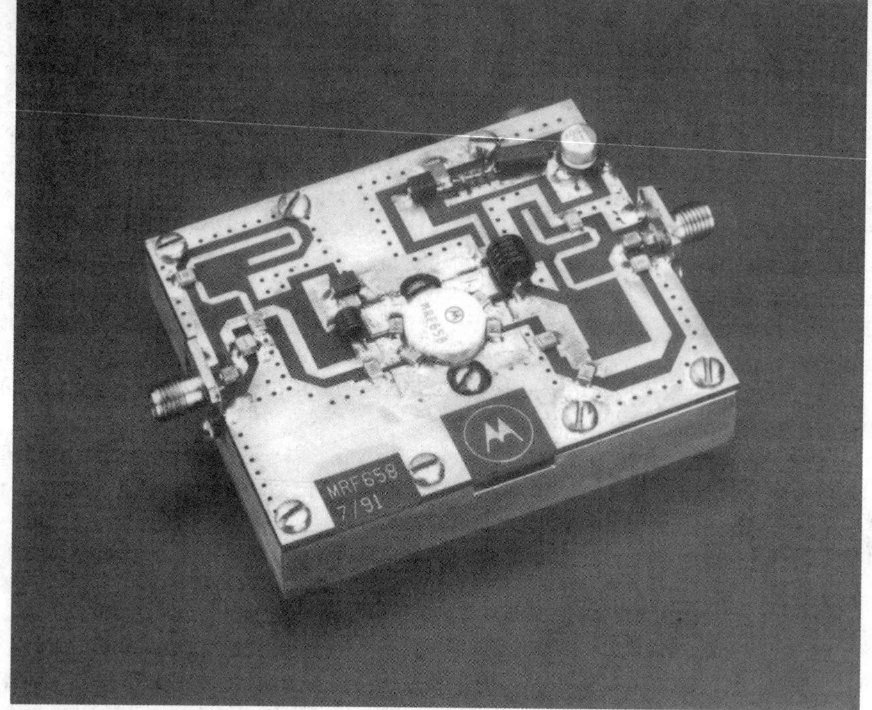

Figure 13–48 The strip-line amplifier uses trace lengths as tuned circuits. (Photograph courtesy of Motorola)

Figure 13–49 A stripline opposed-emitter transistor package.

MICROWAVE POWER MEASUREMENT

Microwave Power Meters

Radio frequency power measurements at microwave frequencies are usually done with an instrument that measures the amount of heating effect that a calibrated fraction of the primary signal will produce. The instruments designed for these measurements are based upon the thermistor as a sensing element. A thermistor is placed into a specially designed bridge circuit that cancels out the effect of ambient temperature.

The attenuation of microwaves as they go through coaxial cables is very substantial. A few feet of coax can lose 90 percent of the applied microwave power as it passes through the cable. Since it is not practical to couple and uncouple waveguides, short lengths of cable may be used at microwave frequencies for test purposes, but the attenuation of the cable must be known and taken into account. See Figure 13–50.

A small sample of a transmitted signal passing through a waveguide is taken by means of a microwave coupler. This is a pickup loop with a known amount of sampling. For instance, a coupler may be marked as having a –20 dB factor. This coupler would provide a .01 *power* sample of the energy traveling within the waveguide. The loss of the necessary short length of test coax cable at this frequency is known in this case to be 7 dB. The power meter reads what is left, an average of a mere 2 milliwatts. The total 27-dB energy ratio may be applied to this reading to calculate the average power within the waveguide. Using the mental calculations already explained in this chapter, the reading of 2 milliwatts could be increased mentally to a level of 2 watts by applying a 10X factor three times, (30 dB) giving 2 watts traveling through the waveguide. Then, the final power would be halved to account for the 3 dB that are yet unaccounted for. Thus, the power in the waveguide would calculate to be an average power of 1 watt.

A microwave power-measuring instrument is a powerful troubleshooting tool when servicing and troubleshooting microwave systems. All that is

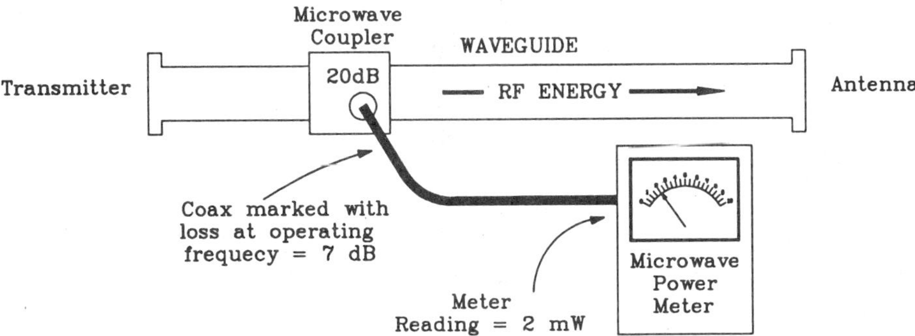

Figure 13–50 Proper method of determining RF power flow through a waveguide.

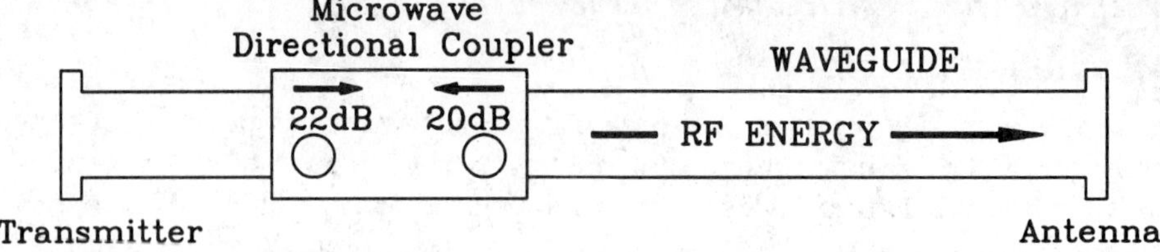

Figure 13–51 The microwave bidirectional coupler will monitor RF passing in only one direction for each output.

needed to make the job easy is a permanently installed bidirectional coupler in the waveguide near the transmitter. The bidirectional coupler independently samples the energy passing through the waveguide in only each direction by means of two output connectors. See Figure 13–51.

The bidirectional coupler is used with the same type of calibrated-loss coaxial cable previously mentioned. Comparisons are made between the incident (direct) and reflected power indications. Excessive reflections are an indication of a problem in the antenna circuit or the waveguide above the coupler.

Many applications of microwave power are pulsed transmissions. Marine radar, for instance, operates at close to 9 gHz. Radar pulses are sent out from the antenna, then echoes are listened for by the receiver as they return from objects in the radar beam.

Microwave power meters read average microwave power. Calculating the peak power is necessary, using the ratio of the peak to the average power of the system. If a system has a peak power of 50 kilowatts, pulsing for 2 microseconds 40 times a second, the average power is calculated as follows:

$$\text{Average Power} = \text{Peak Power} \times \text{Time On}_{\text{secs.}} \times 40$$

This would calculate as:

$$50{,}000 \times .000002 \times 40 = 4 \text{ Watts}$$

This method of calculating peak and average power assumes a perfect pulse without sloping sides. Actual figures are subject to errors because of imperfect pulse shape, but in most practical cases this may be disregarded.

A spectrum analyzer capable of showing emissions well into the gigahertz range is an important instrument for ensuring that transmitted signals do not contain undesirable sidebands. The methods of generating microwave signals, multiplying lower signals, makes it quite possible to have strong radiations at unintended frequencies. The misadjustment of tuned circuits can greatly affect output signals at these frequencies. The spectrum analyzer shows rogue transmissions, and can be used to minimize them through careful retuning of the tuned circuits, while watching the results on the spectrum analyzer.

SPECIAL COMPONENTS FOR USE AT MICROWAVE FREQUENCIES

Amplifying and Detecting Microwave Signals

The GAsFET Transistor. It is possible, though difficult, to amplify very low-level microwave signals at their original frequencies, without immediately heterodyning them to lower frequencies. The normal generation of noise within the amplifier itself places a limit on the smallest signal that can be amplified.

The best component for amplification of very small signals at microwave frequencies is the gallium-arsenide field effect transistor (GAsFET.) This component produces very little noise internally, making it a very good amplifier at microwave frequencies.

Other transistors have been optimized for operation at microwave frequencies. These are best used when signal levels are larger, such as in the amplification and doubling stages of transmitters.

The Schottky, or Hot Carrier, Diode. Diodes that are intended for use at radio frequencies must be made with small junction areas to minimize capacitance which would limit their frequency of use. They should also require less voltage to forward bias them because of the very low voltage signals used in some RF circuits. Schottky (hot carrier) diodes are specially constructed in such a manner as to have no minority carriers, one of the principle frequency-limiting features of a standard PN junction. These diodes are useful well into the gigahertz range, being particularly low in the RF noise they generate.

The *Schottky* or *hot carrier diode* mixer circuit is particularly attractive for use at microwave frequencies (greater than about 1000 MHz) because of the difficulty of constructing practical small-signal amplifiers at those frequencies. By immediately converting microwave frequencies to a lower frequency that is more manageable, such as the common intermediate frequency of 10.7 MHz, the microwave diode enables the use of low-frequency amplifiers with these extremely high frequencies. See Figure 13–52.

The Schottky diode switch from conducting to reverse biased condition is a matter of one or two picoseconds. It is a nonlinear device, which provides a current and voltage curve suitable for mixing RF voltages. Schottky diodes also produce relatively little RF noise during operation. There are several types of these diodes whose reverse voltage limitations ranges from over a hundred volts to as little as 3 volts. Because of this low voltage limitation, testing these diodes must be done with great care. Generally speaking, the higher the frequency of operation, the less the tolerance for reverse voltage breakdown. Exceeding this value of voltage during component testing will burn out the diode, particularly if one of the older volt-ohm-milliammeters is used on the ohmmeter

Figure 13–52 The microwave diode operates as a mixer at UHF and microwave frequencies.

scales. Typical values of forward voltage range from 0.4 V to 0.55 V at 1 milliampere of forward current.

The Microwave Local Oscillator

The Tunnel Diode. The local oscillator of a receiver at microwave frequencies does not need to be capable of much power: a few milliwatts is quite sufficient for signal mixing with an incoming microwave RF signal. A tunnel diode is a good choice for a microwave oscillator. When it is forward-biased by the proper amount and mounted in a suitable enclosure, the diode will oscillate at UHF and higher frequencies.

The Gunn Diode. The Gunn diode is a single piece of n-type gallium arsenide sandwiched between pieces of metal. It is not really a diode, but by applying a DC voltage across the device, a negative-resistance characteristic is encountered that enables them to oscillate. They are often used in cavities as oscillators at frequencies above 25 GHz.

The Impact Avalanche and Transit Time (IMPATT) Diode. The IMPATT diode is used at microwave frequencies. It uses the reverse-biased avalanche and the forward bias transit time to make a negative-resistance characteristic that can oscillate, and is similar in operational circuits to a tunnel diode.

The Limited Space-Charge Accumulation (LSA) Diode. The limited space-charge accumulation diode (LSA) is a bit heavier in construction than the Gunn diode, and it operates above 25 GHz as well. It will produce more power then the Gunn diode; up to 100 Kw of peak pulsed power at the lower microwave frequencies.

The Magnetron. A magnetron is a vacuum tube diode. By passing a current through the tube in the presence of a very strong magnetic field at right angles, radial cavities may be made to oscillate at a frequency determined by their cavity dimensions. See Figure 13–53.

Exposure to microwave radiation of more than a fraction of a watt can cause, at the least, eye cataracts. Higher levels of radiation produce more sinister symptoms, like internal body heating and cooking of the flesh, or possibly cancer. For these reasons a technician should *be sure to have all power off before working on magnetrons or other sources of high-power microwave radiation.*

A magnetron can be pulse-modulated to make it produce a very powerful burst of microwave power. It is often used as the transmitter in a radar set. An abbreviated schematic of a modulator may be found in Figure 10–38.

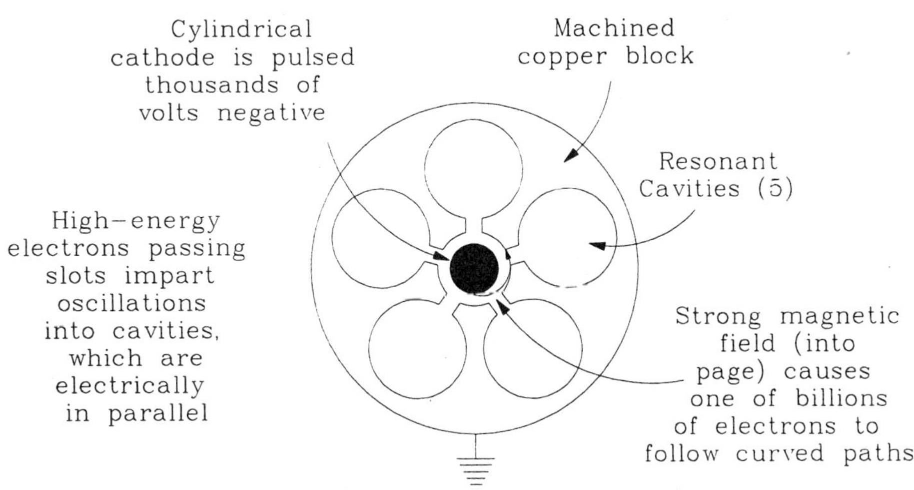

Figure 13–53 Internal structure of a magnetron.

While the magnetron is usually a dependable component, it can occasionally malfunction. The magnets used with these tubes, whether separate or integral, must be of a specified magnetic intensity in order for the magnetron to operate properly. Dropping or jarring one of these magnets can cause it to lose magnetic strength and should, therefore, be carefully avoided. Handle magnetrons gently.

A defective magnetron can also produce an unacceptable spectrum of energy. A spectrum analysis of a malfunctioning magnetron may show this to be the case. If so, the receiver associated with the magnetron, as in a radar set, may not be able to receive signals properly.

Other applications for a magnetron operate it in a continuous manner, such as in a microwave oven. These magnetrons operate at about 2 GHz and have high DC negative voltage applied to the heater circuit of the magnetron. The power supply installed in a microwave oven is potentially lethal because of its voltages and current capability.

Magnetrons must be kept cool during full operation. This is usually accomplished by blowing air through cooling fins on the tube.

Magnetrons are best tested by substitution in the circuit for which they are designed. If it is fed the proper voltage (direct current or pulsed) and yet refuses to oscillate, the unit is defective.

Microwave RF Control and Attenuation: The PIN Diode. The PIN diode (positive intrinsic negative) is a junction diode that has an undoped, neutral semiconductor layer between the positive and negative materials. A PIN diode will act as a normal PN (positive-negative) junction at low frequencies, and will rectify them. At higher frequencies, such as up into the gigahertz range, the neutral zone cannot clear itself of charge carriers fast enough to act as a diode. At these frequencies, the PIN diode acts like a resistor, the value of which is determined by the amount of forward bias current through the junction. The more forward bias current, the lower is the RF resistance of the device.

The PIN diode is a linear device. By varying the amount of forward bias current, the high-frequency RF resistance of the PIN diode can be varied linearly from about 10 K to less than an ohm. This component is valuable as an element of electronically variable RF attenuators, and can also be used for phase shifting, limiting, switching, and modulating at microwave frequencies.

A PIN diode may be tested as a normal PN junction diode with an ohmmeter. Comparison with a known good diode of the same type will provide a more accurate test. Reverse breakdown voltages can be as high as 200 V.

Microwave Frequency Multiplication

The Step-Recovery Diode. A step-recovery diode is similar to a PIN diode, but the current-versus-resistance characteristic is abrupt rather than linear because of special doping of the junction. As the excitation voltage changes from forward to reverse biasing, current through the diode ceases very abruptly (in as little as 60 picoseconds). The effect is that the resistance of the diode will change suddenly from a low to a high resistance. Because of this characteristic, step-recovery diodes are used for producing a rich harmonic output of the applied frequency (comb generator) or as high-efficiency frequency multipliers when using an output tank circuit. These diodes work well up into the gigahertz range. They find use as high-frequency local oscillators, RF drivers, or low-power transmitters. Applications include radar, communications, and telemetry.

Step-recovery diodes may be tested as a normal PN junction with an ohmmeter, comparing an unknown device with a known good one for a conclusive test.

The Varactor Diode. While the varactor diode is normally used as a voltage-controlled variable capacitor, other uses are also possible for this diode. For example, the varactor diode also makes a good frequency multiplier due to its very nonlinear current-voltage relationship. By feeding a fundamental frequency into the diode, the second and higher harmonics can be generated in another tuned circuit connected across the same diode.

CHAPTER SUMMARY

- The Federal Communications Commission regulates radio transmitting equipment and the persons who use and maintain them.
- The quartz crystal is the frequency-determining element of virtually all transmitting equipment and most receivers.
- The variable-voltage capacitance diode (VVCD) is a back-biasing diode with a junction capacitance of as much as 500 pfd, allowing remote tuning and tracking by electronic means.
- The RF wattmeter, dummy RF load, frequency counter, signal generator, audio signal generator, spectrum analyzer, and modulation monitor may all be replaced for radio-servicing needs by a single instrument, the service monitor.
- Only a service monitor, a DC power supply, and a multimeter are needed for a complete two-way radio shop.
- The oscilloscope must have sufficient vertical amplifier bandwidth to measure RF waveform amplitudes accurately.
- RF frequencies to within about +/–5 percent may be determined using an oscilloscope.
- A grid dipper is used to measure isolated tuned circuits for resonance.
- Alignment of RF equipment often requires the use of non-metallic tuning tools to eliminate capacitive loading and reduce shock hazards to personnel.

- The crystal set was the first receiver, giving way to the regenerative receiver, the tuned-radio-frequency (TRF) receiver, and finally to the superheterodyne receiver used today.
- Changing the local oscillator and retuning the RF amplifier, if any, are all that is necessary to change the tuning of a superheterodyne receiver.
- Common IF frequencies used in superheterodyne receivers are 455 kHz and 10.7 MHz.
- 20-dB quieting and 12-dB SINAD are tests used to evaluate receiver performance.
- A receiver must be on-channel and of sufficient sensitivity to be useful.
- Squelch circuits eliminate the necessity of listening to normal receiver noise in the absence of a signal.
- Single-frequency and swept-frequency receiver alignment procedures were explained in detail.
- The dB was explained, along with how it relates to RF system maintenance.
- Mental juggling of dB figures without a calculator or log tables was explained.
- Never key a transmitter without an RF load connected.
- Use a dummy load to protect the RF final amplifier and prevent illegal/nuisance radiations during testing.
- A transmitter must be checked for on-channel operation, proper modulation, and proper power output.
- Transmitters should be checked for spurious outputs by checking with a spectrum analyzer.
- The derivation of a pi-net output circuit was discussed.
- The advantages of using microwaves and some special equipments used when working with them were briefly detailed, including waveguides, waveguide couplers, microwave power meters, and stripline amplifiers.
- The relationship between peak and average power indications was explained.
- Special microwave components for microwave amplification and signal processing are the GAsFET, Schottky (hot carrier) diode, tunnel diode, Gunn Diode, IMPATT diode, LSA Diode, magnetron, PIN diode, step-recovery diode, and the varactor diode.

REVIEW QUESTIONS

1. What must be done if a notice of violation from the FCC is received?
2. What are the two licenses are required for operating a broadcast station?
3. How can one find the actual RF frequency of a given CB channel?

4. What are the three general test areas required for most Ham radio operation?
5. Name three of the types of modulation available for Ham operator use.
6. What licenses are required to operate a marine radio?
7. When are high-seas radio channels to be used?
8. An avionics technician leaves one place of work for another. How does this affect his license?
9. Who certifies the competency of an avionics repair technician?
10. Who licenses an avionics repair technician?
11. What license is required of a technician working for the federal government?
12. What is the purpose of using radio frequency crystals?
13. If a modern radio may be required to operate on one of a great many possible channels, the technician should expect to find the use of a ______ circuit.
14. For what purpose would one use a VVCD?
15. A quick check of RF Class C amplifiers can be made with a DC voltmeter, measuring the voltage drop across an _______ resistor or a _______ resistor.
16. What are the three principal kinds of RF wattmeters?
17. What damage can occur as the result of keying a transmitter without an antenna or dummy load connected?
18. What undesirable effect can occur as a result of keying into an antenna for testing purposes?
19. A frequency counter can be calibrated to _______ as the primary standard by using an AM receiver.
20. Some frequency counters have an input level restriction of as little as _______ volts before damage may occur.
21. If one wishes to measure the output frequency of a transmitter without radiating a signal and without overdriving the input of a frequency counter, the use of a _______ _______ is indicated.
22. A signal generator is required to generator a signal that is precise in both _______ and _______.
23. What is the characteristic (surge) impedance of most RF coaxial cabling?
24. What is the cause of most failures of RF signal generator attenuators?
25. How can the damage of question 24 be most easily avoided?
26. The horizontal axis of a spectrum analyzer is calibrated in _______.
27. A service monitor can take the place of many discrete instruments: Name three.
28. What two additional equipments can be required besides a service monitor for most RF transceiver work?
29. What part of an oscilloscope limits the maximum frequency it can display?

30. The oscilloscope must first be _______ed before it will show RF frequencies with their proper amplitudes.
31. Can an oscilloscope be used at frequencies above its rated vertical response specification?
32. Will an oscilloscope rated at 25 MHz accurately show the amplitude of a frequency of 25 MHz?
33. Calculate the frequency of an RF signal that makes two full cycles in a microsecond.
34. What is the troubleshooter's "weak link"—the first place in which to look for a problem—when dealing with coaxial cables?
35. What are two of the possible consequences of using a metallic tuning tool in RF circuits?
36. Why must one be gentle when adjusting ferrite tuning cores?
37. What are the two tests that can be made to determine radio receiver sensitivity?
38. The SINAD test measures not only the basic receiver sensitivity, but _______ as well.
39. If an FM receiver is exactly centered on an incoming RF signal, one will measure a _______ DC voltage from the _______ circuit.
40. What does CTCSS stand for?
41. Generically speaking, complete realignment of an FM receiver would begin at the _______ stage and conclude with adjustment of the _______ stage.
42. Monitoring the limiter stage of an FM receiver requires a multimeter operating on the _______ _______ scales.
43. When is swept-frequency alignment of a receiver needed?
44. What instruments are required for each of the two methods of measuring receiver stage gain?
45. Is it worthwhile to spend much time to gain a single dB of transmitter output?
46. Is it worthwhile to spend much time to improve receiver sensitivity from 1 to 1/2 microvolt?
47. What internal feature of a service monitor allows one to key a transmitter back into the signal generator attenuator without damage?
48. Can one see the normal FM modulation of an FM transmitter on an oscilloscope?
49. What instrument can quickly check a transmitter for spurious or off-channel radiation or harmonics?
50. Most of the stages within a radio transmitter are operated Class _______.
51. An RF amplifier that can amplify small and large amplitude input signals is called a/an _______ amplifier.
52. Replacement of a component in an RF amplifier circuit may require that the stage be _______ before returning the equipment to service.
53. Where is a stripline amplifier used?
54. What must a technician know about a coaxial cable when using it at microwave frequencies for power measurement?

55. What safety hazard is present in a magnetron circuit?
56. The tunnel, Gunn, IMPATT, and LSA diodes are commonly used to ______.
57. Microwave power measurement generally depends on using a/an ___ ___ as the sensing element.
58. What RF component can be used to tune circuits and also in other applications to generate harmonics?

Troubleshooting Pulse Circuits

14

CHAPTER OBJECTIVES

Analog circuits use mostly sine waves or complex waveforms such as audio. A primary requirement for analog circuits is the distortionless amplification and processing of a signal through the circuitry. Digital circuits, on the other hand, combine timing and on-or-off signal levels using low-voltage digital integrated circuits and/or microprocessors. There is a third kind of circuitry that is neither entirely analog nor digital in nature: such circuits are called pulse circuits. For the purposes of this chapter, pulse circuits are defined as those that generate, process, and control waveforms that are not continuous and sinusoidal. A pulse circuit may involve high voltages, high currents, or both, and it deals with on-or-off voltage levels that are unique for a particular circuit. This chapter will acquaint the technician with the concepts that differ from analog and digital circuits and the recommended methods of troubleshooting. This chapter will cover pulse circuits in three sections; AC power control, low-level pulse circuits, and pulse RF circuits. Each deserves special attention and has special cautions that are appropriate for the specific type of troubleshooting.

PART I—TROUBLESHOOTING THYRISTORS IN AC POWER CONTROL CIRCUITS

14.1 WHAT IS A THYRISTOR?

A thyristor is one of several semiconductor types that are grouped together because of their built-in characteristic of being either completely open or completely saturated. They are not able to conduct in a half-on, half-off manner like a bipolar transistor or FET. Members of the thyristor family are the SCR, TRIAC, GTO, SIDAC, DIAC, SBS, UJT, and PUT. Appendix II provides semiconductor operating curves which help to explain the operation of these devices.

14.2 THEORY OF PARTIAL-SINE WAVE UTILIZATION

Suppose we wish to run a small universal electric motor on the 120-V AC lines, while operating the motor at half its maximum speed. One way to accomplish this is to put, in series with the motor, an appropriate resistance of sufficiently large size to dissipate the sizable amount of power to be wasted. This is a bad idea; not only is it wasteful, it results in a poor speed-torque relationship in the motor output. In other words, even a small load will slow the motor down, making the resistor very hot.

A second choice would be to turn on the 120-V AC for, say, one-fifth of a second and then turn it off for another one-fifth second. The motor would average out these on-off periods into a speed less than full speed (about half normal speed).

The remaining, and best, choice for a way to run the motor at half speed is to turn it on for only half of each cycle by using a simple series power diode. If we discard half the input power, the motor will run at approximately half speed, averaging the remaining power pulses into a rather smooth rotation speed. This will work well until we wish to run the motor at speeds other than half-speed (say, one-fourth normal speed). This requires a whole new approach to the motor speed problem.

The best circuit to fill the requirements for operating the motor at any voltage up to 120-V AC is a circuit that will use part of each alternation, both positive and negative. See Figure 6–14 for an illustration of this principle.

SCRs and TRIACs are the components used for partial-cycle switching in such practical applications as kitchen blenders and variable-speed electric drills. These components are also used in industry to control very large DC motors and for converting AC power into more efficient, DC power. These components and their support semiconductors are the subject of the first part of this chapter. First, let's consider the instruments to be used in troubleshooting pulse circuits.

14.3 INSTRUMENTS FOR THYRISTOR TROUBLESHOOTING

THE AC VOLTMETER ON NONSINUSOIDAL WAVEFORMS

The problem of using an RMS-scaled AC voltmeter on nonsinusoidal waveforms was discussed in Chapter 9. Review this information if necessary.

A true RMS AC voltmeter is the best test instrument to use when dealing with nonsinusoidal waveforms, such as AC power controllers with SCRs and TRIACS. The output waveform from these semiconductors is not a sine wave, but only a portion thereof. A true RMS voltage reading will be needed to calculate important unknowns, such as fuse size in amperes.

An indication of the ability of a true RMS AC voltmeter to respond correctly to nonsinusoidal waveforms can be found in the specifications for the instrument. *Crest factor* is the ratio of the true RMS value to the peak voltage of a given waveform. As an example, an AC sine wave has a crest value of 1.41). The higher the crest specification of a voltmeter, the broader the range of waveforms that can be accurately measured. (For example, the true RMS instrument of Figure 9–5 has a crest value specification of 3 at full scale and 6 at half scale reading.)

USING AN OSCILLOSCOPE IN PULSE CIRCUITRY

While a grounded, 120-V AC–operated oscilloscope can safely handle much of the measuring work required during troubleshooting most circuits, it must be used with great care when working with power-line-related voltages. SCRs and TRIACS are often used in circuits that are referenced, not to ground, but to the opposite side of the power line. Using a grounded oscilloscope in such a circuit can result in equipment damage when a high-voltage, high-current circuit becomes shorted to ground by the simple connection of a 'scope that is grounded at an inappropriate point. For this reason, *always be sure that the oscilloscope ground connection is safe to connect into the circuit before doing so.* A voltmeter can be used to test for voltage between earth ground and the circuit common. If the oscilloscope is plugged into a normal grounded outlet, the outside shell of the BNC connector for the probe is a good ground point to use in this test. Be sure to check for both AC and DC voltages before concluding that there is no substantial voltage difference. When in doubt, do not use a grounded oscilloscope.

A battery-operated oscilloscope, on the other hand, may, theoretically, be connected anywhere in a circuit, just as it is safe to use a battery-operated

DMM. Beware, however, any exposed metal on the oscilloscope can then become an extreme shock hazard if the instrument is measuring high-voltage circuits. *A battery-operated oscilloscope should be used to make measurements in high-voltage, ungrounded circuits only if absolutely necessary.* In this case, the power must be turned off. Then, the instrument should be set up, connected, and electrically isolated as the power is turned on for the readings. Once readings are obtained (*don't* touch the 'scope during operation), the power must be turned off and the oscilloscope must be removed from the circuit.

> ***Caution:*** **Ungrounded operation of an oscilloscope in high-voltage circuits must be left to experienced technicians who are aware of the dangers and who take appropriate safety measures. Since this is a dangerous use of test equipment, one should never work alone under such circumstances.**

Another caution to observe is to be aware that pulse-operated circuits can have unexpectedly high voltages associated with them. A circuit failure can cause voltage spikes of 10 times the DC value in the circuit. The input circuit of the oscilloscope, including the attenuator probe, if used, must not be overstressed by abnormal voltages within the circuit. It is well to remember that the typical 10X oscilloscope probe may have a DC or DC-plus-AC voltage peak limitation of only 500 volts. Beyond this voltage, the probe can be damaged by internal arcing. Damage to the oscilloscope's input circuits is also a possibility. When in doubt, start with a 100X probe (if one is available) to be sure you have normal voltages within the circuit.

The oscilloscope may also be used with a current probe. Although seldom used for routine troubleshooting, the current probe does allow the sampling of circuit currents without physically touching a metal conductor. When using a current probe, the oscilloscope can be used to safely and easily sample current flowing within ungrounded circuits. These current probes usually have severe frequency limitations, making them useful only for frequencies of up to, perhaps, 500 kHz.

Most signal tracing within AC power-control circuits involves looking for a missing trigger or other signal. When SCRs and TRIACS fail, they usually quit operating by shorting or opening.

The signals in pulse circuits must be of the proper polarity and sufficient amplitude to reliably trigger the following stage into conduction. These two effects must be kept in mind during pulse signal tracing. Be sure the pulse is of the correct polarity. It is possible that an amplifier may fail in such a manner as to pass the input signal to the next stage without the normal polarity of the stage. In other words, if the stage reverses the polarity of the input signal, the output may, through a failure, pass the input signal directly to the output without phase reversal. This signal would then be of improper polarity, and the fact that it is merely present could easily mislead a technician.

The technician who is signal-tracing through pulse circuits should keep in mind that although one stage might trigger reliably with a defective, low-amplitude input signal, any following stage may be affected by the lack of amplitude and may fail to trigger. This is caused by the first stage failing to go completely into saturation, as originally designed.

The oscilloscope is a voltage-based test instrument. Pulse circuits frequently operate on the basis of current waveforms. A current waveform may be completely different from the voltage waveform seen on an oscilloscope. For example, to produce a constant current through an inductor for a brief time, the applied voltage must initially be high and then ramp down over a period of time. The best way of ascertaining whether the current waveform is as it should be is to compare voltage waveforms with those provided by the manufacturer.

14.4 TROUBLESHOOTING SCR AND TRIAC CIRCUITS

THE SCR AND THE TRIAC AS POWER CONTROLLERS

A silicon-controlled rectifier (SCR) is a thyristor power device that, if triggered when there is a positive voltage on the anode with respect to the cathode, will suddenly appear as a "short" from anode to cathode. The gate having lost all further control, the device will conduct heavy currents until the anode-to-cathode voltage falls low enough to cause the device to stop conducting. A decrease of anode-to-cathode voltage causes the current through the device to decrease, and when this current falls below a certain level (called the *holding current*), the device opens and ceases to be "shorted" from anode to cathode. This action is best explained by considering the connection of two transistors shown in Figures 14–1 and 14–2.

An inspection of the paired transistors of Figure 14–1 will show that if neither of the transistors is turned on, there will be no current flow from the upper emitter-collector circuit as its base is floating. Likewise, the

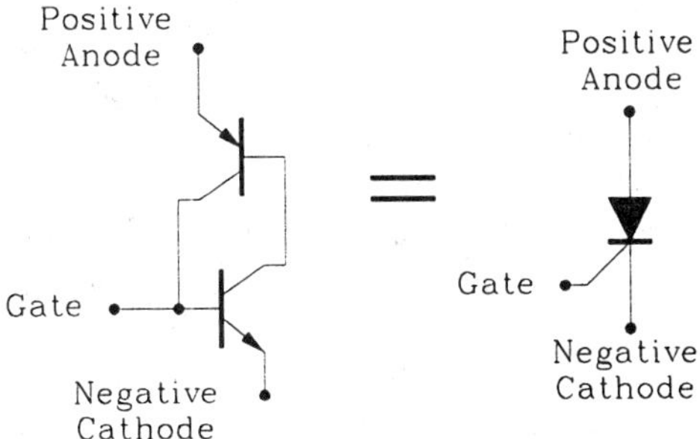

Figure 14–1 The two-transistor analogy of the operation of a silicon-controlled rectifier.

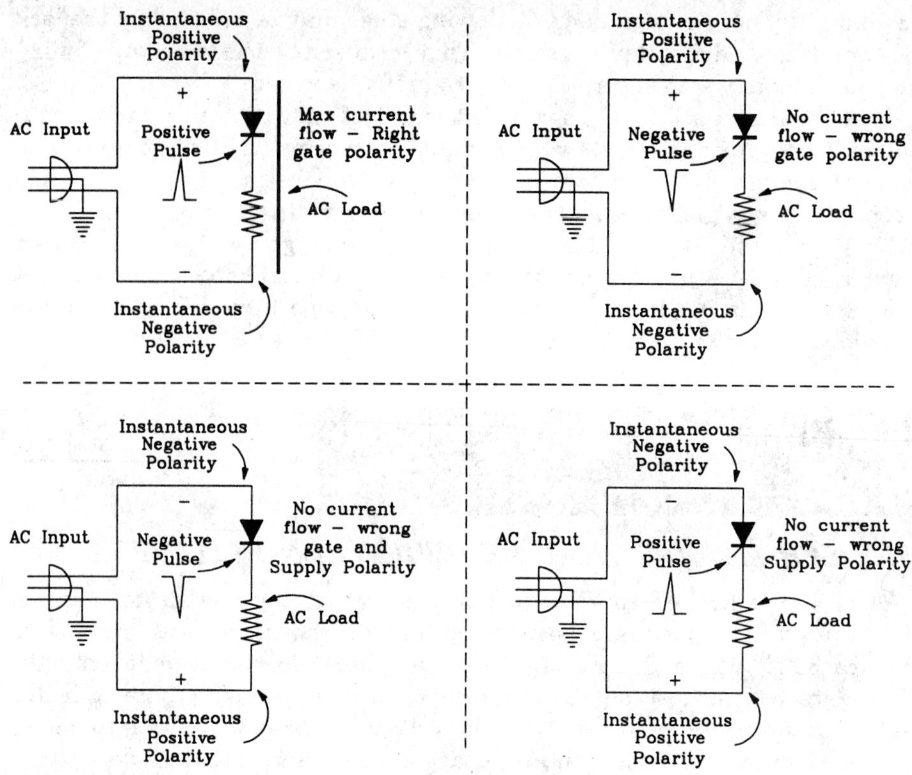

Figure 14–2 Conditions of conduction for the SCR.

lower transistor will have either a floating or a zero input current to the gate, and as a result, it will also be turned off. If a trigger pulse of positive polarity is applied to the gate, the lower transistor will now conduct and will pull its collector low. This, in turn, will turn on the upper transistor, which will then free the base of the lower transistor high. This action locks the two transistors on, with each holding the other in saturated conduction. Since the upper transistor is applying a very strong forward bias to the lower transistor, an external gate signal will be unable to turn the device off. Only an interruption of the current through the emitter-collector circuits will allow them to again open-circuit.

The reference element (the device lead from which voltage measurements are made for troubleshooting purposes) of an SCR is the cathode lead.

An SCR can go into conduction without an input pulse if the voltage applied to the anode increases too rapidly. This is caused by the small amount of capacitance to the gate element. A fast-risetime voltage can couple across this capacitance and cause the device to fire prematurely. Such an event might occur if there were a large spike of noise voltage, which can easily occur in high-power applications such as industrial motor controllers. This unintentional conduction is caused by exceeding the $\Delta v/\Delta t$

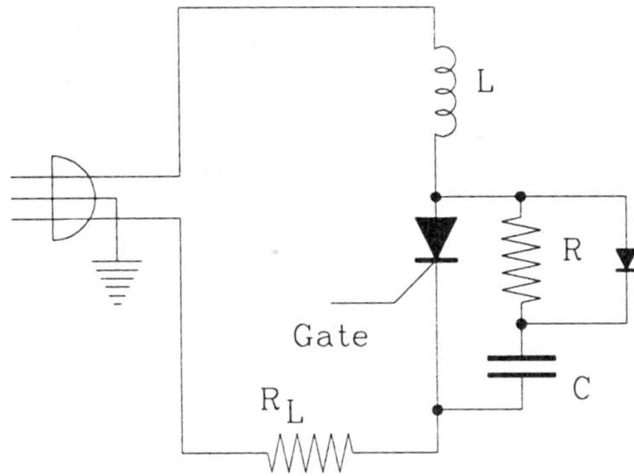

Figure 14–3 A basic Δv/Δt circuit, used to suppress transient voltages that could cause the unintentional triggering of an SCR.

specification for the SCR, resulting in too large a change in voltage (delta-v) in too short a time (delta-t). Circuits using resistors, diodes, inductors, and capacitors can be used to prevent the application of fast-rising voltages to an SCR. These are called *snubber circuits.* See Figure 14–3.

The TRIAC is similar to the SCR except that it will conduct in either direction once it has been triggered. This makes it act much like two back-to-back SCRs. *The reference element for a TRIAC is the MT1 (main terminal 1) lead.* See Figure 14–4.

USING SCRS AND TRIACS IN DC CIRCUITS

If these devices are used on direct current, they trigger and present a short that will not clear as long as DC is applied. The only common and practical circuit using an SCR in DC circuits is the crowbar circuit, covered in Chapter 7.

The SCR can be used in some high-powered applications to convert DC into a waveform closely resembling sine waves. Using an SCR on DC in this application requires the use of a special circuit called a *commutating circuit,* which momentarily reverses the anode voltage just long enough to turn off the device.

USING SCRS AND TRIACS IN AC CIRCUITS

SCR and TRIAC semiconductors are used mainly with the 60-Hz power-line frequency because of the relatively long time required for them to unlatch at less than their holding current and cease conduction. Both devices are particularly useful because the time at which they begin conducting can be controlled rather than allow them to conduct immediately when forward-biased, as with a simple rectifier diode. An SCR or TRIAC can be caused to latch into the conducting mode by the application of a pulse of

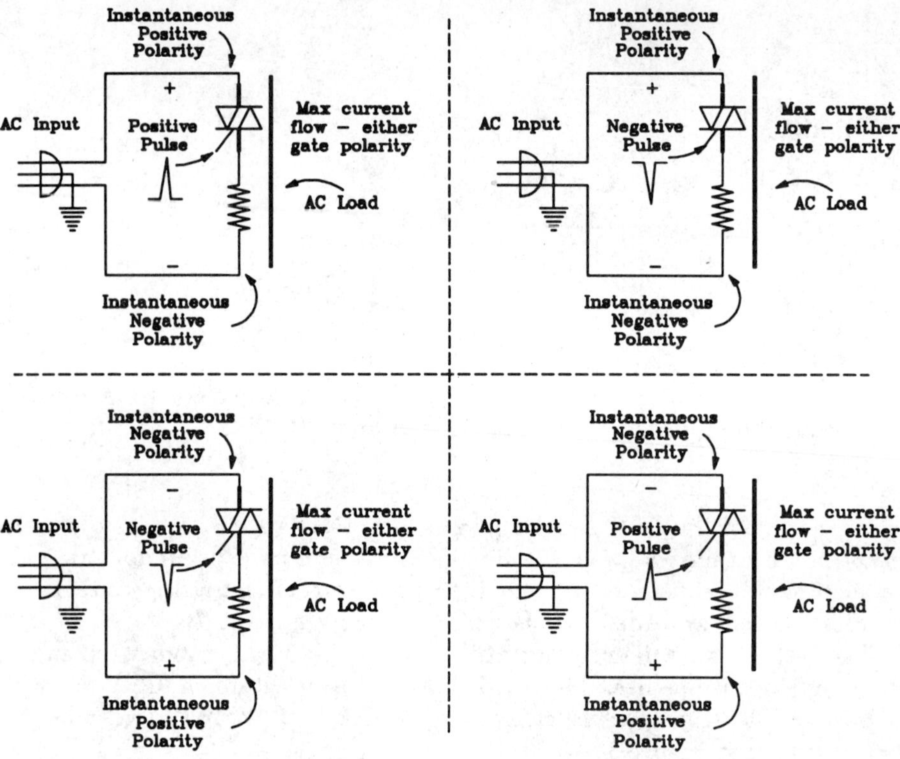

Figure 14–4 Conditions of conduction for the TRIAC.

correct polarity between the gate and the cathode leads in the case of an SCR. A pulse of either polarity applied between the gate and the Main Terminal 1 lead will suffice in the case of the TRIAC.

The SCR and TRIAC allow a very high degree of power amplification since it takes only a small pulse of short duration to trigger them. Once triggered, no further input is required at the gate. This ability to control power with high efficiency can be used to control the average energy applied to the transformer of a power supply, a lighting system, or a suitable electric motor.

Large SCRs can handle very heavy currents (over 400 amperes) and are used in very-high-current industrial applications. TRIACs are available for use only in applications up to about 40 amperes.

TROUBLESHOOTING SCR AND TRIAC CIRCUITS

Silicon-controlled rectifiers are often operated at high voltages, and both the cathode and the anode may be well above ground potential. This makes them difficult to troubleshoot in full operation with an AC line-operated oscilloscope that has one side of its signal input circuit grounded. Since

SCRs operate mostly on 60-Hz AC voltages, use a VOM or DMM. AC voltage readings may be used to help troubleshoot these circuits. A lack of AC voltage across an operating SCR is a strong indication of a shorted device, especially if the SCR is controlling a device that is running uncontrollably at full line voltage. A shorted SCR would probably be suspect in such a case because the load, whatever it might be, operates at full voltage without SCR control.

It may also be possible to compare AC voltage readings between a properly operating circuit and a defective one. Be sure that both circuits are set to operate identically, and then compare the AC voltage readings from cathode to anode of the two SCRs. If one of the SCRs has a substantially higher AC reading across it, you may suspect an open SCR or the lack of a properly timed trigger of sufficient voltage and current capability to trigger the device.

Since these semiconductors often control high voltage and high currents, it is usually safer to troubleshoot them "dead," without any power applied, as covered in Chapter 16, "Dead-Circuit Troubleshooting."

Pulse circuits use high voltage and high currents in their normal operation. Semiconductors in power pulse applications must be protected from the especially high voltage pulses that are caused when the current flow through an inductor suddenly ceases. They must also be protected from voltage spikes that may enter through the primary power lines. Whenever a semiconductor fails in pulse service, any associated protective components should also be checked for proper operation before a new semiconductor is installed. Protective components can include diodes, resistors, and capacitors.

New semiconductors must be properly installed in order to ensure their proper service life. Heat sinks must be firmly bonded to perform their purpose. "Hockey-puck" SCRs must be torqued into their holders with a critical amount of force to dissipate maximum heat yet prevent damage to the SCR from overtightening the mounting bolts. Special holders with a torque indicator are used for this purpose. See Figure 14–5.

SCR AND TRIAC FAILURE PATTERNS

The SCR and the TRIAC share the same kinds of failures. Because of the heavy currents flowing through these devices in normal use, they often dissipate a substantial amount of power. A good thermal bond to a heat sink is essential to their survival under heavy loads. When an SCR or TRIAC fails, it will almost always either open or short from the cathode to the anode, in the case of an SCR, or from Main Terminal 1 to Main Terminal 2, in the case of the TRIAC. Shorting to the gate lead of either device may also occur, but this failure is less common because the gate lead carries much less current than the other leads of the device.

Figure 14–5 The hockey-puck SCR requires a special mounting bracket and precise control of torque on the bolts.

THE SIDAC

The SIDAC can be thought of as a TRIAC that always triggers itself at exactly the same point on the applied voltage, during positive or negative line polarity. This component is advantageous to use when there is a fixed firing voltage. It allows the use of a single component instead of a TRIAC and several other triggering components. The triggering voltage of a SIDAC is typically between 105 and 135 volts. Since this device can pass substantial currents (up to about 20 amperes), it can also be used as an overvoltage protection component, much like back-to-back zener diodes. The circuit symbol for the SIDAC is shown in Figure 14–6.

Once it is conducting, the SIDAC will continue to conduct until the current through it drops to a low enough value to stop conduction; again this is similar to a TRIAC. Failure patterns for the SIDAC include the usual shorting of the two device terminals to each other, or opening.

THE GTO DEVICE

While an SCR can be triggered only into conduction, the GTO (gate turnoff) device can be triggered into and out of conduction by the gate at

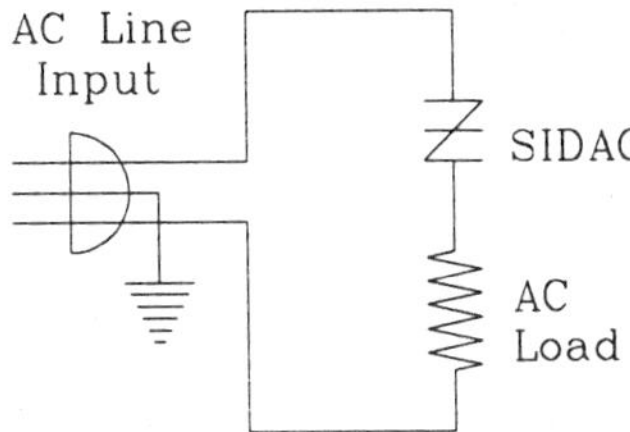

Figure 14–6 The SIDAC symbol and a sample circuit.

any time. This feature makes it useful where the advantages of control of a bipolar transistor and of the current-carrying capability of an SCR are necessary. GTOs are used in high-voltage, high current applications. The GTO, like the SCR, is triggered into conduction by the application of a positive pulse to the gate with respect to the cathode of the device. The application of a negative pulse will turn a GTO off, although the two-transistor model of the GTO does not show this. Figure 14–7 shows the circuit symbol and an approximate equivalent circuit for a GTO.

Note that the two-transistor equivalent is the same as that of an SCR. The turnoff action possible with a GTO is not possible with an SCR, however.

14.5 TROUBLESHOOTING UJT TRIGGER CIRCUITS

Chapter 6 covered the use of the UJT in a phasing power supply, with an explanation of typical circuits. For almost all the SCR or TRIAC circuits, the power devices need to be fired at the proper time during the AC cycle on which they operate. Some means of synchronizing their firing with the

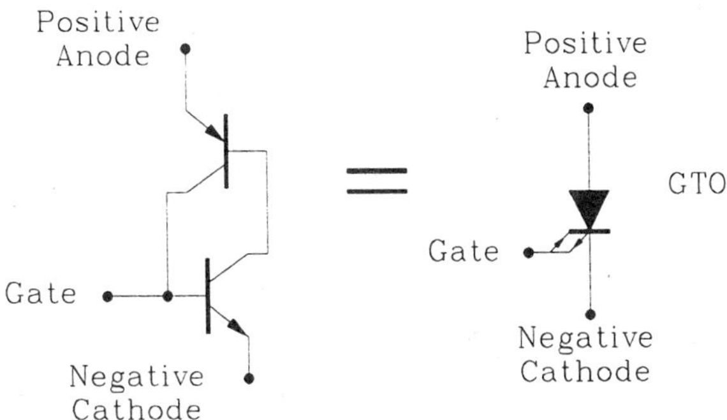

Figure 14–7 Circuit symbol and the internal discrete equivalent for a GTO device.

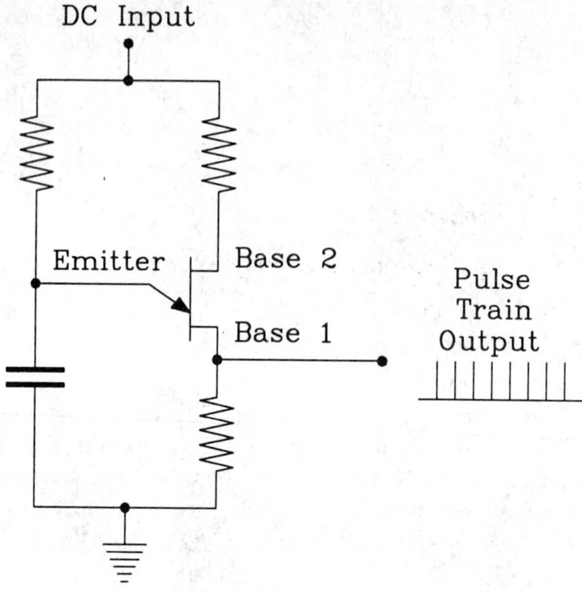

Figure 14–8 A simple oscillator circuit using a UJT.

input waveform is needed. For this job, the unijunction transistor (UJT) is particularly well suited. This semiconductor device is almost always used as an oscillator, although it may be used as a pulse amplifier. A simple oscillator circuit is given in Figure 14–8.

Once a UJT has been fired into conduction, it can be considered a diode with two resistive connections to one end. Figure 14–9 shows the equivalent circuit.

The UJT remains an open circuit between all three elements until the voltage from the emitter to base 1 reaches a critical value. At that time, the UJT develops very low resistance from emitter and from base 2 to base 1. This low-impedance state remains until the voltage at the emitter falls below a certain voltage that is lower than the voltage at which the UJT shorted. At this new voltage, the UJT again becomes an open with three

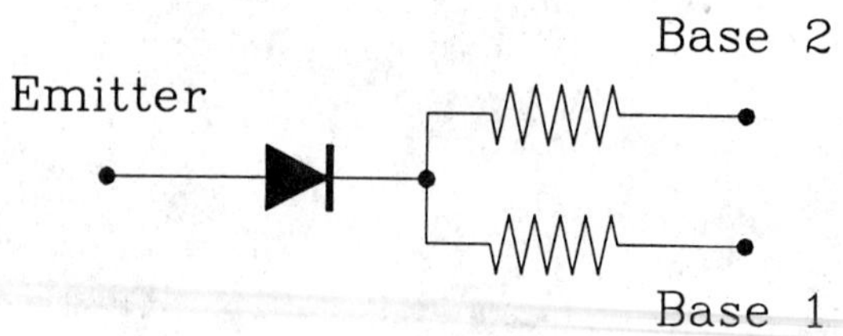

Figure 14–9 Equivalent circuit of a UJT when fired.

leads. The output pulses are relatively short in duration, showing as narrow spikes of voltage on an oscilloscope.

Applying a DC voltage through a high resistance into the emitter circuit of Figure 14–8 will influence the charging time of the capacitor, thus changing the pulse repetition rate (frequency) of the circuit.

When the UJT is powered by a waveform that is full-wave and rectified but *unfiltered,* it can be caused to fire during that waveform at varying times during both the positive and negative input cycles (remember the rectified, but unfiltered, supply voltage). Thus, the output pulses can fire an SCR or a TRIAC. See Figure 6–16.

The UJT, together with a power device and an SCR or a TRIAC, can be used to make a regulated power supply of very high current capability and high efficiency. The DC output of the supply is sampled and fed to the UJT to influence the firing time. These output pulses are then coupled to the power device to control the main power input to a transformer. See Figure 6–15.

UJT FAILURE PATTERNS

The UJT fails in a manner similar to that of a bipolar transistor. Internal shorts and opens will cause a loss of oscillation. If the proper voltages are provided yet the circuit will not oscillate, the UJT should be removed and tested with an ohmmeter or solid-state tester, in accordance with the procedures of Chapter 16. The final word on the condition of the UJT is whether a good replacement UJT works in the circuit.

14.6 TROUBLESHOOTING PUT CIRCUITS

The programmable unijunction transistor (PUT) is often used to trigger an SCR or TRIAC, similar to the UJT just covered. The PUT is different in internal structure, however. It is very much like an SCR except that the input uses the anode as the reference element, and not the cathode. See Figures 14–10 and 6–16.

The PUT triggering voltage can be changed (programmed) by an external resistive voltage divider rather than being a fixed value like a UJT. In addition, the PUT is faster and more sensitive than a UJT. Because of the more sensitive input, the PUT is particularly useful in the design of long-duration timers that use the slow charging of a capacitor through a high resistance.

If the gate of a PUT is made negative with respect to the anode, the device will trigger into its saturated condition, essentially shorting the cathode to the anode. Failure patterns for the PUT are the same as those given for the UJT.

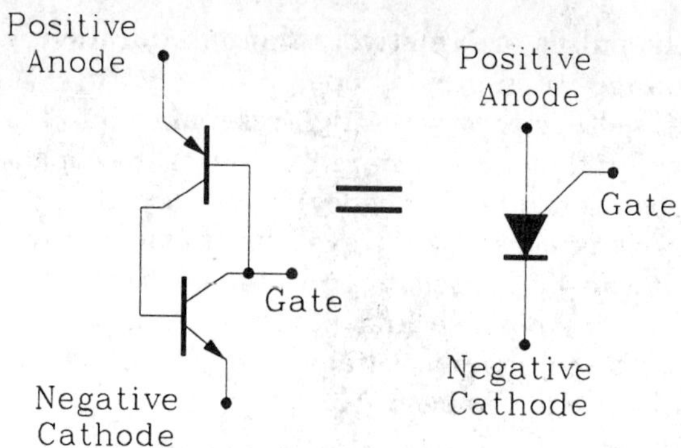

Figure 14–10 Internal structure of the PUT transistor.

14.7 STABILIZING SCR AND TRIAC TRIGGERING

An SCR or TRIAC is subject to small changes in its trigger point when subjected to the normal heating of the device. With changing loads and the resulting change in the heating of the SCR or TRIAC, stabilizing the triggering by providing a sudden trigger is better than providing a waveform that changes gradually. Two devices are available to provide the steep risetime desired: the DIAC and the silicon bilateral switch (SBS).

USING A DIAC

A DIAC is most often used to provide a more reliable trigger for an SCR or a TRIAC when the triggering waveform is a relatively slow-changing waveform. The DIAC is an open circuit until its triggering voltage has been reached, at which time it suddenly starts to conduct. The voltage drop across it almost instantly decreases to a much lower voltage than its triggering voltage. For instance, if a DIAC suddenly fired at a voltage of 35 V, the voltage across it might drop to about 10 V. This sudden conduction at a specific voltage can be used to fire the gate of an SCR or TRIAC. Using a DIAC will also stabilize the firing voltage of an SCR or TRIAC during temperature variations.

The internal structure of a DIAC is similar to a transistor. The two junctions inside the transistor are made to be approximately identical to each other, and the base lead is omitted. See Figure 14–11.

USING AN SBS

The silicon bilateral switch (SBS) is actually an integrated circuit consisting of several transistors, resistors, and zener diodes. This component

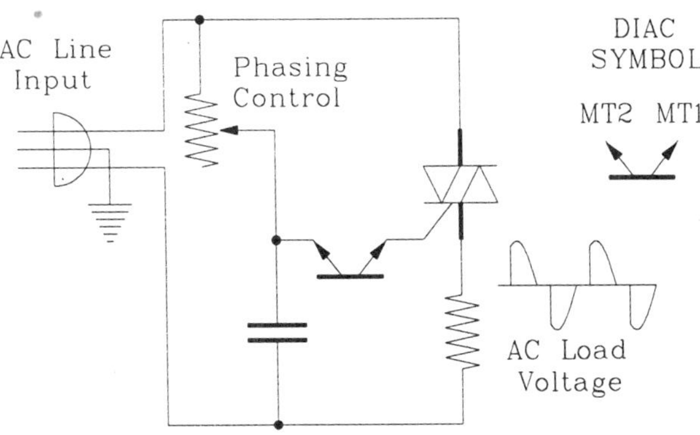

Figure 14–11 Schematic symbol and sample DIAC triggering circuit.

is used to trigger a TRIAC in cases where temperature stability is critical. The gate lead of this device can be used to program the firing voltage of the device, much like programming the trigger point of a PUT. The device will operate quite well without connecting the gate at all. The internal workings of an SBS are shown in Figure 14–12.

The SBS will remain open from Anode 1 to Anode 2 until the voltage reaches about 8 volts, at which time the device will suddenly start to conduct. Once conduction has been established, the device will drop about 3 volts-per-ampere of current flowing through it. Using a zener diode or

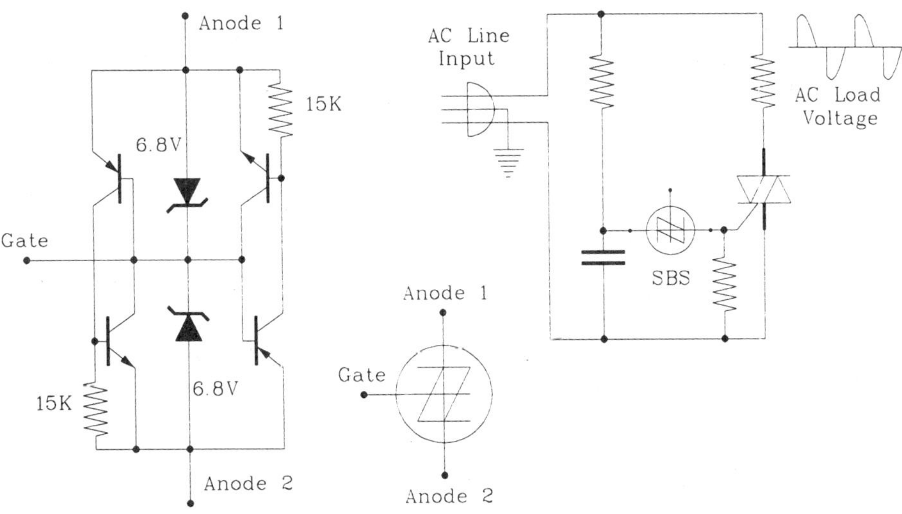

Figure 14–12 The circuit symbol and internal circuitry of a silicon bilateral switch (from the Motorola thyristor manual).

resistor connected to the gate can result in dropping the firing voltage to as low as 4 volts.

TRIGGER DEVICE FAILURE PATTERNS

The DIAC or SBS will almost always fail in one of two ways: by opening or shorting. A shorted device will cause the associated SCR or TRIAC to fire too early in the cycle if it is operated on power sine waves such as 120- or 240-V AC lines. Instead of holding off the trigger current to the power device until a certain voltage has been reached, current may be allowed to flow from the beginning of the cycle. On the other hand, an open trigger device will cause the complete loss of triggering to the power device.

PART II—TROUBLESHOOTING LOW-LEVEL PULSE CIRCUITS

14.8 NONSINUSOIDAL WAVEFORMS

Analog circuits deal with gradually changing voltages. Digital circuits deal with individual steps, using integrated circuits and microprocessors and voltages of less than 18 volts. Pulse circuits are different from both of these in that they commonly use higher voltages and currents than digital circuits. Pulse circuits operate with on-or-off signals and with circuits that amplify only portions of the incoming waveform by the use of Class C stages.

In the past, there were many customized applications that used pulses for such operations as counting events and to divide time into smaller units. These applications have now adopted the use of digital circuits and are no longer called "pulse circuits." Examples of pulse circuits that have "gone digital" include frequency dividers, counters, and all manner of low-voltage gating circuits.

The majority of low-level pulse circuits use Class C operation. Class C is the most efficient of the classes of operation because there is no power wasted when the stage has no incoming signal. The stage is normally cut off without a signal at the input. The incoming signal must be of sufficient amplitude (0.7 or 0.3 volts for a bipolar amplifier) to begin passing the signal through to the output circuit.

Modern low-level pulse circuits use switching transistors. A switching transistor is used because of its low emitter-to-collector resistance when conducting and its high leakage resistance when no signal is applied. A switching transistor must be able to switch quickly from cutoff to saturation and back again. Switching transistors are not designed to be operated on the most linear portion of their operating curve.

Efficienct circuit operation is particularly important when working with high currents. A switching transistor dissipates the most heat during the time when it is actually changing state (a matter of microseconds in a well-designed stage) or when conducting high currents that approach the maximum current rating for the transistor. Since a fully saturated transistor will still have resistance, there will be some power dissipated from the device when it is saturated and conducting heavy currents.

The timing of pulses or their phasing with respect to other signals (also a form of timing) is very important in most pulse applications. The waveshape of low-level pulses can sometimes be of importance, while in other cases, it is immaterial as long as the stage goes fully into saturation and cutoff.

Television sweep circuits provide a good example of pulse circuitry. The amplitude and waveshape of the signal entering a sync separator, for instance, must meet certain specifications for the stage to operate properly. The waveshapes in the CRT sweep circuits are also critical to the proper appearance of the television picture.

Pulse circuits, such as are common in television circuits, use inductors and capacitors to assist in the overall pulse waveshaping in the sweep circuits. When waveshape is important, the documentation for the circuit in question must provide at least a sketch of the proper waveform, along with the normal voltages and timing. This information must be available so that the waveform can be verified by a service technician.

The schematics for television sets and computer monitors may have special markings to identify certain components associated with the sweep circuits. These markings (sometimes a triangle with an exclamation point inside it) indicate that these parts are critical in the prevention of electrical shock of an unsuspecting operator, to reduce possible fire hazards, or to control the level of X-ray radiation from the cathode-ray tube. These parts must only be replaced with the exact same type and value as the original part. The equipment parts list should be consulted for details of these components.

PULSE WAVEFORM TERMINOLOGY

Pulse-Width Modulation

A review of a few terms unique to pulse circuits is approporiate at this point. The first important term is *duty cycle*. See Figure 14–13.

If a circuit is turned on half of the time, it has a 50-percent duty cycle. One example of a 50-percent duty cycle is the "walk/don't walk" sign at a pedestrian intersection. During half the total cycle time you may walk, while during the other half, you may not. The "walk" light itself is often operated at about a 50-percent duty cycle.

An example of a lower duty cycle is the ringing of a telephone. The actual ring is about 1/2 second, with a 4-1/2 second wait between rings. The duty cycle of the ringing is found by dividing the 1/2 second for which the telephone rings by the whole interval of 5 seconds. Multiplying the result by

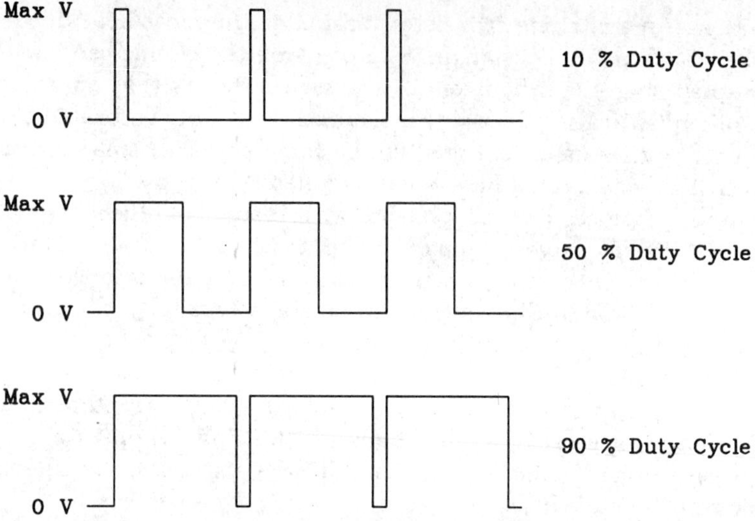

Figure 14–13 Understanding duty-cycle and pulse-width modulation.

100 gives the percentage. In this example, the telephone rings with a duty cycle of .5/5 × 100, or 10 percent.

If we were to apply 12 V at a 50-percent duty cycle to a 12-V incandescent lamp and turn the lamp on and off at a rate of a 100 times a second, the lamp would average the waveform and would glow at about half normal brilliance. Applying a 10-percent duty-cycle waveform to the same lamp would result in barely a glow because of the low average power in a 10-percent waveform. See Figure 14–14.

The duty cycle of a waveform is changed by varying its pulse width while maintaining the same overall period. This process of varying the width of the "on" time while keeping the pulse repetition rate (PRR) constant is called *pulse-width modulation (PWM)*. Many electromechanical devices such as lamps, motors, and solenoids will respond in a nearly linear manner when excited by a PWM driving waveform. For this reason, the PWM control of linear devices should be thoroughly understood.

Terminology of the Pulse

The frequency at which a periodic (repeating) waveform occurs in one second is called its pulse repetition frequency (PRF) or pulse repetition rate (PRR).

There are special terms to describe how fast a pulse waveform switches from one level to the other, how long it lasts, and the common kinds of distortion to such a pulse. Their definitions are shown in Figure 14–15.

The most important terms of this figure are:

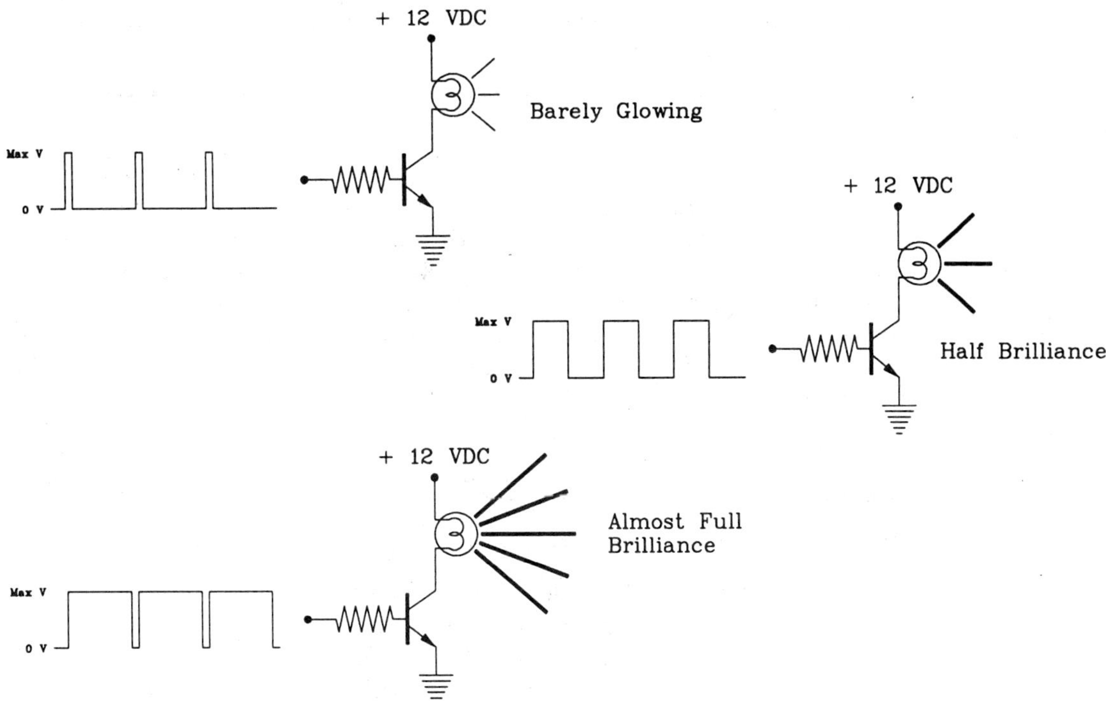

Figure 14–14 The effect of applying a varying duty-cycle waveform to an incandescent lamp.

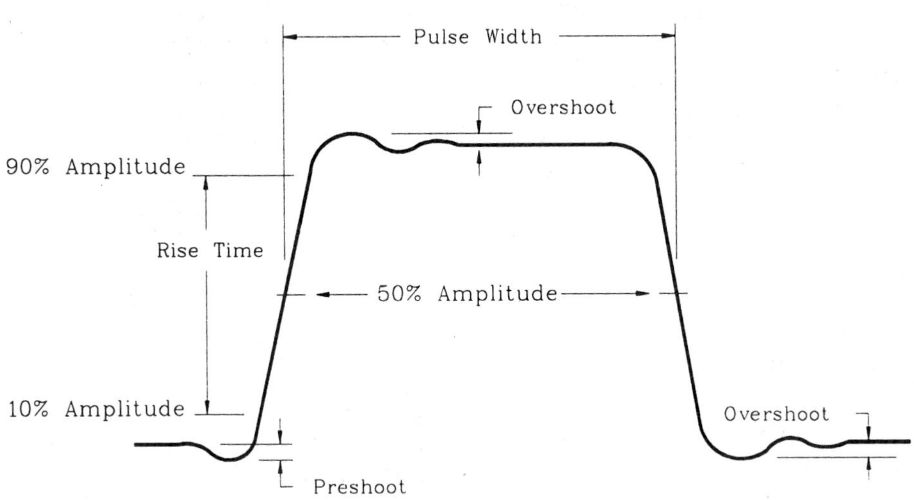

Figure 14–15 Terms used to describe parts of a pulse.

Pulse Width = Time between 50 percent of maximum amplitude and 50 percent on the way back down.

Rise Time = Time between 10 percent and 90 percent of maximum amplitude.

Two more terms that are very commonly used when describing the operation of pulse circuitry are the roughly interchangeable words, *trigger* and *strobe*. These words describe a short-duration signal transition from one state to the other and immediately back again, which is done for the purpose of initiating a process in later circuitry. An example of such an action occurs when the high-energy capacitor of a photographic flash is charged and ready to fire. The flash is then triggered (or strobed) into firing at the correct moment.

SOME TYPICAL PULSE CIRCUITS

The Pulse Driver and Amplifier (Line Driver)

A typical pulse amplifier can be described in simple terms. Without an incoming signal, the stage is idle, passing no current in its output circuit. If the stage receives an input signal of the proper polarity and sufficient amplitude to drive it, the output circuit will conduct with full saturation current for the duration of the input pulse. *Note that two requirements must be met for the circuit to respond: proper polarity and sufficient amplitude of the incoming signal.* These are very important to note when troubleshooting pulse circuits.

A pulse amplifier can be a bipolar transistor, IC, FET, or even a UJT in a few cases. These devices work very well in low-power pulse circuits.

One use for a pulse amplifier is to drive the relatively low impedance of a coaxial or ribbon cable. This application is called a line driver (see Figure 14–16 for an example). Note that the far end of a driven cable must be terminated with a resistor. This resistor, which has the same value as that of the *characteristic impedance* of the cable used, prevents reflections from occurring within the cable when the signal reaches the far end. Either too little or too much resistance at the far end will produce results similar to those on which the Time Domain Reflectometer instrument is based. See the end of Chapter 3 to review TDR.

Switching Circuits

Pulse-switching circuits accomplish such purposes as interfacing digital circuits (TTL and CMOS circuits) to real-world devices. Two simple indicator driver examples are shown in Figure 14–17.

Another circuit that is sometimes useful takes a digital input PWM signal and drives a 12-V permanent-magnet motor. This application is sometimes used in robotic applications. See Figure 14–18.

When driving a coil such as is found in relays and solenoids, it is neces-

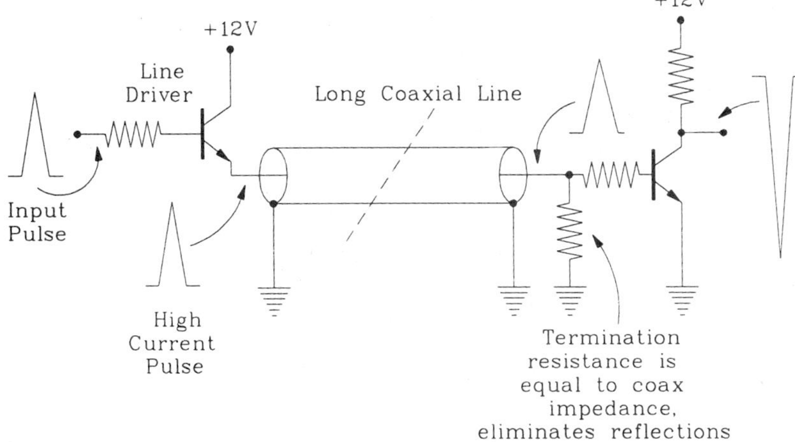

Figure 14–16 A line driver provides the current required to drive a low-impedance cable and the terminating resistor at the far end.

sary to use a kickback diode to prevent damage to the driver transistor by the high voltage spike that occurs when the coil is turned off. Figure 14–19 shows a typical relay-driving circuit that uses a digital signal to drive the higher-voltage relay. The relay in the illustration changes the two sets of contacts together, reversing the current through the armature and reversing the motor.

Dedicated integrated circuits are also available to accomplish switching applications from digital inputs to higher output levels of current and voltage. An example of such a chip is the Sprague UCN 4202. This chip takes a digital forward/reverse bit input and a pulsing input. It controls high-current, higher-voltage outputs to phase-drive the four windings of a stepper motor. See Figure 14–20.

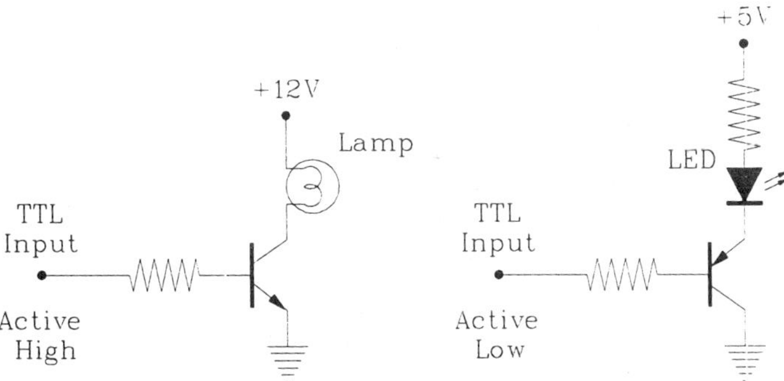

Figure 14–17 Two interface circuits, from TTL levels to real-world indicators.

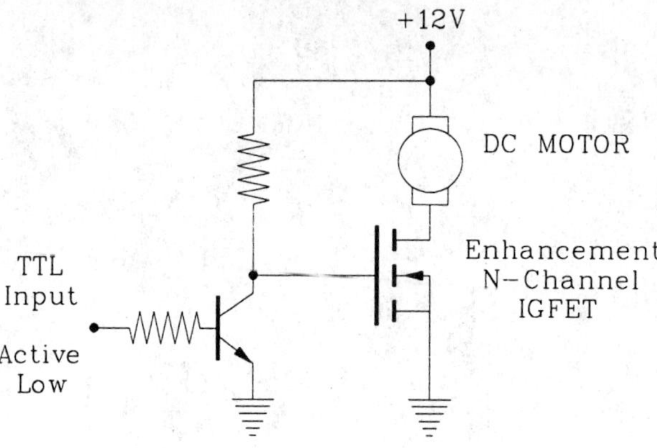

Figure 14–18 This circuit is used to switch a TTL pulse-width–modulated signal into the gate of a power FET, driving the DC motor at various speeds.

Other interface ICs are made for applications such as driving high-voltage neon or fluorescent displays and IC transmission line drivers. ICs are also available for the generation and output of PWM motor-drive waveforms.

CRT Sweep Circuits

The electron beam of a cathode-ray tube (CRT) may be deflected by a voltage difference between two deflection plates between which the electron

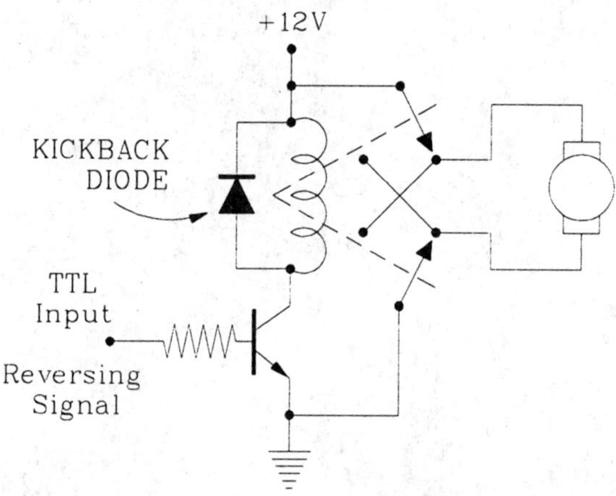

Figure 14–19 A typical relay-driving circuit with kickback diode protection for the transistor.

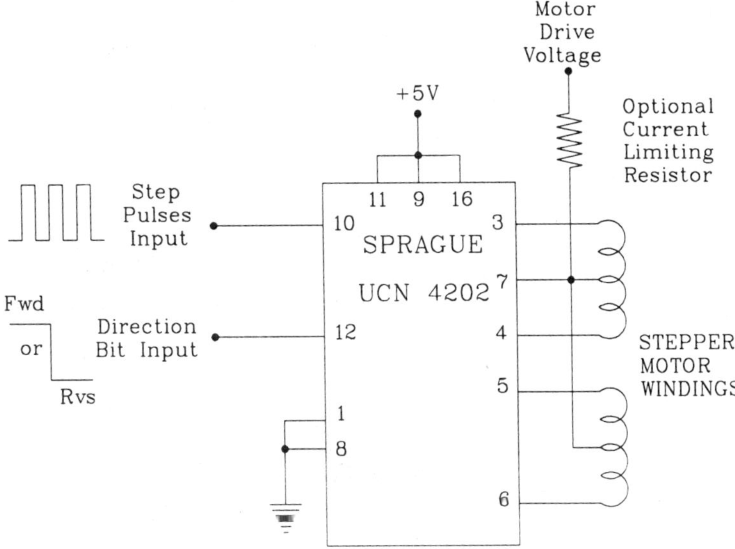

Figure 14–20 An example of an interface chip using TTL logic levels to control a stepper motor.

beam passes. The electron beam may also be deflected across the face of the CRT by making the beam pass through a magnetic field. The deflection coils on the neck of a computer monitor or television set CRT are a good example of this method of beam deflection. See Figure 14–21.

These deflection coils must produce a linear motion of the electron beam across the CRT face. To do this, the coils must have a linear *current* ramp. Because a coil has inductance, the coil cannot accept a linear voltage to produce this ramp, and a special waveform is necessary to obtain the correct deflection. See Figure 14–22.

This application of pulse currents is a good example in which the indicating instrument, in this case an oscilloscope, will read the voltage in the circuit and yet this voltage reading will give no indication of the *current* that is flowing. The voltage and current are not in phase because of the time constants of the inductances and capacities in the circuit. Therefore, *nonsinusoidal applications will require documentation containing normal voltage waveforms within the circuit for troubleshooting purposes.* The voltages present in nonsinusoidal pulse circuits may bear no apparent relationship to the actual currents that flow at a given instant.

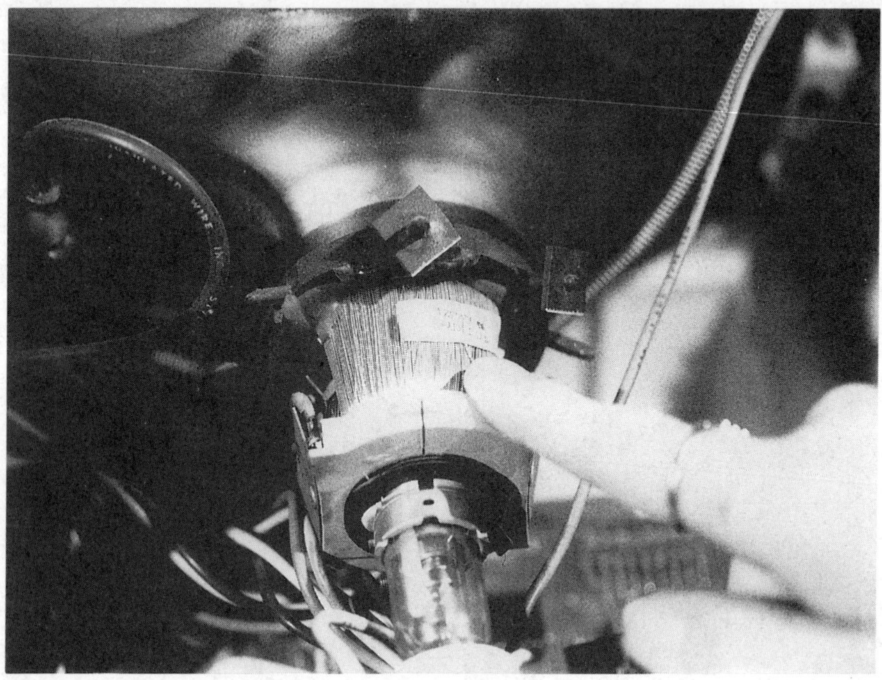

Figure 14–21 Passing current through these deflection yoke coils causes the electron beam within the tube to bend, producing the picture scan.

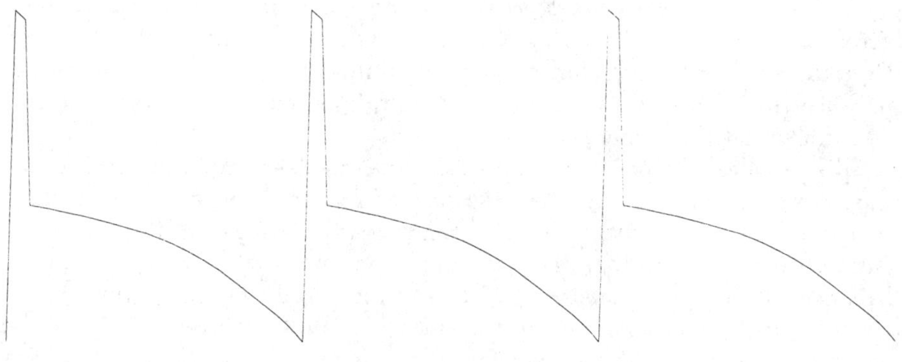

Voltage Waveform to the Deflection Coil
of a Television Receiver

Figure 14–22 This is the waveform required to produce a linear current flow through the vertical deflection coil of a TV.

14.9 INSTRUMENTS FOR PULSE CIRCUIT TROUBLESHOOTING

USING THE OSCILLOSCOPE IN PULSE CIRCUITS

It is well to review the precautions near the beginning of this chapter in regard to the voltage limitations of the oscilloscope input and the probe. Remember that pulse applications, particularly those using inductors, may have voltage pulses well beyond the typical 500-V limitation of a 10X oscilloscope probe. When in doubt as to the voltages that may be present, get and use a 100X probe rather than risk damage to the probe and/or scope input.

Pulse circuits often have low duty-cycle signals. For example, a pulse may occur only 10 times a second, but the signal itself may be a pulse only a few microseconds wide. Attempting to view such waveforms may be difficult. If the sweep speed of the analog oscilloscope is too slow, the 'scope's automatic triggering mode will get in the way, producing a bright baseline between the sweeps showing the waveform. Using the "Auto" trigger mode at sweeps slower than about 40 Hz may also make it impossible to synchronize on the incoming pulse. See Figure 14–23.

Another problem when viewing very low duty-cycle waveforms is that the trace of an analog oscilloscope, even if properly used in the "Triggered" or "Normal" mode, may be very dim (possibly too dim to use). A digital oscilloscope will show such low duty-cycle waveforms with normal brilliance. This instrument is covered in Chapter 24.

Another control which might be of use on an analog oscilloscope is the

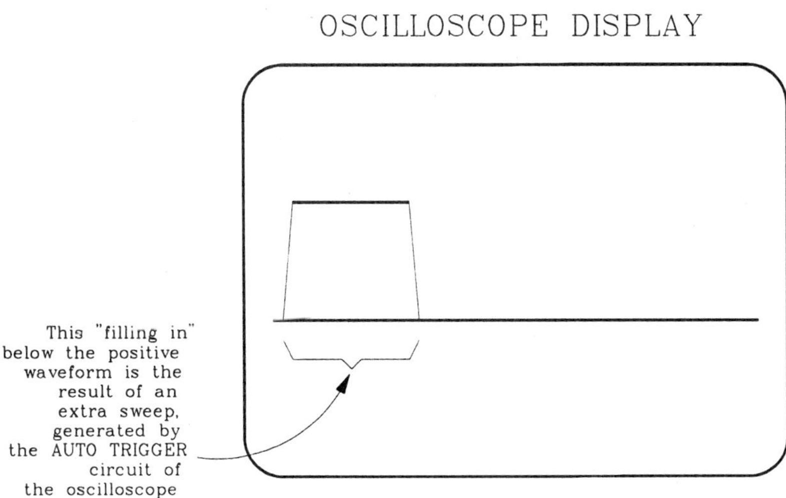
OSCILLOSCOPE DISPLAY
This "filling in" below the positive waveform is the result of an extra sweep, generated by the AUTO TRIGGER circuit of the oscilloscope

Figure 14–23 Viewing slow repetition-rate signals while using the "Auto" triggering mode results in a filling-in of the baseline sweep.

"Holdoff" control. This control is often misused, especially by new technicians who do not understand what it does. It is often left in other than the normal position, making the CRT display dimmer than it should be. This control is useful on perhaps less than 1 percent of the waveforms that the technician may wish to see. Remember to keep it in the normal position, which should be plainly marked on the instrument front panel.

The holdoff control prevents the immediate generation of succeeding sweeps, delaying them before they are started. See Figure 14–24 for an explanation of the use of this control.

USING A FREQUENCY COUNTER IN PULSE CIRCUITRY

Evaluation of Proper Frequency

A frequency counter can be useful in pulse circuitry to determine repetition rate. A caution is in order here when using this instrument: a frequency counter typically has very low signal-input voltage levels. This makes the instrument able to count low-level signals. Exceeding the input voltage limitations will damage the frequency counter, so keep this in mind:

- *The input to a frequency counter may be limited to as little as 2 volts.*

If it is necessary to count pulses up to voltages of about 20 volts, an ordinary 10X oscilloscope probe will work very well. However, a special attenuator may have to be built for signals of more than 20 volts. Some circuits under test provide a built-in preattenuated signal test point (TP) just for this purpose, so be sure to look for such test points on the schematic.

Overdriving the input to a frequency counter can produce improper counts, too, depending on how "dirty" the waveform may be. It is not unusual to produce a count of exactly twice what it should be due to overdriving of the input circuit of the frequency counter. The frequency counter operates by counting the number of cycles or pulses applied to it over a comparatively long, internally generated gate time. Figure 14–25 shows the basic block diagram of a frequency counter.

Period Measurement/Event Counting

When pulses occur very infrequently, say one pulse every 2 seconds, a frequency counter is of no direct use. If the counter is able to measure periods (to function as an event counter), it becomes practical to use it to count events over a specified gate time. See Figure 14–26 for the simplified internal block diagram of an instrument that measures period. EPUT (event-per-unit-time) is an old name for this function of a frequency counter instrument. Note that, basically, the same blocks are used as in a frequency counter, and merely rearranged in their interconnection. Period measure-

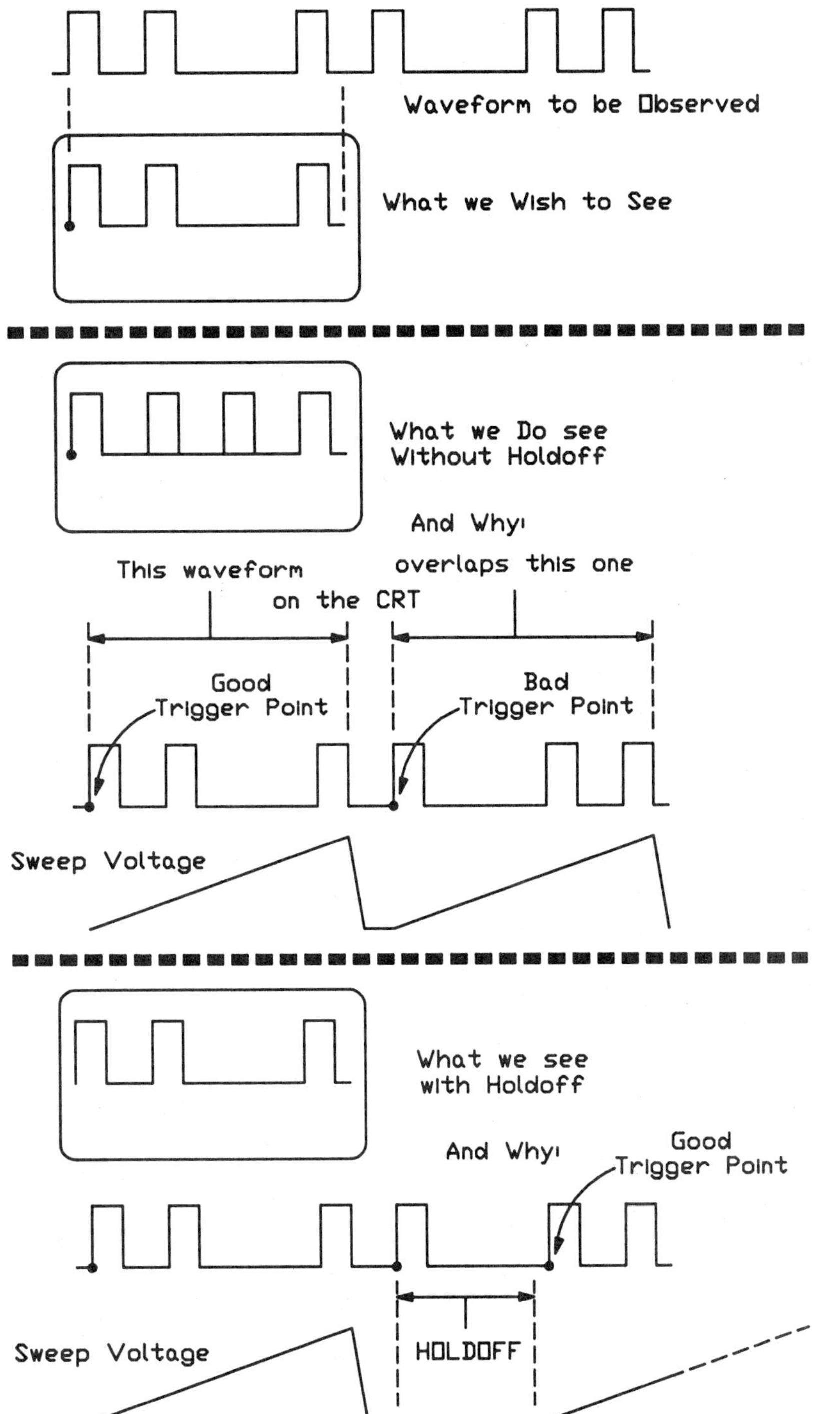

Figure 14–24 The holdoff control allows high sweep-rate analysis of a portion of a longer-period waveform.

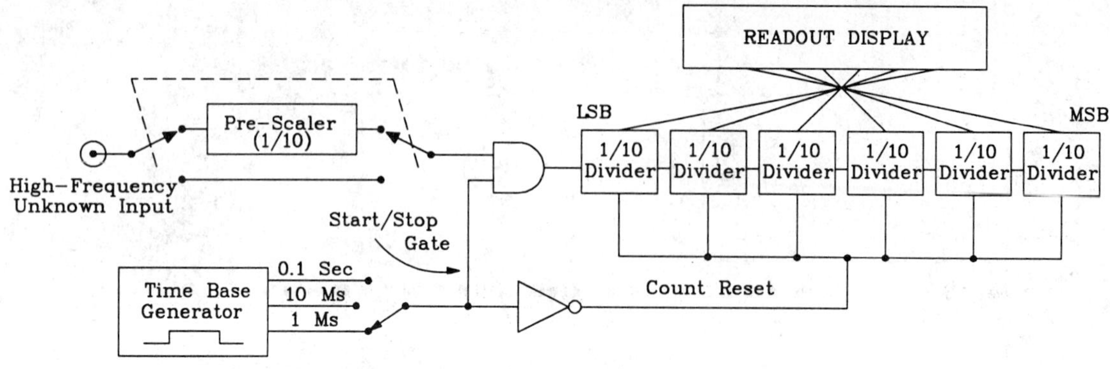

Figure 14–25 Simplified block diagram of a frequency counter.

ment operates by counting a known, fast internal clock frequency during an externally applied gate.

USING A FUNCTION GENERATOR

An Input Signal Source for Pulse Troubleshooting

A function generator can be made to produce several different kinds of waveforms. The most common are the square wave, the ramp, the sine wave, and the triangle wave. See Figure 14–27.

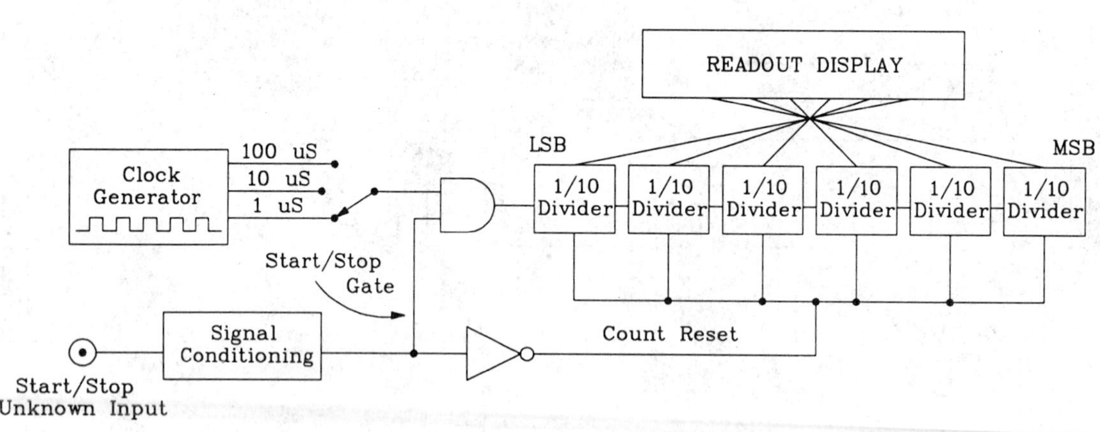

Figure 14–26 Simplified block diagram of a period timer.

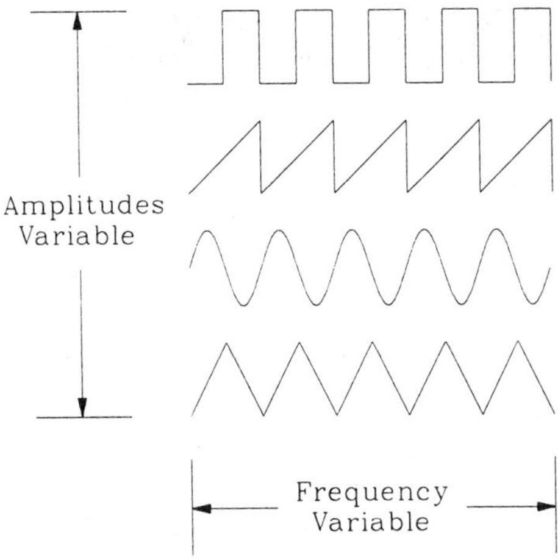

Figure 14–27 Typical waveforms that a function generator may provide.

Function generator waveforms are most often used during the development of a circuit by a manufacturer, but they may also find occasional use during pulse circuit troubleshooting. For most cases, the internally generated pulses within the equipment under test are quite sufficient and a function generator will not be needed. In the rare case in which an external driving signal is required for troubleshooting a pulse circuit, the function generator may prove useful.

If the circuit under test requires very-short-duration pulses, these may be obtained from the function generator's square-wave output by using a small value capacitor in series with the square-wave output connector. Adding a small capacitor will effectively make a differentiator, using the internal resistance of the generator and the load of the input circuit. Varying the capacitor size will vary the pulse width, with smaller capacitors making very-short-duration spikes. See Figure 14–28.

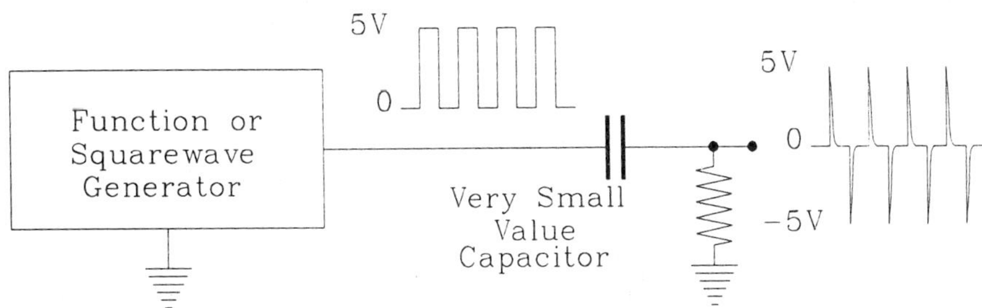

Figure 14–28 The square wave output of a function generator may be used to produce very-short-duration pulses.

14.10 SPECIAL PULSE CIRCUIT COMPONENTS

PULSE TRANSFORMERS

Pulses are often coupled from one stage to the next using pulse transformers. These are commonly used within high-powered AC motor controllers, for instance. These small transformers are used to couple a pulse from one circuit to the next while also providing DC and/or AC isolation between stages. They can also provide impedance matching, converting high-voltage, low-current pulses into high-current, low-voltage pulses. An added feature is that the pulse transformer can be driven with one stage and can trigger more than one following stage by adding the required number of secondary windings, with each winding isolated from all the others.

The pulse transformer is intended to be used only in pulse circuits. It does not have sufficient core material to be used in power handling or power conversion applications.

Because of the requirement for proper pulse polarity to trigger a given stage on the output side, the phasing of the pulse transformer is very important. It is also important when reading a pulse schematic to know what polarity will be produced in the secondary winding when the primary is driven with a given voltage polarity. Standard notation to assist in these problems has been established by the use of *phasing dots* on the transformer and on the schematic. *When a voltage is applied to the primary winding with positive polarity on the end of the winding that has a dot, corresponding dots on the secondaries will also have a positive polarity with respect to the opposite, unmarked end of that winding.* The same rule holds true if a negative-going pulse is applied; the output will then be negative. See Figure 14–29.

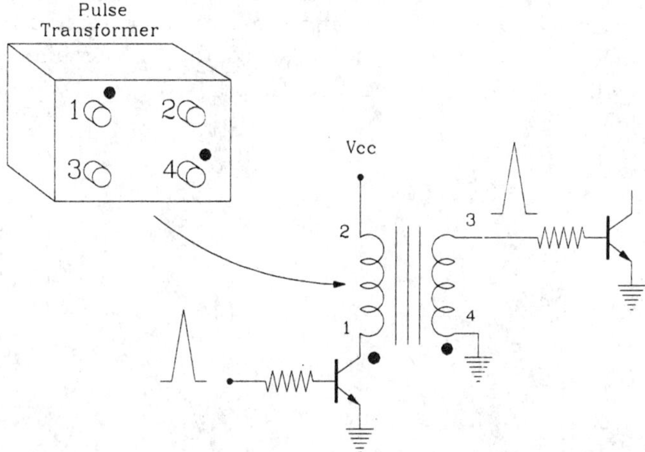

Figure 14–29 Like polarities of transformer windings are indicated by phasing dots on the transformer and on the schematic.

14.11 FAILURE PATTERNS OF LOW-LEVEL PULSE CIRCUITS

Low-level pulse circuits will fail most often because of semiconductor failure, and not because of capacitors or resistors. Any component that dissipates substantial heat in normal operation is a likely candidate for failure. Occasionally, a voltage pulse from an external source may cause the failure of a semiconductor or even a capacitor or a transformer, however, these failures are less likely.

PART III—TROUBLESHOOTING PULSED RF TRANSMITTER CIRCUITS

14.12 EXAMPLES OF PULSED RF AND ITS USES

Another application for pulses is to use them to modulate radio frequencies. *The principal reason for turning RF on for a brief instant is to get range (distance) information.* A pulse is used to gate on, or *modulate* a group of many cycles of radio frequency power.

HOW PASSIVE RADAR USES PULSED RF

Simply stated, a radar cycle begins with a brief pulse of RF that is sent out in a narrow beam from an antenna, at which time an electronic "clock" is started. The returning echo from a distant object is received some time later, whereupon the clock is stopped. The time elapsed on the clock is a direct function of the distance of the object from the transmitter. The direction in which the antenna is aimed indicates the direction of the target from the transmitter. This is the principle of the radar (Radio Detection And Ranging) system. See Figure 14–30.

HOW ACTIVE RADAR (TRANSPONDERS) USE PULSED RF

The main problems with *passive* radar is that it shows stationary objects that are of no concern and it depends on a target's ability to reflect the transmitted pulse. Another means is possible, to get around these obstacles, using special equipment aboard the target. This system is sometimes referred to as active radar.

An active target is one that not only reflects RF energy bursts but *responds* to them. The transponder of an aircraft receives special interroga-

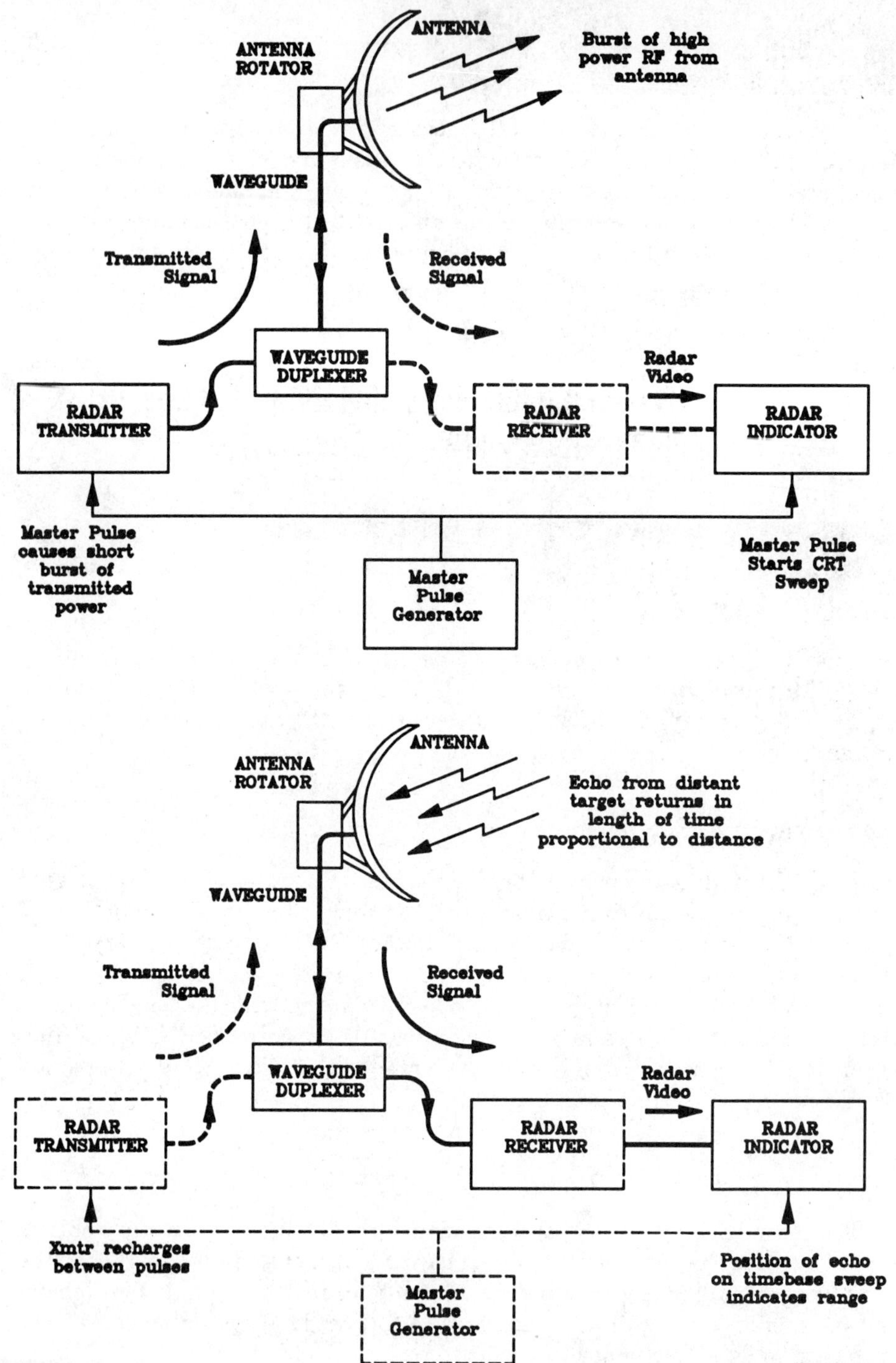

Figure 14–30 Block diagram of pulsed RF as used in a radar system.

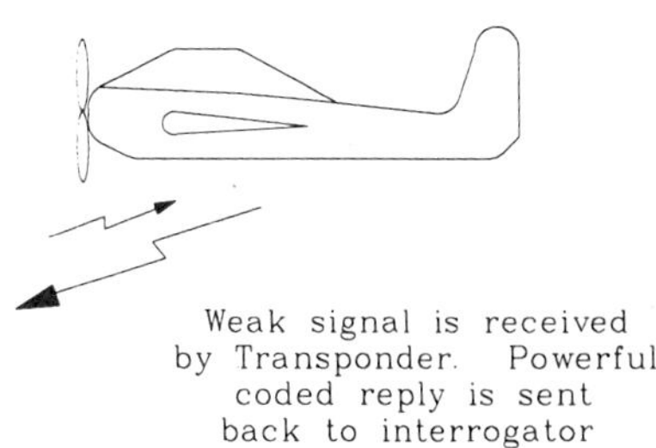

Weak signal is received
by Transponder. Powerful
coded reply is sent
back to interrogator

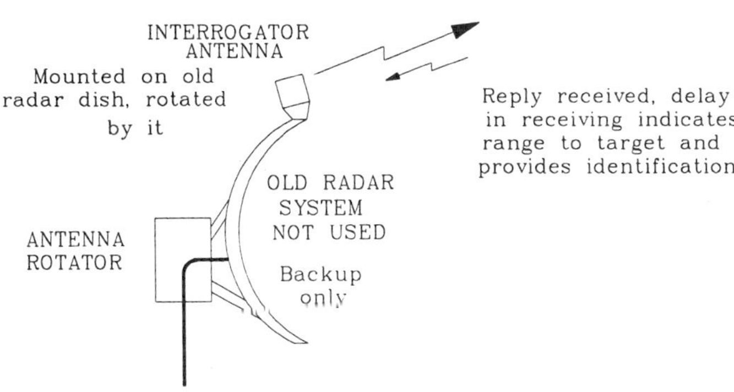

Figure 14–31 Basic diagram showing the operation of an aircraft transponder.

tion pulses from a land-based radar installation. The transponder then replies with a unique numerical code (assigned on a case-for-case trip basis to a specific aircraft) and, in a special mode provided for the purpose, it can also automatically report the current altitude of the aircraft. The interrogating equipment on the ground can tell the range of the aircraft by the delay in receiving the relatively strong, received reply. By processing pulse information within the reply, the computer at the air traffic control facility can also identify the craft by a unique number and show its current altitude on a special CRT display. All this transmitting, replying, and reporting is done without human intervention. See Figure 14–31.

HOW DISTANCE-MEASURING EQUIPMENT (DME) USES PULSED RF

Navigation of an aircraft is made easier by the VHF Omni Range (VOR) navigation system, which is used throughout the world. This system alone will tell an aircraft its direction relative to a transmitting station. Knowing that the aircraft is on a given line is not enough: more information is necessary to pinpoint the aircraft's location. This information may be obtained by getting the aircraft's *distance* from the VOR station. This is the purpose of the DME equipment located on-board the aircraft.

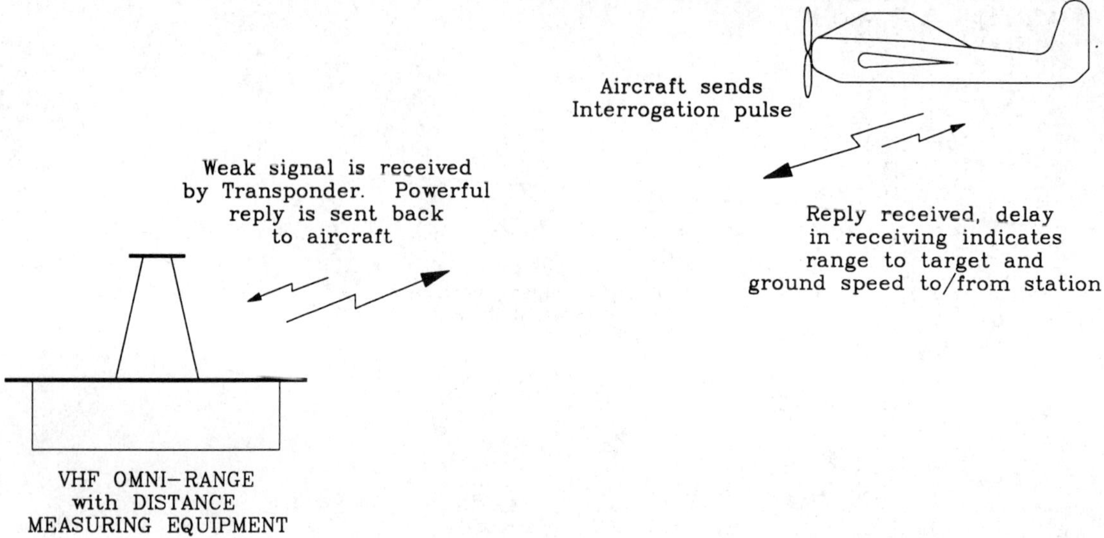
Aircraft sends
Interrogation pulse
Weak signal is received
by Transponder. Powerful
reply is sent back
to aircraft
Reply received, delay
in receiving indicates
range to target and
ground speed to/from station
VHF OMNI-RANGE
with DISTANCE
MEASURING EQUIPMENT

Figure 14–32 Basic block diagram of DME equipment.

The aircraft sends out interrogating pulses, very similar to those of the land-based equipment of the active radar system just described. The VOR station will have colocated transponders that reply to these interrogations. Then, the elapsed time from the interrogation until the received reply is calculated and the distance to the station in nautical or statute miles is displayed for the pilot. With this information calculated against time, the speed of the aircraft may also be calculated as the speed approaching (or leaving) the station. This information may be displayed at the pilot's discretion. See Figure 14–32.

HOW LORAN USES PULSED RF

A system called LOng Range Aid to Navigation (LORAN) is made possible by again using the RF pulse and its transit time as a basis for the system. If two precisely timed transmitting sites were to transmit a short pulse of RF energy at the same instant, the receiver hearing them at exactly the same time would have to be midway, or somewhere on a line drawn exactly between the stations. If one station is received before the other, the receiver must be nearer that station. Mathematical plotting of all the receiving timing differences results in a pattern similar to that of Figure 14–33.

A second LORAN line of position (a line connecting all points of similar

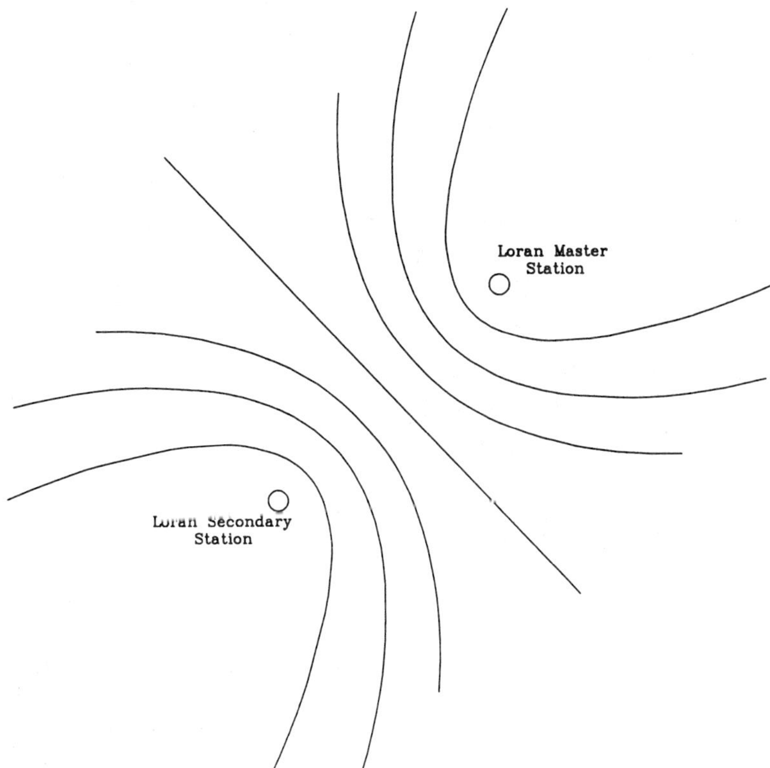

Figure 14–33 Two LORAN stations, showing lines of position with equal time delays.

reading) may be obtained by using another pair of stations. The intersection of these two lines is the location of the receiver.

This is an oversimplification of the LORAN system, but it serves to illustrate the basic principle. In actuality, the receiver must be able to tell the difference between the signals emanating from the stations. Thus, the stations must transmit in sequence with precisely determined timing to prevent one station from ever being received at the same time as another. Three stations can also do the work of four, with one serving double duty in determining the second line of position.

14.13 TROUBLESHOOTING PULSED RF CIRCUITS

PULSE MODULATION CRITERIA

There are several critical parameters for which a pulse RF circuit must be checked.

1. The modulating pulse must be of the correct amplitude. The output circuit of a typical pulse modulator is made so that a low-amplitude modulating pulse will cause the output RF pulse to be too low in amplitude.
2. Some pulse applications will also require that a specific pulse shape be used for the modulation process.
3. The pulse must be of the proper width. Too narrow or too wide a pulse will degrade the system performance, and, in the case of a pulse that is too wide, will waste output power and unnecessarily load the power supply.
4. The pulse repetition rate (PRR) must be correct. If a given amplifier is pulsed too often (at too high a PRR), the amplifier may be overdriven and overheat, the power supply can be overloaded, or other types of damage may occur. Too low a PRR, on the other hand, will result in poor performance of the entire system.
5. Be sure that the RF drive into the modulated stage is the correct value according to the instruction manual. In most cases, the correct DC voltage drop across the RF *driver* emitter resistor will confirm the proper RF drive and modulation of the power amplifier. Pulse waveform voltages and waveshape will be of primary importance in determining the proper pulse output of the modulator. Be sure to consult the manufacturer's test points and make sure that measurements there conform to the specifications.

14.14 INSTRUMENTS FOR PULSED RF MEASUREMENTS

Test instruments for radar, transponders, DME, and LORAN equipment must be specialized. The radio frequencies involved in each vary widely, from 100 kHz for LORAN to about 9 gHz for marine radar. The timing between a transmitted signal and the reception of the RF pulses is critical and must be converted into an appropriate display for the system at hand. While it is theoretically possible to interconnect generic signal generators, pulse detectors, and counters to generate the troubleshooting signals required, it is far easier and less subject to error to use test equipment that has been made for and calibrated for each application.

Since test equipment for pulse equipment is specialized, it will require some time for the technician to learn the equipment and how to operate it. The best instruction that can be obtained without going to a special school is to become familiar with the test equipment book and the manual for the equipment under test. Special test setups may be required for certain measurements. Be sure to use exactly the same kind and lengths of coaxial cable that are called for in the instruction books. Various kinds of coaxial cable have varying degrees of attenuation above roughly 1 gHz (see Appendix X); consequently, using the wrong kind of cable can cause signal strength readings to be far from what they should be. The flexibility of coaxial cable is indispensable in testing, even though its attenuation may be excessive. This must be taken into account whenever signal strengths are part of the test procedure. (See the section on microwave power measurement in Chapter 13.)

CHAPTER SUMMARY

- A pulse circuit is neither completely analog nor completely digital.
- Pulse waveforms are described with unique terms.
- High voltages and on-off operation make pulse circuitry a special category for troubleshooting purposes.
- A power pulse amplifier frequently uses a switching transistor and operates as either cut off or saturated.
- The SCR and TRIAC are the components used in high-power stages of AC line pulse circuits.
- Many AC voltmeters will not indicate RMS voltages accurately on nonsinusoidal waveforms.
- Pulse voltages can often exceed the 500-V limitation of an oscilloscope probe.
- Don't connect the oscilloscope common to an ungrounded circuit.
- Defective pulse circuits usually fail entirely, becoming simple opens or shorts
- The voltage waveforms in circuits that control currents may be misleading.
- Pulse transformers must be phased; consequently, both they and the schematics usually have phasing dots to indicate instantaneous polarity.
- A function generator can easily be made to produce short-duration pulses for troubleshooting pulse circuits.
- A frequency counter may have a very low input voltage limitation (as low as 2 V).
- A power RF attenuator may reduce transmitter power levels to a level that is safe for frequency counters and oscilloscopes.
- The installation of replacement semiconductors in pulse circuits should be preceded by a check of the protective components in the circuit.
- Pulse RF circuits include radar, transponders, DME, and LORAN. These depend on the transit time of RF radiation for range information.
- Specialized equipment is often necessary to troubleshoot equipment using pulsed RF signals.

REVIEW QUESTIONS

AC Power Control Circuits:

1. What is the principal characteristic of a thyristor?
2. Name four members of the thyristor family of semiconductors.
3. The most accurate AC voltmeter to use on partial sine-wave wave forms is one that responds to the _______ value of the waveform.
4. What must you remember if you need to troubleshoot an SCR or TRIAC circuit using an oscilloscope?
5. What is a typical high-voltage limitation of an oscilloscope test probe?
6. What is the criteria for troubleshooting AC pulsed circuits in regard to the appearance of the pulses on an oscilloscope?
7. What internal mechanism can cause an SCR to suddenly begin conduction without a gate signal if the anode/cathode voltage increases too suddenly?
8. What is the reference lead for an SCR?
9. What is the reference lead for a TRIAC?
10. What is the name of the circuit that provides a momentary reversal of anode/cathode voltage to turn off an SCR operating on DC?
11. What are the two most common failures of SCRs and TRIACs?
12. The GTO is very similar to an SCR, except that it can be ________ _______ by a signal to the _______.
13. The reference element of a PUT is the _______ lead.
14. The UJT and PUT are most often used in circuits as a/an _______.
15. Name two semiconductor devices that are used to stabilize the trigger of an SCR or TRIAC.

Troubleshooting Low-Level Pulse Circuits

16. How will the technician know whether pulse waveshape is important for a given circuit?
17. Why might a computer monitor have some components marked with a special symbol, such as a triangle around an exclamation point?
18. What is the duty cycle of a waveform that is high for 33 microseconds and then drops to a low for 55 microseconds?
19. What are the two signal criteria to keep in mind when you are signal-tracing through pulse circuits?
20. The waveform observed on an oscilloscope appears to have extra baselines. What control will probably eliminate them?
21. What should be remembered to prevent damage when applying a signal to a frequency counter?
22. What is the significance of small dots marked next to some of the terminals of a pulse transformer?

Troubleshooting Pulsed RF Transmitter Circuits

23. What is the principal reason for pulsing RF transmissions?
24. What is the difference between active and passive radar?
25. Name the criteria for adjusting or verifying correct operation of an RF pulse modulator.
26. What kind of test equipment will probably be required for working on pulsed RF systems?

Digital Troubleshooting Techniques

15

CHAPTER OBJECTIVES

This chapter will acquaint the technician with the concepts, chips, instruments, and techniques needed to effectively troubleshoot digital circuits. It also forms the basis for detailed troubleshooting in microprocessor circuits (the subject of Chapter 16). At the conclusion of this chapter, the student will understand:

- The three types of digital output circuits: totem-pole, open collector, and three-state.
- The importance of signal timing in troubleshooting digital circuits.
- How to interpret a timing diagram.
- Terms unique to digital circuits.
- The symbols commonly used on digital schematics.
- The primary characteristics and operating levels of the principal logic families: TTL, CMOS, and ECL.
- The use of an extender clip.
- The use of a logic pulser as a digital signal generator.

- How to use an oscilloscope on digital circuits and understand its limitations.
- The detailed use of a logic probe.
- The use of a current tracer with digital signals.
- Basic concepts of using a logic analyzer.
- What a logic comparator is and how it works.
- What signature analysis is and how to use it.
- The use of a logic clip.
- How digital circuits fail.
- Proper steps to use for most digital troubleshooting.
- How to troubleshoot digital-timing problems.
- How to troubleshoot an LCD display.

BASIC INFORMATION

15.1 BASIC DIGITAL CONCEPTS

Digital signals are represented by one of only two voltages: a high level or a low level. The actual voltages that are acceptable as high or low depend on the digital ICs being used (to be discussed later). The high and low voltage levels are separated by a range of voltages that are unacceptable in digital circuits.

IC OUTPUT CONFIGURATIONS

The Totem-Pole Digital IC Output Circuit

Digital signals are usually passed from one digital output to one or more digital inputs, as shown in Figure 15–1.

Most IC output stages pull the output line either up or down, using either of two separate transistors in the output stage within the IC. This circuit is called a *totem-pole output* and is the output circuit usually used in digital ICs. The totem-pole output of a standard 74XX TTL chip (74XX meaning "74 followed by other numbers") will drive up to as many as 10

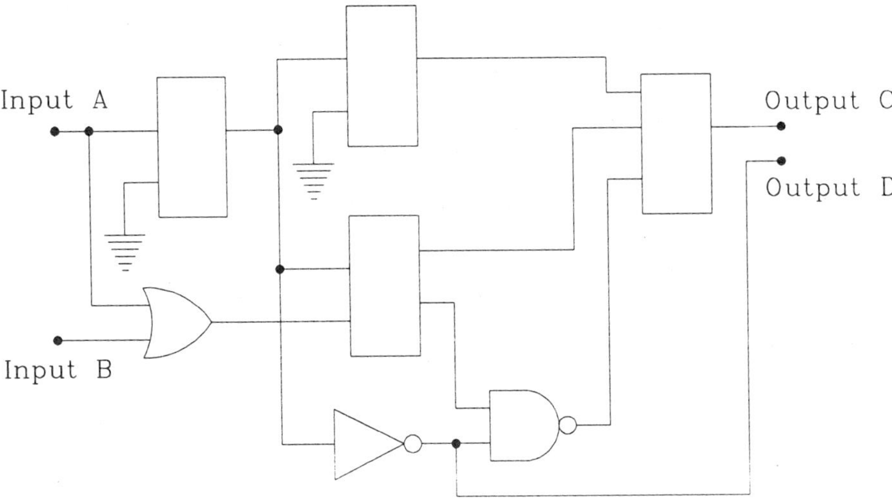

Figure 15–1 Digital circuits often pass signals from one output to one or more digital inputs.

other inputs. This type of connection between *a single output and multiple inputs can be called a Type I data bus*. See Figure 15–2.

When a digital IC with a totem-pole output is operating, there is a very brief time (a few nanoseconds) when both transistors are conducting heavily. This is necessary to prevent "dropping" the output line during the transition time from one state to the other. During this time, a pulse of heavy current is drawn from the power supply. Without special attention to this current pulse, it would be possible for the power supply bus to allow momentary pulses to be carried to other stages, which it could cause unintentional triggering or other timing problems. For this reason, bypass capacitors of about .01 µfd are installed close to these chips and connected from Vcc to ground. With these capacitors in place, the pulse of current is supplied by the bypass capacitor and does not propagate along the power bus into other circuits.

BASIC INFORMATION

The Open-Collector Digital IC Output Circuit

It is easy to abbreviate the totem-pole output circuit to include a single pull-down transistor and then provide an external resistor to pull the output line high when the transistor is not conducting. The resistor connected from the IC output pin to Vcc is necessary to pull the output line high when the transistor in the output stage is not conducting. This arrangement is sometimes used when the output circuit must operate at a higher voltage than the IC chip operating voltage, or when a hardwired NOR configuration is beneficial. See Figure 15–3.

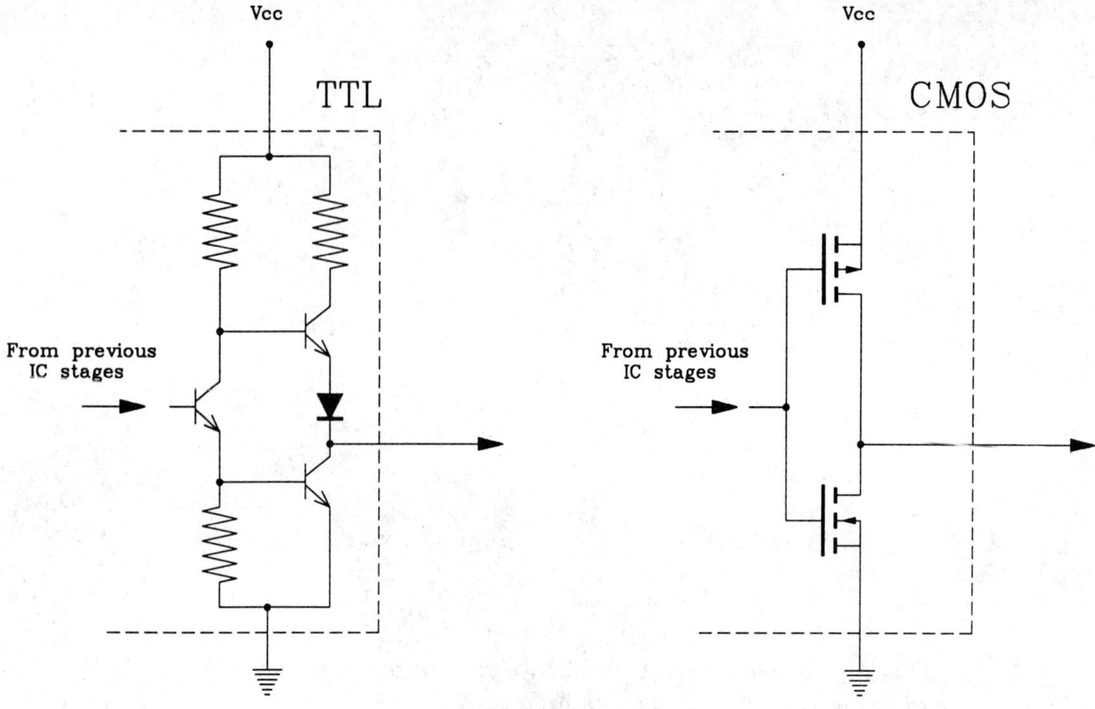
Vcc
TTL
From previous
IC stages
Vcc
CMOS
From previous
IC stages

Figure 15–2 Basic totem-pole output stages, TTL and CMOS.

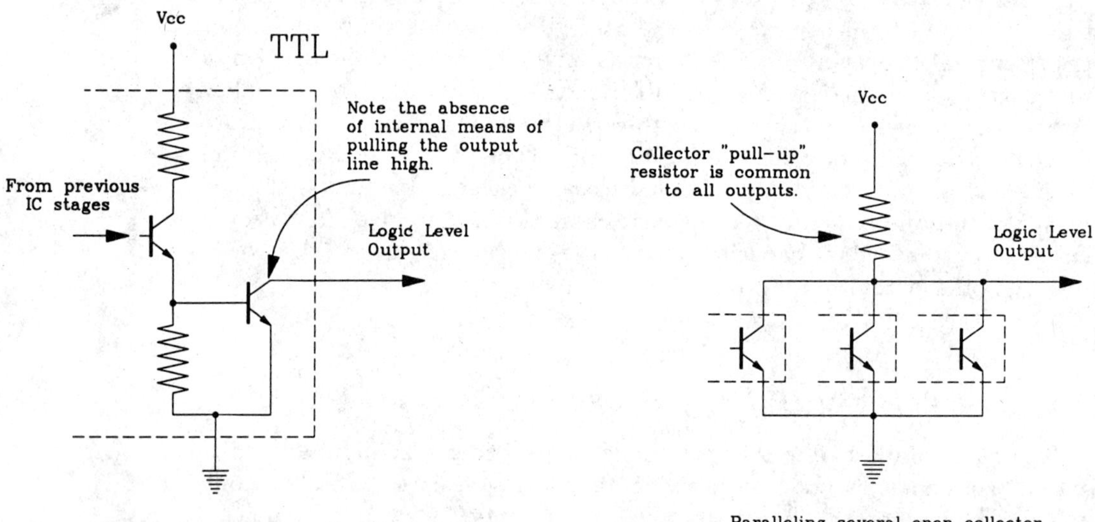
Vcc
TTL
Note the absence
of internal means of
pulling the output
line high.
From previous
IC stages
Logic Level
Output
Internal structure of an IC with
an open collector output configuration.
Vcc
Collector "pull-up"
resistor is common
to all outputs.
Logic Level
Output
Paralleling several open collector
outputs will result in a low
logic output if one or more of
the outputs are low.

Figure 15–3 The open collector IC output stage and how it can be used in a wired NOR configuration.

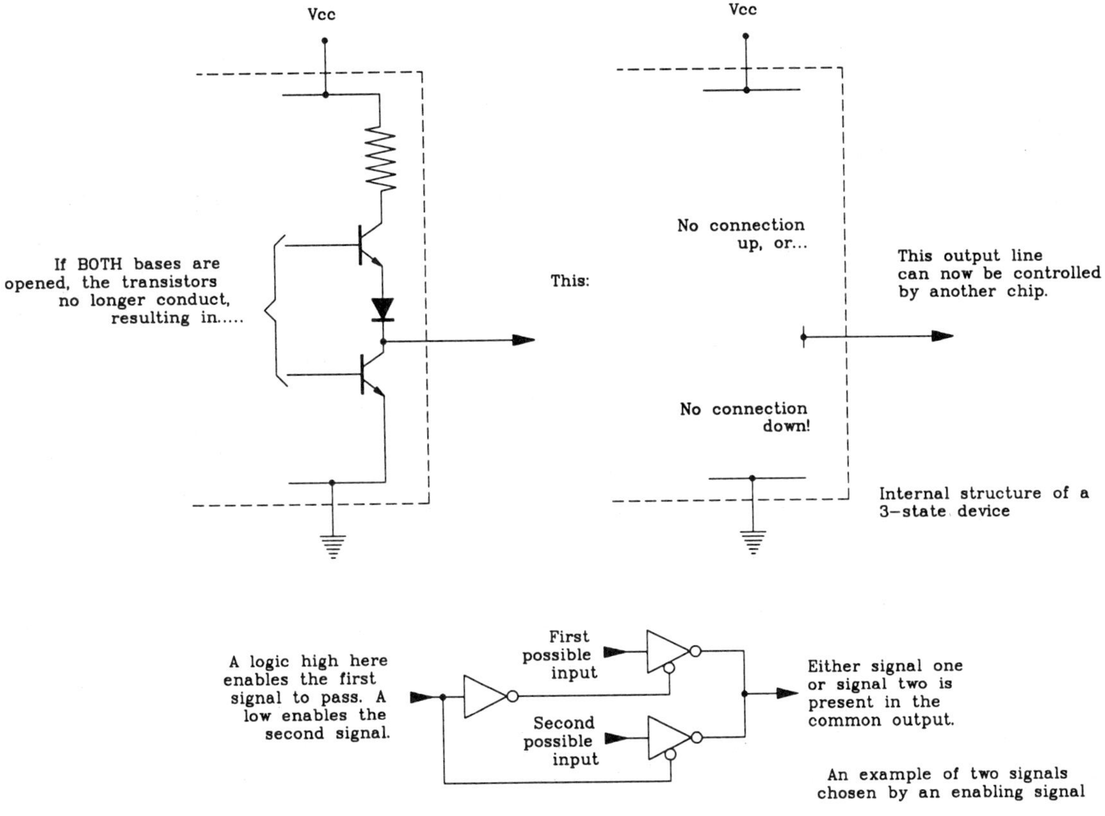

Figure 15–4 The three-state bus allows the interconnection of more than one IC output to a common load.

The open-collector IC output pin can be paralleled with other open-collector chips. If any one of the chips causes a logic low on the output line, the other chips may either agree and help hold the line at the logic low or remain off, thus making them "transparent" and of no consequence to the low-output logic level. This kind of bus structure can be thought of as a *Type II bus, as it has more than one source IC and two or more receiving ICs and uses an open-collector transistor* inside the IC.

BASIC INFORMATION

The Three-State Digital IC Output Circuit

A final variation on the output-to-input scheme is called for when two or more digital output circuits must be tied together to share a common digital line. This requires the *three-state* or *floating output*. Three-state outputs are commonly used in microprocessor circuits where many chips must be able to produce signals on a single given line. Only one of these chips may actually control the line at any given instant. The three-state variation can be called a *Type III bus*. See Figure 15–4.

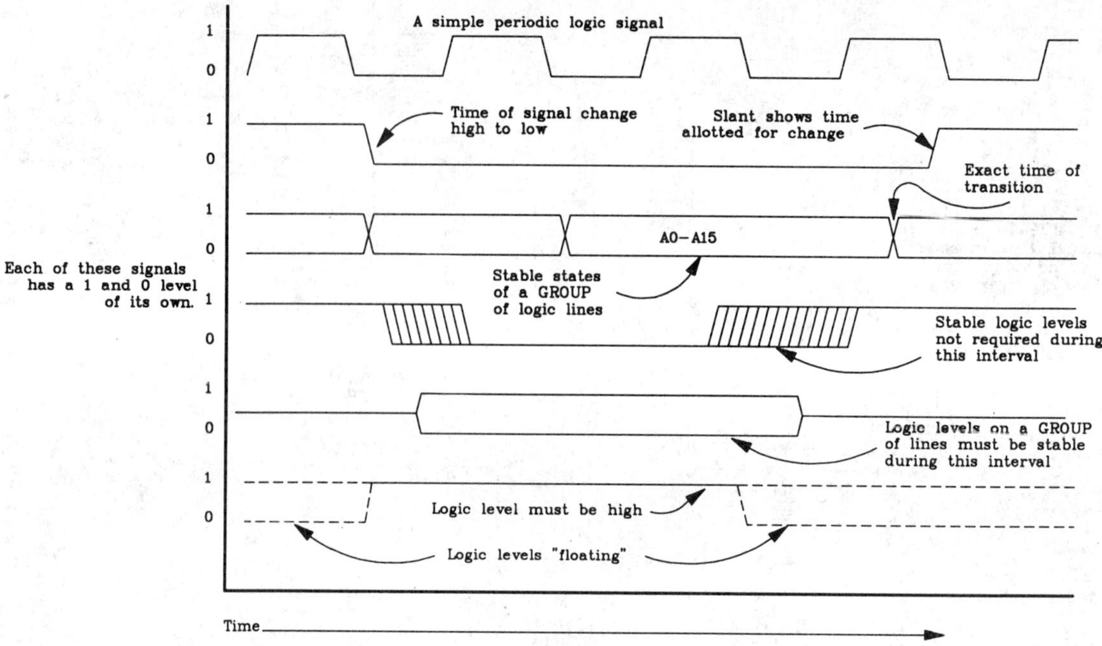

Figure 15–5 The timing diagram explained.

DIGITAL TIMING DIAGRAMS

Timing diagrams, like sheet music, are needed to show what happens in digital circuits, and at what time. Technicians must be familiar with timing diagram symbology, because timing diagrams do not always have a key provided with them. See Figure 15–5.

15.2 DIGITAL SCHEMATICS

PREPARING DIGITAL SCHEMATICS FOR USE

The average digital schematic will show resistors, connectors, and switches, as does any other schematic. The digital chips, however, will take one of two general forms: Individual, simple gates such as NAND and NOR gates will be shown as a standardized symbol for that particular gate. A single chip having several independent gates may be shown, scattered, where needed on the schematic. Other chips are too complicated internally to be shown in this manner, so they will be shown simply as blocks. These blocks are seldom labeled with their purpose or name. To use a digital schematic efficiently, it is wise to customize it, especially if it will be used a great deal. Here are some suggestions for making digital schematics more user-friendly.

Color-Code Your Schematics

Color coding is applicable to digital circuits. Vcc and ground should be colored the standard colors, red and black, respectively. Often, these connections are assumed and do not appear on the schematic. If you feel that it might help you, put these connections on the schematic yourself, along with the appropriate IC pin numbers. Signal flow lines are not quite the same for digital circuits as they are for analog. Rather than showing signal flow, it may be better to color code groupings of similar lines the same color. For instance, a microprocessor schematic might have all the data lines one color and the address lines another. There are generally too many different signals going every which way in a large, complex digital circuit for the term *signal flow* to have much meaning. Of course, a color coding key should be provided on the schematic.

Mark Individual ICs with Their Purpose

With these markings, you will be able to tell that a certain block is a divide-by-eight counter, for instance, or a retriggerable monostable multivibrator. This information is seldom already provided on digital schematics.

Provide Solid-State Tester Patterns

These are very helpful on both digital and analog PC boards. Typical patterns may be shown for many points in the circuit. Use ground as the common reference point.

Mark the Normal Indication of a Logic Probe

Logic probe notations on a schematic are a very good idea. With the circuit in normal operation, the schematic should be marked with a simple code at all appropriate places, indicating one of the following:

A = There is normally an active signal here, with no logic level showing (high frequency).

L = This pin is at a static low level and does not change.

H = This pin is at a static high level and does not change.

F = This pin is floating (bad logic level).

These codes may be used in pairs, as in these examples:

AL = Activity here, but principally at a low level (low duty cycle).

AH = Activity here, but principally at a high level (high duty cycle).

AF = Usually three-stated, but some activity now and then.

There is a movement toward more descriptive notation for digital circuits, to replace the simple blocks. The IEC (International Electrotechnical Commission) has developed a whole system of symbols for this purpose. The complete description takes about 25 pages. If it comes into common use throughout the digital industry, a more detailed description of the system will be necessary. A very brief explanation of some of the more common symbols appears in Appendix II. In Europe, companies are beginning to use these symbols.

THE NEED FOR DIGITAL REFERENCE BOOKS

Having suitable component reference materials for the IC chips used in digital circuits is a must for component-level servicing. While the operation of an analog circuit may be inferable from the components used, the digital schematic diagram often provides only the generic number of the integrated circuits. Sometimes, the ICs have no meaningful markings at all. The function of a digital circuit is seldom given. Without references, the symbols on the diagram are mysteries. Reference books also help in defining obscure terms and special-purpose abbreviations. See Figure 15–6.

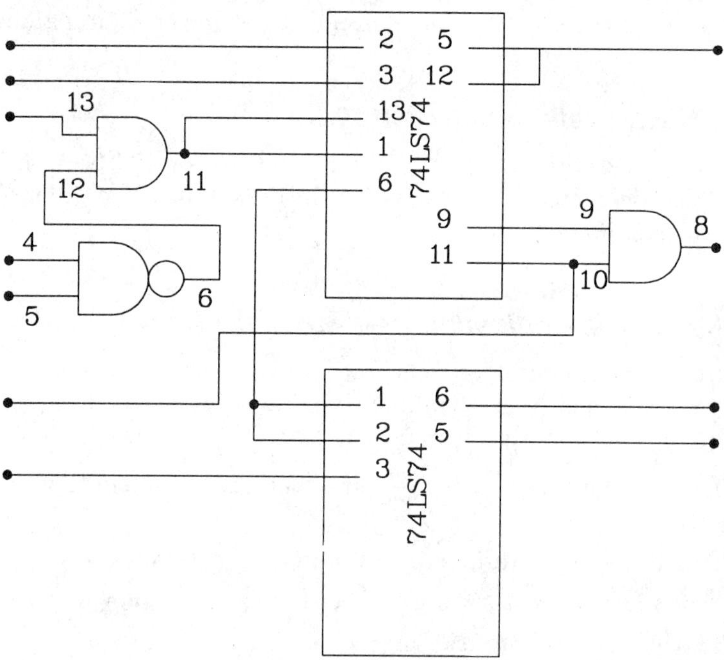

Figure 15–6 Example of a digital circuit that, without a reference for the chips involved, would be all but impossible to understand.

There are two families of integrated circuits in common use, the TTL and the CMOS. The technician should at least have data books for each of these families. They are available through local electronics parts distributors and from the manufacturers of ICs. Information on voltage regulators and operational amplifiers (often used with digital circuits) is found in the linear data book, also published by the same sources.

Digital chips other than generic gates and simple ICs may be encountered and will have to be researched in a variety of references. A particular serial data transmitter and receiver chip, for instance, might be found in a manual that deals only with data communications chips. Memory chips are to be found in a special memory devices manual, while microprocessors will be found in a microprocessor manual. Input/output chips are another category, to be found in a peripheral chip manual. These manuals are published by each different manufacturer for its own line of products, so you can imagine the number of books that are published each year. On top of this, the manuals are updated periodically, so a new set of books comes out with the new products every few years. Add to this the confusion of the tendency of manufacturers to institute their own chip-numbering systems, and it becomes evident that to have information on all the chips you may use may require many books from many different manufacturers. Depending on the chip information needed, the appropriate manuals will have to be obtained to do an efficient job of servicing.

If information is not available for a particular chip, it is often possible to get enough information for the job at hand from an instruction manual for other equipment that uses the same chip. What the schematic may not tell you, the parts list may. Unrelated schematics showing the chip in which you are interested are particularly helpful in answering questions on the connection and/or use of specific pins.

Another possibility for getting scarce information is to visit a reputable electronics parts distributor (see Figure 15–7). Many such businesses make a single copy of references available at the counter for their customers.

If your troubleshooting inquiry can be answered simply, consider calling the manufacturer's representative in your city or a cooperative parts distributor (who may also have the manufacturer's representative's number) and ask for the information. This will require that you cultivate some degree of rapport. Remember that the distributor doesn't memorize the specification books any more than you do. It will take valuable time to look up the information for you, and it *is* a courtesy. Data faxing is possible, too.

A few integrated circuit manufacturers are listed in Appendix IV of this book.

DIGITAL TIMING IS NOT ON THE SCHEMATICS

Whereas analog schematics usually have only a few signals to deal with, digital circuits often have many signals. The dozens of signals of a digital circuit may differ entirely from each other, but they may not necessarily

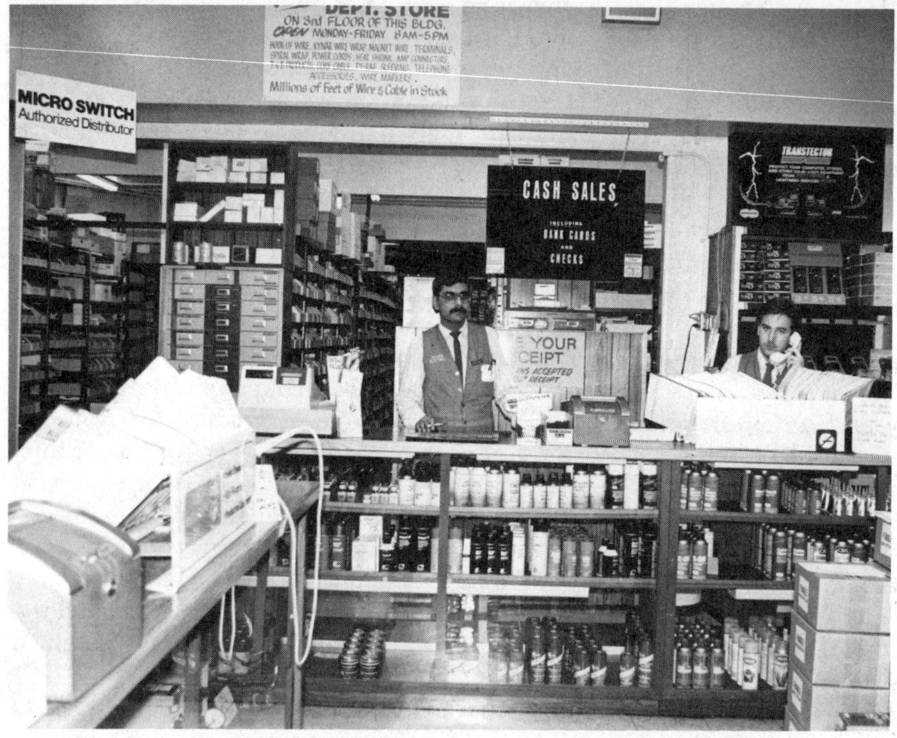

Figure 15–7 An electronics parts distributor may be able to assist in finding parts, getting part specifications, and finding substitute parts.

appear different, even on an oscilloscope. The signals will be at either a logic high or a logic low. These are the only acceptable active levels. *The key to understanding the interaction of the signals in a digital circuit is to understand the timing between these signals.*

Why is timing such an important part of digital circuitry? Take the common AND gate, for instance. Without timing information, there is no way to tell what the output of the circuit might be. We could quote what it is *supposed to do* according to its truth table, but that has little to do with knowing what the instantaneous relationship of the two actual input signals might be. See Figure 15–8.

A little thought about this question will make the point clear that *digital circuits have a timing factor that is not evident on the schematics.* Now let's

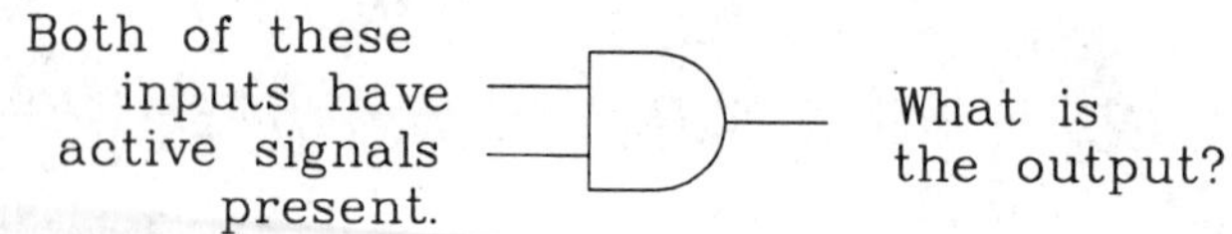

Figure 15–8 What is the output from this digital circuit?

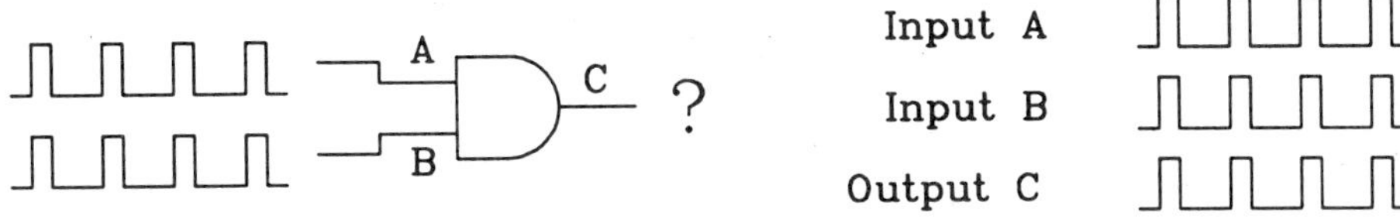

Figure 15–9 What is the output from this digital circuit?

see what adding the dimension of timing will do toward understanding this gate. Take the same gate but provide two identical digital inputs. The relationship of these inputs, with one above and the other below, suggests that they go high and low together. In this case, the output of the AND gate simply follows them both. See Figure 15–9.

Now let us slip the *timing* of one of the input signals so that it arrives later, by exactly one-half of the cycle timing. See Figure 15–10.

Not only is it necessary to know the functions of basic logic gates, flip-flops, registers, and other typical IC circuits, it is just as important to know, for any particular circuit, exactly how the signals are arriving *with respect to one another.*

SUPPLY VOLTAGE AND GROUND ARE NOT SHOWN

It is customary to omit the connections to the supply voltage (Vcc) and to ground when drawing digital schematics. The servicing technician should make it a point to check for the proper voltages right at the chip pins when troubleshooting. *Most, but not all, digital ICs will have a ground connection on pin 7 of a 14–pin IC or pin 8 of a 16–pin IC. The supply voltage is connected to the last pin of the IC, 14 or 16 as appropriate.* Another item that is often omitted from digital schematics is the bypass capacitor that is connected directly across the Vcc and ground pins of many digital ICs. This small capacitor provides the additional, high-frequency filtering necessary to prevent "glitches" on the power bus. These occur during the extremely brief time when, during a change of state from either logic level to the

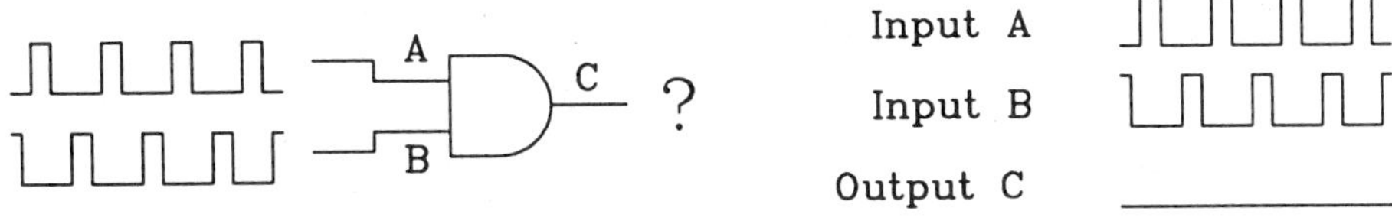

Figure 15–10 Same as previous figure, but with one input signal slipped later in time.

other, both transistors of a totem-pole output stage are conducting. This is necessary to prevent momentary floating of the output logic level.

DIGITAL TERMINOLOGY

Some of the terms used in dealing with digital circuits are unique. Here are some of the common ones and what they mean.

Active

Active simply means, "what satisfies the circuit." The AND gate, for instance, acts as an AND gate when the input 1 AND input 2 are both high. In this way, the gate is *satisfied* that the conditions for an AND gate have been met. The output then goes active. In the case of the AND gate, the output goes high.

If this is confusing, consider the fact that logic circuits can have positive logic, where a logic low is false and a high is true. This is "right-side-up" logic and is easiest to follow. On the other hand, there is also negative logic. Using this "upside-down" logic, the logic high is now false and the low level is true. With these reversals, logic levels are confusing to keep track of while troubleshooting. It is often easier to think of an active high or active low than to be concerned about whether the logic is a "1" or a "0."

Clear

Clear means to change to, or make sure that a logic level remains, a "0." Often used complementary to a Preset input, the Clear input will cause an immediate change of state of a flip-flop to the "0" state, regardless of the clock signal.

CMOS

CMOS stands for complementary metal oxide semiconductor. This comprises a family of logic chips characterized by very low power requirements and a high sensitivity to static damage. Very little power is required to drive them because their inputs are nearly perfect open circuits.

Dynamic

Dynamic means moving or in operation. It is used to describe circuit operation wherein the voltage levels are constantly changing, as during normal circuit operation. The opposite is Static.

Latch

A digital circuit that samples dynamic logic level changes on its inputs, then copies a single sample of the data on its outputs at the instant a strobe signal is received, as a camera "freezes" motion at the instant the shutter is activated.

Preset

Preset implies an input to a digital flip-flop which will cause an immediate change of state to the Set or "1" state, regardless of the clock signal.

Reset

Reset means to change to, or make sure that a logic level remains at, a "0" (zero).

Set

Set means to change to, or make sure that a logic level remains at, a "1."

Static

Static means without motion. It is often used to describe circuit operation wherein the voltage levels remain the same until manually tripped or incremented by the troubleshooting technician. It is the opposite of Dynamic.

Strobe

Strobe is a rapid logic change from one state to the other *and back again*. It is used as a signal to tell another circuit when to operate and it is a commonly used term with circuits that *Latch* data.

TTL

TTL is transistor-transistor logic, which involves integrated circuits that depend mainly on interconnected bipolar transistors to perform circuit tasks. They are characterized by ruggedness, high speed, and operation with a power source of exactly 5-V DC.

SCHEMATIC SYMBOLOGY

Some of the symbology used on digital schematics needs explanation. See Figure 15–11.

A line or bar over the top of the letter designation of an input or output pin means that the input is satisfied, or active, when that pin is at a logic

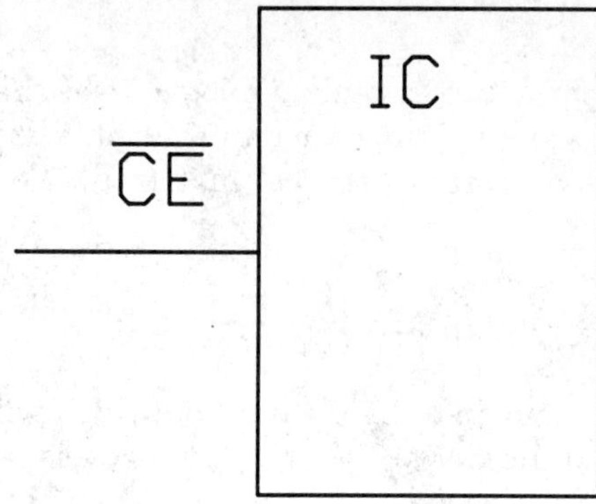

Figure 15–11 A bar over a pin designation means an active low logic level.

low. The lack of a bar over a pin designation *probably* means that the pin is active high. The bar could also have simply been omitted, so it is always a good idea to check a suspicious schematic designation against a data book for verification.

As shown in Figure 15–12, a small "o" at the input or output of a chip, like the overbar, means that this line is active low. On the other hand, the lack of an "o" *probably* means that this is an active-high pin. It could also mean someone was inattentive when drawing the schematic, so check a data book to be sure.

A small triangle just inside the IC symbol indicates that this input is *edge-sensitive* (see Figure 15–13). This circuit will act upon receiving the specified polarity of *transition* on this pin. Without a small "o," this circuit would act on a positive-going signal transition. In other words, at the

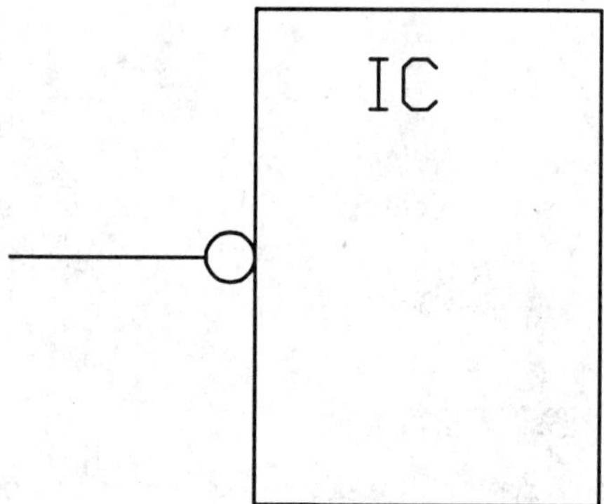

Figure 15–12 A small "o" on either input or output indicates an active low logic level.

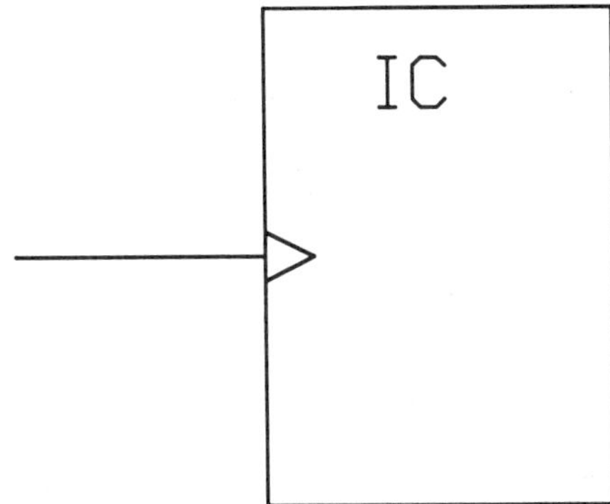

Figure 15–13 A small triangle at an input pin indicates an edge-sensitive input.

instant this input went from a logic-low level to a logic-high, the circuit would act on that information. A transition later from a logic-high to a logic-low would not affect the circuit at all. Adding an "o" at the input would designate this as a negative-going signal input. While it is often used at the clock input pin of a variety of chips, this symbol does *not*, by itself, signify a clock input pin.

EQUIVALENT GATES

When a circuit is designed and a particular chip is used, there are often times when not all the internal gates of the chip are used in the circuit. If a need arises for another gate of a different type, it is a good idea to see if something can be done to use the "extra" gates already on the board instead of adding another chip. For instance, if three NAND gates are used, of the four actually available in a 7400 chip, one will be left over. If it is found elsewhere in the design that an inverter is needed, it is a simple matter to tie the two inputs of the surplus NAND gate together and use it just as though it were an inverter. An alternative is to tie one of the inputs high and apply the input to the single remaining input. See Figure 15–14.

The substitution of one kind of gate for another is often done in digital circuits. One of the most frequent examples has just been discussed, but other combinations are possible. Some of them can be a bit extreme but will nonetheless work. See Figure 15–15.

There is no rule saying that the schematic symbol on the schematic must actually be that of the chip used. Using the NAND gate as an inverter, for instance, may be shown on the schematic as the NAND, with the inputs tied together, or it may be shown as an inverter! Beware of this potentially confusing information.

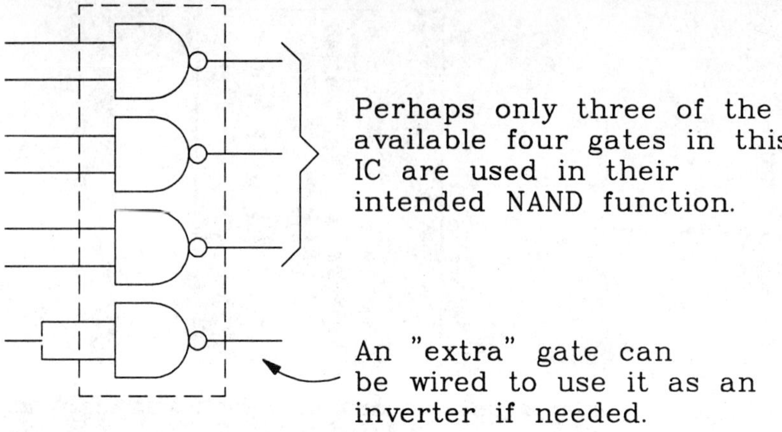

Perhaps only three of the available four gates in this IC are used in their intended NAND function.
An "extra" gate can be wired to use it as an inverter if needed.

Figure 15–14 Using the "extra" NAND gate of a 7400 IC as an inverter instead of adding another IC to the board.

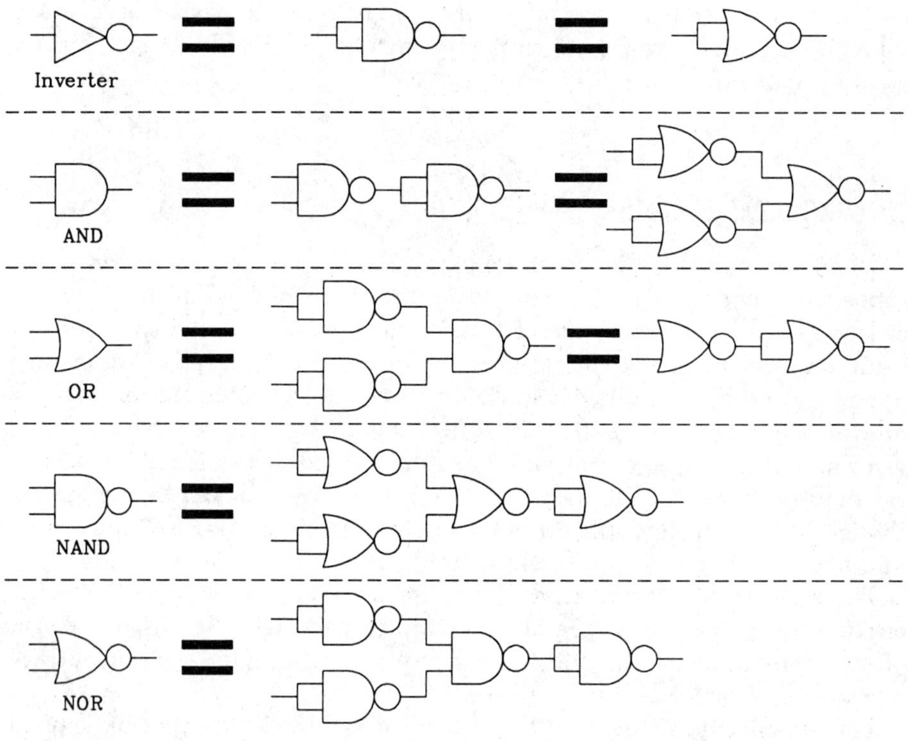

Figure 15–15 Summary of common substitutions of one type of gate for another.

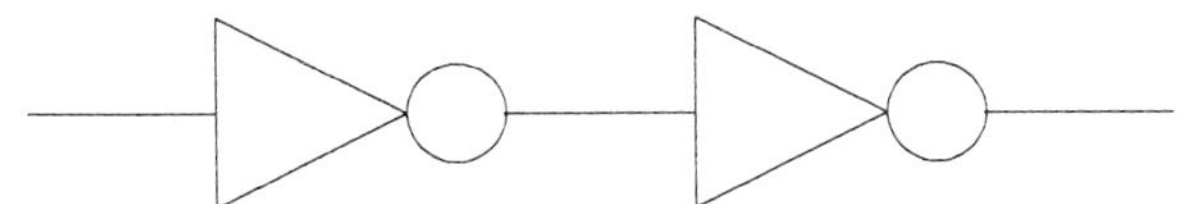

Figure 15–16 Two cascaded inverters can serve an important, though not obvious, function: time delay.

DELAY CIRCUITS

Another circuit that may cause a bit of confusion is shown in Figure 15–16.

This circuit apparently does nothing digital, since the signal comes out with the same logic level with which it went in. There is a change between the input and output signals, though, which is not apparent. The output signal transitions are delayed *in time* from those at the input, due to the delay in getting through both gates. Technically speaking, this circuit depends on the combined *propagation delays* of the two inverters. Propagation delay is the time required from the application of a given set of logic levels to the input of a gate until the proper output is obtained, which may be, roughly, on the order of 50 nanoseconds.

Another possible reason for using two inverters in this manner is to provide more noninverting driving power than was originally available at the input to the first gate. Increased driving power may be needed to operate several additional chip inputs in parallel at the output of the second inverter. This is also called *increasing the fan-out* of the original signal. Fan-out is the maximum number of inputs of a like family that a given chip can drive. One of these gates is used for the increase in driving power, and the other, to reinvert the signal to its original state.

NONSTANDARD GATE SYMBOLS

Some manufacturers make an attempt to draw their schematics so that it is easier to see how they operate. In using nonstandard gate symbols, they indicate what is wanted at the inputs and the function to be performed with those inputs. See Figure 15–17 for an example.

Another example of such a gate is the NOR gate with both inputs indicating an active low. This circuit is the same as a standard AND gate. If these nonstandard symbols are encountered, don't expect to find them by function. They don't exist in any data book. Pay attention to the IC identification number and don't be surprised when the gate in the book is entirely different from the schematic symbol. *The truth tables will be identical for each of them.* An example of this kind of digital notation is given in the partial schematic of Figure 15–18.

And of course:

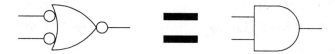

Figure 15–17 Occasionally, a circuit may be easier to understand if the logical complement of the gate is shown on a schematic instead of the actual symbol for the gate.

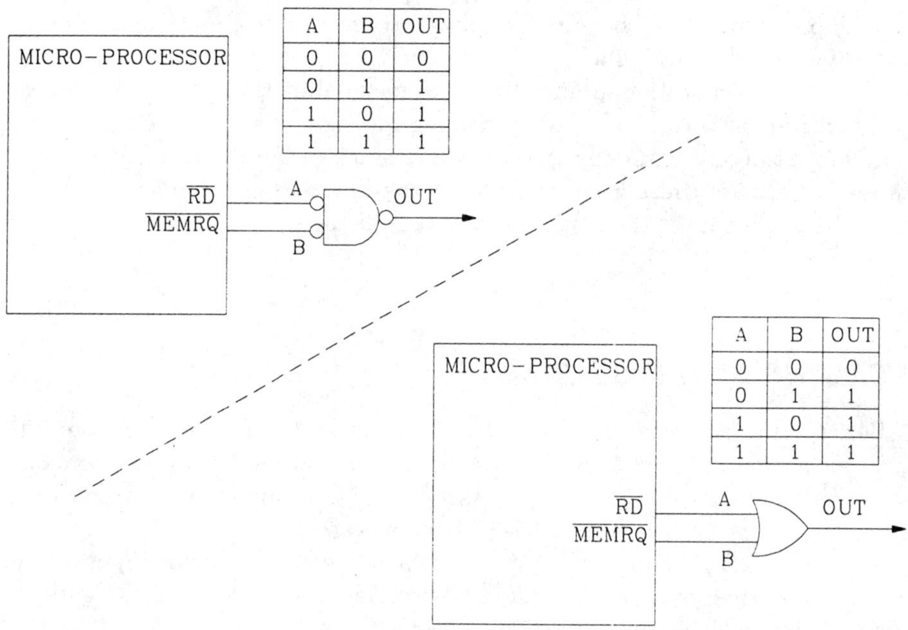

Figure 15–18 To have a line go low when both the RD and MEMRQ lines go low, the circuit could be drawn in either of two ways. Which is easier to understand?

15.3 DIGITAL INTEGRATED CIRCUIT FAMILIES

In the earliest days of digital logic, signals were passed from stage to stage using combinations of diodes and transistors. These were called *diode-transistor logic* (DTL) circuits. Resistors and transistors can also provide logic functions. This type of circuit was known as an RTL circuit. Two kinds of digital chip families are popular today, with a few special applications for a third type. The most often used are the transistor-transistor logic (TTL) and complementary metal oxide semiconductor (CMOS) logic families. A third family, emitter-coupled logic (ECL), is less popular, being used mostly in older, high-speed computers. The characteristics and identification of each are discussed next.

TRANSISTOR-TRANSISTOR LOGIC (TTL)

Characteristics of TTL Chips

The principal characteristics of TTL chips are that, generally speaking, they:

1. Operate on 5.0-V DC, +/- 0.25 volts,
2. Require relatively high power to operate,
3. Interpret an open input internally as a high,
4. Use logic thresholds of <0.8 V for “0” and >2.4 V for “1,” and
5. Operate at high speeds.

TTL chips must have a stable, well-filtered supply of 5.0 volts. This voltage must be within the range of 4.75 to 5.25 volts. Operating outside this range of voltages on the low side can cause these chips to develop “glitches”—short-duration, unintentional spikes of voltage—in their outputs. Glitches are the result of the mismatching of the delay times within the chips. This is particularly troublesome with chips having many internal transistors, such as frequency dividers and decoders. Operation on the high side can cause chip damage by glitch production and/or the simple burn-up of the chips.

The normal operation of a TTL totem-pole output circuit can produce pulses on the Vcc line. This is the reason that well-designed TTL circuit boards have many bypass capacitors (ideally, one for each TTL chip). These capacitors have a value of about 0.01 μfd and should be connected as closely to the ground and Vcc pins of the IC as possible.

TTL Chip Identification

The TTL family of chips requires substantial power for normal operation. Table 15–1 provides a comparison of the various subfamilies of TTL.

Table 15–1 A Comparison of TTL and Its Subfamilies

Family	Switching Speed	Power/Gate	Max. Freq.
Regular TTL (74XX)	10 ns	10 mw	35 MHz
High-Power TTL (74HXX)	6 ns	22 mw	50 MHz
Low-Power TTL (74LXX)	33 ns	1 mw	3 MHz
Schottky TTL (74SXX)	3 ns	19 mw	125 MHz
Low-Pwr. Schottky (74LSXX)	10 ns	2 mw	45 MHz

The basic TTL family is the 74XX family. These chips use bipolar transistors and, in normal operation, drive these transistors heavily into saturation. The military uses high-reliability versions of these chips, with the numbering altered in that they have numbers in the 54XX series. They commonly operate at about 35 MHz maximum frequency. This family offers the greatest variety of logic functions.

74HXX is a series of high-powered TTL chips. These chips operate at slightly higher frequencies, up to about 50 MHz. 74SXX indicates the use of Schottky diodes in the TTL chips. These chips use Schottky diodes that prevent heavy saturation of the internal bipolar transistors. This makes the chip able to change state more quickly, as it does not have to waste time unsaturating the transistors. The principal use of these diodes is to extend the frequency capability of these chips, to about 125 MHz. To help the high-frequency response, the internal resistors used in the totem-pole output are about half the resistance of those in standard TTL. This causes the chips to use about twice the power of a standard TTL chip.

74LXX indicates a low-power TTL chip. By increasing the resistance of the internal resistors to 10 times those of a standard TTL, power consumption drops to about 1/10. On the other hand, along with this drop in power comes a drop in the frequency of operation, to only about 3 MHz. 74LSXX is a compromise version of the last two subfamilies. The Schottky diodes prevent saturation of the transistors and use resistors of five times the standard TTL. These chips use one-fifth the power of a standard TTL yet surpass the regular TTL's frequency capability by operating to about 45 MHz.

74ALSXX indicates an advanced low-power Schottky chip. These chips have frequency capabilities to 50 MHz but with only the power dissipation of the low-powered TTL chips. 74FXX is the last TTL subfamily. These chips are called *fast TTL* and are pin-for-pin replacements for the 74SXX series ICs. They offer an improvement over the 74SXX chips by using only one-quarter the power of that family.

A technician must be aware of a unique failure characteristic of TTL circuits. *If the input to a TTL chip is accidently disconnected, that input*

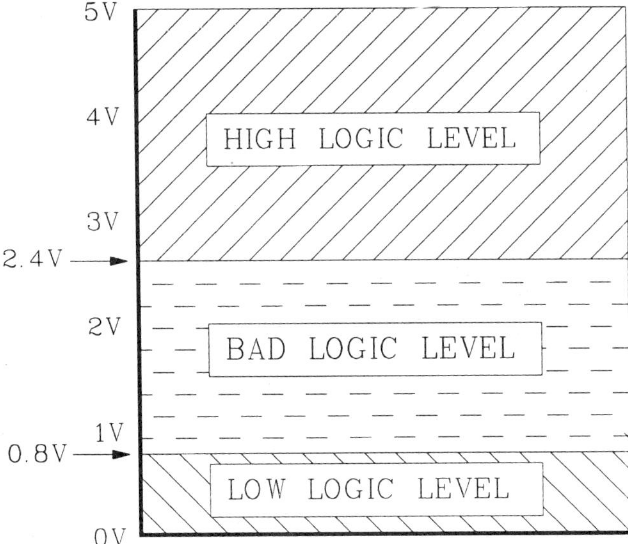

Figure 15–19 Graph of TTL logic-level boundaries.

will float up to a level of about 1.5 to 1.7-V DC. This level will usually be interpreted internally to the chip as a logic high, yet will show only as an indeterminate or "bad" level on the input pin when using a logic probe.

The acceptable logic voltage levels for a TTL chip are shown graphically in Figure 15–19. These levels are important for the technician to memorize.

COMPLEMENTARY METAL OXIDE SEMICONDUCTOR (CMOS) ICs

Characteristics of CMOS Chips

The principal characteristics of CMOS chips are that they:

1. Operate on voltages from 3 to 18 volts,
2. Use logic thresholds of <30 percent of Vcc as a "0" and >70 percent of Vcc as a "1,"
3. Require very low power to operate,
4. Interpret an open input erratically,
5. Are slower than TTL chips, and
6. Are very sensitive to damage from static discharge.

CMOS digital chips have considerable leeway in the Vcc they can use. Voltages from 3 to 18 volts will normally operate these chips. The acceptable logic levels for these chips are a function of the applied Vcc. These levels are shown graphically in Figure 15–20.

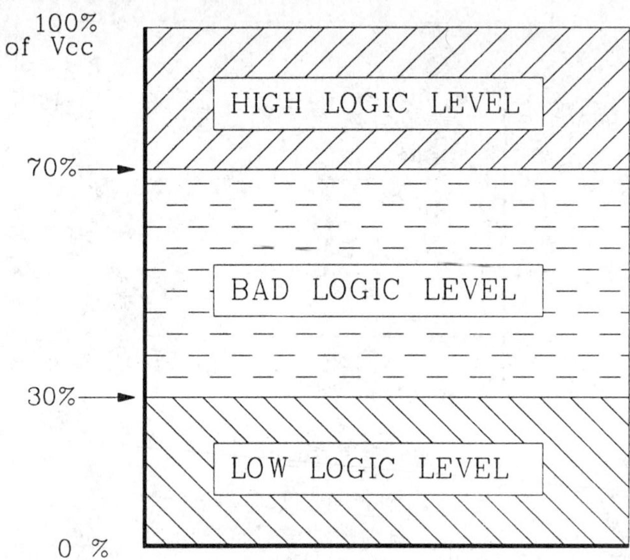

Figure 15–20 Graph of CMOS logic-level boundaries.

The low power requirement for these chips is due to the insulated gate input. Once a CMOS chip has switched and the internal distributed capacitances within the chip have been charged, there is no current flow in the input. Only one of the two totem-pole output transistors is conducting, so there is no direct current path to ground. Current will flow within these chips only while they are actually changing states.

There is a unique failure of CMOS circuits that the technician should recognize: failure caused by an accidentally opened input. Through circuit failure, an input to a CMOS chip may be left "floating," disconnected from any input. This open input is actually an open gate to an internal FET transistor. This gate can "float" to a logic low or high simply because of the static charge on the gate at that instant. Merely touching the circuit with a finger or probe can change the state of the device. Sometimes simply bringing your hand within a few inches of the circuitry can cause a change by inducing a tiny amount of 60-Hz alternating-AC into the gate lead. In summary, *an open CMOS input will be erratic in operation.*

The charging and discharging of the internal capacitances of the CMOS chip through the high impedances of these chips leads to their inability to operate at high frequencies. This characteristic limits the use of standard CMOS chips to low-speed circuits.

Another disadvantage of CMOS chips is their sensitivity to damage from static discharge. The open-circuit nature of their construction will allow the buildup of static charges until the device can be damaged. Most CMOS chips have internal components, such as extra zener diodes or transistors, to minimize static sensitivity. The low-impedance TTL chips, by comparison, tend to load down and bleed away static charges more readily than do CMOS chips.

Electrostatic Discharge (ESD)

A person can accumulate a static charge of electricity in the same manner as a capacitor. Shuffling across a rug on a day when there is low humidity will cause the person's body to accumulate a very high voltage with respect to earth ground. If sensitive microcircuits are handled under these conditions, it is easy to see how a discharge of this static electricity can very easily occur through the components. Estimates of electronic failures caused by ESD damage vary from 5 percent to 25 percent of all failures. The current that flows for even a fraction of a microsecond can cause immediate failure or a failure sometime in the future. ESD failures can occur immediately or long after the ESD damage is first sustained, a fact that explains at least a portion of product call-backs.

Static generation occurs continuously during the workday, caused, for example, by walking across a carpet (to 35,000 volts), walking over a vinyl floor (12,000 volts), opening a plastic bag (20,000 volts), and sitting on a chair containing urethane foam (18,000 volts). Working with certain materials or equipment can cause static buildup, such as working in an area with waxed or vinyl floors, wearing insulated shoes (tennis shoes), and handling ordinary plastic, such as bags, wrapping and envelopes, bubble pack, and styrofoam "peanuts." Spray cleaners, solder-suckers, solvent brushes with synthetic bristles, heat guns and blowers, and even an electrostatic copier can generate large amounts of static electricity. The plastic cabinet of a television can be a source of thousands of volts of static electricity.

ESD damage is caused by the accumulation and discharge of static electricity through a sensitive electronic component. Now that integrated circuits and other components are measured in Angstroms (10E-8 cm), the microscopic spacings can be easily arced over and welded by static electricity discharges. It may take as little as 50 volts to damage a chip, yet a person may not feel an ESD discharge until the voltage level reaches 2,000 volts or more. Voltages up to 35,000 volts can occur during low-humidity conditions, and up to 7,000 volts can routinely occur during 55 percent humidity.

A list of electronic components that are sensitive to static discharge includes: insulated gate and junction-type FETs; operational amplfiers; thyristors; some thin-film resistors and resistor chips; CMOS, ECL, and TTL logic chips; and piezoelectric crystals. Basically, all electronic chips, including microprocessor and computer chips, are susceptible to ESD damage.

Components mounted in a circuit are protected to some degree, but are not immune to ESD damage. PC board edge connectors, in particular, can conduct ESD energy directly into sensitive chips. Conductive materials can be impregnated with carbon to form a semiconducting, resistive shield. Discharge is distributed over the surface rather than being concentrated in any area. Antistatic materials can also be used to prevent static electricity because of surface lubrication, such as pink poly bags. Topical antistatic products, often applied with aerosol cans, can be applied to the surface of insulative materials such as rugs. These products reduce static by lubrication and also by increasing surface conductivity to bleed off static charges.

Grounded wrist straps bleed off personal static by bleeding it off relatively slowly to earth ground. A series resistor of a megohm or more is included in the wrist strap to prevent it from becoming a shock hazard. Antistatic garments made from materials of 65 percent polyester, 34 percent cotton, and a 1 percent stainless steel fiber result in an envelope of conduction for a person, much like a conductive bag for components. Leather-soled shoes with conductive grounding straps can also be used to bleed off static charges. A properly grounded protective table mat can be used to drain away any static charges from equipment placed upon it. In addition, air ionizers are used to remove static electricity generated by the movement of air during low-humidity conditions.

The following is a summary of the precautions to observe when working with components that are static-sensitive:

- Components should be handled only at a static-free work station.
- All circuits and components should be handled and transported in antistatic packing until installed in equipment.
- Discharge the outer surface of an antistatic bag before opening it.
- Avoid using static-generating materials like styrofoam or nylon.
- Insert and remove components only when power to the circuit is off.
- Apply inputs signals only after power is applied to the chips.
- Handle PC boards by their edges, without touching the card-edge connections.
- Ground yourself before handling any components. This can be easily done if the equipment is plugged in and uses a three-wire cord, by first simply touching the chassis.
- When using a spray coolant to test for a thermal intermittent, use one specifically labeled as being "antistatic."

Latch-up

Because of the internal physical makeup of a CMOS device, a unique problem called *latch-up* can occur. If the output of a CMOS device is forced higher than the supply voltage by about a half volt, or by less than a half volt below-ground, the output can latch up and lock at that level. This is because the internal architecture of the chip will connect a pair of transistors, much like an SCR. If latch-up occurs, the chip can be destroyed unless the current through the chip is limited.

CMOS Chip Identification

CMOS chips are marked with a 4XXX series identification, as in the 4002 chip. Motorola modifies this numbering scheme by adding a "1," labeling their 4002 chip as a 14002.

TTL/CMOS HYBRID FAMILIES

High-speed operation is a desirable characteristic of TTL chips. A low power requirement is a desirable characteristic of CMOS chips. This has caused the development of other digital chip families as an attempt to combine the advantages of both and to provide chips that were directly compatible with the different switching levels required of TTL and CMOS. In addition, the TTL and CMOS families were well established in regard to "standard" pinouts. One of the inputs to a hex inverter, for example, was pin 1 for a TTL chip.

74CXX CMOS chips became available in the same pinouts as the 74XX series but had the low power demands of a CMOS chip. The input and output logic levels were CMOS compatible. As such, these chips were more like CMOS chips with a TTL pinout. Frequency capability extended to about 6 MHz.

74HCXX high-speed CMOS chips were then offered, with higher operating speeds than the 74CXX series (to about 60 MHz). These chips could be operated on supplies of 2 to 6 volts. The inputs of this series were CMOS-compatible and the output voltages were the applied Vcc minus 0.1 V, for a logic high, and 0.1 V, for a logic low. This makes the outputs compatible with the inputs of later stages of both TTL and CMOS families. The 74HCXX family is made with TTL pinouts.

74HC4XX chips were the same as the 74HC series, but this family was made with the standard CMOS pinouts.

74HCU chips had CMOS input and output levels but were designed for linear applications, not digital.

The incompatibility of switching voltage levels presented a problem. CMOS output logic levels are acceptable as TTL inputs if both are operating with a Vcc of 5 V. When TTL outputs are connected to CMOS, the 2.4-V high logic-level threshold from the TTL chip will be incompatible with the required 70-percent level required for an input to a CMOS chip (3.5 V is the minimum for a CMOS operated on 5 V).

The 74HCTXX series (high-speed CMOS with TTL input) was offered as the answer to this problem. These chips are basically CMOS chips with TTL pinouts, like the 74HCXX family, and with the addition of an additional buffer stage in their input circuits. This gives them TTL compatible inputs and standard CMOS output levels, making them ideal interface chips between the two families. When using these chips, Vcc must be limited to the range of 2 to 6 V. The input voltage threshold for a logic high is 2.0 V, and 0.8 V for a logic low. The output voltage thresholds are the same as for the 74 HC chips: the applied Vcc minus 0.1 V for a logic high and 0.1 V for a logic low. These chips make excellent replacements for TTL 74LSXX chips.

All the hybrid families are susceptible to static damage and, accordingly, should be handled as CMOS devices.

EMITTER-COUPLED LOGIC (ECL) ICs

ECL chips may be identified by their 10XXX series-numbering system. The principal characteristics of the ECL family of logic chips are that they:

1. Operate on a VEE (negative) supply voltage of minus 5.2 V,
2. Use logic thresholds of –0.9 volt and –1.75 volt, and
3. Are much faster than TTL chips.

ECL chips operate on a negative supply voltage and have negative switching thresholds. These are shown graphically in Figure 15–21.

Individual gates in an ECL chip are made with both active-high and active-low outputs for the convenience of the designing engineer. These complementary outputs are the result of each chip having an internal differential amplifier. Figure 15–22 shows the schematic and logic symbol used for a sample ECL gate having these complementary outputs.

ECL chips operate at very high speeds. In fact, they represent the fastest digital logic today. An ECL flip-flop, for instance, can toggle at speeds up to 500 MHz. At these speeds, the length of the interconnecting lines becomes a problem. The wavelength of a 500-MHz quarter-wave antenna is less than six inches, and any line more than a couple of inches long becomes an antenna. These lines will cause reflections when used with the one- or two-nanosecond switching times of these

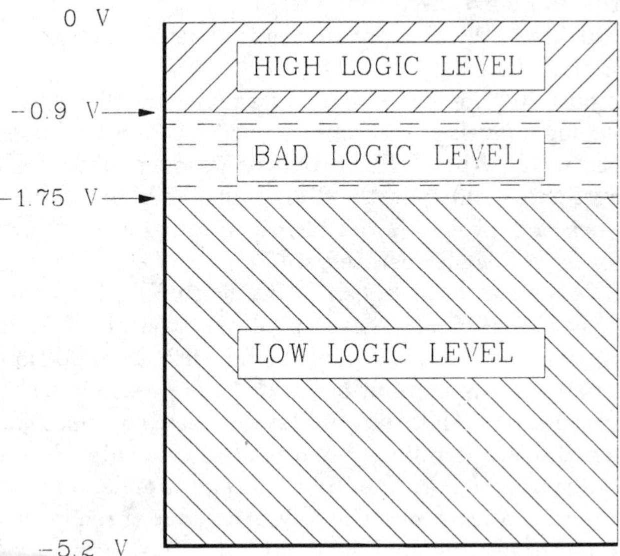

Figure 15–21 Graph of ECL logic-level boundaries.

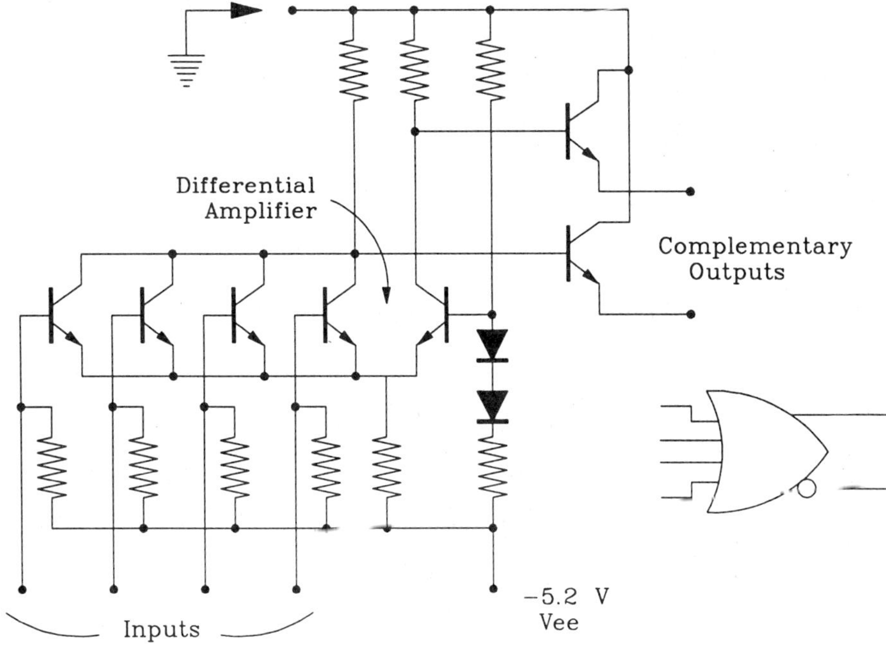

Figure 15–22 Internal structure and symbol of an ECL logic gate.

chips. To avoid problems from reflections, ECL interconnecting lines of more than an inch or so must have a proper terminating resistance at the receiving end to prevent reflections.

The input signal to an ECL chip looks into a resistor and the base of a bipolar transistor. This makes the ECL input a relatively high impedance when compared to the emitter input circuit of a TTL chip, as shown in Figure 15–43. Internal pull-down resistors of about 50,000 Ω are provided internal to the chip so that unused inputs may be left open. The output of an ECL chip, as shown in Figure 15–22, is an open emitter. This provides a very low output impedance from the chip, which is thus able to drive the terminated lines that are often required without special drivers.

ECL chips are sometimes used in critical, high-speed portions of existing systems, interfacing with other logic families.

An interesting feature of ECL chips is that, due to their internal structure, they may be operated in digital or in analog applications.

15.4 NONDIGITAL SIGNALS IN DIGITAL CIRCUITS

If a technician must trace digital signals with an oscilloscope, there are two signals common in a digital circuit that will look as though they are indications of something defective when they are really normal. These sig-

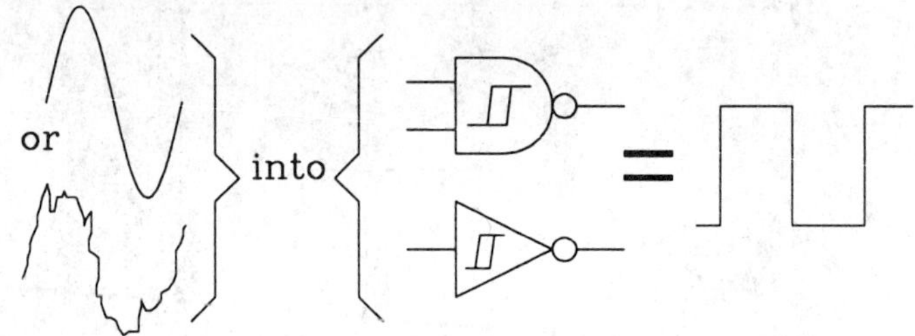
or
into
Input signals to SCHMITT trigger gates can be expected to be analog in appearance.

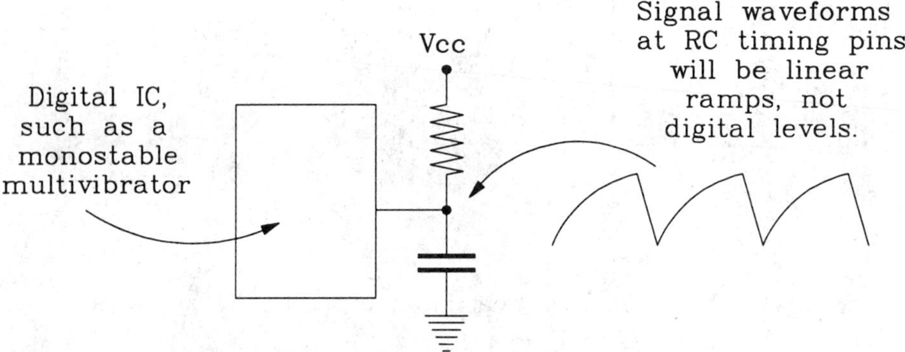
Vcc
Signal waveforms at RC timing pins will be linear ramps, not digital levels.
Digital IC, such as a monostable multivibrator

Figure 15–23 Two examples of nondigital signals in digital circuits.

nals come from the timing resistor and capacitor combination of a monostable multivibrator or any analog input to a Schmitt trigger gate or inverter. Figure 15–23 shows these examples.

15.5 DIGITAL TROUBLESHOOTING INSTRUMENTS

THE EXTENDER CLIP

It is difficult to attach test instruments such as an oscilloscope or logic analyzer to the pins of a digital IC, particularly if there is more than one lead to connect. Attaching many leads is best done by using a special extension clip that clamps right onto the top of the IC. Figure 15–24 shows one of these clips, which is specially built for clamping to chips of 14 or 16 pins.

Extender clips are available for attaching wires to chips having 20, 24, 28, or 40 pins. The small pins sticking up from an extension clip are convenient for attaching test probes or tiny female slip-over connectors which are protected with sleeving to prevent shorting to other pins.

Figure 15–24 The extender clip makes it much easier to connect instruments to digital chips.

SIGNAL SOURCES

Internal Signals

Most digital troubleshooting will be done using the signals that are normally produced within the circuitry. This is the most convenient way to get operating inputs, and it should also provide properly timed signals for the following circuits. A failure of the internal signals to provide one or more signals can be easily detected by using a logic probe. There is a much smaller probability that the timing of a signal may also be wrong, a problem that the logic probe will not identify.

The Logic Pulser

A logic pulser is a small, hand-held instrument that will produce digital pulses and force them into digital circuits, overpowering any digital signals that might be already present. See Figure 15–25.

The logic pulser can be used as a single-bit, single-pulse generator or to generate a train of pulses to apply to any digital pin. This instrument is constructed so that when its control button is pressed, a single pulse is injected into the circuit. The logic level generated by the pulser changes the logic level present in the circuit, which then changes back very quickly. It is designed in such a way that it will pulse a high logic level to low or a low logic level to high. In other words, the technician need not be concerned whether the original logic level was high or low, as the circuit will automatically be pulsed to the opposite state.

The duration of the pulse is very short so that when it is forcing a logic level into a circuit, there will be no damage to any transistors attempting

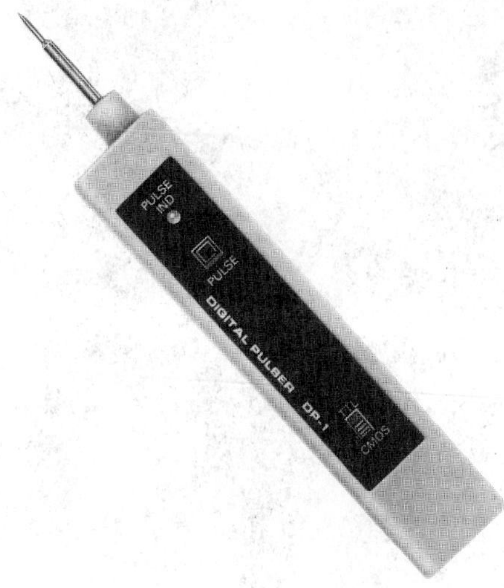

Figure 15–25 A logic pulser is a digital signal generator used for signal-tracing purposes.

to hold the line either high or low. The logic pulser simply overpowers them. The logic pulser output begins at a floating level, not affecting the circuit at all. A short, high logic pulse is generated, followed immediately by a low pulse; then, the pulser floats again. In this way, the pulser forces an opposite logic level to an existing logic state. TTL circuits require a very short, high-current pulse, while CMOS circuits require a longer pulse. Because of these facts, some pulsers have a "digital family" switch that tailors the output pulse as required to the requirements of the digital logic family in use.

DIGITAL SIGNAL INDICATORS

The Oscilloscope

The beginning electronics technician with training in the use of an oscilloscope may have been led to believe that this instrument will be effective in troubleshooting almost any circuit. While the oscilloscope can be used in a few cases for troubleshooting in a digital circuit, it is neither efficient nor appropriate in most cases. The many controls to be manipulated, together with the necessity of having a repetitive signal to show a stable display, severely limits its usefulness in digital troubleshooting applications. Besides these major considerations, the average oscilloscope can be used to view only two signals at a time. Digital circuit analysis may require, not only the display of many signals together, but the interpretation of the signals, as well, displaying information in hexadecimal notation, for instance. The logic analyzer solves these problems.

However, there may be times when the oscilloscope is the only instrument at hand for troubleshooting a digital circuit. Keeping in mind its limitations when used on such a circuit, the oscilloscope can at least be used to show the presence or absence of digital activity. The presence or absence of signal activity is sometimes enough information from a failed circuit to enable the technician to locate the source of the problem and repair it.

The information given in Chapter 13 should be reviewed in regard to frequency limitations of the oscilloscope probe and input amplifiers. The use of the low repetition rates sometimes encountered in digital circuits makes it worthwhile to understand the use of the Auto triggering option (explained in Chapter 14), along with the use of the holdoff control of the oscilloscope, also explained there.

A modern oscilloscope may have the ability to show two channels of digital activity, which is a small advantage over the use of a single logic probe. The timing of two signals with respect to each other can be shown, but the operator must be sure that the 'scope is operated properly. The timing relationship between two signals is destroyed if each of the traces is triggered independently, as when *both* A and B are selected as the trigger source. Only one channel should be used to trigger both traces in order to preserve timing information. See Figure 15–26.

The major disadvantages of using an oscilloscope for troubleshooting digital circuits is the complexity of setting up the instrument and the requirement for a *periodic* signal before the instrument will show a stable display.

It takes experience and familiarity with a specific oscilloscope in order to be able to set it up efficiently to view a given waveform. Even old pros will take a lot of time to set up a 'scope with which they have not worked recently. The locations of each pertinent adjustment vary from one instrument to the next, and sometimes the labels aren't exactly what is expected.

If an input signal to an oscilloscope does not vary in frequency, waveshape, or amplitude from one sweep to the next, and if these properties remain consistent, the oscilloscope will show a repeating pattern in the same identical position on the screen. This will *appear* to be a pattern that is standing still. Digital signals are often *aperiodic*, meaning that they follow no repeating pattern. For an example of what may appear on the screen, see Figure 15–27. After the initial triggering transition of the aperiodic signal, the time for which the signal remains positive varies with each cycle of the waveform, accounting for the gradual dimming of the top horizontal portion of the trace. In a similar manner, the time at which the negative portion begins varies. The overall result of multiple, different traces is almost useless.

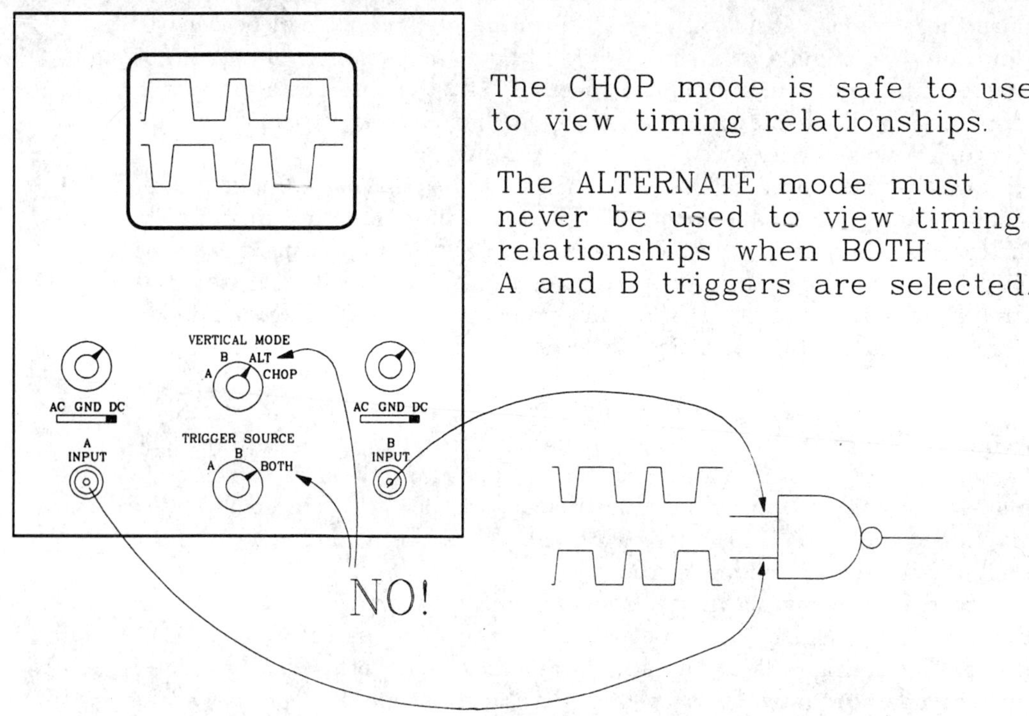

Figure 15–26 Be careful when observing timing relationships with an oscilloscope.

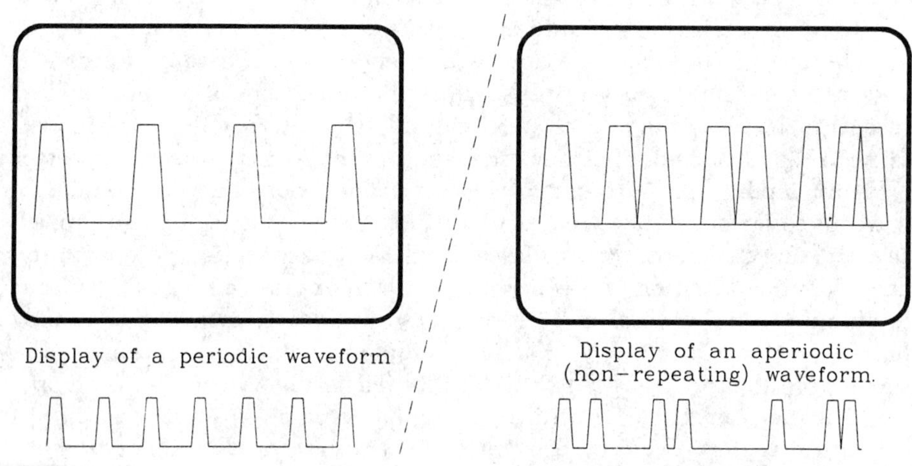

Display of a periodic waveform
Display of an aperiodic (non-repeating) waveform.

Figure 15–27 Only *periodic* waveforms will appear stationary on the oscilloscope.

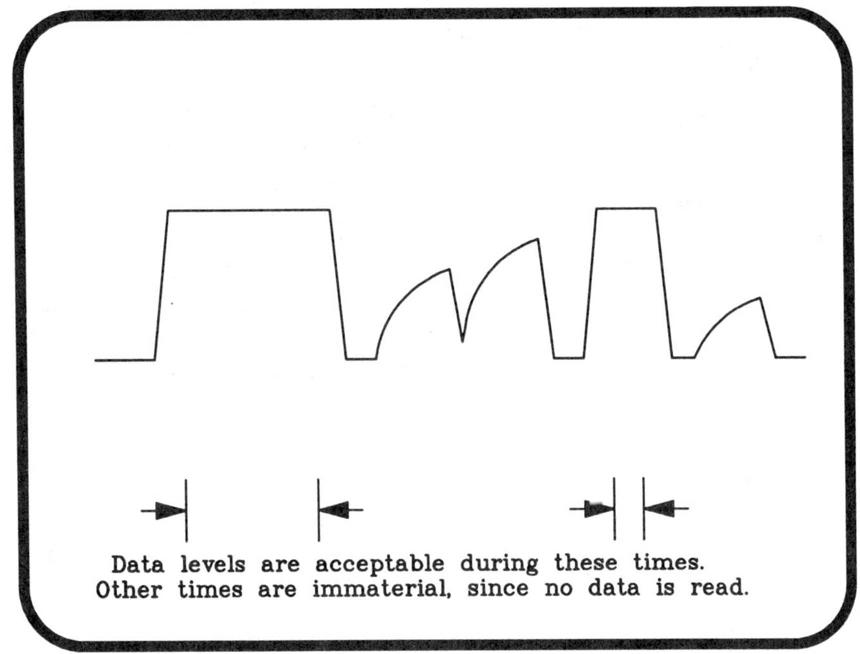

Data levels are acceptable during these times.
Other times are immaterial, since no data is read.

Figure 15–28 Normally floating lines in a microprocessor circuit may appear as "bad" logic levels.

A further disadvantage in using an oscilloscope for troubleshooting three-state chips is that the waveforms shown while monitoring them may appear to have bad logic levels for part of the time. Three-state devices are usually turned on and off under the control of a microprocessor. There are times when none of the chips is transmitting data and the bus lines may float to any voltage. The oscilloscope may show the logic levels as apparently bad, indeterminate levels. The only time when the levels on a three-state bus must be at proper high or low logic levels is when data are actually being read by another chip. The levels at any other time are of no particular consequence. See Figure 15–28.

A final problem encountered during the use of an oscilloscope is that it can easily cause the operator to miss signals of extremely short duration. Sometimes, the only clue to a technician that one of these extremely short signals is occurring is that the oscilloscope is triggering in the "normal" mode (do not auto-trigger on slow digital signals) without a visible vertical signal. As confirmation, removal of the triggering input probe will cause the loss of the trace. These very short signals could trigger the oscilloscope but not be visible because of their extremely short duration. If the input signal changes polarity and immediately changes back again, there may be no visible spot to show up on the CRT's phosphor screen to mark the signal.

Oscilloscope Transient Response

An oscilloscope with a fast risetime specification will display digital signals more accurately than an instrument of lesser capability. For example, an oscilloscope with a risetime of 30 nanoseconds is superior to one having a 100-nanosecond risetime.

If the risetime specification of an oscilloscope is known, that number of nanoseconds should be multiplied by 5 to determine the fastest signal input transition that can be displayed with less than 2 percent distortion. In other words, the scope must have a risetime time at least 5 times faster (five times less risetime) than that of the signal to be observed. Attempting to use a scope with a risetime specification that is too slow for the waveform will make the waves appear more rounded-off than they really are. See Figure 15–29.

It is appropriate here to mention that one of the features of a high-quality oscilloscope is the presence of a *vertical delay line* in the vertical amplifier. The delay line usually takes the form of several loops of coaxial cable tucked away inside the instrument. Its purpose is to delay the depiction of the vertical waveform for a few microseconds, which is sufficient for the trigger circuit to initiate the sweep and get it under way. With this feature, you can see the event you are triggering on.

If only the bandwidth specification for an oscilloscope is given, the risetime of the instrument can be easily calculated. Simply divide the constant

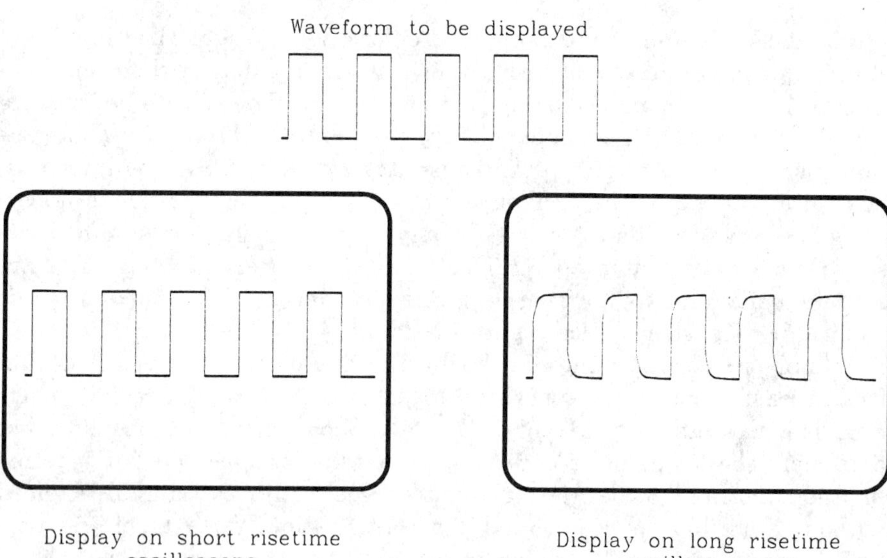

Figure 15–29 Using an oscilloscope with poor risetime will round off digital waveforms.

of 350 by the stated bandwidth in MHz. Use whole MHz figures, not basic units. The result is the instrument's risetime figure in nanoseconds. For example, an instrument of 35 MHz has:

350/35 = 10 nanoseconds risetime.

10 nanoseconds for the instrument means that it could be used to display signals having risetimes of 50 ns or more and display them as they really are. This also works in reverse, of course; divide 350 by the risetime in nanoseconds and you have the bandwidth in MHz.

The Logic Probe

While it is necessary to understand the circuit timing to really understand how a digital circuit operates, *it is often quite sufficient for troubleshooting purposes to know merely if there is digital activity present.* About 75 percent of digital IC failures involve an open circuit, either at the input or the output of an IC. The remaining 25 percent of the failures involve shorted inputs or outputs.

Open circuits are found with voltage-based test instruments while short circuits are traced with current-based instruments. Some thought will verify why this is true: an open circuit cannot generate any current, and the short circuit cannot develop a voltage across the short. Troubleshooting the 25 percent of digital problems that involve shorted digital circuitry is covered under the explanation of the current tracer instrument, the next topic in this chapter.

For the 75 percent of the problems that ICs cause, all that is needed is a means of looking for the presence or absence of a signal with a voltage-sensing instrument. The most convenient instrument is the *logic probe.* See Figure 15–30.

This little instrument is handy to carry and very easy to use. It can tell the technician enough about most situations to narrow a problem down to two among all the ICs on the board. If a required signal is not present between two ICs, it could be either the transmitting or the receiving IC that is shorted and causing the symptoms. More will be explained on this instrument's use in section 15.6. For now, the indications need explanation.

Logic Probe Indications

Circuit Activity. One of the handiest features of most logic probes is the "pulser" or activity light. This LED will flash relatively slowly whenever the tip detects logic activity going on between logic levels. It also flashes once if the logic level changes only once. One of the logic probe's strongest points is that this activity indicator will *stretch* a short pulse lasting for as little as 50 nanoseconds and make a long flash from it. This flash enables the technician to detect extremely short logic pulses.

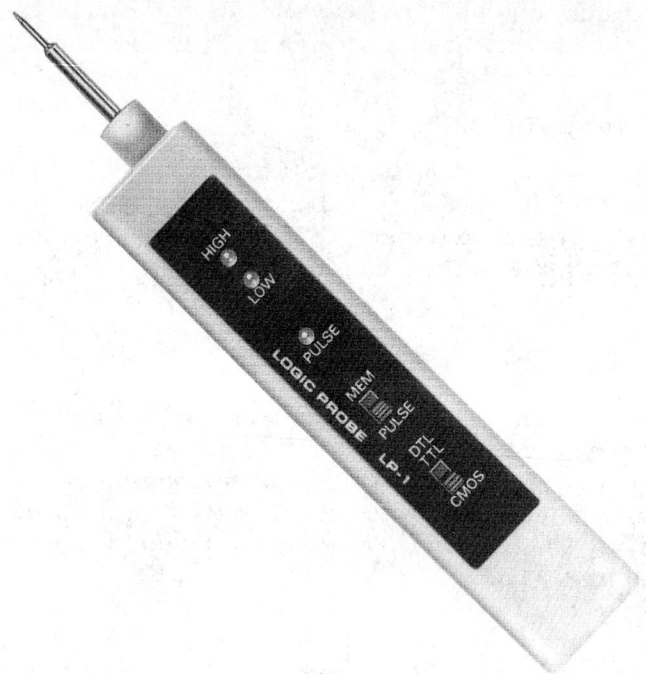

Figure 15–30 The logic probe is so handy for troubleshooting digital circuits that it is sometimes called a "digital screwdriver."

Logic High. Another LED will light when the probe is in contact with a logic high. This LED lights with an *intensity that varies with the duty cycle and with the frequency of the sampled signal.* This LED and the one for logic low often have a much lower capability of responding to high-frequency or short-duration signals. As a square wave goes higher in frequency than about 100 kHz, the logic probe's high- and low-level LEDs may become progressively dimmer. The pulse LED, however, should continue to report the presence of a high-frequency signal far beyond this frequency. One probe manufacturer cites a frequency of 1.5 MHz for the pulse LED of one probe mode model, and 50 MHz for another. The higher the frequency of response, the better the probe.

Logic Low. This LED and circuitry are the same as that of the logic high LED, just explained. Of course, this LED lights when there is a logic low at the probe tip.

Indeterminate Levels. When none of the LEDs of the logic probe light, this is an indication of a floating or disconnected line.

NOTE: If none of the three logic probes LEDs light, this is an indication of an open line. *Input* lines to a digital IC should never be left open, although some very poorly designed TTL circuits are made in this way.

Such TTL input lines will show as indeterminate but will be interpreted within the chip as a logic high. CMOS inputs left disconnected will be erratic, causing erratic intermittent symptoms. Either TTL or CMOS unused *outputs* should be at either a logic high or low. Three-state outputs may be normally indeterminate if the chip output-enable pin is not active.

IC Family Switching. The switch labeled *TTL/CMOS,* which is sometimes available on a probe, allows the use of a single probe on both these popular IC logic families. The switch changes the threshold high and low voltage levels that the probe reports via the LEDs. When switched to TTL, the probe conforms to standard TTL logic level definitions, above 2.4 V is a high and below 0.8 V is a low.

On CMOS circuits, the logic voltage thresholds are interpreted differently. CMOS circuits may operate on a supply voltage from 3 V to as much as 18 V. The logic high and low thresholds are determined as a *percentage of the voltage powering the probe.* The probe must be powered using the same voltage as the circuit under test. Under these conditions, the logic high will be shown for any voltage sampled that is more than 70 percent of the Vcc, and a logic low will be shown for voltage that is less than 30 percent of Vcc.

Pulse Memory. This option allows the logic probe to act as a digital "watchdog." If the probe tip is applied to the circuit under test and then the "Memory" switch is thrown, the activity LED assumes a new function. The activity LED should be extinguished under these circumstances, and will remain so until a logic change occurs at the sampled point. This could be a complete, one-time change; the appearance of a normal on-and-off signal, or a very short pulse of only a few nanoseconds. Any change from the original logic level (whether originally high or low) should cause the activity LED to come on and remain lit. (Test the probe you use to see if this is the case for your instrument.) Think of the LED as a telltale sign, informing you that, even if you didn't notice, at least one logic change did occur. The pulse memory must be manually reset with the same switch to indicate further changes.

Sound Effects. Some logic probes provide a low-toned beeping sound when the probe is connected to a logic low and a higher sound when connected to a logic high. Some technicians may find this helpful, while others consider it an irritation.

Using the Logic Probe

In summary, the LED lights of the logic probe can be interpreted according to Table 15–2.

The logic probe can be used on both static and dynamic digital circuits. A static circuit is one that has logic levels present but none of them are

Table 15–2 Logic Probe LED Interpretation Table

HIGH LED	LOW LED	ACTIVITY LED	
OFF	OFF	OFF	Indeterminate level; disconnected circuit; TTL circuit input open.
OFF	OFF	FLASH	Normal signal, frequency of operation too high for high and low LED circuits.
OFF	ON	OFF	Constant low level.
OFF	ON	FLASH	Normal signal, very low duty cycle.
ON	OFF	OFF	Constant high level.
ON	OFF	FLASH	Normal signal, very high duty cycle.
ON	ON	OFF	Not a valid reading.
ON	ON	FLASH	Normal digital signal.

changing. A clocked logic circuit without clock activity is one example of a static circuit, and an unclocked circuit without changing inputs is another. Intelligent use of the indicator lights of the logic probe will tell a great deal about the circuit under test.

The Current Tracer

The current tracer is an instrument that allows a technician to trace a pulsing digital *current* flowing in a circuit. It will respond only to pulsed signals, not to pure DC current levels. The current tracer is an analog device that shows the relative intensity of a small current. It can be used to trace a shorted digital signal trace right to the shorted component. See Figure 15–31.

The tip of this instrument has an extremely tiny magnetic pickup coil. When this coil picks up a pulse of magnetism, the lamp is caused to light, providing at the same time a pulse-stretching capability similar to that of the activity light of the logic probe.

The current tracer is sensitive to two variables: the orientation of current flow past the tip and the intensity of the current pulses. Orienting the pulser with the alignment of a trace by rotating the instrument in your hand is necessary to provide the proper sensitivity and indications. If the tip is rotated 90 degrees from the direction of current flow, there will be no indication, even if the current flow is substantial. For this reason, the instrument should be constantly rotated to maintain alignment as a trace is followed in its meanderings around the board. There is a small rubber boot on the tip of the

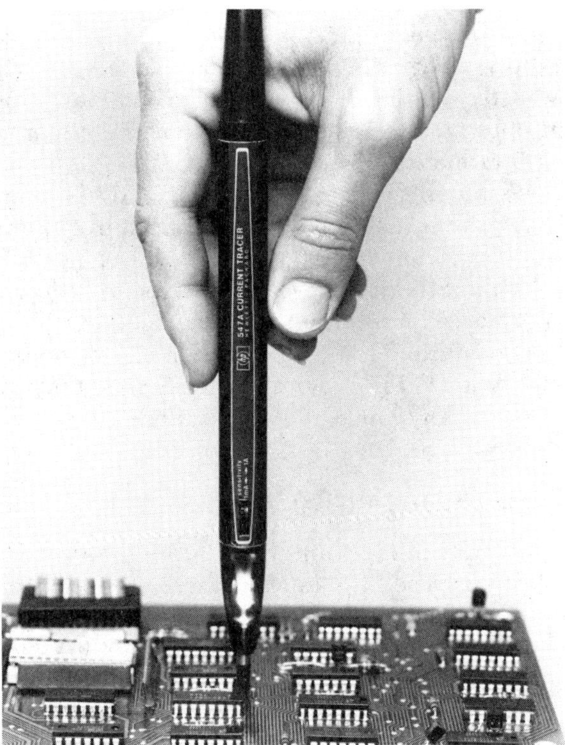

Figure 15–31 The HP current tracer, a current-sensing instrument for tracing digital current paths on PC boards.

instrument that can be rotated to align the two holes in its side to the direction of maximum sensitivity. Then, using the holes as an indicator, align the instrument for current flow "into" or "out of" these holes.

The sensitivity of this instrument to current pulse intensity is so great that there is a decided difference in the lamp indications when the current flow encounters a widening or narrowing of a circuit trace. When the trace narrows, there is an increase of current density and the lamp will glow brighter while monitoring the same current. This is one reason why experience with the instrument is necessary to be effective in its use. To help visualize this, one can consider a given current flow as a stream of water in a creek. As the creek narrows, the flow increases in velocity. This accounts for the increased indication of the instrument when encountering narrowed traces.

The Logic Analyzer

DC and low-frequency AC circuits require a multimeter as the basic troubleshooting instrument. Analog circuits require an oscilloscope to troubleshoot properly. Digital circuits, particularly those associated with microprocessors, require either a probe or a logic analyzer. The logic probe is much simpler, faster, and more convenient to use than a logic analyzer, but the probe can only monitor a single point in the circuit, and it does not provide timing information.

The typical logic analyzer can monitor logic levels at many points in a digital circuit simultaneously. The analyzer requires many connections to be made to the circuit under test, at all of the points of interest. A logic analyzer records all of the logic levels connected to it over a period of time. This digital information is recorded in its memory, much as a movie camera captures motion on film. The logic analyzer can be used only for digital troubleshooting, because the input circuits respond only to the logic "1" or "0" levels, and not to any analog values between them.

The Two Kinds of Logic Analyzers

There are two kinds of logic analyzers, *timing* and *state*. There is a big difference in their purpose, use, and the kind of information obtained from them. Some logic analyzers are designed for one purpose only, while others offer partial use as either kind of analyzer. Such dual-purpose analyzers may require two connections to a given point in a digital circuit to obtain the dual information. At least one logic analyzer is available that will record either timing or state information, requiring only a single connection to each point in the circuit under test. This analyzer is shown in Figure 15–32.

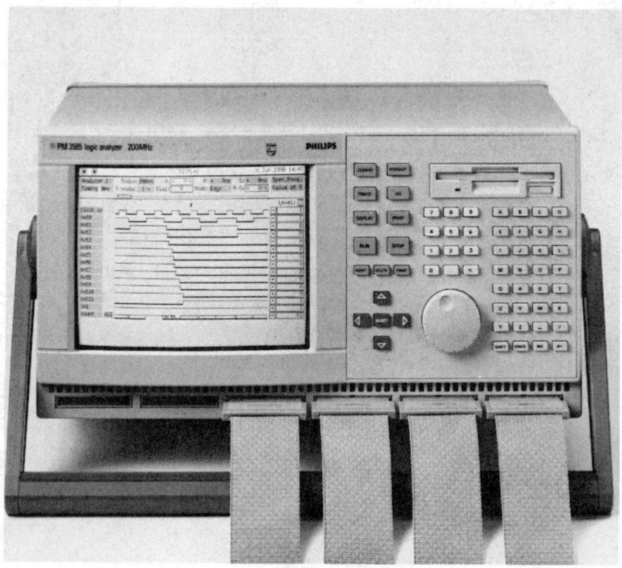

Figure 15–32 The logic analyzer will record many digital channels for later analysis.

The difference between timing and state logic analysis may be better understood by again comparing the two functions to types of cameras. Two different cameras will be needed for our analysis, a movie camera and a still-photo camera.

Imagine a photographer at work taking annual high school photos of the students. He is set up with a still camera, taking pictures of each of the students as they sit on a chair. This is analogous to a *state logic analyzer.* Notice that the photographer is synchronized with the events occurring in front of the camera; the students give him a sign when they are seated, facing the camera, and smiling. The photographer waits until this occurs and then takes a single shot, without need for any hurry. *A state logic analyzer is synchronized to the circuit under test. An external clock from the circuit under test is, therefore, required* for the analyzer to stay in step with the external events. *A state logic analyzer is used primarily, though not exclusively, for testing microprocessor software,* discrete steps that must occur with absolute precision. Information between circuit clock pulses is unimportant in the debugging of software.

Imagine, now, a photographer who uses a movie camera to record the same students as they chat before their photo is taken, leaving the camera running while the students take their turn, seat themselves, remove their chewing gum, and so forth. This corresponds loosely with a *timing logic analyzer.* The timing logic analyzer and the movie photographer are able to take split-second, detailed recordings of events, slice by very thin slice, that are *unsynchronized with the action taking place.* Depending on the speed of the camera (logic analyzer), very detailed information can be recorded. *A timing logic analyzer is used primarily, though not exclusively, for testing hardware* of either microprocessor or discrete digital circuits.

Logic Analyzer Specifications

Logic analyzers are defined as either state or timing analyzers or as a combination of both. Logic analyzers also have other important specifications, such as the amount of memory available for recording, the speed of the analyzer in the timing mode, and the maximum number of channels that they will record.

The memory provided within the logic analyzer is used to record digital information. A second memory may also be provided that can copy data from the recording memory. This now leaves the recording memory free for a second run of data collection, data that can then be compared to the previous recording run. Other functions may include the ability to record data onto floppy diskettes or to send it via a cable to a computer for further analysis.

The speed of the logic analyzer determines how fast it can acquire information: how thin the slices of time are when collecting data *in the timing mode.* High speed is seldom needed when working with most clocked circuits in the state mode. The instrument of the last figure is able to take digital pictures at the rate of 200 MHz: a frame every 5 nanoseconds! At these speeds, it is easy to see the propagation delay through individual digital gates.

The number of channels that a logic analyzer can record was originally limited to eight. This was a natural outgrowth of the two-channel oscilloscope, thus quadrupling the ability to observe digital signals. However, eight channels became insufficient for serious work right away. The 16-channel analyzer came into use during the reign of the 8-bit microprocessor, some 15 years ago. The growth of microprocessors to 16 and more data lines made more channels necessary in the logic analyzers used to develop them. This trend continued, and we now have logic analyzers capable of more than 100 channels. Channels usually come in multiples of 8, with 24, 32, 48, and 64 channels being common today.

Connecting a logic analyzer to a circuit involves connecting small wires to the circuit at various points of interest or placing large pre-cabled clips directly over selected chips, usually the microprocessor. The leads from the logic analyzer terminate in some sort of pod or cable connector, out of which small wires are provided for the actual connection to the circuit under test.

Starting and Stopping the Logic Analyzer

Now that we have described the logic analyzer as a sort of digital high-speed camera, it follows that some means must be provided to control it. It would do little good to have the logic analyzer ready to record and have to manually hit a push button to cause it to record all its memory (use all its film) and then stop. It would be impossible to capture specific events when the events are occurring millions of times per second, with perhaps only 1,000 frames of film available. A *trigger event* is necessary to begin the process of recording, and the recording should stop when all the "film" has been used. *The trigger event is a series of one or more predefined logic levels that are simultaneously present at the sampled circuit points.*

A logic analyzer uses a high-speed memory to record digital information. An important fact to keep in mind when using a logic analyzer is that once it is set up and ready for recording data, the operator initiates the recording action. *The logic analyzer continually records digital information in a memory loop, writing over the oldest data with the latest information.* This would be analogous to using a video camera and endlessly recording on a looped film cassette.

When the trigger event occurs, the recording of information continues for a predetermined number of memory locations and then stops. The data recorded in memory consists, then, of data, some of which occurred before the trigger event, the trigger event itself; and data that occurred after the trigger event. The selection of how the trigger point will relate to the information that recorded is variable, enabling the operator to place the trigger event in the middle of memory (providing an equal amount of data before and after the trigger event) or in either direction from memory-center. This provides the ability to record mostly after the trigger event or to concentrate on what happened *before* it.

While an oscilloscope is triggered to begin a sweep, thus showing an event that occurs after the trigger in time, the logic analyzer, with its recording ability, is triggered to *stop* recording data. The data can then be displayed and analyzed in detail.

The logic analyzer can be set up to trigger in a great many different ways. In the simplest way, it can trigger on a single logic level, much like an oscilloscope. One of the leads to the analyzer is simply designated (via the logic analyzer's software) as the triggering signal.

The analyzer can also be set to stop recording data after reaching any combination of logic levels among the data lines that it is recording. Suppose we want to know what happened at about the time when the logic levels were "0" on the first data channel, D0; a "1" on the second, D1, line; "0" on the third, or D2, line; and a "1" on the fourth, D3, line. (This process can be extended to include all the available data channels.) If we had only 4 of 16 channels connected, we would set up the logic analyzer to trigger on a "word" of XXXX XXXX XXXX 1010. Remember that binary values begin with the least significant value on the right and that an "X" means "any value."

Setting Up the Logic Analyzer

Setting up a logic analyzer for use involves several separate steps:

1. Set up the logic analyzer: plug it in but leave it turned off during the connection of the channels.
2. Connect the channels to the circuit under test, again without power to the circuit under test. (**Note:** Some analyzers require that power to the analyzer *must* be applied before power to the circuit under test is applied to prevent damage to the channel input elements within the analyzer.)
3. Determine if state or timing information is required. Hardware analysis usually uses timing analysis, while software uses state analysis. This decision determines whether to connect an external clock. Connect an external clock from the circuit under test to the logic analyzer if state analysis is desired.
4. Determine the trigger event according to what information is desired about the circuit. Enter this information into the logic analyzer.
5. Press the "Run" button. This begins the recording loop which is terminated when the trigger event occurs.

Note: Failure of the logic analyzer to stop recording, remaining in the recording loop "forever," is the result of the trigger event not occurring as entered into the logic analyzer. The two most common reasons for this are (a) the event is not occurring at all, as expected, or (b) there is a wiring

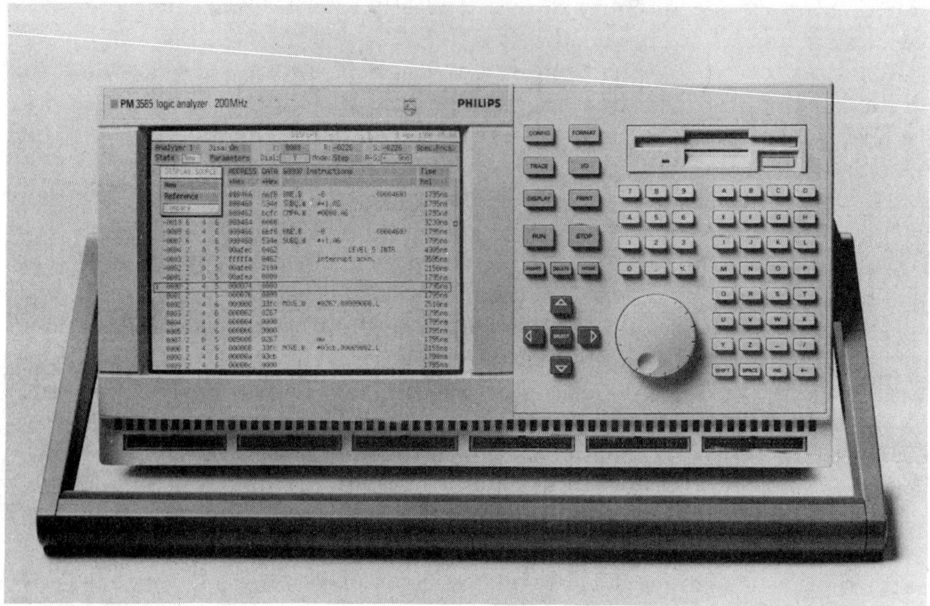

Figure 15–33 The state display is used primarily in troubleshooting software problems.

error in connecting the channels to the circuit under test. Be sure to check your channel wiring carefully.

Using Logic Analyzer Data

Once the logic analyzer stops, its memory will be full of data from the circuit under test. There are many different ways to use this information. If the state analyzer is used (external clock connected), it is probably more advantageous to show a *state display,* a readout of the hexadecimal (or any other numerical base) of the steps that occurred in the circuit. If a microprocessor is being analyzed, it may be possible to use special *disassembler* software with this data to show, in assembly language, the steps that occurred. These steps can be manually compared to the good program to see where the errant program went astray. See Figure 15–33.

Another common way of displaying information is the *timing display,* in which a timing diagram shows high-speed recording of the logic levels as they actually changed in respect to one another. See Figure 15–34.

A third common use of data is to compare, or *correlate,* data with previously recorded, correct data. The logic analyzer is able to quickly pinpoint differences between good and bad files, highlighting them and showing the operator exactly where the information differs. See Figure 15–35.

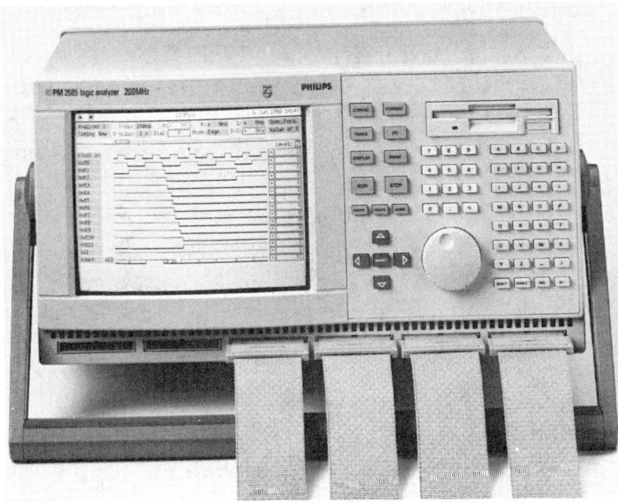

Figure 15–34 The timing display is of most use in finding hardware problems.

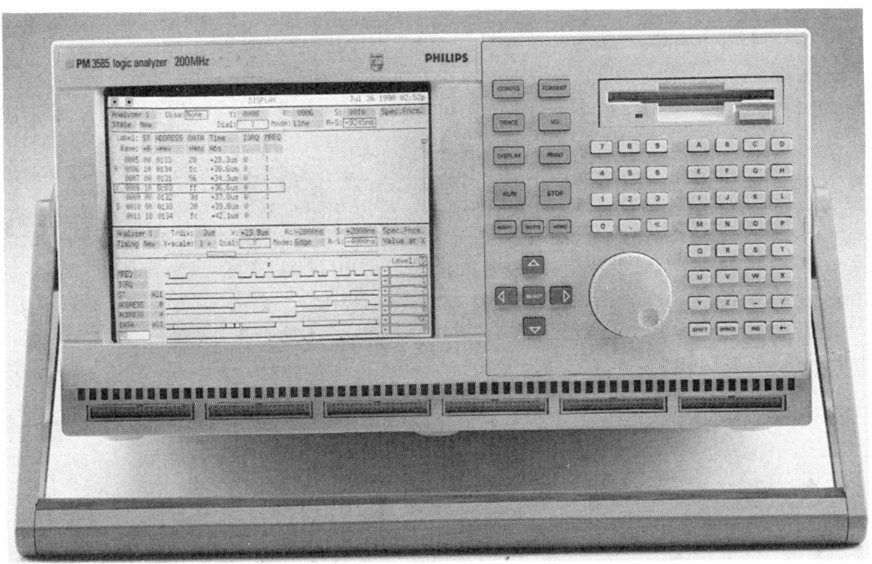

Figure 15–35 The correlation display pinpoints discrepancies between good and bad digital performances.

Using the Logic Analyzer on Microprocessor Circuits

The logic analyzer is particularly well-suited to the troubleshooting of microprocessor circuits. Before it can be used with real effectiveness, the program operating the processor must be available The hardware will merely follow the dictates of the program; therefore, software information is a must.

Perhaps the greatest help in debugging a microprocessor problem is the source code listing with the microprocessor codes included. This is called the "print" or "list" file. One of these files is usually generated when the original program is assembled on a computer. See Figure 15–36 for an example, noting the hexadecimal numbers on the left side. These correspond to the address and data of the actual microprocessor program.

The instructions that the microprocessor should be following are listed down the left side of this printout. The logic analyzer can be set up to show each of these instructions as steps in a timing diagram. This is mainly intended for troubleshooting the hardware of the circuit. The logic analyzer should be set up as a state analyzer to troubleshoot the program itself. Each tick of the processor clock will take a "picture" of what is happening as the program is executed. These individual "snapshots" of the actual execution can be compared with what should be happening to debug the software.

Proficiency in the use of the logic analyzer will come only with daily use of the instrument.

The Logic Comparator

This instrument allows a technician to verify whether an operating circuit is occasionally missing pulses or is erratic in such a way that other instruments may miss the cause of the problem. It is used strictly for hardware failures. Its principle of operation is quite simple. A duplicate IC of the one under test is inserted into the comparator and, by means of a multipin clip, it is compared in parallel to the one in question. The IC used as a good comparison is driven by the same input signals as the IC under test. If the IC under test varies at all in output from the good one, the comparator lights a light to indicate a discrepancy. The logic comparator is particularly good for finding missing pulses, glitches, and other intermittent problems caused by defective 16-pin ICs. A stock of duplicate ICs known to be good is necessary for use as standards.

The Signature Analyzer

The signature analyzer for troubleshooting microprocessor circuits is an innovation of the Hewlett-Packard Company. Its principle of operation is similar to that used in an analog system where there is a library of precise oscilloscope waveforms available for standard signals within the equipment under test. The signature analyzer uses a specific diagnostic program with

```
AVOCET SYSTEMS Z80 ASSEMBLER -  VERSION 1.04M  SERIAL #00413

SOURCE FILE NAME: DIAGS.ASM

                ;
                ; (DIAGS.ASM)
                ;
                ;This assembly language program will test all of the chips used
                ; in the Microcontroller.  It is designed to rotate a "0" thru
                ; all of the 24 output lines of the 8255.
                ;
                ;System Constants:
                ;   ROM Addresses from 0000H to 07FFH.
                ;   RAM Addresses from 0800H to 0FFFH.
                ;   I/O Addresses - See System Equates, below.
                ;
                ;
 1000           PORTA   EQU     1000H
 1001           PORTB   EQU     1001H
 1002           PORTC   EQU     1002H
 1003           CONTL   EQU     1003H
 0FFF           RAMTOP  EQU     0FFFH
                ;
                ; The main part of the program begins here:
                ;
 0000 31FF0F            LD      SP,RAMTOP   ;Give the Micro a Scratchpad in RAM
                ;
                ; Initialize the 8255
                ;
 0003 210310            LD      HL,CONTL
 0006 3E80              LD      A,80H       ;Code for all ports as outputs
 0008 77                LD      (HL),A
                ;
                ; Put all output lines high
                ;
 0009 3EFF              LD      A,0FFH
 000B 210010            LD      HL,PORTA
 000E 77                LD      (HL),A
                ;
 000F 210110            LD      HL,PORTB
 0012 77                LD      (HL),A
                ;
 0013 210210            LD      HL,PORTC
 0016 77                LD      (HL),A
                ;
                ;
 0017 CD3000            CALL    WAIT
                ;
 001A 3EFF              LD      A,11111111B
 001C 210010    HERE:   LD      HL,PORTA
 001F 77                LD      (HL),A
                ;
 0020 210110            LD      HL,PORTB
 0023 77                LD      (HL),A
```

Figure 15–36 A "print" or "list" file, showing the hexadecimal numbers of each microprocessor program step.

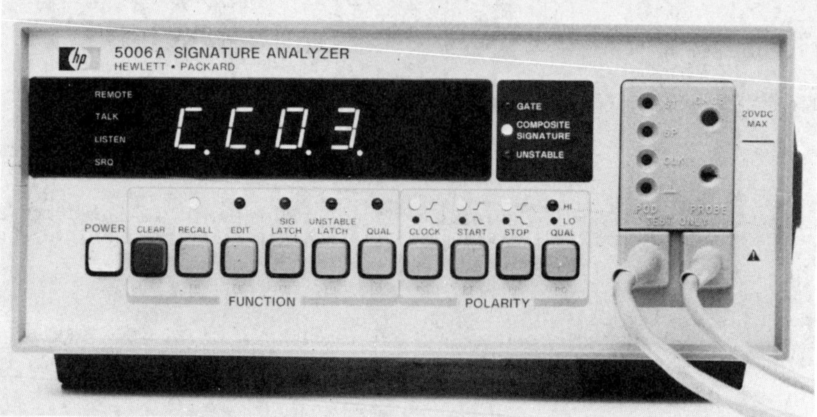

Figure 15–37 The signature analyzer.

the microprocessor system under test. Instead of presenting an analog output, as would be the case using an oscilloscope, the signature analyzer gives an alpha-numerical display to be compared to values in separate flowchart documentation. See Figure 15–37.

An advantage of signature analysis is that, with proper software and documentation, a technician can tell quickly which circuit is malfunctioning.

The biggest disadvantages are that the technician must have documentation with which to compare readings, and the equipment under test must be operated with specific software for the test run. Those few technicians who are fortunate enough to have this test equipment available will find it a very fast and efficient way to troubleshoot compatible microprocessor equipment.

Troubleshooting using signature analysis test equipment consists of following a troubleshooting flowchart to find the defective part while monitoring special test signals designed to exercise the circuits. Figure 15–38 is an example of such a flowchart.

In those relatively few situations where signature analysis has been built into a digital system as part of the original documentation and testing procedures, signature analysis can tell where a digital signature varies from normal. Due to the complexity of such troubleshooting, the use of a troubleshooting tree, or flowchart, is necessary to make effective use of signature analysis.

Basically, a standard input is provided to the circuit under test: a test program in most cases. The signature analyzer is then connected to the circuit at specified points according to the troubleshooting procedures published for that specific model of equipment. Next, the instrument is set for the proper triggering criteria. It will provide a hexadecimal number to be

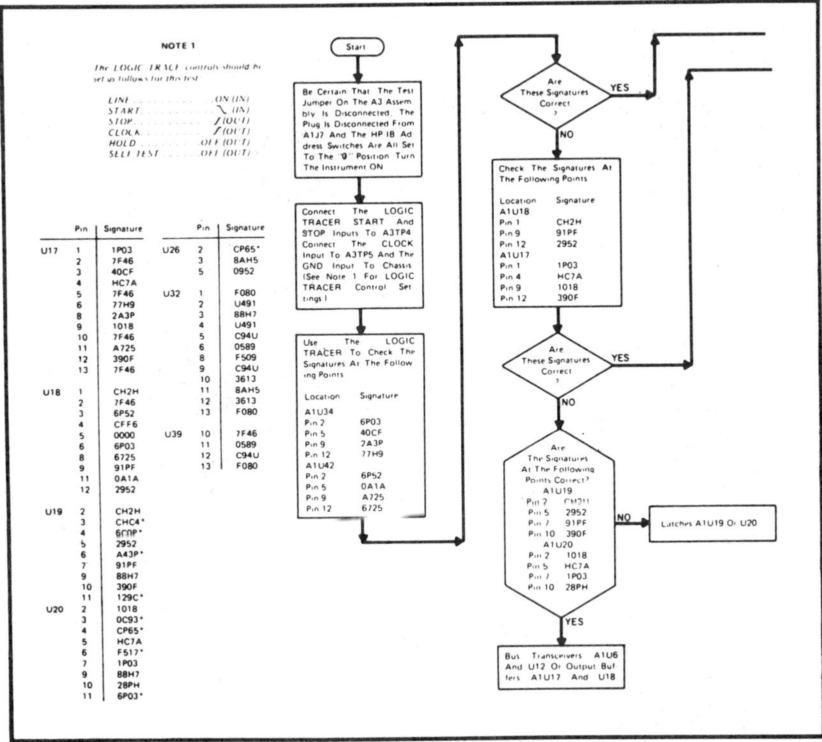

Figure 15–38 Signature analysis troubleshooting requires a flowchart to find the problem.

compared to the troubleshooting chart. If the numbers agree on this test point, all preceding circuitry is assumed to be 100 percent normal and the instrument can be moved further into the circuitry for another test. When a reading is taken that does not match the troubleshooting chart, the chart itself suggests the defective card or module to be replaced.

The Logic Clip

This small instrument is attached to the IC in question in a piggyback manner. It shows on LEDs the high or low status of all the pins of the IC simultaneously. The instrument of Figure 15–39 may be attached to either TTL or CMOS chips. It finds the supply and ground leads automatically, without any effort on the part of the operator. When an LED is lighted, the corresponding IC pin is at a logic high. The Vcc and ground pins will show appropriate logic levels, too.

If this 16-pin instrument is used on an IC of less than 16 pins (14 pins for instance), the pins left hanging over the end of the chip will default to an indication of a logic high. This will require the operator to be careful in

Figure 15–39 This instrument, the logic clip, simultaneously reads the logic levels at each of the pins of a 14- or 16-pin IC.

determining which pin is which, because the logic clip will indicate 16 pins, thus making specific pin identification from the top of the instrument a bit more difficult.

The logic clip is of real value only with static logic circuits. Static logic circuits are those in which the logic levels do not change. Dynamic logic circuits (those in operation with rapidly changing logic levels) will cause some of the LEDs to glow with partial brilliance, indicating average logic levels rather than discrete high or low levels. The LEDs can give only a rough indication of duty cycle, since the logic clip does not contain pulse stretchers on any of the LED indicators. Some clocked logic circuits can be made to operate in a static mode if the clock is stopped. After analysis of an individual "single-frame picture" by the logic clip has been done, the circuit can be manually advanced to the next step by inserting a single pulse from a logic pulser. This next step can then be analyzed by the logic clip. Operating a clocked circuit with a pulser to step it through the various states is called *single-stepping* the circuit.

One way to disable the clock for this test is to simply short the clock signal to ground. This does not harm TTL circuits, as explained in Figure 15–40.

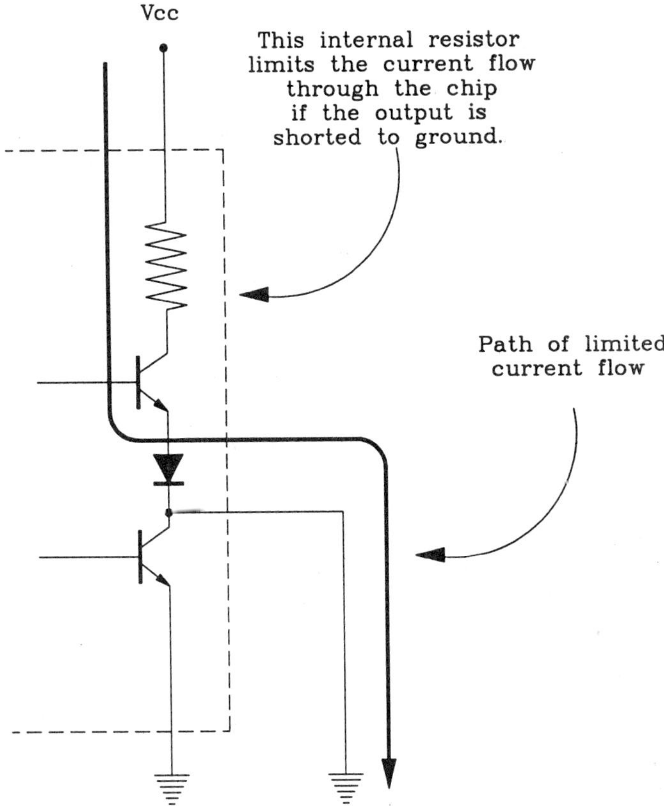
Vcc
This internal resistor limits the current flow through the chip if the output is shorted to ground.
Path of limited current flow

Figure 15–40 Why shorting a TTL output to ground does no harm.

15.6 DIGITAL TROUBLESHOOTING TECHNIQUES

HOW DIGITAL CIRCUITS FAIL

It is worthwhile at this point to investigate how digital circuits usually fail. Since about 75 percent of digital circuit failures involve open circuits at one point or another, voltage-based troubleshooting instruments can be used effectively in finding the problem. Voltage-based instruments include the voltmeter, oscilloscope, logic probe, logic clip, and logic analyzer.

About 25 percent of digital circuit failures involve shorts, either internal or external to the ICs. Most of these shorts involve the ICs themselves, with perhaps only 10 percent being caused by shorts external to the chips. This analysis assumes that the circuit has been in full operation before, and is not fresh off the assembly line. New units often develop shorted-trace problems, particularly with modern surface-mounted devices and their very close-spaced traces. Finding a short on a PC board requires a current-based instrument like the current tracer.

SOME CAUTIONS ABOUT TROUBLESHOOTING DIGITAL CIRCUITS

It is wise to use proper test leads. Taking measurements in circuits on modern PC boards requires that the test leads make good contact and, more important, do not slip. An accidental slip of a probe can cause a great deal of damage. Be sure that the probes are of small diameter to avoid accidentally shorting traces or IC pins together. Using sharp points on the test leads will make it easier to make contact with the traces through any possible solder resin that may be left on the board or to penetrate the solder-mask. The solder-mask is used to prevent covering all of the traces with solder and often appears as a green or blue "paint" on the traces between soldering points. Refer back to Figure 5–1.

While a sharp test lead should be used for voltage and ohmmeter measurements, they should not be used for current measurement in excess of about one ampere. Forcing heavy currents through the fine tip can overheat and burn it.

Any test leads should be used with extreme care when working with surface-mounted devices, however, because these tiny components can be damaged or changed in value if the probe is allowed to rest on the component itself at any point. Probe only the circuit board traces when troubleshooting SMD circuits, and not the ends of the components.

Oscilloscope probes should be used with either the clip-tip installed on the probe, using them in conjunction with an extender clip over the ICs, or you can sharpen the tip on the probe in lieu of the clip-tip. Again, the sharp tip helps prevent slipping and makes a much better contact than other tips. See Figure 15–41.

Even the tip of a logic probe can be sharpened a little to help control

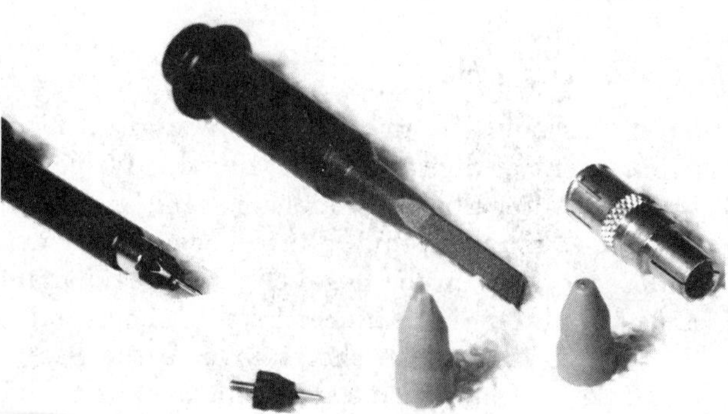

Figure 15–41 Use these optional tips in cases where they may help prevent shorting accidents.

possible slippage. If sharpened, any kind of tip should have a piece of small, slip-on tubing or piece of foam slipped over it for protection when not in use. This also prevents punctured fingers.

Most of the components used in modern digital circuits are susceptible, to some degree, to being damaged by the accidental discharge of static electricity accumulations. If the discharge path for a static charge happens to be through some of these components, they will either fail immediately or at some later time because of it. It may be well to review the ESD precautions described in Chapter 1.

FIRST CHECKS IN FINDING A DIGITAL PROBLEM

There are three things a technician should check before becoming deeply involved in troubleshooting a digital circuit to the component level:

- Make a careful visual inspection,
- Check the power supply for proper voltage(s), and
- In clocked circuits, check the clock for activity.

A visual inspection of a PC board should include a very careful inspection of the board, using a bright light if available. A magnifying glass may also be helpful. Look at both sides of the card. Watch for solder splashes that may be shorting two traces together, ICs with a slight discoloration or raised dimple in the center, obviously overheated parts, and poor solder joints. Components that have physical stresses on them in normal operation, such as connectors, will often develop bad solder joints due to that stress. Watch also for cracks in the board itself. This is sometimes caused by mechanical overstressing of the board or abuse such as dropping it. If a PC board is cracked, it might be worthwhile, depending on the board's value, to make a splint of wire across the break, soldering it on each end. If the traces are very small, parallel a longer, insulated wire across the break, joining the soldered terminals nearest the break. If you are dealing with a multiple-layer board, you cannot repair the break as easily. A multiple-layer board will require a good schematic to find either end of a break internal to the board, on one of the sides where you can get access to the line. A jumper can then be placed between these two points.

A circuit cannot be expected to operate without the proper supply voltages. It is easy to check for proper supply voltage to the chips. Don't rely on a digital probe to give a good reading of Vcc, however. The probe would indicate a healthy high even if the supply voltage to a TTL chip was only 2.5 volts. Use an accurate voltmeter and check for voltage on the component side of the board. *Be sure to also check for excessive ripple by switching to an AC scale.* More than a few millivolts of ripple is excessive. One could also, in troublesome cases, look for high-frequency noise on the Vcc supply line using an oscilloscope. Checking for supply voltage and a good ground connection from the top, component side of the board also checks the condition of the board-to-IC connection. The supply line for a TTL chip must be 5.0 V, plus or minus only a quarter of a volt. A reading of more than a few millivolts from the power-supply ground to the ground pin of an IC is an indication of a poor or open connection from the pin to supply ground.

Later in the troubleshooting process, a digital signal line that may be found to be stuck low—at a 0 voltage—is another good reason to look for the proper supply voltages to the chip that drives that particular data line.

The positive voltages within these circuits are usually referred to as the Vcc line. Sometimes it is called a *Vdd supply*. The negative line of the supply is usually ground. Grounds are usually called just that, or they might be called *Vss* or *Vee*. *Vss* or *Vee* may also be voltages *below* ground potential, or negative supply voltages.

Many digital circuits depend on a central clock to keep all of the digital signals in proper synchronization. This corresponds to the heartbeat of the entire system. One of the first and simplest tests you can make on such a circuit, particularly if the equipment is "dead," is to be sure there is a clock available where it should be. A logic probe will suffice for this simple, but vital, check.

THE NEXT STEP: DETAILED WORK WITH A LOGIC PROBE

Interpreting Logic Probe Indications

There are three basic ways to interpret what a logic probe may indicate:

1. Compare logic probe indications with an annotated copy of the schematic diagram, as suggested under the section titled, "Preparing Digital Schematics for Use," earlier in this chapter.
2. Determine the proper signal you should see on the logic probe first, and then take the reading. If the logic levels are not statically logic-high or -low, duty cycle and frequency may be major factors to consider.
3. Consult the chapter on theory of operation in the maintenance manual for the equipment for statements (or at least hints) as to what should be expected at important points. It is possible that actual indications will be called out for important test points.

The LED indications of a logic probe and what they mean have already been covered in this chapter. The actual use of this instrument involves three basic areas of interest:

1. Tracing signals between digital ICs,
2. Tracing signals from digital ICs to discrete devices, and
3. Tracing signals from discrete devices to digital ICs.

Each of these topics will be covered separately in the following paragraphs.

Tracing Signals between digital ICs

Most digital troubleshooting will involve tracing signals as they are passed from one digital IC to another. A typical input and output stage, as used inside a digital IC, was shown in Figure 15–2. Notice that in this configuration, the two transistors in the output stage of a totem-pole IC allows a forced-high or forced-low logic level. See Figure 15–42.

There are a several possible failures that can occur when one IC chip drives signals into another. These are shown in Figure 15–43.

Probing a digital circuit such as this with a logic probe will likely produce one of the following symptoms:

1. Check the output and input pins of the ICs involved. If the source IC output pin indicates that the signal is being generated but is not

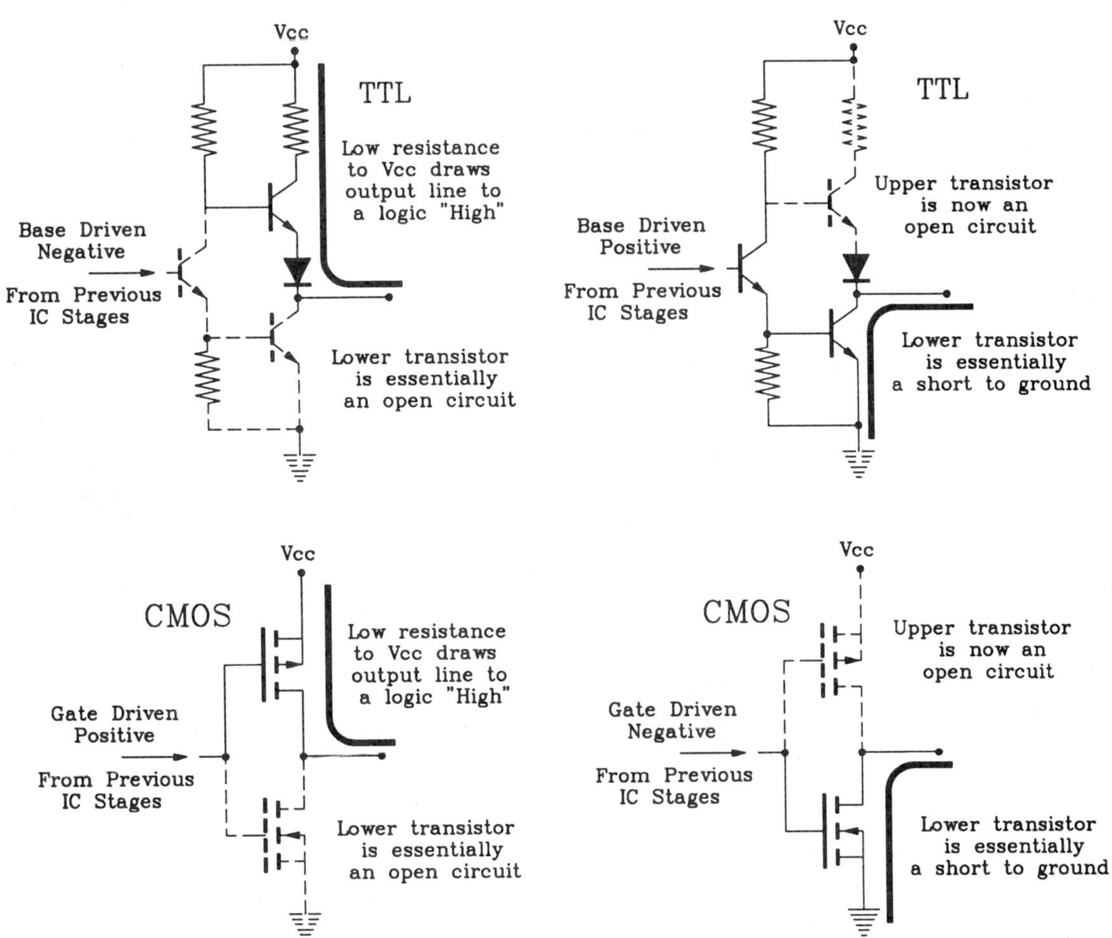

Figure 15–42 How the totem-pole output produces logic levels.

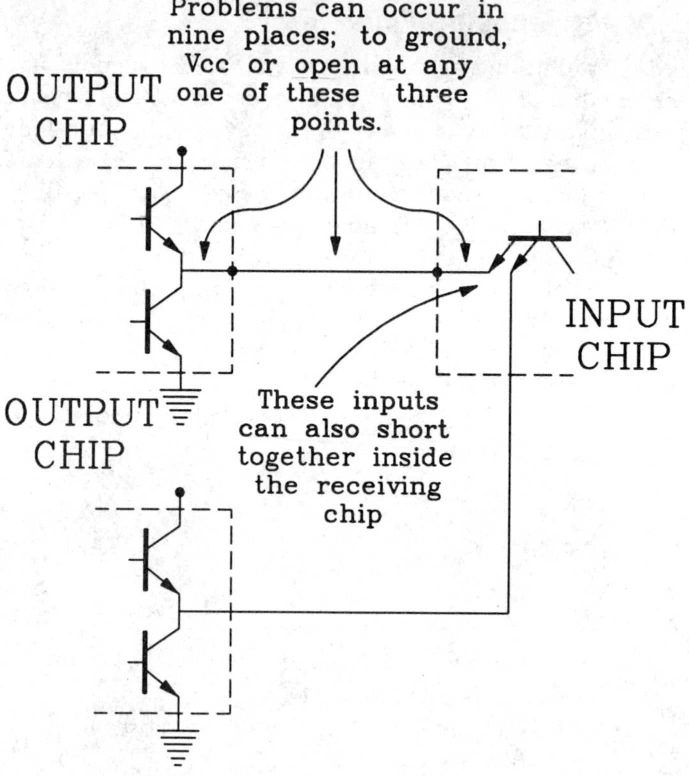

Figure 15–43 Some of the possible faults that may occur when one IC transmits to another.

reading the input pin of the following stage, there is obviously an open in the PC board trace between the ICs. See Figure 15–44.

- In TTL circuits having an open trace, the input pin will show no activity on the pulse LED and a "bad" digital level; neither the high nor the low LED on the probe will be lighted.
- In CMOS circuits, the input pin will probably be very sensitive and will act erratically; it may switch logic states or "lock up" when the probe is touched to the input line.

Tracing the open line is easy. Simply progress along the trace from the source IC until activity is lost. That is the point of the break.

2. Failure of either of the transmitting transistors may pull the output line high or low. For instance, *activity normal, high LED normal, low LED extinguished* can mean either a *normal* signal with a very high duty cycle that causes the LED not to respond. See Figure 15–45.

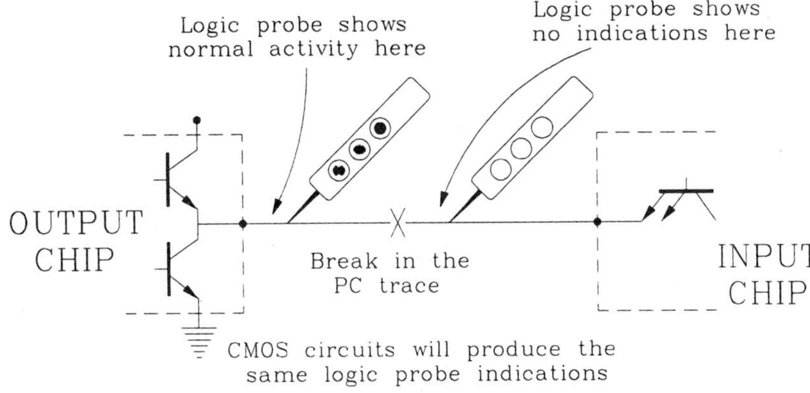

Figure 15–44 Tracing along an open PC board trace to find the break.

The same symptoms can be caused by an open low source transistor. This bad transistor will result in the logic level driving from an intermediate logic level to high. If TTL logic is used, the receiving IC will interpret this as a constant high level.

In a similar situation, if the technician finds activity normal, the low LED lighted, and the high LED extinguished, this may mean either a *normal* signal with a very low duty cycle or, possibly, an open transistor in

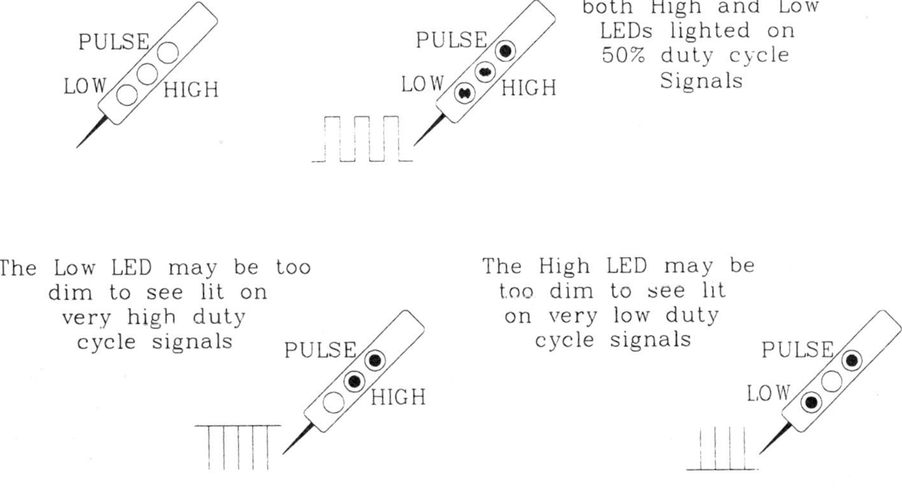

Figure 15–45 How the duty cycle of a digital signal may present confusing indications.

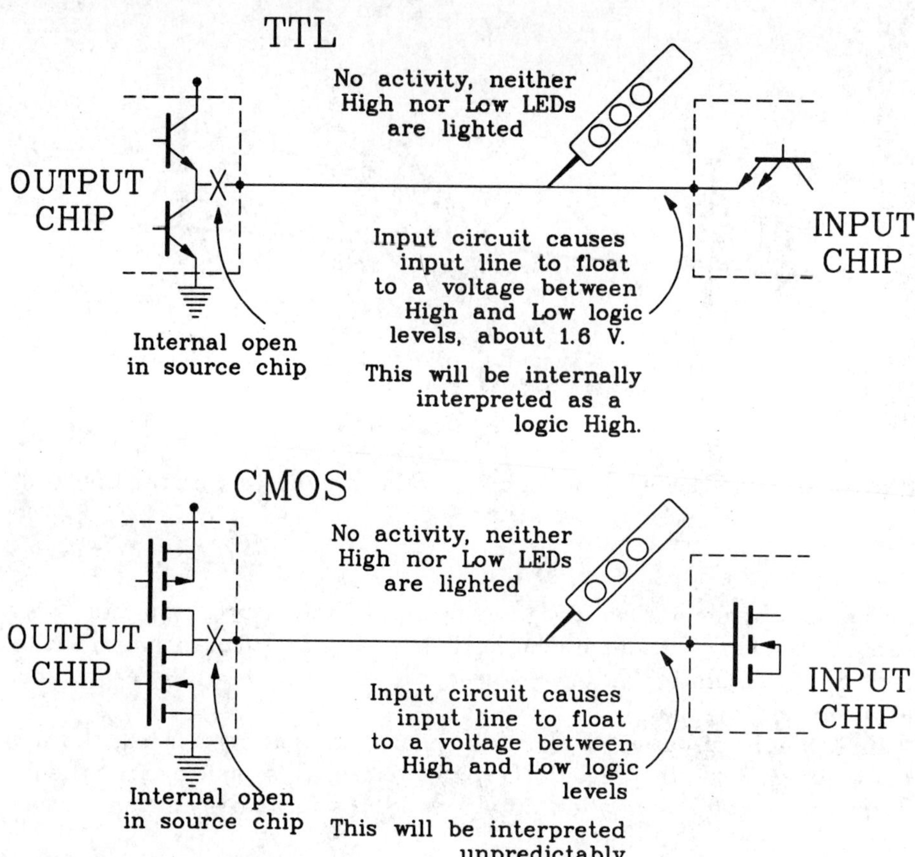

Figure 15–46 The effect of an internal open in the source IC.

the totem-pole output from the output line to Vcc. This was also shown in Figure 15–45. In this case, the logic high is being provided by the receiving IC, pulling the line to about 1.6 V when the source transistor is not saturated. This open input line is usually internally interpreted as a high within the receiving chip.

3. Failure by the opening of both output transistors or an internal open lead to the output pin of the source IC will, in the case of TTL chips, result in a constant indeterminate logic level at the source IC. See Figure 15–46.
4. If there is no digital activity and a constant high or low logic level at the source pin, this is called a *stuck bus*. See Figure 15–47.

An internal short to either ground (the digital signal is stuck in a low state) or to Vcc (the digital signal is stuck in the high state) can cause the

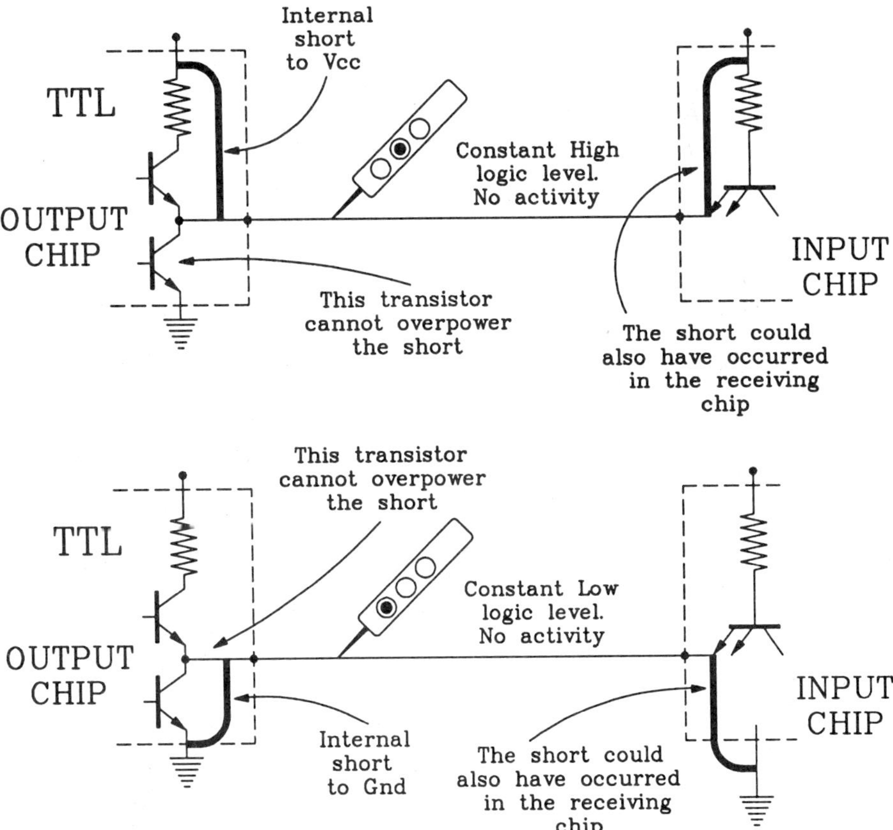

Figure 15–47 How an internal short in either the source or the load IC can cause a *stuck bus.*

line between ICs to be held at these levels. The problem is that the actual fault in this case can be caused by either the source or the load IC.

Before proceeding further, *be sure that the proper combination of digital signals is present at the input to the source IC* and that the output should indeed have activity. Remember that the *timing* of the input signals in relation to one another is of utmost importance in determining the output of a digital IC. If in doubt, remember that the trace feeding a gate can be safely grounded to force a logic low into it.

A stuck bus due to an internal short in either of the ICs is part of the 25 percent of digital IC failures that cannot be directly detected by using a voltage-based instrument such as a logic probe. Methods to use in determining which of the chips is at fault (and if they cannot be easily and simply replaced) are covered later in this chapter under the section titled, "If You Find a Missing Signal."

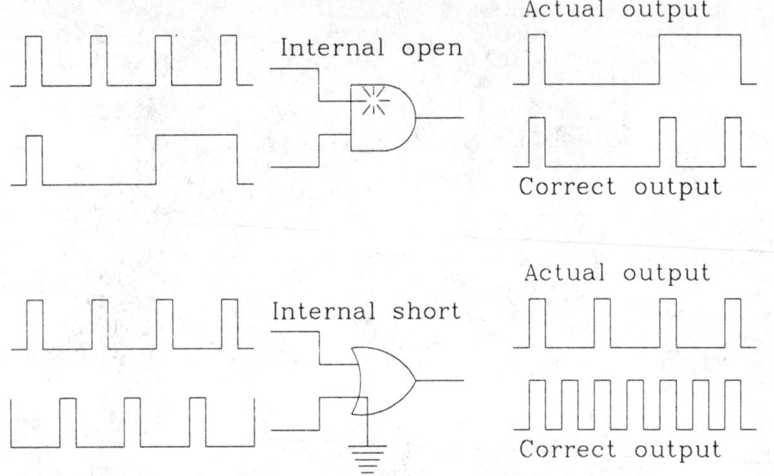

Figure 15–48 How an open AND input or a grounded OR input failure that is internal to a chip can cause an input to be ignored.

5. If the signal between ICs appears normal yet is being *ignored* inside the receiving IC because of an internal failure, the signals may appear as shown in Figure 15–48.

This is a more difficult situation to confirm. If the chip truth table allows an output from the chip with all other inputs tied low, the remaining inputs to the chip can temporarily be individually tied low (to ground) to eliminate possible confusion with these signals. Then, apply a signal to the suspected input with a logic pulser, looking for activity at the output.

If a simple IC gate is suspected to be ignoring one of its inputs, this possibility can often be verified with a dual-channel analog oscilloscope.

6. A less common fault can occur when two inputs to a chip are shorted together inside the receiving chip. Verification of this problem is done by applying a pulser signal at one input and then detecting the same signal coming out the other input, using a logic probe. Reexamine Figure 15–44 to see how this can happen.

Tracing Signals from ICs to Discrete Devices

Using Totem-Pole IC Outputs. Digital circuits communicating with the "outside world" usually do so with the help of components that are not ICs. Transistors are common components used in this application. These cir-

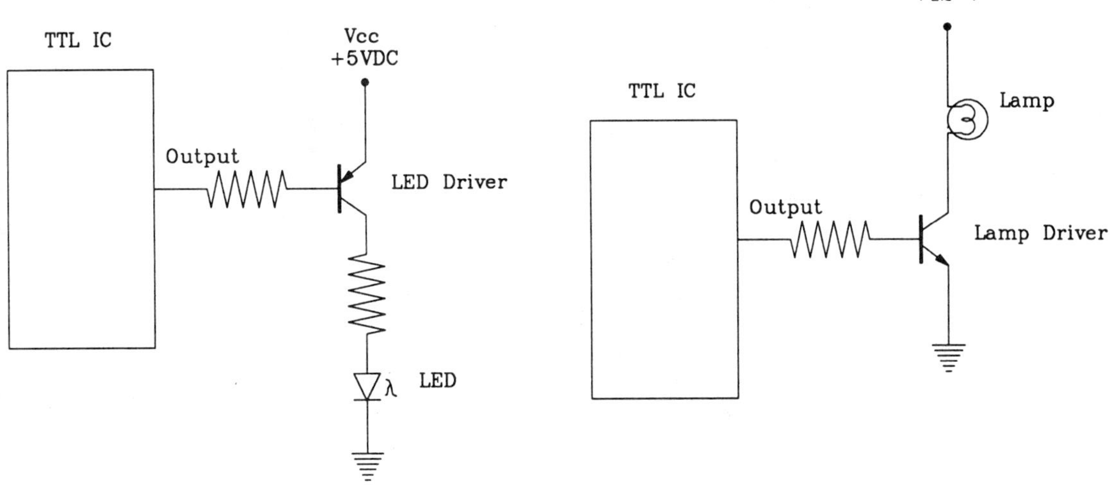

Figure 15–49 Sample interface circuits from ICs to the real world.

cuits are often very simple, since they operate Class C; they are either fully saturated or in complete cut-off. In this way, transistors are used as a switch and are, therefore, called *switching transistors* in the data manuals. Switching transistors are designed to come out of full saturation quickly and they have a steep collector current curve. Figure 15–49 shows some representative circuits of how a digital IC might pass on-off signals to a transistor.

In these circuits, the digital IC is the source component. Note that in some cases, the digital IC is shown connected to a transistor. The transistor provides the current needed to operate the actual output device. *The series resistor in the transistor base circuit provides the technician with an excellent monitoring point* because it effectively isolates the digital IC from problems that the transistor might develop. For instance, if the transistor shorts from base to emitter, the signal fed to the input end of the resistor from the IC would change very little from normal. The voltage on the base circuit end of the resistor, however, would change considerably.

Check the logic levels at the output of the digital IC with a logic probe. If the logic levels are good, the problem must lie with the transistor or components later in the signal path. If the logic levels are not good, then the problem is almost certainly either within the IC or prior to it.

Checking the voltage levels within the transistor amplifiers should be done using an oscilloscope. If the transistor is converting the logic levels to another voltage or, worse yet, to a negative voltage, the logic probe will not give valid indications. Remember that the logic probe is intended for use in circuits using from 0- to 5-V DC in the case of TTL ICs, or from 3 to 18 volts

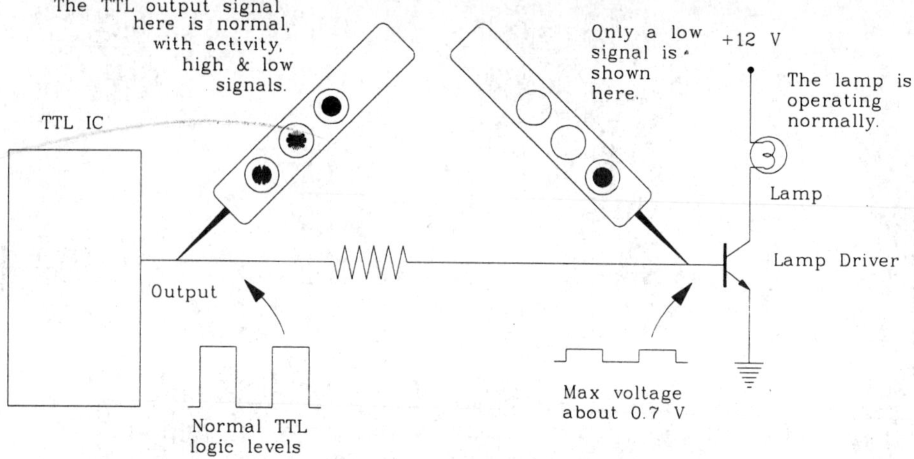
The TTL output signal here is normal, with activity, high & low signals.
TTL IC
Output
Normal TTL logic levels
Only a low signal is shown here.
+12 V
The lamp is operating normally.
Lamp
Lamp Driver
Max voltage about 0.7 V

Figure 15–50 Why a logic probe will provide misleading information on some circuits.

for CMOS ICs. The high- and low-voltage levels reported by the probe depend on two definite thresholds. These thresholds will not apply to the transistor circuit. See Figure 15–50.

Using Open-Collector IC Outputs. Another circuit that the technician may encounter in interfacing circuits is the IC with an open-collector output stage within the chip.

Compare the output circuits of totem-pole and open-collector configurations, Figure 15–51. Notice that the open-collector output stage has no transistor for forcing a logic high on the output pin.

The open-collector IC can usually be recognized in a circuit, even if it is not specifically labeled as such on the schematic, by the presence of a resistor from the output pin to a source of positive voltage. This external voltage can be a different voltage source from that powering the remainder of the chip. This resistor is called a *pullup* resistor. Its function is to provide a logic high on the output line when the internal transistor open-circuits. When the internal output transistor conducts, the output line is forced low.

If the output transistor of the open-collector chip should develop an open, the chip will not produce a logic low and the output will be stuck high. On the other hand, if the internal transistor should short, the symptoms would reverse; the output would be stuck low. The failure of a different power supply than that powering the chip can be easily overlooked, making a good open-collector chip seem defective. Failure of the +12-V supply of Figure 15–52 would cause such an apparent failure of the IC.

In summary, when dealing with interfacing circuits that are not IC chips at both the source and receiving ends, the logic probe must be used with caution and the technician must be able to interpret its indications cor-

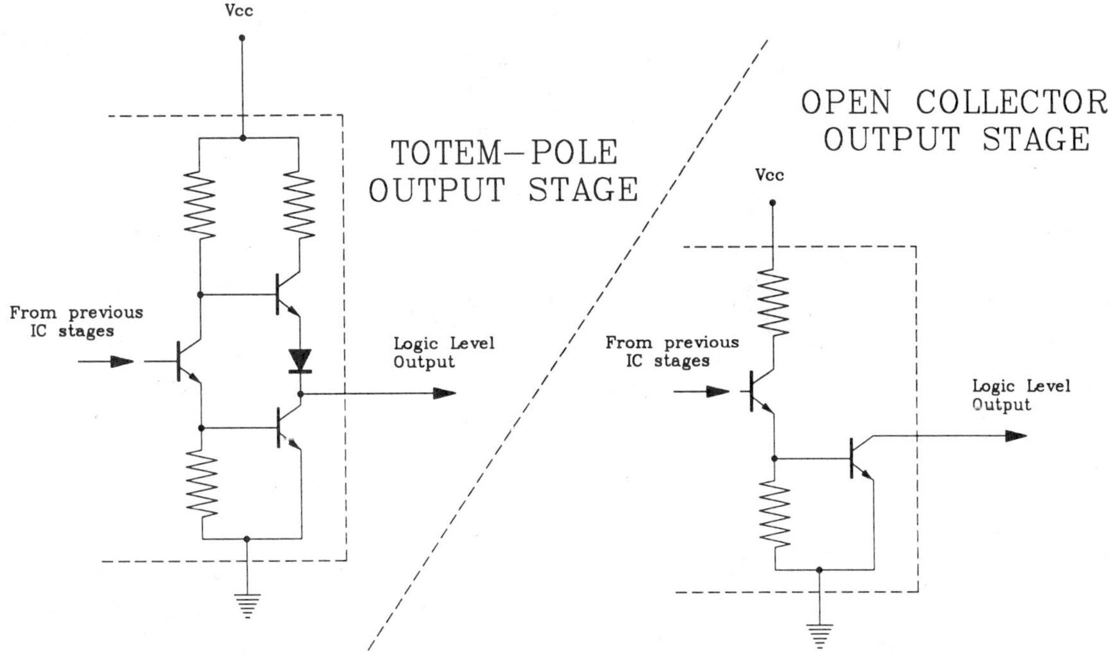

Figure 15–51 Comparison of totem-pole and open-collector output circuits within digital IC chips.

rectly. An oscilloscope is better at analyzing voltage levels when the signals are not occurring directly between logic ICs.

Tracing Signals from Discrete Devices to Digital ICs

Signals applied from an analog world must be converted to definite on- or off-states when connecting them to digital circuits. One would think that something as simple as a switch, for instance, would provide a good "on" or "off" condition that could be properly interpreted by the digital circuitry. See Figure 15–53.

If the switch itself were perfect, then this circuit would work fine. Like people, however, switches are not perfect. They consist of metal contacts that are made to come into physical contact with each other. This coming together results in *switch bounce*. See the example waveform in part A of Figure 15–54.

The switch is only one example of the many different inputs that must

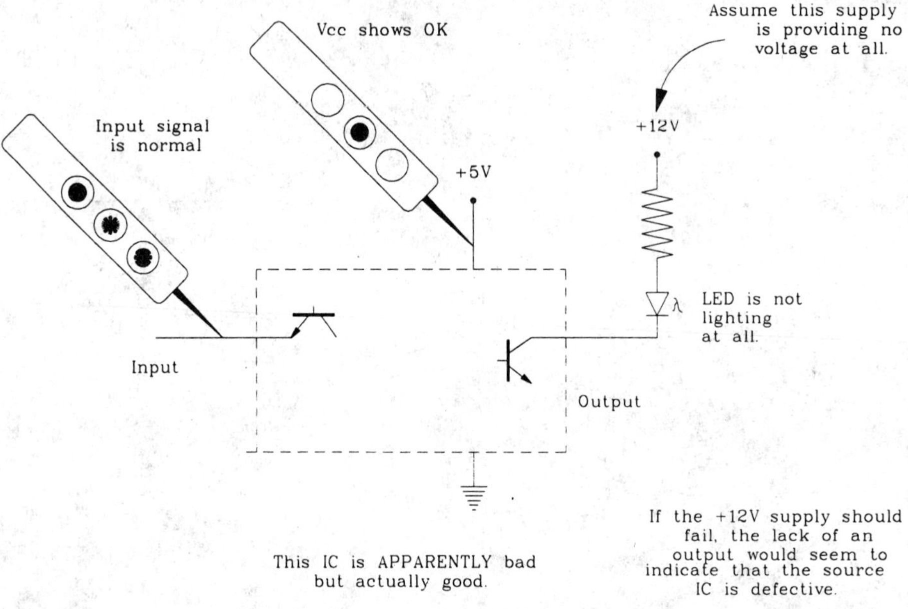
Vcc shows OK
Assume this supply is providing no voltage at all.
Input signal is normal
+12V
+5V
LED is not lighting at all.
Input
Output
This IC is APPARENTLY bad but actually good.
If the +12V supply should fail, the lack of an output would seem to indicate that the source IC is defective.

Figure 15–52 Circuit showing how the failure of a different supply can cause the output of an open-collector IC to appear bad.

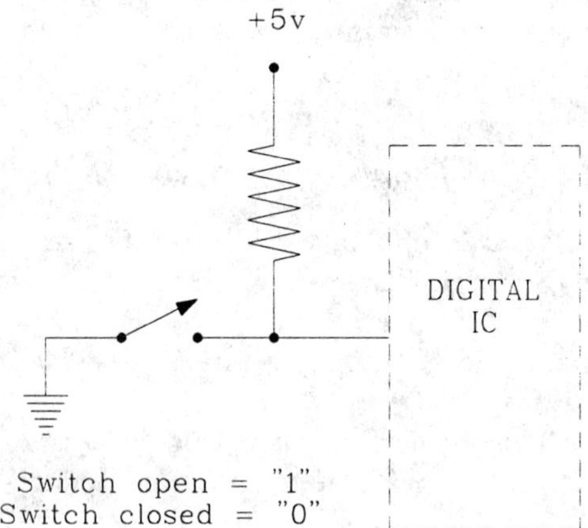
+5v
DIGITAL IC
Switch open = "1"
Switch closed = "0"

Figure 15–53 A switch-and-resistor combination that supplies either a high or a low logic level.

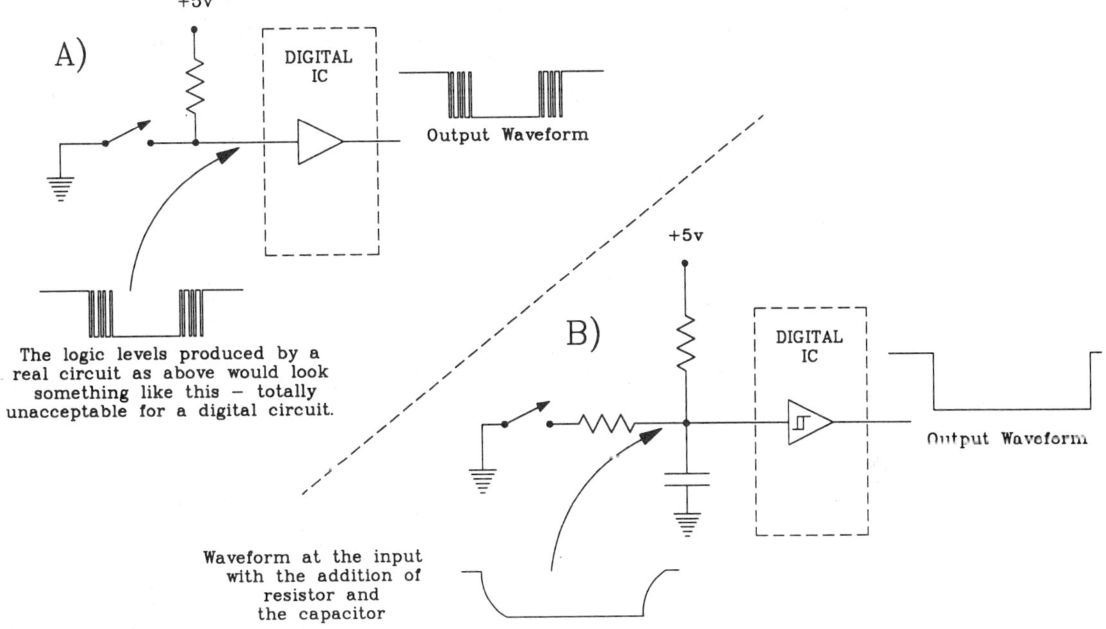

Figure 15–54 Waveforms of switch bounce and how a Schmitt trigger circuit can be used to "clean up" the waveform.

be *conditioned,* or made suitable, to provide the sharp on-off transition required by most digital circuits. A failure of conditioning circuitry will usually cause the digital circuits to also malfunction. An example of signal conditioning is also shown in part B of Figure 15–54, using a Schmitt trigger circuit. Schmitt triggers are available in inverters, buffers, and NAND, AND, NOR, and OR gate configurations.

The logic probe is inconclusive in interpreting analog signals because it is digital in its interpretations. The oscilloscope must be used to show if the incoming signals to a Schmitt trigger gate are high enough in amplitude for the circuit to operate. The Schmitt trigger requires definite levels of input signal before the output will toggle from one state to the other. The exact levels at which the circuit toggles depends on the Vcc supplied for CMOS chips. TTL Schmitt triggers typically trip at 1.6 V for a positive-going signal and 0.8 V for a negative-going one. Without *at least* this much input voltage swing, the circuit will not toggle. If the input signal is of sufficient amplitude and the IC still lacks the proper output, the IC is suspect and should be replaced.

The dual NAND gate signal-conditioning circuit of Figure 15–55 is sometimes used to eliminate the effects of switch contact bounce.

The dual NAND gate circuit will toggle on the very first pulse of a switch, bouncing or not, and hold that logic state at the output, whether or not the

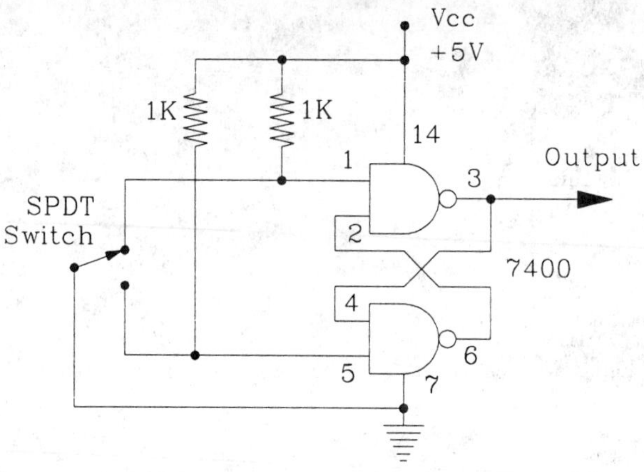

Figure 15–55 Circuit for a bounceless switch.

switch then opens the circuit. It will toggle the other way only if the switch actually contacts the opposite side, when the switch is changed to the opposite state.

LOOK FOR SIGNAL ACTIVITY: FULL-SPEED TESTING

Digital circuits usually fail by having one or more signals simply fail to toggle: a signal is missing. Further downstream in the signal flow, many other signals can be missing because of the failure of a single signal earlier in the circuit. It is the job of the technician in such a case to *find the earliest missing signal* in the signal flow path.

Finding the missing signal on a digital board, especially if it is a large and complex one, may not be easy. One method is to mentally divide the schematic in half, looking for signals halfway through the circuit. Another is to proceed sequentially, beginning at either the input or output end of the circuit and working one's way to the opposite end of the circuit. Look for signal pins that have no activity. Activity is the thing to watch for at this point in the troubleshooting procedure.

There are a few cautions to keep in mind when looking for missing signals:

1. If the unit under test is a microprocessor board, the technician must be certain that the software generates a signal where it appears to be missing.
2. Be sure to check the special pins on a chip that set, reset, enable or disable, or select. All these inputs must be correct for the chips to have activity on their output lines.

3. Because of timing considerations, the presence of an input signal does not necessarily mean that the signal is timed properly to allow an output from the chip.
4. Remember that a floating TTL input pin will show as indeterminate on a logic probe and will have no activity. It will be interpreted internally as a logic high input.
5. A floating CMOS input pin will be erratic. A floating CMOS input can also cause the chip to overheat, since both output transistors, high and low, may be partially conducting.

An example of the importance of verifying the logic levels of all input and output pins levels is shown in Figure 15–56.

Once a missing signal has been identified, it should be verified that a signal at that point is really required. When comparing logic probe indications against notations on the schematic, be sure that the signal input conditions are the same. If you are not absolutely sure, check the inputs to the chips in question, including their timing, to be sure they are correct. If they are, then either that chip *or the following chip* is the problem. Remember that a short to Vcc or to ground in the receiving chip can cause an output chip to appear bad.

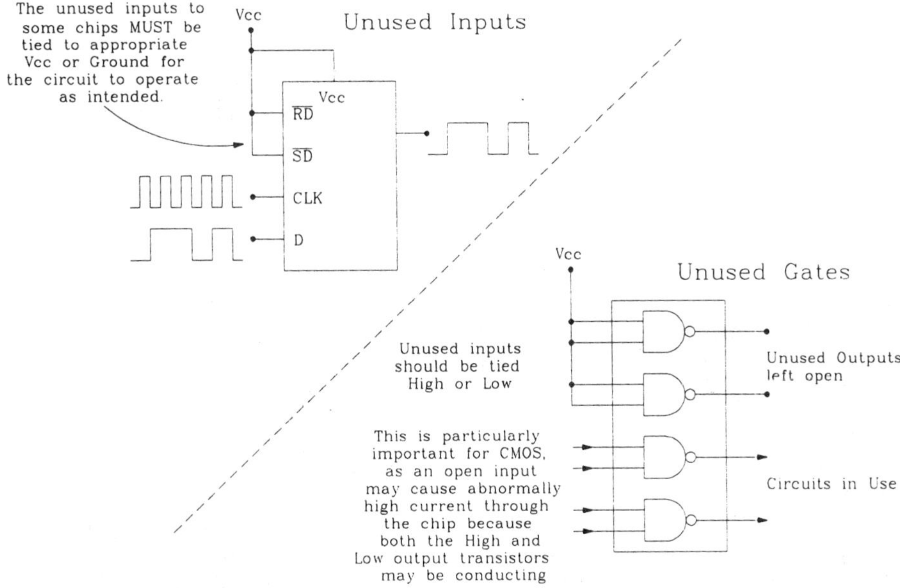

Figure 15–56 Unused logic inputs should be tied either high or low. Unused outputs should be left open.

If, upon checking an input to a chip, a missing input is found, continue tracing the missing signal back through earlier stages until the offending chip has been identified.

Logic Pulser/Logic Probe Verification of Shorted Trace

If it is determined that there is a stuck bus and that the inputs to the source IC chip are all correct, then the problem of identifying the bad chip—source or receiving—remains.

The next step is to turn off the power and measure the resistance of the stuck bus to whatever it is stuck to: to ground, in the case of the bus stuck low, and to the Vcc bus, in the case of the bus stuck high. A reading of less than 2 Ω indicates a shorted trace (shorted to the corresponding ground or Vcc). A reading of more than about 2 Ω indicates a bad IC connected to the bus. If both the source and receiving chip(s) are installed in sockets, a simple replacement of one of the chips should cure the problem.

If the chips are soldered into the circuit, the logic pulser and the current tracer can be put to use. If a current tracer, as shown in Figure 15–30, is available, the technician can find which of the two chips involved is causing the stuck bus problem. Hold the current tracer, paying attention to the proper orientation of the tip, against any trace on the board that has normal digital activity. Adjust the tracer for a glow *slightly less than maximum*. Then, place it over the trace that goes from the suspected source IC to the receiving IC, again with proper orientation. If the short is in the source IC, there will be no flow; if the short is in the load IC, however, a bright glow will be evident. See Figure 15–57.

If there are several receiving chips tied to the source chip, this method will also identify the offending chip. Simply trace the overcurrent right up to the offending pin. See Figure 15–58.

DIGITAL TIMING PROBLEMS

If testing with a logic probe indicates that there are signals throughout the PC board where they should be, a timing problem is indicated. Timing problems will usually involve a bad input signal to the board or the failure of a component on the board that affects signal timing. The logic probe is ineffective to identify timing problems. However, two instruments are of use at this point: the oscilloscope (good only for one or two signals at a time) and the logic analyzer. To efficiently check the timing of more than two digital signals requires the use of a logic analyzer. This is the instrument of choice, particularly when the circuit involved is a microprocessor.

Testing circuit timing will require an intimate knowledge of the circuit and thorough documentation. Microprocessor circuits will require the availability of the program being used.

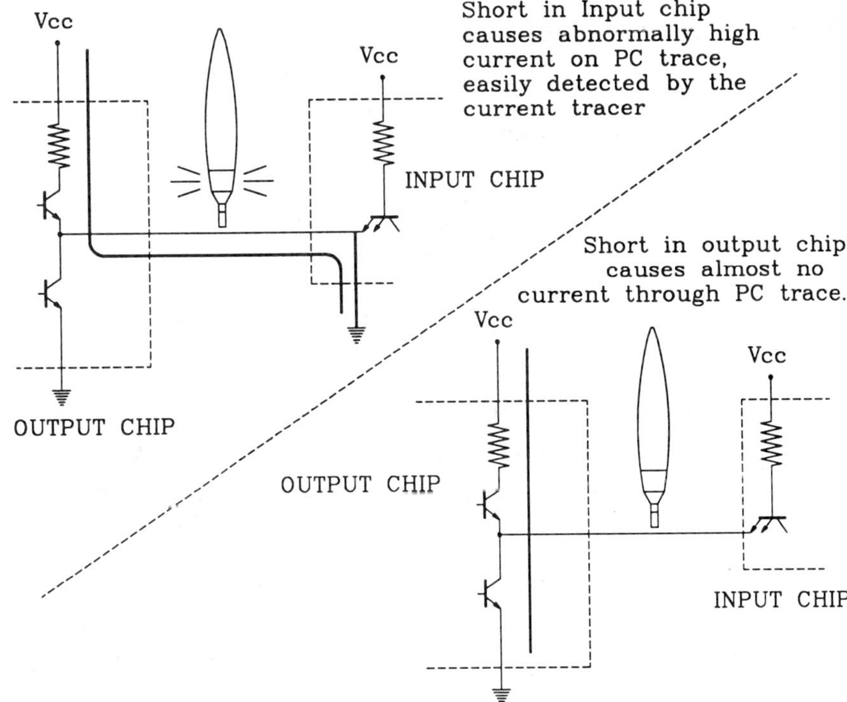

Figure 15–57 Using normal digital signals to determine whether the source or receiving IC is causing a stuck bus.

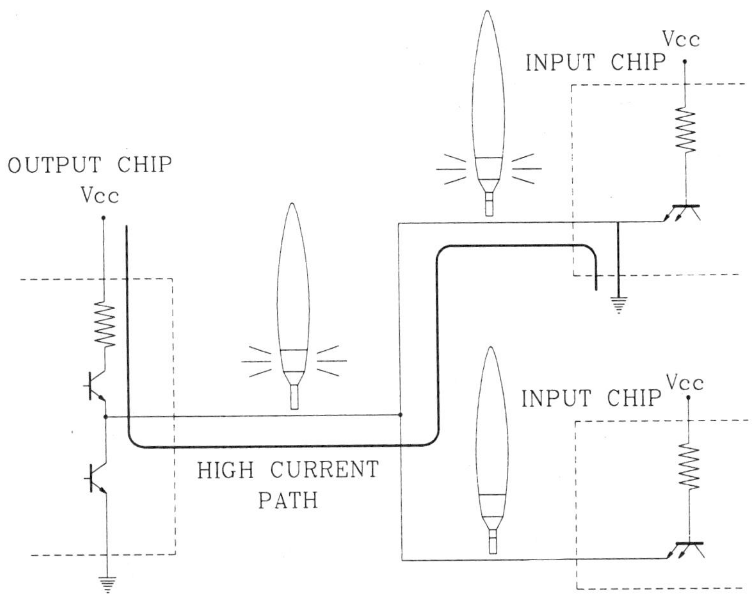

Figure 15–58 The current tracer will find the one of many possible receiving ICs that is shorted.

Look for Inputs Being Ignored

If the digital circuit apparently has all necessary signals yet is still not operating properly, there is a small possibility that one of the inputs to a logic chip is being ignored because of an internal failure in an IC. This was shown in Figure 15–48.

Troubleshooting this kind of problem will require the use of an instrument that can analyze the timing relationships of all the active inputs to the chip in question. Most chips will have some active inputs, with other inputs possibly tied high or low. The verification of the static high or low logic levels can be done with a logic probe.

If a Signal Is Bad Only Part of the Time

Microprocessor circuits often share a common bus line between two or more chips that drive the line to high or low logic levels. Since a line can be driven by only one chip at a time, an accidental enabling of two chips at once will result, sometimes, in a disagreement as to the logic level of the bus. This is called *bus contention*. See Figure 15–59.

Be careful to note the voltage levels of 0.8 and 2.4 volts on the CRT screen, as normal operation of digital circuits often causes the logic levels to vary within the legitimate levels. While an oscilloscope might be able to see this contention, *a logic analyzer may only show contention as very short*

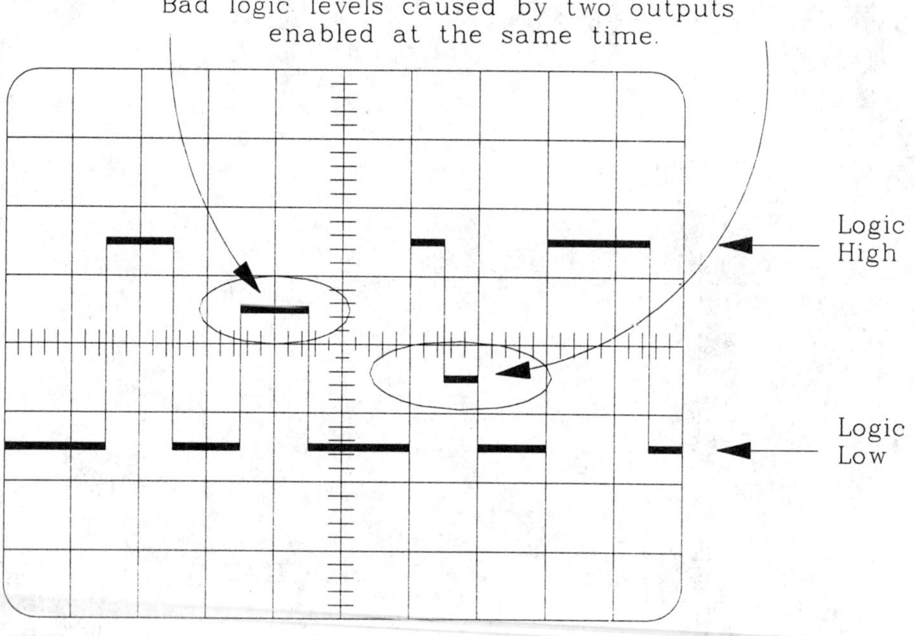

Figure 15–59 Bad logic levels can sometimes be seen on an oscilloscope.

pulses where a good logic level should appear. This is the result of one chip momentarily overpowering the other.

IF ALL ELSE FAILS . . .

If the use of a logic probe and the logic analyzer does not find the problem for any reason, there are two instruments that can be used at this point, the logic comparator and the solid-state tester. The logic comparator is particularly adept at catching erratic problems caused by 14- and 16-pin chips. It can be set to operate for long periods, waiting for the suspect chip and a "standard" chip to disagree (days, if necessary).

One other possibility exists that may yet save your day. If you have a duplicate, good board against which to compare the defective unit, consider using a solid-state tester to find the difference between the boards. The use of this instrument is covered in detail in Chapter 17.

15.7 TROUBLESHOOTING LIQUID CRYSTAL DISPLAYS

THEORY

The liquid crystal display (LCD) operates on the principle of alignment of molecules when a voltage is applied to a certain liquid. When the voltage is applied, the liquid aligns in such a way that light is absorbed, producing a dark area instead of the normal, light-colored blank screen. Since the LCD reflects existing light rather than emitting it like an LED, the display cannot be seen in dim light or darkness. Reading an LCD under such conditions can be done if a separate source of light behind the LCD structure is provided, however.

An external control must be provided for an LCD display to determine the display contrast. This control is a potentiometer that adjusts the voltage on one pin of the circuitry that drives the display. Adjustment at one extreme causes the display to become all dark, and at the other extreme, all blank (white). The misadjustment of this control can sometimes be a problem caused directly by the operator, and is, therefore, the first thing that should be checked on a "bad" display.

The pin-for-pin control of an LCD display is complex. As an example, a 5 × 7 character box for 12 characters per line and 4 lines means coordinating the placement of 1,680 individual character elements on the display. If you combine this requirement with movement of the cursor between characters, independent of the letters showing, the blinking of any or all characters, and the possible scrolling of characters across the display, and the complexity becomes clear. Just as in a computer printer, there is a need for a small microprocessor to handle the large amount of information. With a dedicated

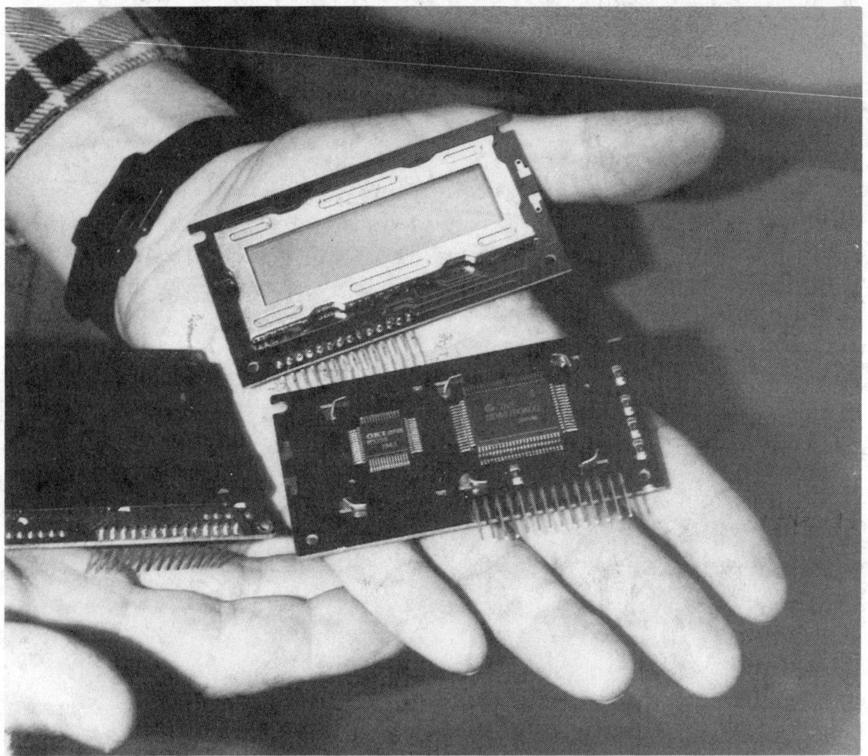

Figure 15–60 These liquid crystal displays require a small micro-processor just to drive them.

processor to handle the task, all that is needed is to provide coded data and control information, and the processor will take care of all the details.

Displays that are placed into mass-produced, special equipment can be controlled by custom processor chips made for the specific purpose. The LCD driver and circuitry for the Fluke digital multimeter of Figure 9–5 is an example of this kind of integrated display system.

Less highly specialized applications make use of a generic module that consists of the display, a PC board, and the necessary chips to drive the display, including the specialized microprocessor. See Figure 15–60.

The processor of such a display recognizes ASCII (American Standard Code for Information Interchange) codes for letters, including perhaps upper and lower case, and symbols such as the diagonal, dollar sign, percent sign, and so forth mapped out within an internal ROM (Read Only Memory). All that needs to be done, to put it very simply, is to provide the ASCII binary combination desired to be shown at the 14-pin connector. The processor on the LCD board takes this data, converts it to an appropriate series of dots, and sends these dots to the display. Internal housekeeping chores such as keeping track of where the next letter goes, and so forth, are all taken care of by the processor. Control codes are also available to make the display do such things as blink the display, clear it, or scroll it.

More complex LCD displays are capable of displaying graphics in addition to the text mode. All this capability is made possible by the use of a separate microprocessor to drive the display. The display of a laptop computer is a good example of a large display.

LCD displays are not tolerant of high temperatures. Under conditions considered hot by humans (above 100° F, approximately), the display has a tendency to darken. Readjustment of the contrast pot will help restore normal contrast under such conditions. More heat than this may result in the display staying dark despite any adjustment of the contrast. The solution is to simply cool the display to more reasonable temperatures.

FAILURE PATTERNS

The very first item to check is the setting of the contrast control. Misadjustment will cause the display to either go blank (white) or become very dark. Since this is a manual adjustment, and a mechanical one at that, the pot itself is subject to wear and, therefore, suspicion if the display is blank or completely dark. The way to check the pot is to verify that its output, which is right on the arm of the pot itself, varies smoothly as the control is turned, producing a voltage that is, at all times, between the voltage on the outside terminals of the pot.

The microprocessors used to drive LCDs are almost always soldered onto the circuit boards. Because of this, it is most timely and cost-effective if the entire module, with or without the LCD itself, is replaced as a unit. If the new one works well where the old one did not, either the connections to the old one weren't making proper contact or the old display/driver was bad. This can be verified by temporarily reinstalling the old display.

If the display module circuitry is separate from the LCD display itself, it may be possible to replace only the display to determine whether it or the driving circuitry is at fault. Handle the LCD displays carefully, and do not place your fingers directly on the face of the display. Such pressure can cause the display to discolor and is a needless stress on the display. Handle it by the edges only.

CHAPTER SUMMARY

- Most digital chips have a totem-pole output circuit which pulls the output line high or low.
- An open-collector chip only pulls the line low, depending on an external resistor to pull it up.
- A three-state digital chip can open-circuit its output lines, leaving them "floating."

- Timing diagrams provide timing information that is not shown on the schematic.
- Preparing digital schematics for use enhances their value to the technician.
- Digital references are necessary to show information that is not on the schematics.
- The two most common families of digital chips are the TTL and CMOS groups.
- Hybrid families related to both these basic families are also available and are used for interfacing between the basic families and for adding features.
- ECL is a third family of digital chips that is very fast and uses a negative supply.
- The extender clip brings digital chip pins up where instruments can be more easily connected.
- The logic pulser can provide a single pulse or a train of pulses for digital troubleshooting purposes.
- An oscilloscope is not the best instrument for digital troubleshooting, but it can be used in some cases.
- The logic probe is the easiest digital troubleshooting instrument to use and can tell a great deal about circuit operation if the LEDs are properly interpreted.
- The current tracer is useful in finding short-circuit problems in digital circuits where a voltage-based instrument cannot.
- A logic analyzer can simultaneously record many channels, more than 100 on some sophisticated models.
- A logic comparator compares a known good chip against a suspected chip, indicating any difference, at full operating speed.
- The logic clip will read out the logic levels of a 14- or 16-pin IC but contains no pulse stretcher and, consequently, is useful only for static circuit troubleshooting.
- Digital troubleshooting begins with a visual inspection, looking for proper Vcc and checking the clock, if any, for a proper signal.
- The logic probe is the next step, looking for missing signals.
- The logic probe is best used only between digital chips, and not on interface circuitry.
- If all signals are present on a malfunctioning board, the problem may be a timing error.
- Timing problems are shown by an oscilloscope for two signals, or a logic analyzer for more than two signals.
- The logic analyzer is able to record logic levels on up to 100 different points in a circuit simultaneously.
- The timing logic analyzer is good for finding problems in hardware.
- The state logic analyzer is good for finding problems in software.
- As a last resort, the digital comparator or the solid-state tester may be useful to find elusive problems.

REVIEW QUESTIONS

1. Name the three typical output circuits used within digital integrated circuits.
2. What pulls the output line of an open-collector IC to a logic high?
3. What is the configuration called involving several open-collector ICs tied together to a common output line?
4. When only one of several chips can "communicate" at one time on a common bus, the use of a _______ output circuit will be required in all the chips.
5. On a borrowed digital schematic, you find hand-written notes to make troubleshooting easier. On one point, you see a marking of *AH*. What might this mean?
6. What very important factor that determines digital circuit operation *does not* appear on a schematic?
7. What is the purpose of using multiple bypassing capacitors in digital circuits?
8. What is the term meaning the opposite of dynamic?
9. If a signal line is reset, what is the logic level?
10. How many NAND gates are required to make an AND function?
11. How many NOR gates are required to make an inverter?
12. You see on a schematic a NOR gate with negated inputs. When the two inputs are low, the output goes low. What logic function would you expect to find in a data book for this chip?
13. Name the five principal characteristics of TTL chips.
14. Name four of the six basic families of TTL chips.
15. Name the five principal characteristics of CMOS chips.
16. What are the two numbering systems commonly used to designate CMOS chips?
17. What is "latch-up," and what causes it?
18. Name three of the hybrid chips that are neither entirely TTL or CMOS.
19. What is the third popular digital IC family besides TTL and CMOS?
20. If you suspect that there is a short somewhere on a PC board, what kind of instrument, generically speaking, will be most effective in finding the cause of this current-based problem?
21. What does the TTL/CMOS switch on a logic probe do internally?
22. What feature of a logic probe allows one to perceive a strobe of short duration, perhaps only a microsecond long?
23. What voltage level is indicated if a logic probe shows no lighted LEDs at all?
24. What is indicated when a logic probe shows neither logic level LED to be lighted, yet the activity LED is flashing?
25. What are the two types of logic analyzer and their uses?
26. Once a logic analyzer has been started up by the operator, what does the analyzer do until it is stopped?

27. When a logic analyzer registers the trigger event, what does it then do?
28. What is the principal difference between an oscilloscope trigger and a logic analyzer trigger?
29. What are the five main setup steps for a logic analyzer?
30. The logic clip is useful only on _______ digital circuits.
31. If a program is executed one step at a time, this is called ________ ______ the circuit.
32. What approximate percentage of digital circuit failures involve open circuits at one point or another?
33. What are two reasons for using test probes with sharp, small-diameter tips?
34. When should sharp-tipped test leads *not* be used?
35. Name three quick checks to be made before detailed troubleshooting of a clocked digital circuit.
36. The logic probe is most useful for tracing signals in what area of a digital circuit?
37. Whenever you touch a CMOS input with the logic probe, it changes state. What is the probable problem here?
38. How will an open input to a TTL chip be interpreted internal to the chip?
39. You believe you have found a stuck bus. What should you do next?
40. What are the two failures that may result in an "ignored input"?
41. Is the logic probe useful on digital interfacing circuits?
42. You find several missing signals throughout a digital circuit. Where is the problem indicated?
43. You find a stuck bus between two digital chips. The timing and input signals are correct. Consequently, the problem could be caused in one of three places. What are they?
44. Is a logic probe useful to check digital signal timing?
45. If an oscilloscope shows indeterminate logic levels for part of the time, this could be caused by _______ _______.

Troubleshooting Microprocessor Circuitry

16

CHAPTER OBJECTIVES

This chapter will discuss, as generically as possible, the troubleshooting options available for *any* equipment that contains a microprocessor, from microcomputers to printers and automotive computers to programmable logic controllers. At the conclusion of this chapter, the student:

- Can identify the three basic problems these circuits develop: hardware, software, and configuration problems.
- Can recognize power-supply problems.
- Will be able to test a ROM effectively.
- Will be able to localize a floppy disk problem.
- Will know substitution procedures to be used to localize a problem to a unit, and then to a board within a unit.
- Will be aware of internal switches that are often used for initializing equipment.
- Will look for diagnostic software to do most of the troubleshooting.

- Will be able to compare logic probe readings to help localize a problem to a chip.
- Will be able to use a one-line program for microprocessor circuit testing.
- Will know what an emulator is and what it does.
- Will know what additional information is necessary to use a logic analyzer most effectively.
- Will know where to look for software substitution and configuration problems, and how to cure them.

16.1 THE THREE BASIC MICROPROCESSOR PROBLEMS

FAILURE OF HARDWARE

The circuitry that makes up all electronic equipment, including circuitry under the control of a microprocessor, can develop hardware problems. Besides the usual failures of broken wires in cables, bent pins in connectors, blown fuses, and physical damages such as cracked PC boards, the semiconductors can also fail.

Semiconductor failure has been shown to be caused by static electricity discharge through the devices. Although most such failures are immediate, some can occur a long period after the damage—even days or weeks later. Return calls to repair previously failed microelectronic problems can be reduced by the proper use of ESD prevention products and procedures during servicing.

After long months of use, equipment may break down due to IC or other semiconductor failures. (These might be called "normal" failures.) Such breakdowns may cause an immediate failure of the equipment, or the performance may merely suffer and limited service can still continue.

Whatever the problem, a hardware failure is most quickly localized by the method of substitution. Whether at the equipment or the board level, an exact substitute can be made, one unit or PC board at a time, to identify where the problem lies. This will be discussed in detail in this chapter.

DAMAGED OR WRONG SOFTWARE

If there is a microprocessor involved, there will be a program to operate it somewhere. The program can be contained in one or more PROM (Programmable Read Only Memory) or EPROM (Erasable Programmable Read Only Memory) chips. A program placed into such a chip is called *firmware*. Other times, for the smaller micro applications, the processor itself can contain the program in an internal PROM or EPROM. Other applications require that the software be loaded from a medium such as a floppy disk. Floppy disks and hard disks can become damaged and, therefore, give incorrect binary codes to the microprocessor. In these cases, the software on the floppy disks must not only be undamaged, it must be compatible with the processor. As an example, Apple computer software will not run on an IBM™-compatible computer.

WRONG CONFIGURATION OF EITHER HARDWARE OR SOFTWARE

Another consideration must be made, depending on the equipment under test. This is whether the program itself needs to be changed slightly to fit the actual hardware at hand. A computer's software, for instance, must be "told" what kind of a monitor is connected in order to display information correctly.

The modification (configuration) of software can be done in two ways: by using hardware switches read by the microprocessor during boot-up or by running the program in a special way (setup mode) to make the appropriate changes.

16.2 IDENTIFYING THE TYPE OF PROBLEM

There are some symptoms that strongly suggest the kind of problem, and the obvious cure. The first is the most obvious: the lack of power.

NO LIFE AT ALL

When there is no indication of power applied to the equipment, then whatever it is, the source should be checked first. In equipment that depends on the 120-V AC line, remove the line cord from the outlet and plug in something else, like a lamp, to be sure that the outlet is "live." If not, check the fuse panel.

If the outlet is supplying power, check to be sure both ends of the line cord are connected and *firmly* seated. Some line cords must be very firmly pressed into their connectors at the equipment end to ensure good contact.

If there is a fuse accessible from the outside of the computer, by all means check it. If the fuse is blown, be sure to put exactly the same type (fast or slow-blowing) and current rating as was originally installed. (Review the material on fuses in section 6.1. If the fuse blew "hard," silvering the inside of the glass, there is no sense in installing another fuse, as it, too, will blow immediately.

Assuming that power is being correctly applied to the equipment, it will be necessary to open the equipment case and begin troubleshooting the power supply to see if it is doing its job. If it is not, it must be replaced or repaired. Chapter 6 provides the techniques to use in finding power supply problems.

If the power supply is providing the proper voltages to the rest of the equipment, then troubleshooting will require substitution into the equipment of spare boards that are known to be good. It will be necessary to have documentation on the equipment to begin troubleshooting, using the techniques of Chapter 15 of this book.

IS THE PROGRAM REPLACEABLE?

If the program is contained in external, separate ROM chips, it may be possible to substitute identical ROM chips from another identical computer to test the originals. This is the quickest and easiest way to test ROMs. ROMs can also be copied, with a set saved as "masters," to program additional ROMs. Be careful not to violate a copyright, however.

Another way to test ROMs is to see if the internal digital numbers add up to the same *"checksum"* as is noted on the label attached to the chip. Some ROMs have this number, and some don't. The checksum is rather like the total deposit figure for a bag of money deposited at a bank. If the deposit total does not match the cash in the bag, something is wrong. Similarly, if the sum of the bytes inside the ROM does not match the checksum, there is something wrong with the ROM. Testing the checksum of a ROM requires a piece of equipment programmed to do just that: a board tester or a PROM programmer can be used to accomplish the job.

On the other hand, the program loaded for execution may come from another source (often a floppy diskette, as is the case for microcomputers). The program from the floppy is copied into RAM (Random Access Memory), where it is then executed. Programs are never executed directly from a diskette. A failure to load a program from a diskette into RAM and execute it could be caused either by the diskette drive, its electronic driving circuitry, or any of the chips within the microprocessor circuit, including the RAM chips.

If one is using a diskette to load programs, the loading of several programs of different types should be attempted. If none of these programs will operate, the problem is almost certainly of hardware origin and located in the drive, its circuitry, or the microcomputer system itself. One item that should be checked is the proper setting of any hardware setup switches provided. These are usually tiny switches in banks that are suitably small to plug into an IC chip socket, and called DIP (dual in-line plastic) switches. The proper setting of these switches, particularly if they have been disturbed, must be checked by consulting the instruction book.

Finding a hardware problem beyond this point will require the substitution of each module of the equipment with identical modules until the offending piece is identified.

If some programs run while others don't, the hardware is probably running just fine. If the programs use the same hardware features, then the software programs must be the problem. This can be verified by considering the status of the software that does not work: did it ever work on this particular equipment? If it did run, but does not now, there has probably been damage to the software. This could take the form of diskette damage because of mishandling: subjecting the diskettes to magnetic fields or physically damaging them. If, on the other hand, the software has never been used with this equipment, it most likely needs to be configured to the hardware in actual use in this system.

A single program that is new to this particular equipment will usually require a slight modification for it to operate the hardware of the system properly. A microcomputer, for instance, might be loaded with a word processing program for the first time. Upon loading up the program, the first step to be accomplished would be to invoke the *configuration menu* and step through all the options presented on the monitor screen, making the correct choices throughout. After completing this step, it is not unusual for the operator to be requested to exit the program and reload it in order for these new choices to be read and used.

A common problem with microcomputers occurs when each of two computers work very well on its own, yet the diskettes used on one are not readable or reliable when taken to the other. This situation can also occur between two drives on a single computer. One of the drives uses its own diskettes, but the diskettes cannot be interchanged between the two. This kind of problem suggests that when one or both of the drives in question are drifting *out of alignment*. The cure is to identify the bad drive(s) and replace them. The clue here is that a bad drive will not reliably read a "perfect" diskette, such as one on which original software is recorded.

16.3 HARDWARE TROUBLESHOOTING

SUBSTITUTE KNOWN GOOD UNITS IN THE SYSTEM

If it is possible to break down a microprocessor system to units or equipment, get and use identical units and substitute them to find the offending equipment. A printer in a computer system is a good example. Be sure to also check any external or internal cables. Examine the ends of cabling carefully for bent or missing pins.

Once the bad equipment has been identified, substitute internal PC boards and modules, if possible, to identify the bad card. Once the bad card has been identified, it can be analyzed to the component level using the techniques of Chapter 15, or perhaps it can be returned to the factory for replacement or repair, depending on the warranty status. In some cases, discarding the old card is also practical, provided the new one is available and the cost of a replacement is reasonable.

HARDWARE CONFIGURATIONS: PRINTERS AND COMPUTERS

When a piece of equipment uses a microprocessor, there open all manner of possibilities concerning how to operate the equipment. Many choices have to be made when possibilities are present. For instance, if a printer has the capability of operating via a parallel or serial port, which of the two is used upon power-up? (The printer cannot use both.) The easiest way to configure equipment is by the use of DIP switches. These switches are set according to instructions provided with the equipment. In the instructions, the operator is asked to make choices and set the switches accordingly. See Figure 16–1.

When the equipment is first powered-up, the DIP switches are read and the equipment hardware is operated accordingly. In our example, the microprocessor might know by the *on* setting of the second switch on DIP switch 3 (SW3–2) that the serial port is to be used rather than the parallel. The actual marking appearing on a label near SW3–2 might be the abbreviation *S/P*.

The DIP switches are usually located inside the equipment, just inside a small door (usually hidden) or accessible through a small hole in the rear or through the bottom of the equipment. If there is any chance that some-

Figure 16–1 These DIP switches are used to set microprocessor-based equipment to a specific configuration upon power-up.

one might have changed these switch settings from their proper position, stop and verify that they are correct before going further. Keep in mind that *internal setup switch settings are read only during power-up,* and if they are changed, the equipment must be turned off and then back on again for the new settings to be effective.

If you are going to make any changes to DIP or setup switches, *write down the original settings* so you can easily return to them if you should get confused or discouraged.

INVOKE THE INTERNAL DIAGNOSTIC PROGRAM

The easiest way to troubleshoot the hardware of equipment that operates under the direction of a microprocessor is to invoke the internal diagnostic program, if one has been provided. A diagnostic program will detect most hardware problems in the equipment.

An example of a diagnostic program can be found in almost all dot-matrix printers. Somewhere in the instruction book, you will probably find the key combination to invoke this program. It is usually called up by holding down one, two, or three switches on the printer *while power is first turned on.* After a moment, the keys may be released, and the printer should go through a loop, repeatedly printing all possible characters for the full width of the carriage. The cable to a host computer does not even need to be connected to invoke this diagnostic test. The pattern of the printing will tell if there are problems such as missing pins in the matrix. See Figure 16–2 for an example of a printer's self-test.

Computers, on the other hand, have two ways of running diagnostics: power-up and special diagnostic programs. Most computers will run a diagnostic program as one of the normal booting-up software routines. For example, if the diagnostics finds no problem, a microcomputer will usually emit a single "beep" from its speaker, indicating that no problem was found. Other audible codes, which were originated by IBM™ and are sometimes used by other manufacturers are:

No beep, no display: power supply problem.

Continuous or repeating beeps: power supply problem.

One long, one short beep: main board problem.

One long, two short beeps: monitor adapter problem.

One beep, no display: monitor problem.

Two short beeps: keyboard problem.

The power-up diagnostics of a microcomputer might also include a routine that flashes an error code—a number—on the screen. Other manufacturers may or may not use these same codes. If an error code number appears on the computer screen during power-up, consult the computer instruction manual for the probable meaning.

Figure 16–2 Typical result of a printer's built-in self-test.

Diagnostic programs can also be loaded from diskette. The programs can test memory, input/output ports, and disk drives. Bulletin boards are a good source of such software. Of particular value to a computer technician are one or more programs that give the current status of the machine, showing the hardware as "perceived" by the computer.

Once the microprocessor-based equipment has detected a hardware problem, it must have some means of informing the operator about the nature of the problem. Depending on the equipment's output capabilities, the output may be visible on a monitor, printed out on a printer in message or number code format, or communicated by means of a beeper of some sort. The method used will depend on the manufacturer's selection.

SUBSTITUTION OF CHIPS IN SOCKETS

One of the less sophisticated methods of troubleshooting microprocessor equipment is to simply replace the chips in sockets with ones known to be in good condition. Just removing and reinserting a chip can cure a problem *if* it was caused by a bad contact to the socket. Be sure to observe all static-discharge prevention rules and to use a static grounding mat and a wrist strap. This will prevent the very likely possibility that damage could be caused as the boards and chips are handled.

At the conclusion of changing all the socketed chips, one by one, one may find that the chips that were replaced were not causing the problem: it is still there. Only the board itself, the edge connector, and the chips that are soldered into the board remain as causes of the problem.

The edge connector of a PC board occasionally develops microscopic corrosion that can interfere with good contact to the socket. The edge connectors can be cleaned by removing them from the connector and gently rubbing them with an eraser. Wipe away all the rubber filings and firmly reseat the card into the connector.

USING THE LOGIC PROBE ON MICROPROCESSOR CIRCUITS

Without going deeply into the operation of a microcomputer's internal workings, it is still possible to troubleshoot a hardware problem on a microcomputer board by comparing logic levels between a board that is running properly and one that is not. This is the next step in complexity beyond simply changing of chips.

In order for a comparison to be valid between identical boards, each must be running the same software and each must have the identical setup for the jumpers that are often part of the board layout. Typically, activity will differ greatly from one board to another, with dozens of different logic probe indications. *The principal symptom for which to look is a floating input to one of the chips.* A floating input indicates that a defective chip is driving that line or there is an open circuit of the trace between the driving and the driven chips.

THE HERE-JUMP-HERE PROGRAM

An effective way to troubleshoot the basic chips of a microprocessor is to place the micro in a tight program loop, executing the same instruction over and over. When properly operating, such a simple program will allow logic probe testing of the processor itself, to some extent, as well as of some of the circuit memory, the clock, the control lines, the data lines, and some of the address lines. All the technician needs is a special ROM program to put the micro into the loop.

While this method cannot be used to test a microprocessor that contains its own ROM internally, it is well suited for those circuits that use an external, separate ROM chip. If an application uses a microprocessor chip with an internal ROM, a new one can be programmed for this purpose, but the original chip must be removed, thus not allowing it to be checked.

The test ROM should be programmed with a simple assembly-language instruction, such as:

HERE: JUMP HERE

Use whatever microprocessor mnemonic is necessary. Be sure to precede this instruction with any necessary initializing instructions.

Once this ROM is available, the schematic of the circuit should be annotated with the normal indications of a logic probe, as suggested in Chapter 15 under the heading, "Preparing Digital Schematics for Use." When a defective circuit is encountered, these indications can be compared and the problem can be located.

The simple repair of a once-functioning circuit will usually mean no more complex troubleshooting than has been discussed to this point: the use of diagnostic programs, substitution of chips, or use of a logic probe to compare boards. Troubleshooting beyond this level will very seldom be done in the field as a repair. The microcomputer board will probably have to be replaced in service with a good board, and the bad board will have to be either returned to the manufacturer for repair or discarded.

USING AN EMULATOR

An emulator is a piece of equipment that "acts like" a microprocessor. The microprocessor in a given circuit is removed and the emulator is plugged into the socket in its place. The emulator can now operate all the circuit memory, input and output circuits, and the other hardware as well. See Figure 16–3.

An emulator can be manipulated through its keyboard so that only part of the program in the circuit is executed. The technician can instruct the emulator to perform program steps to a specified point in the program and then stop. This will allow detailed pin-for-pin troubleshooting with a logic probe to find a problem with the hardware in a known logic state. This is a valuable troubleshooting instrument for prototyping new circuits, where it is used to debug the hardware.

An emulator would be useless without the details of the program to be run. All the program information must be available in assembly-language format. Of course, the emulator must be tailored to take the place of a specific microprocessor as well, since each type has a different pinout and software.

USING A LOGIC ANALYZER

A logic analyzer is useful for troubleshooting both hardware and software problems. It is relatively expensive, but its results can be extremely thorough. Using a logic analyzer will require a considerable investment of time

Figure 16–3 An emulator takes the place of a processor, making detailed troubleshooting easier.

to acquaint the operator with the concepts of the instrument and its controls.

Hardware problems within a microprocessor circuit are best detected by using a *timing logic analyzer*. This kind of analyzer runs at high speed, recording the logic levels of the circuit under test. Once recorded, the logic levels at any given instant of time can be analyzed with respect to each other. Very short transitions of logic levels can be detected with this instrument. For example, changes of logic state are recorded every 5 nanoseconds with the logic analyzer in Figure 15–32.

Depending on the troubleshooting requirements, logic analyzers can be obtained with more than 100 channels. Each channel is recorded at the same instant of time, regardless of the number of channels in use.

A logic analyzer is of little use without full documentation on the program to be operated by the circuit. One must know what *should* be before what actually *is* will make sense.

One of the advantages of using a logic analyzer is that it can store digital information. If the normal digital operation of a circuit is stored on diskette for future use, the operation of a defective circuit *running identical soft-*

ware can then be compared to this stored file. A logic analyzer can be used for automatic comparison of such files, called *reference and sample,* and to highlight the first mismatch during the program execution.

The logic analyzer also finds use in detecting the presence of very-short-lived, undesired, logic-level changes that may occur between normal signals. Such a logic transition from one level and back again is called a glitch. A glitch is caused by a switching problem related to the mistiming of logic levels and usually caused by the normal delay of signals as they travel (propagate) through the various digital chips of a circuits. If one signal meets with a given delay and another signal arrives a few nanoseconds earlier or later than necessary for normal operation, a glitch can occur. See Figure 16–4.

16.4 SOFTWARE TROUBLESHOOTING

THERE'S A PROGRAM IN THERE SOMEWHERE

Whatever kind of microprocessor is involved, there is a program located somewhere in the circuit. The usual place for a program is in a ROM chip. If there is no apparent hardware problem, it is a good idea to try another ROM chip, but it must have the same program as the original in order to identify the original chip as having a problem.

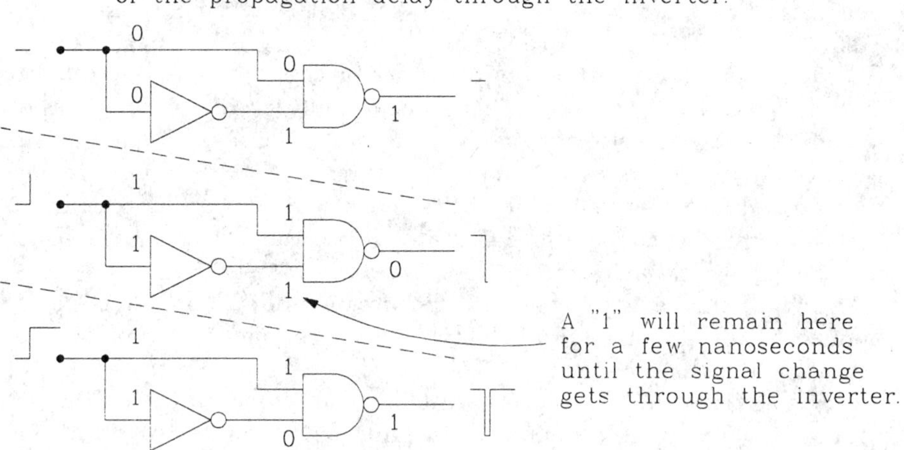

Figure 16–4 An example of how small timing errors due to propagation delay can cause "glitches."

SUBSTITUTION OF A KNOWN GOOD COPY

Other applications use a floppy or hard disk to store programs. These programs are read into RAM memory, where they are executed. If there is a problem with the stored program, there are two ways to identify it. One way is to get a known good copy of the same program and attempt to run it. If the new program runs, the old one was bad. The cure is simple: copy the good program over the original, bad copy. If it still does not work, the floppy diskette itself is probably bad.

A second way to identify a software problem is to use the suspected program in a known good computer or microprocessor circuit. If it runs there, the software is not the problem with the first circuit. This would indicate a hardware problem in the first circuit.

SOFTWARE CONFIGURATION

Software can be written and copied an infinite number of times without degradation. Because of this, programs are written and copied (and distributed) millions of times. Each copy of the software must make certain assumptions about the hardware on which it is to be operated. Microcomputers provide a good example of this concept. A word processor program, for instance, might be written with the assumption that all users will have a monochrome monitor. The software must be written with at least *some* assumptions in order for the program to run on every computer. Once coupled with a given computer, the software can then be modified, as provided for by the original programmer, to use the actual hardware of the computer at hand. This process of slightly modifying the software to take advantage of the specific hardware to be used is called *configuring* the software. It is often done through the use of a special program for that purpose, called a *setup* or *installation program*. Using such software, the main program can be tuned up for use with, for instance, a color EGA (Enhanced Graphics Adapter) monitor rather than a monochrome monitor.

New software, particularly complex application programs like word processing and CAD (computer-aided drafting and design) programs, must be configured before it will work properly. If incorrectly configured, it can do such unpredictable things as making the display go blank, the keyboard lock up, or the printer refuse to work. The configuration of software is one of the most important things that must be done with a computer to make it efficient to use.

The method of configuring software varies with the particular program, but it often involves special computer files, called *drivers*, to accomplish the modifications necessary to the main program. The instruction manual that comes with the program should detail the steps that are necessary to perform a proper configuration of the software.

CHAPTER SUMMARY

- Microprocessor circuits can develop either hardware or software problems.
- Such circuits can often troubleshoot themselves through special programming called diagnostics.
- Hardware problems can often be traced to improper setup of DIP switches.
- A microprocessor circuit that is completely dead probably indicates a power-supply problem.
- Replace the software to identify the problem as either a hardware or software problem.
- Substitute units of a microprocessor-driven system to localize a hardware problem.
- Invoke the diagnostic program, if any, to help identify a problem within a unit.
- Numerical error codes require a cross-reference to identify the specific problem.
- Some applications, such as computers, automatically run a power-up diagnostic routine.
- Chip substitution for socketed ICs can identify a bad chip.
- The logic probe is the least inexpensive choice for routine troubleshooting of digital circuits.
- An emulator or logic analyzer is most often used during circuit development, in debugging hardware and software problems.
- A "Here-Jump-Here" program will provide a constant, short program for troubleshooting many microprocessor problems.
- Software troubleshooting can be done in one of two ways, by using the suspect program on another microcomputer or by substituting known good software.
- New, complex software often requires configuration before it will work within a given hardware system.

REVIEW QUESTIONS

1. The presence of a microprocessor in a circuit opens the possibility of a troubleshooting program called a _______ program.
2. If there is no indication of power applied, yet the outlet is supplying power, the _______ circuit of the equipment is the next thing to check.
3. A program is typically contained in a _______ or _______ IC chip.
4. A common way that hardware is configured is through the use of _______ _______s.

5. If two programs that use the same hardware are tried, and one runs while the other doesn't, where is the problem?
6. What hardware technique can be used to isolate a problem to a bad board?
7. After making changes to the configuration switches on a microprocessor-controlled piece of equipment, what must be remembered to use the new settings?
8. What should you do before making experimental changes to configuration switches?
9. What is a typical way to invoke the internal diagnostic program on a computer printer?
10. The use of a logic probe is a valid option for locating a problem, even without documentation, if _______ is available.
11. What is the shortest operational program possible to continually exercise some of the hardware of a microprocessor?
12. How can one determine if the program at hand is the problem?
13. What must often be done to sophisticated programs written for a great variety of hardware?

Dead-Circuit Troubleshooting and Part Removal

17

CHAPTER OBJECTIVES

There are two occasions for dead-circuit testing: (1) after signal tracing has narrowed down a problem to a stage or several possible components (the object at this point is to verify that the suspected component is actually bad, preferably before removing it from the circuit or (2) when a technician is handed a circuit and asked to repair it with no other information—no schematic, no cables to connect it to power, no history of likely failures—in fact, he or she may not even be informed about the board's use! At the conclusion of this chapter, the student will:

- Know the two alternatives to working on a live circuit, to find a problem.
- Know why in-circuit resistance readings are usually inconclusive.
- Be aware of the probabilities of failure for most commonly used components.
- Be able to use a VOM or DMM ohmmeter effectively to trace a problem in a dead circuit.

- Be able to use a Huntron Tracker™ to find a problem in a dead circuit.
- Be able to use an ohmmeter or Huntron Tracker™ to verify the condition of a questionable part after removal.
- Know the fundamentals of soldering and the tools used to accomplish a soldering job.
- Know the cautions to be observed when unsoldering components.
- Know the alternative methods for removing a good component from an old board or a bad component from a good board.

This chapter will guide the technician in isolating the defective component, removing it from the PC board, and verifying the failure once the component is out of the circuit.

17.1 IS THERE REALLY A BAD COMPONENT?

If the circuit problem is merely one of marginal performance, an adjustment or the substitution of the suspected component with a known good one may be the next logical step in the repair. There is no need to verify such a problem with an ohmmeter or a solid-state tester because it is likely one of adjustment or tuning, or a radio-frequency reactive component may be out of tolerance for the circuit under test. Neither the ohmmeter nor a solid-state tester will detect such problems. In this case, the suspected component should be adjusted (if applicable) or simply replaced with a new one installed.

However, most electronic failures will involve a leaky, shorted, or open component. If the suspected problem involves a short, changed resistance, leakage, or an open, such defects should be verified before removing the component from the board. If testing conclusively indicates that the suspected problem is *not* the case, continue troubleshooting to track down the cause rather than unsoldering the component. Soldering operations stress the circuit board a great deal, and they can often be avoided by careful troubleshooting and some logical thought about the failure.

If the problem has been progressively tracked down to this point, the technician should have a very good idea of just where the defect lies (usually within a group of about a half-dozen components or less).

On the other hand, as mentioned in the chapter objective, it may be that the technician must do *all* the troubleshooting without applying power to the circuit. For either reason, only two instruments are of any practical value.

17.2 THE DEAD-CIRCUIT INSTRUMENTS: OHMMETER AND SOLID-STATE TESTER

If the technician has previously signal-traced a problem down to a stage or a few components that could cause the problem, the next step is to turn off all power and verify that the suspected component is defective by using the dead-circuit methods of this chapter.

Testing electronic components for shorts, leakage, and opens without normal power applied to the board requires that the test instrument apply a voltage. The technician then interprets the results. The ohmmeter applies a small DC voltage, and then measures the resulting current to indicate resistance. The Tracker™, one model of solid-state tester, applies a small AC signal and shows the resulting current and/or voltage on the two-axis CRT display.

17.3 IN-CIRCUIT RESISTANCE READINGS ARE OFTEN INCONCLUSIVE

Before going further into dead-circuit testing, the technician must be aware that ohmmeter or Tracker™ tests are often not as definite as one would like. An ohmmeter, for instance, reads the results of a small DC current that is made to pass through the circuit under test. Now let us consider the two scenarios of troubleshooting at this point: with and without a schematic diagram.

With a schematic, the technician can see what components, if any, are located across the suspected component (in parallel with it). These components, depending upon what they are *and whether they are defective,* can be taken into consideration in estimating the resistance to be expected between any two given points in the circuit. The chances are very good, in any specific case, that there will be several paralleling paths for the ohmmeter's DC current flow. All these paths must be taken into consideration *together* in order to evaluate how they will affect the resistance reading to be taken. Don't forget that the power supply and bleeder, if any, may not appear on the schematic, but they nonetheless may be connected in some cases. After the *total* expected resistance reading is estimated for a normally operating circuit, the actual resistance reading is taken. Differences between the estimated and actual readings should, if interpreted properly, give a strong indication of which is the bad component.

Without a schematic, the technician can be only partially effective in predicting the proper resistance reading to expect between any two points within the circuit. In this case, there are two possibilities:

1. Compare resistance readings with a known good circuit, point for point, or
2. Evaluate readings with a great deal of analysis.

Evaluating a resistance reading with logic means that the resistance reading is evaluated, knowing that there may or may not be components in parallel with the single component across which you may be reading. Readings other than those taken directly across a component are valueless for this method. Take the case of reading across a resistor. If the resistor is marked with a value of, say, 10,000 Ω and a tolerance of 10 percent, one would expect approximately that value to show on an ohmmeter. If the measured reading was lower than about 9,000 Ω, it would be reasonable to assume either that some other DC component was in parallel with the resistor or that the resistor was out of tolerance. A paralleling component becomes more likely as the measured value goes farther below the 10 percent low-tolerance value. Thus, this reading is not conclusive. On the other hand, if the measured value is over 11,000 Ω, the resistor must either be out of tolerance on the high side or is open, and the ohmmeter is reading a paralleling path. The open resistor is more likely. Again, the reading is not conclusive, but the resistor does need replacing, regardless. If the measured value is well above the upper tolerance limit, one could be sure that the resistor was open. The third possibility is that the expected resistance reading is just what was expected. However, this could be misleading. It is possible, particularly if this is a power circuit, that there are two such resistors, placed in parallel with each other for the added power dissipation capability, and the ohmmeter is measuring across an open resistor but reading its mate.

If all this discussion of in-circuit resistance readings makes you uneasy, I have accomplished my purpose. In summary, in-circuit resistance measurements are usually inconclusive. However, due to the ease with which these measurements can be made, the technician should go ahead and make them, but should apply a good deal of thought to the results.

17.4 SOME COMPONENTS ARE MORE LIKELY TO FAIL THAN OTHERS

It helps during troubleshooting at this level to keep in mind the likelihood of certain kinds of component failures. For instance, if there is a paralleled resistor and capacitor that together measure almost zero Ω, consult Table 17–1, checking the list for each of these components, to determine the problem.

Table 17–1 Component Failures in Order of Likelihood: Most Frequent Failures First

Component	Ohmmeter Failure Patterns
Batteries	Wear out; Ni-cads may short; Normally wear out by use. Too-frequent replacement may be caused by leakage or a defective on-off switch.
Fuses	Often open. Usually fail due to circuit malfunction or shorted Vcc source, or excessive load.
Capacitors	Usually short; sometimes leaky, occasionally open or out-of-tolerance. Often fail themselves; rarely caused to fail by other failures.
Connectors, Sockets	Develop poor connections, broken wiring where attached.
Semiconductors*	May short or open; often leaky; Short or open by themselves; often caused by other component failure.
Resistors	Sometimes open; occasionally out-of-tolerance; do not short. Usually open, almost always caused by associated semiconductor or capacitor shorting.
Switches	Permanently open or closed; occasionally erratic. Usually fail due to mechanical means; may fail due to excessive current.
Relays	Contacts often erratic; coils rarely open; Contacts become mechanically erratic, seldom caused by other components.
Vacuum Tubes	Wear out; break; Fail due to hours of operation alone; occasionally caused by associated biasing problems.
Microphones	Cords often erratic or open; Cords fail due to normal wear-and-tear.
Speakers	Occasionally open; often rub; Fail by mechanical rubbing against magnet and complete failure caused by overdriving.
Inductors	Occasionally open; seldom partially short; Open or occasional shorted turns caused by shorted components on load side of the circuit.
Transformers	Occasionally open; seldom partially short. Open or occasional shorted turns caused by shorted components on load side of the circuit.
Meter movements	Occasionally open; often break; Electrical abuse; overload; mechanical failure; mishandling.
Crystals	Seldom open; occasionally break; circuit usually at fault; physical breakage from dropping, out-of-tolerance condition.
Neon indicators	Become dim only; occasionally break; Aging causes darkening of glass. Insufficient current limiting greatly speeds this process.

*Includes bipolar transistors, FETs, integrated circuits, UJTs, SCR, TRIACs, diodes, and LEDs.

17.5 OHMMETER TESTING OF DEAD CIRCUITS

DON'T RUIN YOUR OHMMETER!

The common way of damaging an ohmmeter is to apply voltage to the test leads. This happens most frequently when a technician is troubleshooting and simply forgets to turn off the equipment under test before going to ohmmeter testing. A VOM is much more likely to be damaged than a DMM, but both are susceptible.

The best way to avoid having power in equipment is to remove the plug from the outlet rather than relying on the power switch to turn off the unit. If the plug is left in the receptacle, there is still 120-V AC present within the equipment, certainly near the power switch and possibly exposed on some internal parts such as the terminals of the fuseholder. Battery-operated equipment should have the batteries removed.

Even after the removal of all sources of power, the large electrolytics in the power-supply circuit are capable of retaining enough energy to damage an ohmmeter. For this reason, the large capacitors of a power supply should always be manually discharged using a test lead or screwdriver to short the leads. On very large capacitors, it would probably be a good idea to discharge the capacitors through a 5-watt, 100-ohm resistor for a few seconds rather than with a direct short. The resistor will dissipate the energy without the excessive current flow of a short circuit. After a few seconds with the resistor across the capacitor, all the charge should be dissipated. To ensure that the resistor has not opened, however, it is also wise to finally short the capacitor with a screwdriver.

USING THE VOM

The venerable volt-ohm-milliammeter has been around a long time, and it has served technicians well for many years. The transistor does not technically match well with a VOM, though. The VOM produces relatively very high currents on the lowest ohms scale. Before development of the transistor, this presented no particular problem. The transistor, however, is a very low-current device, and a VOM can easily damage it. Add to this the fact that some ohmmeters use batteries of up to 30-V DC to measure very high values of resistance, and one can see that the VOM must be used with great caution and thought when testing solid-state devices of any kind. As a basic rule, *do not use the lowest or the highest resistance ranges of a VOM on semiconductors.*

The following currents and voltages were present when a popular VOM, the Triplett model 630 meter, was tested for current with the ohmmeter leads shorted, and then for voltage with the test leads open:

Scale	*Current*	*Voltage*
RX1	300 ma	1.5 V
RX10	35 ma	1.5 V
RX100	3.5 ma	1.5 V
RX1K	0.35 ma	1.5 V
RX100K	35 μa	30 V

The resistance scale of VOMs is printed from right to left, which is backwards compared to the other scales. The zero-ohm marking is at the right of the scale and the maximum readings are on the left. This fact alone requires a little getting used to. One will also note that the graduations from right to left keep changing in value, as the scale is nonlinear. Whereas one-tenth of an ohm per minor graduation is used on the right end of the scale, 100 ohms per graduation may be used in one area of the scale on the left. This, too, makes some practice necessary to read the scale.

To be accurate, a VOM must be zero-adjusted after each resistance range change. The adjustment for one range is usually not quite right for the next range selected. To zero-adjust the meter, just short the test leads together and adjust the proper meter control until the needle exactly coincides with the zero, right-hand end mark. If you cannot adjust the needle to the end mark, the battery within the instrument needs replacing or the meter has suffered damage.

When the Ohmmeter Zero Is Unstable

If the VOM does not stay in calibration on the lowest range and the zero apparently drifts above and below the end mark when the instrument is moved or tapped, the problem is almost always caused by a poor connection to the battery (a 1.5-volt flashlight cell, in most cases). If bypassing the spring clip of the battery holder with a soldered-on jumper wire does not cure the problem, try taking off the outer covering of the cell and making a soldered contact to the case of the battery. When dismantling the outer covering of the cell, you will probably find that there is a round "washer" on the bottom of the cell that originally depended on a rubbing, physical contact with the zinc casing of the cell for contact. Removing this "washer" and making the soldered connection will cure the erratic contact problem that was designed into the cell.

Ohmmeter Lead Polarity

The polarity of the test leads is important if you wish to identify the cathode of a diode or determine whether a transistor is an NPN or a PNP type. It is a good idea to check your ohmmeter's lead polarity before such a need arises, since some meters switch polarity when using the resistance function.

With the test leads in their proper jacks in the VOM (red is positive and

THIS METER HAS CORRECT
OHMMETER POLARITY

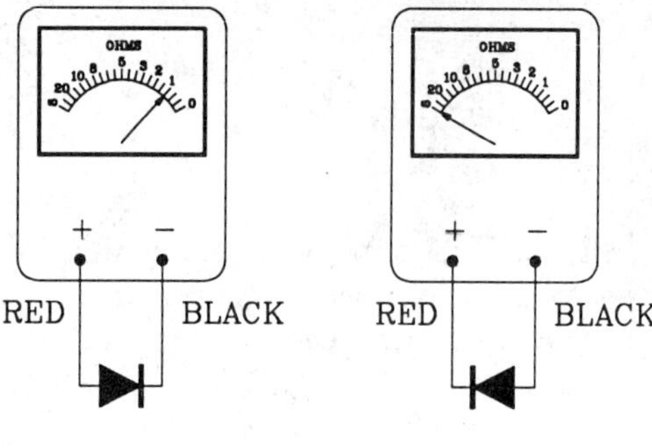

THIS METER HAS REVERSED
OHMMETER POLARITY

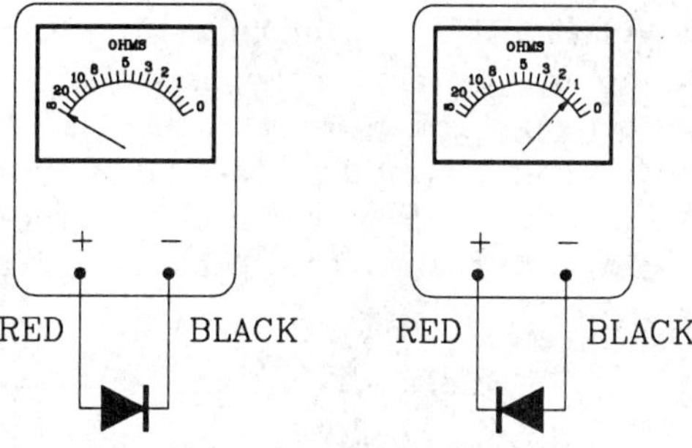

Figure 17–1 Testing your VOM for polarity reversal on the resistance scales.

black, negative) attach the test leads to a diode that already has the cathode end plainly marked. The cathode of a diode is usually marked with a band around it. Using the R 100 or R 1,000 scales, take a resistance reading across the diode. See Figure 17–1 for an explanation of the tests to make.

If you find that the meter reverses polarity on the resistance scales, this could confuse you when using it later. A small label saying something like, “Reverse leads on ohms” should be attached to the meter front as a reminder. Then, when junctions are tested, the technician will be reminded to reverse the leads at the meter (red in the negative jack and black in the positive) so that the colors of the leads show the correct polarity, thus avoiding confusion.

Use an intermediate ohmmeter range to tell if a transistor is an NPN or PNP. Place the red lead of the ohmmeter on the base of the transistor and the black lead on the emitter or the collector. If the ohmmeter reads a low resistance, indicating forward conduction of the junction, the transistor is an NPN. If the ohmmeter shows an open, the transistor is a PNP. If one of the junctions shows open or shorted both ways on what should be a diode junction, the transistor is defective.

USING THE DMM

The digital multimeter with its ohmmeter scales is the best instrument for working with semiconductors. First, the meter does not require zeroing on any of the ohmmeter scales. This alone provides a reduction in work load when taking many different readings. Second, consider the advantage of the autoranging feature that is offered by the instruments of Figures 5–4 and 9–5. These features make most resistance-measuring jobs a simple touch-and-read operation.

The DMM is a more accurate instrument than a VOM. The VOM accuracy is typically +/–5 percent, where a DMM is often better than 1 percent accurate on the ohms scales. Besides its greater accuracy, there is no chance of misreading the scale as there is with a VOM.

The DMM of Figure 9–5 offers a feature that makes the measurement of very low resistance readings more accurate; the test lead resistance can be "canceled out" by shorting the leads together, waiting for the reading to settle, and then pressing the "relative" button. This makes the reading go to zero, mathematically subtracting the known resistance of the leads.

There are a couple of things to keep in mind when using a DMM, however. While not really a disadvantage, autoranging may not settle on a range when testing circuits containing semiconductor junctions. This is caused by the instrument changing ranges while the junction also changes resistance because of the different current used on the new range. The result is that the instrument may continue to change ranges from one to another, without stopping. The answer is to use the scale intended for junctions, which is marked on the instrument face with the symbol of a diode. This is a fixed range and is tailored to the requirements of testing junctions. About 1 milliampere is the maximum current capability on this range, which is sufficient to reliably turn on a semiconductor junction. The open-circuit voltage at the test lead probes is limited to about 3 volts. *The scale of the diode function reads in volts, not ohms.* Using this feature, the DMM can distinguish between germanium junctions (about 0.3 volt) and silicon junctions (about 0.7 volt). This scale will indicate nearly zero volts when reading across a shorted junction, and more than 0.7 volt (*OL* or "overrange" for a Fluke meter) in both directions when the diode is open.

Another point to keep in mind is that *the normal ohmmeter function of a DMM often has insufficient voltage to turn on semiconductor junctions* when testing components in-circuit. Because of this, the instrument can read resistors placed in parallel with diodes or transistor junctions without considering the presence of the junction. To prove this is the case in any specific application, simply reverse the test leads in the circuit. If the junction is not turning on, the resistance reading will remain the same.

An important use for a DMM is to test for *continuity* in a circuit.

There is no absolute definition of "continuity," just as there is no fixed definition of the term "high." One must set a fixed value for a digital device, a go or no-go definition. The Fluke 77 meter in Figure 5–4 uses a set value of 175 Ω. Below 175 Ω, the meter will audibly report continuity with a beeper. Above that value, there will be no continuity reported, nor any audible signal. The detection of a forward-biased junction, however, will result in a single short "beep" from the device. The Fluke 87 in Figure 9–5 allows the user to define the "continuity" value as any one of 40, 200, 2,000, 20,000, or 200,000 Ω by locking the instrument on specified resistance ranges.

The continuity function is valuable when checking for continuity in circuit traces, wiring, or switch and relay contacts. The continuity tester may also feature a "stretcher," which will cause the beeper function to beep for long enough to be heard, even though the contact may be for as little as a millisecond.

In-Circuit Tests with a DMM

The DMM is simplicity itself to use when measuring resistance in cases where components are in a circuit. The interpretation of the readings, however, is another matter, for the reasons previously discussed. Paralleling resistance paths around the component in question will make the actual reading lower than anticipated. The only reliable resistance reading of a component is one made after the component is disconnected from any possible sources of reading error: in other words, out of circuit.

17.6 HUNTRON TRACKER™ TESTING OF DEAD CIRCUITS

The Huntron Tracker™ is a unique instrument for testing multiple components in-circuit or single components out-of-circuit. See Figure 17–2. Whereas the ohmmeter injects a small DC current into the circuit under test via its test leads, the Tracker inserts a small AC voltage. This difference allows the technician to observe circuit response over a range of voltages rather than a single voltage, which will display much more information about the circuit or component. Because of its AC input to the circuit, capacitors and inductors may now be registered, whereas an ohmmeter will report only an open or a near-short.

The Tracker will allow the identification of most components, even those connected in parallel to one another. Its principal strength is in comparing known good and suspected components, rather than providing absolute readings of resistance or reactance. Because of the ability to test reactive components, test results using this instrument are much more conclusive than those using only an ohmmeter.

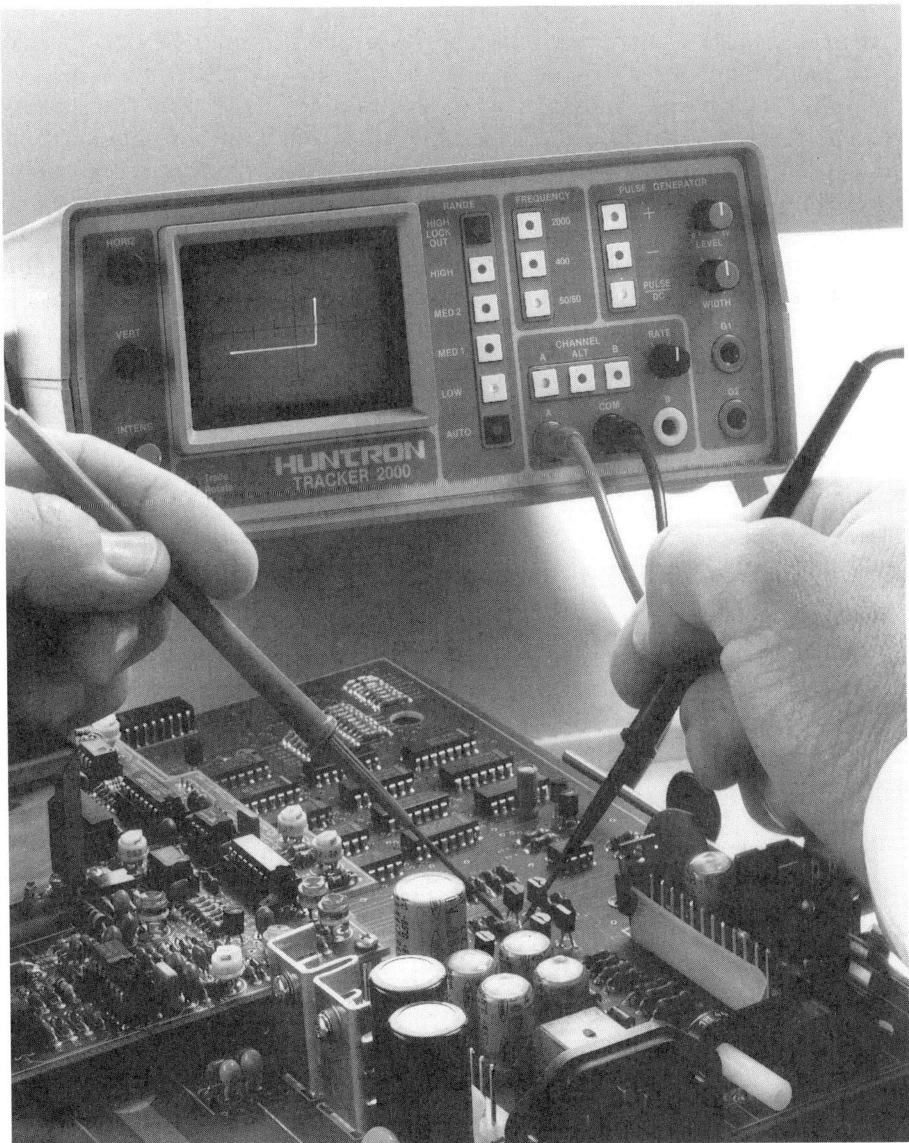

Figure 17–2 The Huntron Tracker™ provides signatures that are used to find defective parts.

OUT-OF-CIRCUIT TESTING OF INDIVIDUAL COMPONENTS

Much of the chance of success in using the Tracker is directly related to the operator's familiarity with the instrument. The more it is used and the more the technician relates the display to the component under test, the better the results. This familiarity begins with an understanding of the instrument.

Opens and Shorts on the Tracker Display

Refer to Figure 17–3 for examples of the displays in the following discussion. The display of the Tracker is a small cathode ray tube. On the face of the tube, the vertical represents current and the horizontal represents voltage. If the test leads are left open, the trace will show a single horizontal line. This line represents the AC voltage at the probe tips, without any current flow between them.

The horizontal line does not appreciably change length, but the technician should be aware that the horizontal voltage available at the tips of the test leads varies with the range selected. The highest range has a peak voltage of 60 volts. As the ranges are decreased through Medium 2, Medium 1, and Low, the peak voltage changes from this value to 20 volts, 15 volts, and 10 volts.

If the Tracker test leads are shorted, the display changes to a vertical line. This line represents a shorted current between the leads across which there is negligible voltage, and thus, no horizontal deflection. See Figure 17–3.

Diodes on the Tracker Display

We will next demonstrate how a diode shows both an open and a short, depending on the instantaneous polarity of the AC voltage applied. To properly set up for this test, be sure the Tracker is set for 60-Hz sweep

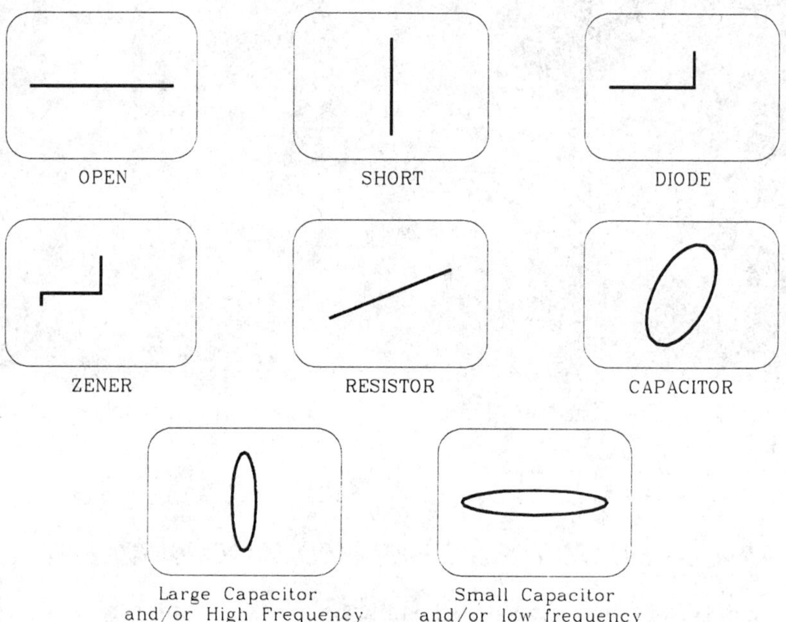

Figure 17–3 Basic patterns of single components, as shown on a Huntron Tracker™.

frequency and that the low impedance range is selected. *The low impedance range should always be used when testing single junctions.* Connect the test leads to the instrument and carefully center the horizontal trace vertically on the screen. Then, short the test leads and center the trace horizontally. When the leads are alternately opened and shorted together, the trace should inscribe an *X* exactly on the center of the screen.

Rectifier and Signal Diodes. Now, connect a good diode across the test leads. A waveform should appear, as shown in Figure 17–3. *If the waveform seems inverted, this is immaterial. If the test leads were reversed on the component, the pattern would be identical but with the waveform righted. Since the Tracker uses AC for testing, it is never necessary to reverse its leads.* The horizontal portion of the waveform occurs when the AC polarity back-biases the diode with a negative on the anode end. The vertical portion occurs when the AC polarity reverses, placing the positive on the anode. Note that there is a small displacement of the vertical line off-center. This is caused by the small voltage drop of the diode in the forward direction, before the voltage is sufficient to cause conduction. This is the familiar 0.3 V (for a germanium diode) or 0.7 V (for a silicon diode). Thus, the Tracker can be used to identify the type of diode in question.

Zener Diodes. Let's take this examination a bit further and place a zener diode across the Tracker leads. The zener must have a breakdown voltage of less than 60 volts in order for the breakdown to occur, since this instrument provides only a 60-V peak amplitude on the highest impedance range.

Connect the zener across the test leads. Note that the display now shows two voltages at which current occurs, one near the center (forward conduction of the diode) and one further away, on the opposite end of the horizontal trace. The distance from the vertical center to the far end breakdown is caused by the zener breaking down and avalanching, and occurs at the rated zener voltage of the diode. Changing ranges on the Tracker may result in losing this breakdown voltage because the instrument decreases voltage with lower ranges (20-V peak on the Medium 2 range, 15-V peak on Medium 1 range, and only 10-V peak on the Low range).

Resistors on the Tracker Display

Testing resistors is very easily done with a Tracker, but the results will be only approximate. Simply attach the resistor to the test leads and observe the display. The angle of rotation is related to the resistance and to the range in use. The ranges of Low, Medium 1, Medium 2, and High represent center-range resistance values of about 50 Ω, 1K Ω, 15 KΩ, and 50 KΩ, respectively, for a 45-degree tilt of the display. As the resistances on each of these ranges increase from the center values, the line increasingly approaches the horizontal, while decreases in resistance tilts the display more to the vertical. Using the various ranges, the Tracker will present approximate resistance comparisons (the angle of the display is difficult to read otherwise) for resistors of about 2 Ω to almost 1 megohm. Comparing resistances (using one of known value) gives a better idea of whether two resistors are similar in value.

Capacitors on the Tracker Display

A capacitor connected to the Tracker will result in the display of a reactive component. This causes the horizontal sweep to separate into forward-and-back lines rather than a single, retraced line. The displays of a capacitor are more easily understood if the basic open-horizontal, shorted-vertical system of the display is kept in mind while also remembering that a lot of capacitance at high frequency is effectively a short. Conversely, a small capacitor at low frequencies is an open.

Besides the ranges, the frequency of operation becomes a factor in the display when testing reactive components. The Tracker has three selectable frequencies of operation for testing frequency-sensitive components like inductors and capacitors. A capacitor that shows a near-open on the low range can be made more visible on the display (usually for purposes of comparison with a good, known-value capacitor) by increasing the frequency of operation. A given capacitor will register more like a short as the frequency increases. Thus, a capacitor that appears very open at 60 Hz will become more of a circle as the frequency is changed to 400 and then to 2000 Hz by pressing the appropriate buttons on the Tracker.

The largest capacitors (up to 1000 μfds) are best tested with the Low range at 60 Hz. Capacitors as small as .01 μfd or less will display best using the High range and 2000 Hz. All capacitors in between will require intermediate values of frequency and range to obtain a near-circular pattern, which is the best suited and most sensitive for comparing components.

Inductors on the Tracker Display

An inductor will also show a circular or elliptical pattern on the Tracker, very similar to that shown by a capacitor. The difference in the two patterns is an invisible change in the direction of rotation of the trace.

Inductances are the opposite of capacitors, and therefore, the higher the range used and the higher the frequency of testing, the more the inductor will resemble an open. (This fact allows differentiating between an inductor and a capacitor.)

Bipolar Transistors on the Tracker Display

Three tests must be made on a bipolar transistor to determine if it has the required two junctions (one from the base to the emitter and another from the base to the collector). Check these junctions as you would a diode, looking for a short in one direction and the open in the other. A shorted junction will show as a vertical line, and an open will show as a straight, horizontal line. Remember, you do not need to reverse the leads of the Tracker because the AC effectively does that for you. The remaining reading to take is from collector to emitter. Some transistors may exhibit an apparent breakdown at the higher-range test voltages, resulting in a small hook on one end of the open indication. This is normal and is caused by the base-to-emitter junction going into zener avalanche.

A Darlington transistor is actually two connected transistors, as shown in Figure 17–4.

The only difference between a bipolar transistor and a Darlington pair, as far as the Tracker is concerned, is that there is a higher voltage from base to emitter before the display goes from open to shorted. This is because we are now checking two junctions in series rather than a single junction.

FETs on the Tracker Display

A junction field effect transistor (JFET) is basically a diode tied into the approximate midpoint of a resistor. The JFET diode can be tested by connecting the Tracker across the gate and the source lead. The familiar checkmark pattern should result. If the diode is damaged, leakage (resistance) or a shorted pattern will show. This is the most common problem with a defective JFET. The specifics of testing FETs are covered in the Tracker manual, step by step, with typical displays for each set of conditions.

The patterns shown while testing insulated gate FETs (IGFETs) vary greatly, depending on the stimulus of the input gate. There should be an open between the gate and either of the two remaining leads for any kind of IGFET.

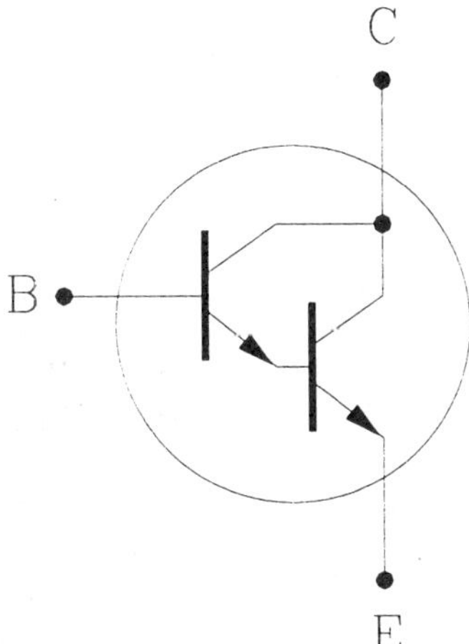

Figure 17–4 The internal connections of a Darlington Pair.

If an enhancement IGFET is being tested, there should be an open between source and drain when the gate is connected to the source lead (observe normal polarity appropriate to the device). Then, connect the gate to the drain and check for a normal low resistance from source to drain. If you are in doubt as to the readings obtained, compare them with readings from a known good device.

The depletion IGFET will always show leakage, whether the gate is connected to the source lead or the drain. The resistance from source to drain should be much lower when the gate is connected to the drain.

The different patterns resulting from depletion and enhancement IGFETs under differing conditions of loading and gate stimulus are available in the Tracker manual for those who need specifics of those procedures and test setups.

Thyristors on the Tracker Display

The Tracker also includes a pulse generator for testing thyristors out-of-circuit. Thyristors are characterized by their triggerable operation; once triggered, they conduct heavily until the applied voltage decreases to near zero. (Chapter 14 covers these components in further detail.) The normal output terminals of the thyristor are connected to the usual test leads of the Tracker. For a UJT, this means the base 1 and base 2 leads; for an SCR, this means the anode and cathode; and for a TRIAC the MT1 and MT2 leads are connected. The output pulse from the Tracker's pulse generator is then connected to the input element of the semiconductor, emitter, or gate, respectively, of the above-mentioned devices. The output pulse width and amplitude of the trigger (up to 5 V) is adjustable. This allows the comparison of two devices, a known good and the suspected bad component. Malfunctions of misfiring, erratic triggering, and opens and shorts within thyristors are easily detectable using this pulse-triggering feature of the Tracker.

Because of the wide range of instrument setups and displays, the Tracker instruction manual should be referred to for specifics on testing these devices.

Integrated Circuits on the Tracker Display

Integrated circuits, even the simple ones, consist of multiple transistors connected in various combinations of series and parallel within the chips. Most IC failures involve either the input or the output circuits of these chips. While the detection of input and output circuits is usually very easy with a Tracker, it cannot detect defects in the internal driving circuits.

ICs should be tested using either the Medium 1 or Medium 2 ranges. This applies a slightly higher voltage to the device under test, which is necessary with ICs because of the multiple junctions in series that are encountered.

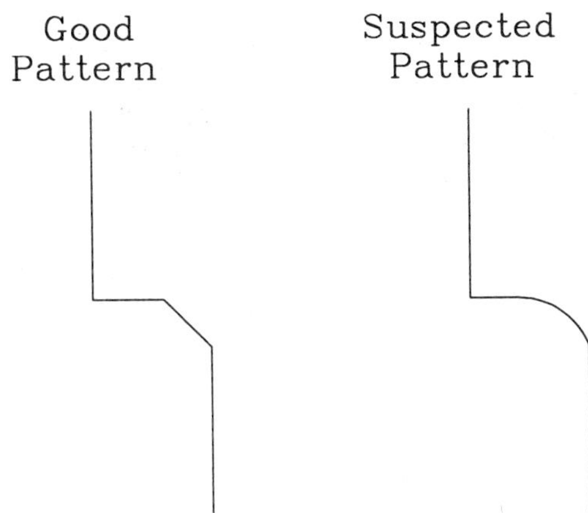

Figure 17–5 Generic waveform of an integrated circuit. Note the curved portion of the "bad" waveform.

The basic waveform most often seen looks like a high-backed chair, without back legs, as seen from the side. See Figure 17–5. The technician attempting to identify good and bad traces without any specific information should look for waveforms with straight sections. Many straight sections is generally good a sign, but any curved lines or portions of patterns signal cause for a more detailed look. A comparison with a good part or circuit, of course, will give a better evaluation of the pattern.

Occasionally, one may encounter an IC waveform that has what appears to be a small flutter or oscillation between line segments. This is caused by a fracture of the internal crystal structure of the device, which is sufficient cause to replace the device, even though it may still be working quite satisfactorily in the circuit. This defective pattern is sometimes called a "fractured knee."

IN-CIRCUIT TESTING OF INDIVIDUAL COMPONENTS

Once the technician has become familiar with the basic patterns of the junction, resistors, and capacitors, the waveforms obtained while testing in-circuit components become much more understandable. Consider the waveforms of Figure 17–6.

It would be useless to attempt to list all possible combinations of components, since there may be three, four, or more units simultaneously affecting the display in a given instance. Because of the infinite combinations possible, *the value of the Tracker as a troubleshooting instrument is in its ability to compare units rather than to read absolute values.*

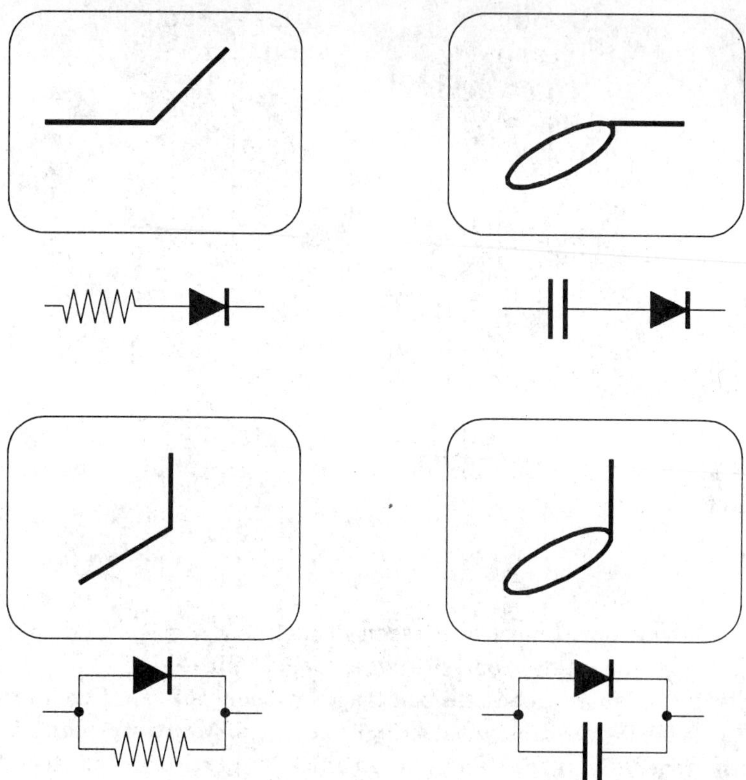

Figure 17–6 Combinations of basic resistive, junction, and capacitive patterns that may occur in actual in-circuit tests.

Selecting a Reference Point for Comparisons

Just as a technician routinely takes voltage or ohmmeter readings from the common measuring point of ground, the Tracker usually uses this point as well. As with a voltmeter or ohmmeter, however, this is not always the case. As the occasion demands, the reference point may be changed, usually to test a specific, ungrounded component in the circuit.

The reference may also be the Vcc power bus for the circuit in question. If dead-circuit waveforms taken with the ground as reference are not satisfactory, try a second set of readings using the Vcc bus as common.

The Three Tracker Troubleshooting Methods

There are three ways in which to use the Tracker: by visually interpreting each display, by comparing displays to recorded "good" displays, and by comparing good and defective circuits.

Individual Display Interpretation. The simplest way to use the Tracker is to connect it to a given circuit and look at the display. A schematic will be necessary to properly interpret the display. A comparison must be made between the actual display and what the technician would expect the display to be when connected to the components shown on the schematic. This method will require familiarity with the Tracker and all its basic displays of resistance, junctions, and reactance. (Some of these combinations were shown previously in Figure 17–6.)

Using Recorded Patterns. Recorded displays provide the information needed for a technician to quickly find the problem in a specific board. For each important point of interest, the Tracker display must be written down, preferably on the unit's schematic. This is similar to the marking of typical voltages on the schematic of a piece of equipment; thus, the information of what is normal is right at hand, requiring no estimate on the part of the technician and speeding up the job a great deal. This method is efficient when the technician may be required to troubleshoot a number of identical boards.

Direct Comparison with a Known Good Circuit. The fastest method of finding a PC board problem with the Tracker is to use it to compare two boards, one of them good and the other defective. Set up a common reference point such as ground (or, alternatively, the Vcc bus) and set the instrument to "Compare." This is done by pressing the ALT button on the instrument's front panel. This will cause it to alternately connect first one test lead and then the other into the input. Each of the two boards under test must have the same reference point, and they must both be connected to the Tracker's center, COMMON test jack. See Figure 17–7.

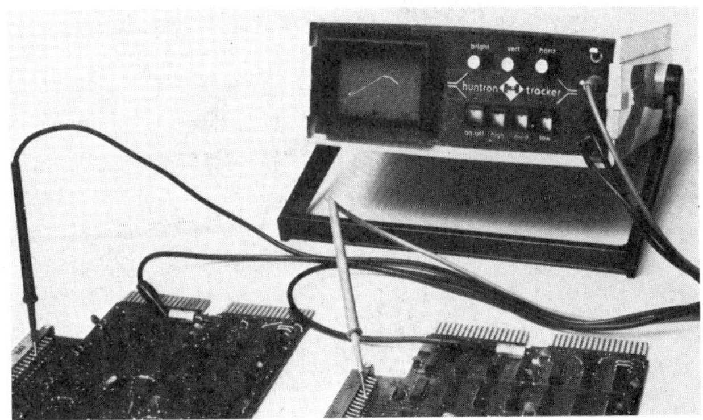

Figure 17–7 The Huntron Tracker™ also compares properly functioning and defective boards.

When both "hot" test leads are connected to the same point on each board, the display on the instrument may seem to have a very short jerk, but the pattern shown will be essentially stable. If the two boards are not electrically the same at that point, perhaps due to a defect in the bad board, the pattern on the instrument will "flip" back and forth and show two different patterns. The board with the faulty pattern can be distinguished by removing one of the test leads, leaving only one "hot" lead connected. Ignore the horizontal line shown for the disconnected lead and read the remaining pattern.

Testing Integrated Circuits with the Huntron Switcher™

The Huntron Switcher™ is an accessory for the Tracker. After connecting the switcher, alternating comparisons between two ICs, either in- or out-of-circuit, can be made quickly and easily. Just press a single button on the Switcher to compare a given pin on one IC with the same pin on a second. By pressing the buttons in any order, all the pins of the two ICs can be compared. See Figure 17–8.

While most IC failures can be detected with the Tracker, certain failures deep within the chips, in the driver circuits, will not be detectable with this instrument. Only substitution of the chip will verify this as the cause of an IC failure. Most failures of IC chips involve abuse of the input or output circuits, however, which should be easily detectable.

Figure 17–8 The Huntron Switcher™ makes it easy to compare chips, whether in or out of circuit.

Tracker In-Circuit Testing Levels

Testing a PC board with the Tracker is best done by following several levels of troubleshooting, in order:

1. Test for a Vcc-to-ground short.
2. Test major, likely failed components.
3. Test the edge connector.
4. Test all individual components.

These will be discussed in detail in the following paragraphs.

Test for a Vcc-to-Ground Short. Many failures are caused by a short from the Vcc supply bus to ground. These failures are most often due to a solder splash or similar direct short between traces, a shorted filter or bypass capacitor, or an IC that has failed by shorting internally. Each of these possibilities is explained, along with the methods for finding them, in section 6.5. To verify such a problem, use the Tracker, connecting it between the Vcc and ground buses. Using the low range and 60 Hz, there should be *no* vertical line. The vertical line indicates that there is a short. Remember, of course, that very large value filter capacitors (1,000 μfd and greater) will normally appear as a short at 60 Hz.

Test Major, Likely Failed Components. Components that dissipate power are the most likely ones to fail. This places power transistors at the top of the list by the sheer weight of statistics. Check the power transistors, whether bipolar, FET, TRIAC, or SCR. Your chances of going directly to the problem are very good: perhaps 50 percent!

Electrolytics have very small spacing internally between the active plates. This small spacing permits them to be easily damaged by small voltage overloads or ordinary failure without external cause. Be sure to check the capacitors on the board, especially the physically large ones. The size of an electrolytic increases with the rated operating voltage and the capacitance of the component, both of which also increase its chances of failing.

If an electrolytic capacitor has a metallic case, this can be used as a test point, too. The case is often at an intermediate value of the overall capacitance of the unit, but because of its ready accessibility from the board's top, it is a very handy point for a quick check. Again, a comparison with a good board is the method of choice.

Test the Edge Connector. The edge connector of a PC board, the contacts through which the board may be plugged into another board—provides a very convenient and likely place to find a fault. By comparison to another board (or by referring to recorded displays), the technician can very likely find the problem. This is because most problems on a board involve the input or output circuits, those same points that are available at the edge connector.

If a certain pin is found to have a very different pattern from that of a good board (again using the comparison method), the defect will often be traced back on the PC board to an open or a short. If the difference seems minimal, keep in mind that a *small* difference in patterns is often caused by the use of chips from different manufacturers.

To trace the defect further, the trace of the board is followed back to the source IC or other component, if practical. Several chips may connect to a given pin, making it necessary to test several rather than a single component. Be sure to watch very carefully for solder splashes on the trace if the defect shows as a short.

Test All Individual Components. If the repair of the board is of the highest priority and, for some reason, other traditional methods prove inappropriate, it is possible to individually check all the components on the board with the Tracker. The chances of finding the problem are good, even under these conditions. All that is required is a good set of recorded waveforms for each pin, or, more conveniently, a known good board for comparison. One of the Huntron seminars mentioned that by using the Tracker, an experienced operator can achieve a success rate of approximately 90 percent in finding the bad component on any given board.

When the bad component has been tentatively identified, it is time to remove it from the circuit for out-of-circuit testing. We shall, therefore, consider the removal of parts in detail in the following paragraphs.

Some equipment is at least partially constructed with the use of pop rivets. These handy fasteners are a once-only proposition. Once installed, the only easy way to remove them is to drill them out. Use a drill a few thousandths of an inch less than the hole into which the rivet was placed. After drilling through the fasteners with the proper size drill, it is a simple matter to pick off any remaining pieces of rivet.

17.7 REMOVE THE COMPONENT, THEN VERIFY THE FAILURE

DESOLDERING COMPONENTS

It requires a bit of skill and practice to avoid damage to printed circuit boards during unsoldering and resoldering operations. While the part being removed may not be worth a lot of money, the board itself may be very valuable. It is important to work quickly and to use the minimum heat necessary for both operations.

Today's circuit boards require the use of a heat-regulated soldering iron. Using an unregulated iron will subject the board and the components to excessive heat. A nonregulated iron might be sufficient for hobby work, but

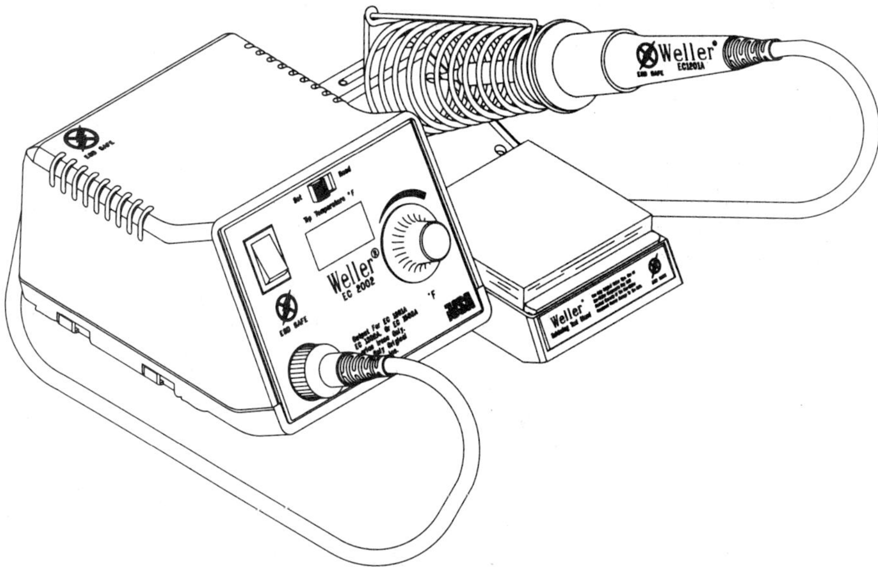

Figure 17–9 The temperature-regulated soldering iron is the safest tool for PC boards and components alike.

it does not belong in a professional shop, where work must meet the highest standards. See Figure 17–9.

Care of the Soldering Iron

Heating the connection to be desoldered is best done with a clean, tinned soldering iron. A dirty tip will not heat the connection nor melt the solder properly, as the dirt will prevent the conduction of heat.

The tinned portion of the tip of an iron is "wetted" with the molten solder. A tiny amount of solder applied to a tinned iron will provide a good heat transfer and result in the intended connection being heated to the proper temperature in a minimum of time. Be sure to apply only a small amount of solder to conduct the heat. If the tip of the iron is merely tinned without a bit of excess solder, it will be considerably more difficult to heat a connection properly and quickly. Besides, it is better for the iron if it is kept well tinned with a bit of excess solder at all times.

A damp sponge is good for cleaning dirt off the soldering iron tip. The technician should not keep the tip stripped of solder all the time, however. To strip the tip and allow it to sit in the holder for long periods will result in its oxidation, and an oxidized tip will not transfer heat. Properly clean the tip of dirt and oxidation with the sponge and put a bit of solder on it before leaving it idle. An already oxidized tip can sometimes be rejuvenated by alternately cleaning it on the damp sponge and applying very small amounts of rosin core solder over as much of the tip area as will accept it. When the tip becomes dripping wet with solder, remove the solder by wiping on the sponge and repeating the process again. It may take several minutes to reclaim a burned tip, but stubborn cases will require its replacement.

Never file the tip of a plated iron. Filing the tip will remove the special thin plating, ruining the tip.

Rosin is available in a paste form for heavy soldering jobs. Paste should not be used directly on a temperature-regulated iron. The excess flux can work its way up into the threaded sleeve of the iron and into the internal parts, where it will burn and prevent the disassembly of the iron by jamming the threads.

Solder

There are two very general kinds of solder, one with rosin flux within tiny cores in the solder and one with an acid flux. *Only rosin-core solder should be used for electronic work.* Acid-core solder is for use on plumbing, where corrosion is heavier and a more powerful cleaning agent is needed. Acid-core residues can badly deteriorate PC boards. Solder containing acid flux should *never* be used on electronic equipment. Leave it for the plumbers.

Rosin flux is a cleaning agent that makes the solder flow readily into the connection and bond to the metal. Under the heat of the iron, rosin does not last long. The burning of the rosin is what makes the smoke during a soldering operation. If an old connection is merely reheated while attempting to make a better joint, there will be no cleaning action, and the connection will probably not be as good as possible. This is often called a "cold solder joint." The application of a fraction of an inch of fresh solder to an old joint is often all that is needed to improve the joint's quality.

Rosin-core solder is available in several different ratios of tin to lead. Electronic work is best done with a 63:37 ratio. This combination melts at the lowest possible temperature and hardens quickly without an intermediate "mushy" state.

Soldering Tools

For various soldering and desoldering operations, a few items are helpful to have on hand:

A pair of hemostats for component removal and placement.

Denatured alcohol for removing rosin residue.

Old toothbrush for use with above.

Vacuum solder-removal tool (solder-sucker).

Desoldering braid for solder removal.

Magnifying glass for solder joint inspection.

Desoldering Methods

If the technician is working at a large enough company, particularly one that deals with government contracts, there may be a special and expensive piece of equipment intended solely for soldering and desoldering operations. It will probably include a motor-driven vacuum pump for sucking up molten solder and a sophisticated iron for both operations. Very close control of the soldering iron temperature is possible on some of these machines.

Other times, the technician must work with simple hand tools to remove and install components. Removing two- or three-lead components is usually quite easy. Just gently pull on the component (rocking it, if it has three legs) while each joint is heated successively. One can remove most components in this way without a lot of desoldering. The holes remaining after the component has been removed can be cleaned easy, using desoldering braid or a vacuum solder-sucker. Be very careful not to lift the pads or traces of the board with excessive pressure or too much heat.

Multiple pinned components like ICs are more difficult to remove. There are four basic methods of IC removal:

1. Clip the pins and remove the stubs.
2. Desolder using braid.
3. Desolder using a solder-sucker (with the board either vertical or horizontal).
4. Heat-gun desoldering.

Each of these methods will be covered in the following paragraphs.

Clip the Pins and Remove the Stubs

There is an easy way of removing an old IC with minimal heat being applied to the PC board, if the old chip is either proven to be bad or if it is so inexpensive that it can be ruined in the removal. *This method is probably the best to use in all but special circumstances.* See Figure 17–10.

Once the old IC is off the board and the stubs have been removed, either braid or a solder-sucker may be used to remove the remaining solder in the holes. This IC removal method subjects the board to the least amount of heat of all techniques.

Desolder Using a Solder-Sucker

When the PC board and the IC are both to be saved, a solder-sucker is the next best method to use in IC removal. There are two ways to use this tool: with the board vertical, working with both sides at once (preferred), and with the board horizontal, working from the back side of the board only.

Working with the board vertical allows the technician to heat the connec-

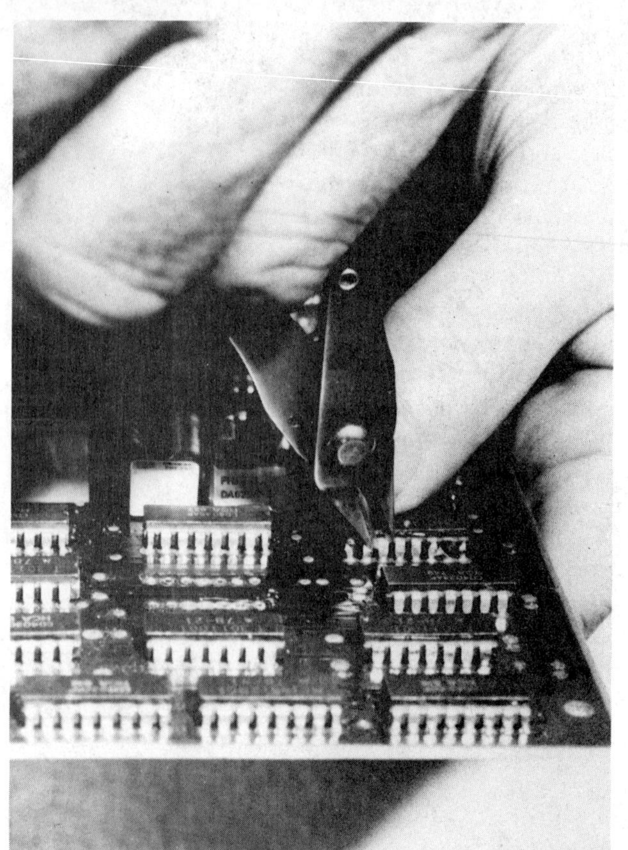

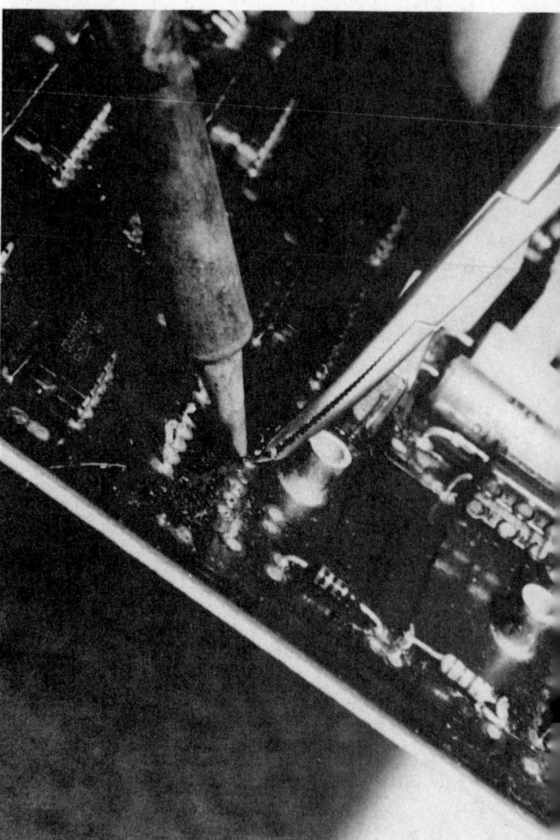

Figure 17–10 If the old chip is bad or of low quality, clipping the pins is probably the best desoldering method as it will cause the least damage to the board.

tion from the component side of the board, holding the solder-sucker to the opposite side of the connection. When the solder melts, just press the release of the solder-sucker. Almost all of the solder should be sucked from the through-hole pad into the sucker. See Figure 17–11. An alternative method is to place the board on the bench with the foil side up, as shown in Figure 17–12.

Heat the connection with the iron in one hand, holding the solder-sucker ready in the other. When the connection becomes molten, remove the iron, place the solder-sucker over the connection, and press the trigger, all in one smooth movement. This method requires speed and a bit of practice. Hesitation in getting the solder-sucker onto the connection and pressing the trigger will allow the connection to cool, and the whole operation will then have to be repeated. The result will be that both the board and the IC will become heated, which is something that must be kept to a minimum.

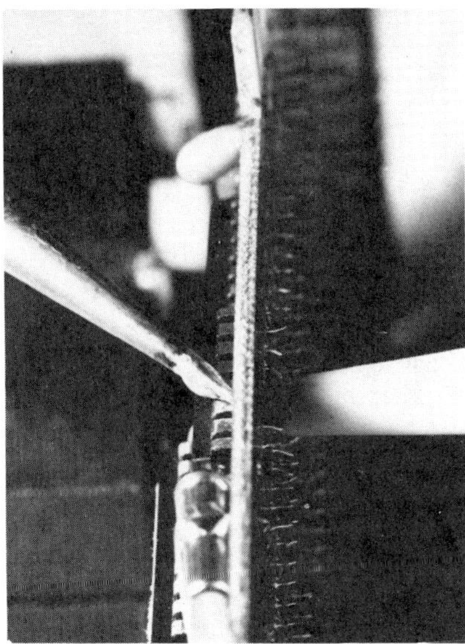

Figure 17–11 Working from both sides of the board is the best way to remove good components with a solder-sucker.

Figure 17–12 Working only from the foil side of the board requires coordination and speed.

Desolder Using Braid

If one does not have a solder-sucker and both the board and the IC are to be saved, the use of desoldering braid is suggested. Desoldering braid can be purchased in small rolls or fabricated from the shield of a piece of small coaxial cable. The braid should have a small amount of rosin flux spread through the weave to encourage the wicking action that absorbs molten solder. See Figure 17–13. The braid can also sometimes help when other solder removal methods are only partially effective. It should be placed between the tip of the soldering iron and the work. As the work heats, the solder becomes molten from the heat transferred through the braid. Capillary action then absorbs the molten solder, much like a terrycloth towel absorbs water. When the braid becomes saturated, clip off the stiff part of the braid and continue working.

Figure 17–13 Soldering braid may help when other methods are not completely successful.

Heat-Gun Desoldering

It is possible to use a heat-gun to desolder multipin components such as ICs. Just apply sufficient heat with the gun to the trace side of the board (not the component side) until the solder holding the component is melted, and then use a pair of pliers or hemostats to pull the component free. This method is potentially the most damaging of all desoldering methods, but it can be used when the board is of no consequence but the part to be removed is. Plan on ruining the board for future use. An occasion to use a heat gun for desoldering might arise when an IC must be salvaged from a "junk" board.

DESOLDERING SURFACE-MOUNTED DEVICES

Surface-mounted devices (SMDs) are extremely small, probably reaching the limit at which a technician can work with individual components by hand. To properly see the markings, if any, will require a strong magnifying glass.

Special tools are recommended when working on boards using surface-mounted technology (SMT).

Temperature-regulated iron with 1/16" or small tip, 500–600°.

SN62 solder with 2 percent silver, 0.015" dia., rosin core.

Stainless steel tweezers (hemostats).

Magnifying glass.

Solder removal braid of the smallest size available.

Dental picks.

Standard ICs have pins spaced 0.1" apart. Surface-mounted devices have pin spacings of .05" or even .025" for the smallest components. Because of this close spacing, a very small tip on the soldering iron must be used and great care must be exercised to make successful repairs on these tiny circuits. Additionally, all SMDs should be handled in accordance with the rules for handling static-sensitive devices.

The removal of two-lead devices such as capacitors and resistors may be done by first lightly gripping the device with the tweezers. Alternately heat both ends of the device with the iron, and *twist* the part to remove it. Lifting the component runs the risk of lifting the traces to which it is attached. These small parts are often held in place with a tiny spot of epoxy under the component. This epoxy held the device in place while the entire board was wave-soldered at the time of original assembly.

Once the part has been removed, clean the solder pads of excess solder with the braid. Remove the remains of epoxy by gently scraping it away with a tiny chisel or dental pick. If left in place, the old epoxy will elevate the new part, making it more difficult to solder it into place.

IF THE COMPONENT IS BAD, WHAT IS THE REASON?

It is not enough to simply find a bad component and replace it. It is equally important to attempt to determine *why* the part failed in the first place. Review Table 17–1 for the most common failures of electronic components *and their causes.* Take particular note of the failure patterns for semiconductors, resistors, and inductors. Whenever one of these components is found to be defective, the technician should investigate further to find a possible second, primary cause of the problem.

Semiconductors often fail by themselves. A semiconductor that dissipates a substantial amount of heat will be particularly prone to failure simply because heat destroys semiconductors. The failure of a heat sink to make good contact with the device is a common contributing cause of heat-related failures. Semiconductor biasing should also be checked carefully before replacing these devices to be sure that the correct bias for the component is actually being applied. A failure caused by a bad bias circuit can immediately destroy any new device that is installed unless the bias circuit defect is corrected first.

Resistors are the prime example of a component that fails much more often because of another related component failure than due to resistor failure itself. However, one exception is worth mentioning here. If the resistor is a high-power resistor (greater than about 5 watts) and is normally operated at the full rated power, the resistor might well fail, usually by opening of its own accord.

ALTERNATIVES IF THE REMOVED COMPONENT WAS GOOD

If the suspected component checks out as good once out of the circuit, leave it out for the time being. This will leave the circuit more accessible to use of the ohmmeter or Tracker to make further tests of the circuit. The removal of a part will often open several possible parallel paths, making the readings more meaningful and easier to interpret.

It is possible to temporarily install a part, including integrated circuits, into the circuit by the method shown in Figure 17–14. The toothpick method will work reliably only when the PC board has plated-through holes.

Whenever a component, especially an IC, is replaced, the technician should consider whether to install a socket for it. With a socket, future replacements will be much easier. The reason why sockets are not put into circuit cards by the manufacturer is their cost and the fact that they introduce the distinct possibility of poor connections. Manufacturers usually prefer to rely instead on the reliability of the original components. Later, it may be the case that a particular component is stressed in normal operation enough that it may occasionally fail, a point not known to the manufacturer. The installation of the socket can be very handy for components that have shown a high failure rate in the past. Sockets should not be used in radio frequency circuits that operate at more than about 30 MHz be-

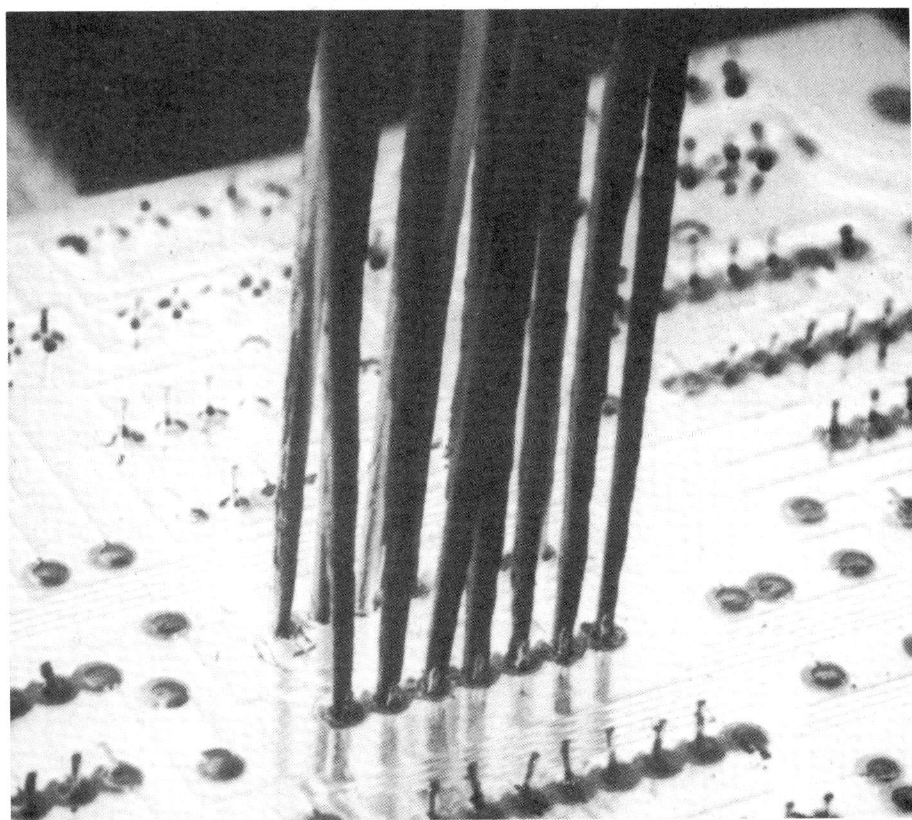

Figure 17–14 The toothpick method allows electrical installation without soldering.

cause lead lengths may be critical when operating at these high frequencies. Other applications in which sockets should not be used involve those that must tolerate high vibration levels.

Occasionally the technician may find that a removed component checks out as good and that all the components in the vicinity do as well. In this case, two options are possible: (1) replace the good-but-suspected component with a new one or (2) reinstall the old component and resume troubleshooting. This will make it necessary to begin over again, starting with the original bad symptoms and redoing the troubleshooting job from scratch.

In cases of doubt as to whether the old component caused the original "bad" symptoms, *the final conclusive test of a part is to compare operation of the old part with that of a new or otherwise known good part.*

17.8 VERIFYING A BAD COMPONENT OUT-OF-CIRCUIT

BATTERIES (CELLS)

Two or more cells make a battery of cells or, simply, a battery. Through common usage, a flashlight cell is often improperly called a battery. Both terms will be used properly in this chapter.

Since we are considering now the testing of suspected components, the logical place to start is the testing of cells. They are, of course, never tested with an ohmmeter. Instead, a voltmeter must be used.

The only valid test of the condition of a battery is to measure its voltage while it is providing a heavy current to a load!

The true test of a battery is to subject it to a heavy load for a short time and see if it can deliver relatively heavy current. Since battery failures are usually evident in that they can no longer sustain a high-current drain, this is the test of choice. An automobile battery should be tested for the correct terminal voltage while delivering very high currents (maybe 100 amperes). This will ensure that a battery that passes the test will certainly be able to crank the engine of a car. Special testers are available for car and other batteries. These instruments are both a voltmeter and a high-power load resistor.

Smaller cells such as those used to power hand-held radios, watches, and calculators should also be tested while under load. Keep in mind that these are severe loads and should not be held on the cell for any longer than necessary. Note also the wide difference in load resistances recommended for these cells (see Table 17.2).

BIPOLAR TRANSISTORS

For a discussion of bipolar transistors, see the heading "Transistors."

BRIDGES

Diode modules are available in prepacked, potted assemblies with three or four leads. The three-leaded components are generally two diodes (half of a bridge). See Figure 17–15.

These are used when a full-wave, center-tapped transformer is providing the AC input. Four-leaded devices have all four diodes required for a full-wave output. Each of the internal devices can be tested individually through the leads. See the entry titled "Diodes" for the details of testing these components. If any reading is bad, the whole component must be replaced.

CABLES, MULTIPLE-WIRE

The testing of cables, both multiple-wire and coaxial, are covered in section 3.4.

Table 17–2 TEST CRITERIA for SMALL CELLS

Cell Type*	Load R (Ohms)	Minimum V (Volts)
Cylindrical Cells and Batteries		
1.4-V hearing aid	60	1.2
1.5-V carbon-zinc (general use)	10	1.1
1.5-V alkaline	1	1.1
1.2-V ni-cad	1	1.1
6-V camera battery	1,200	4.4
6-V lantern battery (dry cell)	40	4.4
9-V carbon-zinc	250	6.6
9-V alkaline	15	6.6
Miniature Cells		
1.4-V mercury		
watch and calculator		
high-drain	200	1.0
low-drain	3,000	1.0
camera	300	1.1
hearing aid	1,000	1.2
1.5-V general-use manganese	200	1.0
1.5-V silver		
watch and calculator		
high-drain	200	1.3
low-drain	3,000	1.3
camera	300	1.1
hearing aid	1,000	1.2
1.5-V carbon-zinc	200	1.0
1.5-V lithium-iron	3,000	1.0
3.0,V lithium-manganese	600	2.0

*Information courtesy Eveready-Union Carbide.

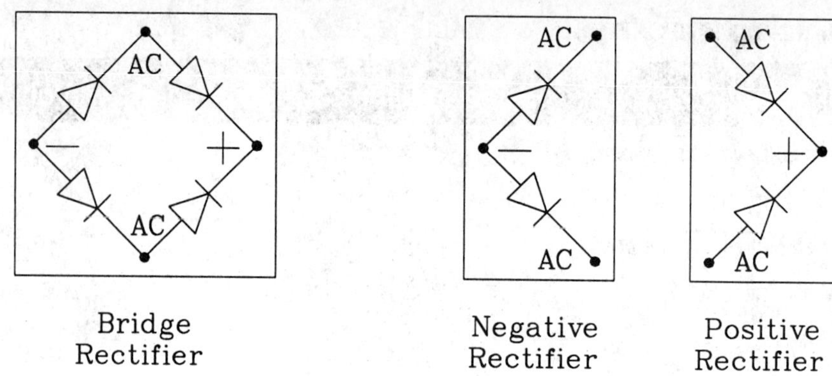

Figure 17–15 Examples of the diodes within prepackaged bridges and partial bridges.

CAPACITORS

Color codes for many different styles of capacitors can be found in Appendix I.

Capacitors fail by shorting, leaking, opening, or, rarely, by changing value. The shorted capacitor is easily identified using an ohmmeter or a Tracker. The open capacitor is another matter, however. Substitution is the most reliable method of determining if the original was defective.

It is possible that the capacitor does not have the same capacitance at all voltages. This may be demonstrated by using a Tracker. If the pattern shown is a "kinked" circle or ellipse rather than a smooth curve, this indicates a poor capacitor.

A VOM or DMM, when locked on a single ohmmeter range (autoranging is not appropriate here), may be used to compare capacitors, too. Select a range of the instrument that will allow the charging curve of the capacitor to be shown in 3 to 5 seconds or so. Compare the charge time of the suspected capacitor and a known good one. Begin the timing from the instant a short is removed from the capacitor until the charge reaches, for example, two-thirds of the full scale in use. The VOM and DMM will use lower resistance scales for larger capacitors, and high ranges for small-value capacitors.

Incidently, the meter of Figure 9–5 has a special feature that can quickly and directly measure capacitors with values between about .005 and 5.8 μfds. With some precautions, even smaller values can be measured.

CELLS

See the previous section titled, "Batteries (Cells)."

CIRCUIT BREAKERS

A circuit breaker is a switch that will switch itself to the "off" position during an overcurrent condition. Testing such a device will require a closely controlled source of current (very low voltages will suffice) and a means of monitoring the current passing through the circuit breaker. A variable power supply able to supply at least twice the rated current of the breaker will be required. In addition, it will be necessary to have the complete information on the particular type of circuit breaker. This is necessary because breakers do not instantly open when the rated current is passing through them. They are designed to remain closed during an overload for a specific amount of time before opening, with the duration related to the percentage of overcurrent that is flowing.

The best test of a circuit breaker, lacking the test equipment, is to simply replace it with one of the correct rating. If the new breaker remains closed under the same load conditions that frequently caused the old one to trip off the line, it is reasonable to assume that the old circuit breaker was defective.

COAXIAL CABLES

The testing of cables, both multiple-wire and coaxial, is covered in section 3.4.

CONNECTORS

Other than the visible damage that sometimes occurs in connectors, a suspected bad connection can be difficult to troubleshoot because of mechanical restraints. Some connectors do not allow easy access to the soldered connections for testing purposes.

Most problems with connectors will show up as a mechanical intermittent. Bend the mating halves of the connector back and forth, and the connection of one or more pins may open at that exact moment, indicating the mechanical intermittent. Depending on the kind of connector, it may be possible to respring the contacts, obtaining an acceptable contact. Other kinds of connectors cannot be resprung at all because of their construction. In this case, the replacement of one or even both halves of the connector may be the only reliable fix.

Another common problem with connectors is the situation in which the wires going into the connector are broken at the point where they are soldered to the connector. In some cases it may be feasible to resolder the broken wire to the connector if the wire is not too short. If the wire is too short, it may be necessary to unsolder all the wires, completely resoldering them.

Whenever a connector is reassembled, be sure that the clamping mechanism, if any, holds the cable securely. The most common cause of connector failures is by improper assembly, making the individual wires of the cable take stress at the soldered connections rather than passing the stress to the entire cable via a proper clamp.

CRYSTALS, QUARTZ

Quartz crystals are a circuit component that ensures the proper frequency of operation. The crystal itself is a small, mechanically resonant, precisely shaped and ground chip of quartz. The quartz is usually manufactured for purity. See Figure 17–16.

Each crystal is meant to have a particular *capacitive load* on it. This capacitance is usually below about 60 picofarads. The operation of a circuit without the proper load capacitance (including stray capacitance of the circuit) can mean off-frequency operation or even complete nonoscillation of the circuit.

The end result is that only the substitution of a known good, identical crystal can determine if the original crystal is defective. Be sure to check for the proper frequency of operation if another crystal is used.

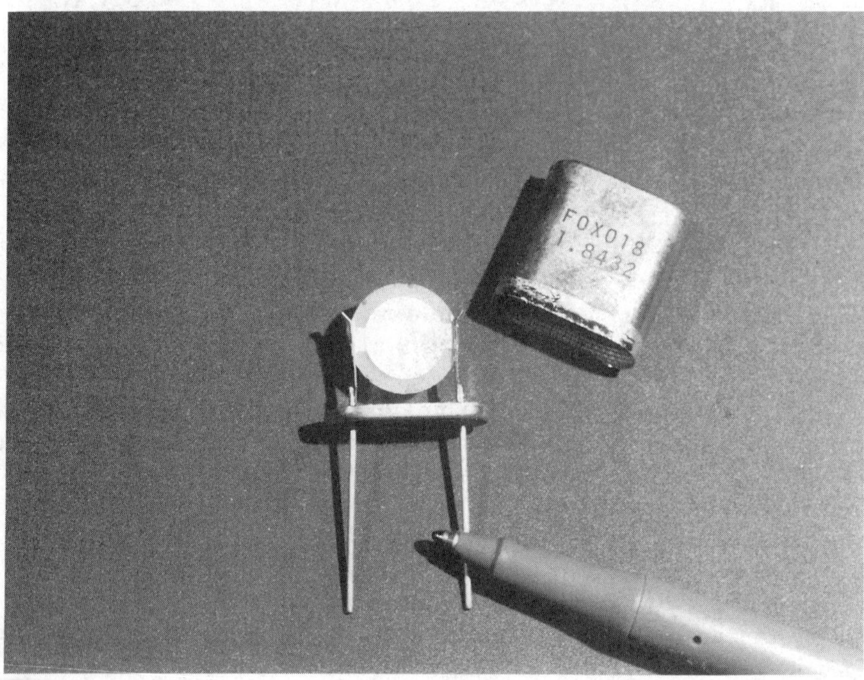

Figure 17–16 A radio frequency crystal is a wafer of quartz with two electrodes attached.

DIODES

Power Diodes

Power diodes are usually the silicon variety and should have a 0.7-V forward voltage drop. This voltage can be easily checked with a digital multimeter, using the special diode scale. When the DMM leads are reversed, the meter should indicate an open. However, the use of the resistance scales of a DMM will produce invalid readings. A VOM will test power diodes quite well using any scale, since the high current of the low ranges and the high voltage of the highest range should be well within the specifications of a power diode.

Signal and Tuning (Varactor) Diodes

Signal diodes are much smaller than a power diode and cannot withstand high currents or voltages. Restrict the testing of small diodes to the ranges *other* than R 1 and R 1,000 (the highest ohmmeter range) of a VOM because of the sensitivity of small diodes. A DMM, on the other hand, should not damage small diodes because of the very low voltages and currents used for testing. The Tracker should be used on either of the Medium ranges.

Light Emitting Diodes (LEDs)

LEDs may be quite easily tested with an ohmmeter. A VOM may be used in the middle ranges of the instrument, avoiding the highest and lowest ranges. Check for forward conduction and an open in the reverse direction. Compare the unit with a known good LED if there is any doubt. LEDs usually open rather than short.

A TRACKER will brightly light an LED using the Low range. The meter of Figure 9–5 will make a good LED light when connected with the proper polarity, but only enough to see if viewed in subdued lighting.

LEDs can best be tested while in operation (in-circuit). When an LED is lighted, it should have a specific voltage drop across it. This voltage depends on the color of the LED. The remainder of the supply voltage is dropped across at least one resistance, in series with the power source. Section 11.1 includes a listing of the *voltages* that may be expected across LEDs when they are operated in a circuit.

LED Displays

LED displays are really just seven or eight individual diodes placed in such a manner that they can represent decimal figures when selectively energized. An eighth diode may be provided for a decimal point. See Figure 17–17.

The seven-segment display is usually driven with a decoder chip, either a 7447 or a 7448 TTL chip. A binary input is encoded for the display output.

Figure 17–17 The seven-segment display will show numbers by lighting combinations of individual segments.

Note that numbers from 0 to 9 can be displayed, but higher binary inputs may result in encoded displays as shown in Figure 17–18.

Each segment of an LED display can be individually tested as an LED. It will probably be more convenient, however, to simply unplug the suspected display and see if a new display works where the original did not. Occasionally, a display will go bad when a segment "dies."

Additional segments can be designed into displays to enable them to show letters or symbols. These are called alphanumeric displays. Due to the complexity of encoding the individual segments, such displays are usually operated with custom-designed driver chips for that specific display or by a microprocessor and software.

Photo Diodes

Photo diodes are sensitive to light. They are usually back-biased by placing them in series with a resistor. The junction point is the output. See Figure 17–19.

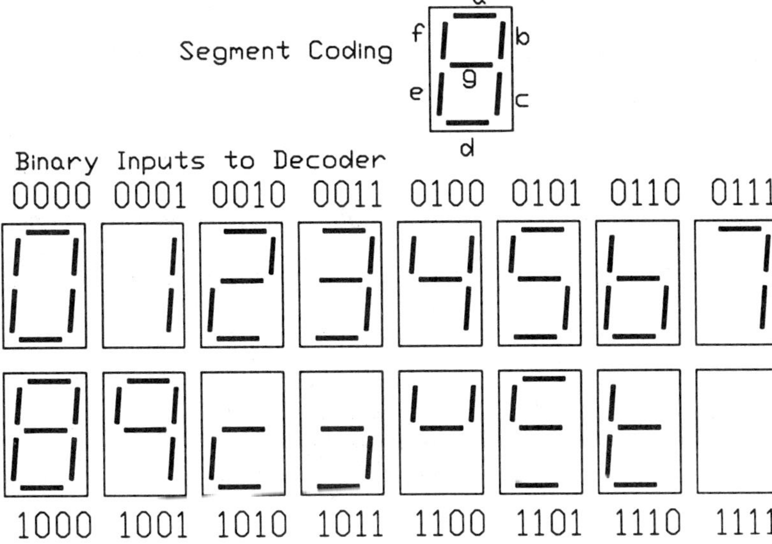

Figure 17–18 Seven-segment display-segment coding and the patterns resulting from various digital inputs.

It is faster in most cases to replace the photo-sensitive component in question, noting the improvement in circuit performance when the new part is installed. Of course, a sample circuit such as the one just given could be put together and the outputs compared between known good and suspected components.

Gunn, Impatt, and Step Recovery Diodes

These are microwave diodes. While they are intended only for use at microwave frequencies, they may be checked safely by substitution, *not* with an ohmmeter or Tracker.

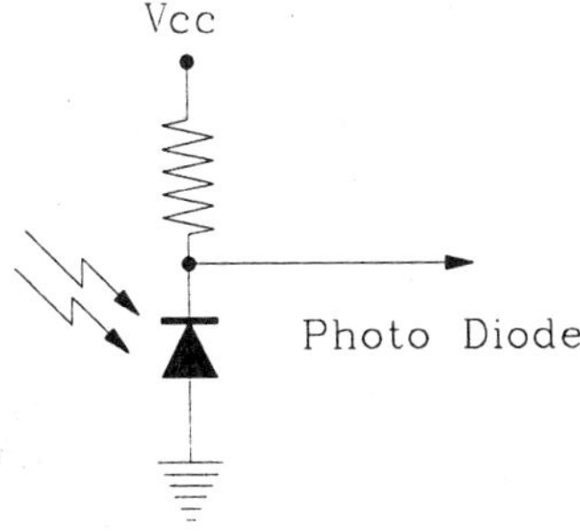

Figure 17–19 Typical schematic for a photo diode.

PIN Diodes

A PIN diode may be tested as a power diode, as described previously.

Zener Diodes

A zener diode may be tested with a VOM ohmmeter or a DMM meter on the diode scale, as a normal diode. Depending on the zener voltage rating, there will probably be an open in the back-biased direction. At least, the ohmmeter or DMM will show if the device is shorted, a common mode of zener failure.

A better zener test uses the Huntron Tracker™. Diodes of up to about 60 V can be checked with this instrument, comparing the test pattern of a suspected device to that of a known good device.

The most precise method of testing zeners to is apply a DC voltage of a few volts above the zener rating of the diode, through a current-limiting resistor of about 1,000 Ω. Read the actual voltage across the zener alone with a voltmeter. This test will show the zener voltage at low current. The voltage will increase by a few percent when the device has normal operating current through it and heats slightly.

FLUORESCENT DISPLAYS

A fluorescent display uses relatively high voltages, typically 75 volts. They are similar to neon lamps in that they use a current discharge through a gas to emit light. Because of the requirement for a high voltage, the best method of determining lamp condition is to compare a suspected display with a known good one, using the same driving circuit.

FUSES

Any fuse over about 1 ampere should measure as a short with an ohmmeter or a Tracker. Fuses of less than this rating may show some internal resistance; the lower the rating of the fuse, the more resistance will be indicated. Be very careful when testing very-low-current fuses with a VOM because of the high currents used for testing. Remember that a VOM can produce up to 0.3 ampere on the lowest ohmmeter range.

Solid-state fuses are now available that protect circuitry by effectively opening the current path to the power source. These small units, which resemble a small capacitor, use the heating effect of current to make semiconductor material within the fuse increase dramatically in resistance. As long as the overload is sustained, the semiconductor fuse keeps its temperature high enough to limit the flow of current. When the overload is removed, the temperature of the fuse drops and it regains its normal low resistance. Thus, the solid-state fuse is self-resetting over a period of a minute or two. Notice that the symptoms of normal cycling of such a fuse might suggest an intermittent power problem.

HALL EFFECT TRANSISTORS

A hall effect transistor is sensitive to magnetic fields. It requires other circuitry to operate, an amplifier being the most important. The output voltage of a hall transistor is very small. Only the substitution of a known good transistor will easily indicate whether the original was defective.

IGFETs (INSULATED GATE FIELD EFFECT TRANSISTORS)

Insulated gate FETs vary resistance from drain to source according to the static charge connected to their gates. If an ohmmeter is connected with the proper polarity to the drain and source (positive to the drain for an N-channel device, and opposite polarity for a P-channel FET) and the gate is shorted to the drain also, there should be a relatively low resistance read on the ohmmeter. See Figure 17–20.

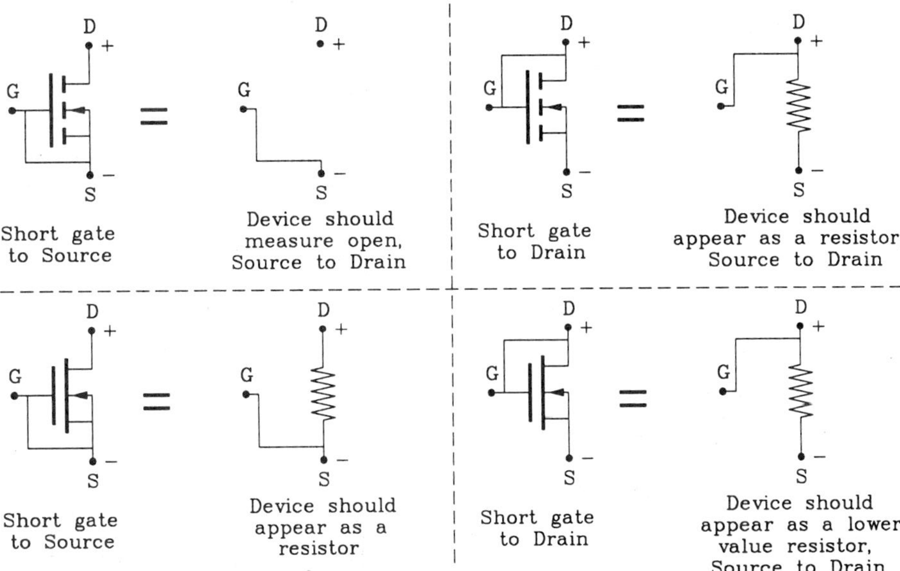
OHMMETER TESTING OF N-CHANNEL FETs
D
G
S
+
−
Short gate to Source
Device should measure open, Source to Drain
Short gate to Drain
Device should appear as a resistor, Source to Drain
Short gate to Source
Device should appear as a resistor
Short gate to Drain
Device should appear as a lower value resistor, Source to Drain
Note: P-Channel devices may be tested by reversing the polarity of the ohmmeter leads.

Figure 17–20 Testing IGFETs with an ohmmeter.

Exact readings can be compared between original and known good components.

The most common problem encountered with FETs is that the gate insulation to the substrate is punctured. The gate should always measure open to any other lead of the device. Any reading of other than open is reason to discard the FET.

More exacting resistance tests using the Tracker are possible. The operating manual for the instrument can be consulted if detailed testing of FETs is desirable.

INCANDESCENT LAMPS

Incandescent lamps are just resistors that are supposed to glow from orange to white-hot. A peculiarity of incandescent lamps is that they measure a low resistance when cold. Under normal operation, their internal resistance can increase to 10 times the cold resistance. This is called a *positive temperature coefficient*; resistance increases as temperature also increases. Because of this characteristic, the resistance reported by an ohmmeter will be far below what would be expected if the operating voltage and current were used to calculate it.

INDUCTORS

An inductor should appear as a long piece of wire to an ohmmeter. As such, the ohmic value should be very low, often indicating less than 1 ohm.

An inductor will often open due to other circuit defects, such as a short to ground. An open inductor is easily detected, as shown in Figure 12–8.

Because of the normally very low resistance of a good inductor, an inductor that has shorted turns will be difficult to detect. The substitution of a known good inductor is the best way to determine if a suspect inductor is defective.

INSULATED GATE FIELD EFFECT TRANSISTORS

See IGFETs.

JUNCTION FIELD EFFECT TRANSISTORS (JFETs)

An ohmmeter or Tracker will register the drain-to-source leads of a junction FET as a resistance, leaving the gate open. The gate to either of the other two leads should show as a diode, with relatively low resistance in one direction (use the diode function of a DMM) and an open with the opposite polarity applied. See Figure 17–21.

The most common problem that develops to ruin a JFET is that when it is back-biased, the diode develops a leakage or a short instead of being open.

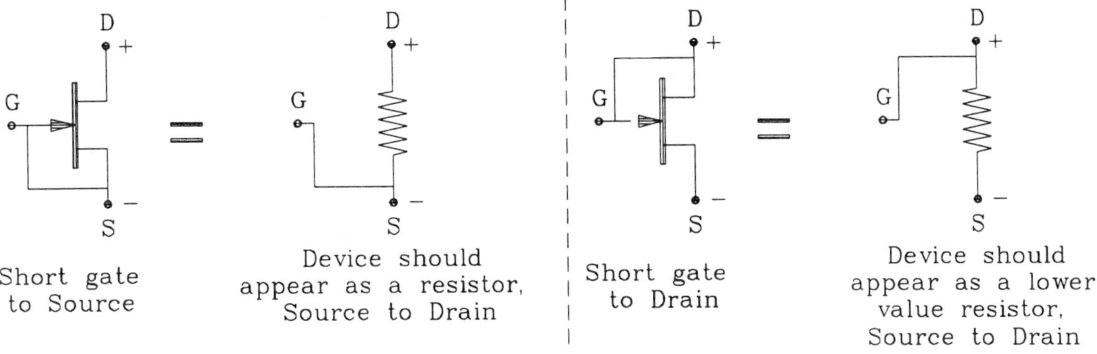
OHMMETER TESTING OF N-CHANNEL JFETs
D
+
G
S
−
Short gate to Source
Device should appear as a resistor, Source to Drain
Short gate to Drain
Device should appear as a lower value resistor, Source to Drain
Note: P-Channel devices may be tested by reversing the polarity of the ohmmeter leads.

Figure 17–21 Testing the JFET with an ohmmeter.

LAMPS

For a discussion of lamps, see under specific type (e.g., incandescent, fluorescent, neon).

LIGHT EMITTING DIODES (LEDS)

For a discussion of LEDs, see "Diodes."

LIQUID CRYSTAL DISPLAYS (LCDs)

LCDs require a square-wave driving waveform to prevent clouding of the display. For this reason, testing them out-of-circuit is not practical. It is best to substitute a known good display to see if the original was bad.

METAL OXIDE VARISTORS

See MOVs.

METERS

A sensitive meter can be damaged by careless testing! Some D'Arsonval meter movements are sensitive to as little as 50 microamperes for a full-scale reading. If they are tested thoughtlessly with a VOM on the low range, and if the current supplied by the VOM is 250 milliamperes, the poor meter experiences a 5,000 percent overload. Only a DMM should be used to test a meter movement. Start from an upper ohmmeter scale, going lower with each value until a useable reading is obtained.

An alternative way to determine the internal resistance of a meter is to provide plenty of external resistance in order to make the meter read exactly full-scale with a given low-variable supply voltage. Then, parallel the meter with another resistance (a 1,000 Ω potentiometer will do nicely) and adjust that resistance until the meter reads half-scale. Remove and measure the paralleling resistance in the usual way. It will be the same as the meter movement resistance, since it diverted half the current away from it.

The best way to test meter movements other than through a D'Arsonval movement is to replace them with an identical meter to determine if the original was defective.

MICROPHONES

There are four basic types of microphones in common use today. Each will be discussed in turn.

The Dynamic Microphone

The dynamic microphone is a small speaker used in reverse: impinging sound waves produce very small voltages across a tiny voice coil attached to a diaphragm that moves in a magnetic field. Because the voltage is so small, and considering that the current produced is sizable, a small transformer is usually included within the microphone structure. It is often located in the stem that holds the microphone or, sometimes, hidden at the base of the instrument. The transformer steps up the voltage and reduces the current, commonly matching the low impedance of the moving coil to a 600-ohm load. Taps at 150 and 300 ohms are sometimes also provided at the transformer. See Figure 17–22.

Testing the microphone with an ohmmeter should show a resistance: the resistance of the matching transformer secondary winding. This resistance will be approximately 150 Ω if tapped for 600 Ω output.

A better check of the whole microphone mechanism, if it is equipped with a matching transformer, would be to use the amplification capabilities of a DMM on its AC scale. After connecting the output leads of the microphone to the DMM, the word *four* (pronounced "fowwwwer"), spoken solidly into the microphone, should produce a few millivolts AC on the DMM.

The Carbon Microphone

The carbon microphone varies its resistance in response to the incoming sound waves. Although the carbon microphone does not have the quality of a dynamic mike, it is very rugged. The resistance of the mike element

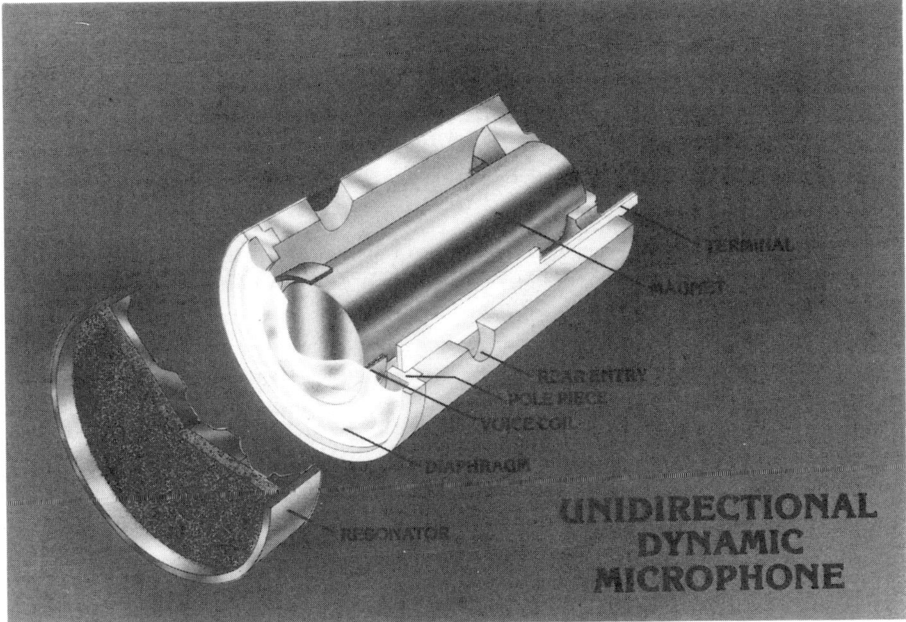

Figure 17–22 A dynamic microphone is like a speaker in reverse. (Photo courtesy of Shure Brothers, Inc.)

(don't confuse the usual push-to-talk switch connections with the microphone connections) can vary between less than a hundred ohms to several hundred. The resistance will change considerably if the microphone is gently thumped against the heel of your hand.

If the carbon microphone ('phone) has the standard microphone connector, it appears as a shaft of a little less than a quarter inch in diameter, with two insulated connections at the end. The microphone element should be connected to the long "sleeve" and the next segment of the plug, the "ring." The push-to-talk switch is usually connected between the "sleeve" and the "tip." *Tip, ring,* and *sleeve* are the usual way to refer to these parts of a 'phone plug.

As long as the microphone is available for testing, it wouldn't hurt to check the push-to-talk (PTT) switch for reliable operation. Check for solid continuity between the sleeve and the tip of the plug, moving the cable and flexing it, particularly at the ends. Watch for any erratic ohmmeter reading, which would indicate a bad switch or cable.

Distortion may become a problem with a carbon microphone. This is often caused by moisture "packing" the carbon granules within the mike. A *gentle* rap against a solid surface will often cure the problem.

The Crystal or Ceramic Microphone

A crystal microphone operates on the piezoelectric principle. The piezoelectric effect occurs when a material such as quartz is physically bent, as by a sound wave. The bending produces a voltage across the crystal face. Because of the thinness of the crystal, a crystal microphone can be quite fragile and should be handled with reasonable care. A ceramic microphone is very similar except that it is made with a ceramic rather than a crystalline material.

The output voltage of a crystal or a ceramic microphone is quite easily detected with a DMM on the AC scales. The word *four*, as mentioned for the dynamic microphone, makes a good spoken word to use in testing. The voltage output of a crystal or ceramic mike is several millivolts.

The Condenser Microphone

The condenser (an old name for capacitor) microphone is just that: a capacitor. It requires a special circuit and a high-gain amplifier to use its varying capacitance output. The only check of a condenser microphone that can be made with an ohmmeter or Tracker is that it should measure as an open.

MOTORS

DC Motors

Motors that run on direct current will usually have brushes to carry current to and from the armature as it rotates. An ohmmeter should read the same between any two segments of the armature. Basically, the armature consists of windings connected between segments, forming a single, large circular winding with the segments representing taps on that winding. A sudden large difference of resistance reading between two segments indicates an open coil on the armature.

The magnetic field may be permanent magnets or electromagnets. If they are electromagnets, they may be tested as though they were inductors.

Stepper Motors

Most stepper motors are made with a permanent-magnet rotor. The stators may be two separate coils (four-lead steppers), two center-tapped coils, with or without a common center tap lead (five- and six-lead steppers), or four separate windings (eight-lead steppers.) See Figure 17–23.

By counting the number of leads coming from the motor, one can estimate where to expect high and low ohmmeter resistance readings. Each winding can be identified, along with the winding center tap, if any. Resistances will range from 3 Ω upward, depending on the size and operating voltage of the stepper. As a matter of comparison, a typical small stepper motor in a 5-1/4" computer diskette drive runs on 12 volts and reads 150 Ω across one center-tapped winding.

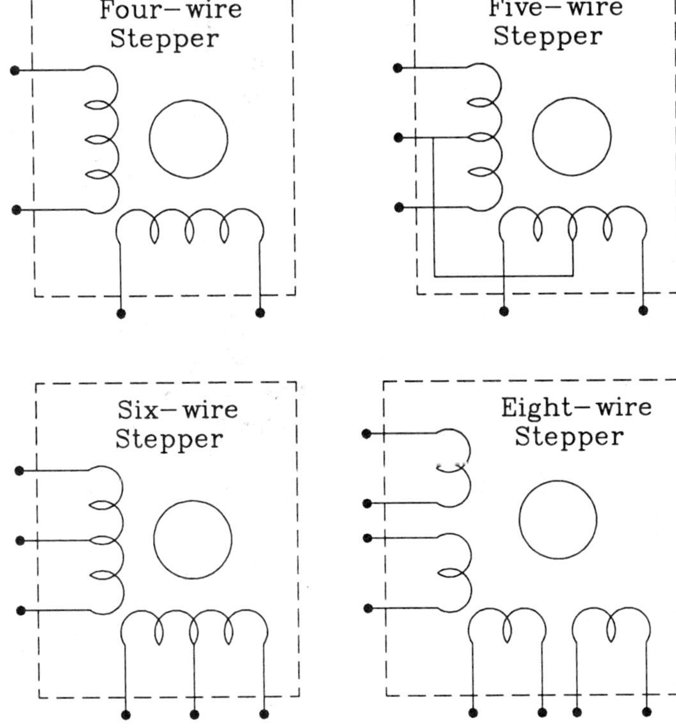

Figure 17–23 The number of leads coming out of a stepper motor provides a clue to the internal wiring.

Induction motors

An induction motor has field windings which may be thought of as the primary of a transformer. The secondaries are shorted turns on the rotor. No practical checks can be made on the rotor, but the field windings can be tested with an ohmmeter. Expect low resistances, as they are just another form of an inductor. Chapter 22 shows schematics and descriptions of various induction motors which may be helpful.

MOVs (METAL OXIDE VARISTORS)

A shorted MOV will be evident when tested with an ohmmeter or Tracker, which should probably be the first and most convenient test of an MOV. See Figure 2–7 for an illustration of the various forms this component can assume.

A metal oxide varistor may be tested as though it were two zener diodes in series, back to back. Because most varistors have breakdown voltages well above the voltage capability of even a Tracker, a special test setup will be necessary to test them. Being very careful because of the potential shock hazard, connect a variable DC power supply, capable of perhaps 200-V DC, to the MOV through a 10,000-Ω resistor. Connect a voltmeter across the MOV. Slowly increase the power supply voltage output and note the voltage when the MOV voltage no longer rises along with the application of ever-increasing voltage. This is the voltage at which the MOV will clip transient voltages when used on AC voltages.

NEON LAMPS

A neon lamp "fires" at about 75 to 90 volts. Up to that voltage, it should be an open circuit. After firing, however, the voltage across the lamp drops immediately to about 60 volts. If the voltage falls substantially below 60 volts at the source, the lamp will again extinguish and will require another rise to 75 volts to fire again.

Testing a neon lamp requires the use of a current-limiting resistor. Without that resistor, the lamp will conduct excessive current and may explode if too much energy is absorbed.

To test a neon lamp, put between 100,000 Ω and 1 megohm in series with it, and then connect them to a source of 120-V AC. If the lamp lights, it is good, if not, it is bad.

PICKUP COILS

A pickup coil may also be called a recording head or a read or write head. It is basically a very small inductor, and may be tested as such. If the performance of a suspected head is bad, the substitution of a new head is the best test by far. A great deal of the high-frequency performance of a head depends on its recording information with exactly a 90-degree orientation to the recorded information on tape. Because of this, the mounting for a read/write head may include adjustments for changing the head's azimuth. This adjustment is adjusted for maximum high-frequency response.

PHOTOCELLS

There are basically three kinds of light sensors: photo-resistive (light-sensitive resistors), photo-emissive devices (solar-cells), and photo-conductive devices (photo-semiconductors).

Photo resistors

A photo-resistive device can often be recognized by a small glass window covering a ceramic-like material, into which is etched a pattern vaguely resembling a venetian blind. It is a resistor and, therefore, is not polarity-sensitive. The resistance of the element takes a drastic drop as the amount

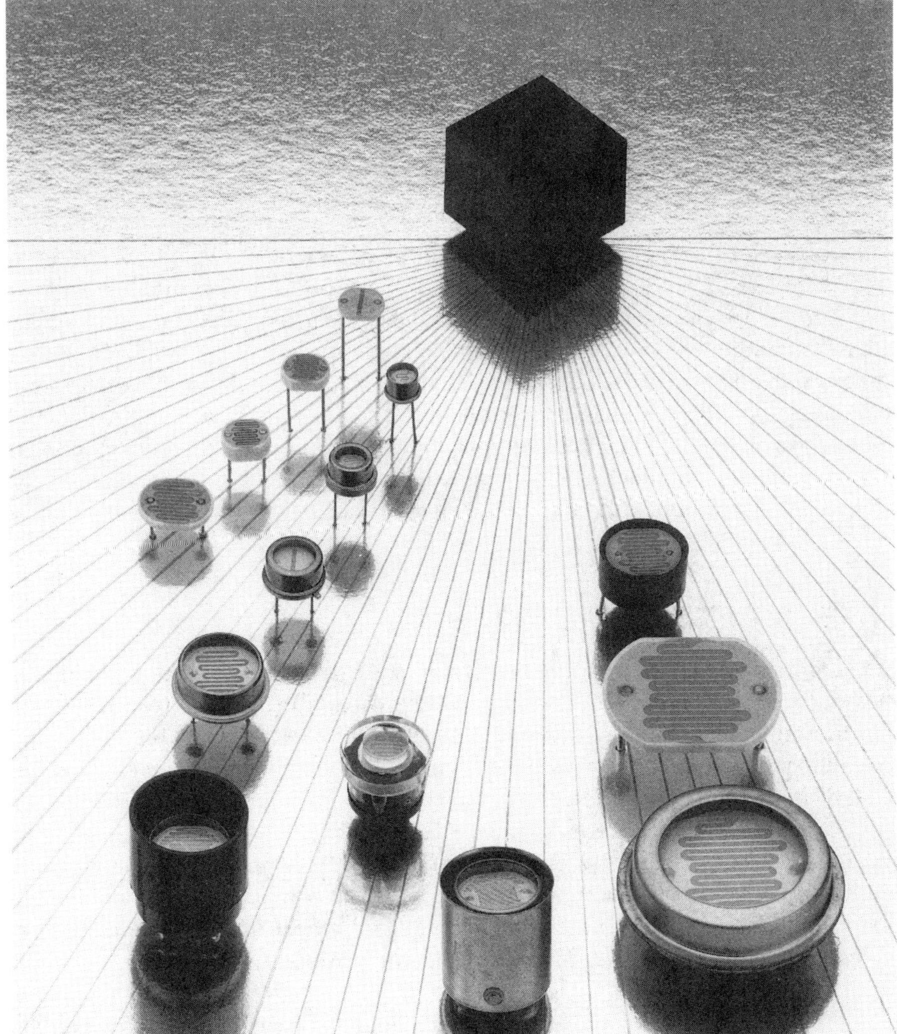

Figure 17–24 A photo-resistive (light-sensitive) cell. (Photo courtesy of Silonex, Inc.)

of light shining into the window increases. Resistance comparisons can be made between suspected and known good cells to determine their condition. See Figure 17–24.

Photo-Emissive Cells (Photo Cells)

A photocell produces electrical power in response to the stimulus of light energy. Each photo cell may produce only a fraction of an ampere at less than a volt, but many photo cells connected in series-parallel can produce substantial amounts of power. The cell under test should produce the same amount of energy as a good, new cell under the same lighting conditions.

Photo-Conductive Devices (Photo Diodes and Transistors)

A photo-conductive device is a semiconductor whose conduction is determined by the amount of light striking it. The photo diode and photo transistor must be connected to an external power supply. When light strikes the semiconductor, the diode acts as though it were very leaky (it is normally connected in a back-biased fashion in the circuit) or the transistor acts as though it had base current applied.

Because of the need to build a sample circuit to check these components, the easiest way to check them is usually to substitute a known good component in the circuit and compare the results.

POTENTIOMETERS ("POTS")

A potentiometer is simply a resistor with a movable tap that can be moved from one end of the resistor to the other. They can be tested with an ohmmeter from end-to-end for the rated, total resistance of the "pot," and then checked from the movable tap, called a "wiper," at either end. As the control is rotated, the amount of resistance should change smoothly as the pot is rotated from one end of travel to the other. A common defect is for the pot to open at one end. An open at one end of the pot will show up as an infinite resistance from end to end, yet the wiper will show normal resistances at all positions except at one end where it will suddenly open at one rotational extreme. The connection at this end of the pot is open to all other connections.

Potentiometers for audio work are not linear. These controls are deliberately tapered so that as they are rotated, the sound signal coming through them is increased logarithmically with a smooth rotation of the control. This is necessary to offset the logarithmic response of the human ear to sound intensities. The testing of one of these pots will show a drastic increase or decrease of wiper-to-end resistance on one end of the pot but not the other.

Multiple turn (usually 10-turn) potentiometers are used when repeatable accuracy is necessary, as in precision voltage dividers. They should be checked just like any other pot.

One of the failure modes for a potentiometer is to develop a great deal of noise when moved from one position to another, as when used for a volume control. At the extreme, portions of the adjustment may even become "dead," providing no output at all. One cure is to apply a special radio-television cleaner meant for just this problem. However, the best cure is to replace the control.

QUARTZ CRYSTALS

For a discussion of quartz crystals, see "Crystals, Quartz."

READ/WRITE HEADS

For a discussion of read/write heads, see "Pickup Coils."

RELAYS

A relay is just an electromagnetically actuated switch, rather than a manually operated one. The application of power to the coil of the relay causes the contacts to activate: to open, close, or do both. See Figure 17–25.

As with any switch, the contacts take the beating of normal operation. Wear, arcing across the contacts, and oxidation of the contact points all contribute to the relatively high failure rate of relays. Generally speaking, once a relay is determined to be the cause of a problem, the technician should replace it rather than attempt to repair it or adjust the contacts by bending them.

The contacts of a relay can be tested by forcing the relay into any condition (energized or not) in which the technician *knows* that a given set of contacts *should* be closed as designed, but suspects they aren't doing so.

Figure 17–25 A relay is little more than an electrically operated switch.

Each set of contacts can be treated separately, like a simple switch: Take a test lead or other suitable wire and short from one side of the switch contacts to the other side where it should be making contact. If the load, whatever it may be, now responds, then the contacts must *not* have been making contact as they should. Be careful not to connect across contacts that should be *open*, however. Bridge only those contacts that are supposed to be closed at that particular moment.

Occasionally, a relay coil will open. This can be checked just like an inductor, except the coil of a relay can measure thousands of ohms on a sensitive, high-voltage relay.

Another common problem with relays occurs when they have been in the vicinity of metal-drilling operations, which can cause the relay pole-piece to collect small metal filings. When the coil is energized, these filings may stand straight up from the pole-piece, causing the armature to fail to come all the way down on it. This problem can sometimes be seen in a relay when viewed from the side. Sometimes, all it takes is a firm puff of air to blow the filings away from an *unenergized* relay.

RESISTORS

A resistor is made to have a certain resistance. Within the allowable tolerances, it should have a measured resistance, as marked. The marking of resistors was discussed in Chapter 1, including some of the text-coded marking schemes. Appendix I details the rest of the color codes used on resistors, including both the two- and three-significant figure codes.

Armed with the information concerning what the resistor should measure, it becomes simply a matter of connecting a DMM with the autoranging feature to the resistor to get the actual value. If that value is within the tolerance for the resistor, then the resistor is good. If not, it is defective and should be replaced.

The Tracker will provide only rough comparisons of resistances.

RHEOSTATS

A rheostat is just a potentiometer with only a single terminal on one end of the main resistive element. It is a variable resistor that cannot be used as a simple voltage divider, as the potentiometer can.

Rheostats are generally of much lower resistance than pots. They are used as dimmers on incandescent light arrays, for instance, where low resistance and high power dissipation are needed.

The rheostat may be tested as a variable resistor. It should have essentially zero resistance at one extreme and the maximum resistance for the device at the opposite end. Some rheostats are supposed to have a full open position at the "far" end in order to turn off the power altogether, thus acting as both a dimmer and a switch.

SILICON-CONTROLLED RECTIFIERS (SCRs)

SCRs should test as a diode action between the cathode and the gate if the gate is connected to the anode. All other leads of the SCR should test open. If not, the SCR is defective. Common problems include a short from gate to any other lead and a short from the anode to the cathode.

Some of the largest SCRs have an internal resistor from gate to cathode, which is evident when the back-biased direction is checked on the gate-cathode diode. This resistor helps prevent premature triggering and stabilizes operation at higher operating temperatures.

The Tracker is very useful for testing SCRs and TRIACS. The instruction manual for the instrument details some of the tests that can be made and gives typical results. These tests are particularly good for comparing suspected devices with known good ones.

SOLENOIDS

For a discussion of solenoids, see the section titled "Inductors."

SOLID-STATE RELAY

The input of a solid-state relay is a light emitting diode. The input DC may range from 3-V DC to as much as 32-V DC without external current limiting, depending on the specific device. Simply apply enough current to light an LED and the output will respond.

The output component of a solid-state relay is usually a TRIAC. This allows the control of any AC-operated device. The TRIAC can control 10 amperes or more at 240-V AC, controlled by only the input LED-driving current. No other application of power is necessary. See Figure 17–26.

Testing a solid-state relay requires that it be put into full, normal operation. Therefore, substitution with a known good unit is the best way to determine if the original unit was at fault.

Testing a solid-state relay in full, normal operation requires that the input LED have driving voltage applied to it with proper polarity. If the solid-state relay is functioning properly, the load "contacts" (actually a TRIAC in conduction) should be closed under these conditions, with very little AC voltage across the output terminals.

SPEAKERS

A quick check of a speaker that you suspect of creating distortion can be made with just your fingers. Gently press on both sides of the speaker's central cone, with two fingers about three quarters of an inch apart. A good speaker should not produce a scraping or rubbing sound when gently pressed inward and released.

If the speaker passes this "scratch test," apply an ohmmeter on the low-

Figure 17–26 The solid-state relay has a DC input and operates AC devices with its output.

est range to the voice coil terminals. If a VOM is used, the high current of the meter should produce a scratching noise from the speaker cone. (A DMM does not have sufficient current to make this test.) With either instrument, the indicated resistance should be from half to almost the rated impedance of the speaker; 2.4 to 3.8 Ω for a 4-ohm speaker, 4.8 to 7.6 Ω for an 8-ohm unit, and 9.6 to 15.2 Ω for a 16-ohm speaker.

A single dry cell (1.5 V) can be used to determine proper phasing of the speakers. Speakers used together on a given system, particularly large ones, should be phased so that they move in and out together with a given polarity. If they do not, there will be a decrease in the intensity of the output, especially the low tones. To phase the speakers, put the 1.5-V battery directly across the speaker terminals. Note which way the speaker cone moves, and reverse the battery if necessary so that the speaker cone moves *outward*. Mark the terminal of the speaker that has the "+" end of the battery, using a dab of paint. (Red fingernail polish is handy for this use.) Phase all speakers in this manner. When connecting the speakers to the main amplifier, be sure that the same lead of the amplifier is connected to the terminals marked with the "+."

SWITCHES

When a switch is open, it must be just that: open. When closed, it must have zero resistance. Problems occur when, through corrosion and arcing, the switch contacts build up resistance. Normal current flowing through the resistance causes localized heating, and the corrosion problem gets worse. Replacement is required of any switch that has resistance when closed.

Some switches can be repaired under emergency conditions even though they were not constructed to be opened. Opening a switch may involve gently drilling out the end of a rivet or uncrimping the case with a pair of pliers. *Hold the switch tightly together as you break into it and be very careful when actually opening it, as it will usually fly apart because of the springs inside it.* Anticipate the possibility of small parts dropping out of the switch by working over a table or bench. Once the switch is apart, it may be possible to clean up the contacts or stretch a tired spring to make the switch operate again. Sometimes just cleaning it out with denatured alcohol is enough to get many more hours of operation. To reassemble the switch, gently tap the crimp back together or install tiny screws and nuts to hold it. Once dismantled, a switch should probably be replaced at the first opportunity to prevent more failures.

A special type of switch called a *reed switch* is also available. Instead of having the contacts exposed to air, they are sealed in a long glass tube. See Figure 17–27.

The contacts are brought together by bringing a magnet close to the switch or by turning on a solenoid wound around the contacts. The switch reeds pick up the induced magnetism and bend toward each other, closing the circuit. To test a reed switch, place an ohmmeter across the sealed contacts and bring a small magnet up against the glass tube. The contacts should close. Since the strength of the magnetic field is a factor, you can use the magnet with which the reed switch is supposed to operate for a better check.

THERMISTORS

Thermistors are basically resistors but are designed to change value a great deal depending on their temperature. See Figure 17–28.

Testing a thermistor will require information as to what resistance it should be at a given temperature. One such resistance at room temperatures may be given as, for instance, "50 Cold." This would mean that the thermistor should read approximately 50 Ω out-of-circuit (with no current flowing). If heated to 100 degrees, the same resistor might measure twice that value. Only the specification sheet for a particular resistor can give the correct information on temperature changes with changes in resistance.

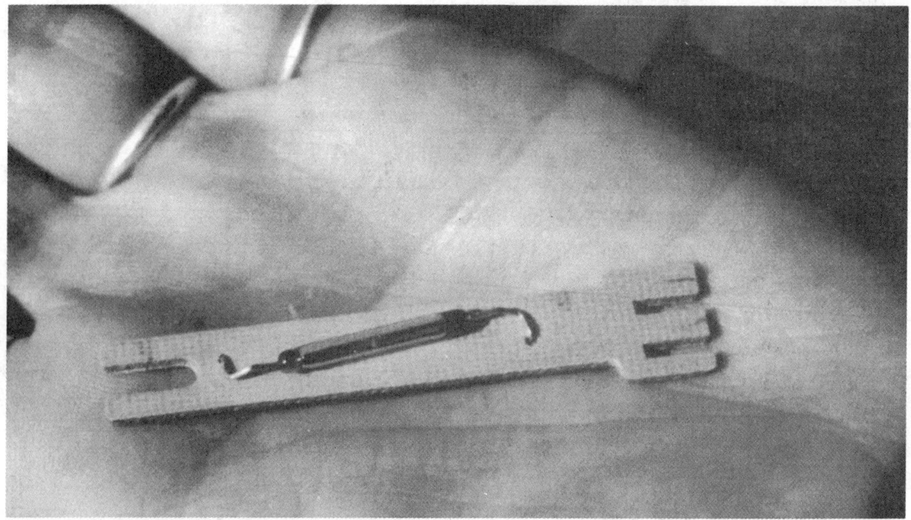

Figure 17–27 The reed switch has contacts sealed in a glass tube and is activated by an external magnetic field.

THERMOSTATS

A thermostat is a temperature-operated switch. It is supposed to actuate at a given temperature and then reset to the original condition when the temperature falls again. Most thermostats are made to actuate and then deactivate at a temperature *below* that which actuates it. See Figure 17–29.

The temperature difference between the switch when actuated and when deactuated is called the *temperature differential.* This differential serves to prevent the arcing that would occur if the contacts were separated by a few micro-inches at a critical temperature.

Testing a thermostat will require some means of raising and lowering its temperature. The temperatures at which the switch should open and close must be known and then compared to the actual operation of the thermostat. Lacking temperature-testing equipment, substitution with a known good thermostat is probably easiest.

TRANSFORMERS

There are basically three different kinds of transformers, for which testing methods will vary: the power transformer, thc audio transformer, and the RF transformer.

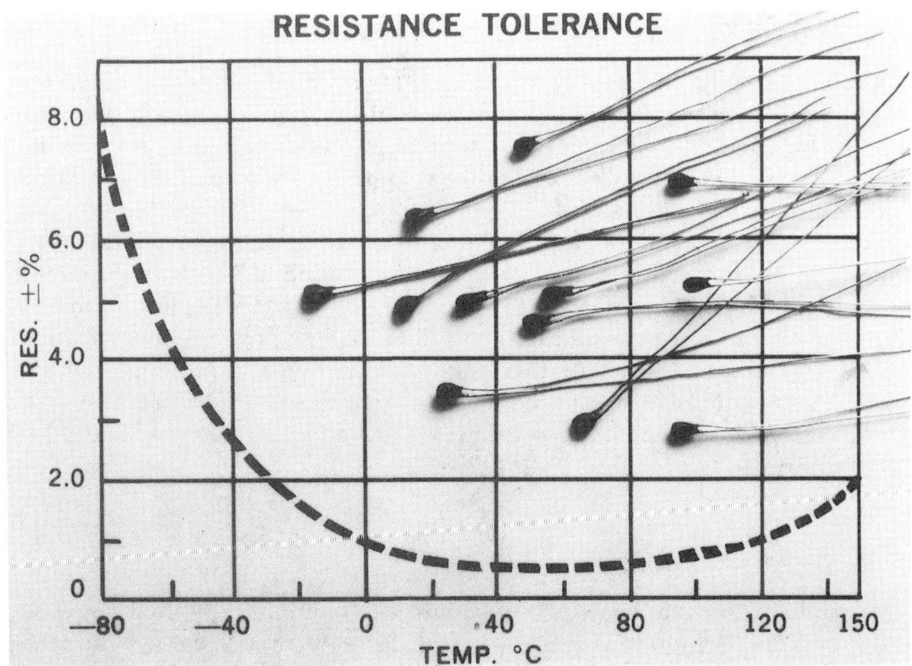

Figure 17–28 A thermistor is simply a resistor that is very sensitive to changes in temperature. (Photo courtesy of Fenwal Electronics, Inc.)

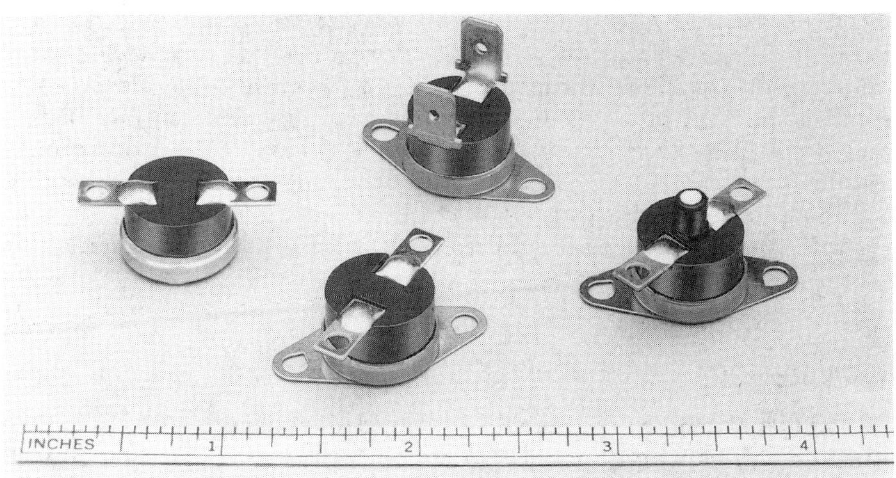

Figure 17–29 A thermostat is a temperature-sensitive switch. (Photo courtesy Selco Products Co.)

The Power Transformer

A power transformer can first be tested for open windings and for shorts or leakage between windings. Depending on the physical size of the wire within the windings, a continuity check from end to end of a winding can range from a 0-ohm reading to perhaps 20 ohms. Leakage between windings should be over a megohm.

Don't forget to also test for shorts or leakage to the core of the transformer. A short here results in a short to ground if the transformer is mounted to the chassis. Once the windings are tested with an ohmmeter, the transformer can be tested for shorted turns by applying power without a load on the transformer. If there are shorted turns in any winding, the transformer will become hot within the span of anywhere from a minute to a half-hour. After extended operation, an unloaded transformer should be barely warm to the touch.

The Audio Transformer

An audio frequency transformer should be tested as explained above for a power transformer: test each winding for continuity, leakage to other windings, and leakage to case ground.

An audio transformer winding with shorted turns is rare and may be difficult to isolate. If the transformer is a power audio transformer, it may heat abnormally, but this is *not* a good test criterion. A substitution of the transformer and comparison of the amplifier performance is the best test.

The RF transformer

It is possible, but extremely rare, that an RF transformer can become defective by shorting internally between windings. Substitution and a comparison of stage gain is the test procedure to follow to determine the transformer's condition. Remember that an RF transformer is probably tuned, perhaps at both input and output windings, and top and bottom cores are provided for this purpose. These will have to be retuned upon installation of another transformer before the stage can operate properly. Mistuning is a far more common problem of an RF transformer than an actual failure. A tuning core can become dislodged and even fall out of the transformer altogether.

TRANSISTORS (BIPOLAR)

Small transistors may be tested as two diode junctions, back to back. The use of a VOM ohmmeter or a DMM on the junction scale will require six readings, all combinations of polarity across the three leads of the device. A Tracker will require only three readings, since the AC of the Tracker does the "lead reversal" for you.

Table 17–3 Sample VOM Ohmmeter Readings on Several Bipolar Transistors

Ohmmeter Lead	Polarity	Bipolar transistors					
+	–	npn Power 2N1486	npn Signal 2N388	npn Signal 2N377	pnp Power 2N1164	pnp Signal HEP636	pnp Signal 2N2907
Base	Emitter	2000 Ω (X1000) 33 Ω	600 Ω (X1000)	800 (X1000)	∞	∞	∞
Emitter	Base	∞	∞	∞	10 Ω (X10)	800 (X1000)	3K (X1000)
Base	Collector	2000 Ω (X1000) 40 Ω	700 (X1000)	700 (X1000)	∞	∞	∞
Collector	Base	∞	∞	∞	10 Ω (X1000)	600 (X1000)	3 K (X1000)
Emitter	Collector	∞	∞	∞	200 (X10)	∞	200 K (X1000)
Collector	Emitter	∞ (X1000) 500 K (X100,000)	50 K (X1000)	75 K (X1000)	∞	∞	∞

Figures in parentheses are range used.

∞ = open

The Tracker may detect and show a breakdown when measuring from collector to emitter. This is caused by the base-to-emitter junction going into avalanche, much like a zener diode. This is an abnormal polarity to apply to a transistor, and such a reading is, therefore, to be expected. The larger the transistor, the more it is prone to base-emitter avalanche.

Table 17–3 gives some examples of bipolar transistor readings made with an ohmmeter.

A simple transistor checker can be built to test small devices. This might be a good project if the technician has a frequent need to test or comparison-select transistors. See Figure 17–30.

Often, the simple use of a VOM or a DMM on the diode scale will suffice for routine transistor checking.

Darlington Transistors

A Darlington transistor is actually two transistors in a single package. The collectors are connected, and the emitter of the first stage connects

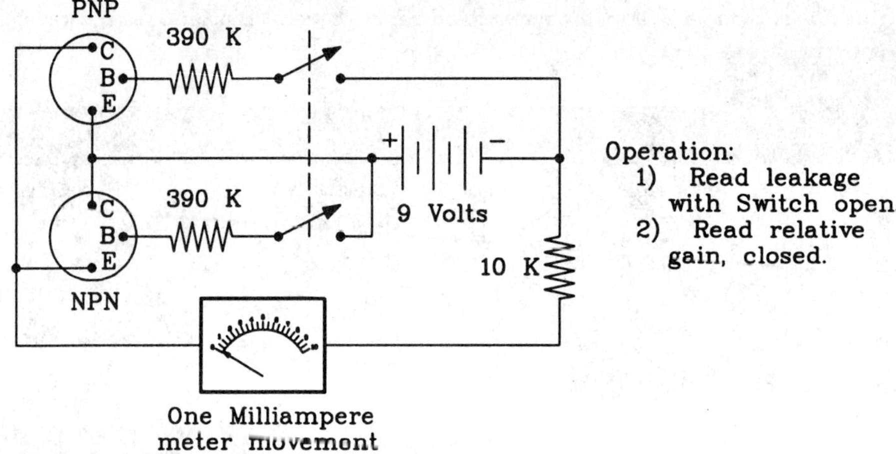

Figure 17–30 This quick-tester for transistors will identify NPN and PNP transistors along with providing relative gain and leakage figures.

directly to the base of the second transistor. This gives a great deal of gain in a single package. Darlington transistors are often used in switching applications where they are operated either saturated or cut-off. Refer to Figure 17–5.

Testing a Darlington transistor is similar to testing a single transistor, except that the voltage drop in the forward direction from base to emitter is about twice what one would expect. A reading of 1.4 V rather than 0.7 V will register due to the two base-emitter junctions in series.

Photo Transistors

A photo transistor has a window into the device through which light may fall. The light striking the base junction causes current flow through the device just as though a forward bias had been applied to the base of the transistor. The base connection, if provided, may be left disconnected, or it may be tied to the emitter with a very high resistance.

To test a photo transistor, it must be set up in a proper test circuit. However, it is easier *and* more conclusive to put a new transistor into the existing circuit under test to see if a new transistor cures the problem.

TRIAC

A TRIAC, as explained in Figure 14–4, should conduct under control of the gate with either polarity applied to the MT1 and MT2 leads. To test a TRIAC, apply ohmmeter leads to MT1 and MT2 without regard to polarity.

There should be an open. Now connect the gate lead momentarily to the MT2 lead, and the TRIAC should latch on. If both sections of the TRIAC are good, the same results should be obtained when the test is run with the ohmmeter leads reversed on the MT1 and MT2 leads.

Larger TRIACs may have an internal resistor connecting the gate to terminal MT1. This is added to improve triggering stability at higher operating temperatures.

TUBES

Receiving Tubes

Small vacuum tubes used in receiving and similar applications may be tested on a tube tester. The best test, however, is substitution. A tube tester usually checks tubes with DC signals rather than the AC or radio frequencies of an actual circuit. For this reason, it provides only an indication, not proof, of whether the tube will work in a given circuit. Major failures such as open heaters, however, can be detected reliably with the tube tester.

Power Vacuum Tubes

A test setup suitable to test larger tubes is impractical to consider. The normal operating circuit should be used as a test setup, substituting tubes to compare them. If "good" tubes test as bad, there is probably something wrong with the circuit rather than any of the tubes. This kind of testing is applicable for cathode-ray tubes (CRTs), magnetrons, and all high-power RF amplifier tubes.

UNIJUNCTION TRANSISTORS (UJTs)

A unijunction transistor should look like a resistor from base 1 to base 2, with either polarity of ohmmeter applied. The emitter should appear as a diode tapped into the approximate center of the resistance between base 1 and base 2. The diode scale of a DMM should be used to check these devices. See Figure 17–31.

Table 17–4 gives some examples of unijunction transistor readings made with an ohmmeter.

Table 17–4 Sample Ohmmeter Readings on Several Unijunction Transistors

Ohmmeter	Polarity	Unijunction Transistors		
+	–	2N1671B	2N491	2N4870
Emitter	Base 1	4 K	3 K	3 K
Base 1	Emitter	∞	∞	∞
Emitter	Base 2	10 K	7 K	4 K
Base 2	Emitter	∞	∞	∞
Base 1	Base 2	9 K	6 K	5K
Base 2	Base 1	9 K	6 K	5 K

X1000 Range of VOM used.

∞ = open

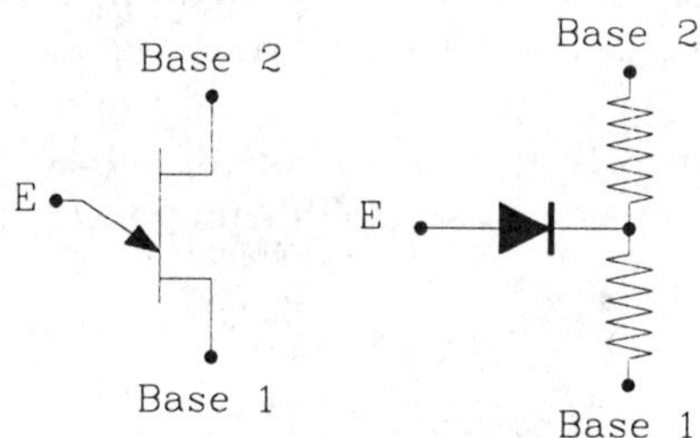

Figure 17–31 How an ohmmeter reads a UJT.

CHAPTER SUMMARY

- This chapter provided the basic information necessary to evaluate two kinds of circuits: those that have been troubleshot to the stage level and those that come across the bench "cold," without information, a means of applying power for signal tracing, or any documentation.
- The two types of instruments suitable for testing such circuits, the VOM and DMM ohmmeter or the Huntron Tracker™, were discussed in detail along with cautions as to their use and limitations.

- The inconclusiveness of ohmmeter readings in-circuit was explained and the odds of particular components being defective were presented.
- Each component that is routinely encountered in electronic circuits was discussed with a view to testing with dead-circuit instruments.
- The substitution of a suspected part with a known good part is the most conclusive test of all.

REVIEW QUESTIONS

1. What two instruments are the only options available to repair equipment that, for one reason or another, cannot be turned on?
2. What is the principal reason why in-circuit resistance readings are usually inconclusive?
3. What electronic component is most likely to fail? What component is least likely?
4. You wish to use an ohmmeter in a circuit and have just unplugged it to avoid applying power to the meter. What else must be done first?
5. What VOM ranges are *not* recommended to be used with transistor circuits?
6. Why should ohmmeter polarity be checked?
7. An ohmmeter indicates low resistance when the cathode of a test diode is connected to the red, plus lead of the meter. Is this meter polarity reversed on the ohmmeter function?
8. Some DMMs have a special button that can be used to cancel the test lead resistance. How is this button labeled?
9. A 1,000-Ω resistor is in parallel with a diode. A DMM resistance reading will probably indicate _______ Ω.
10. A vertical line on a Huntron Tracker™ indicates a _______.
11. A check mark pattern on a Tracker indicates a _______.
12. What is the usual reference point when using a Tracker?
13. What are the three methods of using a Tracker?
14. What will a technician look for, generically speaking, when using a Tracker for testing integrated circuits?
15. When is a Huntron Switcher™ used?
16. Two known, good chips of the same generic type show different patterns when using a Huntron Tracker™. What is a probable cause of this difference?
17. What four steps can be used when using a Tracker to find a problem on a board?
18. What kind of solder is best for general electronic use?
19. What is probably the best method of IC removal, subject to certain conditions?
20. What type of motion should be used for SMD removal after melting the solder on both ends?

21. What should be done with a part that was removed, but tested good?
22. Under what conditions is a voltage check on a battery valid?
23. What is the normal voltage drop across an infrared diode?
24. If a 12-volt incandescent lamp calculates to a resistance of 120 ohms, will the lamp draw 50 milliamperes on 6 volts?
25. You wish to measure the internal resistance of a sensitive meter movement using a VOM on the resistance scale. Is this permissible?
26. How is an MOV tested?
27. A neon indicator shows as being open on a DMM ohmmeter. Is this normal?
28. What technique will verify if a set of relay contacts is not making contact as it should?
29. What should be done with large speakers to ensure that they work well together on low frequencies?
30. What quick test will tell if a speaker is rubbing?
31. Basically speaking, what is a thermostat?
32. What is the most common failure associated with an RF transformer?
33. What is a Darlington transistor?
34. What is the best test of a vacuum tube?

Replacement with a New Part

18

CHAPTER OBJECTIVES

This chapter takes the technician from the point of having found a bad component and removed it to the stage where the new part has been found (or a substitute for it has been made) and replaced into the board or circuit. At the conclusion of this chapter, the student will know:

- Where to obtain most generic parts for replacement purposes.
- What to look for when substituting generic replacement parts.
- How to use a semiconductor replacement guide.
- The cautions to observe when handling static-sensitive replacement parts.
- How to test new components before installation.
- How to install replacement components.

18.1 GETTING NEW PARTS

Once the technician knows for sure which component or components are bad, new ones must be obtained. These replacement parts fall under one of the following categories, each of which is considered in detail in the following paragraphs:

Single-source permissible,

Manufacturer only possible source,

Direct-order items, and

Generic replacement permissible.

SINGLE-SOURCE PERMISSIBLE

There are applications for which the technician is restricted to a single source for parts. Using parts from any other source is simply not permitted. The U.S. military, for instance, has its own huge stocking system of generic and special components, and all replacement parts must be obtained from this source.

Another application that may require parts from a single source is aviation. The parts used in aircraft, for instance, may have to meet exacting specifications for humidity, altitude, temperature, corrosion resistance, and so forth. Parts from any other source may seriously affect the reliability of the equipment and, therefore, must not be used. Generally, only the parts provided by the manufacturer of the equipment are permitted.

In extreme cases, failure to use the proper replacement part (or using an inferior part) may subject the person making the substitution to disciplinary action.

MANUFACTURER AS ONLY POSSIBLE SOURCE

All the parts mentioned in this paragraph are called *proprietary parts*. They include custom-built parts, ROMs (read only memories), and PAL™ (Programmable Arrays of Logic).*

The manufacturer of a given part may simply be the *only possible* source for a particular part. For instance, major electronic manufacturers have been making their own large-scale integrated circuits (LSIs) for several years now, with more manufacturers doing so as time goes by, for reasons of industrial security. When only one company makes a part, the replacement must obviously come from that company. Some companies needing particularly specialized or precision parts will make their own, often to tolerances far exceeding any "off-the-shelf" component. These parts are only available from the original source. One last category of part is the

*Registered trademark of Monolythic Memories, Inc., 2175 Mission College Blvd., Santa Clara, CA 95050

customized part that basically is a generic product but has been modified by the manufacturer for a specific application. An example is a meter. A meter scale can be custom-designed for a particular use, while the mechanism itself is a generic part. Such specially modified parts must also be procured from the manufacturer.

A read only memory (ROM) is a programmable logic device that has bit patterns of 1s and 0s within it. Programs within a ROM chip are called *firmware.* If a ROM chip fails in a given application, only the manufacturer can provide the information within that device. The ROMs are available inexpensively, but the information within them is only available through the people who originally put information into a given ROM for a specific application. Be sure to provide the information labeled on the ROM for the manufacturer to ensure that the proper program is put into the replacement chip.

Another kind of part that must be procured from the manufacturer is a Programmable Array of Logic (PAL™). These chips are loosely analogous to a ROM in that they are programmable. They are programmed for a specific logic function at the factory. Without the programming information, it is all but impossible to determine the logic gating within the device. Instead, a replacement must be obtained from the manufacturer. When ordering such a part, it is imperative that the exact information be provided as it appears on the chip, usually on a small, stick-on tag. This tag identifies the version and the exact information needed to locate a proper, direct replacement.

In order to force customers to return to the factory for parts, whether for economic or quality control reasons, some manufacturers conceal the "true identity" (the generic marking) of a part (usually with ICs). This is done by removing the generic marking, putting the manufacturer's own cryptic numbers on parts, or by ordering quantities of parts from the part manufacturer with special markings to conceal their generic identity. In any case, these nongeneric numbers can seldom be traced back to a generic part indication. Instead, the technician making the repair will be forced to go to the manufacturer for a replacement.

DIRECT-ORDER ITEMS

There is one component that can best be custom-made for a given application by the component manufacturer, bypassing the middleman or parts distributor. Quartz crystals must be ground for a specific circuit, a specific loading within that circuit, and a specific frequency of operation. Several companies are available for making custom-ground crystals, one of which is CAL Crystal Lab Inc. (1124 N. Gilbert St., Anaheim, CA 92801, 1–800–333–9825). All the technician need do is determine as much of the following information as possible for the crystal to be made:

Equipment Make, Model, Serial Number, Circuit Symbol (X-2).

Overtone or fundamental mode.

Frequency of operation.

Series or parallel resonant, if known.

Circuit capacitive load.

Standard or special tolerance.

Oven or nonoven operation.

GENERIC REPLACEMENT PERMISSIBLE

The remaining replacement parts, if permitted by the application, may be substituted for by other parts not exactly like the original. This is a broad category, including most:

Batteries, capacitors, circuit breakers, coaxial cable, fuses, incandescent lamps, inductors, LEDs, meters, microphones, MOVs, photocells, potentiometers, relays, rheostats, resistors, semiconductors of all kinds, including ICs, solid-state relays, speakers, switches, and thermistors, and some transformers.

Nonstandard Replacement of Parts

Lacking the proper replacement, the following components and combinations are sometimes used in place of the original part.

Batteries. Batteries are required to supply a given voltage at a current level determined by the circuit supplied. When the original battery is not available, other cells can be substituted. The total capacity of any given battery is roughly proportional to the battery's mass. Thus, compared to a 6-volt battery weighing 2 pounds, a 6-volt battery of 4 pounds will probably last about twice as long with the same load.

Cells may be connected in series until the required voltage is obtained. Keeping this in mind, the common cells listed below may be considered to have the voltages listed.

Cell Type	*Volts/Cell*
Alkaline	1.4 V
Carbon-zinc (common flashlight cell)	1.5 V
Lead-acid	2.0 V
Ni-cad	1.2 V

When making up a battery by connecting cells in series, one must be careful to use the correct number of cells. As an example, an 8-cell carbon-zinc battery of 12 V would require 10 cells if ni-cads were used instead.

Physically larger cells have more internal plate area and are thus able to deliver more current than smaller cells. An equal number of heavier cells can directly substitute for smaller cells, with an expectation of greater operating time with a given load.

Cells may also be connected in parallel to increase the current capability of the battery in time or intensity. For instance, if a 6-V battery delivers

300 ma into a load and lasts 6 hours, it is reasonable to place a second battery in parallel with the first to obtain 300 ma for twice as long, or about 12 hours. On the other hand, adding the second battery in parallel would permit an increase in load to 600 ma and still allow the battery to last the original 6 hours.

Capacitors. If a direct replacement is not available, some leeway is allowed in most applications for the substitution of different kinds of capacitors.

Fixed-value RF capacitors should be replaced with a part identical to that originally used if at all possible. The type of capacitor used will probably have restrictions as to the temperature coefficient required and, perhaps, the value tolerance.

Bypassing and filtering applications are relatively flexible on the specifications for the capacitor. A simple bypassing capacitor can be doubled or quadrupled, in almost every case, without degrading circuit performance. The use of a disk ceramic capacitor for another type may cause problems, though. This is because the disk ceramic capacitor has considerable internal inductance and is also very temperature sensitive. At higher RF frequencies, it can be resonant or, worse, inductive! Most bypassing applications *will* work well with monolithic, ceramic, glass, or mylar capacitors.

The older-style electrolytic capacitors in aluminum cans are intended for relatively low-frequency use. As such, they are useful up to approximately the upper limit of hearing, about 20 kHz. Beyond this, their internal inductance, which can be substantial, may make them ineffective as a filter. To be effective at all frequencies, bypassing should include paralleling a small-value, different-type capacitor such as a monolithic or mylar. The newer tantalum electrolytics are better at higher frequencies.

Connecting capacitors in parallel for additional capacitance presents no particular problem. This is sometimes done because of space restrictions, which may often make it easier to use two smaller capacitors than a single large one.

Connecting capacitors in series is also sometimes done to obtain a given value when two of them are available, each having twice the value needed. In other words, two 0.02-μfd capacitors in series have a total capacitance of only 0.01 μfd.

Another reason for placing two capacitors in series is to increase the voltage rating of the capacitor. Thus, two 50-V capacitors in series may be placed across 100 V: with one condition, however. The DC voltage division across two capacitors is determined solely by the leakage resistance of the capacitors. A resistance that is one-tenth or less of the worst-case leakage resistance of the capacitor must be placed across each of the capacitors to force a more equal division of the DC voltage. This was explained in Figure 6–9.

Circuit Breakers. A circuit breaker replacement may require the same current/trip characteristic as the original. If a substitution must be made, be sure that the circuit is protected at least as well as the original. The same type and rating of the overload mechanism should be used, together with any special features, such as arc suppression. The trip-out time under overload of the replacement unit should be equal to or less than that of the original.

Coaxial Cables. If it is necessary to use another kind of coaxial cable than the original, the frequency of operation and the permissible power level for that cable must be considered. Some coaxial lines are able to pass higher frequencies without appreciable loss, while other cables, which physically look the same, are just long attenuators at high frequency. It seems logical that the replacement cable must be at least as good as the original to prevent problems due to the replacement. Consult the information available in Appendix X when selecting a different coaxial cable.

Fuses. Basically, a fuse should be replaced only with the identical type recommended by the equipment manufacturer. *The installation of a larger fuse should only be done if continued operation is more important than the probable damage that can occur.* If an emergency substitution is made, order and replace with the proper fuse as soon as possible.

There are two ratings of interest: the fuse rating in amperes and the time-delay or lag of the fuse. Fuses that are meant to "blow" or open immediately when an overload occurs are called *fast-acting fuses.* Others, called *slow-blow fuses,* are meant to open only after a specified delay, holding an overload current for a length of time. If the overload is gone before the time runs out, the fuse does not blow. Such capability is important when fusing loads that have a heavy influx of current for a few cycles, after which the load reduces dramatically. A standard transformer-rectifier power supply, for instance, requires a great deal of current for a few cycles, until the capacitors reach full voltage, at which time the current demand will drop to normal values. An electric motor will have similar characteristics, drawing a large level of inrush current until the motor reaches near-normal operating speed.

Fuses are seldom marked with their time-lag characteristics, but this specification is identified by the codes on the fuse, in accordance with Table 18–1.

Incandescent Lamps. Sometimes you just can't find the correct incandescent lamp to replace in equipment. Refer to Appendix XI to select the nearest substitution. Remember that variations in the type of socket used by the substitute may require changing the socket, too.

Inductors. Generally speaking, replacing an inductor means that you must use an exact replacement. The mounting of inductors alone may require an original replacement. Size and cabinet space restrictions may also make this necessary. If space and mounting conditions permit, you can use an inductor of the same inductance and current-carrying capacity.

Table 18–1 Time-Lag Characteristics for Electronic Fuses

Fuse Type		Time-Lag Characteristics
3AB	Normal-blow	200% for 15 seconds
1AG	Fast-blow	200% for 5 seconds
2AG	Fast-blow	200% for 10 seconds
3AG	Fast-blow	200% for 5 seconds
4AG	Fast-blow	200% for 5 seconds
5AG	Fast-blow	200% for 5 seconds
7AG	Fast-blow	200% for 5 seconds
8AG	Fast-blow	
9AG	Fast-blow	200% for 5 seconds
216	Fast-blow	210% for 30 milliseconds
217	Fast-blow	210% for 30 milliseconds
218	Slow-blow	210% for 2 minutes
ABC	No-delay	110% of rating
AGC	Fast-acting	110% of rating
AGX	Fast-acting	
FLA	Time-delay	135% for 1 hour
FLM	Delay	200% for 12 seconds
FLQ	Delay	200% for 12 seconds
MDL	Time-delay	

RF inductors are used for two purposes, in tuned circuits and in filters. RF inductors used in tuned circuits must be identical to the original, and particularly so at higher radio frequencies. Filtering applications will require at least the original current-carrying capability (in amperes or milliamperes), but the inductance of the substitute can safely be increased.

Meters. Depending on the physical appearance required of the circuit, it is sometimes possible to substitute a generic meter having a slightly different scale or size than the original. The "standard" D'Arsonval meter movement is rated at 1 milliampere for full-scale deflection and has a resistance of 50 ohms. If the original meter had similar electrical characteristics, the two may be interchanged, even if the scales are completely different: full-scale is still 1 milliampere, regardless of what the scale may read. With this in mind, a substitute meter can be used with the addition of a small tag near the meter face saying something like, "Multiply meter reading by 10 x," or something equally appropriate.

Potentiometers. Potentiometers are seldom operated at their rated power. It enhances the resistor's reliability to operate it well below its maximum heat-dissipating rating. Thus, the principal rating of a potentiometer becomes simply the resistance from end to end.

The technician must be aware that potentiometers are not always linear: they do not have a linear change as the shaft is rotated. Some pots, particularly those used in audio circuits, have a logarithmic taper instead. This corresponds to the response of the human ear. Using a linear pot where a log-taper pot was originally installed will make the pot critical to adjust at the low-volume end, but the high-volume end will seem to be flattened out, and little change will be made in response to a given rotation of the shaft.

While precision circuit replacement pots must have the same resistance as the original to avoid uncalibrating the circuit, many applications will not suffer if the value of the potentiometer is changed from the original by a factor of 100 percent or more. Thus, an original control of 50 K might use a substitute of either 25 or 100 K without degrading the circuit excessively. A tone control is an example of such an uncritical application.

Relays. There are basically two parts to the substitution of a relay: the coil voltage, and contact arrangements and specifications.

The coil of the relay determines the voltage that is required to operate the relay. When a relay is replaced, the new component should have the same voltage rating as the coil. (Don't confuse the switch-contact voltage rating with that of the coil itself.) If a direct replacement is not available, a relay of less operating voltage may be pressed into emergency service. If a relay can be found that has, for instance, half the voltage requirement of the original, this can probably be used if an appropriate series resistor is used to reduce the voltage to the relay. A 6-V relay, for instance, can be used quite well on a 12-V circuit if a resistor is used in series with the coil.

As an example, suppose a 12-V relay coil opens, and a similar 6-V relay is found with the required contact arrangement and current ratings. Whereas the original coil might have had a resistance of, say, 250 Ω, and our replacement might have a 100-Ω coil. The original coil drew:

$$\frac{E}{R} = 0.048 \text{ Amperes}$$

Our new coil will draw:

$$\frac{6}{100} = 0.060 \text{ Amperes}$$

Since the new coil requires 6 volts, we still have 6 volts to "get rid of," or drop. This will require a resistor of 100 Ω having a power rating of at least:

$$P = I^2R$$

Thus, the power dissipation required of the resistor is:

$$0.06^2 \times 100 = 0.36 \text{ Watt}$$

A relay intended for use on AC voltages will have a small copper piece attached to the end of the magnetic core, underneath the movable armature. This copper core prevents the relay from buzzing when operated on AC. An AC relay can be operated on DC, but there should be a suitable resistor in series to drop the DC voltage below the AC coil rating. This is because the relay depends in part on inductive reactance to keep the AC current to a safe value. There is no inductance on DC, so an external resistance will be required to keep the coil from overheating. The easiest way to determine the required resistance is to substitute power resistors, one at a time, in series with the AC coil and the DC voltage. Find the resistance value that will just allow the relay to close when voltage is applied, and then install a permanent resistor of half that value.

A DC relay can be operated on AC if the AC is first rectified with a diode. Operating a DC relay on AC may result in the relay buzzing and perhaps not closing as definitely as it should, due to the inductive reactance of the coil. A filter capacitor of perhaps 10 or more μFds connected across the coil will help this problem. It may be necessary to install a series resistance, too, to keep the current through the coil at a safe value, in a manner similar to that discussed in the previous paragraph.

Relays can be made with a mercury wetting that all but eliminates contact pitting and contact bounce in certain critical applications. These relays must be installed with a specified orientation, and the case is usually marked with "This end up" or similar markings.

SAFETY NOTE: Do not disassemble a mercury relay! These relays often have reed-type contacts sealed in a high-pressure glass vial. If disturbed, the contacts can explode, throwing glass fragments. Mercury is also poisonous.

Rheostats. A rheostat is a manually variable power resistor. A replacement should have nearly the value of the original for best results, and at least the same power-handling capability. To use too physically small a rheostat for a replacement is to invite another failure due to simple overheating of the device.

Resistors. Anyone studying electronics is aware of the series and parallel arrangement of resistors and the resulting single-resistor value. Briefly, resistors in series add to one another to produce a total. Thus, two 10-Ω resistors in series will substitute for an original 20-Ω resistor.

Resistors in parallel act differently, of course. Two 10-Ω resistors in parallel allow twice the current flow as one; thus, the total resistance is half that of any one resistor (or 5 Ω). Three 10-Ω resistors in parallel result in 3.33 Ω total, or one-third of the individual resistances.

The power dissipation required of a series or parallel arrangement must be calculated for high-power applications to be sure that no one of the resistors will be required to dissipate more than its rated amount.

Speakers. A speaker has three basic ratings; its impedance, power-handling capability, and frequency response. Speaker impedances are commonly available in impedances of 4, 8, or 16 Ω. It is usually permissible in noncritical applications to substitute a speaker that is a single step from the original impedance. If, for instance, you found it necessary to replace a 16-ohm speaker in a CB radio, you could use an 8-ohm speaker. Do not substitute a speaker of different impedance or less power rating in more expensive or critical equipment.

Switches. Switches have current and voltage ratings. A substitute switch should have the same or higher ratings.

Replacement switches may have extra sets of contacts. It is common practice to parallel unused contacts of switches to help share the current flow, thus extending the life of the switch.

Rotary switches must usually be replaced by exact substitutes. There are a great many variables with rotary switches, and some very complex switching arrangements can be accomplished with a single switch. The more complicated the unit, the more unlikely it is that you will be able to find a generic replacement.

It is appropriate when discussing rotary switches to make the reader aware of the terms *make-before-break* and *break-before-make.* These terms are best explained through the use of an illustration (see Figure 18–1).

Thermistors. The thermistor is a temperature-sensitive resistor. Because of its sensitivity, a replacement thermistor should, depending on the application, be similar in the temperature/resistance curve. This information is seldom available to the technician, who is usually restricted to perhaps a single temperature and resistance reading. Thus, the substitution of the original part number is the safest way to replace a thermistor.

Transformers. A transformer should be replaced by an equal or better transformer. The total number of windings, their voltages, and their current ratings must be equal or better in each case. Unused windings must be left open (disconnected).

Although it is theoretically possible to connect secondaries of identical voltage in parallel, they will not share the load equally if they are wound with different sizes of wire. The basic rule is to parallel transformer windings only if they are *identical,* and preferably made by the same manufacturer.

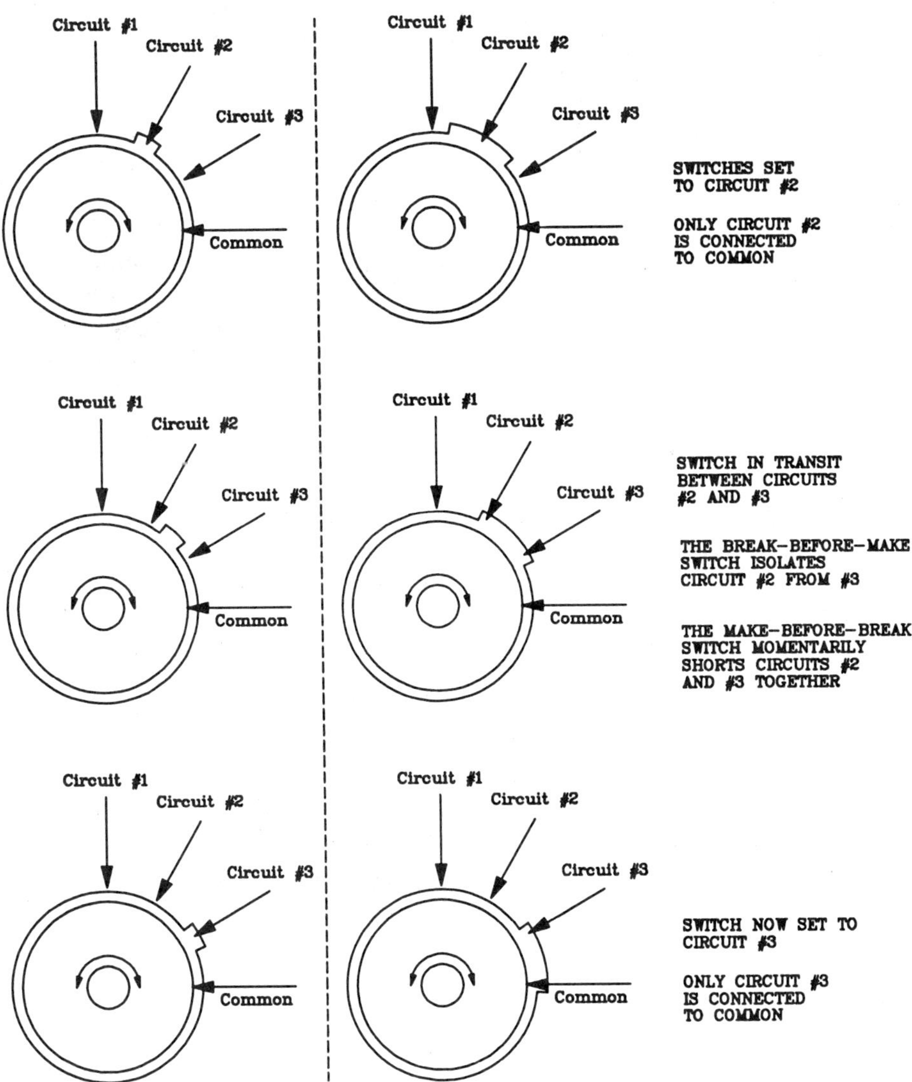
BREAK-BEFORE-MAKE
MAKE-BEFORE-BREAK
Circuit #1
Circuit #2
Circuit #3
Common
SWITCHES SET TO CIRCUIT #2
ONLY CIRCUIT #2 IS CONNECTED TO COMMON
SWITCH IN TRANSIT BETWEEN CIRCUITS #2 AND #3
THE BREAK-BEFORE-MAKE SWITCH ISOLATES CIRCUIT #2 FROM #3
THE MAKE-BEFORE-BREAK SWITCH MOMENTARILY SHORTS CIRCUITS #2 AND #3 TOGETHER
SWITCH NOW SET TO CIRCUIT #3
ONLY CIRCUIT #3 IS CONNECTED TO COMMON

Figure 18–1 Explanation of the rotary switch terms, *make-before-break* and *break-before-make*.

Transformer windings can be connected in series to obtain otherwise unattainable voltages. The phasing of each winding will determine if the voltages will add to or subtract from one another. It is also possible to add to or subtract from the incoming line voltage, as demonstrated in Figure 2–4.

Local Parts Distributors

The best place to get replacement parts is through a local parts distributor. Parts distributors buy in quantity from the part manufacturers, which enables them to get lower prices. They mark up the prices, and then sell the parts to you. In many cases, the technician cannot get parts directly from the manufacturer of a given part because of the low cost per part and the fact that it simply isn't worth the time to sell a 3-cent part through the mail when the postage is now over 25 cents! Manufacturers of small parts usually have a limit of how much they will consider for a single order (often $25 or more). The local distributor is your most cost-effective choice in most cases. If the technician works for a large enough company, it may be worthwhile to stock some items, taking advantage of the volume buying that a distributor uses. Of course, there must be sufficient use of a given part before buying in quantity becomes profitable.

The parts distributor should be able to take care of almost all your parts needs, either from stock directly or by ordering for you. This may require the distributor to buy 100 units, pass on to you the 10 you requested, and stock the remaining 90 units in the hope of selling them to others.

It is common for a given parts distributor to handle only one generic brand of semiconductors. A distributor handling the Motorola brand, for instance, will probably not have RCA (Radio Corporation of America) or Philips replacement parts on hand. If you are able to identify a replacement for a given semiconductor within the given line of products, however, the distributor will probably have a replacement for you.

A technician can use name-plate data or the markings on a given part to provide the parts distributor with enough information so that a replacement part can be found. The manufacturer's logos in Appendix IV can be of help in identifying the part manufacturer, particularly if it is an IC. Of particular importance are the telephone numbers provided there. It may be possible to get information on a given chip over the telephone. It is possible to get limited information (for a single chip, for instance) by requesting that they send the information to you by fax machine.

It is also an alternative to order parts by mail. Some mail-order suppliers of electronics parts and kits will give very good service, mailing your order within a day or two of receipt. The price of parts from these suppliers is often substantially lower than from any local supplier.

Semiconductor Replacement, "Equal or Better"

NTE, RCA, Motorola, and Philips are some of the companies to realize the great interchangeability of all manner of semiconductors. Using this information, they categorized most of the transistors in use by specification. They may have found, for instance, that 350 different transistors in use share almost the same specifications, including voltage, current, frequency, and power dissipation. Then, they made a single transistor that would work in any of the circuits in which the 350 varieties worked. The replacement transistor was equal to, or better than, any of the 350 transistors. Taking this further, a special line of only a relatively few semiconductors could substitute for *thousands* of other transistors. This is the basis for the semiconductor interchangeability guides published by these semiconductor manufacturers.

One can stock a relatively few transistors that will be suitable to replace thousands. This is a great advantage in the service industry. All the technician need do is to look up the number of the transistor to be replaced in the guide. This entry gives the generic replacement device that can be used to replace the specific faulty transistor.

A replacement guide will typically list bipolar transistors, IGFETs, UJTs, JFETs, digital and analog ICs, and consumer ICs found in televisions and radios. These replacement guides can also be used to give an *indication* of the nature of a given semiconductor and its specification. Look up the specific part number in the guide, and then look up the specifications for the generic replacement part. Keep in mind, though, that the replacement part may possess improved specifications compared to those of the actual part under consideration.

A copy of an interchangeability guide can sometimes be obtained from your parts distributor.

18.2 HANDLING NEW COMPONENTS

New components should, generally speaking, be left in their original packaging until they are actually needed. All surface-mounted devices and semiconductors of all types should be handled in this manner.

In addition to electrostatic damage prevention, the technician must be careful to prevent mechanical damage to components during their insertion into or upon the circuits. Surface-mounted devices and metal-film resistors are susceptible to damage or changes in value if handled roughly with tools such as pliers or tweezers. Handle these parts with care and minimal force.

If the leads to a device are stressed too much, this can also cause damages. Glass-encapsulated or sealed devices are very prone to damage or outright destruction if they are carelessly bent during installation. As a basic caution, if there is glass or a glass seal involved, bend the leads by first gently holding the device with a pair of pliers connected very near the component, then make the bend beyond the pliers. See Figure 18–2.

18.3 TESTING NEW COMPONENTS

When it is convenient, the new component can be checked for proper value. If the part cannot be checked without a test circuit, go ahead and install it. The probability of getting a bad part "off the shelf" these days is very small (probably less than 1 percent).

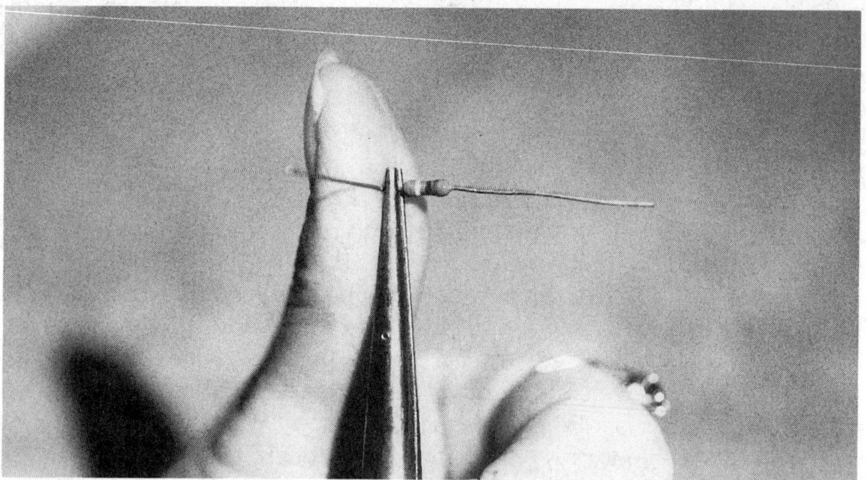

Figure 18–2 Use pliers to protect small components from damage while bending their leads.

The options of using a "toothpick test" or installing a socket for the component in lieu of soldering the new one directly into the board should also be considered. If there is any chance that the component may have to be replaced again, a socket makes it much more convenient next time. These options were covered in Chapter 16.

18.4 INSTALLING PARTS

Most modern electronic parts should be installed at a static-free workstation. This should include, as a minimum, a grounded antistatic mat on which to work and a wrist-strap to ground the technician, preventing any accumulation of static charges.

The technician must make a conscious effort to double-check the installation of polarity-sensitive parts. Installing a part backward is bad enough, but applying power to the board under these conditions just about guarantees further damage. *Always check your work, particularly the polarization of parts, before applying power to a board.* Some of the parts that are polarity-sensitive include diodes, electrolytic capacitors, transistors of all types, integrated circuits, and LEDs.

It is sometimes best to install nonpolarized components with a particular orientation in order to make the board more organized. Resistors, for instance, are usually installed with the color bands all reading toward one end of the board.

SOLDERING NEW PARTS

A competent technician *must* be able to solder expertly. Severe board damage can be done with an improper iron or by operator clumsiness.

New parts should be installed using the correct solder. A tin-to-lead ratio of 63:37 is the preferred mixture for modern electronics. Surface-mounted devices should use a similar solder with 2 percent silver added.

Parts should be positioned before soldering to help keep the necessary amount of heat to a minimum. Using minimal heat helps prevent damage to the PC board traces and the component. Excessive heat will lift the traces from the board and can either damage the component irreparably or, at the least, change its value.

A small amount of paste or liquid soldering flux must be applied to the connection if rosin-core solder is not available.

INSTALLING SURFACE-MOUNTED DEVICES (SMDs)

Surface-mounted devices must be handled very carefully. Tweezers and a light touch are essential for handling these tiny components.

An SMD that has been removed from a board should never be reused. It will have received too much mechanical and thermal abuse to be reliable. Use only new components, handling them carefully to minimize possible damage.

The heat applied to an SMD should be kept between 500 and 600° F, the minimum necessary to do the job.

The new SMD should be installed by first cleaning each of the pads with solder braid to remove excess solder on the pads. Put a tiny amount of solder on one pad, as a beginning. Put the new SMD on the board, using the tinned pad as the first soldering point. Be sure to heat the connection, rather than the component. A small spot of special epoxy made for the purpose can be used to hold the part in place while soldering it, but simply holding it down in position with the tweezers is probably more convenient. If there are only two leads on the device, solder its remaining end.

If there are more than two connections on the device, there is a recommended sequence of soldering the second and remaining leads. See Figure 18–3.

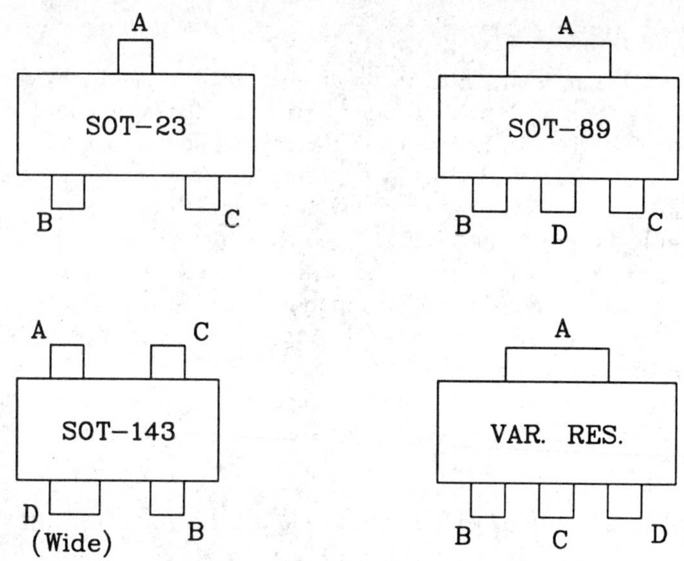

Figure 18–3 Sequence to follow when soldering surface-mounted devices.

CHAPTER SUMMARY

- While some applications leave the technician no choice but to obtain parts from a single source or from a manufacturer, many components are generic in nature.
- Similar parts can often be used without degrading circuit performance.
- Most replacement parts can be obtained through a local parts distributor, often with the assistance of an interchangeability guide.
- Special precautions are appropriate when replacing SMD devices.
- Electrostatic discharge (ESD) precautions are always appropriate.

REVIEW QUESTIONS

1. You have determined by substitution that a particular PAL chip is bad. How can you get a replacement?
2. You see only the numbers "6773452–157" on a particular IC. Where can you get a replacement?
3. You must replace a quartz crystal that was ruined when you dropped it on the floor. What information is necessary to replace it?
4. What is the cell voltage for an alkaline cell; for a ni-cad?
5. How long should a "4AG" fuse last under a 200 percent overload?

6. What voltage and current are required for a type 47 incandescent lamp?
7. How can one often identify a relay that is intended for use on AC voltages?
8. What determines whether two transformer windings will aid or buck each other in voltage?
9. A semiconductor interchangeability guide can help you find a ______ replacement for a given transistor.
10. Why should component leads never be bent right at the component body?
11. What must be remembered about replacing electrolytic capacitors, diodes, transistors, and all ICs?
12. What is the recommended soldering sequence for a SOT-23 SMD part?

Final Inspection and Return to Service

19

CHAPTER OBJECTIVES

By now, the technician has found the problem and probably has corrected it by replacing a part or two. However, this does not end the job. This chapter will make the technician aware of some of the less obvious tasks that must be accomplished, subject to actual working conditions, to completely finish the job. At the conclusion of this chapter, the student will:

- Know tips on reassembling electronic equipment.
- Learn test criteria that must be met during the final checkout.
- Have been introduced to the concepts of test equipment calibration.
- Have been made aware of general paperwork requirements and the reasons behind them.
- Be advised to keep a personal notebook and when it may prove valuable.
- Know what not to use when packing electronic equipment.

19.1 EQUIPMENT REASSEMBLY

Once the problem has been found in a piece of equipment and the offending parts have been replaced, it is time to reassemble the equipment, check it, and make it ready for delivery to the customer.

Reassembling equipment is relatively easy, especially if you were the person who took it apart in the first place. Hopefully, if you are new to the job at hand, you will benefit by the good working habits of the person who began the job. Quality workmanship demands that the necessary nuts and bolts, wire clips, and so forth be on hand when it is time to put the equipment back together. Such small parts should have been stored in a small container and kept with the job through completion.

Great care should be taken when reassembling equipment, and one should not hurry the job, thus sacrificing quality for speed. It is very easy to make common mistakes that can, at the least, waste time. At the worst, poor workmanship or rushing the job can cause damage to the equipment which requires a great deal more time to remedy.

If there were any internal wiring clips or other internal hardware removed originally, now is the time to replace them. If you are dealing with high-frequency radio circuits, the exact placement of some wiring can be very critical to the proper operation of the circuit. Such critical circuits should have been pointed out in the equipment documentation.

Be sure that all the internal PC boards (if used) are firmly seated in their connectors. Route cables and wiring out of the way of the cabinet to be reinstalled.

Be careful that the internal wiring folds naturally out of the way when the cover is reinstalled on the unit. It is very easy to damage internal wiring by applying unnecessary force when putting the cover on. Internal connectors are often dislodged during reassembly of the case.

Another point to watch is the installation of screws into the equipment at any point of reassembly. Putting the wrong size screw into a matching hole can ruin the threads if forced. More damaging is the installation of a long screw in a location where it does not belong (putting in too long a screw to replace a lost one). This can cause damage by touching circuit boards or wiring inside the unit. It is essential to use screws of the right length.

If the unit under repair has fragile controls, such as a keyboard or small switches, be very careful not to tilt or stand it facedown on these items while installing covers. Sometimes, the weight of the equipment alone is enough to bend or break them.

19.2 FINAL EQUIPMENT CHECKOUT

It is not enough that the specific repair passes the final operational test. The entire piece of equipment should be tested for proper operation because of the very strong possibility that other damage may have been caused, directly or indirectly, by the work performed on it. The best way to thoroughly test any piece of equipment is to run the tests necessary to ascertain that all its specifications can be met. For instance, a transmitter may have developed a problem with the modulator. Once repaired, it is not sufficient to merely test to be sure the transmitter now modulates. Rather, all the appropriate tests should be made to be sure that all aspects of transmitter operation are correct. Since the unit is in the shop already, now is the time to accomplish these tests. Checks should be made for frequency, modulation, and power output at the very least.

Any equipment that has failed because of an intermittent problem must be run for extended periods to prove that the problem has been corrected. It is not at all unusual for a technician to replace a suspected intermittent part, as judged by sound troubleshooting methods, only to have the unit fail again later. In such a case, an overnight burn-in test is often a good idea.

DOES THE UNIT MEET SPECIFICATIONS?

Once a repair has been made, certain circuit adjustments may require a touch-up to put the circuitry back into its proper alignment. This was already discussed in Chapter 13 for the topic of alignment of RF circuits.

Precision circuits, such as DC amplifiers, may also require adjustment after repair. For example, adjustments may be provided to calibrate the equipment to meet very exacting specifications of precise gain. The calibration of electronic equipment must, in some cases, be traceable to the standards maintained by the National Institute of Science and Technology in Boulder, Colorado. Standards for physical quantities such as weight, resistance, and voltage are examples of the kinds of standards maintained by this agency.

There is one rule on which calibration laboratories operate: *the standard used must be at least 10 times more accurate than the device being calibrated* in order for the calibration to be considered effective and reliable.

After the equipment has met all the important specifications, it can be repacked and shipped to the customer.

19.3 PAPERWORK

Every job has at least some paperwork. The technician doing repairs will probably have to fill out a work sheet for each job accomplished. This will normally include items such as the time spent on the job, the symptoms originally reported, and the parts used to cure the problem. This work sheet, whatever its form, will be used to calculate the time and materials for the customer's bill. It is the technician's responsibility to report all these items as accurately as possible for the billing to be fair.

Besides the required paperwork, a technician would be well advised to also keep a personal written account of the daily details of the job. Items like time and parts costs are a matter of work-sheet record. The dates of job completion and when the equipment was shipped out, along with any personal notes about the job, can come very handy later. If the customer should call in regard to a particular job, the notebook can be used to refresh your memory and allow you to answer questions quickly and accurately. The personal notebook also finds good use in recording information like details of road trips, meal costs, and overnight expenses relating to jobs. If original claim reports are lost, a notebook such as this can save the day when it comes to reimbursement for money spent on behalf of the company.

Billing the customer may or may not be part of the technician's job. Company policy will determine how much customer contact a technician will have. Often, the technician simply reports the pertinent details of a job to the company. The company then bills the customer, and the technician is not involved with the monetary aspects of business at all. Billing of a customer will depend heavily on the information provided by the technician as to the time spent and the parts used, plus any road time or associated expenses.

A routine repair of equipment will mean that parts will be expended from the company stock room. The identification of these parts is included in the customer's bill. These parts may also have to be replaced in preparation for a future anticipated need for them. The specific means by which the parts are ordered will again depend on company policy. Responsibility sometimes rests entirely on a technician to order replacement parts for stock. Of course, computers are being used more frequently these days to keep track of parts inventories. However, when a computer is used, inventory can be very exact, but *only if all parts are logged in and out,* without exception.

If repair parts are tightly controlled, the problem of using parts temporarily comes up. If a new part is needed to verify the condition of a questionable part, how does the technician get the new part for temporary use? What happens to the new part if it does not remain in the equipment (after having showed that the original part was all right)? These are the questions that the technician must be able to answer after a short period of employment with a given company. Many stock rooms will charge out a part to a specific job (usually by job number) but will not restock that part once it has been installed. The part is now a known good part, but it need not be installed. What, then, is to be done with it? Find out how your company handles this situation.

An inventory of at least a small store of spare parts is usually maintained by electronic service companies. If a required part is temporarily out of stock or is not stocked as a spare, the technician can have it ordered and simply put the partially repaired equipment aside until the new part arrives. Priority repairs will require that a replacement part be obtained as soon as possible. Local electronics parts distributors can usually supply such parts quickly, having them ready for immediate pickup by the technician. The exact method of getting a part locally will depend on the company's relationship with the supplier.

19.4 PACKING EQUIPMENT

While some repair jobs can simply await the arrival of the customer for pickup, other equipment must be packed for mailing or shipping to the customer. Sometimes there is a special department that will take care of the actual packing, but it often falls to the technician to do the packing as part of the job.

The best packing for any given piece of equipment is that in which it originally arrived from the manufacturer. Although it is nice to keep such packing stored somewhere in case it is needed, original packing is more often discarded or used to ship some other unit. If the equipment is very expensive, such as some shop test instruments, it might be a good idea for someone to request a proper shipping container from the manufacturer.

If the original shipping container is not available, equipment can be wrapped in bubble-wrap, using many layers. Do not use any form of styrofoam, like "blankets" of styrofoam or styrofoam "peanuts," because of its highly static nature. This material is potentially dangerous to use in packing any static-sensitive circuitry. If you are unsure how to physically pack electronic equipment, imagine dropping the finished job on one corner of the box: would the equipment survive the fall?

If any equipment is to be returned to a manufacturer for replacement or repair after failing, whether or not it is under warranty, there a telephone call should be made first. Many manufacturers and some distributors require that any equipment sent to them for repair or replacement must be done so under a return authorization number, or *RA*, as it is known in the trade. Sometimes the abbreviation *RMA* is also used, for return material authorization. Equipment shipped blindly, without an authorization, can easily become lost because its status is unknown.

CHAPTER SUMMARY

- After reassembling equipment when a repair has been completed, testing should be done to ensure that the equipment is performing up to original specifications.
- The equipment instruction book will give the specifications, and the technician must be sure that they are met or exceeded before proclaiming the job finished.
- Retuning, alignment, or calibration may have to be performed as a result of repairs that were made or circuits that were disturbed as part of the troubleshooting process.
- A calibration standard must be at least 10 times more accurate than the unit to be calibrated.
- Besides the required company paperwork, a personal notebook can

be handy when dealing with customers and as a backup to other paperwork.

- Be sure that any parts expended from stock are replaced in a timely manner.
- Pack repaired equipment carefully, without using styrofoam products. Use the original shipping cartons whenever possible.

REVIEW QUESTIONS

1. After making a repair and closing the cabinet of a piece of equipment, what should be done next?
2. You wish to check the calibration of a VOM meter, using a digital meter as a standard. How much more accurate must the DMM be to act as a standard for the VOM?
3. Why check all the functions of a unit if only one was repaired?
4. Who provides parts and repair time information for customer billng?
5. What is the best way to pack equipment for shipping?
6. What is an RA number?

Equipment Installation and Preventive Maintenance

20

CHAPTER OBJECTIVES

An electronics technician may sometimes be in charge of, or take part in, the installation of new equipment. Technicians also frequently get involved in routine maintenance of equipment that at the moment is working fine. This chapter will acquaint the new technician with some of the more important highlights of both these activities. At the conclusion of this chapter, the student will be familiar with:

- Generic requirements for preventive maintenance.
- The instruments used for transmission line and antenna maintenance.
- The need for cleaning and dusting out equipment.
- The general dos and don'ts of mechanical lubrication.
- The cautions to observe when using cleaning solvents.
- When equipment logs are required and why.
- Things to watch for when placing equipment in storage or returning it to service after long storage periods.

20.1 INSTALLING EQUIPMENT

The installation of new electronic equipment requires only a moderate amount of special instruction. Be sure that crates and boxes of equipment are in the proper, "This Side Up," position before unpacking them, and take special care when unpacking new equipment to avoid damage to the cabinets. Watch for the instruction manuals, warranties, and other paperwork that is packed with the equipment. Keep the instruction manuals at hand, but take shipping documents to the proper person for accounting. It is important to process these papers to be sure that the correct type and quantity of equipment has been received.

The actual installation of equipment will have to be carefully researched by consulting the instruction book or the manual specifically addressing the matter of installation, the installation manual. This manual will contain very important information on how the equipment should be mounted and how any accessory equipment, such as antennas, must also be taken into account during the installation.

When an installation requires the services of a professional, such as an electrician or a carpenter, be sure to get one. Do not attempt such work unless you are competent to do so. An installation should be done correctly, and this often requires outside services.

Installation frequently requires wiring between major units of a system. This kind of wiring is best done by using overhead wiring racks. Be sure to follow the installation manual as it pertains to the kinds of wiring and cabling to be used. The use of other than recommended cabling can result in poor performance of the finished installation.

20.2 ROUTINE MAINTENANCE

Routine maintenance is work performed on equipment to keep it in working condition, before any failures have occurred. Some electronics applications will require maintenance, while others will not. Many applications for electronic equipment can benefit from the adage, "If it isn't broken, don't fix it." Problems can be easily caused by a technician overzealously disturbing equipment that was working fine.

REMEMBER INTERLOCKS

Be careful of opening any potentially dangerous, operating equipment with which you are not completely familiar. Interlocks may be provided to turn off dangerous circuits, and in the process, to shut down the equipment. A commercial broadcast transmitter is an example of such equipment. The doors of these high-powered transmitters are equipped with interlocks to protect personnel. A curious or not particularly astute person who has no business poking around inside such equipment is thus protected from harm. It is equally effective for a technician who unthinkingly opens the cabinet due to overfamiliarity with the equipment. The interlocks should operate as designed and shut down the equipment, taking the station off the air. If you don't want to go off-air, don't open the doors.

WHEN IS ROUTINE MAINTENANCE PERFORMED?

Whether routine maintenance will be performed may be a matter of law, common sense, or company policy. In the case of some aviation equipment, FAA regulations state that no more than a certain interval of time may pass before performance checks are made to equipment such as distance measuring equipment (DME) and Transponders.

Critical equipment, such as the instrument landing system at an airport, is one type of equipment that is routinely checked and maintained to ensure the highest possible degree of reliability. These applications may also include complete redundancy: a second backup system that can come into service immediately, and sometimes automatically, upon failure of the primary system. In this case, the failed system can be repaired while the backup is on-line.

Scheduled maintenance is maintenance that takes place at regular intervals. Items to include in these routines are vacuuming out dust and dirt from the equipment and, perhaps, at least partial performance verification, using installed monitoring devices.

As-needed maintenance include those items of work that can be accomplished as the need for them arises, like clean air filters. When the filters are relatively clean, they need not be replaced, but if dirty, they will be replaced at the first opportunity.

BATTERY MAINTENANCE

Most electronic equipment is operated by 120-V AC from the public power lines. There are some applications that, due to their critical nature, cannot be interrupted even if the primary power fails. These applications will require some form of backup electrical system. There are two choices here to take over the load: battery or generator. A combination of batteries and at least one generator provides short- and long-term backup capability.

Extremely critical electronic installations cannot tolerate even a momentary interruption of primary power, particularly because of the computers used to facilitate their operation. In aviation, an enroute air traffic control facility is an example of such an installation. There is a need for maintenance of the batteries used in these power backup systems. The electrolyte level must be maintained, and the connections to the batteries must be kept clean and tight. Old batteries must be replaced periodically with new ones. The maintenance of these battery systems may fall to a technician, a topic covered in Chapter 21.

ANTENNA MAINTENANCE

Antennas need occasional maintenance. Wire antennas, vertical towers, and many other kinds of antennas often have insulators that must be kept clean. One of the ways that the need for insulator cleaning can be ascertained is by using a very-high-voltage ohmmeter to see if there is leakage across the face of the insulators. See Figure 20–1.

If the insulators become dirty, the *megohmmeter*, or *megger* as it is usually called, can detect it, indicating that they should be cleaned. A megger is shown in Figure 20–2.

A megger can be battery-operated or can be a manual generator of high voltage. The meter indicates the amount of leakage across the test leads of the instrument.

> ***Caution:*** **A megger typically produces 500-V DC for testing. Do not touch or otherwise come in contact the leads during operation, and do not permit others to contact the antenna under test. Be sure the antenna structure is disconnected from any source of RF power before using the megger.**

A megger is also good for testing the leakage condition of long runs of coaxial cable. As cable ages, its leakage increases. Replacing leaky coaxial cables can prevent burnout of the cable and the failures that could cause.

An antenna tower will often be constructed atop a strong base insulator.

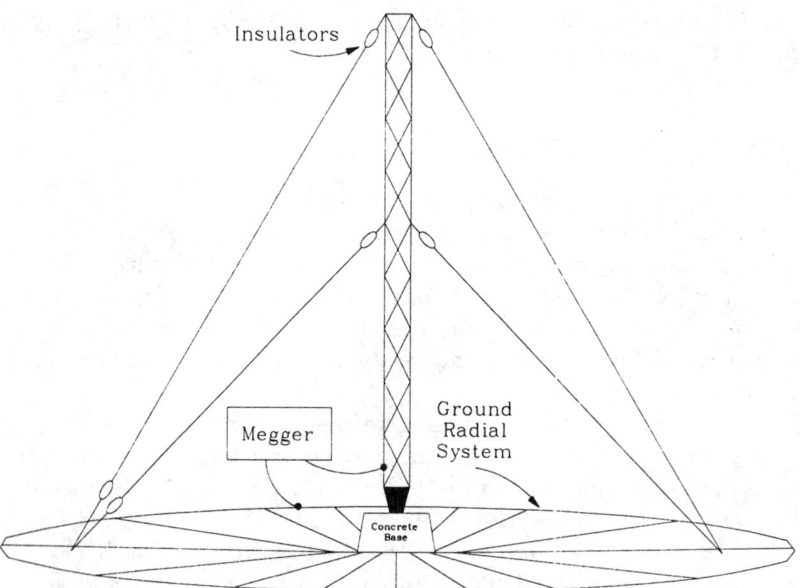

Figure 20–1 Use a megohmmeter, or "megger," to test the leakage condition of all antenna insulators.

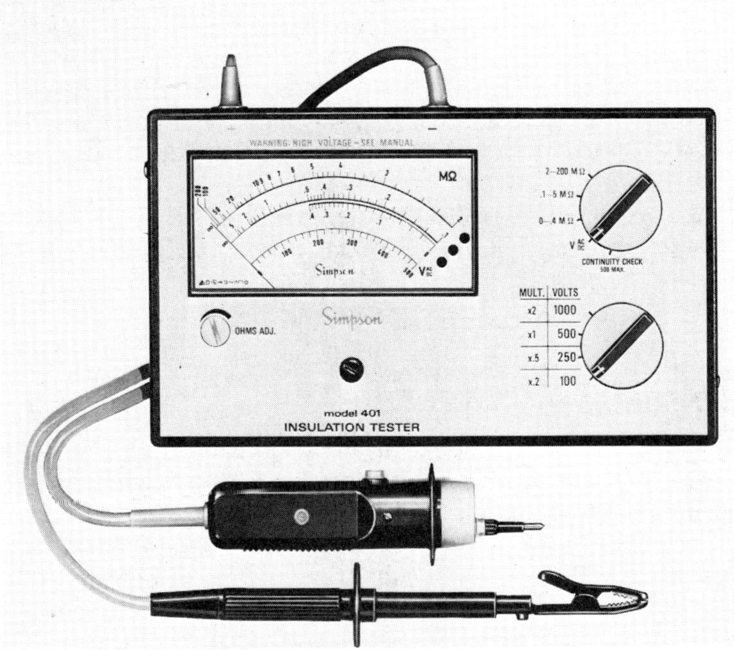

Figure 20–2 The megohmmeter uses up to 500-V DC to test for insulation breakdown. (Courtesy of Simpson Electric Co., Elgin, Illinois)

The leakage condition of this insulator is also tested by using a megger. This insulator is usually at ground level, where it can be cleaned of dirt and dust with a clean cloth and warm, soapy water. Rinse thoroughly, dry, and retest for leakage.

Antenna tower cleaning and painting are done by commercial contractors trained and equipped for the job. Technicians are not expected to be steeplejacks as well. A possible exception to this may be when a technician is asked to climb an antenna tower to replace bulbs in the red aircraft warning lights. A refusal to climb a tower is no sign of cowardice, however, and this option should be exercised when one is uncomfortable with the thought of climbing to great heights. There should be a substantial monetary compensation to the climber for this hazardous job, proportional to the height of the tower.

TDR FOR TRANSMISSION LINES

Transmission lines can also be tested at regular intervals. This preventive measure can detect gradually deteriorating cables. The time domain reflectometer instrument, mentioned at the end of Chapter 3, can detect the smallest problem before it becomes a big one. This instrument is particularly good to use every six months or so in marine applications, such as naval ships. As the vessel bends and flexes in normal seagoing service, the coaxial cables running up the mast can fail due to chafing. The movement of the vessel can also rub into their protective covering and expose the fragile inner braid to the corrosive effects of salt water. This invasion of the braid can be detected by a good TDR instrument before it becomes a major problem.

If the application is not critical, the schematic of Figure 20–3 will provide a crude TDR generator, provided an oscilloscope of 35 MHz or better is available for a readout.

VACUUM TUBE MAINTENANCE

Vacuum tubes are still in use today. Transmitting equipment often uses tubes because of their relative inexpensive high-power capability. It may be up to a technician to maintain such equipment.

The safety of the technician is of primary importance when working with high-power, high-voltage vacuum tube transmitting equipment. Voltages of thousands of volts are commonly encountered in such circuits. The only way to safely handle these circuits is to be provided with, and to wisely use, a dead-man stick, as will be covered in Chapter 23.

Vacuum tubes gradually wear out because of a lack of electrons boiling off the cathode. Some tubes can be partially rejuvenated by the application of higher-than-normal heat to the cathode, thus bringing up some electrons from deeper within its material. A transmitting tube with a *thoriated tungsten* filament is one type.

The harmonic radiation of a given transmitter can be reduced if the final

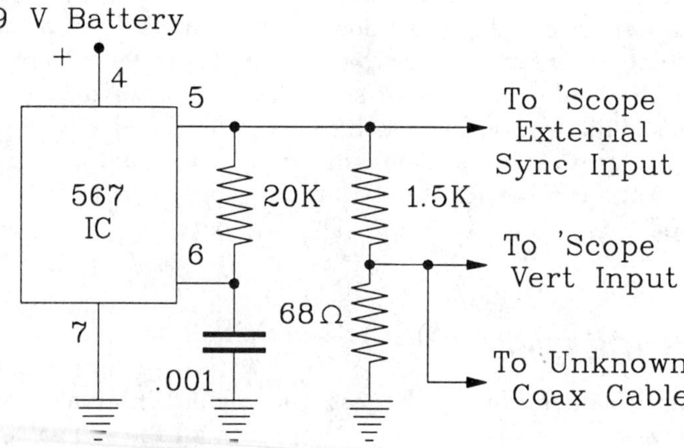

Figure 20–3 An inexpensive TDR generator circuit.

amplifier is designed to have two tubes in push-pull. These applications may require the balancing of tubes to minimize such radiation. Tubes are balanced when they conduct the same current with the same bias voltage. A technician may have to replace tubes, logging the individual currents drawn, until a good match has been made.

New tubes, particularly those that have been in storage for years, should be started out in the equipment at reduced plate voltage. After a certain length of time, the plate voltage can be increased until the maximum operating voltage is reached. The exact method and timing needed to "bake-in" a new tube should be documented in the information that accompanies it. Basically, the larger the tube and the longer it has been stored, the more likely that it will benefit from a gradual rise to normal operating conditions. When in doubt, it does no harm to bake-in large transmitting tubes for too long rather than too short a time.

MANUAL MAINTENANCE

Most of the work of routine maintenance takes four basic forms; using a vacuum cleaner to remove dirt, changing air filters, lubrication, and cleaning.

Blowing Out or Vacuuming Equipment

Blowing out dirt and dust makes a big mess, but is sometimes more effective in cleaning equipment than vacuuming. Vacuuming should be done first to remove the majority of the dust that will normally accumulate in equipment that has been in service for long hours. The remaining dust in the corners may respond better to the blowing function.

A vacuum cleaner can cause a great deal of static electricity. The nozzle should never touch the actual circuitry; be careful to touch only the grounded chassis of the equipment, if anything. The equipment should be turned off during vacuuming.

Air Filters

Many kinds of electronic equipment make use of an internal blower to circulate air, particularly if the component density is high. Many of these *forced-air systems*, as they are called, include an air filter. The circulation of the air is fine for cooling, but without a filter, dust is also deposited within the equipment.

A properly fitting air filter may have to be specially ordered from the manufacturer of the equipment. A supply of these filters should be kept on hand to avoid having to operate with a dirty filter. As an air filter performs its function, it gradually becomes clogged with dust. Running equipment too long without changing the filters can cause temperatures to soar, causing failure of the equipment. Keep the filters clean, and replace them as needed. A few kinds of air filters are washable. In that case, wash them according to the instruction manual for the equipment, replacing them when they become worn from use or if they develop holes.

Lubrication

The only parts of equipment that need lubrication are those that move in relationship to some other part. The bearings in blower motors, panel bearings, and slide rails are common lubrication points on equipment.

Lubrication is mainly used to provide a more friction-free contact between two surfaces, thus preventing excessive wear of the contact surfaces. While desirable in bearings and on slide rails, *lubrication products must be kept clear of belts and friction drives* or they will cause the immediate failure of these mechanical devices. Belt drives will slip if they are contaminated by lubricants. Friction drives are commonly used within tape-recording mechanisms, for instance, where the rotating shaft squeezes the tape between itself and a rubber roller.

These days, bearings are often sealed, requiring no lubrication for the life of the bearing. See Figure 20–4.

If bearings are to be lubricated, they should first be cleaned in an oil solvent, and then dried before repacking with the recommended grade and quantity of grease. This procedure of repacking a bearing with lubricant, if required, should be well documented in the equipment maintenance manual. Do not try to dry a bearing by spinning it with compressed air, as this can cause chipping of the bearings or races due to the high speeds encountered.

Some motors used in association with electronic installations will require the replacement of bearings when they become worn and noisy. After disassembling the motor, the old bearings are pulled off with a bearing-puller tool made for that purpose. See Figure 20–5.

Use only the proper size of puller for the bearing at hand, however. A new bearing can then be placed on the shaft and *gently* tapped into position *with a soft-faced mallet*. Do not use a steel hammer of any kind to seat a bearing, as damage can very easily result.

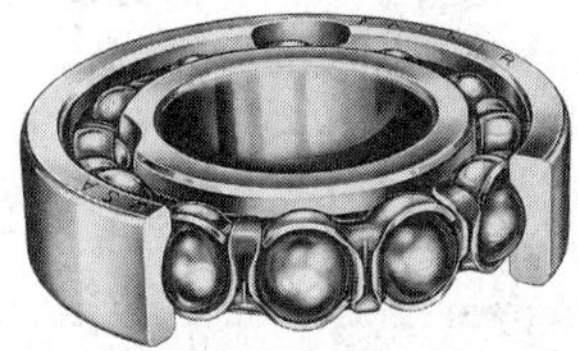

Figure 20–4 Sealed bearings cannot be lubricated. On the other hand, unsealed bearings may have to be manually cleaned and repacked periodically. (The Torrington Co., Fafnir Bearings Division)

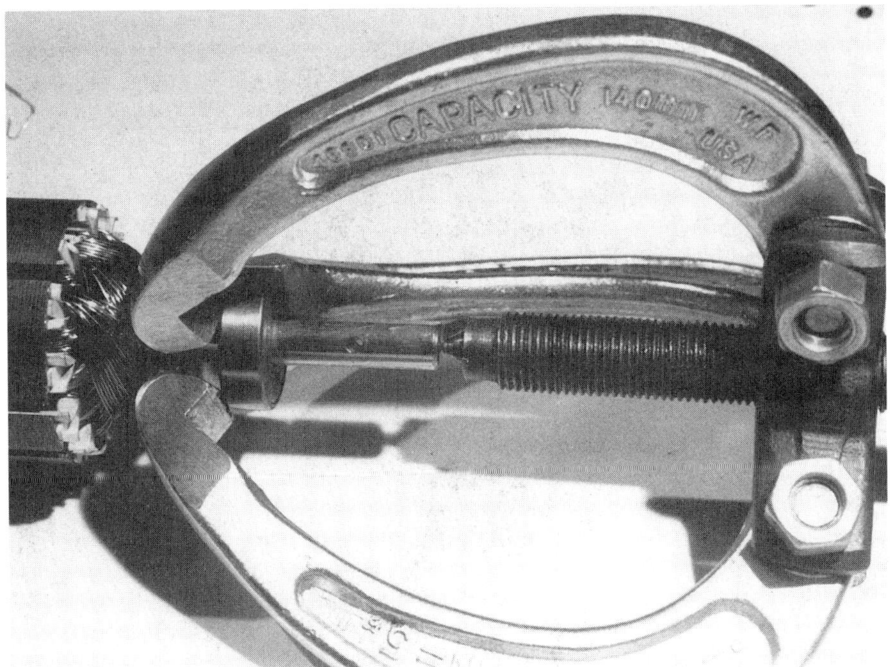

Figure 20–5 This small bearing puller is a typical size for maintaining the bearings on small blower motors.

Another component that can benefit from proper lubrication is the drawer-type slide that is often used with rack-mounted electronics. These slides may develop binding and prove hard to use if they are not lubricated along their mating surfaces. See Figure 20–6.

Slides will often develop dirty grease because of the heavy loads on them. If the old grease remains but is dirty, clean off the old grease before installing a new layer.

Sometimes, controls make use of a shaft passing through a collar in the front panel of the equipment. These applications will operate more smoothly if a tiny bit of light grease or a drop of oil is placed where it can work into the bearing surface. The "feel" of such a control will improve right away, making the equipment more pleasant to operate.

20.3 EQUIPMENT LOGS AND THEIR USE

Really critical applications of electronics equipment may require periodic logging of pertinent readings on the system. This information can be recorded automatically in some cases by using strip-recording equip-

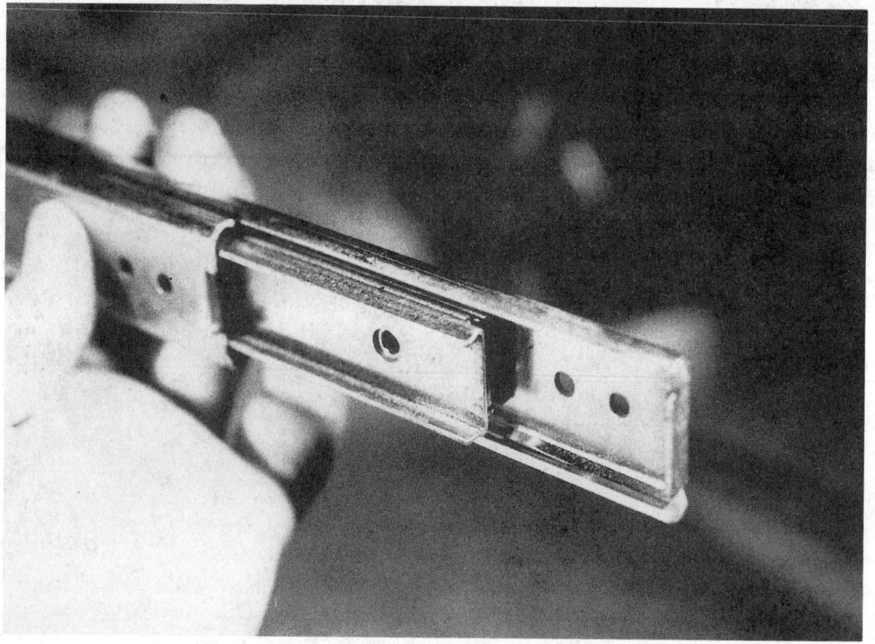

Figure 20–6 These drawer slides may benefit from cleaning and relubricating with fresh, light grease.

ment. Computer logging is also a possibility, using appropriate software for the purpose. One of the instruments available for this use is shown in Figure 20–7.

The Hydra™ provides the necessary interfaces between real-world data such as temperature, RPM, and so forth, and digitizes it so that a computer can then record it. Even time-stamping of data is possible by using the clock within the computer.

Manual logging of important system readings may be required. In this case, the operator or technician on duty may be required to log important readings at specified intervals. This accomplishes three purposes: to log information that may be of use in determining trends toward a possible failure, to help ensure continued legal operation by frequent inspection of important readings, and to force the operator or technician to take periodic notice of what is occurring.

Whatever the method of logging, this form of preventive maintenance is typically pursued when the equipment is operated 24 hours a day. If maintenance is required, scheduled downtime can be arranged for preventive measures unless backup equipment can take over the job while a second system is being worked on.

Figure 20–7 The Hydra™, a convenient system for logging equipment readings via computer. (Reproduced with permission from John Fluke Mfg. Co., Inc.)

20.4 SHUTDOWN, OR LONG-TERM MAINTENANCE, AND POWER-UP

Most electronic and electrical components can tolerate long periods of storage without detrimental effects. However, this is not the case with unsealed inductors and transformers or with some electrolytic capacitors.

TRANSFORMER AND INDUCTOR LEAKAGE

Some transformers and inductors are sealed within metal cases, which often are also cooled by oil within the case. These units can be stored indefinitely without degrading their specifications. However, it is the unsealed unit that presents an occasional problem. An unsealed transformer or inductor can absorb moisture from the air during long periods of storage. This is particularly true of inductors used in underground environments. These units should be checked for leakage to their case ground before being placed into service. Excessive leakage, as compared to leakage in a unit presently in operation or very recently taken from service, may be detected by using one of three instruments: a megger, a hi-pot tester, or a nano-siemens meter.

A megger is probably the instrument of choice to determine if a given coil is acceptable for service. The megger will subject the insulation to the stress of approximately 500-V DC and will detect leakage up to perhaps 100 megohms or more. In the event of an insulation failure, little or no damage is done because of the very tiny amount of current that is produced, even though a full 500 V is available during the test.

An even safer method for detecting leakage is to use a meter capable of measuring nano-siemens, the reciprocal of resistance. These meters can detect leakages of up to about 10,000 megohms yet use a voltage of less than 9 V for the test. See Figure 20–8.

The last method to use to determine the leakage of an inductor or transformer is to subject it to a voltage test. The leakage at this high voltage must be less than an amount determined to be satisfactory by the manu-

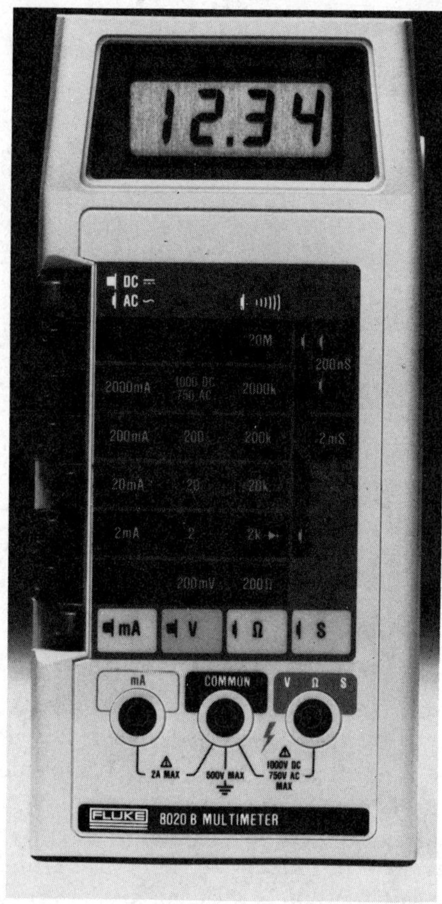

Figure 20–8 This Fluke meter will measure up to 10,000 megohms of leakage using less than 9 volts. (Reproduced with permission from John Fluke Mfg. Co., Inc.)

facturer. This test can be destructive if the amount of available current is also high. It is commonly used to pass or fail a new component after manufacture. The passage of a high potential test is usually identified by a notation somewhere on the device, reading *"HIPOT 500 V PASSED"* or something similar.

If an inductor or transformer should fail to pass a leakage test, it is possible to help the situation by heating the device. In some cases, a few days under a protective cover with a 100-W light bulb may do the job, while in others, it will be necessary to "bake" the device in an oven. Raising the temperature of a coil only 25 or 30 degrees over a period of many hours will often suffice to drive out the moisture that is causing the leakage. In some cases, a current of suitable intensity can be sent through the coil itself to raise its temperature sufficiently to dry it.

CAPACITOR FORMING

The electrolytic capacitor normally has a certain amount of leakage. The more recently it has been used, the less will be the internal leakage. Capacitors in storage can develop very low resistances, sufficiently low that a sudden, full application of the rated working voltage may cause a short as well as a complete failure of the capacitor. Modern electrolytics may not have this problem often, but the older the capacitor, the more likely that it should be *formed* before being placed into full service. An electrolytic capacitor can be formed by the application of its normal operating voltage, but supplied instead via a series resistor of very high value. As the capacitor forms, its terminal voltage increases gradually and gently, with the current being severely limited by the very high series resistance. The value of a forming resistor can be approximated (this is not critical) by the following formula:

$$R_{\text{Megohms}} = \frac{100}{\text{Capacitance}_{\text{Microfarad}}}$$

CHAPTER SUMMARY

- The installation manual must be read carefully before installing new electronics equipment.
- If you are involved in routine maintenance, remember the interlocks that may have been provided.
- Routine maintenance may be required by law or may be performed periodically or on an as-needed basis.
- Battery maintenance duties may fall to the technician.
- Antenna maintenance starts with watching for excessive leakage across the insulators due to dirt and contamination.
- The cleaning and painting of antenna towers is a matter for professionals in that field.

- The replacement of lamps is an extra pay situation, which should provide compensation proportional to the height of the tower.
- TDR is very effective for keeping a watch on coaxial cables and preventing sudden cable failure caused by cable deterioration.
- Maintenance of vacuum tube circuits may mean the need to balance tubes in high-power applications.
- Some large vacuum tubes may require a gradual break-in to normal operating voltages.
- Manual routine maintenance of equipment requires the removal of dust and dirt, replacement of air filters, lubrication, and cleaning.
- Equipment logs force attention to operation for legal or failure-prediction purposes.
- The storage of inductors, coils, and electrolytic capacitors may require testing, baking-in, or forming to prevent failures when components are subjected to normal operating voltages.

REVIEW QUESTIONS

1. What should be done with the enclosed shipping documents if you unpack new equipment for your company?
2. What is routine maintenance?
3. What instrument is used to detect dirt on antenna insulators?
4. Is the replacement of tower aircraft warning lights a normal part of a technician's job?
5. What is the best method to detect deteriorating coaxial cable?
6. What should be done with new, high-power tubes that have been in storage for a long time?
7. What three jobs are commonly performed during routine maintenance?
8. What are the three purposes of manually logging meter readings on a large system?
9. What two components can deteriorate during long-term storage?

Batteries for the Electronics Technician

21

CHAPTER OBJECTIVES

This chapter will acquaint the technician with the fundamentals of commonly used batteries, their construction, and the normal maintenance required to keep them in operating condition. At the conclusion of this chapter, the student will:

- Be familiar with the need for a load during battery testing.
- Know the cautions for disposing of various batteries.
- Know the strengths and weaknesses of each major type of battery for comparison purposes.
- Know the construction and operational details for the most common cells and batteries.
- Know how to maintain secondary cells.
- Know the dangers of handling and maintaining common battery types.
- Be familiar with the differences between major kinds of lead-acid batteries in use today.
- Know how sizes and ratings of lead-acid batteries are expressed.
- Know how to use and maintain ni-cad batteries and how to prevent their early failure.

21.1 GENERIC INFORMATION ABOUT BATTERIES

The basic unit for the chemical storage of electrical energy is the cell. Cells placed in series, parallel, or series-parallel combinations with other cells are called a battery. Cells placed in series increase the voltage available. Cells in parallel increase the discharge current capability and/or the discharge time before requiring replacement or recharging.

> ***Caution:*** **The technician must be cautioned that some of these batteries contain caustic, hazardous liquids. Large batteries are quite capable of sufficient current to produce fires and explosions because of the gases they can produce. Consequently, the maintenance of batteries should always be done with great care. Eye protection is particularly important, since these caustic chemicals (sulfuric acid and caustic potash, for example) can cause immediate and serious eye damage. Protective clothing that will withstand the chemicals involved should be worn if battery work is done often. Gloves can provide protection in case of spills and for the normal handling of batteries which often bubble over and spill chemicals on the outside of the cases.**
>
> **Cells of any kind, and particularly alkaline and some nickel-cadmium cells, should not be disposed of in a fire. The cells used within these batteries are often sealed in metal, and excessive heat can cause them to explode, with potentially dangerous results.**

A battery of any kind must have a suitable load placed on it before testing for the unit's condition. One of the ways in which a battery can become defective is to develop a higher than normal internal resistance. The detection of an increased internal resistance requires the attachment of a load that will stress the battery to approximately its full, normal load.

It is interesting to note at this point that one of the common symptoms of a receiver, when operated on a failing battery, is to develop either a low- or a high-frequency oscillation, which can be a tip-off to an observant technician. This oscillation varies with the equipment at hand, from a low growl and excessive receiver distortion to a high-pitched squeal (particularly if the receiver is at a high-volume setting). The oscillation is caused by the battery voltage varying up and down due to the discharged condition, rather than holding a constant voltage, as the demands of the audio section increase momentarily. This oscillation effect is sometimes called *motorboating.*

Cells come in two basic types: primary and secondary. Primary cells are used once and then discarded, because their chemical makeup cannot be reversed. Secondary cells, on the other hand, are reversible. Forcing a current through them in the opposite direction of the discharge cycle over a suitable period of time will cause them to regain most of their original charge.

21.2 PRIMARY CELLS

THE CARBON-ZINC (CZ) CELL

One of the oldest cells in common use is the carbon-zinc (CZ) cell. This is the familiar, inexpensive flashlight cell. It is made by placing a carbon (+) rod in a caustic electrolytic paste, which is all contained within a zinc container. The top of this cell is often sealed with a tar-like substance. The normal cell voltage is about 1.5 volts. Discharging a CZ cell causes the erosion of the zinc container. In severe cases of discharge, holes are eaten into the container, releasing some of the electrolyte. This caustic material will attack all manner of metals, leaving them rusted and corroded within a few days. For this reason, always remove discharged CZ cells immediately, and remove even good CZ cells from any equipment before long periods of storage.

CZ cells normally develop small bubbles along the carbon rod during high discharge rates. If the cell is allowed to "rest" for a few hours, the bubbles dissipate and the cell can again supply large currents. This characteristic makes them seem to "recharge themselves" after sitting for a while.

The chief advantage of the CZ cell is that it is relatively inexpensive. Its shelf life can be extended if it is stored at a low temperature but not allowed to freeze. (The author keeps several of these cells on hand in the refrigerator butter-storage compartment—not the freezer—ready for use. In one case, a special 30-V battery was stored in this way for years and was later put into a meter, where it then performed well for several additional years.)

The CZ cell is tested, as all cells are, by placing a normal-to-heavy load on the cell while monitoring its terminal voltage. The testing of various sizes and types of cells was covered in Chapter 17. Since a weak CZ cell must be discarded, there is no maintenance to be performed on it other than replacement. For capacities of the various types, see Table 21–1.

ALKALINE-MANGANESE CELLS

The alkaline-manganese cell is often similar in appearance to the CZ cell, being available in the same basic sizes for use in flashlights, camera flash units, and portable radio equipment. One will note the heavier weight of the alkaline cells, however. The normal alkaline cell voltage is 1.4 volts. These cells can directly replace the 1.5-V CZ cell in almost any application. The alkaline's slightly lower cell voltage is offset by its ability to supply heavier currents than a CZ cell.

The lower internal resistance of the alkaline cell can be deduced from the

Table 21–1 Capacities of Various Carbon-Zinc Cells and Batteries

	Eveready	NEDA	Voltage	Capacity
AAA	912	24F	1.5	20 ma for 21 hours
AA	915	15F	1.5	54 ma for 20 hours
C	935	14F	1.5	20 ma for 140 hours
C	1235	14D	1.5	37.5 ma for 97 hours
D	950	13F	1.5	20 ma for 360 hours
D	1150	13C	1.5	375 ma for 15.8 hours
D	1250	13D	1.5	60 ma for 139 hours
N	904	910F	1.5	22 ma for 22 hours
WO	201		1.5	0.1 ma for 650 hours
	750	704	3.0	20 ma for 37 hours
	715	903	4.5	120 ma for 90 hours
	724	2	6.0	60 ma for 175 hours
	509	908	6.0	187 ma for 40 hours
109	206	1611	9.0	12 ma for 40 hours
127	226	1600	9.0	12 ma for 61 hours
	276	1603	9.0	20 ma for 350 hours
117	216	1604	9.0	9 ma for 50 hours
	228	1810	12	12 ma for 59 hours
	420	225	22.5	5 ma for 60 hours
	482	207	45	40 ma for 125 hours
	490	204	90	10 ma for 63 hours

Source: Thomas J. Glover, *Pocket Reference,* Morrison, Colorado: Sequoia Publications), 1992.

recommended loads, as shown in Table 21–2. Again, the condition of an alkaline cell can be determined only if there is a load on the cell during the voltage check. This lower internal resistance and the lack of internal resistance increase due to bubbling enable this cell to supply relatively large currents into heavy loads. This makes the alkaline cell a good choice for providing high cell voltage under heavy-current conditions.

Since alkaline cells are primary cells, they cannot be recharged. In fact, the alkaline cell is sealed and it can explode if disposed of in fire or if

Table 21–2 Capacities of Various Alkaline Cells and Batteries

	Eveready	NEDA	Voltage	Capacity
AAA	E912	24A	1.5	37.5 ma for 25 hours
AA	E91	15A	1.5	20 ma for 107 hours
C	E93	14A	1.5	37.5 ma for 160 hours
D	E95	13A	1.5	50 ma for 270 hours
G	520	930A	6.0	375 ma for 59 hours
N	E90	910A	1.5	9 ma for 90 hours
	532	1308AP	3.0	20 ma for 35 hours
	531	1307AP	4.5	20 ma for 35 hours
	522	1604A	9.0	18 ma for 33 hours
	539		6.0	18 ma for 30.5 hours

Source: Thomas J. Glover, *Pocket Reference* (Morrison, Colorado: Sequoia Publications), 1992.

recharging is attempted. Recharging current will only result in heating, which may even be sufficient to cause the cell to burst.

Alkaline cells have a very good shelf life, and if stored in a cool place, they will last even longer. This is the kind of cell that is valuable when stored for use during emergencies such as power outages, tornadoes, and floods. For capacities of the various types, see Table 21–2.

OTHER PRIMARY CELLS

The mercury cell also has a low internal resistance for its physical size. The normal cell voltage is about 1.4 volts. These cells will last a long time under suitable loads, and thus they have become very popular for subminiature applications like power sources for watches, hearing aids, and small calculators. The loads given in Table 17–2 can be used to test these tiny cells.

Lithium cells were made to answer the need for cells with an exceptional shelf life. Normal shelf life of up to 10 years can be expected of these cells. They are particularly suited for emergency applications, such as a power source for emergency radio-locating beacon transmitters in aircraft. After years of storage, they can be actuated automatically by impact forces during an aircraft crash, and efficiently power an emergency VHF locator transmitter.

Lithium cells should be replaced in such critical applications according to the recommendations on the battery itself. Although the battery may register as being in good condition, one would not want to take chances with a very old battery, lithium or not.

21.3 SECONDARY CELLS

LEAD-ACID CELLS WITH LIQUID ELECTROLYTE

The lead-acid battery is most commonly recognized as the battery in cars. Although in common use, these batteries generate large amounts of hydrogen gas, especially when fully charged. The bubbling sound sometimes heard at high charge rates is from the production and dissipation of this highly explosive gas. When mixed with the oxygen of the normal atmosphere, a very dangerous mixture is produced. All it takes is a small spark to ignite this gas, which is lighter than air and therefore rises. If ignited, the battery can explode, sending a spray of sulfuric acid for a considerable distance.

> ***Caution:* Working with high voltages requires that you remove metal jewelry to help minimize skin contact and reduce the severity of an accidental shock. Although batteries do not generally produce high voltages, the removal of metal jewelry is still a very valid safety measure. Batteries, particularly large ones or Ni-Cad batteries, can produce extremely high currents. These currents can cause metal jewelry to become red-hot: while you are wearing it!**

The normal voltage of a lead-acid cell is between 2 and 2.25 volts. This figure is somewhat influenced by the battery's temperature. The terminal voltage of a battery can be calculated by multiplying the 2-volt figure by the number of cells. A six-cell battery would be a 12-volt unit. The actual voltage of a battery under normally operating conditions and under a moderate charge is closer to 13.8 volts. This is the voltage input figure most often stated for automobiles and for some aircraft electronic equipment.

The electrolyte for a lead-acid battery is a diluted solution of water and sulfuric acid, which is very corrosive and can eat holes in clothing in a matter of hours. Any spills of the electrolyte can be neutralized with a solution of baking soda (not baking powder) and water. Dissolve the baking soda in water (preferably warm water for the quickest neutralizing action). A quart of water with about six tablespoons of soda makes a good mixture. Pour the solution over any spills (and keep it out of the battery cells). The bubbling is a visual indication that the acid is being neutralized.

There is a natural tendency for lead-acid cells to have material flake off from the plates, thereby reducing their capacity over long periods of time. The bottom of most of these batteries includes an empty space for the accumulation of this material, which is necessary to prevent it from building up to a depth at which it might short the plates above it. A lead-acid battery should not be inverted because of the settled material in the bottom. If the material is disturbed by tipping or inversion, it can ruin the cells.

Construction

A lead-acid battery is available in several variations, each of which is suited to a particular use.

Conventional Engine-Starting Batteries

The most common use for a lead-acid battery is to start either a gasoline or a diesel engine. In this application, the battery must produce a very high current for a short period of time. An automobile can require several hundred amperes of current at a terminal voltage of perhaps 9 volts to start the engine. A diesel vehicle will require even more power to turn it over, mostly due to the higher compression within the engine.

The internal construction of a conventional engine-starting battery consists of many thin, porous plates. Both the positive and negative plates consist of grids, with the spaces in between filled with a mixture of lead and antimony (as a hardener). The cells are vented to allow the free gassing of the cell under charge. Because of the thin plates, a conventional battery sheds quite a bit. This shedding of material limits the life of a conventional automotive battery in normal use to about three years. *The conventional car battery should be maintained near maximum charge at all times.* If a battery is allowed to discharge, it will develop a hard coating on the plates, called *sulphation*. This will limit the amount of current the battery can supply, effectively increasing its internal resistance. Keeping it charged minimizes this effect; the higher the charge, the less sulphation will occur.

A conventional battery should not be deep-discharged because of the attendant shedding of lead material from the plates, which, again, increases the internal resistance.

The gassing of a conventional lead-acid battery during charging causes the loss of water from the sulfuric acid solution. After a small loss of liquid, the level should be brought back up to normal by the addition of pure, distilled water. Practically speaking, the addition of any clean water should do, but adding distilled water will prolong the life of the battery because it lacks the chemicals commonly found in ordinary tap water. Distilled water can be purchased at most supermarkets.

Deep-Cycle Batteries

Deep-cycle lead-acid batteries have thicker plates than a conventional battery. This thicker plate structure results in less shedding of the plate material. A deep-cycle battery can be routinely discharged to a dead state with less damage than would occur with a conventional battery. Although a deep-cycle battery will still start an engine, it will not crank it as fast as a conventional battery because of the lack of surface area. Under deep-cycle service, a deep-cycle battery will last from three to five times longer than a conventional battery under the same conditions.

Low Maintenance

The gassing of a lead-acid battery under charge can be minimized if the amount of antimony within the plates is reduced. The less antimony, the less gassing and the less liquid is lost during normal operation. These batteries are still vented for the release of hydrogen during charging, but they will require the addition of water less often than a conventional battery. Although they are an improvement due to their less frequent requirement for maintenance, they will still require the addition of water now and then.

Maintenance-Free

The maintenance-free lead-acid battery uses calcium instead of antimony to harden the lead within the plates. There are no visible filler caps and no obvious venting holes for gassing. However, there is a very small hole provided for the normal "breathing" of the cells. The shelf life of a no-maintenance battery is very good; in fact, it is the best of the lead-acid battery family.

The internal construction of a maintenance-free battery is considerably different from that of other lead-acid batteries. The positive plates of the battery are enclosed in a special ion-permeable bag which all but prevents shedding and the accumulation of buildup in the bottom of the cells. With little shedding, the sump at the bottom of the cell can be reduced, leaving more room for the initial liquid level to increase at the top of the cells.

Marine Battery

A marine lead-acid battery is simply a battery that has screw terminals and perhaps a handle of some sort to facilitate its handling while installing it in a boat. These batteries are available in either the conventional or the deep-cycle varieties.

Dry-Charge Battery

A dry-charged battery is one that has been conditioned at the factory and shipped without any liquid in the cells. The absence of the electrolyte increases the shelf life of the battery tremendously: in fact, the cell will age very little. The only reason for dry-charging is this single advantage. Once activated, there is no advantage to its original status of being a dry-charged battery.

Activation of a dry-charged battery is simple enough: just add sulfuric acid of the proper specific gravity ("thickness") and let the cell sit for an hour or so. After this time, the battery should be charged until the specific gravity of the cell electrolyte reaches a value of 1.260 times the specific gravity of water. The addition of the acid should be done outdoors or in a well-ventilated area, because the smell will be quite bad—like rotten eggs—until the battery stabilizes.

Lead-Acid Battery Specifications

Lead-acid batteries are available in many different case sizes. The case sizes have been standardized, and each is called a "group." Specifying a battery group really means specifying the physical dimensions of the battery. There are about 24 different group sizes for passenger cars, 27 for light trucks, and 31 for heavy trucks.

The *ampere-hour rating* of a lead-acid battery is the number of amperes that the battery can supply for one hour. It is an inconclusive and now obsolete rating, having been replaced by the more comprehensive Cold Cranking Performance Rating.

The Cold Cranking Performance Rating takes into account temperature, which can cause major variations in the capability of a battery to deliver heavy currents. This rating specifies the number of amperes that the battery can deliver in a cranking condition at low temperatures. These conditions are precisely defined as the number of amperes that can be delivered for 30 seconds when the battery begins at a temperature of 0 degrees, maintaining at least 1.2 volts per cell. For a 12-volt battery, this would be a voltage of 7.2 volts. As an example, the common automotive cell of a group 24 size will typically deliver 400 to 500 amperes under these conditions.

At one time, there was considerable emphasis on the number of plates per cell. This specification means little, however, and the cold cranking specification is much more informative.

Charging of Lead-Acid Batteries

One of the advantages of the now-obsolete ampere-hour (AH) rating was that it gave an indication of how heavy a current could be used to charge the battery. A slow charge was in the neighborhood of one-tenth the ampere-hour rating. Thus, a battery with a 40 AH rating could be slow-charged at 4 amperes for about 12 hours to bring it to fully charged status. If the current was then changed to a *trickle-charge* of about one-tenth that amount, or 0.4 amperes, the battery could be maintained for long periods with minimal deterioration. All that needed to be done is to keep an eye on the electrolyte level, topping it off as necessary. Following this procedure minimizes sulphation and provides a fully charged battery when needed.

Batteries that are used seasonally, such as motorcycle or snow-mobile batteries, should be disconnected from their loads and, with occasional checking of the liquid level, should be placed on trickle-charge during the months of nonuse. This will extend the life of the battery from one to three years, depending on many other factors. *Never subject a discharged battery to freezing temperatures.* A discharged battery has an electrolyte of a low specific gravity, making it very likely to freeze. A frozen battery will expand, breaking the case.

It is possible to quick-charge a lead-acid battery, but this should not be done with a good battery. Heavy charging currents heat the battery and may cause the internal plates to buckle and short one or more cells. Under heavy charging, there is a lot of activity in the electrolyte, greatly increasing the flaking off of the plate material. Add to this the increase in sediment stirred up by the circulation of the electrolyte, and one can easily predict the probable result of quick-charging. It is far better to allow more time for charging, particularly if the battery is basically a sound one that is simply low on charge.

Lead-Acid Battery Testing

There are several ways to test a lead-acid battery to determine its current state of charge. As the cells discharge, the voltage per cell also decreases slightly. When an automotive battery reaches an open-circuit voltage of about 1.6 volts per cell—10 volts for a 12-volt battery—the battery is completely "dead" and will not provide substantial current. A good battery should read at least 12.5 volts before you can expect it to make a decent showing under load.

An even better way to tell the status of a battery is, of course, to place a load upon it. An automobile battery can be conveniently tested while running the load of the headlights for a few minutes. With the load of the headlights, the battery should still read 12 V across its terminals.

The very best way to determine if a battery is really good is to put a full charge into it and then connect a very heavy load, such as cranking an engine for a few seconds. Measure the terminal voltage while cranking. The battery voltage should remain over about 10.0 volts after cranking for perhaps 10 seconds. This test assumes a warm summer day; slightly lower voltages should be expected in lower temperatures.

The state of charge of a lead-acid battery can be determined by measuring the specific gravity (SG) of the electrolyte in the cells. The hydrometer in Figure 21–1 is the instrument for this measurement.

The hydrometer provides a very good indication as to the amount of charge that the cells have accumulated. As the cell increases from about 1.100 to 1.260 SG, the cell varies from 0 percent to 100 percent of full charge. If needed, a correction can be made for variance of temperature,

Figure 21–1 The hydrometer, which is used to check the state of charge of a lead-acid battery.

according to the chart or table provided with this instrument. This instrument finds its principal use in evaluating a battery after what should have been a full charge and to find "dead" cells within a battery.

Still another way to test a battery is to use a load tester. This instrument is a combination of a very low-resistance, heavy load and a voltmeter. When using it, the tester is held firmly against the battery terminals for a moment. Then the voltmeter is read. A minimum voltage must be maintained while under the load.

LEAD-ACID CELLS WITH PASTE ELECTROLYTE

The basic liquid-electrolyte lead-acid cell has the disadvantage of gassing and the hazard of spillage of the electrolyte. Cells similar to these are now available that avoid the hazards of a liquid electrolyte by changing it to a paste instead. These cells (often called Gel-Cells) do not spill when tipped to any angle. They do not produce excessive gas, either. These cells are particularly attractive for use in emergency lighting systems for large, public buildings and for robotic use.

A Gel-Cell cannot be quick-charged without permanent damage. Rather, it must be charged strictly in accordance with the charging instructions packed with each new battery. Thc charging rate varies greatly with the size of the battery. In the absence of charging information, do not exceed a charge rate of one-fourth the ampere-hour rating.

A paste-electrolyte lead-acid battery should always be kept charged, for the same reasons already discussed under "Conventional Engine-Starting Batteries."

Disposing of Lead-Acid Batteries

In this day of environmental awareness, batteries with their caustic liquids can easily be seen to be a hazardous commodity. The disposal of batteries in landfills is illegal in some areas. They should be disposed of in accordance with local regulations. The easiest way to get rid of an old battery is to simply turn it in when you buy a new one. The old ones can be recycled into rebuilt batteries with a new lease on life.

NICKEL-CADMIUM CELLS (NI-CADS)

Basically, the ni-cad battery is a big improvement over the lead-acid battery. If it were not for their cost, these batteries would be used in automobiles. There is still danger, however, from the gassing of the cells during high charge rates, especially at full charge. The hydrogen gas is produced, presenting the same hazard of explosion as with the lead-acid battery. Accidental shorting of the terminals of a ni-cad battery can cause fire and explosion in some cases. The big advantages of the ni-cads are that they can be stored in any state of charge without damage and, in the case of sealed cells, can be used in any position.

The state of charge of a ni-cad of any type cannot be determined by measuring the cell voltage. Cell voltage is 1.2 volts, regardless of the state of charge, until the cell goes suddenly and completely "dead" at 1.0 volt per cell or less. The only way to be 100 percent sure of the state of charge of a ni-cad cell is to simply put a known, full charge into it.

Ni-Cad Construction

Ni-Cads are available in both wet and sealed constructions. The wet ni-cad uses a liquid solution of caustic potash in water as the electrolyte, whereas the sealed version has no visible electrolyte.

Ni-Cad Wet Cells

Although not often seen, the ni-cad wet cell is used in applications such as helicopter turbine starting, where very high currents are necessary for short periods of time. The internal resistance of such wet cells is extremely low, and is the lowest of any battery. Dropping a metal wrench on top of the intercell connectors of such a battery can cause an almost immediate explosion because of the extremely high discharge currents that occur.

These cells can be replenished when the electrolyte gets low by simply adding distilled water. The facilities for maintaining ni-cad wet cells and lead-acid batteries must be kept separate, as one type uses an acid electrolyte and the other uses an alkaline electrolyte. Mixing the two battery types can have violent results, so the tools and containers must be kept completely separate from one another. A wet ni-cad cell should have new water added only when it is fully charged and still charging. This is when there is the most gassing and when the addition of more water will not cause an overflow later.

Ni-Cad Dry Cells

Ni-cads are also available in the more common form of the flashlight-type battery and in custom-designed plastic packs of series-connected cells for specific applications.

Since there is no reliable way of determining the state of charge of a ni-cad cell or battery, a full charge is applied before depending on the battery to deliver full performance for the specified time.

Ni-cad cells are easy to charge. Their rating in ampere-hours is divided by .1 to determine the amount of current to apply to the cells for a normal charge. This current should be supplied for 14 hours to allow for a 40 percent overcharge due to the inefficiency of the charge-discharge cycle. Thus, a 4-AH flashlight battery requires a charge of 400 milliamperes for 14 hours to completely recharge it. Sealed ni-cads also have a cell voltage of 1.2 volts. This voltage should be maintained for all normal loads on the cell.

A fully charged ni-cad cell will begin to heat when the end of the charge cycle has been reached. Normally, the heating does no harm under recommended charging currents. Gasses are produced within the cell, but they are immediately reabsorbed and the internal pressure will remain within safe limits.

Overcharging a cell that is designed only for a normal .1-AH charging current can cause the cell to develop excessive internal pressures. In extreme cases, the pressure will rise sufficiently to trigger the internal pressure-release mechanism, which is a sharp point touching a diaphragm in the top of the cell. Once this pressure has been vented through the release mechanism, the cell has been breached and the electrolytic will seep out. The seepage can be identified by the corrosion on the ends of the cells. Such cells should be replaced.

Special cells can be made to take advantage of this heating effect to terminate a higher-than-normal charge rate. As the end of the high-charge-rate cycle nears, the cells heat up rapidly. A temperature detector held against the cell case will detect this and will reduce the charge rate to a trickle or turn it off altogether. When the cell cools, it gets another jolt, again heating it and thus keeping the cell at full charge. One cannot expect such radical treatment to result in a great many charge/discharge cycles, however. It is better to use a smaller charge current for a longer time and reduce the stresses on the cells.

A ni-cad cell can be tested under load for proper terminal voltage, as with any other cell. Remember, however, that the terminal voltage bears no relationship to the amount of charge remaining. A ni-cad will deliver nearly full terminal voltage of 1.2 volts until the cell is almost completely discharged. Only a full charge cycle can assure a fully charged cell. See Figure 21–2.

Ni-cads are often used in packs of series-connected cells. The prolonged use of such battery packs will eventually result in the pack failing to deliver the advertised voltage. This is usually caused by the actual shorting of one or more of the cells inside. Instead of the normal 12-V battery pack, only 10.8 volts will show, even after charging. A drop to 9.6 volts would indicate that two cells shorted, and so forth. Once a cell has shorted, it can be individually rejuvenated by a very strong pulse of charging current and can apparently recover from its shorted condition. Such a cell should not be placed back into service in critical applications, however, because it will no longer be dependable. Internal shorting occurs from the microscopic growth of a crystals within the cell. One short may be cleared, but there will probably be others ready to short soon after.

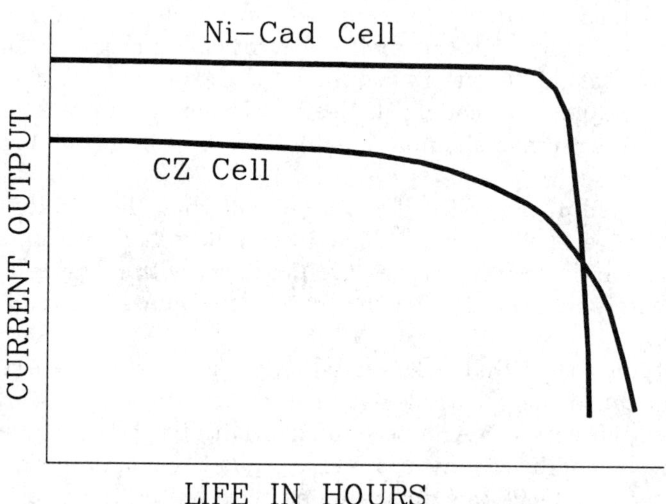

Figure 21–2 Comparison of discharge curves of carbon-zinc and nickel-cadmium cells.

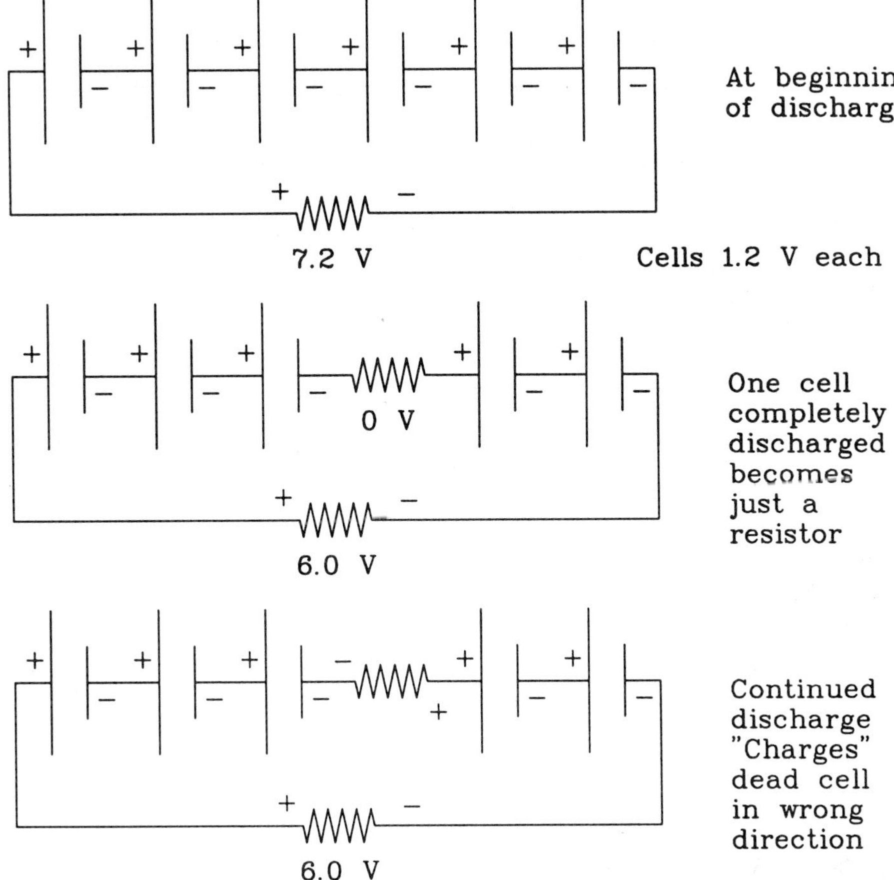

At beginning of discharge
7.2 V
Cells 1.2 V each
0 V
One cell completely discharged becomes just a resistor
6.0 V
Continued discharge "Charges" dead cell in wrong direction
6.0 V

Figure 21–3 Schematic of voltage drops when one, weaker cell goes into polarity reversal.

One of the main factors in the internal shorting of a ni-cad cell is the accidental reversal of current through a cell as it discharges in series with other cells. See Figure 21–3.

If a bank of ni-cads is repeatedly discharged only partly and then recharged, they may not deliver their full rated energy output when finally taken to complete discharge. This is called ni-cad cell "memory." The cure for a "short memory" is to take the cells to a discharge voltage of 1.0 V per cell (never lower than this voltage due to the danger of reverse-charging a cell), and then recharging with a normal charge cycle. Repeated several times, nearly new performance should result.

Although overcharging ni-cads does them no harm, it also does them no good as it heats the cells unnecessarily. After the 14 hours of normal charge, either remove them from the charger or switch the charger to a trickle-charge setting if available. Remember that ni-cads do not have a

Table 21–3 Ni-Cad Capacities for Common Cells and Battery Packs

	Eveready	NEDA	Voltage	Capacity
AAA	CH12AVP-2	10024A	1.2	180 ma-hour
AA	CH15	10015	1.2	500 ma-hour
C	CH35	10014	1.2	1.2 ampere-hour
Sub C	CH1.2	10022	1.2	1.2 ampere-hour
D	CH50	10013	1.2	1.2 ampere-hour
D	CH4	10013HC	1.2	4.0 ampere-hour
N	CH150	10910	1.2	150 ma-hour
	CH22		8.4	80 ma-hour

Source: Thomas J. Glover, *Pocket Reference* (Morrison, Colorado: Sequoia Publications).

Note: CH cells are standard-charge, and CF are meant to fast-charge.

particularly good shelf life, so recharging them for a few hours every week or so is a good idea in order to maintain them at peak efficiency. For capacities of various types, see Table 21–3.

CHAPTER SUMMARY

- Batteries are made up of cells.
- Don't discard batteries carelessly in fire or attempt to charge primary batteries: this can be extremely dangerous.
- The true test of a battery includes applying a substantial load while at the same time checking cell or battery voltage.
- Motorboating is usually caused by failing batteries.
- Primary cells cannot be recharged and must be discarded when their life is finished.
- Secondary cells can be recharged and returned to service.
- The carbon-zinc flashlight battery seems to recover between uses because of internal bubbles of gas that dissipate when the battery is allowed to rest.
- The CZ cell has a terminal voltage of about 1.5 volts.
- The alkaline cell is an improvement over the CZ cell, having lower internal resistance and a terminal voltage of about 1.4 volts.
- Other primary cells include the tiny mercury cell and the cell with a 10-year shelf life, the lithium cell.

- The two secondary cells in common use are the lead-acid and the ni-cad.
- The lead-acid cell presents chemical and thermal burn dangers, plus dangers of explosion.
- The conventional automotive battery is made to provide short bursts of very high current and should be maintained at full charge at all times.
- The deep-cycle battery can be discharged further without much damage.
- Deep-cycle batteries will last three to five times longer than conventional batteries when used in deep-cycle service.
- The low-maintenance automotive battery requires less water than a conventional battery due to the use of less antimony in the lead plates.
- The maintenance-free battery uses almost no water due to the substitution of calcium for the antimony.
- The internal construction of a no-maintenance battery includes ion-permeable plastic bags to help prevent shedding of the plate material.
- A marine battery may be either the deep-cycle or conventional variety and is usually provided with a handle and screw terminals instead of the tapered posts used in automotive service.
- A dry-charged battery is one that has been activated by the addition of sulfuric acid upon delivery to the customer, having been kept in a dry state for storage until that time.
- The physical sizes of lead-acid batteries are classified into "groups."
- The old ampere-hour rating for lead-acid batteries has been replaced by the Cold Cranking Performance Rating.
- The Cold Cranking Performance Rating is the current that a battery at a temperature of 0 degrees Fahrenheit can deliver for 30 seconds while maintaining a cell voltage of at least 1.2 volts.
- The electrolyte level of a lead-acid cell can be replenished by the addition of pure water.
- Keeping a lead-acid battery charged prevents sulphation, which otherwise increases the internal resistance of the cells.
- Quick-charging can damage any kind of battery.
- Trickle-charging maintains a battery at peak charge without overcharging.
- The condition of a lead-acid battery can be determined by voltage measurement under load or by the use of a hydrometer.
- A lead-acid battery with a paste electrolyte can be used in any position and will not gas appreciably.
- Dispose of lead-acid batteries by recycling them.
- Ni-cad batteries are available in wet form, but sealed cells are more common.
- Sealed ni-cad cells that have vented are defective and should be replaced.

- The ni-cad cell has a nominal voltage of 1.2 volts.
- Ni-cad sealed cells should be charged for 14 hours at one-tenth their ampere-hour rating.

REVIEW QUESTIONS

1. A cell or battery having sealed units should not be disposed of by _______.
2. Concerning primary and secondary cells, which is used one time only and then discarded?
3. A CZ cell of size "D," number 950, can supply a load of 10 milliamperes for about _______ hours.
4. An alkaline "C" size cell can supply a current of 37.5 ma for about _______ hours.
5. What is the principal advantage of a lithium cell?
6. You see a lead-acid battery that has an unusual count of 4 cells in the battery. What is the nominal terminal voltage of this battery?
7. What is the electrolyte of a lead-acid battery?
8. How should a conventional car battery be treated with regard to charging?
9. What chief advantage does the deep-cycle battery offer?
10. What is the currently accepted performance specification for lead-acid batteries?
11. How may the *state of charge* of a lead-acid battery be determined?
12. Do wet ni-cad cells gas when charging?
13. Can the state of charge of a ni-cad battery be determined by a voltage test under load?
14. What are the terminal voltages of a charged and a discharged ni-cad?
15. How can one tell when a ni-cad battery has reached full charge, particularly at high charging currents?
16. What is the significance of a ni-cad cell that has begun leaking?
17. Why should a series of ni-cad cells *not* be discharged below a voltage of 1.0 volt per cell?
18. A ni-cad "D" cell with a NEDA number of 10013HC will provide a terminal voltage of 1.2 volts and a current of 2 amperes for about _______ hours.

22

Troubleshooting Power-Line Circuits and Motors

CHAPTER OBJECTIVES

Since the electrical energy that powers much of today's electronic circuits comes from the 60-Hz power lines, it makes sense that an electronics technician should have a basic knowledge of electrical wiring and electrical motors. Appendix II may be consulted for appropriate symbology throughout this chapter. At the conclusion of this chapter, the student will:

- Have a general understanding of how power is wired into a residence as 120/240-V AC.
- Understand how a two- and three-station switch can control a single load.
- Be introduced to the distribution and use of three-phase power.
- Learn how high-energy power is safely monitored.

- Learn why the clamp-on ammeter is preferrable to a sensitive meter in maintaining power circuits.
- Become familiar with common three-phase rectifier variations.
- Learn how an electrician refers to transformer windings and how to strap them for different operating voltages.
- Be introduced to the major kinds of electrical motors for both DC and AC operation.
- Be able to reverse the direction of any kind of electrical motor.
- Be able to explain the operation and control of any kind of generator or alternator, AC or DC.
- Know the general operation of synchros and resolvers.
- Be familiar with the use of relays and ladder logic.
- Know generally how to read a ladder logic diagram.
- Be familiar with a three-wire control and how it works.

22.1 RESIDENTIAL WIRING

240/120-V WIRING

Residential wiring supports the needs of homes and small businesses. The maximum voltage used is 240 V, which is used for high-energy applications such as room heating, water heaters, clothes dryers, and kitchen ranges. This higher voltage is used to reduce the current demand through the house wiring. Delivering 5,000 watts of power with 240 V requires about 21 amperes (A). If 120 V were used to deliver this same power, twice the current, 42 A, would be required. While this does not seem like much of an advantage, consider that the power lost in the wiring will be *one-fourth* if the current is dropped to just half. In this light, the advantage of 240 V over 120 V for high-current circuits becomes more understandable. The power lost in the resistance of the wires is found by the familiar formula:

$$P = I^2R$$

The energy supplied to a residence or small business is the result of distributing electrical energy from the generating plant to the consumer at high voltages, to keep the current and, therefore, the line losses at a minimum. Outside the residence, usually on a power pole, one can find the transformer that converts this high voltage (typically 2,400 or 4,600 V) to the relatively low voltages of 240/120 V. The diagram of Figure 1–2 shows the basic idea of how this transformer is wired. The secondary is center-tapped, with 120 V appearing on each side of the center tap. Loads requiring 240 V are connected across the full secondary, while 120-V loads are placed between the tap and one end of the secondary.

A technician should use Figure 1–2 to become familiar with the terms *safety ground, neutral,* and *hot* sides of the incoming power lines. It is also important to note that electrical wiring is backward from what technicians are accustomed to working with: *the black wire is the hot, the dangerous side of the line,* and the white side is the neutral side. The earth-grounded line is usually green or simply a bare wire.

When a building is wired, the 120-V loads should be approximately equalized on the transformer secondary. This is called "balancing the load." Under these conditions, the load on the transformer is across the 240-V outside connections with little or no current flowing in the neutral wire. See Figure 22–1.

When the load becomes unbalanced, as it usually does due to turning loads on and off at various times, the neutral line carries current, too. See Figure 22–2.

One of the first rules that an electrician learns is to *never break the neutral* with either a switch or a fuse. The reason for this can be shown by comparing the previous figure with Figure 22–3.

A poor connection of the neutral at some point is evident when any of the loads in a building are getting too much voltage or if any load voltage varies when certain other loads are turned on.

Most wiring in small buildings is straightforward: a simple circuit is made from the power panel hot, using a *black wire* to a switch, then to the

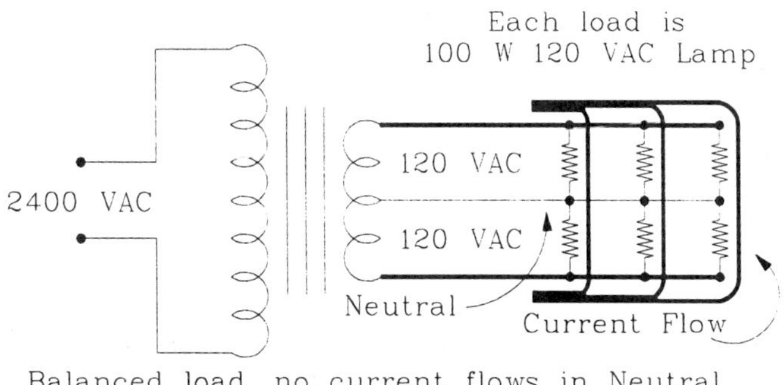

Figure 22–1 A balanced load on 240-V AC.

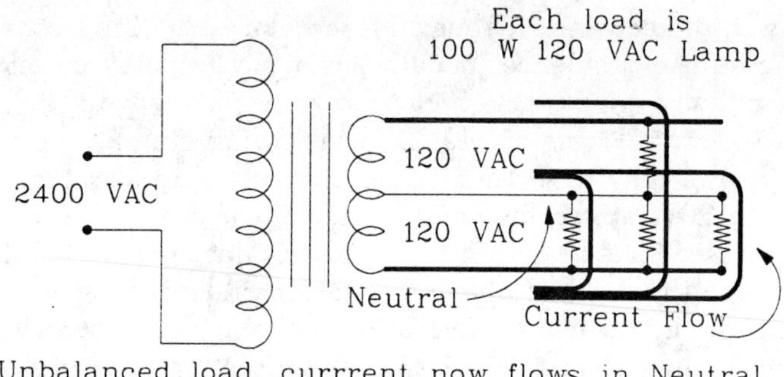

Figure 22–2 A normal, unbalanced load on 240-V AC.

load *with a black wire,* and then back to the neutral at the power panel using a white wire.

A variation of this simple circuit is shown in Figure 22–4, in which two switches at different locations control a single load. Note that changing either of the switches, one at a time, reverses the status of the load, whether on or off.

When a third controlling switch is added, the circuit looks like that in Figure 22–5. Again, changing any of the switches will change the load status.

Additional switch stations, identical to the wiring of the center switch, may be installed anywhere between the two single-pole double-throw switches. Any number of control stations can be used.

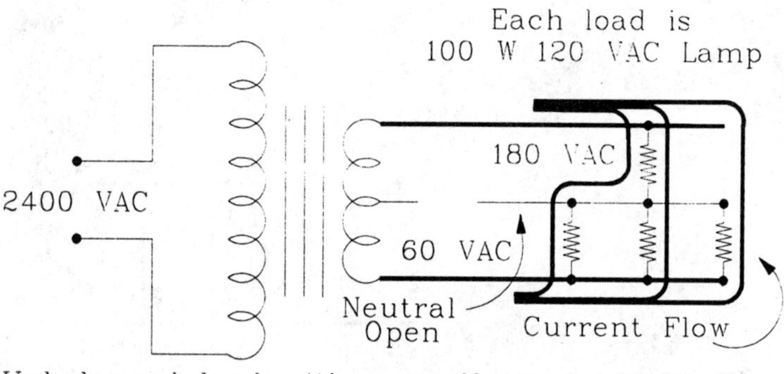

Figure 22–3 The result of an open neutral line.

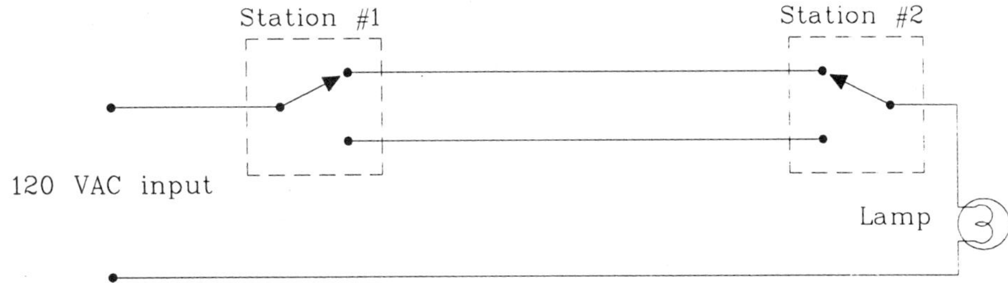

Figure 22–4 Two-station control of a load.

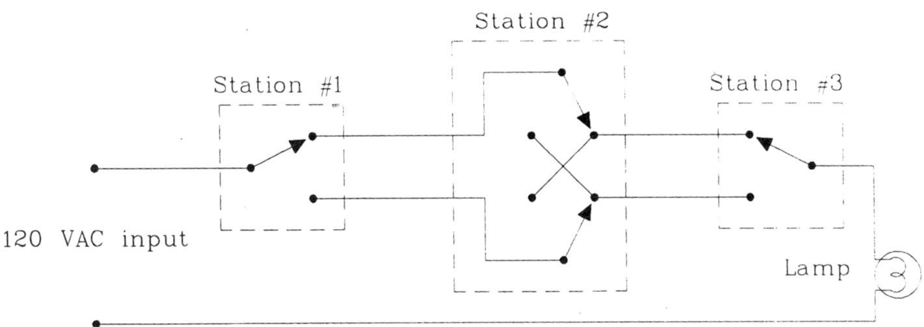

Figure 22–5 Adding a third control station.

22.2 COMMERCIAL WIRING

THREE-PHASE POWER WIRING

Two wires can carry moderate amounts of electrical energy quite well from one location to another. However, a heavy demand for energy, such as found in most industrial applications, will exceed the reasonable capability of a pair of power lines.

By properly adding just one more wire to the original two, the system can carry about three times the energy carried by a pair. This is done by phasing three different voltages exactly 120 degrees apart from one another. By proper circular placement of the generating coils in the generators at the power generating plant, while one coil is at maximum, a second is on its way to a full maximum in the opposite direction, while a third coil is beyond the negative maximum and is now going positive. See Figure 22–6.

The AC power coming from a source in just a pair of wires will go through zero volts, at which time no current flows. The use of three phases

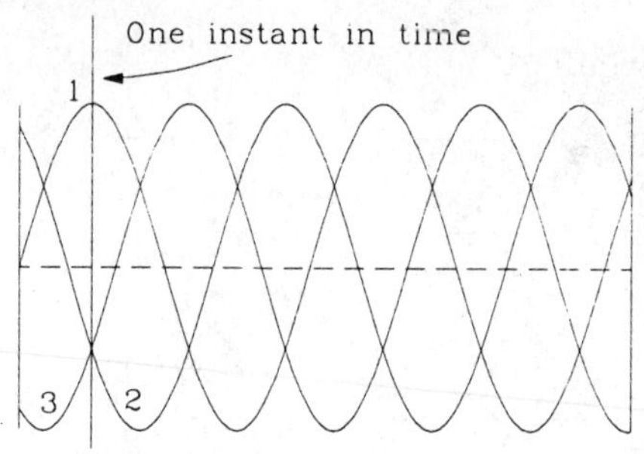

Figure 22–6 Relationship between the three voltages of a three-phase power system.

results in power always being available on at least two combinations of the three wires. Thus, a much more constant availability of energy results. In fact, the total instantaneous power to a resistive balanced load is equal at all instants in time.

Large industrial power applications are progressing toward solid-state controls rather than using mechanical switches and circuit breakers. It may become the resonsibility of electronics technicians to maintain or monitor the operation of these newer methods of power control.

The transformers used in a three-phase system can be separate units or they can be combined in the form of three separate windings on a single "E" shaped core. See Figure 22–7. (If you ran an "E" and an "I" together, the resulting rectangle with two square holes in it would describe the shape of the iron core.)

Notice that the step-up or step-down ratio of a transformer, as used in a three-phase system, is the ratio of a single transformer, reading primary to secondary, without regard to any other transformer being used with it.

For safety's sake, a fourth wire is often provided. This is the earth ground wire, which is often used also as a neutral line. Figure 22–8 shows these two methods of transmitting three-phase power, the delta and the wye (star) wiring configurations.

Delta connections are used when no connection to ground is desired, as in some power-isolation circuits. The wye connection is most often used when a ground point is desirable. Notice that the relationships of the voltages within a three-phase wye system can provide two different voltages depending on whether we connect to the neutral line and one of the hot lines or from one hot lead to another. The voltage from the neutral to a hot line is called a *phase voltage*. The voltage from one line to another is called a *line-to-line voltage* or, simply, *line voltage*.

The relationship between phase and line voltage in a wye configuration is based on the square-root of 3 (a value of 1.73). Since the line voltage is always the larger, it is 1.73 times the phase voltage. If the line voltage is the only figure known, the phase voltage will be the result of the line voltage divided by the 1.73 factor.

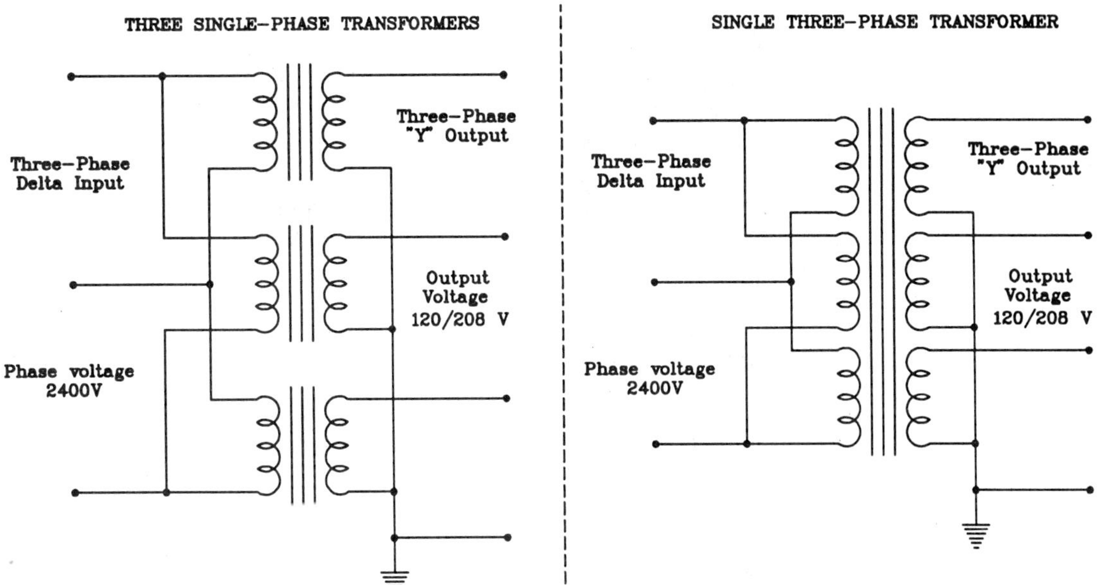

Figure 22–7 Transforming three-phase power using separate transformers and special three-phase transformers.

This relationship of line to phase voltages gives rise to several common combinations of voltage pairs that are used in industry:

Phase Voltage	Line Voltage
120	208
277	480
1,200	2,080
1,387	2,400
2,400	4,160

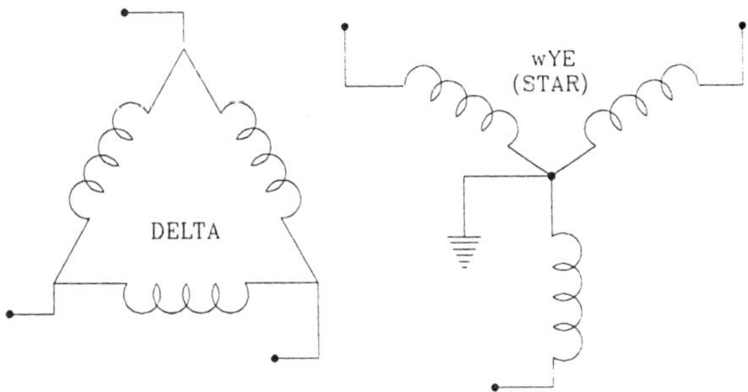

Figure 22–8 Using transformers in delta and wye configurations.

Voltages of 120/208 are used in buildings that have light industrial loads, such as a large school building. The loads within the building are balanced, as much as possible, between each of the three phases. This is done by using special power distribution panels designed to encourage balancing by making power from each of the phases available consecutively as one proceeds down a single row of circuit breakers. Going down the row and wiring up the breakers one at a time will pretty well balance the load without deliberate planning.

MONITORING HIGH ELECTRICAL ENERGY

As can be imagined by the examination of the level of voltages just shown, some very high and extremely dangerous voltages are used in industry. It would be foolish indeed to attempt working with such high voltages directly while the power is on. How can one safely measure these high voltages and safely monitor the currents flowing at these potentials? The answers to both questions lie in the capabilities of the transformer.

The Potential Transformer

High-energy high voltages can be safely monitored if they are first converted down to a reasonable voltage. This is the purpose of a special transformer called a *potential transformer*. This transformer is built to provide a very precise ratio from primary to secondary. It is not intended to supply any appreciable load, being used only to provide a precision voltage reduction ratio that, in turn, operates a voltage-monitoring device. See Figure 22–9.

Note that the secondary winding of the transformer is solidly grounded. If an interwinding short should occur within the transformer, it will blow the fuse rather than put the meter at a high voltage above ground, which would make it a very serious hazard for operators. A common ratio for a potential transformer is 100:1. When not being used for voltage monitoring, the secondary circuit is left open-circuited.

The Current Transformer

A current transformer can also be used to monitor the current flowing in a high-voltage, high-energy line. A current transformer looks like a large doughnut through which the main line passes without touching. See Figure 22–10.

While a potential transformer's secondary must be left open when a meter is not connected, the current transformer secondary must be *shorted out* in the absence of a meter. Leaving it open could cause extremely high voltages to be produced because of the step-up relationship of the winding ratios. Note also that the secondary winding is again referenced to ground

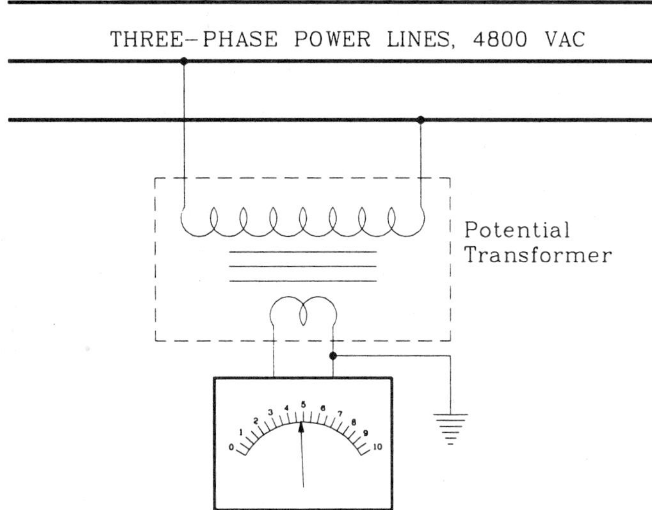

Figure 22–9 Using a potential transformer.

for safety reasons. A common step-down ratio for a current transformer is 1,000:1.

THE CLAMP-ON AMMETER

Troubleshooting high-powered circuits is often done by using a clamp-on ammeter. Three-phase circuits are especially well suited to the use of this instrument. A clamp-on ammeter was shown in Figure 5–14. This instru-

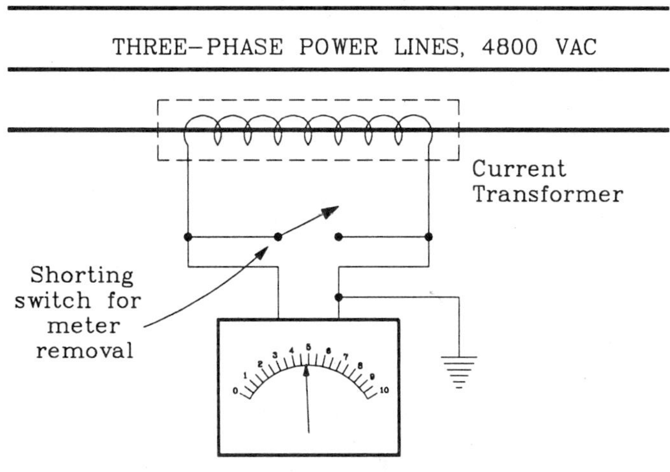

Figure 22–10 Using a current transformer.

ment is capable of measuring either AC or DC currents, as the sensor is a hall effect transistor.

Most clamp-on ammeters use a transformer action to monitor the current that is flowing. The clamp is opened, placed around the conductor through which the current is to be measured, and then allowed to snap shut. The clamp is now a single-turn magnetic coupling which picks up the magnetic field surrounding the wire. The more current flowing in the conductor, the more intense the magnetic field. Inside the instrument, the magnetic field flows through a coil which drives the meter in the instrument. The stronger the magnetic field that is coupled into the meter circuit, the more voltage will be produced by the coil and the higher the meter will read. See Figure 22–11.

The clamp-on ammeter is often combined with a voltmeter into a single hand-held isntrument. The voltmeter is provided with detachable leads so that voltage measurements can be made in the conventional way. This voltmeter is intended for use on AC power circuits in cases where sensitivity is not a factor. Because of this, a meter of 5,000 or 1,000 Ω per volt sensitivity is quite adequate. In some cases, the lower input impedance of this meter is an advantage, in that it will not indicate on "stray" AC voltages. See Figure 22–12.

One of the features commonly provided with a clamp-on ammeter is a meter needle lock. This feature allows the repair technician to reach into a cabinet and take an ammeter reading even when it is difficult to see the meter face. Once in position and one simply switches the needle lock to the "lock" position, then disconnects the instrument. When removed from the circuit, the reading remains on the meter for convenient interpretation.

The use of a clamp-on ammeter as a voltmeter carries with it an element

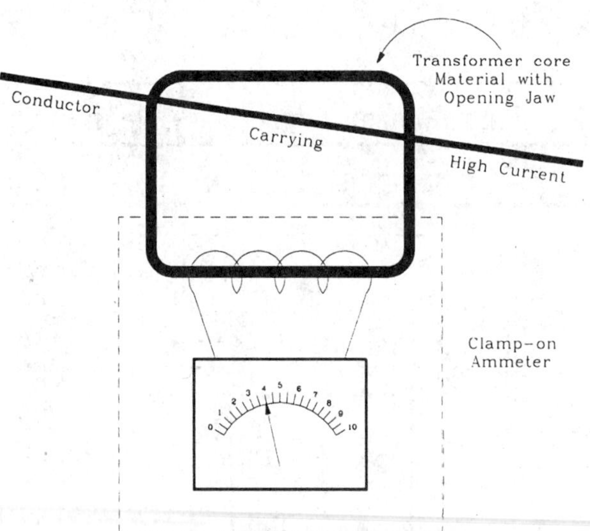

Figure 22–11 How an AC clamp-on ammeter works.

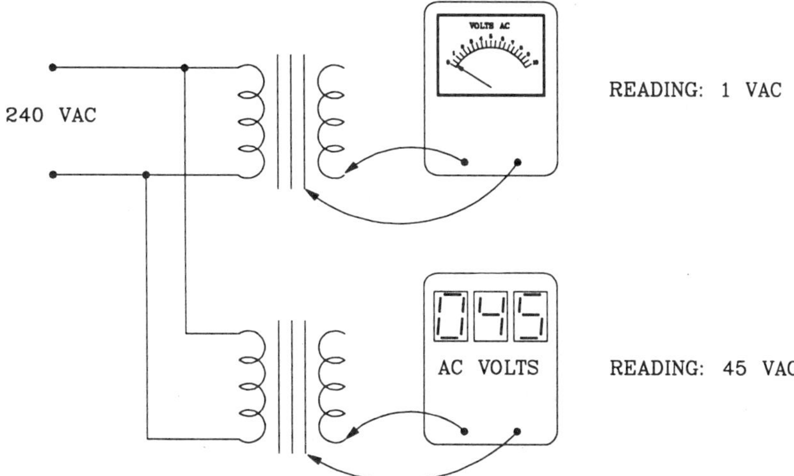

Figure 22–12 Using a high- versus a low-impedance meter produces different results on high-impedance "stray" voltages.

of danger if the locking mechanism is forgotten, however. If the meter lock is put "on" while the needle indicates zero, the meter will indicate zero voltage while testing for voltage, when in actuality there may be hundreds of volts in the circuit. Therefore, *be absolutely sure the meter is not locked when using the voltage function of a clamp-on ammeter!* To do so could be hazardous due to the false information it would provide.

THREE-PHASE RECTIFIERS

A technician should be familiar with the kinds of rectifiers that may be found in three-phase equipment, since these circuits are common in heavy industrial equipment. The two most common three-phase rectifier circuits are the three-phase, full-wave and half-wave rectifiers. See Figure 22–13.

The amount of DC that is recovered from a three-phase rectifier can be controlled by varying the firing angle of three SCRs, used together with three normal rectifier diodes. Unless one of the SCRs fires, the associated diodes will not conduct either. See Figure 22–14.

TRANSFORMER WINDINGS

Electricians identify transformer windings by a simple criterion; the winding with the most number of turns (the highest voltage winding) is the *H* winding, and secondaries are designated as *X* windings. A simple step-down transformer, for instance, will have two *H* terminals and two *X* terminals.

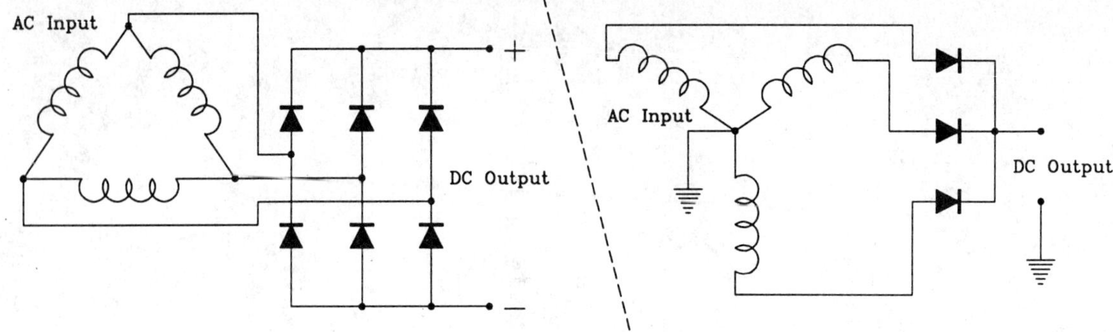

Figure 22–13 Three-phase full- and half-way rectifiers.

It is very possible that an electronics technician will be asked to change the strapping of a suitable transformer from a 120-V configuration to a 240-V setup, or vice versa. Transformers are commonly configured so that this will be an easy task. Such transformers require four terminals to be restrapped. See Figure 22–15.

22.3 ELECTRIC MOTOR CONTROL

It is to the technician's advantage to know the fundamentals of how various motors operate, their principal characteristics, and how to reverse their direction of rotation.

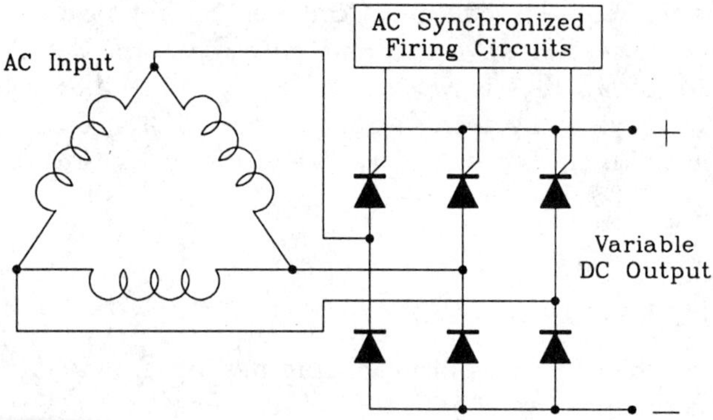

Figure 22–14 A full-wave, three-phase bridge rectifier with adjustable output via the use of SCRs.

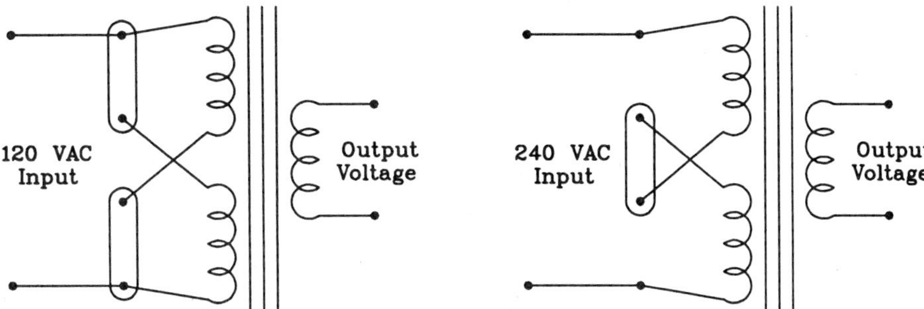

Figure 22–15 Changing the power straps of a transformer between 240 and 120 volts.

DIRECT CURRENT (DC) MOTORS

Before going into the details of the various types of DC motors and how they operate, this is a good point to explain one of the fundamentals of controlling and operating motors: the relationship between the amount of current flowing and the motor's speed.

As a motor turns, it acts like a generator. When stopped, such as immediately before starting, the motor will have very little resistance. The armature of most motors has resistance measured in ohms or fractions of ohms. When starting such a motor, heavy current flows according to Ohm's law. As the motor begins to turn, however, it acts like a generator and produces a voltage in parallel with the applied voltage. This opposing voltage is called *counter-electromotive forces*, or CEMF for short. The CEMF voltage produced by the motor cancels much of the applied voltage, resulting in only a portion remaining to produce a current flow. When the motor reaches final speed, only the load on the motor and frictional losses keep it from producing a voltage that exactly cancels the applied voltage. As an example, a voltage of 12 volts applied to a 12-volt motor might, under light load conditions, result in a voltage difference of only 1 volt, which is left to actually operate the motor. Placing a load on the motor reduces the amount of voltage generated by it. Thus, there is less canceling effect, and the motor will draw much more current from the supply.

Permanent-Magnetic Motors

A permanent-magnet DC motor has a permanent magnet to produce the fixed, stationary field. Voltage is applied to the rotating armature coils via a series of carbon brushes. Depending on the polarity supplied to the armature coils, the magnetic field produced by the coils interacts with the field, either repelling or attracting, to rotate the coil away from or closer to alignment with the field. However, before the final alignment is reached, the switching action produced by the *commutator bars* on the armature switch the voltage to a different set of coils, which then take over the rotating action. This is much like the carrot held in front of a mule: like the mule, the armature never actually reaches the goal, but work is done in the continual attempt.

The presence of a commutator basically identifies a motor or generator as being a DC device, with two exceptions to be mentioned later. Figure 22–16 shows two kinds of DC permanent-magnet motors, and Figure 22–17 shows the schematic symbol for them.

A permanent-magnet (PM) motor has good starting torque (twisting force) and a relatively constant speed once full voltage and load have been reached. Reversal is easy, requiring only the reversal of the input voltage to accomplish the task.

One of the advantages of the PM motor is that its speed is easily controlled. If the input voltage is decreased, the motor settles quickly and smoothly to a slower rate of revolutions per minute (RPM). Speed is approximately proportional to the voltage applied.

When it is desirable to control the speed of a PM motor using only a fixed, single supply voltage, this can be done using the technique of *pulse width modulation.* By generating a rapid on-off switching of the supply voltage at an audio frequency, the motor will respond by running at the

Figure 22–16 Typical "pancake" and PM DC motors.

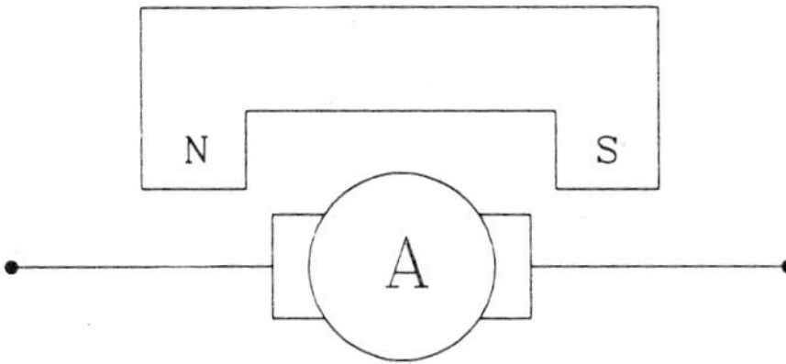

Figure 22–17 Permanent magnet motor symbol.

average voltage of the input waveform. This is very similar to the response shown in Figure 14–15.

One of the major uses for a permanent-magnet motor is as a tachometer. When a PM motor shaft is turned mechanically, the armature produces a DC voltage that is proportional to the speed of rotation. These tiny motors are often used to monitor the speed of other motors as part of a large motor-controller servo system.

Series-Wound DC Motors

If the stationary magnetic field of a motor is generated by passing a current through a coil rather than using a permanent magnet for the purpose, some interesting characteristics arise. There are two ways of passing current through field coils, either in series with the armature or in parallel to it.

If the field coils are placed in series with the armature windings, the motor is known as a series-wound motor. See Figure 22–18.

It is basic to DC electric motors that if the magnetic field of a motor is strong, the motor will run relatively slow but with high torque. A weak magnetic field means less torque, but a higher speed of rotation.

The starter motor of an automobile is a series-wound motor. When the starter is first engaged, it must develop a tremendous amount of torque. The series motor provides this torque by passing all the armature current through the field windings, producing a very strong field. The accompanying high torque requirement is thus provided. High starting torque is a major characteristic of a series-wound motor. A second pair of field coils can

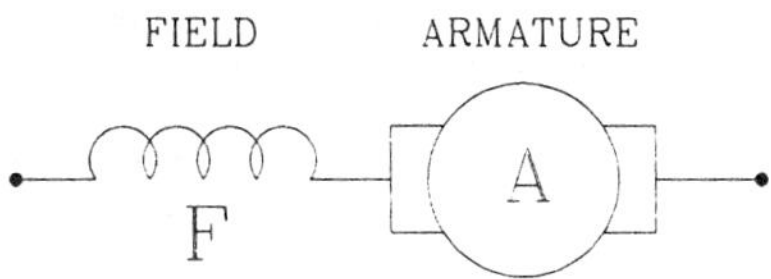

Figure 22–18 Schematic symbol for a series-wound DC motor.

Figure 22–19 A motorcyle starter motor, one example of a series-wound DC motor.

be added along with a second set of brushes to double the torque, in effect, making two motors with a single armature. See Figure 22–19.

As the load on a series-wound motor decreases, the series motor develops CEMF, thereby causing a reduction in the total amount of current drawn from the battery. This causes decreased current flow through the field windings, causing the motor to run faster. Because of this chain reaction of decreasing current-less field-faster running, another principal characteristic of a series wound motor is that it has poor speed regulation.

A series-wound motor can be reversed in rotation only by physically changing the wiring within the motor. Either the armature polarity (at the brushes) or the field windings must be reversed. Reversing the input voltage polarity will not change the direction of rotation, since both the polarities of the armature and the field winding will reverse and no reversal of rotation will occur. An alternate way to reverse direction is to physically rotate the brushes around the commutator to a new position.

Very large series motors can increase their speed too much if the load is accidently disconnected and no protective circuitry has been provided. Without a load, the motor can continue to accelerate until the windings are thrown off the armature, destroying the unit.

An Ingenious Ammeter

This is a good place to make the technician aware of a special ammeter that is available, often at automotive suppliers, to measure the relatively

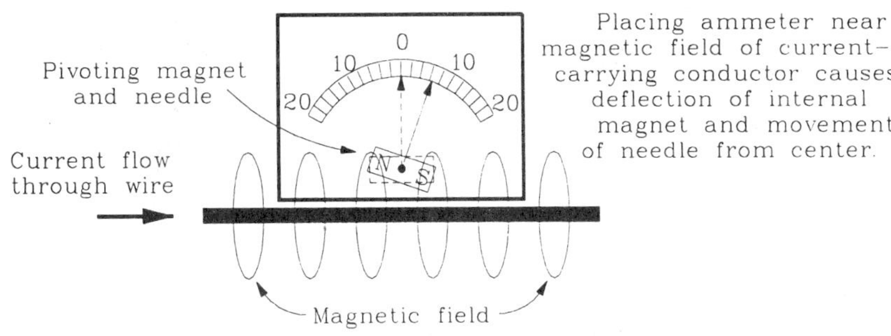
Pivoting magnet
and needle
0
10
10
20
20
N
S
Placing ammeter near
magnetic field of current-
carrying conductor causes
deflection of internal
magnet and movement
of needle from center.
Current flow
through wire
Magnetic field

Figure 22–20 How the wireless DC ammeter works.

large DC currents that are frequently encountered in automotive electric starter motor and charging circuits. See Figures 22–20 and 22–21.

This wireless ammeter needs no direct connection to a high-current circuit. Inside the meter is a small magnet suspended by a pivot. A needle that sweeps over the scale is also attached to the magnet. When a wire is placed correctly in contact with the back of the meter, the magnetic field around the wire interacts with the internal magnet to deflect it from the normal centered position. One cannot expect such a meter to be very accurate, but for troubleshooting automotive starter and charging circuits, it is quite adequate and very convenient to use.

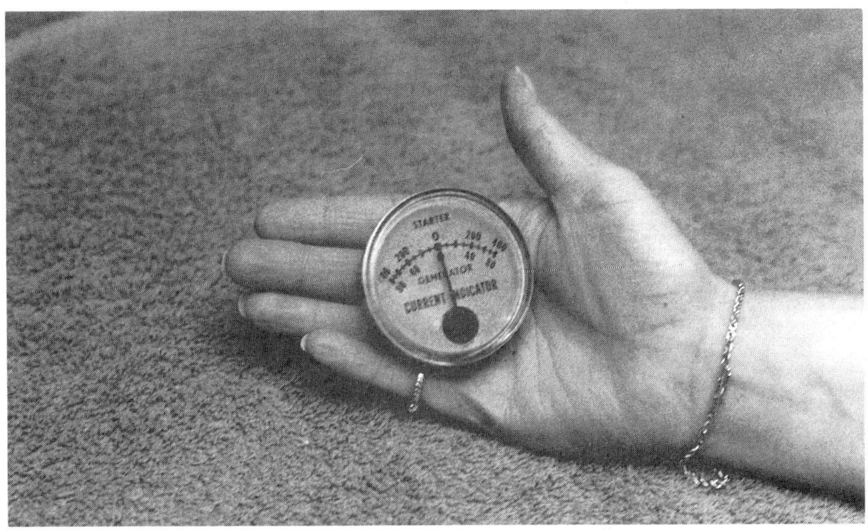

Figure 22–21 An example of a wireless ammeter.

There are usually two scales to this meter. Charging circuits deal with much less current than starting circuits. The selection of the appropriate scale is made by positioning the wire behind the meter in one of two different, marked locations. One location is nearer the internal magnet than the other, thus providing a more sensitive indication. The location farthest from the internal magnet is intended for testing very heavy currents like those of the starter circuit.

Shunt-Wound DC Motors

A shunt-wound DC motor has a field that is wound with much finer wire than that used in a series motor. This is necessary because the field winding is placed in parallel, directly across the DC voltage driving the motor armature. See Figure 22–22.

The shunt-wound DC motor has a relatively constant RPM with varying mechanical loads, which is one of its positive characteristics. It has moderately good starting torque, but much less torque than the series-wound motor. DC shunt-wound motors find use in automotive applications, such as windshield wipers, where the speed of wiping should be somewhat constant.

The speed of a shunt-wound DC motor can be changed by varying the input voltage, just as is done with the series motor. The shunt motor also provides a second way of varying its speed with a given voltage: change the field current. Remember that a weakening field means a higher RPM: this fact can be put to use to regulate the speed of these motors to some extent. A stronger field during starting will increase starting torque, while a weaker field will increase the motor's RPM.

The direction of rotation of a shunt-wound motor can be changed by reversing the connections of either the armature or, more conveniently, the field winding.

Very large DC shunt-wound motors used in industry must be provided with a special circuit to turn off the current to the armature in the event that the field current ceases for any reason. Without this protection, a large motor could increase to higher and higher RPMs until it destroys itself. This protection is called a *no-field protection circuit*.

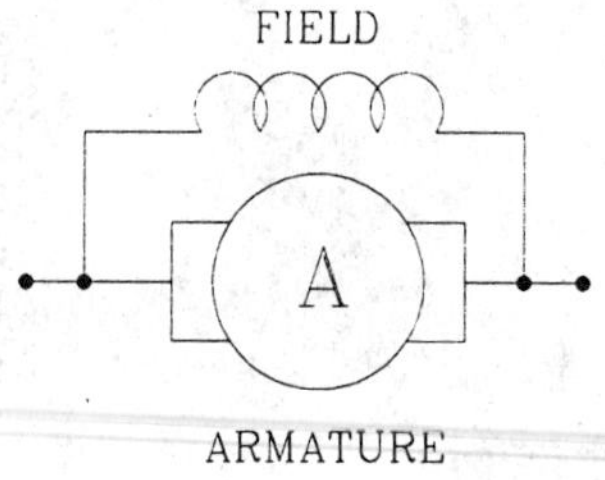

Figure 22–22 Schematic symbol for a DC shunt-wound motor.

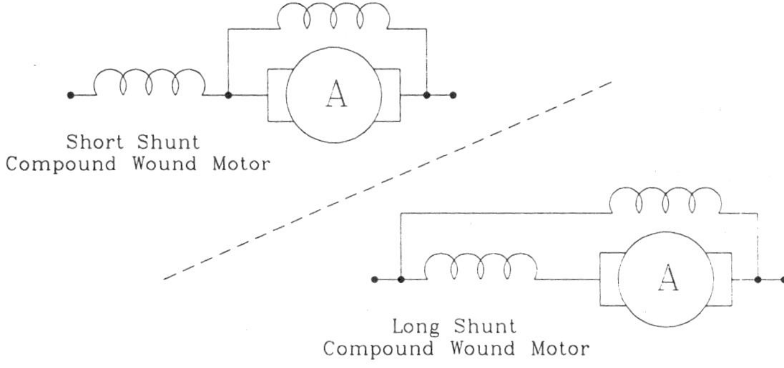

Figure 22–23 Schematic symbols for long- and short-shunt, compound-wound DC motors.

DC Compound-Wound Motors

Industry finds occasional applications for a DC motor that has some of the characteristics of both the series- and the shunt-wound motors. Such a motor can be built with both series and shunt fields to obtain a compromise between these two kinds of motors. These motors are called compound-wound motors and are wired in either of two ways. See Figure 22–23.

As one can see from the figure, the shunt field can be connected in parallel to either the line itself or to only the armature. Connecting to the line directly will make the torque-versus-speed characteristics of the shunt-wound motor more dominant than those of a series-wound motor. Connecting the shunt field in parallel with the armature will cause the series-wound motor characteristics to become pronounced.

The direction of rotation is determined by the magnetic interaction of both fields with that of the armature. To reverse the direction, one must either reverse the connections to the armature or to *both* of the fields.

The DC Motor Drive for Large DC Motors

The greatest advantage of DC motors over AC motors is their ease of control for precise torque and speed requirements. By monitoring the actual rotational speed of a DC motor, the input voltage can be carefully controlled to maintain any given speed to within very close tolerances. Because of the ease with which a DC motor can be controlled, it finds frequent use in industrial applications where this ability is required.

The control of a large DC motor can be accomplished by equipment designed for that purpose, called a *DC motor controller*. A DC motor controller will have a rectifier to change the incoming AC to a DC, a means of controlling the DC level sent to the motor, and a means of monitoring the motor's actual speed of rotation. Using the speed feedback, the input voltage can

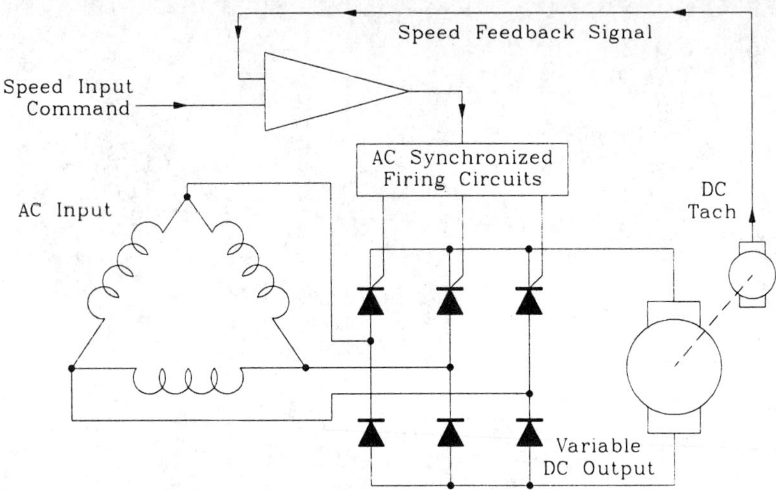

Figure 22–24 Block diagram of a large DC motor controller.

compensate for changes in the load on the motor, maintaining a constant speed under varying load conditions. See Figure 22–24.

The size and complexity of such a motor controller depends on the size of the motor for which it is designed. A controller for a 5-horsepower motor might be as large as a four-drawer filing cabinet. The internal circuitry will involve principally analog circuits, often with many operational amplifiers.

The Brushless DC Motor

Another motor worth mentioning is the brushless DC motor. Since any DC motor will probably eventually fail due to brush or bearing wear, eliminating the brushes can extend the useful life of a motor without requiring any additional maintenance. In addition, this motor is not hazardous to use in explosive atmospheres and produces no electrostatic interference.

The purpose of the commutator of a DC motor is to switch the armature coils on at the proper instant, turning off the previous coils. This causes the physical wearing away of the brush material, which will eventually cause motor failure if the wear is not caught in time and the brushes are not replaced.

A brushless motor consists of a permanent magnet armature (*rotor*). The field coils (*stator*) are turned on and off at the appropriate times to rotate this magnet. Since the operation of the field coils must be synchronized with the rotating magnet, some means must be provided to detect the passage of the magnet as it rotates. This can be done with a small hall effect transistor, a transistor that is sensitive to magnetic fields. See Figure 22–25.

Since the hall effect transistor is a semiconductor, it will not wear out

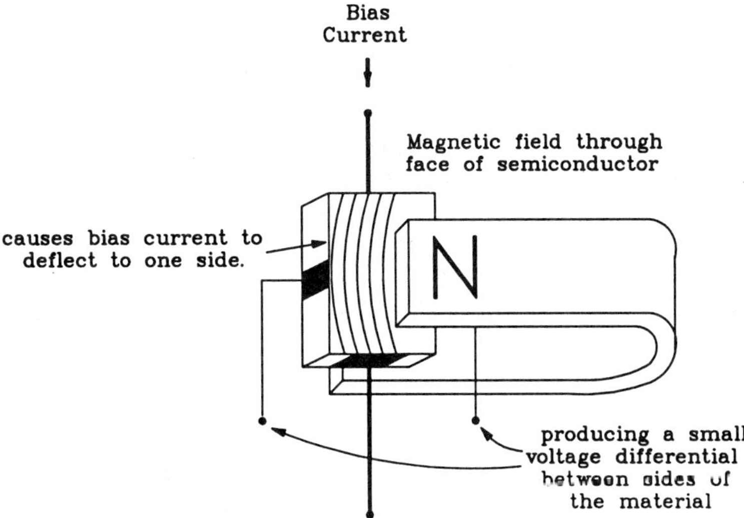
Bias
Current
Magnetic field through
face of semiconductor
causes bias current to
deflect to one side.
N
producing a small
voltage differential
between sides of
the material

Figure 22–25 How the hall effect transistor works.

like a set of brushes. Using this device, a small electronic circuit can detect the instantaneous position of the rotating magnet and pulse the field coils at the proper time to cause the magnet to rotate continuously. The internal workings of a DC brushless motor can be seen in Figure 22–26.

The Synchronous DC Motor

There are a few applications that require a DC motor to rotate at a very precise speed. One of these is the rotation of a digital storage device: a floppy diskette or the hard disk drive of a computer system. These applications can be designed in either of two ways. The older method is to use a DC shunt drive motor and carefully monitor its speed with an analog feedback servo circuit. This circuit will change the level of input voltage to the motor in the proper direction to maintain as constant a speed as possible. The second way, which has gained much popularity, is to use the frequency stability of a precision electronic oscillator to drive the coils of a DC motor that is constructed just like a brushless DC motor. The rotating armature is a permanent magnet, and the field is a series of coils. The coils are driven at precisely the correct time, as synchronized to the precision oscillator, to maintain a precise rate of rotation. See Figure 22–27.

ALTERNATING CURRENT (AC) MOTORS

The Universal Motor

By proper design, a series DC motor can be made to operate on AC voltage. If the armature and the field are made of laminations to reduce

Figure 22–26 A brushless motor uses a hall effect transistor to trigger the stationary field coils.

Figure 22–27 This synchronous DC motor drive is used to turn at a precise 300 RPM.

Figure 22–28 A typical universal AC/DC motor.

eddy-current losses, AC will operate these motors quite well. The inductance of the field winding of a series motor is relatively low, allowing sufficient current flow to operate the motor. Other kinds of DC motors do not run on AC because their windings have too high an inductance when used on AC, severely limiting the current flow through the winding.

The universal motor is a DC series-wound motor, which will run very well on DC, too; hence, the term *universal.* This motor finds application where high starting torque and operation at a fairly high RPM are necessary. Household blenders, vacuum cleaners, electric drills, and "shop" vacuum cleaners use these motors. See Figure 22–28.

The universal motor can be controlled for speed and direction of rotation, as explained under "Series-Wound DC Motors," earlier in this chapter.

AC Synchronous Motors

An AC synchronous motor will operate perfectly in step with the frequency of the applied AC voltage. After 34,543 AC cycles, for instance, the final position of the motor is precisely predictable.

For this reason, small motors of this type are often used in applications where precision of rotation must be exact: for use as a timepiece, for example. For many years, electric clocks have used this motor to drive the geared mechanism that rotates the hands of a clock. The internal construction of the small AC synchronous motor is almost identical to that of the DC synchronous motor: a rotating magnet turning in an AC field.

Industry uses large AC synchronous motors, too. Once they are turning and have been locked to the incoming power line cycles, their position in time is also predictable. Since they present a capacitive power line load, they have the added advantage that they help correct the lagging power factor caused by using induction motors elsewhere in the factory. These large motors have many field windings. The more field coils, the more constant the rotating torque and the stronger the motor will be.

AC Induction Motors

As mentioned during the discussion of the brushless DC motor, the presence of brushes in a motor means maintenance requirements and potential failures. An AC motor can be built that takes advantage of transformer action to induce currents into the rotating *(rotor)* part of the motor from the field (*stator*) without using brushes at all. The magnetic field induces currents into the armature just as a transformer induces a current from the primary winding into its secondary. No sliding or mechanical contact to carry the energy to the armature is necessary when using AC.

The armature of an induction motor consists of shorted turns. When currents are induced into the armature from the field, the strong currents in the shorted turns produce magnetic fields that interact with the stationary field to produce rotation. As long as the armature is free to rotate, the armature will closely, but not exactly, *line-lock* to the incoming frequency of the AC, rotating in unison with it.

In order for a current to be induced in the armature, there must be *relative motion* between the armature and the field. There is a small amount of slippage that keeps the armature from reaching the exact line-locked speed of rotation. Instead of running at a precise speed of 1,800 RPM, for example, an induction motor under normal load will run at about 1,750 RPM due to slippage.

A single-phase AC induction motor will have almost no starting torque at all. Once running, however, the motor has very good torque because it is line-locked. However, getting it up to speed is a problem that must be solved.

The Shaded-Pole Motor. The simplest AC motor is the shaded-pole motor. See Figure 22–29.

The shaded-pole AC motor is used in applications in which starting torque requirements are very low, as in small fans or blowers. It is also sometimes used in small jobs such as to rotate advertising signs in supermarkets. If provided with a geared transmission, the torque of the motor will be greatly increased, at the expense of rotational speed.

Figure 22–29 A typical AC shaded-pole motor.

While the starting torque of the shaded-pole motor is not very good, its speed of rotation is relatively constant as it is locked to the frequency of the line voltage at about 3,500 RPM. This is the result of slippage in RPM from the 3,600 cycles per minute of the line voltage.

When looking at a shaded pole motor, one can see that there are two small loops of copper wire at the ends of the field pole-pieces. The direction of rotation of a shaded-pole motor is determined by these shorted loops of wire. The armature turns in a direction that takes it from the center of the pole piece toward the shorted loops. See Figure 22–30.

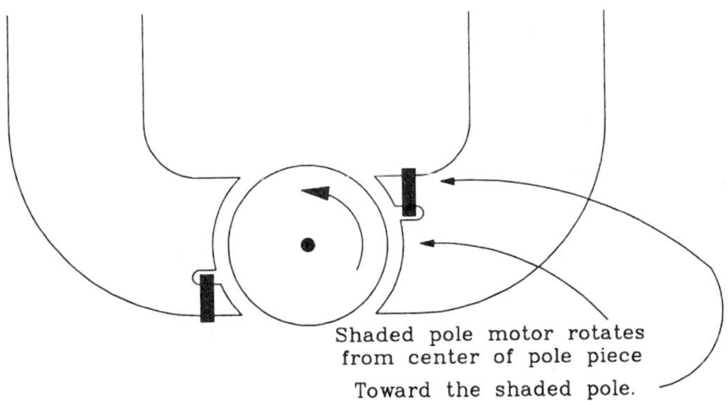
Shaded pole motor rotates
from center of pole piece
Toward the shaded pole.

Figure 22–30 Explanation of the direction of rotation of a shaded-pole AC motor.

The direction of rotation of a shaded-pole motor is fixed by the orientation of the field/shorted-loop. If reversal is required, the motor must be dismantled and the field must be physically turned over.

Split-Phase AC Induction Motors

In most of the several types of single-phase AC induction motors, the problem of starting the motor is solved by providing a second phase. This is done by including a running winding and a starting winding, each with a different phase of current flowing through it. It is the difference in the two phase currents that starts the motor in a specific direction. These kinds of AC motors are called split-phase AC induction motors.

AC Split-Phase Motor. The first type of split-phase motor is one in which there are two windings with different reactances. The difference in reactance causes a different phase of current to flow in them, thus giving the motor its starting torque. Both windings remain connected to the main line at all times. The reversal of this kind of motor is done by reversing the connections to either winding.

A second type of split-phase motor is very similar to the one just mentioned except that one winding has a bipolar electrolytic capacitor placed in series with it to improve the starting torque. A bipolar electrolytic capacitor is an electrolytic capacitor that is designed to run on reversing polarity, with large capacitance in either direction. Again, both windings are across the AC lines at all times. Reversal is done in the same way: by reversal of either the running winding or the capacitor-fed winding.

Capacitor Start Split-Phase Motor. The starting torque of an AC induction motor can be greatly increased if the second, starting winding has a much lower reactance. While this will create a good starting torque, the motor would overheat if this low reactance winding were connected to the AC line at all times. This problem can be solved by providing a centrifugal switch within the motor. When the motor is running well above stall speed, the switch installed inside the motor will open, disconnecting the starting winding. At normal speed, the motor runs at about 1,750 RPM on the running winding only.

The capacitor-start AC induction motor finds use in domestic clothes washers and dryers, in-sink garbage disposals, and some kinds of water pumps: wherever a high starting torque is needed to get a heavy mechanical load moving quickly. The direction of rotation of a capacitor-start motor can be reversed by reversing either the starting- or the running-winding connections.

The centrifugal switch within this kind of motor is mechanical and is a prime source of failures of these motors. If the contacts refuse to close, the motor will not start under load and will quickly overheat. To preclude this problem, these motors are often provided with thermal overheat protection.

If the motor becomes too hot for any reason, the thermal overload will trip and cut power to the motor. Overheating can be caused by a failure of the starting winding circuit, or a dead-stall condition of the motor. These overload circuit breakers often have a red "reset" button that must be manually reset for the motor to regain power. If the capacitor-start circuit should again fail to disengage after resetting once the motor reaches operating speed, the motor will again overheat.

Three-Phase AC Induction Motors

Large, high-powered motors run better on three phases than on a single-phase. These motors are slightly smaller for a given horsepower when operated from three-phase lines. No provision need be made for starting windings since there are three phases already connected, thus ensuring the proper direction of rotation.

The reason why three-phase motors need no special provision to determine the direction of rotation lies in the separation of the windings. Six windings are connected into three pairs. As one pair reaches a peak AC voltage and begins to decline in voltage, a second pair will be increasing in strength. With three-phase power, the windings are separated by 120°. This will dictate the direction of rotation. With single-phase motors, successive windings are placed 180° apart, resulting in ambiguous rotation and therefore requiring a special means of determining direction.

Three-phase motors develop smooth power to a mechanical load because power is always available to turn the motor and there are no zero-crossover points as in a single-phase power source. The rotational speed of three-phase induction motors is almost completely line-locked (there is still a requirement for slip). *Feeding AC motors with lower-than-normal voltage makes them weaker, but does not slow the rotation.* The direction of rotation for a three-phase motor can be changed by reversing any two of the three lines connecting the motor to power.

Once a three-phase motor is running at full speed, the failure of one line coming into it will cause the failure of two of the phases, leaving the motor to run on a single phase. This causes a great loss of torque and may cause the RPM to drop to the point at which the motor will draw excessive current. Electrical means should be provided to protect large motors against this possibility, which is called *single-phasing* of a three-phase motor.

The AC Motor Drive for Large AC Motors

Industrial uses dictate that the speed of rotation must be variable, even if the motor is an AC induction type. This is quite possible, and it is often done. Remember that the induction motor speed is essentially line-locked to the *frequency* of the power provided to it. What is needed is a *variable frequency drive.* See Figures 22–31 and 22–32.

The variable frequency drive takes the incoming power and rectifies it

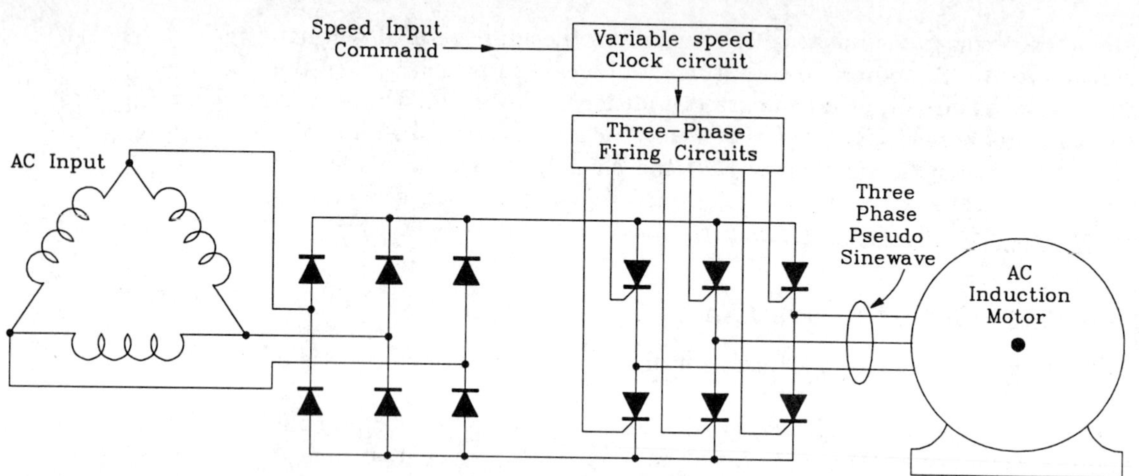

Figure 22–31 Diagram of a variable-frequency motor drive.

Figure 22–32 A large, variable-frequency, induction motor drive. (Courtesy Eaton Corporation, Electric Drives Division, 3122 14th Ave. Kenosha, WI 53141.)

into DC. This more pure form of energy is then chopped up by SCRs or gate turn-off devices (GTOs) into either a single- or a three-phase output voltage waveform that closely approximates a sine wave. This voltage is then connected to the motor windings. As the *clocking speed* of the SCRs or GTOs is varied, the motor RPM will respond proportionately.

In order to operate an SCR from a DC source, some means of turning off the device is required. A special circuit called a *commutating circuit* is used to accomplish this task. (This use of the word *commutating* should not be confused with the commutator of a DC motor.) The commutating circuit provides a turn-off pulse, a very short-term reversal of the polarity across the SCR sufficient to turn it off even though the main DC source is still connected.

GTOs (gate turn-off devices) are finding widespread use in motor control applications. A GTO will turn off under control of the gate, without requiring a commutating circuit. The GTO was discussed in Chapter 14.

ELECTRIC MOTOR FAILURE PATTERNS

Electric motors and generators usually fail in one of two ways: either the brushes wear and fail to make good contact with the rotating armature's commutator or slip rings or the bearings wear out.

Brushes are usually replaceable. The surfaces against which the brushes move are harder than the brushes themselves, so most of the wear just removes brush material, resulting in the brushes becoming shorter and shorter. After a time, the springs holding them against the rotating commutator or slip rings can no longer make good contact. The brushes will then begin to spark excessively as contact is intermittently lost. Carried to an extreme, even the commutator or slip rings can be damaged by this sparking. If the commutator or slip rings are at all pitted or out-of-round, the motor must be dismantled. The commutator or slip rings must be trimmed down and trued on a lathe before new brushes are installed.

The bearings used in most modern motors cannot be lubricated since they are sealed at the time of manufacture with lubrication already inside them. If the bearings fail due to long use, they must be replaced. Replacing the bearings is a simple operation after the motor has been dismantled. The bearings are gently pressed off the shaft with a bearing puller. Using the number stamped into the side of the bearing, replacements are purchased from a bearing supplier. The new bearings must be carefully installed, being sure that they are inserted straight on the shaft. Use a collar to tap the bearing gently on the shaft by applying the taps to the *inner* race only.

Once in a great while, a winding on either the stator (stationary part) or the rotor (rotating part) may short to the case, which is usually connected to ground in one way or another. The motor will probably have to be disassembled to isolate the stator from the rotor for testing with an ohmmeter. Motors, alternators, and generators operating with DC sources of 24 volts and below, particularly in automobile and marine applications, are made with a deliberate internal connection to the case. Motors intended for use with 120 and higher AC voltages isolate the windings carefully from ground. Safety ground is connected by a separate line to the unit's case.

After determining whether the winding in question should be grounded, the actual status can be checked with an ohmmeter. If a winding is found to be shorted to the case of the unit and it is determined that this should not be, the motor can be sent to an electric motor shop for rewinding. This would be the right approach if the motor is expensive or a replacement is not available for a reasonable price. Smaller motors being less expensive, it is probably be more economical to simply discard the motor and purchase a replacement.

22.4 GENERATORS AND ALTERNATORS

DIRECT CURRENT (DC) GENERATORS

The Permanent-Magnet Generator

A permanent-magnet generator is identical to the PM motor, discussed earlier. The only difference is its application. In a PM motor, voltage is applied to produce rotation. Used as a generator, the same device is rotaed by a mechanical force and produces DC voltages.

The PM generator is most often used to indicate rotational speed. It is the monitoring transducer used to provide the feedback in a closed-loop motor servo system, which is used to operate the motor at variable RPM. Refer back to Figure 22–24. The PM generator can also produce small amounts of power, which is useful in a few applications. The generator that bicyclists sometimes use is a PM type. The shaft of the generator rubs on the tire, producing enough power to run a single headlamp—if the cyclist pedals fast enough.

The DC Generator

The DC generator was used in automobiles until about 30 years ago. It has been replaced by the alternator, for reasons to be explained later. The DC generator may still be encountered now and then in old cars and a few other special applications. This generator has some strange quirks. Basically, it is a shunt motor, and is driven by a belt from the engine. When the field was *excited* by an external voltage, the armature produced a voltage and current that were used to maintain the electrical system of the vehicle, including charging the battery.

Once running, the DC generator works quite well. It is getting it started for the very first time that is somewhat difficult. Until it comes up to proper output voltage, the generator is isolated from the battery by the regulator. This is necessary in the regulator design to keep the generator from discharging the battery when the generator is not turning. Since the field has no current flowing, the armature will have no output, so the whole generator will do nothing—except that, if it has been magnetized once, the field will retain some small amount of magnetism even when the excitation current is cut off. It is this *residual magnetism* that bootstraps the generator into producing the first few volts. These volts energize the field, causing the generator to come up to normal operating speed.

When purchased, the generator field has to be *flashed* in order to first magnetize the field. Once it is working, it will bootstrap itself from then on without further attention. After sitting for a long time or having been dismantled, the generator may have to be flashed again to establish the weak residual magnetism it requires.

Flashing the field of a generator is done by disconnecting the field lead from the regulator (never flash to the regulator connection) and momentarily applying a full +12 V to the field wire. The other end of the winding is already internally grounded. Reconnect the field lead to the regulator when done.

There are problems with this type of generator. It does not charge well at low RPM. The main output current flows through the brushes, which require periodic maintenance and replacement. If not disconnected by the cutout (reverse-current) relay within the voltage regulator, the generator will "motorize" and run down the battery quickly if the engine is not running.

The regulator used with the generator is often a three-relay regulator. One is the voltage regulator, and a second is the current regulator. By critically setting the spring tension and contact spacings of these relays, mechanical control is exerted over the field to prevent overcharging a battery with too high a current or voltage. The cutout relay prevents the motorizing of the generator when the engine RPM falls too low for charging.

ALTERNATING CURRENT (AC) ALTERNATORS

The alternator that is now in common use in almost every vehicle is a great improvement over the generator. It charges well at low engine RPMs and is easy to control. It also requires very little maintenance.

The alternator is basically an AC generator, as the name implies. Inside the case of the alternator are six diodes that convert the low-voltage AC produced by the alternator into DC suitable for automotive use. See Figure 22–33.

These rectifier diodes also provide the reverse-current prevention required, disconnecting the alternator when it stops or rotates too slowly to run the electrical system.

An inspection of the internal construction of an alternator will show that the field rotates and that the energy produced by the alternator is taken from the stator: exactly the reverse of the DC generator.

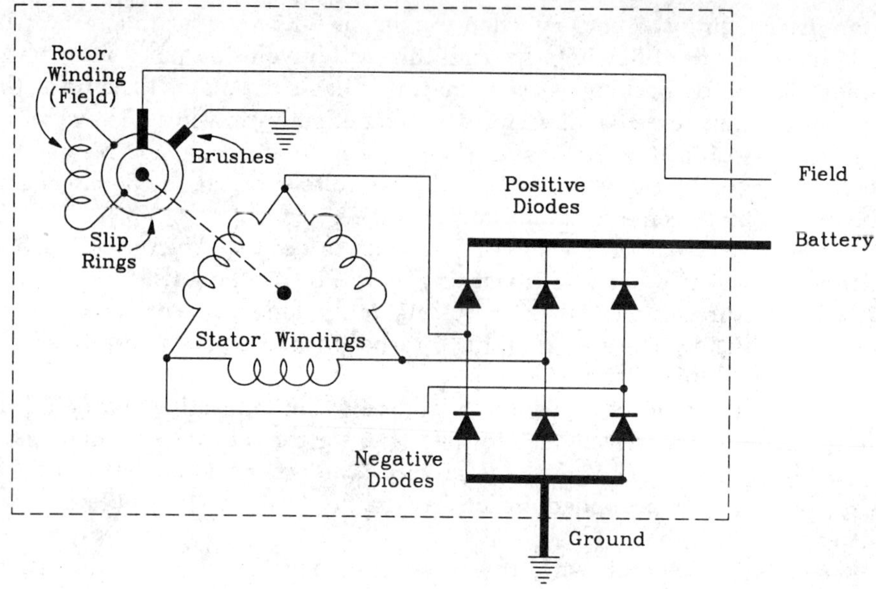

Figure 22–33 Block diagram of an automotive alternator.

The rotating field requires much less current than that produced by the output of the alternator. A few amperes is sufficient to operate the field. This relatively small current does not excessively wear the small brushes and the slip rings that carry excitation to the rotating field. Slip rings are provided to pick up the DC at the brushes and deliver it to the field winding on the rotor.

The output of the alternator is low-voltage, three-phase AC. The voltage regulator for an alternator is small, often so small that it is placed within the shell of the alternator itself. The regulator samples the output voltage of the alternator and reduces it by reducing the average DC applied to the rotating field via the slip rings. With less voltage applied to the rotating field, the output voltage of the alternator decrease. Reducing the voltage to the field is accomplished by turning it off and on in a pulse width–modulated manner, effectively controlling the field in an analog manner.

22.5 SYNCHRO TRANSMITTERS AND RECEIVERS

Synchros are really transformers with a rotatable winding. See Figure 22–34.

The input AC voltage is applied to the movable winding. Depending on the angular relationship between this movable winding and the three stator windings, each of the stators produces an AC voltage that varies in

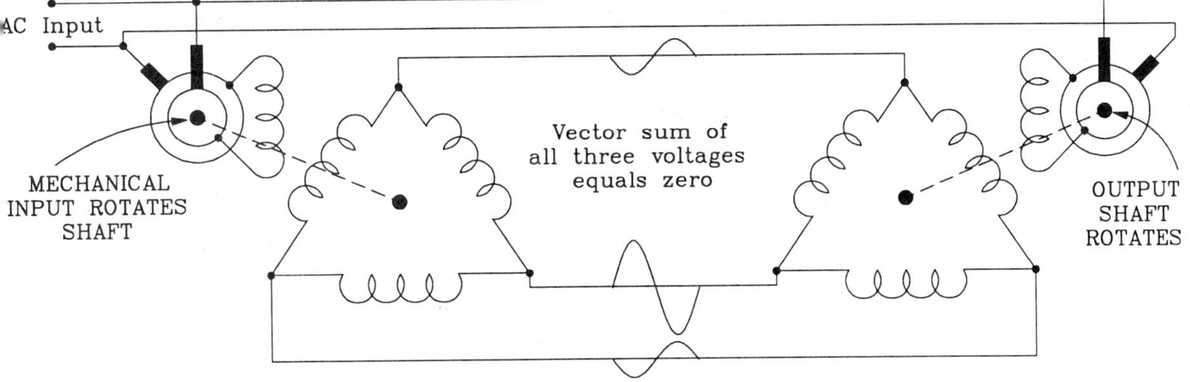

Figure 22–34 Schematic of the interconnection of two synchro transformers.

amplitude and is either in-phase or 180 degrees out of phase with the excitation voltage.

These three voltages are then sent from the *transmitter synchro* to a *receiver synchro*. The receiver synchro is electrically identical to the transmitter but includes a special mechanical oscillation damper on its output shaft. The receiver synchro is fed the same excitation voltage as the transmitter, along with the three voltages generated by the transmitter. The shaft of the receiver will take up the same angular position as the transmitter shaft as it integrates all four of the voltages applied to it. The end result is remote, mechanical angular positioning using only electrical means.

A third type of synchro, the *differential transformer*, can be inserted as shown in Figure 22–35.

The differential transformer is used to insert an additional angular input

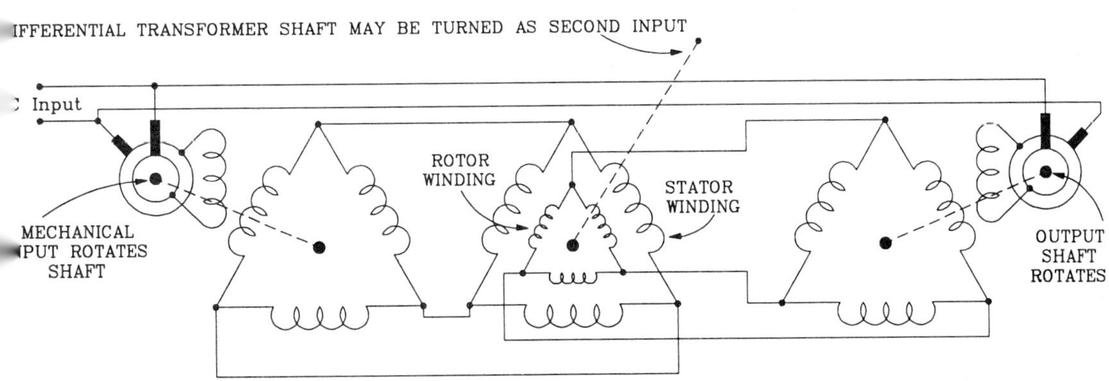

Figure 22–35 Adding a differential transformer for an angular offset.

to the system, with the receiver reporting the difference between the transmitter and the differential transformer.

22.6 RESOLVERS

A resolver is a modern component that provides a very precise indication of the amount by which its input shaft is turned. It is used as a feedback mechanism in servo mechanisms, to produce precise motion to a given position. Although it may look like a small motor, the resolver is actually a kind of transformer. See Figure 22–36.

A resolver requires two excitation voltages for its operation. These are AC sine wave voltages that are exactly 90 degrees out of phase and of equal amplitude. The phase of the output sine wave varies linearly with the rotation of the shaft, completing 360 degrees of shift for a full turn of the shaft. The output of the resolver is often squared by digital circuitry and used in closed-loop servo amplifier systems.

22.7 LADDER LOGIC

RELAY BASICS

Electrical relays are still among the most common components used in industrial applications. The relay provides electrical isolation between input and output circuits and also, in a manner of speaking, amplification; a relatively small current passed through a coil can cause a set of contacts to close which can, in turn, control a much greater level of current.

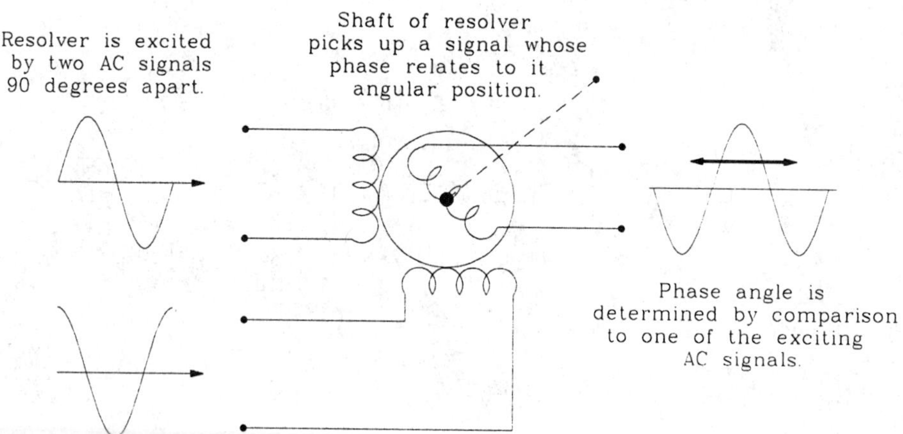
Resolver is excited
by two AC signals
90 degrees apart.
Shaft of resolver
picks up a signal whose
phase relates to it
angular position.
Phase angle is
determined by comparison
to one of the exciting
AC signals.

Figure 22–36 How the resolver works.

Relays are used to turn on and off other relays or equipment of many different types. Interconnected properly, they can perform all the basic logic of digital gates. They are slow, however, and cannot be used for high-speed operations. They are also power-hungry when compared to digital chips. However, they can handle very large currents through their contacts without appreciable power loss. Relays are available in a wide variety of contact configurations. Appendix II shows these *relay form designations*.

The subject of ladder logic and how to read it is sufficient material for a whole book. A very brief summary of the diagrams and how to read them will be given here, however. It is basic to understanding relay diagrams to know that *relay contacts are always shown on diagrams as though the coil is not energized.* When showing a relay that has a simple set of contacts that close when the coil is energized, this relay will always be shown with the contacts open.

Relays usually fail because their contacts develop dirt, contamination, or a misalignment that prevents them from closing properly. If the contacts can be seen to be apparently touching yet there appears to be no contact, simply bridge the contacts momentarily with a short wire. If the load then responds, you have proven that the contacts were not contacting properly. This is a primary way of determining whether relay contacts are working.

LADDER LOGIC DIAGRAMS

Ladder logic diagrams use different symbols than those used by the electronics technician. Appendix II, "Electrical Symbols," lists the common electrical symbols used in a ladder logic diagram.

Ladder logic diagrams are set up differently, too. Whereas an electronic schematic puts the positive DC at the top of the diagram and a ground or negative at the bottom, the electrical ladder logic diagram is an interconnection of relays, their contacts, and their loads across an AC source of power. The AC is applied to the circuits vertically, down each side of the diagram. The rungs of the ladder represent individual circuits across the AC supply. See Figure 22–37.

Ladder logic diagrams are read by proceeding from the top of the diagram downward. As the relays in the upper part of the diagram energize, they provide a sort of timing diagram. By examination, the technician can see that there is a sequence whereby certain relays must close before others. Thus, ladder logic diagrams can indicate the order in which events occur. Remember that all relays are shown as though they were *not* energized.

One of the difficult tasks in reading a ladder logic diagram is to associate a set of contacts with the proper coil, even though the two may be widely separated on the diagram. Some sort of coding is used, such as a "5CR" meaning "#5 Control Relay." Elsewhere on the diagram the contacts (no doubt you will recognize the contact symbol as a capacitor symbol), the normally open contacts mounted on this coil might also be labeled "5CR." This is the symbology used in Figure 23–37. Normally closed relay contacts

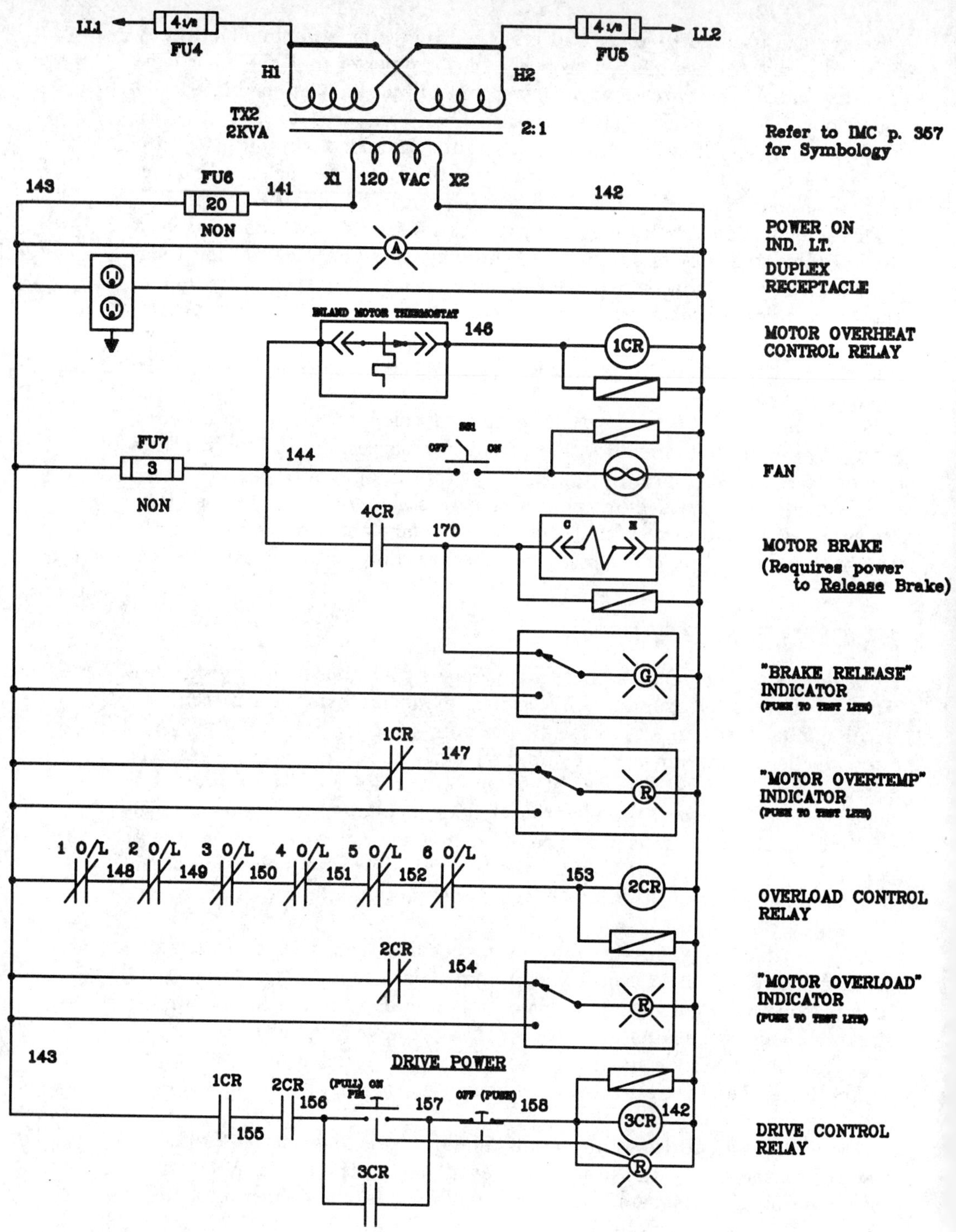

Figure 22–37 A typical ladder logic circuit. (Courtesy Lloyd Controls, Seattle, WA.)

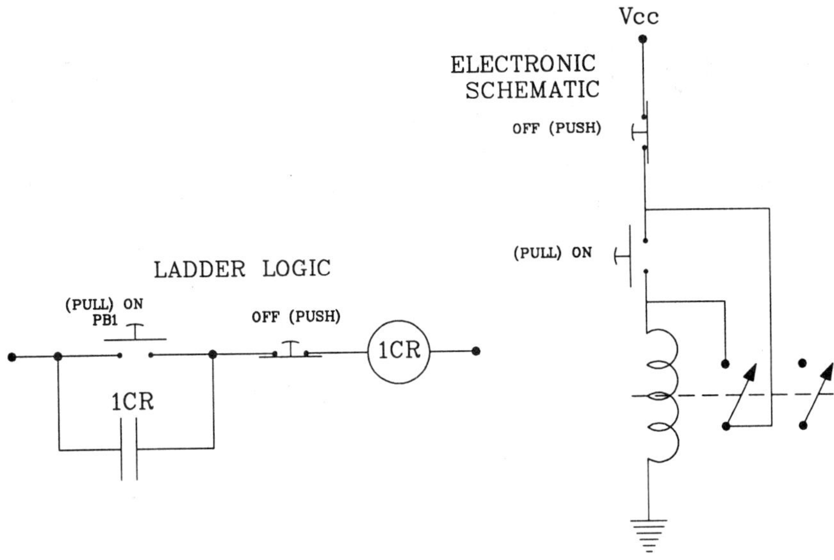

Figure 22–38 Two ways of drawing the three-wire control circuit.

look like a capacitor symbol with a line diagonally through it. Again, remember that the normally open and normally closed designations refer to an *unenergized* relay (with no current flowing through the coil).

THE 3-WIRE CONTROL CIRCUIT

One of the common circuits used in industrial systems is the three-wire control system. Through the use of relays, a heavy-current load can be controlled from a relatively long distance away by using a relay. The relay latches itself in the on position via one of its own contacts. Once latched, it will stay in that condition until the circuit is interrupted, at which time it will turn the load off and be ready to recycle. Figure 22–38 shows a ladder logic diagram and a schematic of the circuit. One way of identifying this circuit in the real world is that both the controls, on and off, are push-buttons rather than ordinary switches.

CHAPTER SUMMARY

- Residential and small commercial buildings are wired for 240/120-V power.
- Industrial applications use three-phase power.
- Phase voltage is taken from a star-configured, three-phase system from ground (neutral) to one of the phase voltages.

- Line voltage is taken from one hot line to another.
- Line voltage is 1.73 times the phase voltage.
- The two configurations for three-phase wiring are the delta and the wye (star).
- The potential transformer and the current transformer allow safe monitoring of high-energy power lines operating at thousands of volts.
- The clamp-on AC ammeter is a valuable tool for troubleshooting power AC circuits.
- Using the voltmeter function of the instrument (if provided) can be dangerous because of the needle clamp feature, which is used mostly when measuring current.
- Three-phase rectifiers can be either half- or full-wave.
- Using SCRs or GTOs allows the regulation of the resulting DC from a three-phase rectifier.
- Electricians designate the highest voltage winding of a transformer as *H* winding, with the lower voltage winding as *X*.
- DC electric motors include the permanent magnet motor, the series-wound and shunt-wound motors, and the combination, compound-wound motor.
- Each motor has unique torque and speed characteristics.
- DC motors can be precisely controlled for both speed and torque by a DC motor controller.
- The brushless DC motor uses a hall effect transistor to tell when to energize the field coils.
- The synchronous DC motor runs at very precise speed.
- AC motors include the shaded-pole and induction motors.
- The universal motor is a series-connected DC motor.
- AC synchronous motors turn with precise positioning by the applied AC.
- AC induction motors use transformer action and a slight slippage to couple energy from the field windings into the shorted armature windings.
- AC induction motors are locked to the line frequency for their rotation speed.
- A capacitor-start induction motor uses a centrifugal switch to turn off the starting winding before final rotation speed is attained.
- A three-phase motor must be provided with all three phases or it may quickly overheat.
- Motor controllers are available to drive AC induction motors at variable speeds.
- Variable-frequency motor controllers work by converting power-line AC into DC and then building from the DC an AC output waveform that can be varied in frequency.
- The basic DC generator is the permanent-magnet motor.
- It is often used as a tachometer, providing a DC output proportional to the rotational speed of the device.
- The DC generator is seldom used today, having been almost entirely replaced by the alternator.

- An automobile alternator has a rotating field (the rotor) and stationary, three-phase AC output windings.
- The AC from an alternator is immediately converted to DC by a three-phase bridge consisting of six diodes.
- This rectifier is often located inside the alternator frame.
- Even the alternator regulator can be contained within the alternator itself: this is called an integral regulator.
- Synchros provide a means of carrying information on rotational position by electrical means from one location to another.
- Offset information can be inserted into such a system by using a differential transformer.
- Synchros operate by means of three AC voltages that vary in amplitude and polarity (not by their phase.)
- A resolver provides electrical information related to the position of the resolver shaft.
- Ladder logic is a type of electrician's diagram that explains the logical progression of control circuitry using relays as the logic elements.
- Ladder logic diagrams are read from the top down.
- The side rails in ladder logic diagram represent the applied control voltage, commonly 120 V.
- A relay provides isolation and amplification.
- A relay's contacts are always shown as though the relay was turned off (unenergized).
- A relay's contacts may be shown widely separated from the coil that energizes them.
- Suspected open contacts of a relay can be verified by bridging them with a jumper wire.
- If the circuit connected to the contacts responds only when bridged, the contacts are not "making" (making contact) as they should.
- A relay form chart (see Appendix II) shows the contact configurations commonly available.
- The three-wire control circuit enables an operator to control power to a heavy load from a distance, using small wires and a pair of push-buttons.

REVIEW QUESTIONS

1. If a household range were operated from 120-V AC instead of 240-V AC, one could expect to lose ________ times as much power in heating the wiring supplying the stove.
2. As an electronic technician, what must be remembered when working on AC power lines as far as color coding is concerned?
3. What is the fundamental rule regarding the neutral wire of a power AC circuit?

4. Industrial power applications sometimes have four wires to supply power. What are these wires?
5. What are the two configurations for three-phase power?
6. What other voltage would you expect to be associated with 2,400-Volt phase voltage?
7. What is the potential transformer used for?
8. What is a current transformer?
9. What is the danger of using the voltmeter function of a clamp-on ammeter?
10. How many diodes are required to full-wave rectify a three-phase power source?
11. How many SCRs are required to controllably rectify full-wave three-phase AC power?
12. How does one reverse the direction of a permanent-magnet motor?
13. How can the speed of a PM motor be efficiently controlled with a fixed power source?
14. What kind of DC motor is used to crank an automobile engine?
15. What kind of DC motor develops great torque but has poor speed regulation?
16. What kind of DC motor has a good speed regulation but poor starting torque?
17. What kind of motor is easiest to control for speed and torque?
18. What is the key component of a brushless DC motor?
19. What is a universal motor, basically speaking?
20. Name two applications for a universal motor.
21. The direction of rotation of a shaded-pole AC motor is _______ the shaded pole.
22. A single-phase induction motor must have a second winding to determine the _______ of the motor.
23. How can the direction of rotation of a single-phase induction motor be reversed?
24. A capacitor-start motor hums loudly and then trips off-line. What is the probable cause?
25. How may the direction of a three-phase induction motor be reversed?
26. How may the speed of an induction motor be changed?
27. An automobile alternator puts out a three-phase voltage which is immediately changed into DC by a _______.
28. What does a resolver do?
29. Electricians use a _______ logic diagram to show relay closure sequencing.
30. The contacts of a relay are always shown as though the relay were _______.
31. Ladder logic diagrams are read from _______ to _______.
32. A ladder logic diagram ties a set of contacts to a coil by what means?
33. What is the name of the circuit that is commonly used to remotely control the primary power applied to a large machine through the use of relays?

23

Troubleshooting Vacuum-Tube and CRT Circuits

CHAPTER OBJECTIVES

The cathode-ray tube is the most common means of displaying data in monochrome and color in computers and in television sets, even though it is technically a time-honored vacuum tube. Vacuum tubes are still used in high-powered radio frequency amplifiers such as those used in commercial broadcast transmitters. It is to a technician's advantage to have at least a fundamental knowledge of how vacuum tubes work. At the conclusion of this chapter, the student will:

- Be aware of the necessary safety cautions to observe while working with the high voltages commonly used with vacuum tubes.
- Know how to use a dead-man stick.
- Know how to number the pins of a vacuum tube.
- Learn how the basic vacuum tube operates and the voltages to expect on the various elements.
- Become familiar with some of the imedance-matching solutions necessary with vacuum tubes.
- Learn what to look for when troubleshooting vacuum-tube circuits.
- Know how a CRT circuit works and how to troubleshoot it with a voltmeter.

- Be shown the magnetic shielding solutions necessary for CRTs.
- Be introduced to CRT phosphors and several different CRT sweeps.
- Be made aware of some of the special tubes, including gaseous regulators and thyratrons.

23.1 WHY STUDY TUBES?

Granted, vacuum tubes have been largely replaced by solid-state devices: bipolar transistors, FETs, and the like. However, since a few of them are still in service, it is a good idea to be at least familiar with how they operate. You never know when a very old piece of equipment may need repair.

High-powered radio transmitters often still use tubes because they can be made relatively cheaply when compared to the many transistors it would take to do the same job. Besides, the large number of transistors in parallel that would be required to replace a large tube would be very prone to failure as a bank, since the shorting of one would disable the whole group. If the technician enters broadcasting, AM or FM radio, or television, a knowledge of tubes would probably be beneficial.

Cathode-ray tubes operate on many of the same principles as a common vacuum-tube amplifier. Electrons are boiled off, then, they are intensity-controlled, and finally, they are accelerated toward a final, high-voltage target.

A microwave oven and many radar sets use a special tube that is actually a very high-powered oscillator: the *magnetron*. When fed a DC or rectified AC waveform of sufficiently high potential, the magnetron oscillates strongly, producing output frequencies from roughly 1 to 20 GHz. Since these tubes are relatively common, they were covered in Chapter 13.

Antique radios, and even some shop test instruments such as electronic counters and oscilloscopes, still use vacuum tubes. As long as these units are around and being used, they will require maintenance. Knowing how to troubleshoot them may be an advantage in some cases.

23.2 SAFETY

To technicians accustomed to working exclusively on low-voltage circuits, prospect of working on voltages in excess of 100-V DC is not particularly

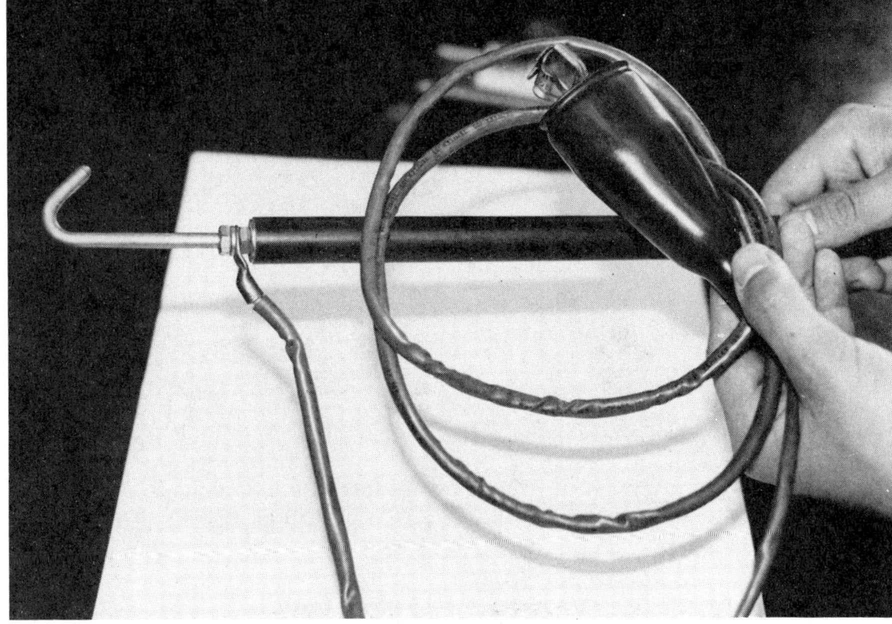

Figure 23–1 The dead-man stick provides safety and a sense of security when working on dangerous, high-voltage circuits.

attractive. With the proper safety precautions being observed at all times, *there is no reason to fear high voltage, but never forget to respect it!*

Receivers using vacuum tubes usually contain voltages of about 200-V DC. High-powered transmitting equipment routinely uses voltages of several thousand volts. Although the heater circuit of a tube is usually relatively low in voltage, the *plate voltage* is the one to be careful of when working inside the equipment.

Transmitters producing about 100 watts of RF power or more often use very high voltages, in excess of 300-V DC. To remove tubes or the associated circuitry in a vacuum tube transmitter, turn off the power. Attach the heavy grounding clip of a dead-man stick to a good, bare metal ground. Touch the metal tip of the stick, holding it by the insulating handle, to any and all points within the equipment that you may contact, whether deliberately or not. In other words, touch everything. Then, while hanging the stick (physically) on the wiring as a backup against accidental start-up, remove the wiring or make the intended changes. The dead-man stick should be removed only when you will not be touching any more internal surfaces, when the equipment is about to be closed up and reenergized. See Figure 23–1.

Whenever work must be done on live circuits, it should be mandatory to have someone present who knows first aid for electrical shock. Most employers have specific, written rules to follow in matters of safety. Ask to read them for your own sake. In addition, now would be a good time to review all of the safety rules.

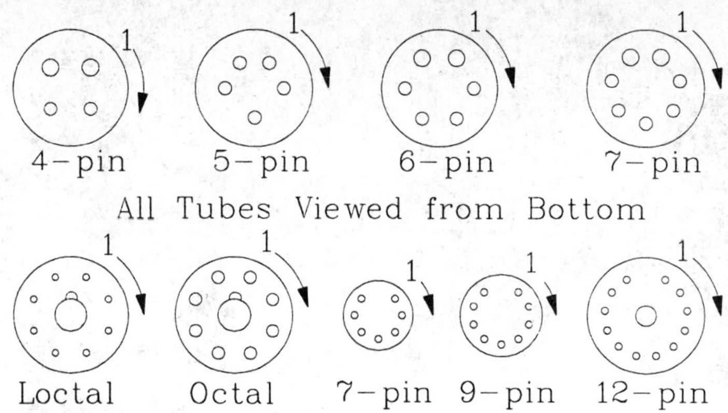

Figure 23–2 Vacuum tube pin-numbering diagrams.

23.3 TUBE ELEMENT IDENTIFICATION

The elements within a tube are identified by a tube-basing diagram with each element numbered. The pins of a tube are usually arranged in a circle. *Numbering begins at a set location and progresses around in a clockwise direction when viewed from the bottom of the socket.* See Figure 23–2.

The elements within a tube are coded with a code that indicates the elements, as noted in Table 23–1.

The codes in Table 23–1 can be combined with additional letters which are used to keep two or more tubes within one envelope separate from one another.

23.4 BASIC-VACUUM TUBE OPERATION

TYPICAL VOLTAGES OF VACUUM-TUBE ELEMENTS

The following paragraphs will progress from the simplest to the more complex kinds of vacuum tubes. Before considering how they work, a

Table 23–1 Abbreviations for Vacuum-Tube Elements

F =	Filament	G2 =	Screen Grid
H =	Heater	G3 =	Suppressor Grid
G1 =	Control Grid	P =	Plate
K =	Cathode	IC =	Internal Connection (do not use)
NC =	No Internal Connection	A1, A2, etc. =	CRT Anodes
IS =	Internal Shield (Ground)		

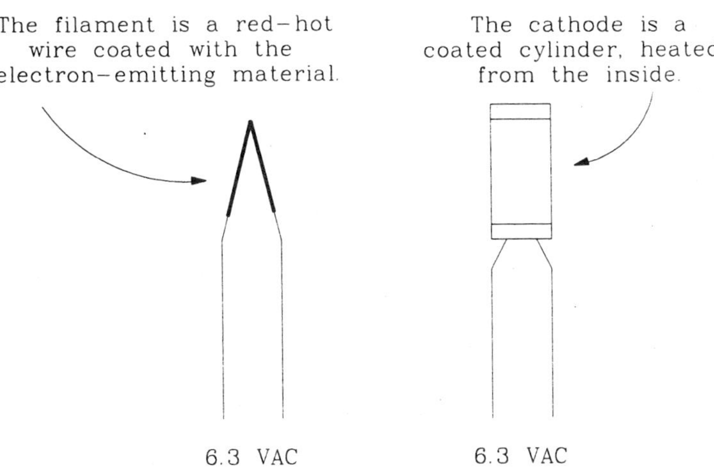
The filament is a red-hot wire coated with the electron-emitting material.
The cathode is a coated cylinder, heated from the inside.
6.3 VAC
6.3 VAC

Figure 23–3 The two methods of producing electrons by thermionic means.

source must be found for the electrons to be controlled. This is done principally by two methods: the directly heated filament and the heater-cathode arrangement. See Figure 23–3.

While the filament is simpler, the heater-cathode arrangement is more rugged and allows some isolation electrically between the heater circuit and the cathode. This helps to eliminate the hum produced in the filament circuit from influencing the electron stream within the tube.

Some tubes are designed for very low, and others for very high voltages to heat them. The two most common heater voltages are 6.3 and 12.6-V AC, which are usually derived directly from a dedicated winding on the 120-V AC power transformer.

Once the filament or cathode has been sufficiently heated—this is the characteristic requirement for tubes to "warm up" before they can operate—the electrons become available. From this point on, the term *cathode* will be loosely used instead of the separate terms *filament* and *heater-cathode*. Now, a place for the electrons to go (while in the process, performing a useful function) is needed.

Adding a Plate: The Diode

The simplest form of vacuum tube is the diode, whose behavior is like that of the semiconductor diode. The vacuum tube diode consists of a source of electrons and a plate to collect them, forming a complete circuit. See Figure 23–4.

This tube, with appropriate modifications and variations, is the active element in DC power rectifiers and in AM and FM detector circuits. It also found use, as semiconductor diodes do now, in clampers, mixers, and clip-

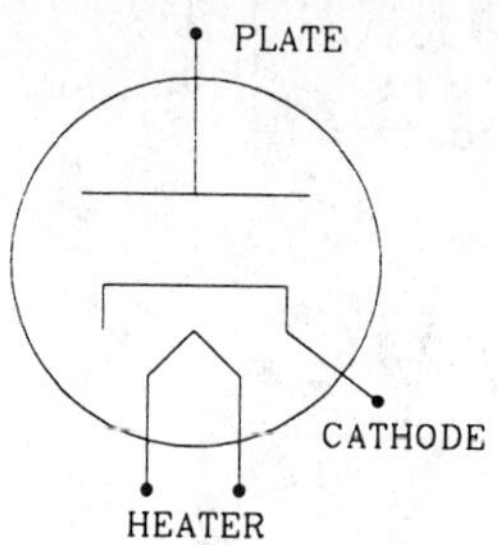

Figure 23–4 The most basic tube, the diode.

pers. The diode conducts only when the plate is more positive than the cathode. With the reverse polarity, there is no current flow through the diode.

Adding a Grid: The Triode

It was found that a loosely coiled grid of wire physically located between the cathode and the plate provides complete control over the amount of current that flows from the cathode to the plate, when the plate is positive with respect to the cathode. See Figure 23–5.

The triode is a voltage-controlled resistor. The more negative the grid becomes, the less current flows to the plate. Without a controlling negative bias voltage on the grid, however, the plate current will be relatively very large.

The reference element for voltage readings on a tube is the cathode. The grid could be held at a negative voltage to operate the triode as Class A, B, or C. Three methods are used in the circuits, as shown in Figure 23–6.

Cathode bias uses part of the normal plate current of the tube to elevate the cathode voltage above ground by a few volts. Receiving tubes operate with biases between 2 and 5 volts, while transmitting tubes may use 50 volts or more. Since the grid is referenced directly to ground, this makes the grid negative with respect to the cathode. This same method of obtain-

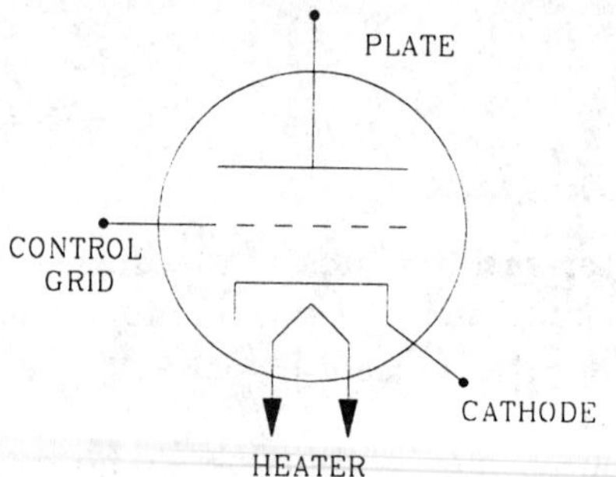

Figure 23–5 The triode tube includes a control grid.

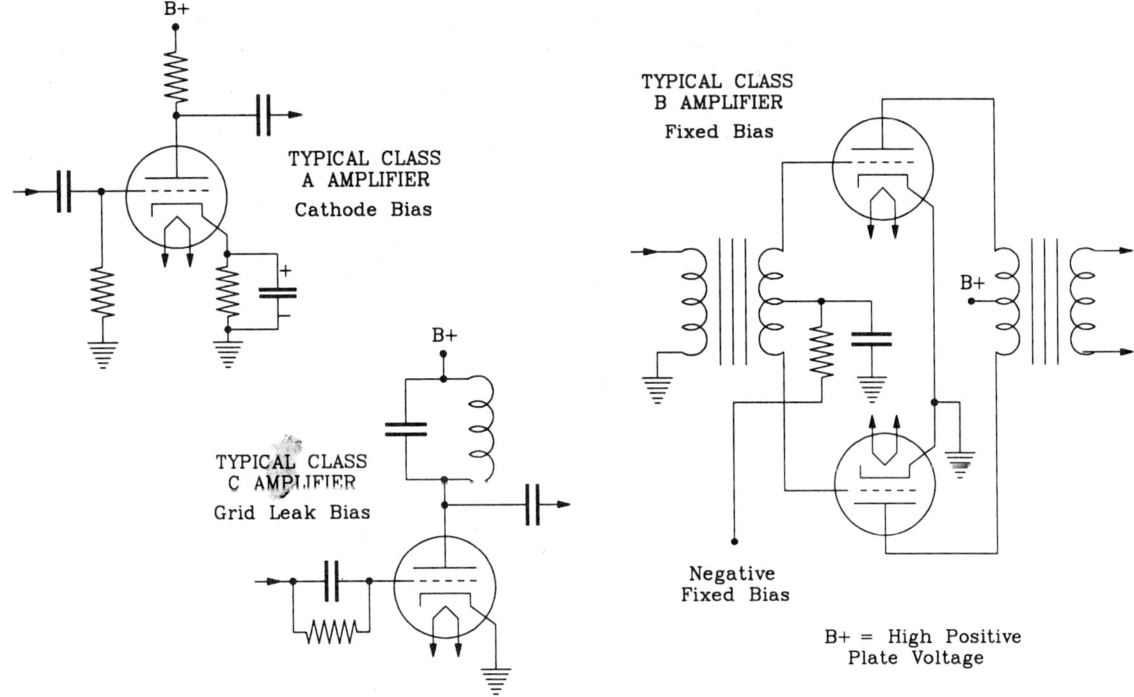

Figure 23–6 Common methods for obtaining the negative bias necessary for vacuum tube operation.

ing a negative bias is used in modern JFET circuits, as shown in Figure 10–19.

Fixed bias is necessary to provide a bias for vacuum-tube DC amplifiers and Class B amplifiers. This requires a separate DC voltage from the power supply. This negative voltage with reference to the circuit common could be done by using a power voltage divider across the entire supply, and then using a junction of the resistors as the common point. Voltages below the junction are negative, and above, positive.

Grid-leak bias can be used when operating Class C, using part of the incoming grid signal to produce a negative bias for the tube. When the grid is driven positive by the incoming signal, grid current is drawn, just as though the grid had become a plate element. The brief current flowing through a series resistor produces the bias. The resistor is called a *grid-leak resistor*. The pulses are filtered to an average DC value by the associated filter capacitor. The stronger the drive into the tube, the larger the bias. This helps protect the tube from excessive driving voltages. The loss of input signal, however, causes a loss of bias and overloading of the tube.

The triode tube was a major advance in electronics, or simply "radio," as the field was called years ago. Radio communication and long-line telephone circuits were the only major applications for electronic circuits.

Vacuum-tube triodes are sometimes used even today in a few high-powered RF amplifiers. (The tetrode, the subject of the next paragraph, is more often used.) When operating at full output, a transmitting triode may glow from reddish to yellow to white at the heater, and the plate itself may glow red or orange due to the normal electron bombardment. Forced air cooling is usually used with these high-powered tubes. However, the triode had some limitations, such as an excessive amount of capacitance between the grid and the plate, which limits its frequency of use and its amplification factor, which is only moderate. Another modification improved these characteristics.

Adding a Screen: The Tetrode

With the addition of a second grid between the control grid and the plate, the capacitance between grid and plate will be substantially reduced. The second grid is called a *screen grid,* and allows more gain from a single tube as well as operation at higher frequencies due to its shielding effect. See Figure 23–7.

The screen grid is usually operated at a high positive voltage, which is only slightly less than the full plate voltage. With less capacitance to the plate than without a screen grid, there is better isolation between the grid and plate circuits. The characteristic curves of the tetrode plate current versus the grid voltage have a "kink" in them, which is caused by electrons that are knocked off the plate by the high-speed stream coming from the cathode. These slower-moving electrons drift back to the second, highly positive screen grid. This is no problem for large-signal, high-powered applications, in which an LC circuit can smooth out the output signal.

Tetrodes are still used today in high-powered radio transmitters as RF final amplifiers, and in the RF drivers for them. As described for triodes, these tubes often glow brightly at the heater and shine red at the plate.

To use a vacuum tube with small signals and get even higher gain, another fix is required in the form of yet another grid.

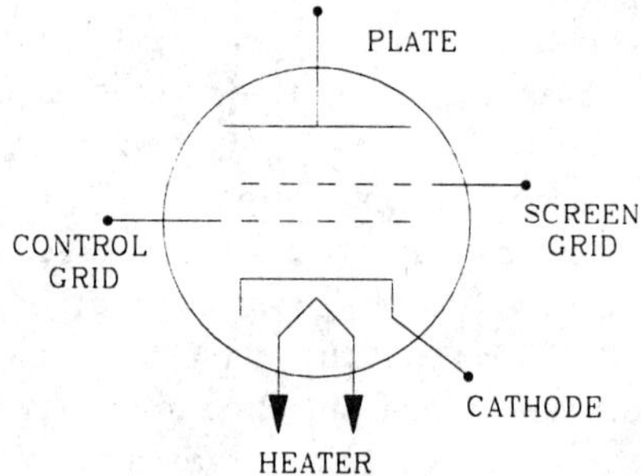

Figure 23–7 The addition of a screen grid provides better capacitive isolation between the grid and plate circuits.

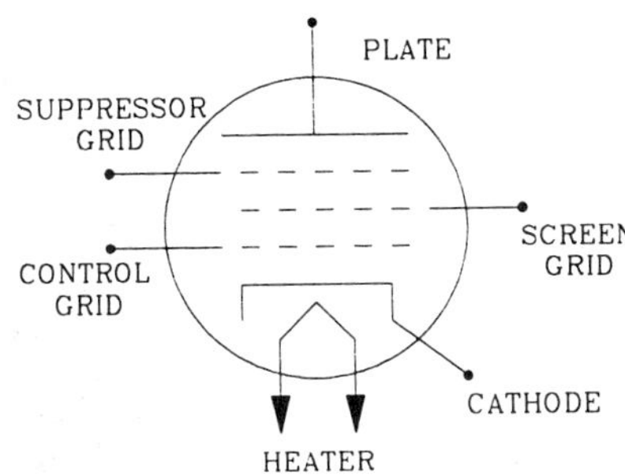

Figure 23–8 Schematic symbol for a pentode vacuum tube.

Adding a Suppressor Grid: The Pentode

The best gain and the advantage of very good shielding between input and output signals are achieved with the addition of a grid between the screen and the plate, called a suppressor grid. The suppressor is connected to a very low-voltage source, which is typically connected directly to the cathode. This grid "straightens out" the "kink" that the screen grid produces in the plate-current versus grid-voltage curves. The pentode is used in small-signal amplifiers for radio receivers and whenever high-gain and high-frequency amplification are required. Because of its widespread use at one time, this is the tube that will be used in following example circuits. See Figure 23–8.

Pentagrid Mixers

The last variety of tube is the pentagrid mixer or pentagrid converter. This tube has five grids, with the first two acting like the first grid and plate of a triode and the last three like the grid, screen, and suppressor of a pentode. This arrangement allows the use of these elements as if they were two tubes in series in order to mix two signals effectively. Both the oscillator and the input signal influence the plate current. The triode portion of the tube is used as an oscillator, and the following three grids and plate amplify a second RF input. See Figure 23–9.

Multiple Tubes in One Envelope

In an effort to save space, it is not uncommon to combine two or three vacuum tubes in one glass or metal envelope. For instance, this is commonly done to combine the two diodes and a triode for the detector and first audio amplifier stages, or to combine two triodes for a flip-flop circuit. Many different combinations of tube elements are manufactured and used.

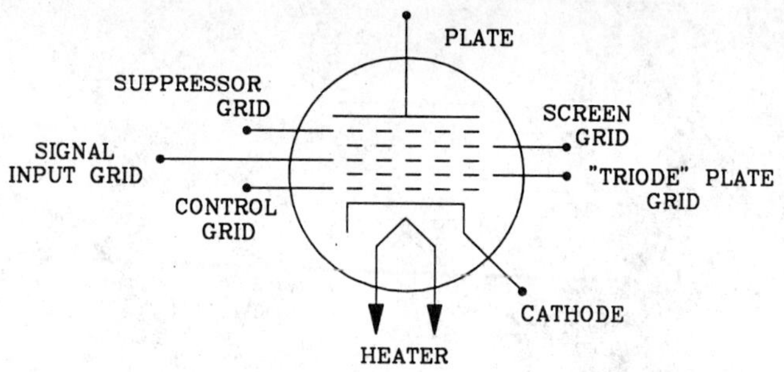

Figure 23–9 Schematic and grid use of a pentagrid mixer.

Nuvistors

With the continuing push to higher frequencies for military and civilian uses, the need for smaller tubes with less internal capacitance became necessary. The nuvistor is a very tiny vacuum tube with a metal case. It found use in the tuners of television sets, which operate at VHF and UHF frequencies. See Figures 23–10 and 23–11.

Figure 23–10 The nuvistor, a miniaturized vacuum tube, is useful at VHF and UHF frequencies.

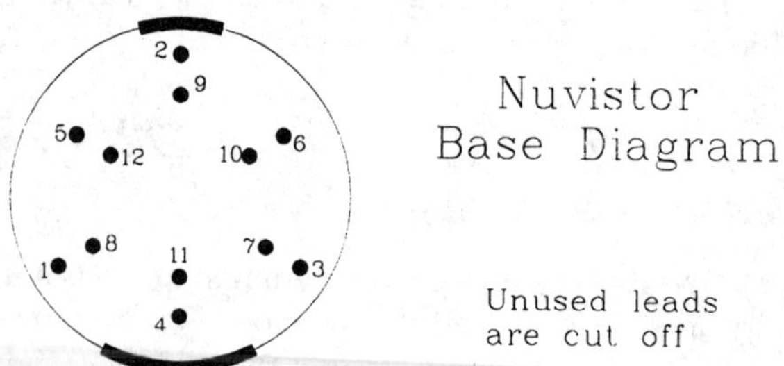

Figure 23–11 Lead identification of a nuvistor tube.

23.5 VACUUM-TUBE IMPEDANCE MATCHING

The vacuum tube is basically a high-impedance device. The input to a vacuum tube is a static voltage, essentially an open circuit in most cases. (The grid can be driven so hard that it turns positive with respect to the cathode and thus draws current, in the process producing a very powerful output for power RF amplification.) The plate circuit is a moderately high impedance, on the order of a few thousand ohms. Consequently, in order to drive low-impedance loads, some form of impedance matching must be employed. At RF frequencies, the RF transformer or the pi-network is used to match to low impedances, such as the common 50-ohm transmission line.

Audio frequency amplifiers are required to match into the very low impedances of speakers, which have impedances of from 16 to as low as 4 v.c. omega. This is accomplished by the use of an impedance-matching AF transformer. Figure 12–19 shows a typical circuit.

23.6 TROUBLESHOOTING VACUUM-TUBE CIRCUITS

Troubleshooting vacuum tubes is easiest and most effective if taken as a step-by-step procedure:

Are the filaments/heaters lit (glass tubes only)?

Is high voltage available at the plate?

Is the screen voltage sufficiently high?

Is the grid bias correct?

Is the cathode resistor value normal?

If the filament or heaters are lit, one should be able to see them, or their indirect glow if the tube is made of glass. Metal tubes are sometimes used, and their heaters may be checked only indirectly by feeling the tubes to see if heat is evident. Whenever any tube is touched, be very aware that you can be burned, particularly when checking large tubes. Even a small tube can be extremely hot if a circuit failure has caused a loss of tube bias. Without a heater, there will be no plate current or heating from that source; consequently, the presence of heat is a confirmation that the heaters are, indeed, operating.

Be careful of a few types of tubes, namely the *klystrons* (a special tube used as a local oscillator in very old radar sets). This tube's entire metal envelope is normally isolated and operating at several hundred volts negative with respect to the chassis! If you are not sure that the case of a metal tube is grounded, do not touch it.

The plate of a small receiving vacuum tube commonly operates at 150 volts for small tubes, with higher voltage, to 300 V, for larger tubes. This voltage should be available, as measured directly on the plate of the tube.

A tube cannot operate without plate voltage. While necessary for operation, the voltage is usually not critical; plus or minus 10 percent of normal voltage is usually quite adequate.

Screen voltage (usually between half and full plate voltage) is also necessary for the tube to operate. This voltage is often derived from the plate voltage supply through a dropping/filtering resistor, filtered again by a bypass capacitor.

The grid voltage of a tube should be measured using the cathode of the tube as the reference point, and not ground. The grid voltage determines the class of operation. Keep in mind the common uses of the various classes of operation to get a good idea of the amount of bias necessary: Class A for DC, audio, and small-signal RF amplifiers; Class B for push-pull power amplifiers and RF linear amplifiers; and Class C for large-signal RF amplifiers and RF oscillators. A grid voltage that is too negative will cut the tube off and probably cause severe distortion, while a bias that is insufficient (not sufficiently negative) will cause tube overheating and distortion.

One of the best points to monitor with a DC meter to evaluate the proper operation of an amplifier is to measure the amount of voltage dropped across the cathode-to-ground resistor. This resistor passes all the plate current. A voltage across the cathode resistor that is too small suggests insufficient plate current, probably due to too negative a grid bias voltage or a loss of screen voltage. Too large a voltage drop across the cathode resistor means excessive plate current, which is probably due to loss of bias voltage.

Most vacuum tubes have a small, silvered mark on the inside of the glass. This is vaporized magnesium. A small piece of this flammable metal is placed within the glass envelope during manufacture. After most of the air is removed, the remaining oxygen is burned by firing this magnesium with an RF pulse, through the glass. Thus, this silvered area on the glass is normal and does not indicate a problem.

Many high-powered vacuum tubes will glow with a faint bluish color, just inside the glass. This is also normal. What is *not* normal is a blue glow *between* the tube elements of a vacuum tube. A blue glow between elements is visual evidence of a severe tube overload, where pieces of the cathode are being blasted away. A gas-filled tube, on the other had, is supposed to have a glow between the elements. These tubes will be discussed later in this chapter.

23.7 THE CATHODE-RAY TUBE (CRT)

The vacuum tube as an amplifier is obsolete for modern circuits. However, the vacuum tube as an indicator is still very much alive in the form of the cathode-ray tube (CRT).

The same source of electrons is used as in the amplifier tube: a heater-and-cathode arrangement. The control "grid" is a cylinder, in the end of

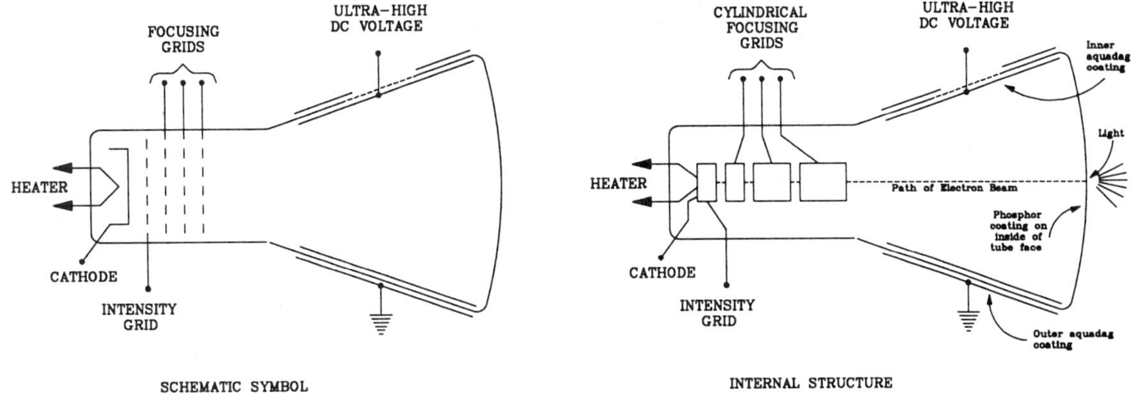

Figure 23–12 Schematic and internal construction of a cathode-ray tube.

which is a small hole through which the electron stream can emerge on its way to the screen. See Figure 23–12.

Once the electrons have been produced and controlled in intensity by the control grid, they are focused and accelerated by two or more additional cylinders, to which are applied progressively higher positive DC voltages. The voltage differences between these grids form electrical "lenses" that can be adjusted to cause the electrons in the beam to converge at the screen in a sharp dot.

Two methods are available to deflect the spot in any direction on the face of the CRT: electrostatic and electromagnetic. The electrostatic method of deflection requires that the electron beam pass between two pairs of deflection plates, one vertically oriented, to deflect the beam horizontally, and a horizontal pair, to deflect the beam vertically. See Figure 23–13. Electrostatic deflection lends itself well to a very broad range of sweep and signal frequencies, as used in oscilloscopes, for instance.

The second method is to use electromagnets placed at the neck of the tube to deflect the beam. This is the method of deflection that is used in television sets and computer monitors. The fixed sweep frequencies, horizontal and vertical, that are used in a TV set are well suited to this method of deflection. Because of the inductance of the deflection coils, electromagnetic deflection is unsuitable for operation over a broad range of frequencies.

UNIQUE PROBLEMS OF A CRT

The CRT is, as might be expected, susceptible to interference from magnetic fields. Transformers should be placed behind the CRT, in line with the CRT neck if possible, to reduce magnetic hum interference of the electron

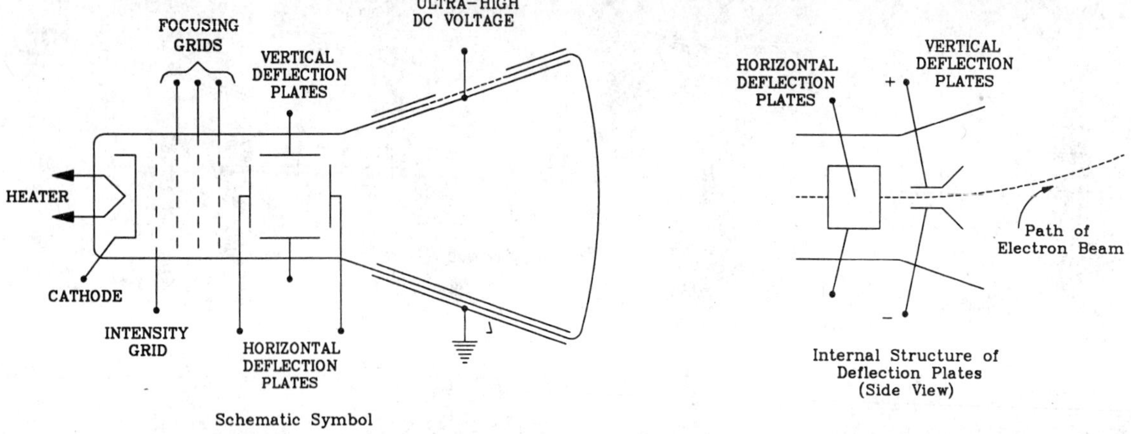

Figure 23–13 Cathode-ray-tube electrostatic deflection plates.

beam. Additional beam deflection interference can be reduced by using a special kind of metal shield around the CRT from neck to screen, made from a material called Mu-metal. This material is particularly suited to shield against magnetic fields.

Working on CRTs within equipment can expose a technician to dangerous voltages. Figure 23–14 shows some of the different way in which voltage is applied to a CRT for various applications. Note that one should never assume that a given circuit is safe to touch. What might be a grounded tube element in one circuit will not necessarily be grounded in a different application.

> ***Caution:*** **In addition to CRTs and vacuum tubes, laser power supplies also produce very high voltages. If you must work on these circuits, be very careful not to complete the wrong circuit with your body.**

GENERATING EXTREMELY HIGH VOLTAGES

Once the electron beam is out of the electrostatic or electromagnetic deflection fields, it must be accelerated by an extremely high DC voltage in order for the beam to strike the phosphor coating on the inside of the face glass with sufficient energy to emit a bright glow. Without this high voltage (commonly 14,000 volts or more), the image will be much too dim to use.

Figure 10–43 gave the generalities of a typical flyback transformer circuit. The collapsing magnetic field of this special kind of transformer produces an extremely high voltage. This voltage pulse is rectified and sent to the CRT. The CRT itself is the filter capacitor. This filter capacitor is formed by coating

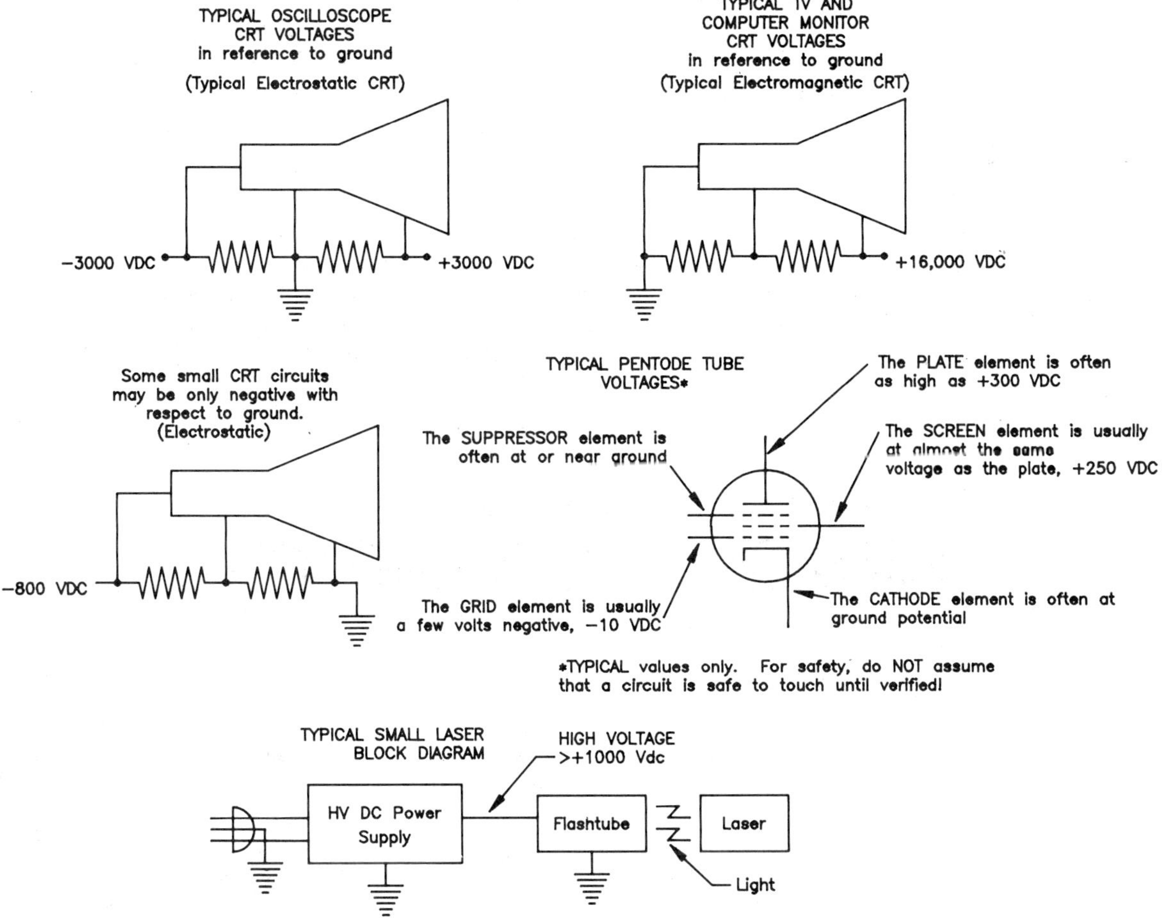

Figure 23–14 Danger points to be aware of when working on CRTs, vacuum tubes, and laser circuits.

the inside and the outside bell of the CRT with a conducting, graphite-based coating called aquadag. The grounded outer coating is omitted near the area where the positive high-voltage lead connects to the glass. The connector on the glass contacts the inner graphite coating. See Figure 23–11.

The high-voltage waveform from the flyback transformer can be directly rectified, or it may be doubled or even tripled by a suitable arrangement of capacitors and diodes before application to the CRT.

CRT PHOSPHORS

When the electron beam reaches the screen of the CRT, it strikes special chemicals that coat the inner surface of the glass. These chemicals glow when struck by the beam. The *phosphors*, as they are called, vary in their persistency (time they glow after the beam is gone) and their intensity and color. These phosphors are number-coded using a "P" prefix; a few examples follow (see Table 23–2).

CATHODE-RAY-TUBE SWEEPS

Once the beam is producing a spot on the CRT face, it can be moved around the face of the tube to represent many different quantities.

The linear sweep is most commonly used to represent time on the face of the CRT, presenting some sort of information in a graphic form as it relates to time intervals. The oscilloscope is the best example of this concept. The

Table 23–2 CRT Phosphor Characteristics

Code	Color	Persistence	Use
P1, P2	Yellow-green	Medium	Oscilloscopes
P3	Yellow-orange	Medium	Oscilloscopes
P4	White	Med. Short	Television
P5	Blue	Med. Short	Photography
P6	White	Short	Obsolete
P11	Blue	Med. Short	Oscilloscopes
P12	Orange	Long	Radar
P14	Yellow-orange	Medium	Radar
P17	Yellow	Medium	Radar
P18	White	Medium	Television
P19	Orange	Long	Radar
P20	Yellow-green	Medium	Radar
P22	Tri-Color*	Med. Short	Color Television
P23	White	Medium	Television
P25	Orange	Medium	Radar
P26	Orange	Very Long	Radar
P27	Red-orange	Medium	Color TV Monitor
P28	Yellow-green	Long	Radar
P31	Green	Short	Oscilloscopes
P32	Purple-blue	Long	Radar
P33	Orange	Very Long	Radar
P34	Yellow-Green	Very Long	Radar
P35	Blue-white	Medium	Photographic

*Three separate electron-beam guns are required to produce a color display.

varying voltage sent into the vertical channel of an oscilloscope is plotted against a ramp of voltage applied to the horizontal deflection plates.

A variation of the time concept is used in the spectrum analyzer. The linear sweep of the analyzer from left to right corresponds to the frequency tuning of the internal or external receiver as it listens to various signals. At the receiver spikes upward upon receipt of a signal at a given frequency, the horizontal position of the sweep provides the frequency at which the spike occurs. Figure 13–35 shows the block diagram of this principle.

Radar sweeps vary according to the information desired. The easiest sweep to interpret is the PPI sweep (Plan Position Indicator). This sweep produces a highly recognizable, map-like display. The PPI sweep is a linear time ramp originating at the center of the screen which rotates around the CRT in exact synch with the rotation of a highly directional antenna. Targets returning an echo will appear at a corresponding bearing from the CRT center, at a distance that indicates the distance from the center of the CRT. The PPI sweep is commonly used in aviation and marine applications. See Figure 23–15 for a few of the many radar sweeps in use.

The *raster scan* is probably the most common sweep of all. The electron beam of a television CRT is swept horizontally at about a 15,750-Hz rate,

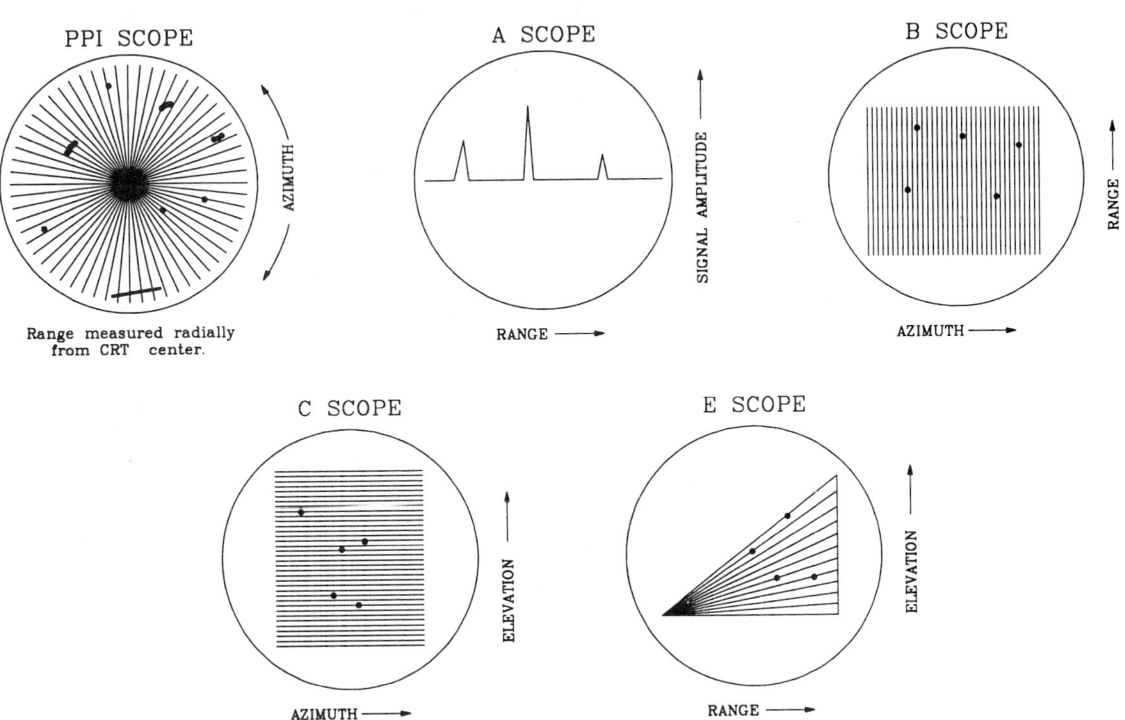

Figure 23–15 Some of the sweep and displays used in radar applications.

all the while being vertically swept at about 60 Hz. The result is a rectangular area of the face of the CRT being illuminated by the spot. At the same time the face is illuminated, the beam is turned off and on or linearly modulated by video information. Signals to modulate the beam are applied to either the cathode or the grid, or both. The result is a picture formed on the full face of the CRT.

The raster scan is used to cover the entire face of the CRT in television applications. In fact, it is adjusted to actually go slightly out of sight at all points on the CRT face. This is called *overscanning* the CRT. Computer monitors, on the other hand, are *underscanned*, with the result that the entire swept area is entirely in sight on the CRT. This prevents a loss of characters on the edges of the CRT screen, as would happen if it were overscanned.

The raster scan rates for various computer monitors are listed for comparison purposes in Table 23–3.

23.8 SOME SPECIAL TUBES

THE GASEOUS REGULATORS

The zener diode provides a relatively constant voltage drop across itself in spite of changes in the currents flowing through it. The vacuum tube family includes the gaseous regulator tubes, tubes which perform a function similar to the zener diode. These tubes are filled with various gases which ionize without needing a heater, requiring only a high DC voltage to begin conduction. Once they conduct, the voltage from cathode to plate drops immediately to a relatively constant voltage, which is used as a voltage reference for power-supply regulators. The normal operation of these tubes can be monitored easily, as they will glow internally with either an orange or a blue color, depending on the gasses used inside the tube. The ionization potential is approximately 15 percent above that of the

Table 23–1 Computer Monitor Scan Rates

Monitor Type	Horizontal Scan	Vertical Scan
Multicolor Graphics Color Array (MGCA)	18.432 kHz	50 Hz
Hercules Graphics (HGC)	18.432 kHz	50 Hz
Color Graphics Adapter (CGA)	15.75 kHz	60 Hz
Enhanced Graphics Adapter (EGA)		
Mode 1	15.75 kHz	60 Hz
Mode 2	16.257 kHz	60 Hz
Monochrome	18.432 kHz	50 Hz
Video Graphics Adapter (VGA)	31.5 kHz	60 to 70 Hz

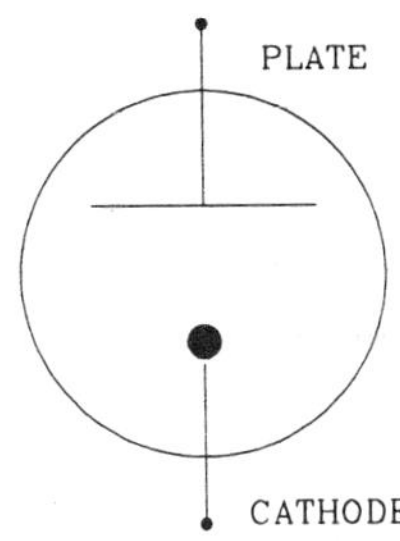

Figure 23–16 Schematic symbol for a gas-filled regulator tube

regulated voltage. A type 0B2 regulator, for instance, regulates at about 90 V DC, but it will require about 105 V to get the regulator to fire. These regulators are available for 75-, 90-, and 105-V voltage references. Figure 23 16 shows the circuit symbols for these tubes.

THE GAS RECTIFIER AND THE THYRATRON

Two more applications make use of a gaseous interior within a tube. Gas-filled rectifiers are commonly used in high-voltage, high-current power supplies, such as those in large radio transmitters. These rectifiers usually contain sufficient mercury to produce a mercury-vapor within the tube, once it has heated sufficiently. These tubes require a definite warm-up time to produce the vapors before plate voltage is applied. In normal operation, they glow *within the elements* with a bright blue glow. The presence of the mercury vapor results in less voltage drop across the tube under heavy current conditions. 15 volts is the typical voltage drop across the tube when conducting.

A variation on the gas rectifier is a gas triode, called a *thyratron*. This tube acts very much like today's silicon-controlled rectifier (SCR). The grid controls the time of firing of the tube. Once fired, the tube conducts without grid control. The plate voltage has to decrease to near zero before the tube will cease conducting and another cycle can begin. The symbols for these two tubes are shown in Figure 23–17.

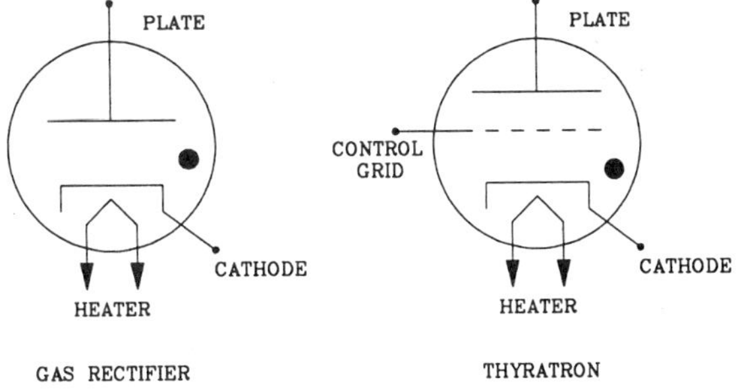

Figure 23–17 Schematic symbols for gas-filled rectifiers and thyratron tubes. Note the presence of the heavy dot, indicating a gaseous tube.

CHAPTER SUMMARY

- A competent technician should have a basic knowledge of vacuum tubes, particularly cathode-ray tubes.
- High-powered radio transmitters still use triodes and tetrodes to generate the RF output voltages.
- Vacuum tubes use very high voltages which are potentially lethal; such circuits must be handled with care.
- The dead-man stick provides safety and peace of mind when working with high voltages.
- Remember to keep one hand behind your back when servicing high-voltage vacuum tube equipment with the power turned on.
- Tube base pins are numbered clockwise, as viewed from the bottom.
- The basic pentode tube consists of the cathode/heater, control grid, screen grid, suppressor grid, and plate.
- The control grid should be negative with respect to the cathode, and the screen and plate should be highly positive.
- The suppressor should be at ground or cathode potential.
- The most common heater voltages are 6.3- and 12.6-V AC.
- Vacuum tubes can be combined in a single tube envelope.
- Impedance matching of vacuum tubes is done with pi-net LC circuits at RF frequencies and with transformers, at audio frequencies.
- Troubleshooting vacuum tubes includes checking the heater, plate, screen, and cathode voltages for normal indications.
- The cathode-ray tube produces an intensity-controlled, focused beam which is directed at the phosphor on the screen.
- Deflection of the spot is done electrostatically or electromagnetically.
- A CRT may be magnetically shielded from stray fields by a Mu-metal shield around the tube.
- The extremely high voltages required for the last anode of a CRT are usually accomplished through the use of a flyback transformer, with or without voltage doublers on its output.
- The phosphor of a CRT will have different colors and persistence, coded with a "P" designation.
- A raster scan can be used to produce letters or graphics on a CRT face.
- Gaseous tube regulators act like zener diodes at voltages of 75-90 and 105-V DC.
- Gas rectifiers can pass heavy currents at high voltages; gas triodes called thyratrons are also used.
- Thyratrons act much like an SCR.

REVIEW QUESTIONS

1. Explain the use of a dead-man stick in making a high-voltage reading with a VOM.
2. Why should one work on high-voltage circuits using only one hand?
3. Tube pins are numbered clockwise from an index mark when viewed from the _______.
4. A vacuum tube with cathode, plate, and control grid is called a _______.
5. Two additional grids wound outside the control grid are called the _______ and _______ grids.
6. What is a nuvistor?
7. What are the five usual checks to be made on a vacuum-tube amplifier stage?
8. What are the two methods of deflecting an electron beam in a CRT?
9. Why must transformers be kept away from CRTs?
10. What kind of circuit is often used to produce the thousands of volts necessary to operate a large CRT?
11. Where is the filter capacitor of a CRT high-voltage supply of 14,000 volts?
12. What determines the color and persistence of a CRT?
13. What is the most common CRT sweep, not counting the time-per-division sweep of an oscilloscope?
14. What is the difference in the scanning coverage of a television and a computer monitor?
15. A gaseous regulator such as the 0B2 is similar in purpose to a solid-state _______.
16. A thyratron is similar in purpose to a solid-state _______.

24

What an Electronics Technician Does

CHAPTER OBJECTIVES

This chapter will acquaint the new electronics technician with what it might be like to work in the field. It is broken into three parts; the assembly-line technician, the bench and field technician, and the engineering assistant. At the conclusion of this chapter, the student will have a "feel" for:

- What an assembly-line technician does.
- The inspection methods used by an assembly-line technician.
- The causes of assembly-line rejects.
- How assembly-line rejects may have to be handled.
- The rework station and how it is run.
- How a field technician's attitude and appearance can affect the customer.
- What to take on a trouble call and why, for various modes of transportation.
- What, in general, to do at the customer site.
- The importance of records of your field work.
- What an engineering assistant does and the job requirements.

- The additional knowledge required of an engineering assistant.
- What circuit prototyping is, and what may be required to accomplish the job.
- General information on the analysis of new circuits.
- Using advanced troubleshooting instruments, such as the digital storage oscilloscope and logic analyzer.
- Basics of data communications and the RS-232C standard.
- Suggestions on knowledge that is often required to operate a personal computer in the workplace.
- Analyzing the initial operation of new circuits, along with environmental testing and burn-in.
- Examples of dedicated test instrumentation and the need to learn it on your own.
- The use of special test equipment applicable to engineering of circuits.
- Suggestions for more rapid advancement in your electronics job.
- Suggestions for further electronics study as applicable to your job.

Part I—THE ASSEMBLY-LINE TECHNICIAN

24.1 ASSEMBLY-LINE TESTING

If electronic equipment is to be manufactured to high standards of quality and reliability, each unit coming off the end of the assembly line will have to be individually tested to be sure it is working. This testing can be done by manual means, running through the various functions of the equipment. On the other hand, automated test equipment (ATE) can be used to good advantage. Automated testing can run many tests very quickly, with little or no human intervention. Whether to use ATE is a management decision based on cost.

THE ONLY OPTIONS: ACCEPT IT OR REJECT IT

The purpose of testing each of the manufactured units is to determine if each one is working properly. If it is, the unit is usually passed on to the shipping department for packaging and delivery to distributors or customers. If the unit fails final tests, the whole idea of assembly-line testing becomes a yes-or-no decision. (This is also referred to as a pass/fail or a go/no-go decision.) The unit is not repaired on the spot but rather is taken from the main assembly flow and put aside for later rework by technicians assigned to that particular task. There is no time during the flow through the assembly process to stop and repair units as they are made. The main idea is to simply reject bad units and keep the assembly line moving smoothly. Little or no training is required in making the basic decision: to accept or reject.

INSPECTION METHODS

The methods used to determine the operational status of any given unit after first assembly vary widely according to what the product really is: a complete unit or only a module of a larger system.

Equipment Burn-In and Initial Testing

A technician may be in charge of operating the burn-in facility of the production line. While a few manufacturers may mass-produce equipment and depend completely on the high reliability of modern components to produce a highly reliable product, many will test their equipment at least once before shipping it.

The greatest percentage of equipment problems will be evident when the unit is first turned on. Faulty equipments will then be sent to an assembly-line technician, where they can be repaired and reevaluated for proper performance.

It is a characteristic of electronic equipment that once it is working, approximately the first hundred hours of operation are critical. If the equipment can operate properly for a hundred hours, it will very likely operate for thousands of hours after that. Equipment that fails during this hundred-hour period is said to have failed due to *infant mortality*.

The equipment in question has to have power connected and may require some means of monitoring normal operation. Once this setup for testing has been accomplished, the equipment will be turned on. If a unit fails, it must be removed from the test setup. The symptoms of failure will probably have to be noted on a standardized form in order for a bench technician to find the problem more quickly.

By noting trends that develop during tests, the technician may detect bad lots of parts from a given parts vendor. Lots of bad parts may be identified as a group by the common date-code of the batch of parts or the lot number.

Environmental Testing

Military contracts are typical of those for which very stringent tests must be met. Equipment may have to operate at extremes of altitude (low air pressure), high humidity, or high or very low temperatures. Some of these factors can occur at the same time, such as high altitude and low temperature. It may fall to junior or senior technicians to work with representatives of the customer to ensure that the equipment properly meets their tests. At the least, the technician will be required to maintain precise logs of equipment test results.

Before critical equipment is released to the customer after such rigid testing, it must usually be "signed off" by someone who passes final judgment on the unit. There will be someone with the job title of Quality Assurance (QA), or, perhaps, Quality Control (QC) Inspector who performs this duty. This person often has a unique "QA" stamp, which is used to imprint a special symbol on the equipment, certifying that it meets all specifications.

Dynamic Testing

Dynamic testing involves making operational tests of equipment while it does its normal job, with all required voltages supplied and test signals being input as required. If the unit is a stand-alone, complete unit, testing will amount to a basic procedure of powering it up for the first time and seeing if it meets the operational specifications. An example might be an audio power amplifier. After assembly, each amplifier goes past a testing station that applies an input using fast connection methods for the wiring. Power is applied and the output is checked using an oscilloscope or other instrumentation.

Modules, on the other hand, may require several inputs, which are sometimes very complex. Power supplies (often more than one or two) must also be applied. The output of the card must probably be checked with an oscilloscope (for analog cards) or a logic analyzer (for digital cards). Special outputs may require special means of determining proper output, e.g., attaching a CRT (as in the case of new monitor driver cards) or stepper motors (as in the case of some servo systems).

If the equipment to be tested must meet exacting test requirements, it may require the use of automated test equipment to run a great number of tests. Besides being faster, the ATE equipment cannot be prone to error, as might a sleepy worker. ATE will also provide neat, hard-copy documentation for each unit tested by putting out the information to a printer.

The rapid connection of a multitude of test inputs and outputs can be accomplished by a special testing device used with ATE. The bed of nails is a series of sharp points suitably mounted to touch very specific test points on the circuit cards to be tested. See Figure 24–1.

A circuit card can be attached to the bed of nails by laying it on the bed and applying a vacuum beneath it. The vacuum sucks the board down onto

Figure 24–1 A bed of nails, used for high-speed troubleshooting with automated testing and troubleshooting equipment.

the probe tips, and the automated testing commences after the card reaches final position. Automated testing can be an integral part of the assembly line, operating at or near the final assembly point for the units being manufactured.

Additional testing may be required for certain components. The insulation of cables, transformers, and capacitors can be stressed to given test voltages to be certain that the insulation can withstand more than normal voltages. Under normal circumstances, the power supply used for this test is required to generate very high voltages but extremely small currents. The power supply is internally protected in the event of a short. This power supply is called a *high potential power supply* or *hi-pot machine* for short. One large company, for example, uses 500 volts to test for leakage or shorts between wires in cables and 1,500 volts to test transformer insulation.

Another test that may be specified for certain equipment is the surge-withstanding capability (SWC) test. One can imagine that telephone equipment and military electronics may occasionally be subjected to nearby lightning strikes. Such equipment can be designed to withstand short pulses of high voltage directly into the input and output circuits of the equipment. The testing of such circuits requires a special pulse-producing probe which is used to fire a high-voltage pulse into the input and output

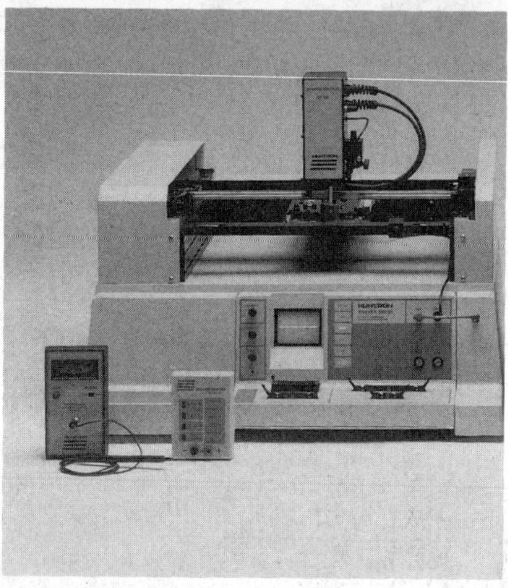

Figure 24–2 The board tester can also be used as part of automated testing. (Courtesy Huntron Instruments, Inc.)

circuits. After being stressed this way, the circuits are then again tested for normal operation. If they still work, they have passed the test.

Static Automated Testing

Another alternative to full-speed, dynamic testing is to use special equipment made for the purpose of testing circuit boards without requiring full power be applied to them. This equipment is an automated form of the Huntron Tracker™, covered in Chapter 17. The board tester will analyze the waveforms found in the circuit in a manner very similar to those read on a Tracker when using manual probing. The board tester will pass the waveform to a companion computer which will digitize and compare the waveforms actually found to waveforms prerecorded as normal for that board. Within preset tolerances, waveforms found to be out of tolerance will be signaled for subsequent human decision. See Figure 24–2.

24.2 TROUBLESHOOTING ASSEMBLY-LINE REJECTS

When a unit is rejected from the end of the assembly line, in the case of small units or boards, it may be discarded. The cost of troubleshooting such items may be higher than the cost of the components to assemble one in the first place. It is common to be required to repair a certain number of units per shift; this is quota work.

A BENCH TECHNICIAN POSITION

The repair of assembly-line rejects will require an electronics technician to do the job. Although the reject information, which is usually a printed sheet from an ATE station on the line, may accompany the bad unit, the symptoms of failure may be "ordinary" (seen before, perhaps many times) or entirely new and unique. A high level of competency in troubleshooting will be required, particularly at the beginning of a long run to establish the nature of the unit's "routine" failures.

Troubleshooting rejects during manufacture is a little different from troubleshooting a great variety of different circuits, as most technicians are expected to do.

First, the setup for troubleshooting rejects will remain fixed, with no need to change the mockup into which the rejects inserted to troubleshoot them.

Second, human and mechanical errors during assembly will prove to be the major problems, comprising perhaps 85 to 90 percent. Of these errors, 30 percent will probably involve faulty soldering. The circuit itself has already been proven to work, but a specific circuit will not function properly. The more common errors found will include:

1. Missing components,
2. Wrong components,
3. Polarized components reversed in circuit, and
4. Soldering errors.

As with most troubleshooting jobs, the first step is to do a very careful visual examination of the unit or board. *Check for all the above-mentioned errors first!* After these have been ruled out, check visually for PC board defects. These will usually take the form of broken or incomplete traces or bridging between traces as the result of incomplete trace etching.

An inspection of the soldering job is particularly important. Most high-volume PC boards these days are soldered by automated flow-soldering machines. See Figure 24–3.

If the flow-soldering machine is not properly and very carefully set up for each run of boards, the soldering job can be very poor. Multiple bridges, dirty solder, and insufficient solder are only a few of the possible problems that might come from this source. The soldering process, by whatever means, is particularly critical to the success or failure of the end product.

The use of surface-mounted devices on PC boards may require a magnifying lens for proper visual inspection. Some of the chips can even have been left standing up rather than in their normal horizontal position, a defect called "tombstoning."

AUTOMATED TROUBLESHOOTING EQUIPMENT

There is computer equipment available that can be programmed to recognize most errors that might cause a problem on a board. Through the use

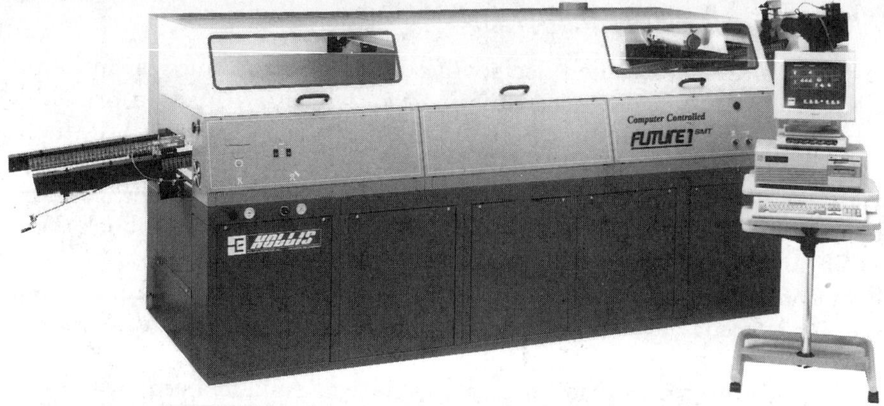

Figure 24–3 A flow-soldering machine. (Courtesy Hollis Automation)

of a computer, many tests can be made throughout the entire circuitry, testing much more thoroughly than the ATE test equipment mentioned earlier. Whereas test equipment can spot a defective unit, the troubleshooting system can pinpoint the problem, even identifying specific components as defective, and thereby suggesting the action that must be taken to fix the unit. Automated testing is valuable when there is a great volume of similar units or boards that must be repaired with the absolute minimum of wasted time.

Dynamic Troubleshooting

Automated troubleshooting equipment can be programmed to recognized the insertion of improper parts, polarized parts placed in backward, missing parts, shorts and opens in PC boards. The more thorough the programming of the controlling computer, the more specific and useful will be the identification of the problems on the completion of testing.

Once a problem has been identified by an automated troubleshooting setup, the unit or board in question will usually be identified by recording the serial number along with the rework to be done. The work to be done is often printed out as a hard copy by a printer, a part of the computer-controlled setup.

This may also be the entry point for defective units returned by customers and warranty work. These units worked at one time but have failed in service, possibly due to infant mortality.

24.3 THE REWORK STATION

The time of a highly trained electronics technician is worth a great deal to his or her employer. It is often to the employer's advantage to keep

Figure 24–4 An electronic rework station. (Courtesy Fluke Instruments)

technicians busy doing technical work rather than having them do the physical replacement of parts. Other employees without the detailed training of the technician can more economically do the actual replacement of parts. A rework station will be operated by a person who should be highly skilled in the manual skills necessary to replace parts. Special soldering and desoldering equipment may be provided for this purpose in large assembly plants. See Figure 24–4.

Once the unit or board has been modified or repaired according to the instructions provided by the automated troubleshooting equipment, it will then be sent back to the end of the assembly line, where it will again be subjected to automated testing.

Part II—THE BENCH AND FIELD TECHNICIAN

This chapter continues with a brief description of what a technician may be required to do if hired for a job working on a bench. These technicians are also frequently asked to make trips to customer sites for repairs. Some companies take this to the extreme, occupying their technician's time mostly with field trips.

YOU REPRESENT YOUR EMPLOYER

Whenever you are called on to make a service call to a customer's place of business, you are the direct representative of your company. It is extremely important that you present yourself as a professional. This includes dressing the part, guided by company policy. Some companies require that their technicians always wear a suit and tie, even when working on equipment that is dirty. Other companies realize that the work can be dirty and will provide coveralls to take the brunt of the dirt. Others will ignore the issue, assuming you have the common sense to dress appropriately. At the least, this means clean denim jeans and a sports shirt. Shorts, torn jeans, or tank-top shirts are not appropriate attire for a field service electronics technician at any time.

Your appearance is only part of the impression that you leave with the customer. Your speech and attitude are even more important than your appearance. If you had a bad day, don't let your customer know about it through a surly attitude. The customer is concerned about his or her own problems, and not yours. A discourteous reply, lack of concern about a customer's problem, or being late for an appointment to repair the problem will add up to a big negative for your company.

Be very careful about what you say about your company, as well. A slip of the tongue in a comment that your company's model of equipment is unreliable or "always fails" can come back to haunt you very quickly. Do not concede any faults with your company's products. If you should agree with the customer (to be agreeable, of course) that this particular equipment is "a lemon," it can result in complaints to your company, with *you* at the center! This is a particularly bad position in which to find yourself.

WHAT TO TAKE

Field trips may be short- or long-haul jobs. Short trips will generally be made by automobile, while long ones will probably involve air transportation. Automobile service trips will be covered first.

On the Road

A field trip using a vehicle for transportation means that any reasonably required instrument can be taken along. Small and large instruments, from a multimeter to an oscilloscope, are commonly used. Specialized equipment like a service monitor might also be appropriate for the type of equipment to be serviced. *Refer to the list of equipment and tools, as given as section 1.11 for what may be appropriate to take along.*

Expensive instruments may be subjected to a considerable amount of abuse, when taken on the road. To minimize this damage, pack large instruments into padded boxes to protect against bumps and scratches. Plywood boxes lined with foam rubber are a very good investment. They can even be provided with locks and bolted to the vehicle to discourage theft. *Be sure the boxes are secured against movement,* such as sliding forward in an emergency braking situation. Since braking forces are more severe than acceleration forces, place heavy equipment as far forward as possible and against something solid. In a pickup, for instance, the load should be all the way forward, against the cab. In a van, place equipment against the backs of the seats or other solid parts of the vehicle.

Spare parts and/or circuit boards, and perhaps even complete replacement units, may also be needed for the job. Since most repairs in the field should be done quickly, it is most common to simply replace bad units or boards, leaving the component-level troubleshooting to be done back at the home office. *Be sure your replacements are in good working order!* It is very troublesome to replace a PC board at a customer's site only to find that new problems have been introduced into the situation because the new board is also bad. At the worst, you may cause further damage by inserting a bad board, while even in the best case, you will increase your on-site time.

If you must use your own vehicle for service calls, your employer will probably reimburse you by paying you a certain fee for each mile you drive on behalf of the company. This will mean that you must keep accurate records as to mileage. Sometimes, your time must also be recorded for the same purpose. The time spent on the repair is particularly important if you end up working overtime, on a weekend, or after regular working hours. Use your personal notebook to keep track of these items, and resist any temptation to "fudge" the figures. It isn't worth it in the long run, and you will sleep better. Another point to clear up about taking service calls is whether you are paid for the time actually on the customer's site or whether you are also paid wages for time travel. This latter category is sometimes called "portal-to-portal" pay.

What if you have an accident on the road while working for your company? Who pays the insurance for this coverage? If your employer does not pay for it, does your insurance company know that you are using your car for company business? Your insurance may refuse to pay a claim if your car was used for commercial purposes unless a special rate is paid to cover that use. Ask before you run into a big problem, and resolve the situation ahead of time. If you must pay a higher premium for insurance because of commercial use, your employer should reimburse you for that extra expense.

It is a fine point, but you should consider what may happen if you get a ticket while driving for the company. Will your employer pay for a speeding ticket if you were asked to hurry to the customer's site? Find out before running into the situation.

The use of a company vehicle also brings up questions that should be answered before actual situations arise. The fueling of the vehicle is usually done via a company credit card which you will either carry all the time or have provided when you use the vehicle. Safeguard the credit card. If you lose it, *notify your company at once* so that it can be canceled, freeing your firm of financial obligation if it is used by someone else. Find out about alternatives you can use if you are running low on fuel and can find no gas station that accepts the company credit card.

Notations about mileage and time will still be required when using the company vehicle in most instances. Traffic tickets that you may receive will probably still be your responsibility, but you should ask beforehand. Your company will provide any insurance needed to cover the vehicle while it is in commercial use.

An important question to ask is whether the company vehicle can be used for personal use at any time. While a few companies allow the use of their vehicles for personal use most do not, and the vehicle must be returned to the company lot each night. This will usually apply even if you have to put in overtime to pass your home to deliver the car and return home in your own vehicle. One of the best ways to get fired is to violate this simple rule. Do not use the company vehicle for personal use—even one mile—without approval from your boss.

Airline Transportation

Travel by air restricts the amount of equipment you can take with you. Referring to the equipment listing in section 1.11, eliminate everything that you can. This may mean that you will travel with basic tools (instead of a full toolbox), a multimeter, a Tracker, and possibly an oscilloscope (the smaller the better). *Never baggage-check an instrument unless it is extremely well protected by packaging.* The reason for taking the absolute minimal weight is that you will probably have to carry *everything* at once, at least for a portion of your trip. Airline terminals are a very poor place to leave any kind of valuable unattended, even for a moment. (Bus terminals are even worse.) Therefore, you will have to carry your overnight bag (if appropriate for the trip) and all your tools and instruments at one time to get to and from the taxi and the terminal.

A very handy instrument to have along for any field trip is Scopemeter™, a combination multimeter and oscilloscope now offered by Philips. It is very lightweight and has all the necessary features you need when using either instrument. Figure 24–5 shows the Scopemeter™.

If you are going on a long trip by air to a customer's site, inquire whether tools might be available for you to use there, thus eliminating the need to carry anything besides specialized tools. While not always appropriate, this is at least a possibility to consider.

UPON ARRIVAL

Whether you are new to fieldwork or an old-timer, you will have moments of self-doubt. You will wonder if your company has misplaced trust in your abilities. You will wonder if you can fix the problem. All sorts of

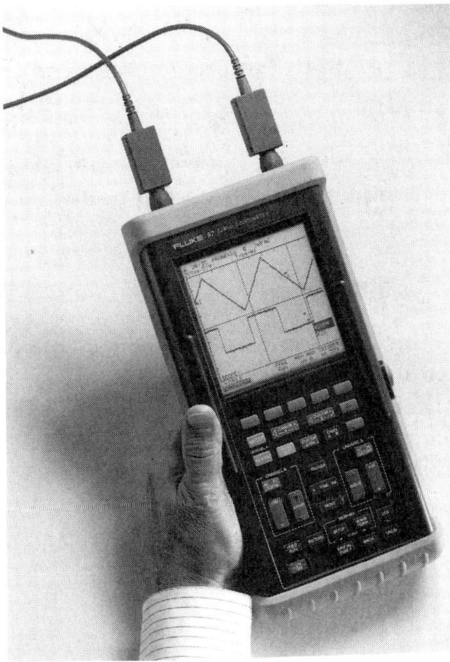

Figure 24–5 The Philips Scopemeter™.

specters may occur to you, but put them aside. Even if there is considerable pressure to make the repair quickly, consider this:

1. Most problems are simple.
2. You can always call your company for technical consultation.
3. No one has all the answers for every situation.
4. No one at the site expects you to be perfect.
5. Your boss does not expect you to be perfect, either.

When you arrive at the customer's site, check in with the receptionist or an employee who is in a position to officially notice you. At the same time, make a note in your personal notebook as to the time and date.

As with most trouble calls, the first thing a technician should do is ask to talk to the person who reported the problem in the first place. Be sure you understand the problem, and eliminate operator error as a possible cause. If you do find operator error, handle it tactfully, because that person is then directly responsible for the cost of your service call. This call can cost the company hundreds of dollars, so be careful. The person will already be very embarrassed, so don't add to the problem.

Once the operator has been eliminated as a source of the problem, begin your troubleshooting. If you are keeping the recommended personal notebook, jot down the serial number, make, and model of the equipment you will be repairing. Be sure power is applied, check the interlocks, and look at the fuses when appropriate to the problem at hand. Remember:

Substitution is the most powerful troubleshooting method.

This applies from the equipment to the component level. Substitute equipment and boards until you have localized the problem.

WHAT LEVEL ON-SITE?

At this time, you must determine whether to repair to the component level on site or to simply bring back the bad board or equipment for shop work. The usual method is to replace to the board level on site, and then take the bad board or equipment with you.

If you have no replacement boards, either your own or the customer's, you may have to repair to the component level if the application is important enough to warrant this. In this case, you can ask if there is a suitable workplace where you can spread out your tools and instruments for further troubleshooting. A Huntron Tracker™ can prove invaluable in this instance, especially if you are in a hurry, lack a full shop of test equipment to use, or may not have a power supply to run the suspected board. Chapter 17 covers this instrument and how to use it.

Getting parts to replace those that were found to be bad during a component-level troubleshooting session may prove to be a problem. You may be in a strange city, without any idea where to get parts. Although the telephone book may help, transportation can be a problem. Having to find a parts store in a strange town will require a map and the ability to read it.

Resist the temptation to use cheap parts just because they may be available. If you have traveled far, don't use second-rate parts because of the increased possibility of a return call should they fail. Deal with a reputable parts store and use brand-name replacement parts. By all means, avoid all parts that do not bear a manufacturer's name. In particular, don't use packages of parts from which the names have been removed or parts that never had markings on them. These parts are often bought from manufacturers as "seconds," parts that don't meet manufacturer specifications. As a result, they do not have the manufacturer's name on them. After all, who would want to claim parts that are not up to quality standards?

FINAL CHECKOUT

After you repair, be sure the equipment, whatever it is, runs properly. Run it with the cabinets installed, back in the rack, or otherwise in the normal running configuration. Let it run a while to be sure the repair is holding as it should. If you have come a long way, a request to operate the unit overnight while you are in the vicinity might be in order. Stay the night in town, checking in the next morning to be sure all is well.

Check with the customer or customer's representative. (This is often the person who made the initial trouble call.) Again, make an entry in your personal notebook concerning the time and date. Now is a good time to also jot down a few lines about the problem, the cure, and any other notes you consider appropriate, such as the names of the persons with whom you have had contact during the repair.

When you arrive back at the shop, note the time and date again for your notebook. Check in with your boss. It may make a very favorable impression if you also present a written report of the field trip, prepared on a computer and printed out neatly.

Part III—THE ENGINEERING ASSISTANT

The remainder of this chapter will briefly explain typical qualifications to advance to the job title of Engineering Assistant. This job may also be called a Research and Development Technician, Senior Technician, or other similar title. In many companies, it is the highest title that may be held without an engineering degree. It can be a demanding job, requiring a broad understanding of electronics, but with the right company and under the right conditions, the pay can certainly be worthwhile. Attention to detail and a good command of English are the keys to becoming an engineering assistant.

24.5 WHAT IS AN ENGINEERING ASSISTANT?

Keep in mind that the traditional electronics technician is primarily in the business of making inoperative circuits, which once worked, work again. The basic job is about the same, whether you are working at a bench or wearing a suit and tie and making customer calls with a toolbox. Basically, the circuit itself is proven, but a failure makes a repair necessary.

An engineering assistant, on the other hand, works on new circuits that may never have worked before. An engineer designs a circuit to accomplish a certain purpose. This circuit must then be put together into a rough-draft circuit called a *breadboard* or *prototype*. Prototyping of a circuit is one of the most common tasks for an engineering assistant, and often requires extensive use of reference materials. The first circuit must be put together both electrically and mechanically. This may require a great of deal time using basic hand and power tools to bend metal, fasten it together, and mount various components.

This first working circuit is then subjected to many different tests to determine if it is working as designed. It usually will not work the first time around, so the engineering assistant will analyze the circuit, often with the help of the design engineer. Together, changes will be made, either formally in writing or based on discussions only. The assistant must have a very thorough knowledge of each component used in the circuit.

The engineering technician then changes the circuit accordingly, rerunning the performance tests. In the process, a great many tests may have to be made, resulting in, perhaps, thousands of readings. For this task, automated testing equipment (ATE) may be used to run the test automatically at high speed, under computer control. It often falls to the engineering technician to set up the testing criteria and to program the ATE equipment for the test run.

The detailed analysis of new circuits that is necessary to be sure they are performing as desired will require, in many cases, the use of advanced troubleshooting instruments.

Once a circuit has become proven, it is then often subjected to environmental testing to be sure it will work under all conditions as stated, such as high or low temperature, high humidity, and so forth.

Each of these job requirements is discussed in greater detail in the paragraphs to follow.

24.6 TYPICAL TASKS FOR AN ENGINEERING ASSISTANT

EXTENSIVE USE OF REFERENCES

Producing a working circuit from a drawing will require the use of numerous data books on the components to be used. Integrated circuits, for instance, must be identified pin for pin. This will require the assembly of a library of reference books, usually obtained from the company that manufacturers the chips.

Besides the integrated circuits and resistors, and so forth, that make up a circuit, other components need to be selected. The best source of information on such items as switches, transformers, and connectors is obtained by poring over the catalogs published by the manufacturers. The standardized method of numbering and, thereby, keeping track of a great many such catalogs may be found in Appendix XIX.

PROTOTYPING CIRCUITS

Wire-Wrapped Circuits

Many new circuits can be laid out using the wire-wrapping method. See Figure 24–6.

Special components are available to support the wire wrapping of new circuits. Special long, square pins are provided on IC sockets of all sizes, and some connectors and other components are also available to support this method of prototyping of circuits. Many different colors of wire are used to wire-wrap, which will make troubleshooting easier later on.

A wire-wrapped circuit is relatively fast to assemble. Changes to the circuit can also be made without rewiring large areas of the board. The later addition of more circuitry is also easy to accomplish.

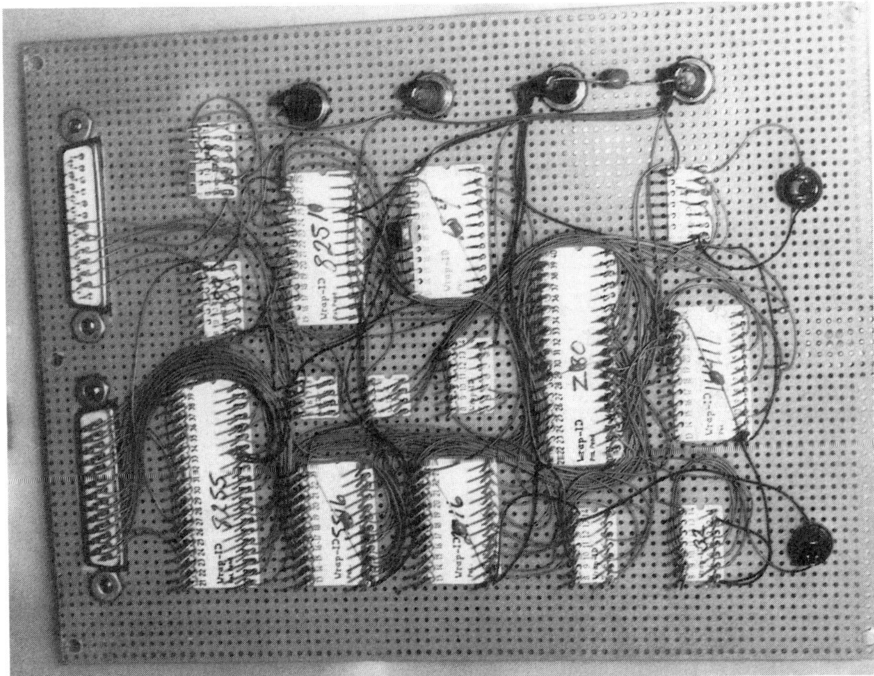

Figure 24–6 A typical wire-wrapped circuit; this technique is widely used for prototyping new circuits.

The skill necessary to make a good wire-wrap connection is easily learned in a few minutes. Basically, a special tool is used to tightly wrap a small wire around the square post of the circuit. The wire is forced into the corners of the post, making a microscopic cold weld, which is gas-tight and has very low resistance. The skill enters in making a joint that will pass quality control inspection. It is easy to get too much or too little of the insulation on the wire wrapped around the post. Too much insulation wrapped on the post results in wasting space, while too little results in needlessly exposed wire, making shorts to adjacent pins likely. See Figure 24–7 for a microphotograph of a good wire-wrap and several bad ones.

Wire wrapping works well up to a few megahertz of operation. Beyond this, printed circuit boards must be used to minimize cross-talk between wires due to excessive capacitance between them.

Printed Circuit Boards

Depending on the size of the company, the layout of a printed circuit board may be done manually on a light table or using sophisticated software for a computer to accomplish the same result.

Figure 24–7 Three bad wire-wrapped joints—one with a shiner (an open area without insulation), a "stacked" wrap, and a pulled wrap—and a good wire-wrapped joint.

The manual layout of a PC board can be done using products such as offered by the Bishop Company, which are specifically made for this purpose. The entire PC board is laid out at twice its final size on a piece of transparent Mylar, a tough plastic. PC board traces, for instance, are made by placing black tape of the proper physical width on the Mylar. Component leads are represented by "dots" of the correct doubled size, again stuck to the Mylar. The entire circuit is thus taped together on the Mylar. This assembly is usually done on a light table. A light table is lit from beneath with fluorescent lamps under a translucent white glass. The final circuit board, including taped-on lettering, if any, is then sent to a commercial firm where the actual PC board is made from the drawing. Compared to the work and cost of the first PC board, costs come down rapidly as the number of boards ordered increases.

The manual preparation of a PC board layout is an art. The first few attempts may take a long time and may not look as nice as later tries. Start learning this method by laying out simple circuits first.

If you are asked to lay out a double-sided PC board, remember that one side of the board should have vertical traces, and the opposite side, horizontal. In this way, the least interference is made, particularly when laying out complicated boards. Look at a large PC board, preferably a digital one, to see how this method of layout is used. Even multiple-layer boards are often laid out in this manner, with a layer positioned either vertically, horizontally, or full-plane, such as used for ground and Vcc.

Really large companies are moving away from storing any information on paper. This also applies to the design of circuit boards. There is very sophisticated software available that will help the layout technician make an error-free PC board, using a computer, the first time. It does this by simply not allowing the accidental shorting of leads, for instance.

Light-Sensitive Products

You may be involved in labeling equipment front panels. Industry has available some amazing products to produce professional results. Light-sensitive products can be used to produce perfect lettering and design the front panels of new equipment. Once the lettering and markings have been laid out, the panel is subjected to a high-intensity light for a specified time. After exposure, the panel is washed in a special solution that removes only the paint that is not wanted, and leaving very attractive lettering.

Chemicals

A technician at any level of experience may be called upon to work with industrial chemicals. The two most common categories are cleaning solvents and various glues and potting compounds.

> ***Caution:*** **Industrial cleaning solvents can be very hazardous. Be very careful to observe all the warnings on the label. There is absolutely nothing wrong with delaying a job in order to get the proper rubber gloves or eye protection called for on the label. An employer would rather have you take the time to be safe than deal with lost time and injuries resulting from being in a hurry.**
>
> **Industrial bonding agents can also be hazardous, not only chemically, but due to the bond they can produce. One example in the home is super-glue. The industrial equivalents of this glue can be very fast and extremely effective in their bonding. Rubber gloves are again a big safety item.**

Potting agents are used to encapsulate certain circuitry. Once a circuit is working well, it is sometimes encapsulated in epoxy-like material to protect it from vibration, weather, humidity, or even unauthorized tinkering or copying. Relatively harmless and slow-acting, potting agents should nevertheless be handled with rubber gloves and eye protection against the possibility of a spill or splash. Potting compounds should always be precisely measured out by weight or volume, rather than by estimation.

Mounting Components

Although electronics assembly personnel often do this job, a technician may occasionally be used to do assembly work. The mounting of compo-

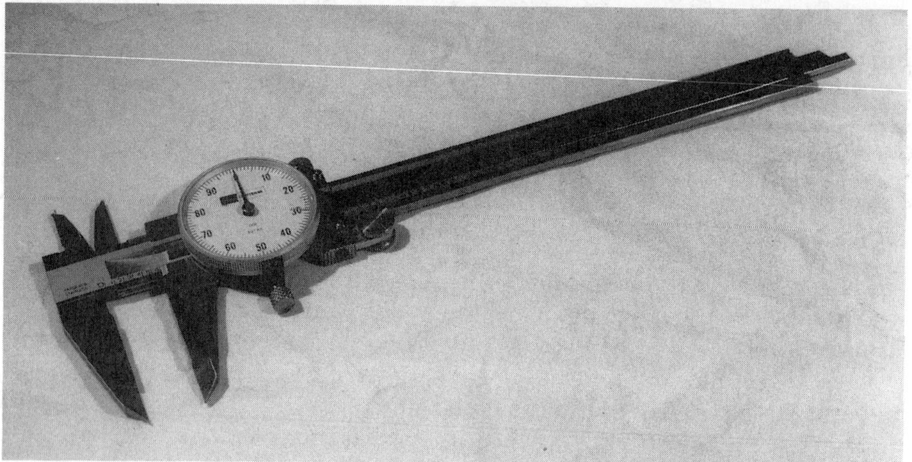

Figure 24–8 These calipers are particularly useful for laying mounting holes for components in new circuits.

nents may require drilling holes and inserting small bolts and nuts. The proper size of drill bit to use for mounting common electronic hardware can be found in Appendix XIV. The three most common bolts sizes for electronics use are the 4–40, 6–32, 8–32, and 10–32 screws. The *4, 6, 8,* and *10* refer to the diameter of the bolt, and *–32* is the number of threads per inch.

Lining up holes in preparation for drilling their mounting holes can be tricky. One method that may be handy for blind-hole location is to use a thin piece of plastic, perhaps half as thick as ordinary cardboard, to mark holes by holding the plastic against the bottom of the component. After drilling the plastic and checking the fit, use it as a template to drill the holes in the chassis.

One of the most useful tools for mounting components is a precision caliper, a machinist's tool costing about $50. This will be useful in determining diameters, inside diameters, thickness of materials, and depth of holes, all up to about 6" for the instrument of Figure 24–8.

Cable Layouts and Lacing

Although this is also chiefly the responsibility of assemblers, a technician may sometimes help to lay out point-to-point wiring. This is common in the installation of controlled machines, burglar alarms, and so on. Sometimes it is necessary to have considerable wiring within enclosed cabinets, especially in industrial applications. The use of cabled wires can be made to appear much neater if the wiring is cabled together with plastic cable ties designed for the purpose. Wires tied together will be less apt to vibrate loose or break off their terminals.

Cables and wiring should be protected against any sharp edges by routing them away from such dangers. Inevitable contact can be cushioned with the use of insulation and wrapping of the wiring. Be sure to leave sufficient slack in the wiring harness if it has to be flexed when the cabinet doors are opened.

Heating and Cooling

Some components, such as power transistors, normally run at high temperatures. The lower these temperatures can be kept, the better the reliability of the equipment overall. When power components require them, heat sinks must be properly attached to carry away heat generated by the components. Additional heat-sinking capability can be obtained by using a heat-conducting grease specially made for the purpose, which is applied between the component and the heat-sink.

Sometimes, it is desirable to place a heat sink against a component yet not allow the voltage potential of the device to be connected metallically to it. For these cases, special insulated washers are used, usually provided with the new components. A heat-conducting compound (mentioned above) is also used in insulated mountings. After installation, these components should be checked with an ohmmeter to be sure that there is electrical isolation between the case of the component and the heat sink itself.

Mechanical Stress and Vibration

Applications for electronic equipment may require that it withstand a considerable amount of physical vibration and shaking. The mountings of components that are held in place by nuts and bolts can be made more secure by using either special lock-washers or special locking nuts on the bolts. A modern alternative is to use one of the liquid locking compounds now available. These compounds come in various degrees of permanency, with the most drastic being a one-time-only assembly compound, with disassembly requiring breakage of the bolt.

Manual Skills

The prototyping of a circuit may require the engineering assistant to make extensive use of hand tools such as wrenches, hacksaws, and the like. In addition to these, a drill press, electric drill, drill press, and chassis punches may also be needed. Even metric tools, and particularly hex wrenches, seem to be needed frequently.

COMPONENT KNOWLEDGE

New circuits usually look good on paper but may refuse to work properly upon their first assembly and testing. The correction of these prototype circuits, as they are called, will require a very thorough knowledge of electronic components. This includes all common components, such as resistors, capacitors, bipolar transistors, integrated circuits, and so forth. The engineering technician must be well versed in the smallest operating details of such components.

As an example of the detailed knowledge that may be required, a silicon controlled rectifier operated in a new DC circuit may not be turning off as expected, even though the anode voltage is turned off for a moment. An engineering technician would look for the *actual* anode current to fall below the *holding current* for that particular SCR, rather than assuming that the absence of the supply voltage instantly reduces the anode current to zero. A filter capacitor might be unexpectedly maintaining current flow during the voltage "off" time. Such a problem would then be reported to the engineer who designed the circuit, perhaps with a suggested cure in the form of a circuit modification.

Some of the best information on semiconductors can be found in the front matter of an appropriate data book, such as the volume published by Motorola. Our example above may require information on the whys and wherefores of SCR holding current. This is explained at the most basic level in the front matter of the Motorola *Thyristor Data Book.*

ANALYZING NEW CIRCUITS

The engineering technician will need a firm foundation in troubleshooting skills, as presented in this text. In addition, the effective troubleshooting of prototype circuits will require experience in a wide variety of circuits, often requiring knowledge of analog and digital circuitry, including microprocessor theory. It will also require a detailed knowledge of components as mentioned previously, knowledge that can be gleaned from component instruction manuals obtained from the component manufacturers.

Analyze Operation and Failures, if Any

Once the new circuit has been completely assembled, power should be applied along with any needed input signals. At this point, the required results can vary a great deal. In the simplest mode, if the circuit works, you are almost done. In other, more involved applications, the work has just begun, with many more tests yet to be made.

Automated Test Equipment

If the new circuit at hand is complex, it may be necessary to take a great many readings. As an example, the design of a wide-band amplifier cannot be said to be finished until its operation is observed *and recorded* over a great many different frequencies. This procedure might require application of 25 or more different input frequencies and the recording of the output signal for each. Even more cumbersome would be a requirement to make these checks on each one of a dozen or more (maybe a thousand?) other amplifiers of the same exact design, later on in the program. This application of instruments and the required readings would be very time-consuming and expensive to perform.

Dedicated ATE Systems

When multiple readings are to be taken on identical equipment, the automated test equipment (ATE) setup becomes very practical and useful. In the simplest form, a few specialized instruments specifically designed to work together are used, under the control of a computer. This might be called a dedicated or mini-ATE system. The engineering assistant then programs the computer to perform the required tests. If the equipment fails a specific test, the computer can be programmed to stop and notify the operator. At the least, the computer keeps a log of the test results and, at the conclusion of the test run, provides a written (hardcopy) printout of the results to accompany the equipment tested.

In a more complex and precise form, commercially available equipment may be purchased that operates under the control of a computer. This equipment usually can operate from an IEEE-488 (Institute of Electrical and Electronic Engineers) instrumentation interface. This interface allows the parallel connection of up to 15 instruments together into a full-blown, complex ATE system. The system controller, a computer, orchestrates the instruments, telling the "listen" instruments what to do, and receiving the "talker" information as necessary to accomplish the tests required. With this system setup and the required software, very complex testing setups are possible.

The IEEE-488 Standard

It is very time-consuming for a technician to manually take and record multiple instrument readings. Known also by the acronyms HP-IB (Hewlett Packard interface bus) or GPIB (general-purpose interface bus), the IEEE-488 interconnection standard is a means by which test instrumentation can be connected together into workable systems for repetitive testing, often without operator intervention. It is particularly valuable on the automated assembly line, where precision equipment being manufactured must be subjected to many tests before being released to customers.

A system of instrumentation can be installed very easily, mostly due to the tight standardization of the IEEE-488. Every combination of signals has been taken into account, and special ICs have been designed to handle all possible combinations of signals on the various lines.

A system is set up by simply connecting all the instruments in parallel, using a special connector. See Figure 24–9.

Each of the instruments is then assigned a digital address, usually by the internal setting of a series of small switches for the purpose. Once set, the

Figure 24–9 This special connector allows the paralleling of up to 15 instruments in an IEEE-488 configuration.

switches are left alone. The software used to run the system then takes over the operation of all the instruments. It must be initialized with the addresses of each of the instruments connected. The master ATE program is then written to read, record, or write information as necessary for all of the tests to be accomplished.

Prototyping Errors

The engineering technician may have to deal with some of the same failures as the assembly line technician; errors in wiring up the prototype circuit, the ever-present problem of using bad parts (particularly if components are reused to wire up different prototype circuits), overstressing and consequent failure of parts due to poorly engineered circuits, unworkable circuits, and circuits that are not reproducible. A *nonreproducible circuit* is one that may work fine with specific parts but refuses to work to specification with off-the-shelf parts, which are not uniform in their characteristics. Such circuits will require hand-selected parts for the circuit to work properly. A circuit intended to have a specific gain, for instance, may have to deal with real transistors that may have off-the-shelf gains which vary from one transistor to another, over a range of from 40 to 250.

Identifying and Curing EMI Problems

One of the more difficult problems that the engineering technician may encounter is that of electromagnetic interference (EMI). EMI may be suspected as the cause of circuit malfunction if the circuit works fine by itself but becomes inoperative when used with other circuits or in the final system. Interaction between circuits on the same power supply, for instance, can cause one circuit to malfunction because of the other. Often, a simple filtering of the common power line between the two circuits will cure the problem. However, other forms of EMI can be more subtle. Certain high-gain circuits can be very susceptible to radio frequency interference. An example would be a public address (PA) system that occasionally picks up a passing citizen's band radio transmission, making the voice audible in the PA system speaker.

Particularly troublesome are such sources of interference as SCRs operating high-powered loads, especially motors. Even touch-controlled living-room lamps make RF electrical noise. Motors that have brushes usually produce quite a bit of interference, and digital equipment, including computers, may also radiate a certain amount. Even fluorescent lighting makes a lot of RF "racket."

The trick to identifying sources of interference is to turn off or otherwise eliminate possible sources of interference until the problem ceases.

Recommend Changes

Once problems have been identified on a new circuit, it will be up to the engineering assistant to recommend changes, either in writing or verbally. Such changes may be electronic, mechanical, or both. Particular attention should be paid to the proper placement of parts. Heat-producing parts like resistors should be kept away from heat-sensitive components like transistors and RF crystals. Transformers can influence each other if mounted too closely to one another.

One of the parameters that is often checked on a new circuit is the range of component operating temperatures. A probe like the one shown in Figure 24–10 is an inexpensive and convenient way to test the temperature of transistors, transformers, and other components.

This temperature probe is an add-on for Fluke DMMs, and is one of many different temperature measuring instruments available from that company. Another way to monitor approximate temperatures is by the use of temperature-sensitive colored stick-on patches. These patches change color as their temperature is changed.

Advanced Use of Prototyping Instruments

The engineering assistant will have to be skilled in the use of all basic troubleshooting instruments in order to discover and correct problems in new circuits. Beyond the basic operation of these instruments, there will be times when new circuits will require the ability to employ the more complex functions of instruments that are normally not used in troubleshooting. The following paragraphs include a brief description of the advanced use of the analog and digital oscilloscope, logic analyzers, the arbitrary waveform generator, and the PROM (Programmable Read-Only Memory) programmer. These will be among the principal instruments that will be used during prototype circuit development.

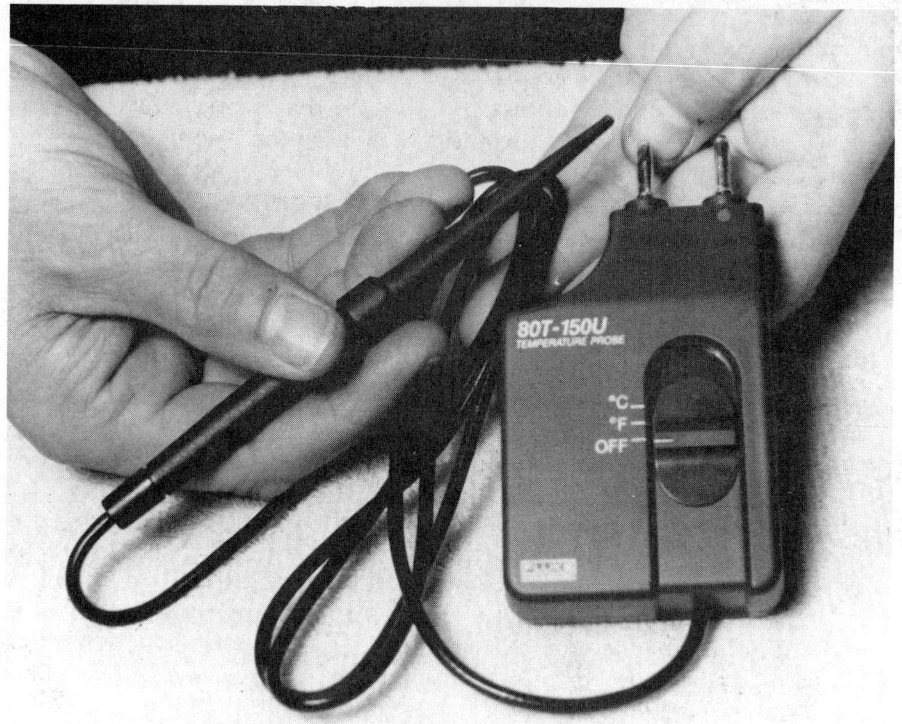

Figure 24–10 This accessory for a Fluke multimeter allows you to measure the temperature of electronic components quickly and easily.

Analog Oscilloscopes

Differential Operation. Besides looking at two channels on an analog oscilloscope, there may be occasions when one is more interested in the *difference* between two signals rather than their absolute voltages. This measurement can be made by first applying the signals to the two input channels of the oscilloscope. To show the difference between the signals, one of the channels, usually the B signal, must be inverted in polarity. After inversion, the two signals are then added together. The result is that the difference between them will show on the scope. Using the oscilloscope in this manner, any signal that is equally induced into both channels will cancel itself out, leaving only their difference on the display.

Dual-Time Base. Dual-time bases on an analog oscilloscope make it possible to look at a short-time event which occurs a relatively long time after the trigger initiates the trace. If an oscilloscope has this capability, it is sometimes called a *delayed sweep oscilloscope.* An analogy may help to understand the principle involved. Converting time to distance, consider what you might do to look very closely at an insect on a highway, as it crosses a painted line. You simply look for the line, then locate the insect. Getting a magnifying glass, one could then see a magnified view of it. But what if you were told that the insect was 23 feet from the line? You would first have to mark out the 23 feet, and *then* get out the magnifying glass to find the bug.

The situation is similar with the dual-time-base oscilloscope. Started by the instrument's trigger (the line on the highway,) one would use one of the sweeps (usually the B sweep) to "measure out" the 23 feet from the trigger. Once there, the second sweep (the A sweep) becomes a magnifying glass to see what can be seen at this distance from the trigger.

The dual-time-base 'scope can be very accurate in determining the delay from the trigger to the beginning of the second trace. This control on the instrument is frequently a ten-turn potentiometer which is very linear. The knob that operates the control is usually calibrated to provide at least a count of 1,000 for the full range of the control, making precise positioning of the second trace fairly easy to accomplish.

It is possible to use the delayed-sweep capability of an oscilloscope to look at a small portion of a signal that does not repeat cyclically except over a relatively long period. The data lines of a microprocessor, with an appropriate program, might repeat a pattern after hundreds of clock cycles. If one could get the instrument to trigger reliably over this long period, the delayed sweep would allow examination of any portion of the sweep to a greater magnification. This will probably require the use of an external trigger signal.

Digital Storage Oscilloscopes (DSOs)

As a benchmark of performance, the Philips model 3365A DSO, as shown in Figure 24–11, is used as an example for the following discussion of the DSO and how it operates.

The digital oscilloscope is the modern version of the analog oscilloscope. Just as the older volt-ohm-milliammeter has been largely replaced by a microprocessor-controlled digital multimeter, the analog oscilloscope is being replaced for many applications by a combination analog and microprocessor-controlled digital storage oscilloscope. Table 24–1 gives a comparison of the merits of both instruments.

Repetitive Signals An example of a repetitive signal is the 60-Hz line-voltage waveform. Each cycle is identical to the last and occurs without variation, time after time. The analog 'scope is exceptionally good at displaying a repetitive signal. Each sweep is followed immediately by another sweep. Getting information from an analog display must be done manually: each amplitude/time relationship must be recorded by hand or, as has been done for years, with a camera.

Table 24–2 Relative Merits of Analog and Digital Oscilloscopes

	Analog	Digital
Display information life	Transient	Forever
Horizontal accuracy	+/– 3.0%	+/– 0.1%
Data interpretation	Manual	Automatic cursor calculations
Display of complex waveforms (e.g., modulated RF)	Real-time, meaningful	Spotty, may be inaccurate
Pretrigger data display	Limited, <200 ns	Virtually unlimited for repetitive signals
Hardcopy capability	None	Yes

A DSO, on the other hand, has a relatively long "dead time" required between each display sweep for all of the storage, calculation, and display of the information. The DSO records information in digital memory. Movable cursors are used to select the area on the waveform of interest, and the 'scope itself calculates the most important parameters of the display. The instrument in Figure 24–11, for instance, will show the following information about a captured waveform:

Vpp, Vrms, Vabs, Vmax, Vmin, Vmean, Frequency, Period, Pulse Width, Risetime, and Falltime

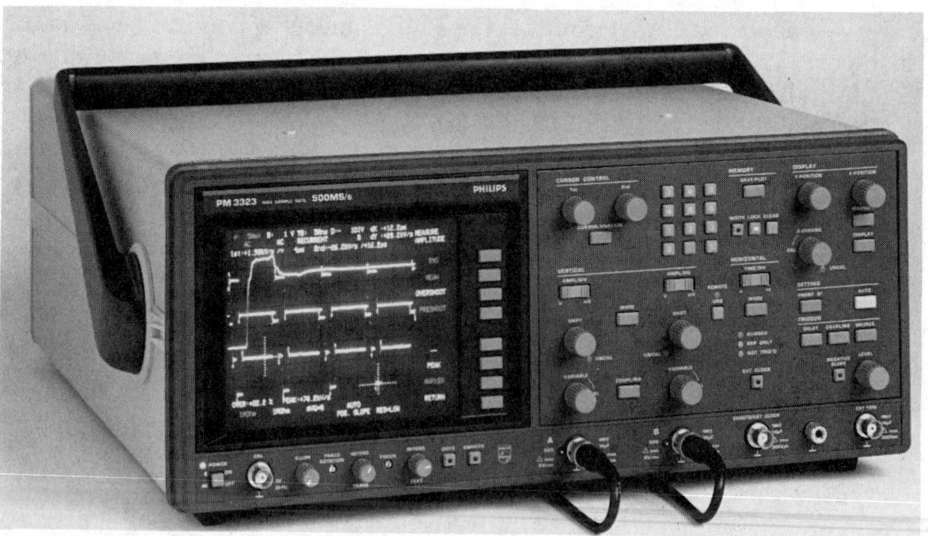

Figure 24–11 A modern analog/digital storage oscilloscope.

The DSO display can be printed out, through the use of appropriate software, as a duplicate picture of the oscilloscope screen, complete with any text notations that it may contain. Thus, it is no longer necessary to manually record voltage versus time. Sample waveforms can be stored and read out at will, using a computer, graphics printer, or a plotter. Displays can even be imported from a DSO into a word processor file to provide excellent documentation of circuit operation.

Single-Shot Events The analog 'scope is inappropriate for signals that are not repetitive. These are waveforms that happen only once, and then disappear forever. They are called *single-shot events*. Analog storage oscilloscopes have been manufactured that will preserve the displayed trace of a single-shot waveform on the screen where, if necessary, it could even be photographed. The higher the sweep speed used, however, the more difficult it is to see and preserve the information.

The DSO uses a quartz crystal–controlled time base rather than a linear voltage ramp, as in the analog instrument. A sample is taken of the DSO input waveform in one of a number of ways. This information is then stored in memory and the process repeated until all of memory is full (perhaps 2 to the 12th power, or 4,096 sampled voltages). Once memory is full, the memory information is then reconstructed and displayed on the CRT.

Because the DSO time base is crystal controlled, the sweep timing is extremely precise. This precision makes it possible to digitally delay the beginning of sampling long after a given trigger, without the jitter that is inevitable on an analog instrument. This method of digital delay takes the place of the analog dual timebase.

The DSO is also capable, when recording repetitive signals, of recording pretrigger information. This is a capability that the analog 'scope cannot provide for more than about 200 nanoseconds.

Sampling Methods There are several methods for digitizing the input voltages to a DSO. The sampling method easiest to understand is the real-time digitizing of a signal. The input is sampled and, depending on the time base selected, digitized from slow rates up to as rapidly as the digitizer can run. This requires a very fast digitizer to be useful at high sweep speeds.

If we use methods other than real-time sampling, we can digitize much higher frequencies. There are three methods used to get data and display it which are not real-time methods. Each of the four methods of digitizing will now be briefly discussed.

Real-Time Sampling *The sampling rate of a DSO varies with the setting of the horizontal time/division switch.* This is an important fact to keep in mind when using a DSO. The sample rate changes with the sweep speed setting so that all of memory is used in 10 times the selected display time (screen width is 10 times this setting), recording perhaps 4,096 individual voltage samples. When memory is filled, the sampling ceases and the display is reconstructed from the data to fill the screen.

One of the fundamental specifications of a digital sampling oscilloscope is the highest frequency at which it can digitize signals. While an analog oscilloscope's capability is largely expressed in a bandwidth figure (the highest frequency at which it will still show a signal as 70 percent of its true value), bandwidth of a digital oscilloscope is not an adequate measure of its true performance.

As stated, the manual selection of the time base determines how often the input signal will be sampled. At regular intervals, depending on the setting of this control, the input waveform is sampled and recorded into random access memory. Real-time sampling requires that the digitizer be able to finish the digitizing process and place the result into memory and on the screen between each sample. The speed of real-time digitizing, or the *real-time sampling rate* as it is called, might be on the order of 100 kHz for a high-quality oscilloscope.

It is generally accepted within the industry that a digitizer must capture *at least 10 samples* of the captured waveform period in order to record a reasonably accurate likeness of the applied waveform. Less than this number of samples can badly distort the input waveform. The more samples taken during the period of a given waveform, the more accurate the reconstruction of the waveform after being digitized. With a 100-kHz real-time sampling rate as an example, the *maximum captured frequency for single-shots,* as it is called, would be only 10 kHz. This can be greatly improved on, as will be explained later.

Repetitive Sampling By using one of two "tricks," sequential or random sampling, the *effective sampling rate* of a digital oscilloscope allows digitizing much higher frequencies, but *only if the signal is repetitive.* Repetitive sampling is sometimes called *time-equivalent sampling.*

Sequential Sampling The speed of the DSO digitizer itself is relatively very slow. The bandwidth of its vertical input channels and trigger circuits are capable of operating at much higher frequencies than the digitizer.

A *repetitive high-frequency signal* can be digitized at relatively low frequencies by digitizing and memorizing only one voltage on the input waveform for each trigger. The first value to be digitized is the value of the input waveform at the moment of triggering, letting the rest of the cycle go by without any more digitizing. When the trigger condition again occurs, a delay of 1/4,096th of the total screen width (one memory location) elapses before another value is digitized and memorized. This process repeats with the following cycle, where a delay of 2/4,096ths of the screen width occurs, then the waveform is again sampled, digitized, and placed into the next memory location. This process continues until all 4,096 memory locations are filled, at which time data acquisition ceases and the data points are reconstructed and displayed.

The effect of sequential sampling is to strobe the sampling point through the screen display taking, in our example, 4,096 samples before the data is complete. Each data point is synchronized by the trigger point on the input waveform. See Figure 24–12.

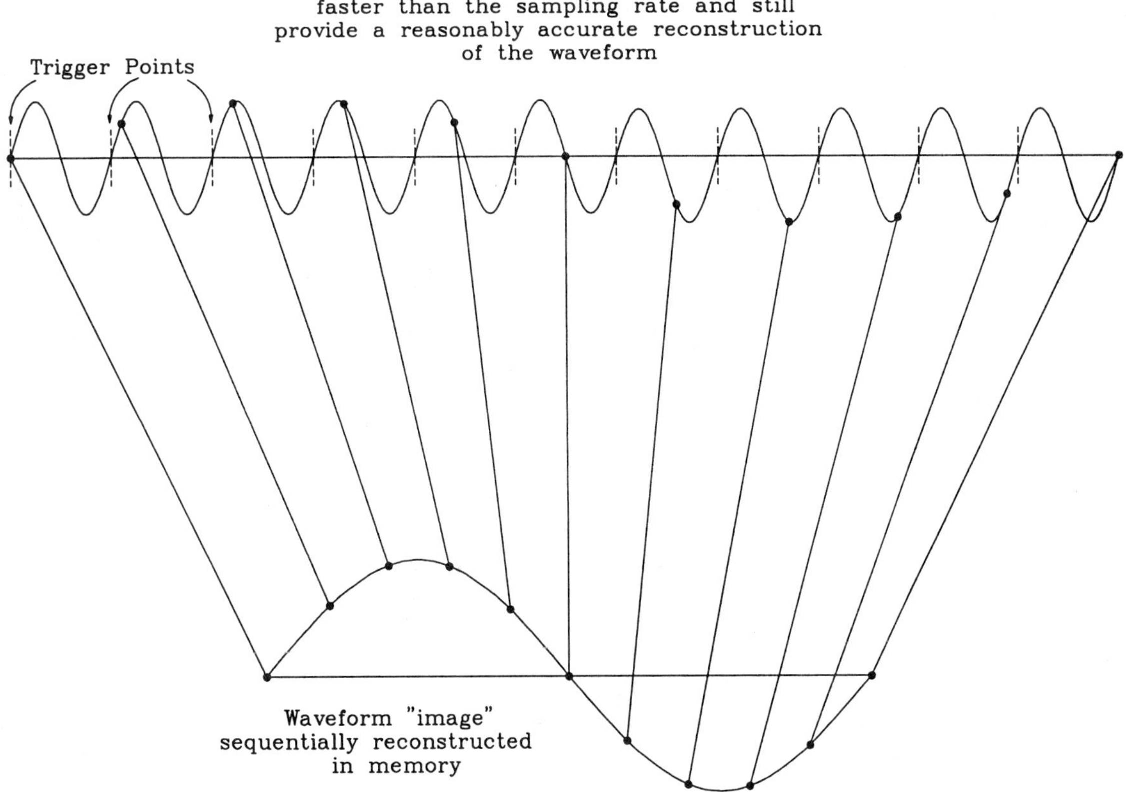

Figure 24–12 Sequential digitizing of high-frequency signals allows the faithful reconstruction of a high-frequency waveform using a low-frequency digitizer.

As with an analog oscilloscope, the sequential sampling method is initiated by the trigger. Because of this, sequential sampling cannot capture pretrigger information. Sequential sampling is also not recommended for the observation of fast rise-time signals.

Random Sampling Random sampling is similar to the sequential sampling technique just discussed. To correct the problem of not being able to see pretrigger events, samples of the input waveform are taken in synchronism with an internal low-frequency DSO clock signal. Random samples of the incoming waveform are taken and recorded. A timing circuit steps through memory. When the unsynchronized sample is taken, the voltage sample is placed at the proper point in memory. The timer continues to step through memory, looping back through the trigger point again. In this way, pretrigger information can be recorded. Random sampling is also well suited for the recording of very fast risetime signals.

The Charge-Coupled Device Thus far, the capture of a single-shot event would be acceptable for signals of only 10 kHz or less. This is simply not enough. A DSO could display even higher frequencies if it had some means of recording a given input waveform at high frequency *in analog form,* and could then later digitize and display the data at much lower speeds. The addition of such circuitry can extend the frequency capability of a DSO by a factor of 1,000.

The Philips company uses a specially developed chip called a *Profiled Peristaltic Charge-Coupled Device,* or P^2CCD. This is a very high-speed *analog recorder chip* that takes analog data and shifts it through the device with each clock signal from the DSO. It is able to directly record data at frequencies up to 250 MHz. When it is full of analog data, the output of the P^2CCD can then be digitized and placed into memory at the much slower rate of 100 kHz. When the memory is full, the data can then be displayed.

At the fastest horizontal sweep speed, the clocking signal for a P^2CCD might be as high as 100 MHz. This means that the highest frequency that could be accurately digitized is now 10 MHz, rather than the 10-kHz maximum without this device. With the P^2CCD, the maximum captured frequency for single shots is extended by a factor of 1,000. *This specification is the limiting instrument specification for the capture and recording of single-shot events.*

The ability to digitize a waveform by either sequential or random sampling is sometimes called the *digital bandwidth* of the instrument. The digital bandwidth of a DSO is limited by the analog bandwidth of the input channels. Stating the digital bandwidth of an instrument implies that the input is repetitive in nature. This is a very important implication to keep in mind when comparing the specifications for a DSO.

DSO Sampling Summary It should be apparent after this discussion of the means of digitizing that two specifications are necessary to fully describe a DSO's ability to digitize data: the real-time digitizing frequency (1/10th the sampling rate) and the *digital bandwidth* for repetitive signals.

Horizontal Resolution The entire memory of a DSO might be 4,096 amplitudes wide in the real-time digitizing mode. This means that there is a *horizontal resolution* of 4,096 different data points across the screen display. This many points is far in excess of that needed to show an entire waveform clearly. Its value is in the ability to allow digital *horizontal magnification* of any portion of the data desired. Horizontal magnification of up to 32 times on any portion of the 4,096 points makes it easy to see fine time details, including voltage changes of very short durations.

The cost of a P^2CCD makes it advisable to have less horizontal resolution. A pair of these devices are alternately recorded into, to provide 512 horizontal data points per channel. The change from the direct mode of digital sampling to the use of a P^2CCD device occurs between the 5-ms- and 2-ms-per-division settings of the time-base switch. This crossover point can be identified by the smooth versus more grainy appearance of the horizontal portions of the sweep when changing between these two settings.

Aliasing Aliasing is a type of error that can occur when digitizing samples of analog data. If a high frequency is being observed at a very slow sampling rate, the result can appear to be a low-frequency signal. The clue to identifying an aliasing situation is that the low-frequency signal cannot be synchronized and caused to stop drifting on the display. Make a quick check if this is suspected by changing the time base to a much faster sweep rate, or temporarily switch to the analog mode. *Because of aliasing, it is best to begin analysis of all high-frequency signals using fast rather than slow sweeps.*

Scrolling Whereas an analog oscilloscope would give only minimal, very temporary information if swept at very slow sweep speeds, the DSO is exceptionally good at showing waveforms on extremely slow sweep speeds. When using a very slow time base (as slow as 50 seconds per division), the input information is sampled at a rate of as low as 8 samples per second. At the end of each acquisition, the entire waveform displayed is advanced in display position 1/4,096th of the width to the *left*. The effect is that the information is very slowly scrolled from right to left. The presentation scrolls from right to left to imitate the action of a recording voltmeter. Thus, a DSO is very effective as a slow-speed chart recorder.

Logic Analyzers

Chapter 15 already covered the basics of using a logic analyzer. The more advanced features offered by this instrument involve the use of a *disassembler*, which effectively "teaches" the analyzer what a specific microprocessor means by the appearance of certain digital combinations. These digital values can be displayed as the assembly-language mnemonics that were used to originally produce the program.

Another use for a logic analyzer is to detect the appearance of glitches, very short-term undesired changes in logic levels. Glitches most often cause problems and must be eliminated at the circuit-prototyping level. If left undetected, a glitch can cause all manner of problems in digital circuits at any time later on.

Once a prototype circuit is working as it should, the logic analyzer can be used to record the execution of normal programming and/or hardware operation. Disk files of the precise action of dozens of digital lines can be recorded, duplicated, and stored for future troubleshooting use.

Arbitrary Waveform Generator

An arbitrary waveform generator is an advanced function generator. Besides generating all the normal waveforms—sine, sawtooth, triangular, and square waves—the arbitrary waveform generator can be used as a sort of digital waveform "repeater." A digital waveform can be loaded into this instrument's memory and then executed by looping through it endlessly, at various speeds. Such an instrument could be of distinct value when developing and testing some of today's sophisticated circuits. See Figure 24–13.

PROM (Programmable Read Only Memory) Programmers

Another important instrument, although it was not directly intended for troubleshooting, is the PROM programmer. This instrument is used to place digital patterns, usually programs for a microprocessor, into a chip. The chip may be a PROM (programmable read only memory), EPROM (erasable programmable read only memory), or EEPROM (electrically erasable programmable read only memory). Software that is placed into a ROM chip is called *firmware.* An engineering assistant will likely be called on to place a program into such a chip, or possibly to read the information already within a particular chip.

One of the most widely used instruments used for programming a great many different PROMs is the Data I/O instrument shown in Figure 24–14.

The programmer is most effectively used when connected to, and operated through, a microcomputer. Choices are made from the software pro-

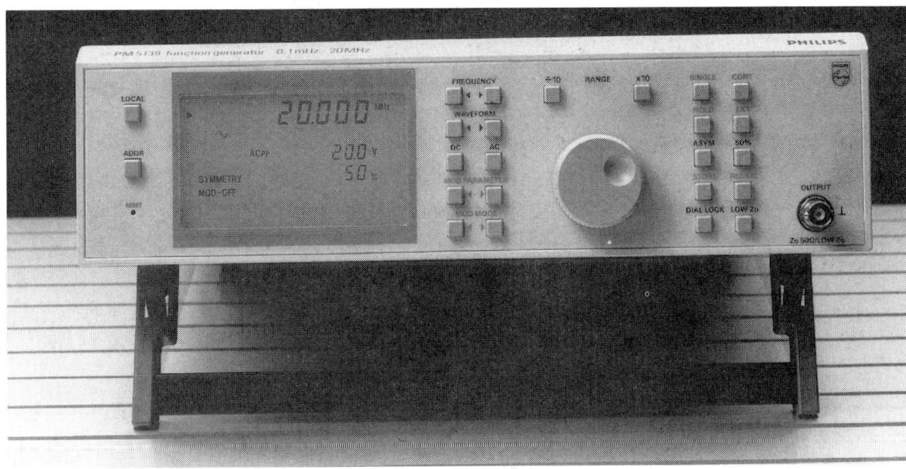

Figure 24–13 An arbitrary waveform generator can produce common waveforms and can also repeat digitized special waveforms. (Courtesy Philips)

gram supplied with the programmer. All manner of data manipulation is possible, from simple programming to the most advanced manipulations.

SERIAL DIGITAL DATA COMMUNICATIONS

The IEEE-488 interface was designed for interconnecting many test instruments to automate measurements. It does very well in this specialized application, but suppose we simply wish to pass digital data

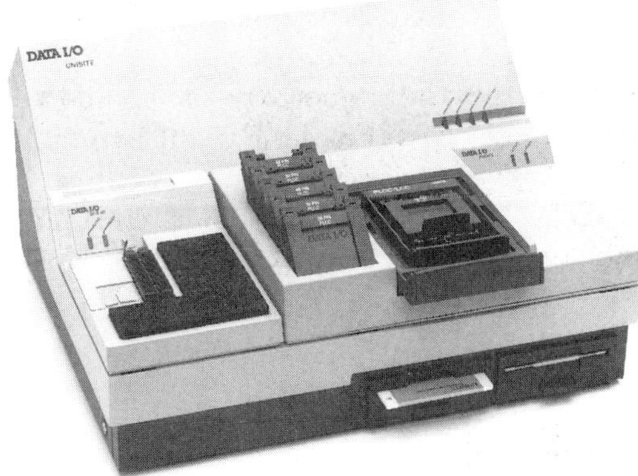

Figure 24–14 A modern ROM programmer, which is also capable of programming PALs. (Photograph courtesy of Data/IO, Inc.)

back and forth between only two instruments? This is a very common need in many applications today. The present data communications standard, called the RS-232C or EIA (for Electronics Industry Association) interconnection standard, was developed years ago. By understanding its origin, we can better understand how and why it has become so diversified and "unstandardized."

The original wiring standard for data communications was intended to satisfy the need for a standardized method of connecting a dumb terminal to a telephone line for the purpose of communicating with a remote computer.

The Electronics Industry Association set the original standard (Recommended Standard number 232, modification C, or RS-232C). While earlier versions used other voltages, version C specified +12 and –12-V levels and the definitions of the lines to be used. It is the standard that is most used today.

All the digital information sent on an RS-232C circuit is serial in format. Each bit is sent, whether a "0" or a "1," by switching between +12 and –12-volt levels on the RS-232C line. Figure 24–15 shows how the digital signals are generated and received on an RS-232C line.

Bits are most commonly grouped as eight data bits. Formerly, seven data bits was popular when only ASCII (seven-bit) files were sent. While there is a possible choice of the number of stop bits to be used, a single stop bit is the most popular.

The original intent of the standard was to provide for all the possible signals needed for a data terminal to communicate with a remote mainframe computer, via a modem. The standard for connecting the modems at either end gave rise to the RS-232C standard of today. See Figure 24–16.

For purposes of the standard, a data terminal is called a DTE (data terminal equipment). The modem is called a DCE (data communications equipment). When the terminal sent data on pin 2, it was received on pin 2 at the modem end. Data sent from the modem was received by the terminal on its pin 3 in both cases, resulting in a straight pin-for-pin interconnection.

According to the standard, the connector used should be a 25-pin connector. The DTE end *should* be a plug (male, DB-25P) and the DCE end *should* be a socket (female, DB-25S) connector.

The original RS-232C wiring table provided for many more functions than are commonly used today. Table 24–2 shows the original RS-232C wiring standard:

Using RS-232C between a Microcomputer and a Modem

Fortunately, only a few of the signal lines provided for in the original standard are commonly in use today. For instance, the serial communications port of a "compatible" microcomputer has only about half the lines

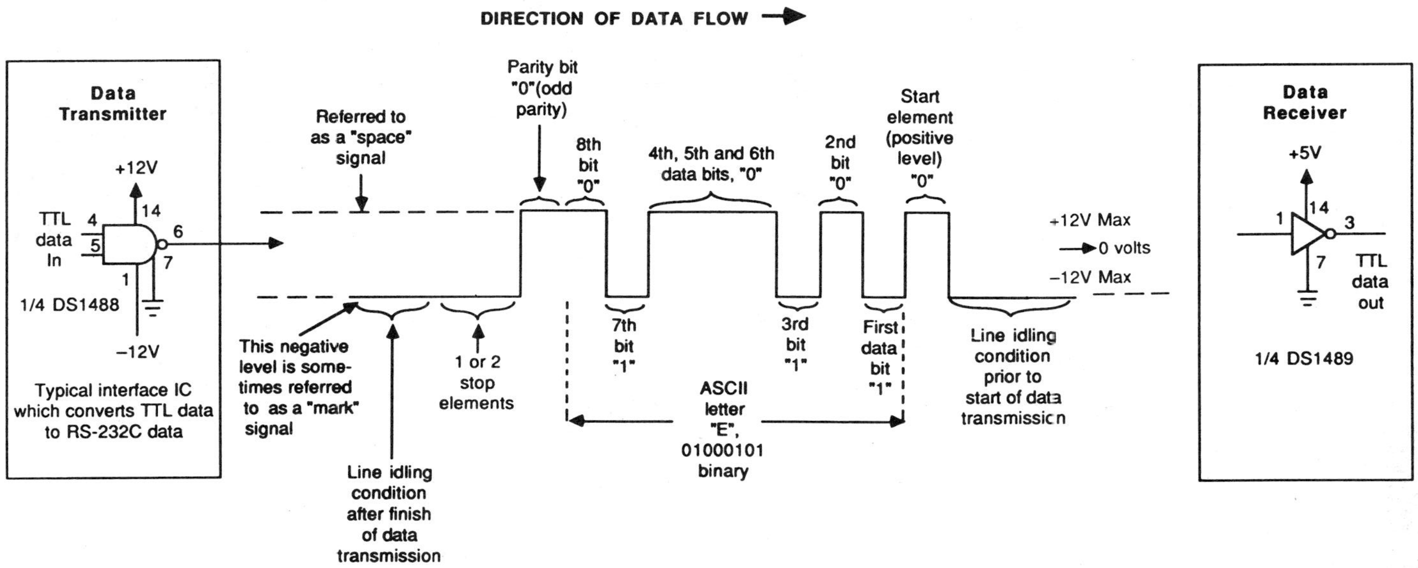

DIRECTION OF DATA FLOW →

Data Transmitter

+12V

TTL data In

4 5 14 6 7 1

1/4 DS1488

−12V

Typical interface IC which converts TTL data to RS-232C data

Referred to as a "space" signal

This negative level is sometimes referred to as a "mark" signal

Line idling condition after finish of data transmission

1 or 2 stop elements

Parity bit "0"(odd parity)

8th bit "0"

7th bit "1"

4th, 5th and 6th data bits, "0"

3rd bit "1"

2nd bit "0"

First data bit "1"

Start element (positive level) "0"

ASCII letter "E", 01000101 binary

Line idling condition prior to start of data transmission

+12V Max

0 volts

−12V Max

Data Receiver

+5V

1 14 3 7

TTL data out

1/4 DS1489

RS232C serial data transmission standards. Note the major points:
Data is inverted to a negative-true convention;
The least significant bit is sent first, most significant bit last;
Voltage levels are either positive or negative, not zero;
Line level idles at a negative voltage.
Control signals, not shown, are positive-true convention and use the same voltage levels as above.

Figure 24–15 How RS-232C voltage levels are generated and received.

Table 24–2 Original RS-232C Wiring Standard

Pin		Name	Direction DTE / DCE	Function
1	*	FG	None	Frame Ground
2	#	TD	→	Transmitted Data
3	#	RD	←	Received Data
4	#	RTS	→	Request To Send
5	#	CTS	←	Clear To Send
6	#	DSR	←	Data Set Ready
7	#	SG	None	Signal Ground
8		DCD	←	Data Carrier Detect
9	*		←	Positive DC Test Voltage
10	*		←	Negative DC Test Voltage
11		QM	←	Equalizer Mode
12	*	(S)DCD	←	Sec. Data Carrier Detect
13	*	(S)CTS	←	Sec. Clear To Send
14	*	(S)TD	→	Sec. Transmitted Data
		or NS	→	New Sync
15		TC	←	Transmitter Clock
16	*	(S)RD	←	Sec. Received Data
		or DCT	←	Divided Clock
17		RC	←	Receiver Clock
18		DCR	←	Divided Clock
19	*	(S)RTS	→	Sec. Request To Send
20	#	DTR	→	Data Terminal Ready
21	*	SQ	←	Signal Quality Detect
22		RI	←	Ring Indicator
23			→	Data Rate Selector
			←	Data Rate Selector
24	*	TC	→	Ext. Transmitter Clock
25			→	Busy

The most important connections used with microcomputers. Other lines frequently not connected.

* Omitted connection on many computers, including the IBM PC

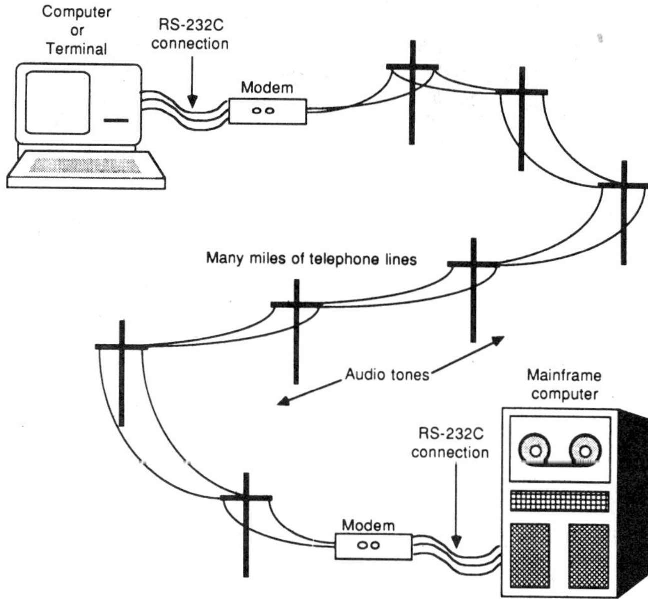

Figure 24–16 The origin of the RS-232C data interconnection standard.

actually wired in. The maximum number of lines are used when connecting to an external modem rather any other serial device, so Table 24–3 will relate the signals to the use of a modem:

As an example, an illustration of the actual connection of a microcomputer to a modem is shown in Figure 24–17.

It is imperative to know the configuration of both ports to be connected

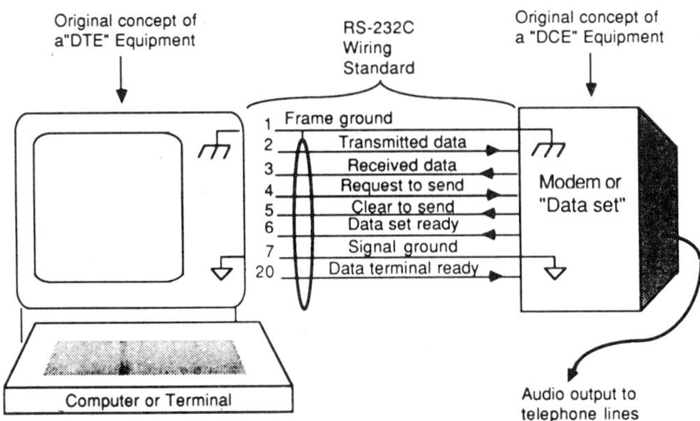

Figure 24–17 A modem connected to a microcomputer port uses all the lines wired to the port within the computer.

Table 24–3 Microcomputer RS-232C Port Wiring Table

	Computer (DTE)	Modem (DCE)	Interpretation of Signal
FRAME	1	1	Frame or shield ground
TXD	2	2	Data out from computer (DTE)
RXD	3	3	Data input from modem (DCE)
RTS	4	4	Computer wishes to send data
CTS	5	5	Modem says OK for computer to send data
DSR	6	6	The modem is on and ready to transmit data
GND	7	7	Signal ground (power supply common)
DCD	8	8	Modem has detected a carrier from a remote modem
DCD	12	12	High-speed indicator*
DTR	20	20	The computer is on and ready for work
RI	22	22	Ring indicator

*Actual speed varies with equipment capabilities. 2400 or 9600 baud are currently the two most common "high speed" rates in use.

via a serial communications cable. *If the ports are of different configurations (one a DTE and the other a DCE), then a simple extension cable will do the job. If they are of the same type (both DTE or both DCE), then a cross-over cable must be used.* See Figure 24–18 for three common types of cross-over (null-modem) cables:

Labeling equipment as DTE or as DCE on the back panel near a port may indicate what it is internally *or* what it is to be connected to, 180 degrees out. The end result is that back-panel labeling is no help at all and should not be relied upon.

In difficult cases, schematic diagrams in instruction books can determine the configuration of a port: *if the output of the data is being sent out to pin #2 of the standard DB-25P, it is a DTE device, and if on 3, it must be a DCE device.* Figure 24–19 shows how two DTE devices might be connected using a null-modem cable.

Using a Breakout Box Most serial ports are configured as they would be on a data terminal (DTE). If there is any doubt, a breakout box can also be used to determine the actual configuration without removing covers or checking schematics. Simply take the breakout box, which is little more than a series of LEDs attached to each of the RS-232C data lines, and insert the box into the circuit. Disconnect one

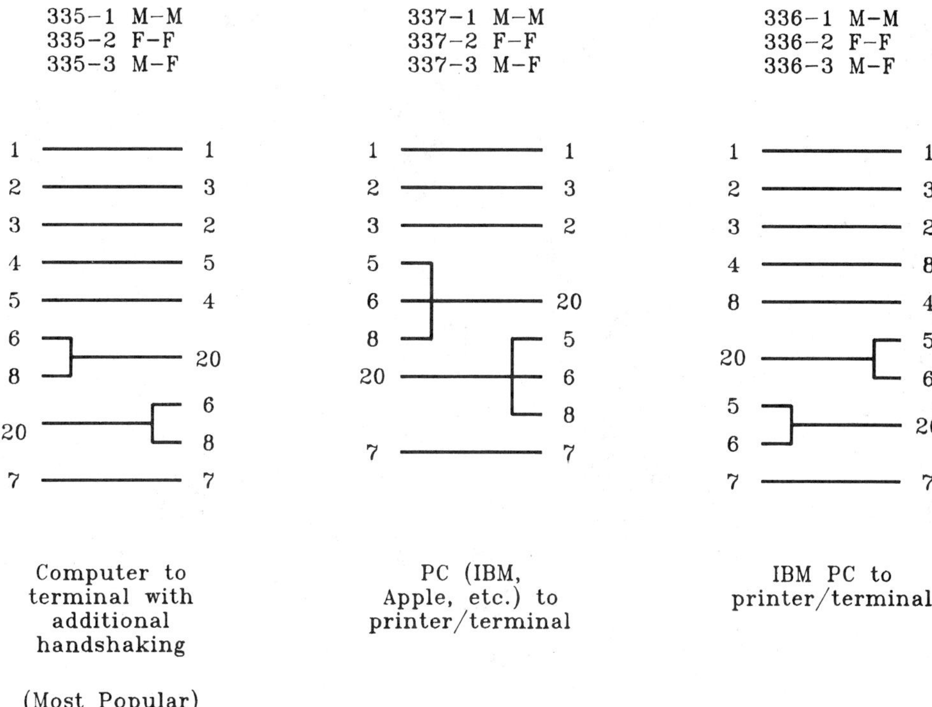

Figure 24–18 Wiring of common null-modem cables for microcomputer use.

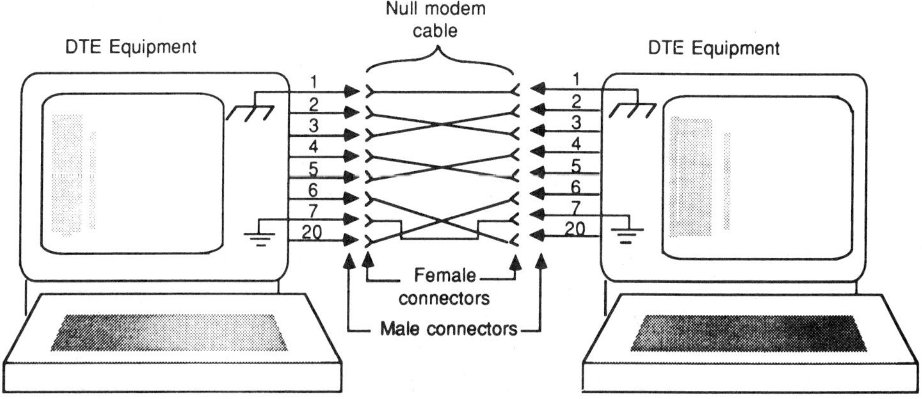

Figure 24–19 Two DTEs, such as these computers, can be cross-connected using a null-modem cable with female connectors on each end.

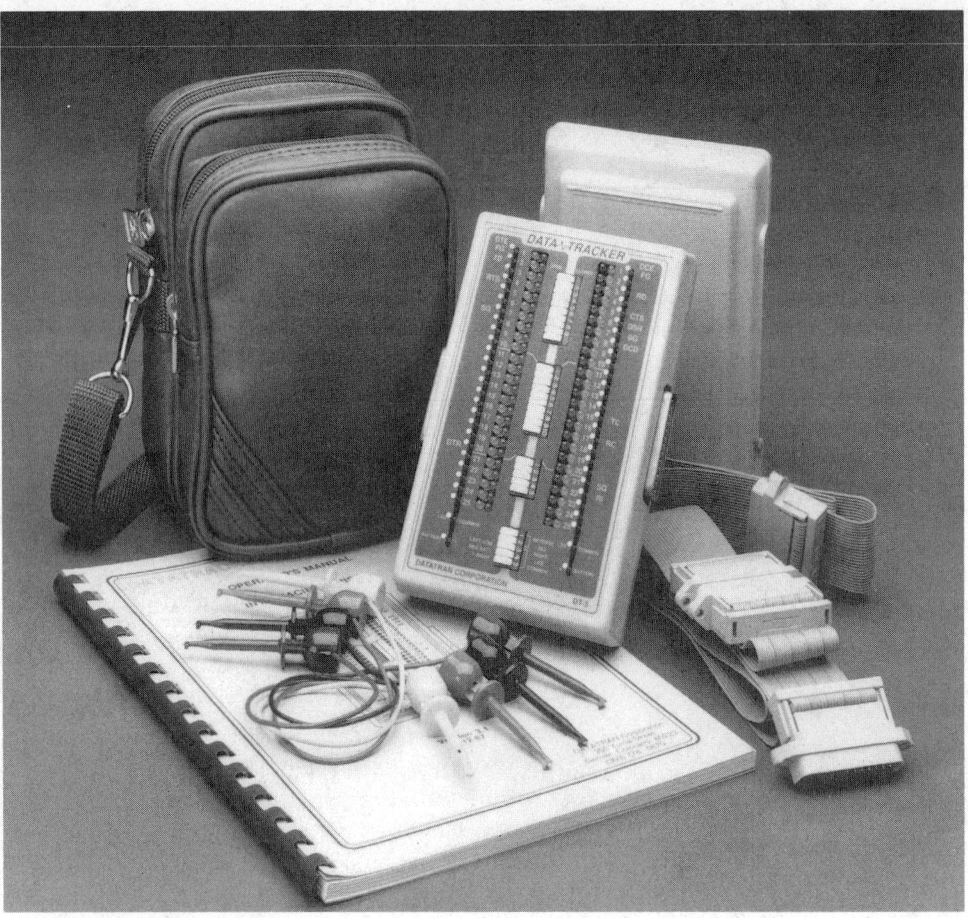

Figure 24–20 This breakout box is a troubleshooting aid for serial data cables. (Photograph courtesy of Datatran Corp.)

end of the cable from a serial port, connect the breakout box and then reconnect the cable into the breakout box on the other side. The box will now show lighted LEDs where there are logic "1" levels and flickering lights when data is passed on a line. See Figure 24–20.

To verify that a microcomputer is a DTE device, use the COPY command of DOS and copy any file to the port. If the number 2 line shows a flickering light, this is a DTE microcomputer port (memory aid: D*T*E *T*ransmits on *T*wo). If number 3 shows the flickering, however, the microcomputer is configured as a DCE port.

The microcomputer is usually configured as a DTE device. A straightforward connection to a DCE device such as a modem will require the use of a straight-through extension cable, where each wire connects to identical pins on each end (the number 2 pin is connected to the number 2 on the opposite end, etc.).

RS-232C between a Microcomputer and Peripherals

The configuration of both the microcomputer and the peripheral port must be determined before connecting them. Although serial ports are by design very forgiving, why take the chance of making a wrong connection? See previous discussion of breakout boxes if you are in any doubt about the configuration of either of the ports.

Using Hardwire Control (Handshaking)

The number of wires required from a serial port to other peripherals is less than would be required for connecting to a modem. Table 24–4 is an abbreviated RS-232C wiring table for hardwire handshaking of peripheral equipment.

Using Software Control (Handshaking)

Sending data to other equipment that uses XON (Transmit On) and XOFF (Transmit Off) handshaking requires only three wires. See Table 24–5 on next page.

The actual hookup might be as in Figure 24–21.

Note that there is now no provision to tell if the printer is on and ready for characters. Characters must be sent by the microcomputer "in the blind," awaiting a software code of XOFF to tell the microcomputer when to wait for the printer to catch up.

The software at the microcomputer end must be set up so that it controls

Table 24–4 Hardwire Handshaking of Peripheral Equipment

	Computer (DTE)	Printer (DTE)	Interpretation of Signal
FRAME	1	1	Frame or shield ground
TXD	2	3	Data out from (Ccomputer (DTE)
RXD	3	2	Data input from printer (DTE)
RTS	4	5	May be used as auxiliary handshaking
CTS	5	4	May be used as auxiliary handshaking
DSR	20	6	The printer is on and ready to receive data
GND	7	7	Signal ground (power supply common)
BUSY	6	20	When logic is low, printer is busy (often connected at printer to number 11, which enables the use of either number 11 or number 20 at the printer end to be used as the printer's "busy" line)

Note: Both the microcomputer and the external peripheral are here represented as being DTE devices, thus requiring pin no. 2 of one connector to be wired to pin no. 3 at the opposite end. This is, therefore, a null-modem cable.

Table 24–5 Abbreviated RS-232C Wiring Table for Software Handshaking of Peripheral Equipment

	Computer (DTE)	Printer (DTE)	Interpretation of Signal
TXD	2	3	Data out from computer (DTE)
RXD	3	2	Data input from printer (DTE)
RTS	4		4 must be jumpered to 5 at computer end
CTS	5		
GND	7	7	Signal ground (power supply common)
DSR	6		6 may have to be jumpered to 20 at the computer end
DTR	20		

microcomputer output in accordance with the incoming serial characters XON (DC1 on the ASCII chart) and XOFF (DC3 on the ASCII chart) from the external device.

CALCULATORS

Just about all of us have used calculators for years now. We are accustomed to them and the basic way to operate them. These are the *algebraic* calculators, having an "=" key.

With an algebraic calculator, *the numbers are simply entered as they would be recited*: for example, "two plus three equals five." The keys for 2, 3, and = would be pressed. This is great for simple equations. However, more complex equations require the insertion of parentheses which complicate the process of entering numbers correctly.

There is another kind of calculator in wide use within engineering ranks,

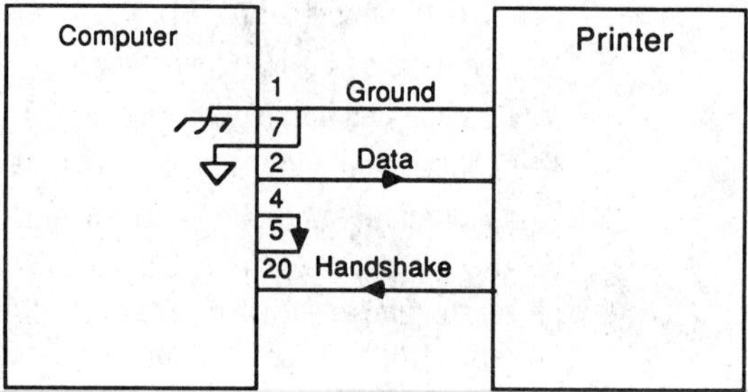

Figure 24–21 Using software handshaking, only three lines are needed to send data to some devices.

those using the so-called RPN (Reversed Polish Notation) method of data entry. RPN was highly developed by the Hewlett Packard Company in their first dramatically different calculator, the HP-35. The engineering technician is well advised to become familiar with this method of entering numerical data.

The RPN calculator, with its *stack,* allows the entry of numbers without using an "=" or parenthesis key. The stack is a rotating 4-number set of registers into which numbers may be placed manually or automatically. This allows very complex mathematical operations to be performed with relative ease. The absence of the "+" key is the easiest way of identifying the kind of calculator at hand. The same equation as before, when entered into an RPN calculator would be "2, Enter, 3," and then "+". The answer would appear immediately after the "+" key was pressed. This way of entering numbers and the use of a memory stack allows engineers to *enter problems exactly as they would be manually solved,* beginning within parentheses and working outward, retaining intermediate answers along the way *automatically in the stack* until the final answer appears.

USING COMPUTERS

As our society moves increasingly toward a digital age, computers are a tool that a good technician simply must master. The computer can interpret, record, do multiple repetitions without tiring or losing accuracy, and even actually design certain kinds of circuits. Although it cannot yet actually create, it is a tremendous tool to those who are paid to do just that.

Basic typing skills are becoming more important as computers become more widely used in technical fields. If you use the hunt-and-peck method, valuable time will be lost and your proficiency ratings may slip a bit as a result.

Since the majority of microcomputers in use these days are those that use MS-DOS (Microsoft Disk Operating System), the technician should be familiar with the following MS-DOS commands. Detailed instructions of their use and the options available within these commands can be obtained from any good DOS reference manual. A listing of the important commands may be found in Appendix XIV.

The senior technician will see the computer's value for inventory control of electronic equipment and parts, drawing of schematics and other documentation for new equipment, and the preparation of reports.

Programming as a Technical Skill

To be really computer-literate, a technician should know at least one programming language fairly well. In some cases, a knowledge of programming can make the difference between job advancement and stagnation.

The easiest programming language to grasp is probably BASIC. The language is very like English and is reasonably powerful to use. It does take the computer a relatively long time to execute programs in BASIC, however.

The fastest-executing language is assembly language. This is the lowest practical level of programming, and probably the hardest to learn. The programming language is different for each manufacturer, although once one has been learned, others are very easy to acquire. Learning assembly language for the first processor can take weeks, yet learning a second processor might take only a few hours.

The "C" programming language is rapidly becoming a major language in writing all manner of programs, especially the technical ones. "C" has three major advantages: (1) A program written in "C" for one computer can often be taken to a completely different computer and with a touch-up can be made to run on the new computer. This is called *program portability* (from one computer to another); (2) Another advantage is that fast-running sections of assembly language can be brought right into the "C" program, thus greatly increasing the speed with which the program can run; (3) Last, "C" programs run relatively quickly, although not as fast as assembly language programs.

Programming skills can be particularly valuable when one is asked to write automated testing routines.

Writing Reports, Drawing Diagrams

The computer is very valuable when used as a word processor. A word processor can be used to put information into a computer, such as written test reports. This takes only slightly less time to keyboard the data with a word processor than it would on a typewriter. The real value lies in the result; corrections can be made very easily and spelling can even be checked for you.

Besides checking for spelling errors, professional words present a problem for spelling checkers. The word "resonator," for instance, may be flagged as "not found." Such words are commonly used in electronics and should be recorded in a supplemental dictionary so that they will be accepted in future documents. Through this supplemental dictionary, your word processor will eventually recognize all of the special electronic terms. This raises the question as to the proper spelling of certain technical words, so they will be recorded properly when encountered. Table 24–6 presents a correctly spelled list of a few of the more commonly misspelled words used in electronic documentation.

Abbreviations will also be flagged as spelling errors. The abbreviations in Table 24–7 are common to electronic technical writing.

The way to becoming an engineering assistant will vary from company to company. Some skills are necessary, others optional. *Competency in the use of English is necessary for job promotion.* One must be able to clearly communicate verbally and in writing, and be able to express one's

Table 24–6 Technical Spelling List

Accumulator	Intermittent	Receive
Alignment	Isolator	Reference
Azimuth	Linear	Schottky
Biased	Maintenance	Silicon
Bipolar	Milliammeter	Stimulus
Calibration	Ohmmeter	Symmetry
Circuit	Oscilloscope	Technician
Comparator	Peripheral	Transient
Complimentary	Preventive	Transistor
Exercise	Programming	Vacuum
Graticule	Proprietary	Vernier
Hysteresis	Protocol	Zener
Impedance	Radial	

thoughts. If a technician hails from another country and hopes to be successful in America, English is the *only* route.

CAD for Drawings, Schematics

Several computer-aided drafting programs are available for microcomputers. Among these are AutoCAD, Generic CAD, and OrCAD. These programs are particularly useful for drawing up schematics and parts layouts, for instance. Proficiency in at least one of these programs may be a big plus in your resume.

Other Inputs for a Computer

Written reports on test results will benefit from the ability of some digital storage oscilloscopes (DSOs) to transfer images and data through digital communications. Once a waveform is digitized by the instrument, it may be possible to download it from the instrument into a computer file. From there, it can be brought into a typewritten document. The calculations that the DSO itself can do include, in the most advanced instruments, the calculation of the following items: addition, subtraction, multiplication, division, differentiation, integration, and Fast Fourier Transforms (which convert real-time signals into frequency domain displays).

The DSO of Figure 24–22 shows one of the most advanced analog/digital storage oscilloscopes which is capable of all of the above functions.

A logic analyzer is also capable of storing timing and state waveforms and information into computer files, where they are available for use in document test results.

Table 24–7 Important Abbreviations

Abbreviation	Meaning
ASAP	As Soon As Possible
ASIC	Application-Specific Integrated Circuit
CCD	Charge-Coupled Device
CD	Capacitive Discharge
CEO	Chief Executive Officer
COB	Close Of Business
COD	Collect On Delivery
DOE	Depending On Experience
DUT	Device Under Test
ETA	Estimated Time of Arrival
ETD	Estimated Time of Departure
ETR	Estimated Time of Repair
FAA	Federal Aviation Administration
FCC	Federal Communications Commission
GMT	Greenwich Mean Time
HVAC	Heating, Ventilation and Air Conditioning
IAW	In Accordance With
LSI	Large-Scale Integration
MOS	Metal Oxide Semiconductor
MPU	Master Processor Unit
MTBF	Mean Time Between Failures
NA or N/A	Not Applicable
OSHA	Occupational Safety and Health Administration
PAL	Programmable Array of Logic
PC	Personal Computer
PCB	Printed Circuit Board
PLC	Programmable Logic Controller
PWB	Printed Wire Board
RAM	Random Access Memory
REV	Revision
ROM	Read Only Memory
SMD	Surface-mounted Device
SMT	Surface-Mounted Technology
TFN	unTil Further Notice
UPS	United Parcel Service; Uninterruptable Power Supply
UUT	Unit Under Test
VLSI	Very Large Scale Integration
WC	Will Call
W/	With

Figure 24–22 A modern digital oscilloscope capable of advanced mathematical treatment of captured waveforms. (Courtesy Philips)

24.7 LESS COMMON TASKS

The items mentioned above are among those that might be considered to be normally expected of an engineering technician. There are many other things that might be done also, but less frequently, depending upon the size of the company at which the work is done, the kind of testing required, and the availability of more specialized test instruments.

SPECIAL TEST EQUIPMENT FOR DEDICATED USES

Special test equipment is available that combines other test instruments into a single piece of equipment, the features of each basic instrument optimized for the special use. The service monitor (section 13.4) is an excellent example of this kind of test instrument. Another is the special toot equipment used to test and calibrate aviation navigational equipment, including radar test sets and distance measuring equipment. Because of the low demand for these specialized instruments, they cost a great deal of money. This large investment is a very good reason for the technician who uses expensive equipment to become very familiar with it and its limitations, mostly to prevent damage to the instrument while in use.

USE OF OTHER INSTRUMENTS

Due to their less common use, the following instruments warrant only a short summary of their use and operation. The engineering assistant may have to use one or more of these instruments, depending upon the job at hand.

RF Sweep Generators

The basic operation of a sweep RF signal generator was covered in Chapter 13. This instrument is also sometimes used to record the response of receivers, attenuators, waveguides, and other-high frequency components over a broad range of frequencies as part of their initial calibration certification. It is used particularly often at VHF and UHF frequencies, well into the gigahertz frequencies. When using a swept-frequency generator as an input signal, the response of circuits or components can be recorded on a digital oscilloscope, which can then produce a hard-copy replica of the test results. A typical test setup might look like that shown in Figure 24–23.

Transistor Curve Tracer

A transistor curve tracer can be used to match or select transistors to meet precision requirements of gain or other parameters. This instrument is basically an oscilloscope, but the horizontal is calibrated in volts and the

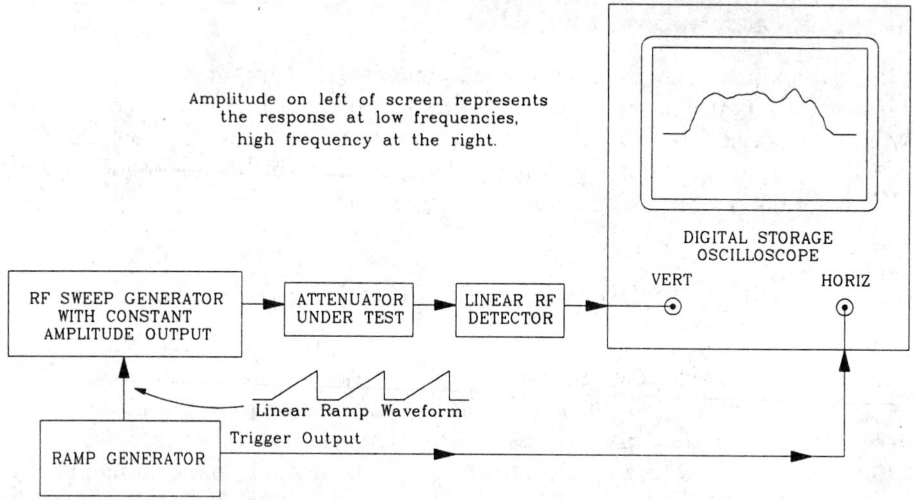

Figure 24–23 An engineering tech may be involved in performing sweep analysis on components or electronic units.

vertical is calibrated in amperes or milliamperes. The instrument automatically steps the base of the test transistor through calibrated steps of very small current while each step is accompanied by a ramp of voltage applied to the collector of the device. The result is a family of curves, each curve representing changing collector voltage with a given base current.

As an example of its use, transistors can be matched for complementary, or critical push-pull, precision differential circuits by using this instrument. The effects of temperature can also be noted if the transistor is operated within a small oven during testing.

Audio Distortion

The use of an audio distortion analyzer was also covered in Chapter 13 in conjunction with the 12-db SINAD test. The distortion meter is used to build and maintain very linear audio amplifiers. The distortion of the signal entering an amplifier is noted, then the output waveform distortion is measured. This often requires the manipulation of controls to zero out the fundamental frequency of operation again. The increase of distortion on the output is the measure of percentage distortion produced by the amplifier.

RF Field Strength Meters

An RF field strength meter is a receiver that is calibrated to read the absolute field strength from a specific transmitter. The meter is tunable and has a special antenna that must be used with the meter in order for the reading to be accurate.

The RF field strength meter is used when proving that the radiated field from a newly installed transmitter is as predicted by engineering calculations. It must also be done when there are changes made to the antenna structure. Specific points, exactly located, are used to accomplish these measurements. The instruction manual for the field strength receiver must be followed very carefully for the readings to be accurate.

LCR Bridge or Measurement Equipment

There are several ways to read the precise values of inductance and capacitance. The LCR bridge (Inductance, Capacitance, and Resistance) is the most popular instrument for measuring these components. Such an instrument might well be used in a prototyping environment to find exact values of components, or to match them for critical use. A digital multimeter is probably the best instrument to measure resistances unless extreme accuracy is required. Precision resistance bridges can be used, as can specially made instruments to read four or five places of accuracy.

Precision EIR Calibrators (Voltage, Current, and Resistance)

These instruments provide highly calibrated values of voltage, current, and resistance for the purpose of calibrating other instruments to them. They act as standards for each of these quantities. When producing a voltage, for instance, they can be used to calibrate a voltmeter. The voltmeter to be calibrated is fine-adjusted until it reads the same voltage as that produced by this instrument. Their only purpose is as a standard, not as a power supply for other uses. See Figure 24–24.

The calibration of equipment requires that the voltage, current, or resistance standard (in this case) be at least 10 times more accurate than the instrument being calibrated. Today's digital multimeters have equal or better accuracy than many of the EIR calibrators of only a few years ago, thus making older EIR machines obsolete.

Microprocessor Board Testers

A microprocessor board tester can be used to test the hardware that is in direct access to the processor itself. Based upon direct memory access (DMA) provisions, the board tester requests access to all of the address, data, and control lines of the processor by driving an appropriate microprocessor pin. This causes the processor to finish what it is doing, then the processor acknowledges the request with another pin, and releases (floats) all of the address, data, and control lines to the chip requesting the busses. In effect, the board tester taps the processor on the shoulder, requesting the

Figure 24–24 EIR calibrator. (Reproduced with permission from John Fluke Mfg. Co., Inc.)

bus. When the processor is ready, it releases them all and the board tester takes over.

After getting control of all of the important lines, the board tester can then read ROM, calculating the checksum of each address to ensure that the resulting sum is as marked upon the ROM chip itself. RAM memory can be tested by saving what is presently in RAM, writing a specific digital byte, then reading it back. The byte must read back the same as it was written, or the RAM is bad. As each location checks good, the original byte is returned to the RAM location from which it came.

Input and output to all manner of ports is also possible using this test instrument, allowing rapid and efficient testing of most of the hardware. It is also possible in some instances to use one of these instruments via a pair of modems and a telephone line. This may allow remote troubleshooting of a specific problem over a telephone line.

Microprocessor Emulators

An emulator is an instrument that takes the place of a given microprocessor chip in a circuit. Through the software included with the emulator, it is possible to run the normally intended operational software, one step at a time, looking for circuit problems. The emulator replaces the microprocessor chip, allowing very detailed software driving of the hardware.

An emulator must be constructed and have the correct operating software for a specific microprocessor. Although this instrument might be expensive, it is a very good way to debug new circuits involving microprocessors.

PROGRAMMABLE ARRAY OF LOGIC (PAL) PROGRAMMERS

It is now possible to program special "blank" chips to take the place of many individual logic gates. By designing circuits this way, the total number of IC chips for a given design can often be drastically reduced, thereby decreasing production costs. Besides this, the programming of these chips makes them a proprietary chip, at the same time assuring a certain level of product security.

The programming of a PAL is irreversible because it uses microscopic "fuses," which it blows deliberately to accomplish the logic function desired.

If there is sufficient call for PALs, a special programmer or one of the universal programmers similar to that shown previously in Figure 24–14 may be purchased.

TEACH OTHERS

As experience is gained at the job, the time will probably arrive when the engineering technician will be asked to help train other technicians on the details of working in the shop.

It is well to inquire about the level of experience of the person you are showing around. To talk too technically or too simply to him or her will not help the situation. Try to explain the things that need explaining, giving credit where credit is due. When possible, arrange for hands-on training, as it is the best teacher of all. Encourage the learning process and, above all, resist the temptation to push the new technician aside with a "never mind, I'll do it myself" attitude. This temptation will always be there when you can do something easier or faster than the person learning. Allow for mistakes, remembering that *you* didn't do things perfectly the first time, either.

Be particularly careful to explain any dangers involved, such as hazardous chemicals, locations, or exposed high voltage. Be sure to observe safety precautions yourself, in spite of the familiarity you may have with the shop. Wear protective clothing, including hard hats, as required.

If you must teach the operation of a given instrument, try to provide the original instruction manual as a reference manual, even if the instrument is a simple one to learn. The instruction manual can answer questions quickly and easily that might go unanswered if it is not available.

Be sure also to carefully explain any paperwork that will be required of others. If possible, provide a notebook of sample forms, made out as you wish them to be prepared. These examples will save time and misunderstanding in the long run.

ENVIRONMENTAL TESTING

Another consideration in the development of new circuits is to be sure that the circuits will work under specified, extreme environmental conditions. Circuits may be required to work at high altitude (aviation and space applications), or under extreme conditions of cold or heat, vibration, high humidity, or contaminating or hazardous (dusty, dirty, or explosive) atmospheric conditions. The engineering technician may be in charge of subjecting prototype circuits to these extremes and then perhaps of determining the components that might have caused a circuit to fail. Special, expensive enclosures are required to subject equipment to these unusual conditions. Together with the engineer, modifications are made to the circuits in an effort to prevent or minimize the failures. The tests are run again to ensure proper operation of the final circuit as specified.

24.8 PATHS TO ADVANCEMENT

Advancement as an electronics technician or engineering assistant can be enhanced by following some commonsense recommendations.

1. Study electronic changes and advances by subscribing to trade magazines and periodicals. The public library is a very good place to go for up-to-the-minute information, too. Just knowing of a new product at the right time could even be the key to getting a promotion. Your company will often pay for such subscriptions if they are addressed to your position at work.
2. Study the equipment you are using daily. Get the instruction book and go over it until you know the equipment very well. This includes the use of each control, and the limitations of the equipment. Test equipment must also be included in your studies. This simple step can put you well ahead of the competition for the next step up.
3. Learn all you can about your company. Know who the "big boss" is, and the other important people within the company. Keep informed about the financial status of your company if it is large enough that it publishes quarterly reports.
4. Last, but not least, keep yourself attractive. Keep personally clean and groomed. Many a promotion is lost to a person who dresses sloppily or inappropriately or who neglects basic grooming. Very few employers will tell an otherwise well-qualified employee that the promotion is available if he or she will take more showers in the future! The competing person, even if not as well qualified, will probably get the job simply because the boss doesn't want the embarrassment of discussing personal issues with an employee.

24.9 SUBJECTS FOR FURTHER STUDY

Each job will be different in the requirements for on-the-job knowledge and performance. Additional qualifications can make the difference between you or the competition getting an advancement, however.

Though it may not be required to do the original job, the FCC commercial General Class License might be the final weight to sway a promotional decision in your favor. This license may take considerable study time, but the reward is official government recognition of your knowledge. No Morse code is required for this license.

Another license that may enhance your future is an amateur radio license. There are five classes of license, from Novice to Extra Class. Each higher-class license grants more privileges than the previous class. Obtaining this license indicates a recreational interest in electronics, which in itself is probably of no particular importance to your job, but it does indicate more than a passing interest in electronics in general.

There are many other more detailed subjects that are not mentioned in this book, but which may have some value in your particular job. The study of these subjects could make you that much more valuable to your employer. The following is a list of some of the subjects that you might want to consider.

Smith charts
RF transmission line theory
Antenna theory
Noise figure
Mathematics at any higher level
Filters, active and passive
Physics
Chemistry
Lasers
Metallurgy
Hydraulics
Fiber Optics

CHAPTER SUMMARY

- Working in a manufacturing environment involves three basic areas of interest for the assembly-line (sometimes called production) technician: assembly-line testing, troubleshooting production line rejects, and rework.
- Assembly-line testing has only two immediately possible results, acceptance or rejection.
- Rejected units may go next to a troubleshooting technician who will make the recommendations as to the work to be done by the last section, the rework station.
- The rework technician may need training in the manual skills of parts replacement or PC board repair, but is generally not required to have extensive electronic training.

- Assembly-line testing may be automated, requiring little in the way of training.
- Bench testing may require a high degree of troubleshooting skill, depending on the complexity of the product.
- Automated test instruments can be used to assist in troubleshooting to greatly increase speed and accuracy of analysis.
- Besides using reference data a great deal, the technician may build prototype circuits and test them.
- The job may require the laying out of printed circuit boards, manually or by using computer software.
- It may be necessary for the technician to use hazardous chemicals and power tools to build and encapsulate circuits.
- Cabling may have to be routed and tied.
- Allowances for circuit heating and cooling may have to be considered.
- Protection of wiring from wear and abrasion may be necessary, along with allowance for possible mechanical wear and vibration.
- A familiarity with wire wrapping is often required to build prototype circuits.
- Components must be thoroughly understood as they relate to the problems possible in new circuits.
- Circuits must be analyzed and failure analysis made of problems which arise in new circuits.
- Circuit changes may have to be recommended, made, and rechecked for proper operation.
- Multiple test readings are the domain of the automated testing equipment setup, which is almost always computer-controlled. Computer control of test instruments gave rise to the IEEE-488 bus.
- Up to 15 instruments can be connected in parallel for automated testing using a special connector designed for this use.
- Prototype circuits may have never run, making troubleshooting more difficult than the simple repair of a proven circuit.
- Electromagnetic interference can be caused by, or cause problems for, new circuits.
- A technician may have to be familiar with modern test equipment, including advanced use of the analog oscilloscope.
- The modern digital storage oscilloscope has functions which make using them easier, and make the acquisition of information very much easier than getting it from an analog 'scope.
- The technician should understand the basics of data sampling and processing to use the DSO.
- Logic analyzers are often used in the analysis of new circuits and require not only knowledge of how to use them, but very detailed information on the circuit under test as well.
- Both the DSO and the logic analyzer can provide recordings of

actual data acquisitions for documentation of circuit behavior, saving many hours of manual data recording.

- The serial data standard most often used is the RS-232C standard, originally used between a dumb data terminal and a modem.
- Today's requirements often use 12 lines or less of the original RS-232C standard.
- An arbitrary signal generator is a digital function generator with the added capability of being able to retain in memory and synthesize a continuous generation of a digitized waveform.
- PROM programmers are often used by technicians to put digital information permanently within these chips.
- Calculators come in two types, algebraic and RPN.
- RPN is the most natural for complex computations, beginning "in the middle" of a complex formula just as one would do the problem manually.
- A computer is a valuable tool in electronics, and the technician who touch-types is a notch ahead of one who does not.
- Microcomputers should be understood by technicians, and certain DOS commands are necessary to do this.
- Besides knowledge of one or more programming languages, skill at using a word processor and/or computer-aided design programming is a big plus when it comes to advancing in the job.
- Equipment burn-in may be part of the technician's job.
- Dedicated test equipment should be mastered for specific uses as applicable to the job.
- Special test equipment, often not used for troubleshooting, may also be part of the technician's job.
- Teaching others the "ropes" of the job is often the senior technician's task.
- Environmental testing for severe environmental use may be required.
- Keep up-to-date, study the equipment and test instruments, learn all about your company and keep yourself clean and well-dressed for the quickest way to advancement.
- Additional study on specialized subjects can increase your chances for advancement, including commercial and amateur FCC radio licenses.

REVIEW QUESTIONS

1. What are the two options available based on assembly-line testing?
2. What does the acronyn ATE mean?
3. What is the purpose and advantage of using ATE?
4. What are failures due to "infant mortality"?
5. What is the primary duty of a QA inspector?

6. What does a high-pot machine do?
7. What are four common errors found on assembly-line rejects?
8. What is a rework station?
9. Where in this volume is there a quick checklist, keyed to the kind of equipment to be worked upon, of test instruments that might be needed on a road trip?
10. What level of troubleshooting is most common for fieldwork?
11. Can the use of a company vehicle for personal use be hazardous to your job?
12. What is the primary reason for assessing the total baggage weight you can carry when traveling by bus or air?
13. What is the first thing to do after checking in at the customer's site on a trouble call?
14. What troubleshooting method will you probably use to begin troubleshooting in the field?
15. How can you identify inexpensive parts that are particularly risky to use?
16. What is the basic difference between the equipment that a field technician works on, and the equipment an engineering assistant works with?
17. A catalog to choose the correct switch for a given application would be found in a filing cabinet under the cataloging number of _______.
18. What are the most common sizes of nuts and bolts used in electronics in the United States?
19. What is the modern way of preventing nuts and bolts from vibrating loose?
20. What is the best way to take a great many performance readings on a great number of identical equipments?
21. What is the purpose of an IEEE-488 bus?
22. What is a nonreproducible circuit?
23. What is EMI?
24. How can one find the source of suspected EMI?
25. What signal is shown on an oscilloscope when operating in the differential mode?
26. What is the fundamental difference between a repetitive and a single-shot event?
27. Name any four of the readouts that a DSO can calculate for you.
28. What is the basic difference between the time bases of an analog and a digital oscilloscope?
29. Name the three methods of digitizing a waveform.
30. What causes aliasing?
31. The scrolling feature of a DSO mimicks the action of a _______ recorder.
32. An arbitrary waveform generator is a function generator that can _______ a complex waveform provided to it externally, replaying it back in an endless loop.
33. What instrument is used to place a program inside an EPROM?

34. What voltage levels are used with the RS-232C standard?
35. What is the rule concerning the kind of cable to use when connecting DTE and DCE equipments in various combinations?
36. How can one tell the kind of device, DTE or DCE, one is dealing with if the schematic is available?
37. When using a breakout box, how can one tell if a piece of equipment is a DTE or a DCE?
38. How can one identify a calculator that uses RPN?
39. Why is it a good idea to get a commercial or amateur radio license, even though it is not required for your job?

Appendixes

Appendix I

Color Codes and Component Lead Identification

The information in this appendix has been collected from a variety of sources. Although it is believed to be accurate, actual values of resistance, capacitance, and inductance should be verified for use in applications where values are critical. Values given for tolerance, parts-per-million, and voltage ratings are not easily verified except through the manufacturer of the component.

RESISTOR COLOR CODES

Note that a resistor-like component that is either unmarked or has a single color band around the middle is probably a jumper wire. The resistor shape is necessary for automatic machine insertion during manufacture. The single color band may be black, yellow, tan, or brown.

COLOR CODE FOR CARBON AND WIRE-WOUND RESISTORS
(Two Significant Figures)

Color	First Digit +	Second Digit	Multiplier	Tolerance
Black	-	0	1	20% #
Brown	1	1	10	1%
Red	2	2	100	2%
Orange	3	3	1,000	3%
Yellow	4	4	10,000	GMV *
Green	5	5	100,000	5%
Blue	6	6	1,000,000	6%
Violet	7	7	10,000,000	12.5%
Gray	8	8	-	30%
White	9	9	-	10% #
Silver	-	-	0.1	10% @
Gold	-	-	0.1	5% @
No Color	-	-	-	20% @

Note: Fifth Band, if any: Brown = 1% (failure rate in 1,000 Hours)
Red = 0.1%
Orange = 0.01%
Yellow = 0.001%

+ Double width means wire-wound resistor; * = Guaranteed minimum value;
@ = Preferred color code; # = Alternate color code.

LETTER TOLERANCE CODES

Tolerance of various components, mostly capacitors, is often provided by the use of letters. The list of tolerance codes is long, but up to 90% of components can be identified by the following common tolerances:

F = 1%

G = 2%

J = 5%

K = 10%

M = 20%

P = +100%/-0% (sometimes referred to as GMV for guaranteed minimum value)

Z = +80%/-20%

Intermediate tolerances can be estimated by inspection, e.g. a D tolerance code would be less than 1 percent tolerance. (Information courtesy Dick Francis, Renton Technical College, Renton, WA.)

COLOR CODE FOR METAL FILM RESISTORS

Color	First Digit	Second and Third Digits	Multiplier	Tolerance
Black	-	0	1	-
Brown	1	1	10	1%
Red	2	2	100	2%
Orange	3	3	1,000	-
Yellow	4	4	10,000	-
Green	5	5	100,000	0.5%
Blue	6	6	1,000,000	0.25%
Violet	7	7	10,000,000	0.1%
Gray	8	8	0.01 #	0.05%
White	9	9	0.1 #	-
Silver	-	-	0.01 @	10% @
Gold	-	-	0.1 @	5% @

@ = Preferred color code; # = Alternate color code.

CAPACITOR COLOR CODES

Note that a single band around one end of a capacitor indicates the lead connected to the outer foil of the device. In noise-sensitive circuits, the band end is the one that should usually be connected to ground or the least noise-sensitive side of the circuit.

There are many different color codes for capacitors. Besides capacitance value, tolerance and voltage ratings are sometimes encoded into the color scheme. Basically, they use standard resistor codes for value, expressed in picofarads. Conversion to microfarads requires moving the decimal point six places to the left of the indicated value.

THREE-DOT COLOR CODES FOR DISK CERAMIC CAPACITORS

Color	First Digit	Second Digit	Multiplier
Black	-	0	1
Brown	1	1	10

Color	First Digit	Second Digit	Multiplier
Red	2	2	100
Orange	3	3	1,000
Yellow	4	4	10,000
Green	5	5	100,000
Blue	6	6	1,000,000
Violet	7	7	10,000,000
Gray	8	8	
White	9	9	

Note: Hold the disk capacitor with the *leads pointing up* and read the dots from left to right. All capacitors of this type are rated at 500 V and 20% tolerance.

FIVE-DOT COLOR CODES FOR DISK CERAMIC CAPACITORS

Color	First Digit (Temp. Coeff. in Parts/Million)	Second and Third Digits	Multiplier	Tolerance
Black	-	0	1	-
Brown	-30	1	10	1%
Red	-80	2	100	2%
Orange	-	3	1000	-
Yellow	-220	4	10,000	-
Green	-330	5	100,000	0.5%
Blue	-	6	1,000,000	-
Violet	-750	7	10,000,000	0.1%
Gray	+30	8		
White	-	9		
Silver	-	-	0.01	10% @
Gold	-	-	0.1	5% @

@ = Preferred color code; # = Alternate color code

Note: Hold the disk capacitor with the *leads pointing down* and read the dots from left to right. All capacitors of this type are rated at 500 V.

COLOR CODES FOR CYLINDRICAL PAPER CAPACITORS

Cylindrical, color-coded capacitors are typically black in color and range in diameter from about 0.25" to over a half inch.

FOUR-BAND COLOR CODE FOR CYLINDRICAL PAPER CAPACITORS

Color	First Digit	Second Digit	Multiplier	Tolerance
Black	-	0	1	20% #
Brown	1	1	10	1%
Red	2	2	100	2%
Orange	3	3	1,000	3%
Yellow	4	4	10,000	GMV *
Green	5	5	100,000	5% #
Blue	6	6	1,000,000	6%
Violet	7	7	10,000,000	12.5%
Gray	8	8	-	30%

Color	First Digit	Second Digit	Multiplier	Tolerance
White	9	9	-	10% #
Silver	-	-	0.01	10% @
Gold	-	-	0.1	5% @
No Color	-	-	-	20%

* = Guaranteed minimum value; @ = Preferred color code; # = Alternate color code
Note: Hold the cylindrical capacitor with the bands nearest the end to the left and then read the bands from left to right.

FIVE- AND SIX-BAND COLOR CODE FOR CYLINDRICAL PAPER CAPACITORS

The capacitance for five-band and six-band capacitors begins with the two significant figures, multiplier and tolerance, as given for the four-band cylindrical capacitors in the table above. A small space separates an additional one or two bands. These two bands represent the first and possible second significant figures of voltage rating, in hundreds of volts. For instance, if two additional bands were brown and black, the capacitor is rated at 1,000 volts. A green band alone would signify a 500-V rating.

Note that if a paper capacitor value is identified in writing, a band around one end identifies the *outer foil,* which is usually grounded.

FIVE AND SIX-DOT COLOR CODES FOR CYLINDRICAL CERAMIC CAPACITORS

Cylindrical ceramic capacitors are typically white in color and less than 1/4" in diameter. The leads are radial and are attached slightly inward from the ends. Hold the capacitor with the dots between the leads beginning on the left. One six-dot capacitors and one dot is isolated outside the radial leads on each end, leaving four dots between the leads. The five-dot system omits the last dot for voltage, outside the leads on the right end.

Color	First Digit Temp (Coeff. in Parts/Million)	Second and Third Digits	Multiplier	Tolerance
Black	-	0	1	20%
Brown	30	1	10	0.1 pf
Red	80	2	100	
Orange	150	3	1,000	
Yellow	220	4	10,000	
Green	330	5	100,000	0.5 pf
Blue	470	6	1,000,000	
Violet	750	7	10,000,000	
Gray	+30	8		
White	-	9		
Silver	-	-	0.1	10%
Gold	-	-		5%

The voltage dot, if present, indicates the voltage rating of the capacitor as follows:

None	600 V
Black	-
Brown	150 V
Red	
Orange	350 V
Yellow	
Green	500 V
Blue	
Violet	
Gray	
White	

COLOR CODES FOR RECTANGULAR MICA CAPACITORS

Rectangular mica capacitors have three- or six-dot color coding schemes. These capacitors usually have a small arrowhead, teardrop shape, or triangular shape to indicate the direction in which to read the color codes (arrow pointing to the right,) or may have lettering on the side to indicate normal left-to-right reading.

THREE-DOT COLOR CODES FOR RECTANGULAR MICA CAPACITORS

Color	First Digit	Second Digit	Multiplier (Picofarads)
Black	-	0	1
Brown	1	1	10
Red	2	2	100
Orange	3	3	1,000
Yellow	4	4	10,000
Green	5	5	100,000
Blue	6	6	1,000,000
Violet	7	7	10,000,000
Gray	8	8	
White	9	9	

Note: These capacitors have a rating of 500 V and a tolerance of 20 percent.

SIX-DOT COLOR CODES FOR RECTANGULAR MICA CAPACITORS

The six-dot color codes are read from left to right, top down, with the arrow or teardrop shape pointing to the right. As indicated by the upper left dot color, three types exist. The first two types use the same color coding.

Type I—Silver Dot in Upper Left Corner

A silver dot indicates a capacitor using the EIA color code standard. It serves only to identify this fact and has no other numerical significance. See the Type II table following for color values.

Type II—Black Dot in Upper Left Corner

A black dot indicates a capacitor using the JAN (Joint Army-Navy) color code standard. It serves only to identify this fact and has no other numerical significance.

In both types I and II, the upper middle dot is the first significant figure, with the second significant color dot in the upper right corner. The lower right dot is the multiplier. The tolerance is shown by the middle lower dot.

Color	Top Middle	Top Right	Lower Right	Lower Middle
Black	-	0	1	20%
Brown	1	1	10	1%
Red	2	2	100	2%
Orange	3	3	1000	3%
Yellow	4	4	10,000	GMV
Green	5	5	100,000	5%
Blue	6	6	1,000,000	6%
Violet	7	7	10,000,000	12.5%
Gray	8	8	-	30%
White	9	9	-	10%
Silver	-	-	0.01	10%
Gold	-	-	0.1	5%
No Color	-	-	-	20%

Type III—Brown Dot in Upper Left Corner

A brown dot in the upper left corner signifies a capacitor with 3 significant figures rather than two as provided for in the previous table. The significant figures appear across the top, following the brown dot, left to right. The multiplier is in the lower right, and the tolerance is the lower middle dot, as shown for types I and II.

Color	Top Left	Top Middle	Top Right	Lower Right
Black	0	0	0	1
Brown	1	1	1	10
Red	2	2	2	100
Orange	3	3	3	1000
Yellow	4	4	4	10,000
Green	5	5	5	100,000
Blue	6	6	6	1,000,000
Violet	7	7	7	10,000,000
Gray	8	8	8	
White	9	9	9	
Silver	-	-	-	0.01
Gold	-	-	-	0.1

INDUCTOR COLOR CODES

Note that inductors are made that strongly resemble carbon resistors. They may be identified by their color code, which begins with a double-width silver band. This band has no numerical significance, serving only to identify the component as an inductor.

The value of an inductor of more than 10 microhenries has the double-width silver identification band, first and second significant figures and a multiplier just like a resistor. A tolerance band is included.

INDUCTORS OF MORE THAN 10 MICROHENRIES (μhy)

Color	First Digit	Second Digit	Multiplier (Microhenries)	Tolerance
Black	-	0	1	-
Brown	1	1	10	-
Red	2	2	100	-
Orange	3	3	1000	-
Yellow	4	4	10,000	-
Green	5	5	-	-
Blue	6	6	-	-
Violet	7	7	-	-
Gray	8	8	-	-
White	9	9	-	-
Silver	-	-	-	10%
Gold	-	-	-	5%

Note: An example might have Silver, Orange, White, Brown, and Silver, meaning an inductor of 390 μhy with a tolerance of 10 percent.

An inductor of less than 10 microhenries has the double-width silver identification band, the first significant figure, a gold decimal-point band, and a second significant figure. The last band is the tolerance.

INDUCTORS OF LESS THAN 10 MICROHENRIES (μhy)

Color	First Digit (μhy)	Second Digit	Third Digit	Tolerance
Black	-	Gold	0	-
Brown	1	Gold	1	-
Red	2	Gold	2	-
Orange	3	Gold	3	-
Yellow	4	Gold	4	-
Green	5	Gold	5	-
Blue	6	Gold	6	-
Violet	7	Gold	7	-
Gray	8	Gold	8	-
White	9	Gold	9	-
Silver	-	-	-	10%
Gold	-	-	-	5%

An example for this color scheme is an inductor with a silver identification band, Blue, Gold, Gray, and Gold bands. This would be an inductor of 6.8 μhy with a 5 percent tolerance. (This information was provided courtesy of Richard Francis, Renton Technical College.)

FUSE COLOR CODE

Note that very small, board-mounted fuses are made that strongly resemble metal-film resistors. These fuses may be identified by their color code, which begins with a double-width red band. This band has no numerical significance, serving only to identify the component as a fuse.

The first two bands are significant figures and the third is a multiplier, denoting the fuse current value in milliamperes. A fourth wide band, if present, indicates a fast-acting fuse. Absence of a fourth band indicates a standard-acting fuse. Standard fuse ratings are as follows:

First Digit Digit	Second Digit Digit	Third Digit Digit	Value (Amperes)	
Blue	Red	Black	.062 Amp or	1/16 Amp
Brown	Red	Brown	.120	1/8
Red	Green	Brown	.250	1/4
Orange	Violet	Brown	.370	3/8
Green	Black	Brown	.500	1/2
Violet	Green	Brown	.750	3/4
Brown	Black	Red	1.000	1
Brown	Green	Red	1.500	1-1/2
Red	Black	Red	2.000	2
Red	Green	Red	2.500	2-1/2
Orange	Black	Red	3.000	3
Orange	Green	Red	3.500	3-1/2
Yellow	Black	Red	4.000	4
Green	Black	Red	5.000	5
Violet	Black	Red	7.000	7
Brown	Black	Orange	10.000	10
Brown	Red	Orange	12.000	12
Brown	Green	Orange	15.000	15

*This information courtesy of Richard Francis, Renton Technical College.

Appendix II

Symbols Used On Technical Drawings

ELECTRONIC SYMBOLS

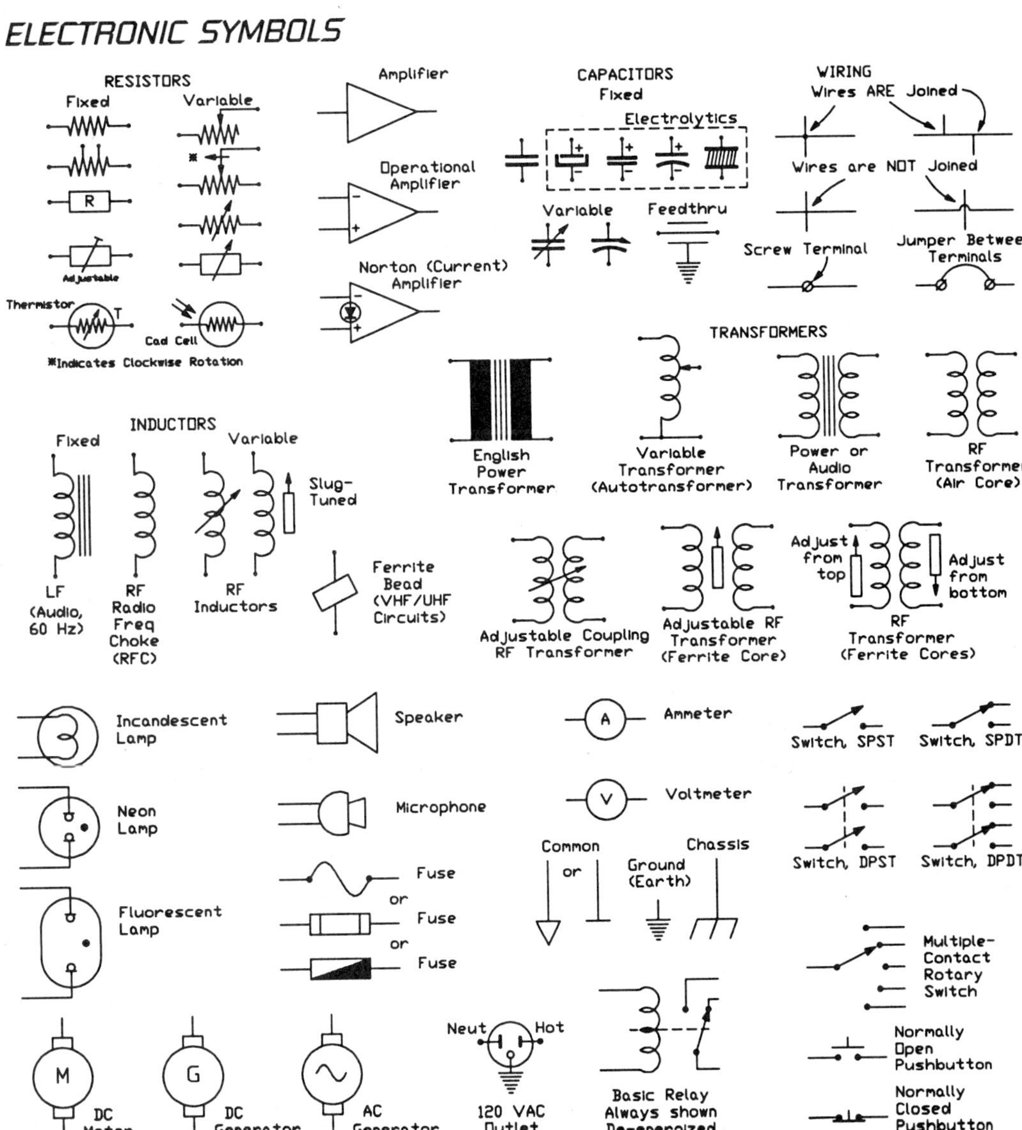

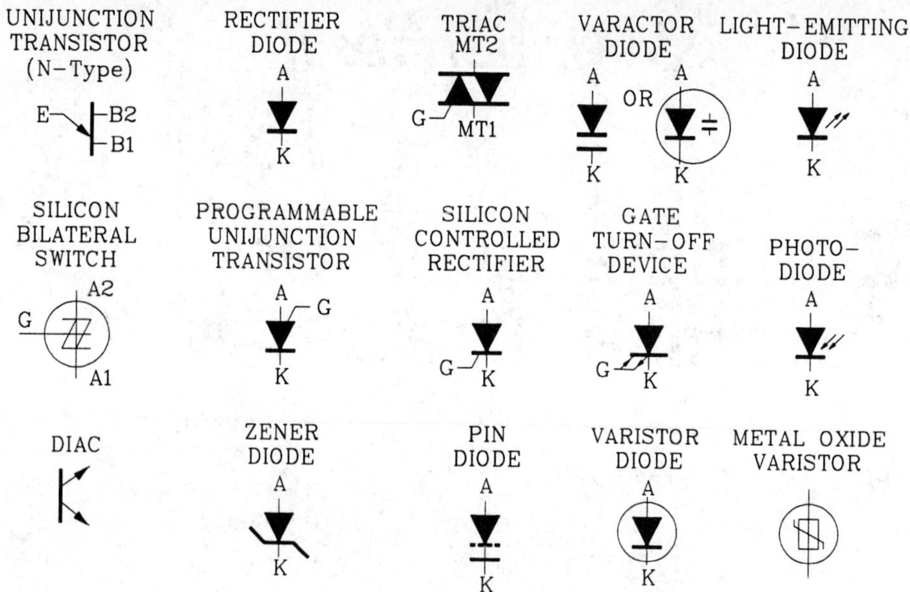
UNIJUNCTION TRANSISTOR (N–Type)
E
B2
B1
RECTIFIER DIODE
A
K
TRIAC
MT2
G
MT1
VARACTOR DIODE
A
OR
K
LIGHT–EMITTING DIODE
A
K
SILICON BILATERAL SWITCH
A2
G
A1
PROGRAMMABLE UNIJUNCTION TRANSISTOR
A
G
K
SILICON CONTROLLED RECTIFIER
A
G
K
GATE TURN–OFF DEVICE
A
G
K
PHOTO– DIODE
A
K
DIAC
ZENER DIODE
A
K
PIN DIODE
A
K
VARISTOR DIODE
A
K
METAL OXIDE VARISTOR

UHF/MICROWAVE SCHEMATIC SYMBOLS

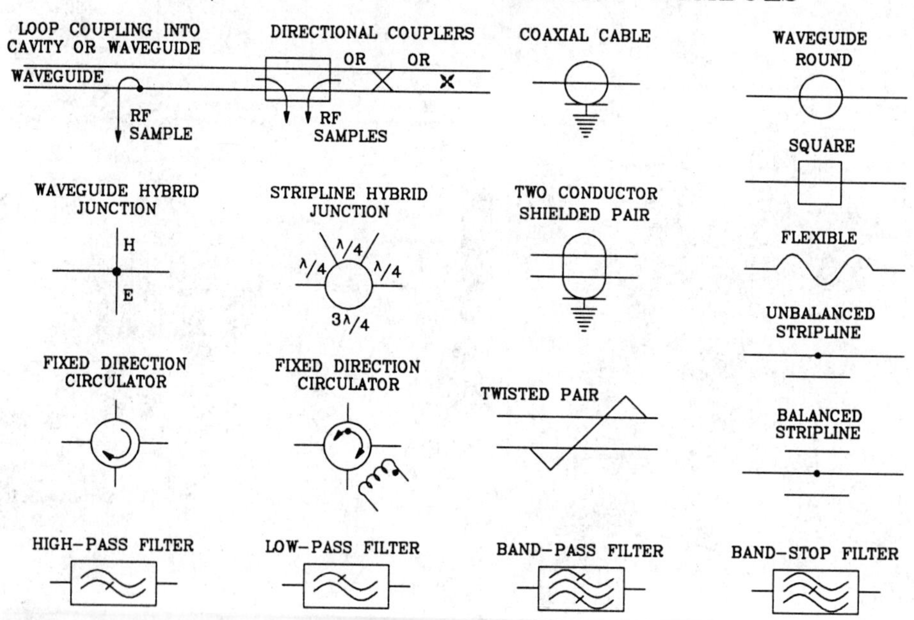
LOOP COUPLING INTO CAVITY OR WAVEGUIDE
WAVEGUIDE
RF SAMPLE
DIRECTIONAL COUPLERS
OR
OR
RF SAMPLES
COAXIAL CABLE
WAVEGUIDE ROUND
SQUARE
WAVEGUIDE HYBRID JUNCTION
H
E
STRIPLINE HYBRID JUNCTION
λ/4
λ/4
λ/4
3λ/4
TWO CONDUCTOR SHIELDED PAIR
FLEXIBLE
UNBALANCED STRIPLINE
FIXED DIRECTION CIRCULATOR
FIXED DIRECTION CIRCULATOR
TWISTED PAIR
BALANCED STRIPLINE
HIGH–PASS FILTER
LOW–PASS FILTER
BAND–PASS FILTER
BAND–STOP FILTER

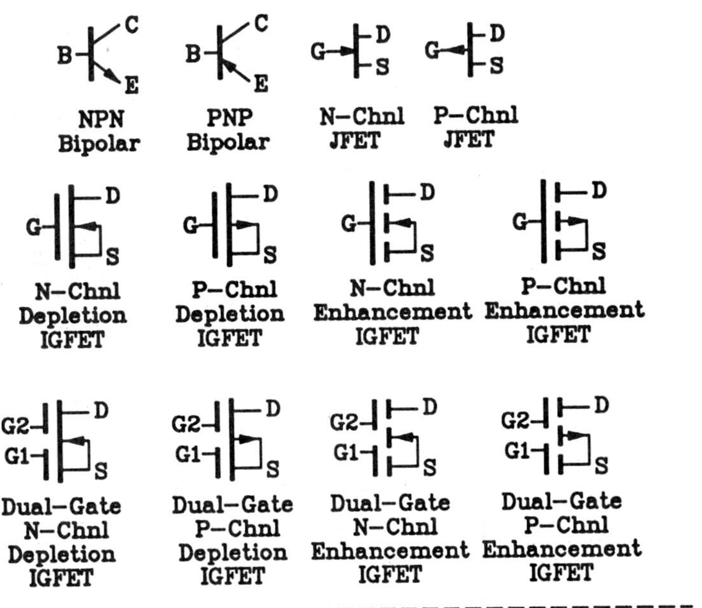

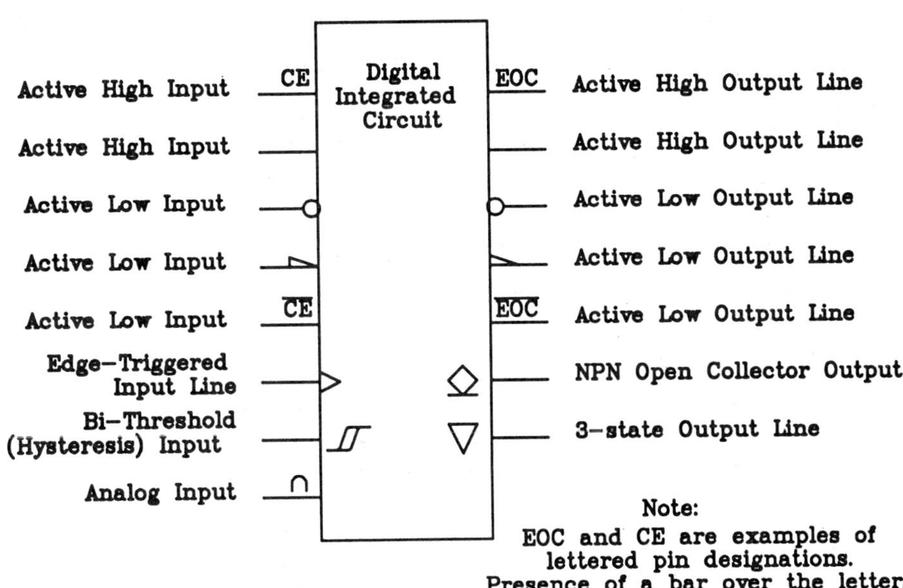

Note:
EOC and CE are examples of lettered pin designations. Presence of a bar over the letters indicates active low state.

DIGITAL FUNCTION SYMBOLS

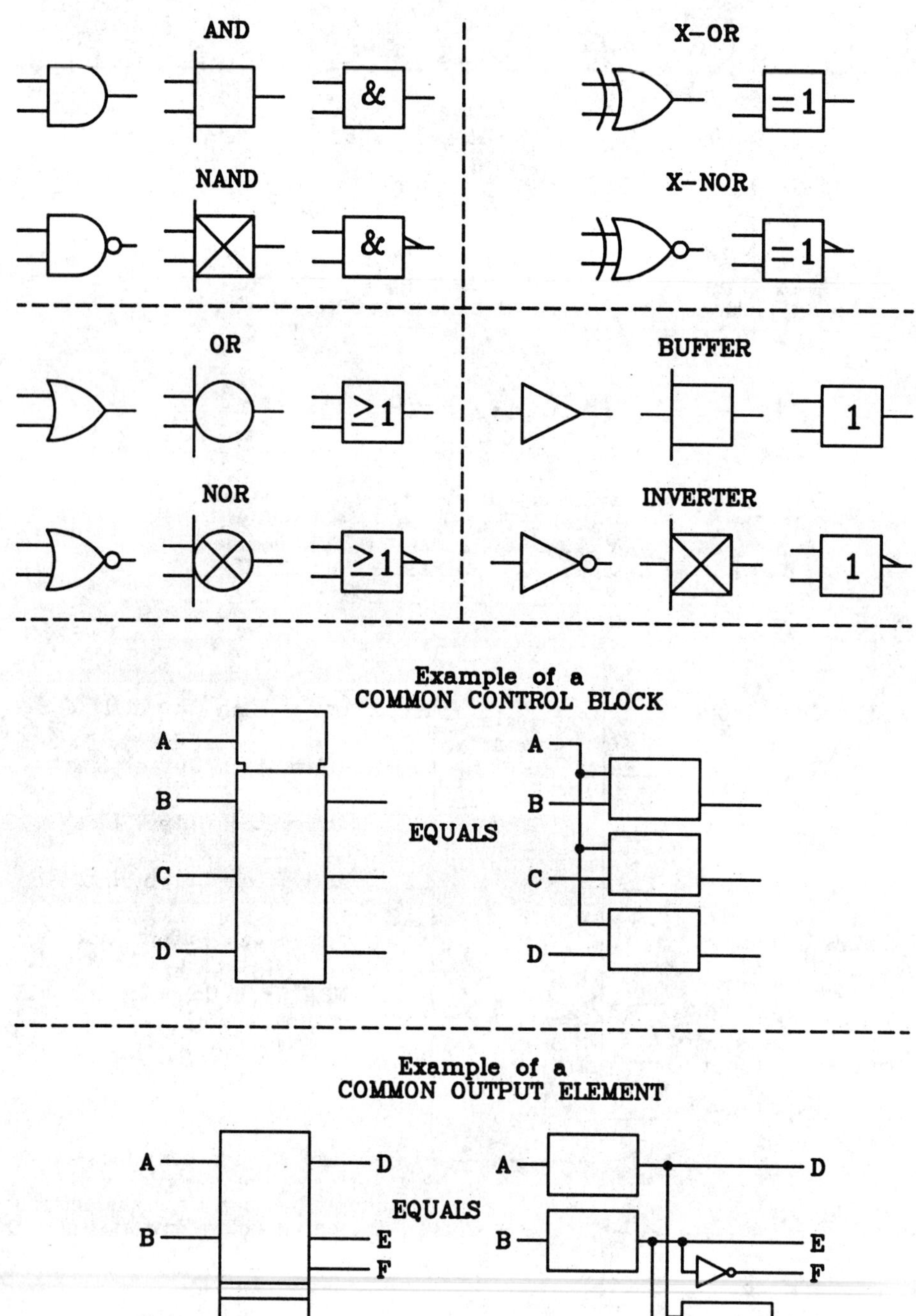

COMMON ELECTRICAL SYMBOLS

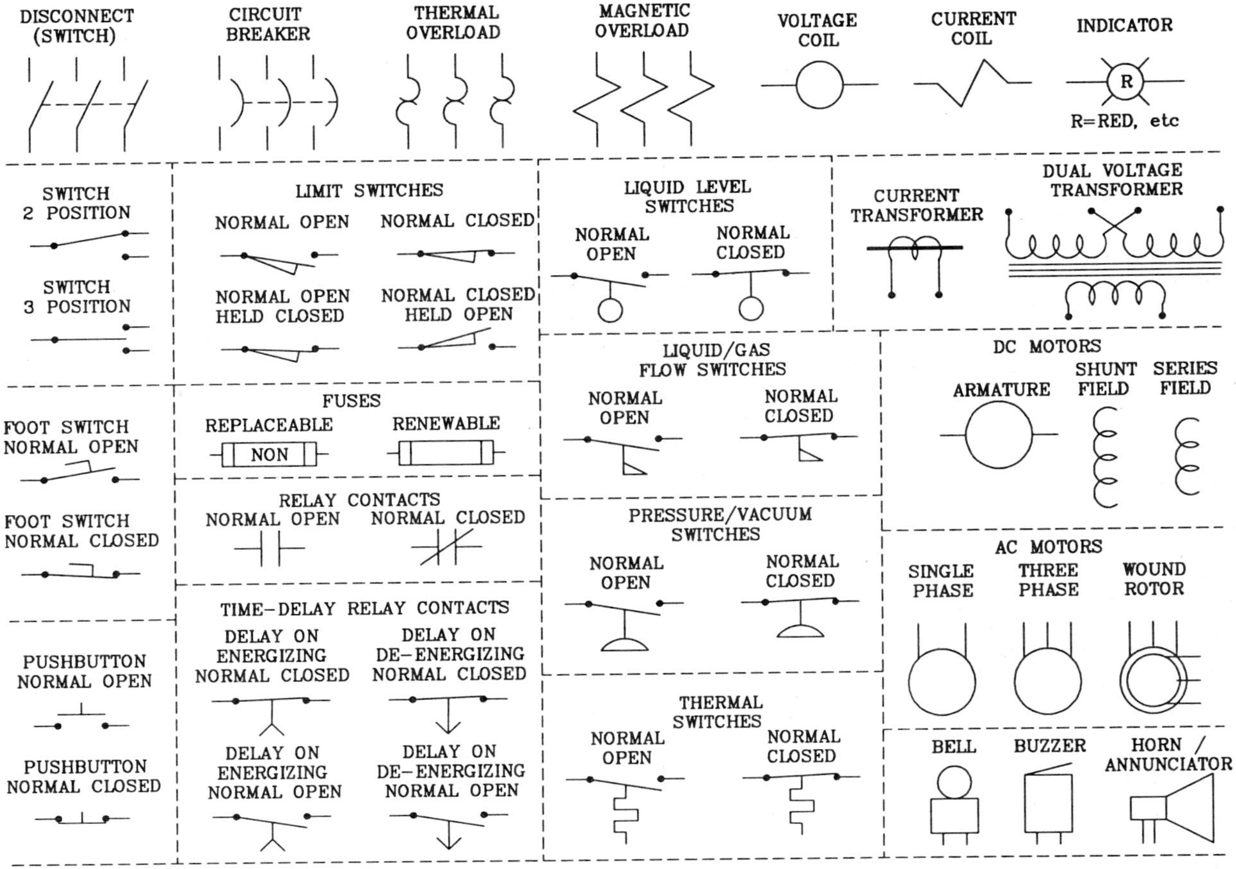

DISCONNECT (SWITCH)

CIRCUIT BREAKER

THERMAL OVERLOAD

MAGNETIC OVERLOAD

VOLTAGE COIL

CURRENT COIL

INDICATOR

R

R=RED, etc

SWITCH 2 POSITION

SWITCH 3 POSITION

LIMIT SWITCHES

NORMAL OPEN

NORMAL CLOSED

NORMAL OPEN HELD CLOSED

NORMAL CLOSED HELD OPEN

LIQUID LEVEL SWITCHES

NORMAL OPEN

NORMAL CLOSED

CURRENT TRANSFORMER

DUAL VOLTAGE TRANSFORMER

FOOT SWITCH NORMAL OPEN

FOOT SWITCH NORMAL CLOSED

FUSES

REPLACEABLE

NON

RENEWABLE

RELAY CONTACTS

NORMAL OPEN

NORMAL CLOSED

LIQUID/GAS FLOW SWITCHES

NORMAL OPEN

NORMAL CLOSED

DC MOTORS

ARMATURE

SHUNT FIELD

SERIES FIELD

PRESSURE/VACUUM SWITCHES

NORMAL OPEN

NORMAL CLOSED

AC MOTORS

SINGLE PHASE

THREE PHASE

WOUND ROTOR

PUSHBUTTON NORMAL OPEN

PUSHBUTTON NORMAL CLOSED

TIME-DELAY RELAY CONTACTS

DELAY ON ENERGIZING NORMAL CLOSED

DELAY ON DE-ENERGIZING NORMAL CLOSED

DELAY ON ENERGIZING NORMAL OPEN

DELAY ON DE-ENERGIZING NORMAL OPEN

THERMAL SWITCHES

NORMAL OPEN

NORMAL CLOSED

BELL

BUZZER

HORN / ANNUNCIATOR

ELECTRICAL RELAY FORMS

Electrical relays may be constructed in such a manner that the contacts cannot be seen. One could not tell, for instance, if the contacts were normally open or closed or whether the contacts would open and close in a set sequence as the relay was actuated. To enable the electrician to convey how the contacts are arranged, a standard arrangement of contacts have been given letter abbreviations, called *forms.* A form "A" contact arrangement, for example, is a simple, normally open arrangement. A relay with "FORM A" written on it would have this particular contact arrangment.

The following illustration shows 18 of the most common contact arrangements.

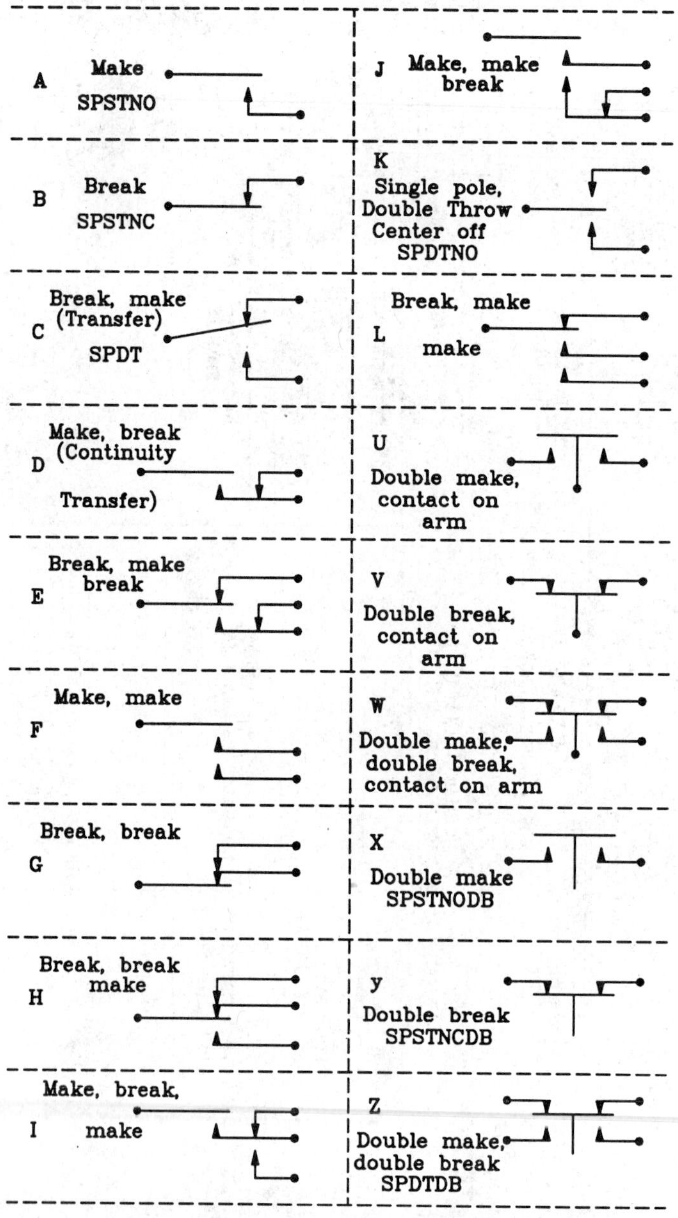

HYDRAULIC AND PNEUMATIC SYMBOLS

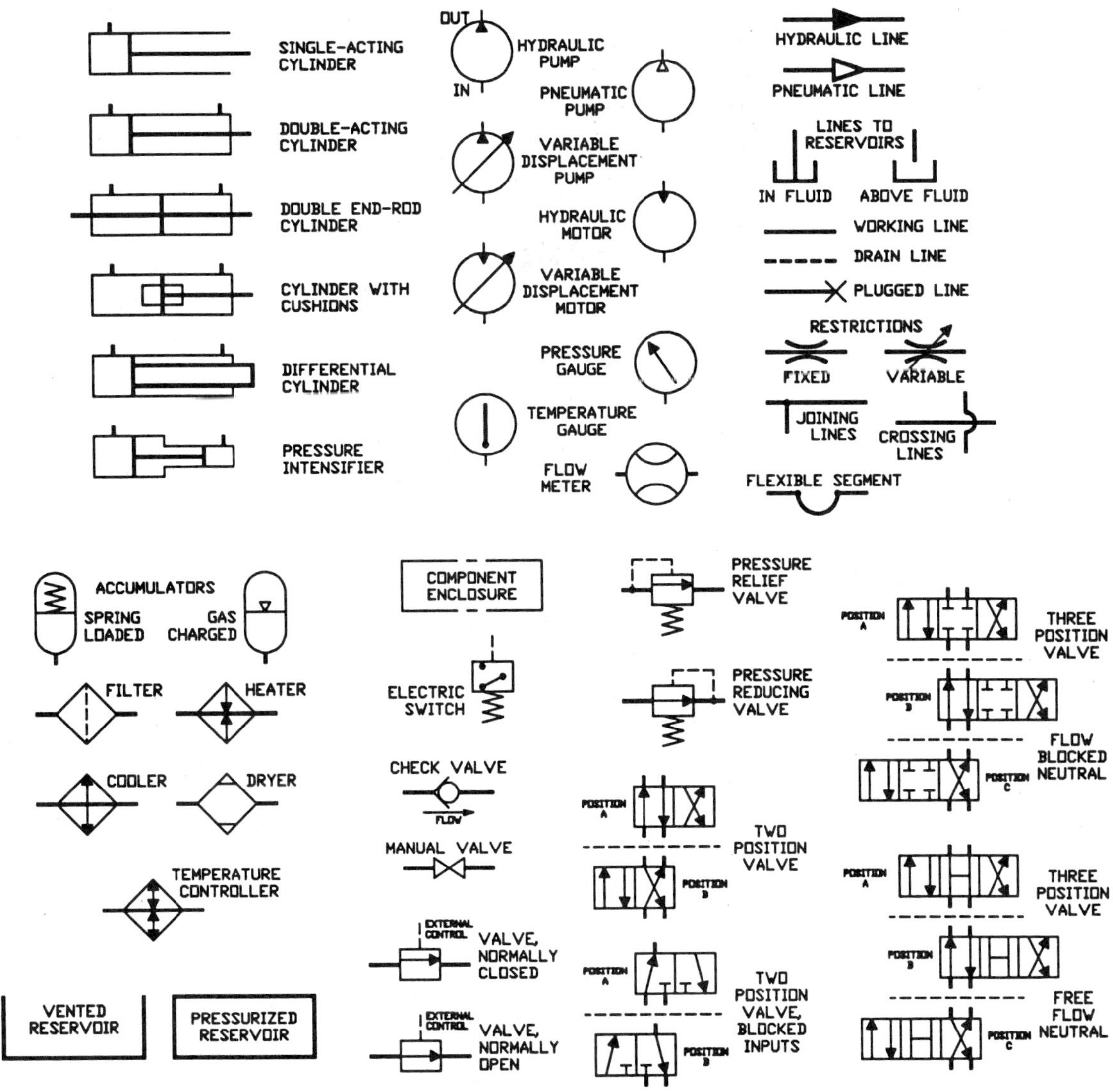

SEMICONDUCTOR SYMBOLS AND OPERATING CURVES

NAME OF DEVICE	CIRCUIT SYMBOL	COMMONLY USED JUNCTION SCHEMATIC	ELECTRICAL CHARACTERISTICS	MAJOR APPLICATIONS
GE-MOV® Varistor		WIRE LEAD, ELECTRODE, INTER-GRAN-ULAR PHASE, ZINC OXIDE GRAINS, ELECTRODE, EPOXY ENCAPSULANT, WIRE LEAD	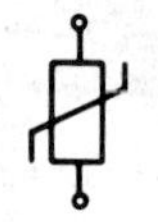 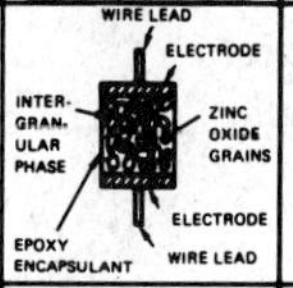 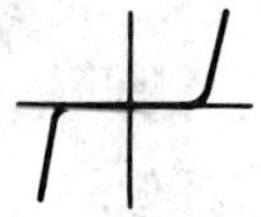 When exposed to high energy transients, the varistor impedance changes from a high standby value to a very low conducting value, thus clamping the transient voltage to a safe level.	Voltage transient protection High voltage sensing Regulation
Diode or Rectifier	ANODE CATHODE	ANODE p n CATHODE	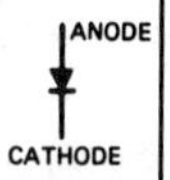 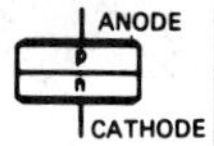 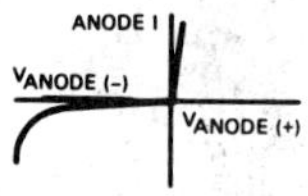 ANODE I; V_{ANODE} (−); V_{ANODE} (+) Conducts easily in one direction, blocks in the other.	Rectification Blocking Detecting Steering
Tunnel Diode	POSITIVE ELECTRODE NEGATIVE ELECTRODE	POSITIVE ELECTRODE p n NEGATIVE ELECTRODE	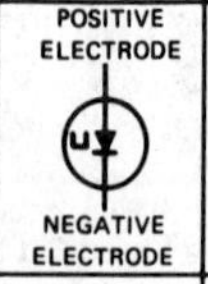 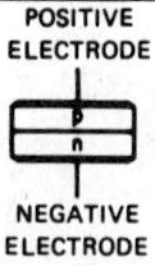 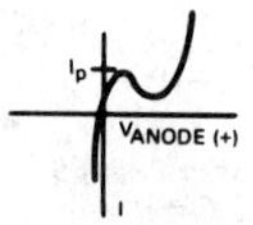 I_p; V_{ANODE} (+); I Displays negative resistance when current exceeds peak point current I_p.	UHF converter Logic circuits Microwave circuits Level sensing
Back Diode	ANODE CATHODE	ANODE n p CATHODE	 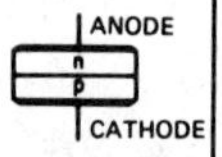 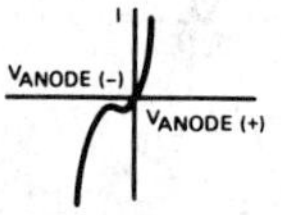 I; V_{ANODE} (−); V_{ANODE} (+) Similar characteristics to conventional diode except very low forward voltage drop.	Microwave mixers and low power oscillators
n-p-n Transistor	COLLECTOR I_C BASE I_B EMITTER	COLLECTOR n p n BASE EMITTER	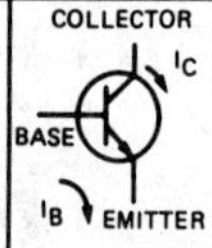 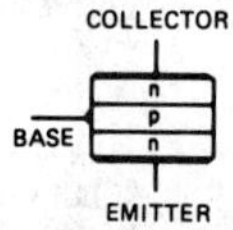 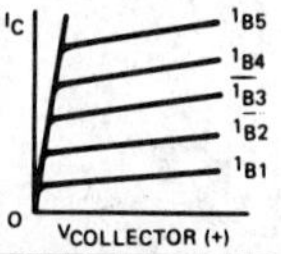 I_C; I_{B5}, I_{B4}, I_{B3}, I_{B2}, I_{B1}; O; $V_{COLLECTOR}$ (+) Constant collector current for given base drive.	Amplification Switching Oscillation
p-n-p Transistor	COLLECTOR I_C BASE I_B EMITTER	COLLECTOR p n p BASE EMITTER	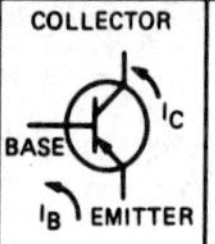 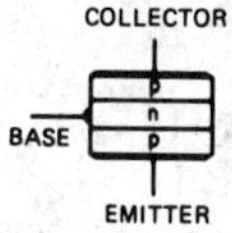 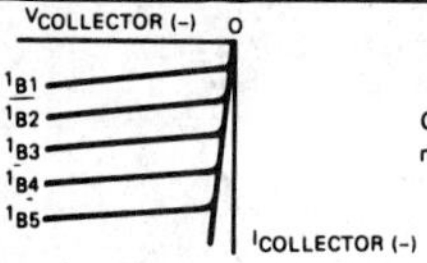 $V_{COLLECTOR}$ (−) O; I_{B1}, I_{B2}, I_{B3}, I_{B4}, I_{B5}; $I_{COLLECTOR}$ (−) Complement to n-p-n transistor.	Amplification Switching Oscillation
Unijunction Transistor (UJT)	BASE 2 EMITTER BASE 1	BASE 2 EMITTER p I_e n BASE 1	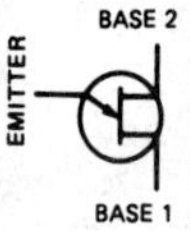 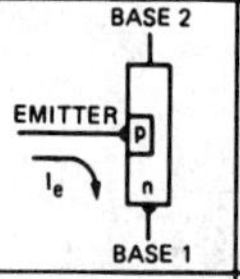 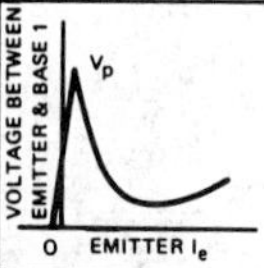 VOLTAGE BETWEEN EMITTER & BASE 1; V_p; O EMITTER I_e Unijunction emitter blocks until its voltage reaches V_p; then conducts.	Interval timing Oscillation Level Detector SCR Trigger
Complementary Unijunction Transistor (CUJT)	BASE 1 EMITTER BASE 2	BASE 1 p n p n EMITTER BASE 2	 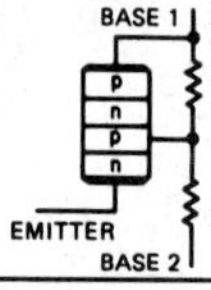 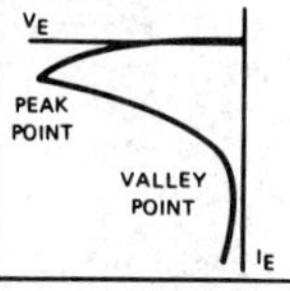 V_E; PEAK POINT; VALLEY POINT; I_E Functional complement to UJT	High stability timers Oscillators and level detectors
Programmable Unijunction Transistor (PUT)	ANODE GATE CATHODE	ANODE p n p n GATE CATHODE	 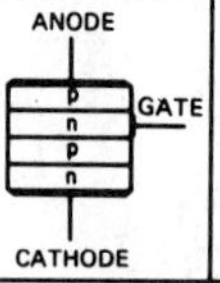 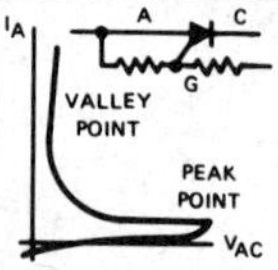 I_A; A C G; VALLEY POINT; PEAK POINT; V_{AC} Programmed by two resistors for V_p, I_p, I_v. Function equivalent to normal UJT.	Low cost timers and oscillators Long period timers SCR trigger Level detector
Photo Transistor	COLLECTOR BASE I_B EMITTER	COLLECTOR n p n BASE EMITTER	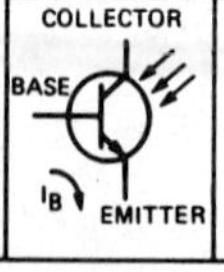 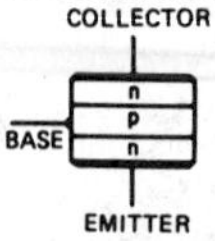 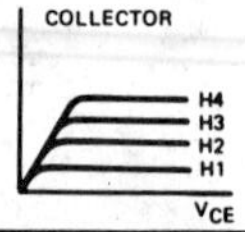 COLLECTOR; H4, H3, H2, H1; V_{CE} Incident light acts as base current of the photo transistor.	Tape readers Card readers Position sensor Tachometers

Reprinted with permission Microwave Products Department, General Electric Company, Owenburo, Kentucky

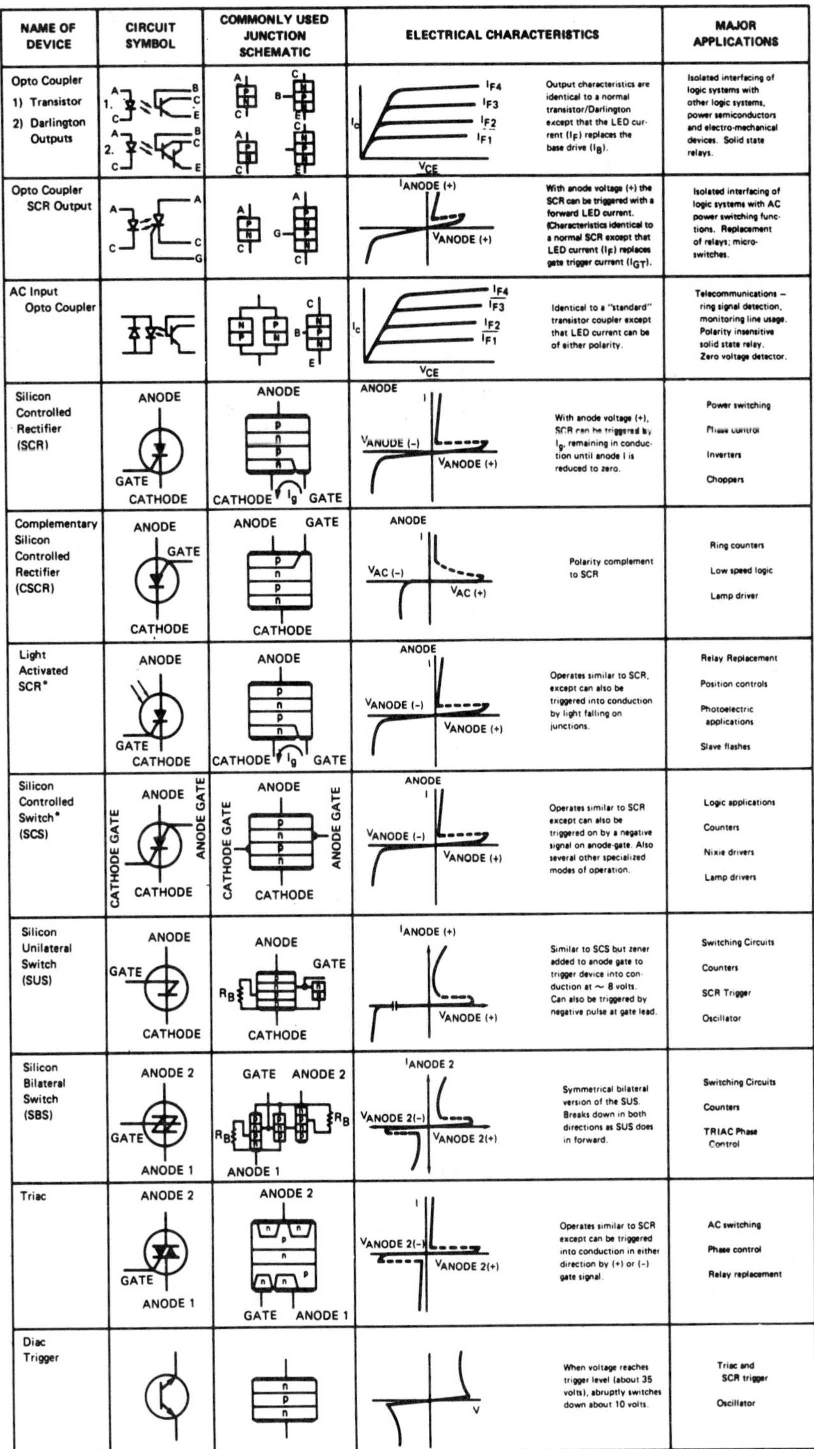

NAME OF DEVICE	CIRCUIT SYMBOL	COMMONLY USED JUNCTION SCHEMATIC	ELECTRICAL CHARACTERISTICS	MAJOR APPLICATIONS
Opto Coupler 1) Transistor 2) Darlington Outputs	1. A, C, B, C, E 2. A, C, B, C, E	A, C, B, C, E	I_{F4}, I_{F3}, I_{F2}, I_{F1}; I_c; V_{CE} Output characteristics are identical to a normal transistor/Darlington except that the LED current (I_F) replaces the base drive (I_B).	Isolated interfacing of logic systems with other logic systems, power semiconductors and electro-mechanical devices. Solid state relays.
Opto Coupler SCR Output	A, C, A, C, G	A, C, G	I_{ANODE} (+); V_{ANODE} (+) With anode voltage (+) the SCR can be triggered with a forward LED current. (Characteristics identical to a normal SCR except that LED current (I_F) replaces gate trigger current (I_{GT}).	Isolated interfacing of logic systems with AC power switching functions. Replacement of relays; micro-switches.
AC Input Opto Coupler		C, B, E; N, P	I_{F4}, I_{F3}, I_{F2}, I_{F1}; I_c; V_{CE} Identical to a "standard" transistor coupler except that LED current can be of either polarity.	Telecommunications – ring signal detection, monitoring line usage. Polarity insensitive solid state relay. Zero voltage detector.
Silicon Controlled Rectifier (SCR)	ANODE, GATE, CATHODE	ANODE; p, n, p, n; CATHODE, I_g, GATE	ANODE, I; V_{ANODE} (–); V_{ANODE} (+) With anode voltage (+), SCR can be triggered by I_g, remaining in conduction until anode I is reduced to zero.	Power switching Phase control Inverters Choppers
Complementary Silicon Controlled Rectifier (CSCR)	ANODE, GATE, CATHODE	ANODE, GATE; p, n, p, n; CATHODE	ANODE, I; V_{AC} (–); V_{AC} (+) Polarity complement to SCR	Ring counters Low speed logic Lamp driver
Light Activated SCR*	ANODE, GATE, CATHODE	ANODE; p, n, p, n; CATHODE, I_g, GATE	ANODE, I; V_{ANODE} (–); V_{ANODE} (+) Operates similar to SCR, except can also be triggered into conduction by light falling on junctions.	Relay Replacement Position controls Photoelectric applications Slave flashes
Silicon Controlled Switch* (SCS)	ANODE, ANODE GATE, CATHODE GATE, CATHODE	ANODE, ANODE GATE; p, n, p, n; CATHODE GATE, CATHODE	ANODE, I; V_{ANODE} (–); V_{ANODE} (+) Operates similar to SCR except can also be triggered on by a negative signal on anode-gate. Also several other specialized modes of operation.	Logic applications Counters Nixie drivers Lamp drivers
Silicon Unilateral Switch (SUS)	ANODE, GATE, CATHODE	ANODE, GATE, R_B, CATHODE	I_{ANODE} (+); V_{ANODE} (+) Similar to SCS but zener added to anode gate to trigger device into conduction at ~ 8 volts. Can also be triggered by negative pulse at gate lead.	Switching Circuits Counters SCR Trigger Oscillator
Silicon Bilateral Switch (SBS)	ANODE 2, GATE, ANODE 1	GATE, ANODE 2, R_B, R_B, ANODE 1	$I_{ANODE\ 2}$; $V_{ANODE\ 2}$(–); $V_{ANODE\ 2}$(+) Symmetrical bilateral version of the SUS. Breaks down in both directions as SUS does in forward.	Switching Circuits Counters TRIAC Phase Control
Triac	ANODE 2, GATE, ANODE 1	ANODE 2; n, p, n, n, n, p; GATE, ANODE 1	I; $V_{ANODE\ 2}$(–); $V_{ANODE\ 2}$(+) Operates similar to SCR except can be triggered into conduction in either direction by (+) or (–) gate signal.	AC switching Phase control Relay replacement
Diac Trigger		n, p, n	V When voltage reaches trigger level (about 35 volts), abruptly switches down about 10 volts.	Triac and SCR trigger Oscillator

Reprinted with permission Microwave Products Department, General Electric Company, Owenburo, Kentucky

Appendix III

Contributing Manufacturers of Test Equipment and Supplies

The author is most familiar with the high quality of the products offered by the following companies. These companies have been instrumental in the preparation of this book and have helped particularly by providing photographs, evaluation equipment, and technical assistance. While other electronics manufacturing companies may have similar products, specifications and quality may differ widely.

AP Products Inc.
9450 Pineneedle Drive
P.O. Box 603
Mentor, OH 44060
(216) 354-2101
IC test clips

Bird Electronic Corporation
30303 Aurora Rd.
Solon, OH 44139
(216) 248-1200
RF wattmeters and power attenuators

Fluke/Philips Test Equipment Alliance
P.O. Box 9090
Everett, WA 98206–9090
(206) 868-1582
Digital multimeters, counters, oscilloscopes, logic analyzers, signal generators, power supplies, etc.

Hewlett-Packard
5301 Stevens Creek Blvd.
Santa Clara, CA 95050-7369
(408) 246-4300
Current tracer, logic clip, logic probe

Howard Sams Publishing Co.
4300 West 62nd St.
Indianapolis, IN 46268
(800) 428-7267
Consumer equipment schematics

Huntron Instruments, Inc.
15720 Mill Creek Blvd.
Mill Creek, WA 98012
(800) 426-9265
Solid-state testers, test leads

Motorola Semiconductor Products Inc.
P.O. Box 20912
Phoenix, AZ 85036-0912
Semiconductors and manuals

Union Carbide Corporation
Section A-2, Old Ridgebury Rd.
Danbury, CT 06817
(619) 279-4500
Batteries

Vector Electronic Company Inc.
12460 Gladstone Ave.
Slymar, CA 91342
(818) 365-9661
Extender boards

Weller Plant
P.O. Box 868, State Road
Cheraw, SC 29520
(803) 537-5167
Soldering equipment

Appendix IV

Manufacturers' Logos and Part Identification

MANUFACTURERS' LOGOS

LOGO	MANUFACTURER/ADDRESS
ADVANCED ANALOG A Division of Intech	**Advanced Analog** 2270 Martin Avenue Santa Clara, CA 95050 (408) 988-4930
AM	**Advanced Micro Devices** P.O. Box 3453 Sunnyvale, CA 94088 (408) 732-2400
TFK	**AEG-Telefunken Corp.** P.O. Box 3800 Somerville, NJ 08876 (201) 722-9800
ANALOG DEVICES	**Analog Devices** One Technology Way Norwood, MA 02062-9106 (617) 329-4700
ANALOGIC	**Analogic Corporation** 8 Centennial Drive Peabody, MA 01961 (617) 246-0300
BECKMAN	**Beckman Instruments** 2500 Harbor Boulevard Fullerton, CA 92634 (714) 773-8603
BURR-BROWN® BB	**Burr-Brown** P.O. Box 11400 Tucson, AZ 85734 (602) 746-1111
CALIFORNIA MICRO DEVICES MICROCIRCUITS DIVISION	**California Micro Devices** 2000 W. 14th Street Tempe, AZ 85281 (602) 968-4431
CHERRY SEMICONDUCTOR	**Cherry Semiconductor Corp.** 2000 South County Trail East Greenwich, RI 02818-0031 (401) 885-3600
	Commodore Semiconductor Group 950 Rittenhouse Road Norristown, PA 19403 (215) 666-7950
	Cybernetic Micro Systems P.O. Box 3000 San Gregorio, CA 94074 (415) 726-3000
CYPRESS SEMICONDUCTOR	**Cypress Semiconductor** 3901 N. First Street San Jose, CA 95134 (408) 943-2600

LOGO	MANUFACTURER/ADDRESS
	Data General Corp. 4400 Computer Drive Westborough, MA 01580 (617) 366-8911
DATEL	**Datel** 11 Cabot Boulevard Mansfield, MA 02048 (617) 339-3000
EG&G RETICON	**EG&G Reticon Corp.** 345 Potrero Avenue Sunnyvale, CA 94086 (408) 738-4266
	EXAR Integrated Systems 2222 Qume Drive San Jose, CA 95161 (408) 732-7970
FERRANTI	**Ferranti** 87 Modular Avenue Commack, NY 11725 (516) 543-0200
F FUJITSU	**Fujitsu Microelectronics, Inc.** 3545 North First Street San Jose, CA 95134 (408) 922-9000
GENERAL ELECTRIC SOLID STATE	**General Electric Solid State** 724 Route 202, P.O. Box 591 Somerville, NJ 08876-0591 (201) 685-6000
GENERAL INSTRUMENT MICROELECTRONICS	**General Instrument** 600 W. John Street Hicksville, NY 11802 (516) 933-9000
GoldStar GOLD STAR CO., LTD.	**Goldstar Semiconductor Ltd.** 1130 E. Arquez Avenue Sunnyvale, CA 94086 (408) 737-8576
GOULD Electronics	**Gould Semiconductors** 2300 Buckskin Road Pocatello, ID 83201 (208) 233-4690
	Harris Semiconductor P.O. Box 883 Melbourne, FL 32901 (305) 724-7000
	Hitachi America, Ltd. 2210 O'Toole Avenue San Jose, CA 95131 (408) 435-8300

LOGO	MANUFACTURER/ADDRESS
HONEYWELL	**Honeywell** 1150 E. Cheyenne Mountain Blvd. Colorado Springs, CO 80906-4599 (303) 576-3300
HUGHES AIRCRAFT COMPANY	**Hughes Aircraft** 500 Superior Avenue, P.O., Box H Newport Beach, CA 92658-8903 (714) 759-2349
	Hybrid Systems 22 Linnell Circle Billerica, MA 01821 (617) 667-8700
HYUNDAI ELEXS AMERICA	**Hyundai Elexs America** 166 Baypointe Parkway San Jose, CA 95134 (408) 286-9800
inmos	**INMOS Corp.** 1110 Bayfield Road Colorado Springs, CO 80906 (303) 630-4000
intel i	**Intel** 3065 Bowers Avenue Santa Clara, CA 95051 (408) 987-8080
INTERSIL	**Intersil** 2450 Walsh Avenue Santa Clara, CA 95051 (408) 996-5000
ITT semiconductors	**ITT Semiconductors** 470 Broadway Lawrence, MA 01841 (617) 688-1881
Jameco ELECTRONICS	**Jameco Electronics** 1355 Shoreway Road Belmont, California 94002 (415) 592-8097 FAX 415-592-2503
λ	**Lambda Semiconductor** 121 International Drive Corpus Christi, TX 78410 (512) 289-0403
LT LINEAR TECHNOLOGY	**Linear Technology** 1630 McCarthy Boulevard Milpitas, CA 95035-7487 (408) 432-1900
3M	**3M/Electronic Products Division** P.O. Box 2963 Austin, TX 78769-2963 (512) 834-1800
MICRON TECHNOLOGY, INC.	**Micron Technology Inc.** 2805 E. Columbia Road Boise, ID 83706 (208) 383-4000
MN	**Micro Networks** 324 Clark Street Worcester, MA 01606 (617) 852-5400
	Micro Power Systems 3151 Jay Street, Box 54965 Santa Clara, CA 95054-0965 (408) 727-5350
	Mitel Corporation 350 Lagget Drive, P.O. Box 13089 Ontario, Canada K2K 1X3 (613) 592-5630
	Mitsubishi Electronics America 1050 E. Arques Avenue Sunnyvale, CA 94086 (408) 730-5900
MMI	**Monolithic Memories** P.O. Box 3453 Sunnyvale, CA 94088 (408) 970-9700

LOGO	MANUFACTURER/ADDRESS
	Motorola 5005 E. McDowell Road Phoenix, AZ 85008 (602) 244-7100
NS	**National Semiconductor** 2900 Semiconductor Drive Santa Clara, CA 95051 (408) 721-5000
NCR	**NCR** 8181 Byers Road Miamisburg, OH 45342 (513) 866-7217
NEC	**NEC Electronics, Inc.** 401 Ellis Street Mountain View, CA 94039-7241 (415) 960-6000
OKI JAPAN	**OKI Semiconductor, Inc.** 650 N. Mary Avenue Sunnyvale, CA 94086 (408) 720-1900
MATSUSHITA	**Panasonic (Matsushita)** 1 Panasonic Way Secaucus, NJ 07094 (201) 348-7000
PLESSEY	**Plessey Semiconductor** 1500 Green Hills Road Scotts Valley, CA 95066 (408) 438-2900
PMI	**Precision Monolithics, Inc.** 1500 Space Park Drive Santa Clara, CA 95052-8020 (408) 727-9222
Raytheon	**Raytheon Semiconductor** 350 Ellis Street Mountain View, CA 94039-7016 (415) 968-9211
Rockwell	**Rockwell International** 4311 Jamboree Road, P.O. Box C Newport Beach, CA 92658-8902 (714) 833-4700
SAMSUNG Semiconductor	**Samsung Semiconductor, Inc.** 3725 North First Street San Jose, CA 95134 (408) 434-5400
SANYO	**Sanyo Semiconductor Corp.** 7 Pearl Court Allendale, NJ 07401 (201) 825-8080
seeq	**SEEQ Technology, Inc.** 1849 Fortune Drive San Jose, CA 95131 (408) 432-7400
	SGS Semiconductor 1000 E. Bell Road Phoenix, AZ 85022 (602) 867-6100
SIEMENS	**Siemens Components** 1900 Homestead Road Cupertino, CA 95014 (408) 725-3531
signetics	**Signetics** 811 E. Arques Avenue Sunnyvale, CA 94088-3409 (408) 991-2000
SG SILICON GENERAL	**Silicon General** 11861 Western Avenue Garden Grove, CA 92641 (714) 898-8121
	Silicon Systems 14351 Myford Road Tustin, CA 92680 (714) 731-7110

LOGO	MANUFACTURER/ADDRESS
	Siliconix 2201 Laurelwood Road Santa Clara, CA 95054 (408) 988-8000
S MOS SYSTEMS	**S-MOS** 2460 North First Street San Jose, CA 95131 (408) 922-0200
S	**Solitron Devices, Inc.** 1177 Blue Heron Boulevard Riviera Beach, FL 33404 (407) 848-4311
② SPRAGUE	**Sprague Electric** 115 N.E. Cutoff Worcester, MA 01613-2036 (617) 853-5000
SPRAGUE SOLID STATE	**Sprague Solid State** 3900 Welsh Road Willow Grove, PA 19090 (215) 657-8400
	Standard Microsystems 35 Marcus Boulevard Hauppauge, NY 11788 (516) 273-3100
STS THOMSON MICRO ELECTRONICS	**STS Thomson Micro Electronics** 1310 Electronics Drive Carrollton, TX 75006 (214) 466-6000
	Supertex 1350 Bordeaux Drive Sunnyvale, CA 94089 (408) 744-0100
TELEDYNE PHILBRICK	**Teledyne Philbrick** 40 Allied Drive Dedham, MA 02026-9103 (617) 329-1600
	Teledyne Semiconductor 1300 Terra Bella Ave., Box 7267 Mountain View, CA 94039-7267 (415) 968-9241

LOGO	MANUFACTURER/ADDRESS
	Texas Instruments P.O. Box 655474 Dallas, TX 75265 (214) 995-2011
TRW	**TRW Semiconductors** P.O. Box 2472 La Jolla, CA 92038 (619) 457-1000
	Thomson-CSF Components Corp. 6203 Variel Avenue, Unit A Woodland Hills, CA 91365 (818) 887-1010
Toshiba	**Toshiba America, Inc.** 9775 Toldeo Way Irvine, CA 92718 (714) 455-2000
UNITED MICROELECTRONICS CORPORATION	**United Microelectronics Corp.** 3350 Scott Boulevard #57 Santa Clara, CA 95054 (408) 727-9239
VITELIC CORP.	**Vitelic Corp.** 3910 North First Street San Jose, CA 95135-1501 (408) 433-6000
WESTERN DIGITAL CORPORATION	**Western Digital** 2445 McCabe Way Irvine, CA 92714 (714) 863-0102
Xicor	**Xicor** 851 Buckeye Court Milpitas, CA 95035 (408) 432-8888
Zilog	**Zilog, Inc.** 210 Hacienda Avenue Campbell, CA 95008 (408) 370-8000

PART IDENTIFICATION PREFIXES

These part-number prefixes may help you in determining the manufacturer or supplier of original parts. The information contained here is believed to be correct, however, no liability to its correctness is assumed by RCA Corporation.

Prefix	Manufacturer
001-	Hammond
010-	Ampex
019-	Hallicrafter
020-	Scott
050-	Hitachi
051-	Automatic
057-	Hitachi
075-	Hammond, Heathkit
1A	Automatic Radio
1N	Diode or rectifier, JEDEC number.
1S	Japanese Rectifier or Diode
1T	Japanese Rectifiers
1W, 1X, 1Z	Farfisa
2A	See G.E. 4JX2A Series
2D	Kimball
2N	Transistor or SCR, JEDEC number.
2S, 2SA	Japanese Transistors
2SB, 2SC	Japanese Transistors
2SD, 2T	Japanese Transistors
3L4-	Philco
3N	Field-Effect Transistor (FET)
4-	Simpson Sears
4C, 4D	General Electric
4JX	General Electric
5E	See General Electric 4JX5E Series
6-, 6A, 6D-, 6L	Automatic Radio
6MC	Automatic Radio
6RS	General Electric
7-	Standel
7A	General Electric, Sherwood
919-	Lowery, Farfisa, Maestro
964-	Zenith
991-, 992-	Lowery
1410-, 1412-, 1414-	Rogers
2057B	Admiral
2093B	Admiral
2400 Series	RCA
3400 Series	RCA
3500 Series	RCA
3600 Series	RCA
3900 Series	RCA
4822-	Philips
7000 Series	RCA
30,000 Series	RCA
40,000 Series	RCA
8-	Blaupunkt
8D, 8H, 8L, 8P	Automatic Radio
13-	Sylvania
14-	Electrophone, Philco
16-	Symphonic
16A-, 16E-	See General Electric 4JX16A/16E Series
20-	Philco
20A	Standel, Gibson
24T-	Standard Kollsman
28-	Electrophone
31-	Philco
32-	Philco, Sylvania
33H	Philips
34-	Philco, Marantz
35-	Marantz, Autolite
40-, 41-	Acoustech
46-	Philco, Simpson Sears
48A, B, C, D, K, P, S	Motorola
51S-	Motorola
53A, 53B, 53C, 53E	Magnavox
56, 57-	Heathkit, Admiral
58	Admiral
62-, 63-	RCA
63B, 63C, 63J	Magnavox
66F-	Fleetwood
69A, 69SP	Standel
73C	General Electric
76	Philco
77-, 78-	Clairtone
79F	Fleetwood
86	Fleetwood, Warwick
85-5000 Ser.	Thomas
88A/B/D, 89B	Automatic
90-, 91-	Imperial
50,000 Series	Conn, Ford
56,000 Series	Leece Neville
58,000 Series	Leece Neville
60,000 Series	Ford, RCA
80,000 Series	RCA
93,000, 94,000, 95,000 Series	Eico
100,000 Series	RCA
161,000 Series	Toshiba
171,000 Series	Toshiba
199,000 Series	Toshiba
530,000 Series	Fleetwood
570,000 Series	Simpson Sears, Sears, Dynaco
600,000 Series	Sharp
612,000 Series	Magnavox
800,000 Series	Emerson
91A	Standel
93	Admiral
93SE-	Clairtone
96-	Blaupunkt
101-	RCA
103-	Zenith
104-	RCA
115-, 118-	RCA
117-	Heathkit, RCA
120-	Hallicrafter
121-	Zenith
132-	McIntosh
156	Westinghouse
173	General Electric
207A	Argos
209-	Dual
212-	Zenith
221-	Zenith
229-	Philco
236-	Allen Organ
247-	Heathkit
294-	Fanon
295	Westinghouse
296	Fanon, Westinghouse
297	Westinghouse
324-, 325-, 344-	Philco
353-	Sony
378-	Dynakit
417-	Heathkit
421-	Zenith
431-	Harmon Kordon
442-, 443-	Heathkit
462-, 464-	Nordmende
465, 469-	
571-, 572-, 574-	Dynakit
624-	Sylvania
690-	Westinghouse
800-	Clairtone, Zenith
880-	Clairtone
801,000 Series	Gulbransen
960,000 Series	Fleetwood
980,000 Series	Fleetwood
1,810,000 Series	Simpson Sears, Sears
2,000,000 Series	Bendix
2,300,000 Series	Hitachi
4,000,000 Series	Bendix
7,570,000 Series	Ampex
23,000,000 Series	Toshiba

A	See 2SA
A	General Electric Rectifier
A	Amperex, Baldwin, Fisher, Nivico
A514-	Baldwin
AA	European Diodes
AC, AD	European Transistors
AF, AI, AL	European Transistors
AMD	Philips
AN	Panasonic, Matsushita
AR, AQ	Philco
AT	Philco
AS, AU, AX	European Transistors
AW01	Hitachi Zener Diode
B	See 25B
B	Bendix Farfisa
BA, BB	European Diodes
BC, BD, BF	European Transistors
BCM	Philco
BF	European Transistors
BN	Maestro, Lowery
BR, BS	European Transistors
BT	European SCR
BU	European Transistors
BY	European Rectifiers
BZ	European Zener Diodes
C	See 2SC
C	General Electric SCR
CA, CD	RCA IC. G.E.
CD, CJ, CS	Simpson Sears, Scott
CDC	Monarch
RM	Raytheon
RR, RS	General Electric, Craig
S	Fairchild, Syntron
SA, SB, SD	Japanese types- See 2SA, 2SB, etc.
SA	Standel
SAJ	ITT, IC
SC	Motorola, Texas Instrument
SC	General Electric SCR
SD	Japanese Rectifiers, Philco
SDT, SES	Solitron, Standel
SE	Fairchild
SF	Texas Instrument
SFC	Motorola
SFT	Farfisa, Simpson Sears
SG	Japanese Rectifier, Telefunken

CDT	Clevite
CS	Continental, Simpson Sears
D	General Electric, Sylvania
DHD	Japanese Rectifier
DM	National IC
DS, DT	General Motors
DTG, DTS	General Motors
E	Fleetwood, Nivico
ECG	Sylvania
EA, ER, ET, EV	General Electric
EP, ES, EV	General Electric
EX	Fisher
FA	Hitachi IC
FJ	Philips IC
FR	Japanese Rectifier
FS	Fairchild- See S No.
FCS	See CS
GB	Philco
GC	Texas Instrument
GE	General Electric
GD	Philco
GM	Japanese UHF Transistors
GP	Texas Instrument
GT	General Instrument
HA, HB, HC	Simpson Sears, Lloyds, Sanyo Hitachi
HD, HE	Admiral, Lloyds
HEP	Motorola
HF, HR	Philco
HS	Lloyds
HT	Admiral
HV	Admiral, Philco
HX	Lloyds
J	Philco
JC	Lloyds
JT	Philco
KB	RCA
SGB	Standel
SIS, SID, SIT	Fisher
SH	Japanese Rectifier
SK	RCA, Motorola, Texas Instrument
SKA	Texas Instrument
SL	Motorola
SM	Texas Instrument
SN	Texas Instrument IC, Japanese Rectifier
SP, SPS, SPF	Motorola
SR, SS, SL	Motorola
STK	Sanyo IC Modules
SV	Transitron
SX	Texas Instrument
T	Philco, Motorola
TA	RCA, Toshiba

KR	Craig
LA, LD, LH	Sanyo IC
LM, LP	
LM	National IC
M4000 Series	Motorola
M5000 Series	Mitsubishi, Sony IC
M7000 Series	Motorola
M8000 Series	Toshiba
M9000 Series	Toshiba
MC, MU, MM, MDA	Motorola
MFC	Motorola
MM	Motorola, Toshiba
MP	Motorola, Philco
MRF	Motorola
MT	General Electric
MV	Motorola
N	Signetics IC
OA	European Diode
OC	European Transistors
P	Lowery
PA	Fisher, Philco, General Electric IC IC
PC	Craig
PD	General Electric IC
PE, PL	Philco IC
PM	Motorola
PR	See Philco AR
PET	See Philco
PH	European Rectifiers
PT	European
QA, QP, QRS	Scott
R	General Electric, Texas Instrument
RC	Raytheon
RD	Japanese Diodes
RE	Raytheon
TAA, TAD	Philips, SGS IC
TD	General Electric, Toshiba
TE, TH	Sanyo
TI, TIS, TIP, TIM, TIX	Texas Instrument
TQ	Sanyo
TR, TRO	Fisher
TS	
TV	Sanyo, Philco
TVC	Sprague
UA, UL	Fairchild IC
ULN, ULX	Sprague IC
UT	Panasonic IC
TZ	Sprague
V	Benco, Fisher
VS	Japanese Rectifier
XB, XC	Clairtone, Motorola
X16	General Electric
ZR	Fisher

Appendix V

Identification Of Surface-Mounted Devices

The demand for smaller and more reliable electronic circuits which can be assembled with automated equipment is making the use of surface-mounted devices (SMDs) the next wave of technology. These components are just like the traditional counterparts, but simply reduced to about half their size. Resistors, capacitors, transistors, and ICs are now being built for pin spacings of 0.05" (compared to the 0.1" spacing of standard-sized integrated circuits). SMDs are sometimes called "chip components." They are mounted on only one side of a PC board, eliminating the necessity of drilling holes in the board.

The identification codes on these tiny parts are not yet standardized. The following parts identification codes are those used by General Electric (GE) and Radio Corporation of America (RCA). Other codes can and will be used by different manufacturers. *The only way to positively identify SMDs is to refer to the proper documentation for the specific equipment at hand.*

CHIP RESISTORS

Chip resistors consist of a ceramic base with a conducting material deposited on it. The ends of such a resistor resemble a letter *C*. See Figure A-V-1.

The color of a chip resistor will be a near-white. One side will be dark (the side with the resistive coating). There should be a three-digit code on the resistor. These digits represent the resistance, a two-digit figure with a multiplier, just like a two-significant-figure resistor color code. See the following for examples:

$$122 = 1{,}200\ \Omega$$
$$331 = 330\ \Omega$$

Note that the use of only a single side makes the use of jumpers a necessity in

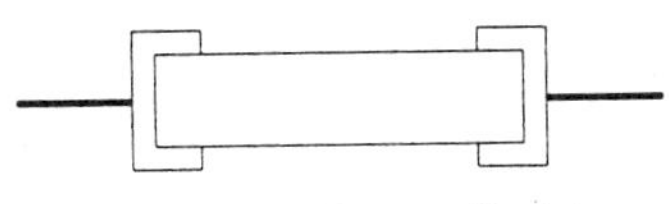

Figure A-V-1 The SMD resistor package.

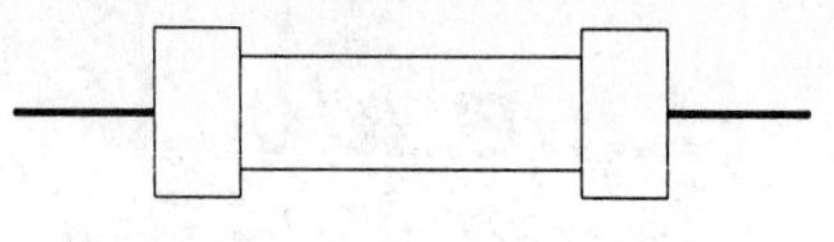

Figure A-V-2 The SMD capacitor package.

most circuits. In lieu of wire jumpers, a zero-resistance "chip jumper" is used. This component is marked with an *H*.

Chip resistors come in two sizes. The first is type 1206, which is 0.125" long × 0.063" wide. This is the 1/8th watt size. The second is type 0805, 0.08" × 0.05", with a rating of 1/10th watt.

CHIP CAPACITORS

Chip capacitors are made up in layers, with alternating conductors connected to the two end caps. Many sizes are possible, depending on the capacitance and voltage rating desired. The end electrodes of a capacitor enclose the end of the component. See Figure A-V-2.

A chip capacitor will be one solid color: brown, tan, gray, beige, or near-white. Common sizes for chip capacitors are: type 1206, 0.125" × 0.063" (thickness is variable); type 0805, 0.08" × 0.05" (thickness is variable); and other sizes, 0.059"–0.22" long × 0.032–0.197" wide.

There are three marking systems in use. The first is the preferred method.

Two-place letter and number.

Two-place letter-and-number, or two numbers.

One-place letter of varying color.

TWO-PLACE LETTER AND NUMBER CAPACITOR CODE

The first letter (upper- or lower-case) of such a code represents 1 of 33 different combinations of two significant figures:

A = 1.0	N = 3.3	W = 6.8
B = 1.1	b = 3.5	n = 7.0
C = 1.2	P = 3.6	X = 7.5
D = 1.3	Q = 3.9	t = 8.0
E = 1.5	d = 4.0	Y = 8.2
F = 1.6	R = 4.3	y = 9.0
G = 1.8	e = 4.5	Z = 9.1
H = 2.0	S = 4.7	
J = 2.2	f = 5.0	
K = 2.4	T = 5.1	
a = 2.5	U = 5.6	
L = 2.7	m = 6.0	
M = 3.0	V = 6.2	

The remaining number is a simple multiplier, where 0 = no multiplier, 1 = 10, and so on. The value indicated is measured in picofarads.

TWO-PLACE LETTER-AND-NUMBER, OR TWO NUMBERS

This method of marking is simple if the code is a pair of numbers. The numbers represent the capacitance directly, without a multiplier. A capacitor marked *75* would have a value of 75 pfd. Values of capacitance over 99 pfd must be represented as follows, where the first letter represents two significant figures:

A = 10	J = 22	S = 47
B = 11	K = 24	T = 51
C = 12	L = 27	U = 56
D = 13	M = 30	V = 62
E = 15	N = 33	W = 68
F = 16	P = 36	X = 75
G = 18	Q = 39	Y = 82
H = 20	R = 43	Z = 91

Note that these are just 10 times the same upper-case values of the previous system. No lower-case letters are used in this code. An example might be a marking of *Y* 1, which would represent 82 with a zero, or 820 pfd. The remaining number is a simple multiplier, where 1 = 10, 2 = 100, etc. The value indicated is in picofarads.

ONE-PLACE LETTER OF VARYING COLOR

This method consists of a single letter representing two significant figures, with a varying color which serves as a multiplier.

A = 1.0	I = 1.8	R = 3.3	Y = 5.6
B = 1.1	J = 2.0	S = 3.6	Z = 6.2
C = 1.2	K = 2.2	T = 3.9	3 = 6.8
D = 1.3	L = 2.4	V = 4.3	4 = 7.5
E = 1.5	N = 2.7	W = 4.7	7 = 8.2
H = 1.6	O = 3.0	X = 5.1	9 = 9.1

The color of the letter is the multiplier (which is very nonstandard) as follows:

Orange = × 1.0
Black = × 10
Green = × 100
Blue = × 1,000
Violet = × 10,000
Red = × 100,000

As an example, a chip marked with a black *Y* would be a 5.6 × 10 or 56 pfd.

SMD INDUCTORS

Tiny SMD inductors can be identified by their relative thickness and black color. Those with a ferrite bead included as part of the package have a rust color at top and bottom. Large inductors look like black-colored blocks with contacts on each end.

The value for inductors is the same as that used for resistors: a three-digit number consisting of two significant figures and a multiplier.

TANTALUM CAPACITORS

These polarized components are recognizable because the two ends are of a different construction.

DISCRETE DEVICE PACKAGES

Diodes, transistors, and FETs are packaged in small plastic packages, as shown in Figure A-V-3.

THE SMC PACKAGE

This two-lead package contains a single diode or a zener diode. The cathode is identified as it is with traditional components by a band at one end.

THE SOT-23 PACKAGE

SOT stands for small-outline transistor. This package is very common and can contain a PNP or NPN transistor, an FET, or a MOSFET. It can also contain a single diode or a zener, or two diodes. Sometimes a transistor is used in a circuit as two diodes, with a common anode (NPN) at the base connection or a common cathode (PNP) at the base connection.

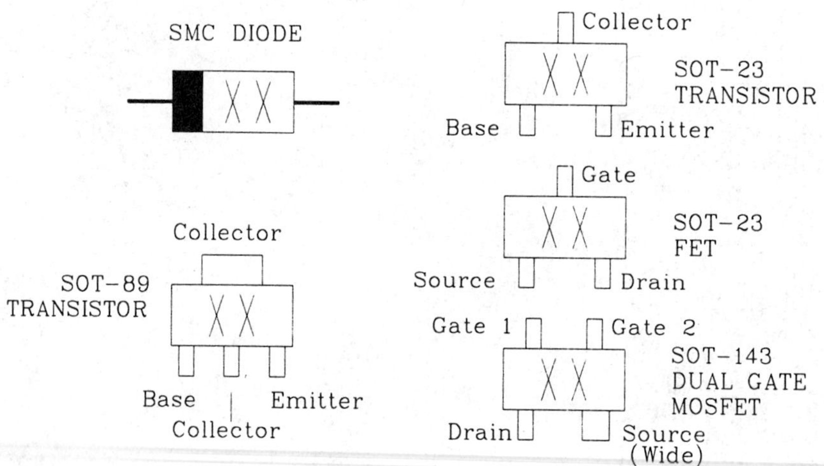

Figure A-V-3 Small-outline packages for active devices.

THE SOT-143 PACKAGE

This package is used to house dual-gate MOSFETs. The widest of the four leads identifies the source connection.

THE SOT-89

This package is used for miniature power transistors of either NPN or PNP types. It presently is the only SMD power device.

THE MELF PACKAGE

Metal electrode face (ELF) bonding is a process used to package diodes, zeners, resistors, and capacitors. They are circular and have metal ends that are soldered directly to the board pads.

INTEGRATED CIRCUIT SMD IDENTIFICATION

There are three basic outlines for ICs. ICs are electrically the same as larger components and are merely repackaged for a smaller size.

The SOIC Package

The small-outline integrated circuit (SOIC) package is identified in the same way as traditional size components. The chips, however, are about half the normal size, with pin spacings of either 0.05" between pins or as small as 0.025". The short wires extending from these chips are sometimes bent to lie along the printed circuit traces and sometimes straight to stand off the board. The leads are identified in the same way as the traditional size ICs. One of the corners has a dot, indentation, or other mark to indicate pin #1. Pins are then numbered counterclockwise (looking at the top of the device) around the chip. The package size is reflected in the designation for the package; for instance an SO-16 package is a standard outline SMD with 16 pins.

The Flatpack

The flatpack is sometimes called a "quad flatpack" because it utilizes all sides of the IC for pins. Pin 1 is identified as the pin just to the left of the trimmed corner. The remaining pins are numbered counterclockwise (looking at the top of the device) around the chip. Up to 80 leads can be accommodated in this package. Both 0.05" and 0.025" pin spacing packages are available.

The PLCC Package

The pastic leaded chip carrier (PLCC) looks like the flatpack. The pins, however, are bent back under the device in a *J* shape. This makes the PLCC able to plug into a socket. Identification of pin 1 is not as simple as the flatpack; lead 1 is midway along the beveled edge. It is in line with a small dimple or depression in the case. Going counterclockwise from this point, the first corner is chamfered. Figure 1–3 of this book shows the pinout method used. From 68 to 124 leads are possible with this chip package.

Appendix VI

Resistive Audio Pads

AUDIO POWER LEVELS

(Reference level = 0 dBm, 1 milliwatt into 600 Ω)

Volts RMS	Milliwatts	dBm
.000775	.000001	-60
.00245	.00001	-50
.00775	.0001	-40
.0245	.001	-30
.0775	.01	-20
.245	.1	-10
.775	1.0	0 dBm

Volts	Watts	dBm
1.1	.002	+3
1.55	.004	+6
2.45	.01	+10
7.75	.1	+20
24.5	1	+30
77.5	10	+40

RESISTIVE ATTENUATOR PADS

Figure A-VI-1 are values required for attenuation pads with 600 Ω input and output impedances. Resistances for impedances other than 600 Ω may be calculated by applying a factor of x/600. For example, pads for 50 Ω circuits would use resistors of 50/600 or 1/12th of the table values.

Note that R3 is half the value of R1.

dB	R1	R2	R3
1	36	5.1K	18
2	68	2.7K	36
3	100	1.8K	51
5	160	1K	82
6	200	820	100
10	300	430	150
15	430	220	200
20	510	120	240

dB	R1	R2	R3
26	500	62	270
30	560	39	270
40	560	12	300

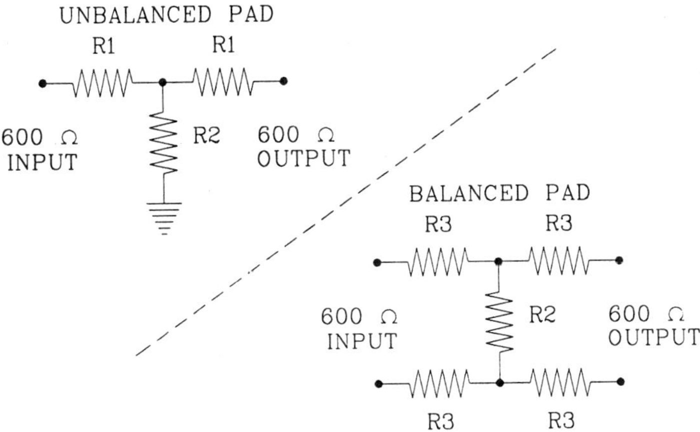

A-VI-1 "T" and "H" resistive attenuator pads for unbalanced and balanced circuits.

RESISTIVE MINIMUM-LOSS PADS

Resistors may be used to match impedances, but their use will result in some loss of signal. The following pads, which were selected for common impedance values, will result in the minimum loss possible when using resistors. The impedances match from either direction.

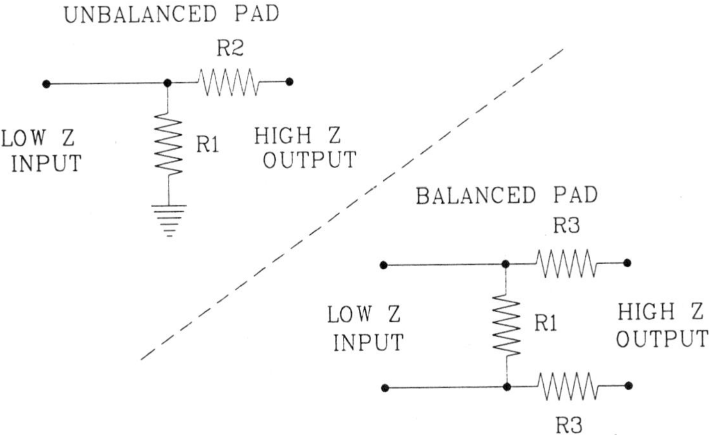

Figure A-VI-2 Resistive minimum-loss pads for matching unlike impedances

dB	Low Z	High Z	R1	R2	R3
5.7	50	75	87	43	22
10	50	150	61	122	61
13.4	50	300	55	274	137
15.8	50	500	53	474	237
16.6	50	600	52	574	287
7.7	75	150	106	106	53
11.4	75	300	87	260	130
13.9	75	500	81	461	230
14.8	75	600	80	561	280
7.7	150	300	212	212	106
10.5	150	500	179	418	209
11.4	150	600	173	520	260
6.5	300	500	474	316	158
7.7	300	600	424	424	212
3.8	500	600	1225	245	122

Appendix VII

Identification Of Foreign Semiconductors

IDENTIFICATION OF EUROPEAN SEMICONDUCTORS

First Letter

A Germanium Device
B Silicon Device
C Other Devices: Gallium Arsenide, etc., >1.3 electron volts (Ev)
D Other Devices: Indium Antimonide, < 0.6 Ev
R Radiation Detectors, Photo, Hall Effect, etc.

Second Letter

A Low-Power Diode, VVCD
B Varicap
C Small-Signal Audio
D Audio Power
E Tunnel Diode
F Small-Signal RF
G Miscellaneous
H Field Effect
K Hall Generator
L RF Power
M Hall Modulators, Multipliers
P Photodiode or Transistor
R Low-Power SCR
S Low-Power Switching
T Thyristors
U High-Power Switching
X Multiplier Diode
Y High-Power Rectifier
Z Zener Diode

Source: Thomas J. Glover, *Electronic Databook*, 4th ed., 1992, TAB Books Inc., Morrison, Colorado

First Symbol
- 0 - Phototransistor
- 1 - Signal, Rectifier, or Varactor Diode
- 2 - Bipolar, JFET, SCR, etc.
- 3 - Semiconductors with two gates

Second Symbol
- S - Semiconductor

Third Symbol
- A - HF PNP Transistor
- B - LF PNP Transistor
- C - HF NPN Transistor
- D - LF NPN Transistor
- F - P gate SCR
- G - N gate SCR
- J - P channel FET
- K - N channel FET

Fourth Symbol—Device Serial Numbers

Fifth Symbol—Alpha Revisions

Source: Thomas J. Glover, *Electronic Databook*, 4th ed., 1992, TAB Books Inc., Morrison, Colorado

Examples:
- 1SS = Signal Diode
- 1SV = Varactor Diode
- 2SA = PNP High-Frequency Bipolar Transistor
- 2SB = PNP Low-Frequency (Audio) Bipolar Transistor
- 2SC = NPN High-Frequency Bipolar Transistor
- 2SD = NPN Low-Frequency (Audio) Bipolar Transistor
- 2SJ = JFET, N-Channel
- 2SK = JFET, P-Channel
- 3SK = MOSFET, IGFET

Appendix VIII

Important Radio Frequencies

Important Marine VHF Radio Channels

Freq. (MHz)	Channel	Use
156.300	6	INTERSHIP SAFETY. *Required an all VHF-equipped vessels.* Safety use only.
156.350	7A	COMMERCIAL. Working channel for business use.
156.400	8	COMMERCIAL INTERSHIP. Same as 7A.
156.450	9	COMMERCIAL AND NONCOMMERCIAL. Marina, dock use.
156.500	10	COMMERCIAL. Same as 7A.
156.550	11	COMMERCIAL/CG (Coast Guard) Vessel Traffic System.
156.600	12	PORT OPERATIONS. Vessel Traffic System, Ports, Waterway, and Lock Traffic.
156.650	13	NAVIGATIONAL—BRIDGE TO BRIDGE. Navigational and safety communications. Locks and bridges. 1 Watt Maximum out.
156.700	14	PORT OPERATIONS. Same as 12.
156.750	15	ENVIRONMENTAL. Receive only, Weather and Notices to Mariners.
156.800	**16**	**DISTRESS/CALLING. Required channel for all VHF-equipped vessels. Monitor at all times. Used to initiate routine calls, switching to other channels upon contact. Distress, monitored by U.S. Coast Guard (USCG).**
156.850	17	STATE CONTROL. Communications with state, local governments. Less than 1 watt required.
156.900	18A	COMMERCIAL. Same as 7A.
156.950	19A	COMMERCIAL. Same as 7A.
157.000	20	PORT OPERATIONS. Traffic handling and safety communications only.
157.050	21A	USCG ONLY.
157.100	22A	COAST GUARD LIAISON. Communications with CG, listen for navigational warnings, weather forecasts. Recommended channels.
157.15	23A	USCG ONLY.
157.200	24	MARINE OPERATOR. Receive 161.800 MHz.
157.250	25	MARINE OPERATOR. Receive 161.850 MHz.
157.300	26	MARINE OPERATOR. Receive 161.900 MHz.
157.350	27	MARINE OPERATOR. Receive 161.950 MHz.
157.400	28	MARINE OPERATOR. Receive 162.000 MHz.
156.275	65A	PORT OPERATIONS. Same as 12.

Freq. (MHz)	Channel	Use
156.325	66A	PORT OPERATIONS. Same as 12.
156.375	67	COMMERCIAL INTERSHIP. Same as 7A.
156.425	68	NONCOMMERCIAL. Working channel, for rendezvous, supplies, and scheduling traffic.
156.475	69	NONCOMMERCIAL. Same as 68.
156.525	70	DISTRESS AND SAFETY CALLING. General calling using digital selective calling only.
156.575	71	NONCOMMERCIAL. Same as 68.
156.925	78	NONCOMMERCIAL. Same as 68.
162.550	WX-1	CONTINUOUS NOAA WEATHER (National Oceanic and Atmospheric Administration). Receive only.
162.440	WX-2	CONTINUOUS NOAA WEATHER. Receive only.
162.475	WX-3	CONTINUOUS NOAA WEATHER. Receive only.

Important Aircraft VHF Radio Channels

Freq.	Use
121.500	Civilian Aircraft Emergency Communications
243.000	Military Aircraft Emergency Communications

Important Marine High-Seas Radio Channels

Freq. (MHz)	Use
2182 kHz Upper Sideband	Emergency and Calling Frequency
2670 kHz Upper Sideband	USCG
2082.5 kHz Upper Sideband	Noncommercial Intership
2638 kHz Upper Sideband	Noncommercial Intership

Citizens Band Channels

Channel	Freq. (MHz)	Channel	Freq. (MHz)
1	26.965	21	27.215
2	26.975	22	27.225
3	26.985	23	27.235
4	27.005	24	27.245
5	27.015	25	27.255
6	27.025	26	27.265
7	27.035	27	27.275
8	27.055	28	27.285
9	**27.065 Emergency Channel**	29	27.295
10	27.075	30	27.305
11	27.085	31	27.315
12	27.105	32	27.325
13	27.115	33	27.335
14	27.125	34	27.345
15	27.135	35	27.355
16	27.155	36	27.365
17	27.165	37	27.375
18	27.175	38	27.385
19	27.185	39	27.395
20	27.205	40	27.405

Appendix IX

TONE MODULATION STANDARDS

Continuous Tone-Coded Squelch System (CTCSS) Frequencies

Freq.	Code	Freq.	Code	Freq.	Code
67.0	L1	136.5	4	273.3	137
71.9	L2	141.3	4A	280.8	107
74.4		146.2	4B	288.5	138
77.0	L3	151.4	5	296.5	108
79.7		156.7	5A	304.7	139
82.5	L4	162.2	5B	313.0	109
85.4		167.9	6	321.7	140
88.5	L4A	173.8	6A	330.5	110
91.5		179.9	6B	339.6	141
94.8	L5	186.2	7	349.0	111
97.4		192.8	7A	358.6	142
100.0	1	203.5	M1	368.5	112
103.5	1A	210.7	M2	378.6	143
107.2	1B	218.1	M3	389.0	113
110.9	2	225.7	M4	399.8	144
114.8	2A	233.6	M5	410.8	114
118.8	2B	241.8	M6	422.1	145
123.0	3	250.3	M7	433.7	115
127.3	3A	258.8	136	445.7	146
131.8	3B	266.0	106	457.9	116

Freq.	Code	Freq.	Code
470.5	147	879.0	128
483.5	117	903.0	159
496.8	148	928.1	129
510.5	118	953.7	160
524.6	149	979.9	130
539.0	119	1006.9	161
553.9	150	1049.6	131
569.1	120	1084.0	P
582.1	H	1120.0	S11
600.9	121	1190.0	S12
617.4	152	1220.0	S2
634.5	122	1265.0	S14
651.9	153	1291.4	S3
669.9	123	1320.0	S15
688.3	154	1355.0	S16
707.3	124	1400.0	S17
726.8	155	1430.5	S7
746.8	125	1450.0	S18
767.4	156	1500.0	S20
788.5	126	1520.0	S9
810.2	157	1550.0	S21
832.5	127	1600.0	S22
855.2	158		

Dual-Tone Multiple Frequency Tones (DTMF)

Figure A-IX-1 shows an outline of a telephone pad with an additional column on the right. This representatation shows the frequencies that are simultaneously generated by the pressing of any key: the vertical column tone is shown above the number, and the horizontal row tone is shown at the right.

Columns

1209	1336	1477	1633	Rows
1	2	3	A	697
4	5	6	B	770
7	8	9	C	852
*	0	#	D	941

Motorola Tone Group Frequencies for Two-Tone Signaling

Tone No.	Mot. 1	Mot. 2	Mot. 3	Mot. 4	Mot. 5	Mot. 6
0	330.5	569.1	1092.4	321.7	553.9	1122.5
1	349.0	600.9	288.5	339.6	584.8	1153.4
2	368.5	634.5	296.5	358.6	617.4	1185.2
3	389.0	669.9	304.7	378.6	651.9	1217.8
4	410.8	707.3	313.0	399.8	688.3	1251.4
5	433.7	746.8	953.7	422.1	726.8	1285.8
6	457.9	788.5	979.9	445.7	767.4	1321.2
7	483.5	832.5	1006.9	470.5	810.2	1357.6
8	510.5	879.0	1034.7	496.8	855.5	1395.0
9	539.0	928.1	1063.2	524.6	903.2	1433.4

Appendix X

COAXIAL CABLE INFORMATION

Cable Number (RG-)	Z	Dia. (Inches)	dBs Attenuation 1 GHz	dBs Attenuation 5 GHz
6A/U	75	.332	11	30
8A/U	52	.405	9	28
8X	50	.242	14	35
11A/U	75	.405	9	28
55B/U	53.5	.206	17	51
58C/U	50	.195	20	60
58-P	50	.163	14	39
59B/U	75	.242	12	41
59-P	75	.190	11	32
62A/U	93	.242	9	30
71B/U	93	.250	9	30
108A/U	78	.235	27	80
122/U	50	.160	30	89
140/U	75	.233	13	36
141A/U	50	.190	13	36
142B/U	50	.195	13	36
174A/U	50	.100	31	97
178B/U	50	.075	45	115
179B/U	75	.100	25	63
180B/U	95	.145	17	50
187A/U	75	.110	25	63
188A/U	50	.110	30	79
188-DS	50	.122	30	79
196A/U	50	.080	45	115
210/U	93	.242	4	9
213/U	50	.405	9	28
214/U	50	.425	9	28
217/U	50	.545	6	19
218/U	50	.870	4	14
219/U	50	.945	4	14

Cable Number (RG-)	Z	Dia. (Inches)	dBs Attenuation	
			1 GHz	5 GHz
223/U	50	.216	17	51
225/U	50	.430	8	21
302/U	75	.206	13	36
303/U	50	.170	13	36
316/U	50	.102	30	79
316-DS	50	.114	30	79
393/U	50	.390	8	21
400/U	50	.195	13	36
401/U	50	.250	8	21
402/U	50	.141	13	36
405/U	50	.085	22	66

Appendix XI

Incandescent Lamp Data

Lamp Number	Mounting	Volts	Current (Amperes)
12	2 Pin	6.3	0.15
12PSB5	Slide	12	0.17
13	Screw	3.7	0.30
14	Screw	2.47	0.30
19	2 Pin	14.4	0.10
24PSB	Slide	24	.073
27	Screw	4.9	0.30
28PSB5	Slide	28	0.04
31	Screw	6.15	0.30
40	Screw	6–8	0.15
40A	Bayonet	6–8	0.15
41	Screw	2.5	0.50
42	Screw	3.2	0.35–0.50
43	Bayonet	2.5	0.50
44	Bayonet	6–8	0.25
45	Bayonet	3.2	0.35–0.50
46	Screw	6–8	0.25
47	Bayonet	6–9	0.15
48	Screw	2.0	0.06
49	Bayonet	2.0	0.06
49A	Bayonet	2.1	0.12
50	Screw	6–8	0.20
51	Bayonet	6–8	0.20
53	Bayonet	14.4	0.12
55	Bayonet	6–8	0.40
57	Bayonet	14	0.24
63	Bayonet	7.0	0.63
67	Bayonet	13.5	0.59
73	Wedge	14	0.08
81	Bayonet	6.5	1.02
82	Dbl Bayonet	6.5	1.02
85	Wedge	28	0.04

Lamp Number	Mounting	Volts	Current (Amperes)
86	Wedge	6.3	0.20
87	Bayonet	6.8	1.91
88	Dbl Bayonet	6.8	1.90
89	Bayonet	13	0.58
93	Bayonet	12.8	1.04
112	Screw	1.1	0.22
120MB	Min Bayonet	120	0.025
123	Screw	1.25	0.30
136	Screw	1.25	0.60
158	Wedge	14	0.24
161	Wedge	14	0.19
168	Wedge	14	0.35
194	Wedge	14	0.27
222	Screw	2.2	0.25
292	Screw	2.9	0.17
292A	Bayonet	2.9	0.17
301	Bayonet	28	0.17
302	Dbl Bayonet	28	0.17
303	Bayonet	28	0.30
305	Bayonet	28	0.51
307	Bayonet	28	0.66
308	Dbl Bayonet	28	0.67
309	Bayonet	28	0.90
313	Min Bayonet	28	0.17
327	Mgt Flanged	28	0.04
328	Mgt Flanged	6.0	0.20
330	Mgt Flanged	14	0.08
331	Mgt Flanged	1.35	0.06
334	Mgt Grooved	28	0.04
335	Mgt Screw	28	0.04
344	Mgt Flanged	10	0.014
381	Mgt Flanged	6.3	0.02
382	Mgt Flanged	14	0.08
385	Mgt Flanged	28	0.04
387	Mgt Flanged	28	0.04
388	Mgt Grooved	28	0.04
656	Wedge	28	0.06
680	Leads	5.0	0.06
682	Mgt Flange	5.0	0.06
683	Leads	5.0	0.06
683AS15	Leads	5.0	0.06
685	Mgt Flange	5.0	0.06
713	Leads	5.0	0.075

Lamp Number	Mounting	Volts	Current (Amperes)
714	Mgt Flange	5.0	0.075
715	Leads	5.0	0.115
715AS15	Leads	5.0	0.115
718	Mgt Flange	5.0	0.115
755	Min Bayonet	6.3	0.15
756	Min Bayonet	14	0.08
757	Min Bayonet	28	0.08
1003	Bayonet	12.8	0.94
1004	Dbl Bayonet	12.8	0.94
1034	Bayonet	12.8	1.80
1076	Dbl Bayonet	12.8	1.80
1133		6.2	3.91
1156	Bayonet	12.8	2.10
1157	DC Bayonet	12.8	2.10
1176	Dbl Bayonet	12.8	1.34
1195		12.5	3.00
1251	Bayonet	28	0.23
1445	Bayonet	14.4	0.135
1447	Screw	18	0.15
1455	Screw	18	0.25
1455A	Bayonet	18	0.25
1458	Bayonet	20	0.25
1487	Screw	12–18	0.20
1488	Bayonet	14	0.15
1490	Bayonet	3.2	0.15
1495	Bayonet	28	0.30
1705	Leads	14	0.08
1764	Leads	28	0.04
1784	Leads	6.0	0.20
1813	Bayonet	14.4	0.10
1815	Bayonet	12–16	0.20
1816	Bayonet	13	0.33
1819	Min Bayonet	28	0.04
1820	Min Bayonet	28	0.10
1822	Min Bayonet	36	0.10
1829	Min Bayonet	28	0.07
1847	Bayonet	6.3	0.15
1864	Min Bayonet	28	0.17
1891	Bayonet	14	0.23
1892	Screw	14	0.12
1895	Min Bayonet	14	0.27
2181	Leads	6.3	0.20
2182	Leads	6.3	0.20

Lamp Number	Mounting	Volts	Current (Amperes)
2187	Leads	28	0.04
3150	Mgt Flange	5.0	0.06
6838	Leads	28	0.024
6839	Mgt Flange	28	0.024
7327	Pins	28	0.04
7333	Mgt Flange	5.0	0.06
7361	Pins	5.0	0.06
7381	Pins	6.3	0.20
7382	Pins	14	0.08
7387	Pins	28	0.04
7632	Pins	28	0.04
7839	Pins	28	0.024
8623	Knurled	28	0.04
8627	Leads	28	0.04
PR-2	Flange	2.4	0.50
PR-3	Flange	3.6	0.50
PR-4	Flange	2.3	0.27
PR-6	Flange	2.5	0.30
PF-7	Flange	3.7	0.30
PR-12	Flange	5.95	0.50
PR-13	Flange	4.75	0.50
PR-18	Flange	7.2	0.55

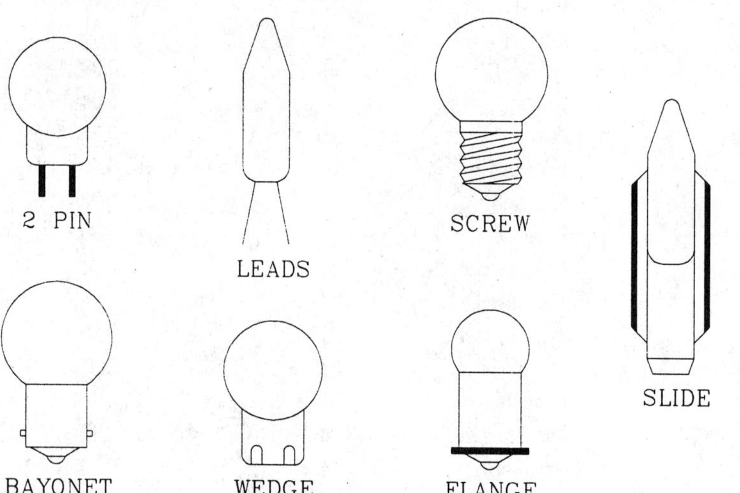

Figure A-XIII-1 Base styles for incandescent lamps.

Appendix XII

Drill Sizes

The following table lists the size drill required to tap a hole for a bolt, or to clear a bolt going through.

Number	Dia.	Clear	Tap
1	.228		
2	.221	12–24	-
3	.213	-	14–24
4	.209	12–20	-
5	.205	-	-
6	.204	-	-
7	.201	-	-
8	.199	-	-
9	.196	-	-
10	.1935	10–32	-
11	.191	-	-
12	.189	-	-
13	.185	-	-
14	.182	-	-
15	.180	-	-
16	.177	-	12–24
17	.173	-	-
18	.1695	8–32	-
19	.166	-	12–20
20	.161	-	-
21	.159	-	10–32
22	.157	-	-
23	.154	-	-
24	.152	-	-
25	.1495	-	10–24
26	.147	-	-
27	.144	-	-
28	.140	6–32	-
29	.136	-	8–32
30	.1285	-	-
31	.120	-	-
32	.116	-	-

Number	Dia.	Clear	Tap
33	.113	4–36, 4–40	-
34	.111	-	-
35	.110	-	6–32
36	.1065	-	-
37	.104	-	-
38	.1015	-	-
39	.0995	3–48	-
40	.098	-	-
41	.096	-	-
42	.0935	-	4–36, 4–40
43	.089	2–56	-
44	.086	-	-
45	.082	-	3–48
46	.081	-	-
47	.0785	-	-
48	.076	-	-
49	.073	-	2–56
50	.070	-	-
51	.067	-	-
52	.0635	-	-
53	.0595	-	-
54	.055	-	-

Appendix XIII

Electronic Component Catalog Listing

Besides what is available in IC data books, it is often necessary to get additional information on components before they are actually in hand. This requires the use of component catalogs and pamphlets. If only a few such catalogs are available, they can be found and used easily. When the number of catalogs becomes too great, however, it will be necessary to use a filing system for them, usually in a file cabinet. Finding the proper component catalog in the drawer will be much easier if a standardized system of filing is used. Such a filing system, keyed by number, is shown as follows:

1100 AMPLIFIER ASSEMBLIES
1300 AUDIO EQUIPMENT AND ACCESSORIES
1400 ENCLOSURES/PACKAGING SYSTEMS
1500 CAPACITORS (ALL TYPES)
1600 CHEMICALS/CLEANERS/COATINGS/MATERIALS
1700 CIRCUIT BOARDS AND ASSEMBLIES/BREADBOARDING KITS
1800 COILS AND CHOKES/ASSEMBLIES/FORMS
1900 COMMUNICATIONS/TELEMETERING EQUIPMENT
2000 COMPUTING AND DATA HANDLING EQUIP., ACCESSORIES
2100 CONNECTORS, TERMINALS, SOCKETS, ETC.
2200 CONTROL SYSTEMS AND COMPONENTS
2300 CRYSTALS/OSCILLATORS, /CRYSTAL FILTERS
2350 DELAY LINES
2400 PANEL COMPONENTS (EXCLUDING LIGHTING AND DISPLAYS)
2450 DISPLAYS AND READOUTS (INCLUDING LAMPS AND LIGHTS)
2500 MECHANICAL COMPONENTS (BEARINGS, CORES, MAGNETS)
2550 ENVIRONMENTAL TEST EQUIPMENT
2600 FANS/BLOWERS/COOLING EQUIPMENT
2700 FILTERS (EXCLUDING CRYSTAL)
2800 HARDWARE (NON-CURRENT-CARRYING)
2900 INSTRUMENTS, MEASURING AND TEST
3000 INSTRUMENTS, GRAPHIC RECORDING
3100 INSULATORS/INSULATION
3130 INTEGRATED CIRCUITS AND HYBRIDS
3400 MICROWAVE SYSTEMS AND SUBSYSTEMS
3450 MICROWAVE COMPONENTS AND ACCESSORIES
3500 MOTORS AND DRIVES
3700 ELECTRO-OPTICAL COMPONENTS AND ACCESSORIES
4000 DC POWER SOURCES
4050 AC POWER SOURCES
4100 PRODUCTION EQUIPMENT/MANUFACTURING SERVICES
4500 RELAYS AND SOLENOIDS
4700 RESISTORS, FIXED

4750 RESISTORS, VARIABLE
4800 SEMICONDUCTORS
4900 SERVOMECHANISMS
5100 SWITCHES/KEYBOARDS/PROTECTIVE COMPONENTS
5300 TEMPERATURE MEASURING DEVICES AND ACCESSORIES
5400 TOOLS (HAND AND POWER) /SOLDERING SUPPLIES
5500 TRANSDUCERS
5600 TRANSFORMERS
5700 TUBES AND TUBE PARTS
6000 WIRE/CABLE/HARNESSES AND ACCESSORIES

Appendix XIV

Important DOS Computer Commands

The modern electronics technician is well advised to know how to operate an MS-DOS–based computer. These machines are widely used for calculations, drawing illustrations, and keeping track of inventories, to name only a few of their uses. If the following commands are understood, the technician can be considered to be competent in the use of a computer.

INTERNAL COMMANDS

DIR Used to find out what files are on a diskette or hard drive.
REN Rename files.
CLS Clear the screen. Useful mostly in batch files.
COPY Make copies of files. Can also be used to change the name on the second copy of a file during the copy procedure. Can be destructive by causing old data to be copied over new data in files with the same name.
VER Tells what version of DOS you are using.
TYPE Put contents of a file on the screen. Terminates at the first ^Z in the file. Useful for checking the contents of data files.
BATCH FILES Powerful feature, consisting of lines (each a DOS command) in a text file whose name ends with ".BAT." Typing the filename causes DOS to execute each line consecutively.
DEL Erase files.
PATH A "standing instruction" to the computer: If this program is not available in this directory, look for it in . . .
CTTY A primitive way of controlling the computer via one of the serial ports (limited in its capabilities).
MD, RD, CD Commands to make, remove, and change the default specified directories.
Root Directory Symbol (\) When leading, used to indicate "starting from the root directory. . ." and as a separator when listing successive directories.
Using Wild Cards (?), (*) When designating groups of files, ? is a single-character wild card and * is a multiple-character wild card.
Meaning of dot (.) and double-dot (..) A single dot means the same as *.* when referring to the current directory. Double dots refer to the directory above the default. As a result, do not try to delete these symbols or you will delete all of the files in one directory.

External Commands

RECOVER A dangerous program, to be used only when problems are reported due to damaged file allocation tables.

FDISK A dangerous program, to be used to divide a hard disk. To be used only when all hard disk files are properly backed up.

FORMAT A dangerous program that will remove all old data from a floppy disk or remove directory of a hard disk.

DISKCOPY A potentially dangerous program that will copy entire diskettes from one to another. Be sure you copy from a good diskette to a bad one, however, or you will have two copies of the bad diskette.

MODE A particularly useful program, to set up the technical parameters for serial ports and to redirect the data heading for one port to a new one.

BACKUP An important program to provide emergency copies of everything on a hard disk, afterward to add the files that have been updated since the last backup. One of the few programs that can split very large files between two or more diskettes.

RESTORE The complement of backup, this program puts the files from backup diskettes back on to a hard drive.

CHKDSK An important program that will run some basic checks on a diskette or hard drive, reporting lost data areas due to improper computer operation such a shut-down of the computer without proper exiting of some programs.

SYS An important program that will place the two hidden files of the operating system onto a diskette or hard disk. Copying of the file COMMAND.COM will usually be necessary to make a proper bootable disk.

Special Files

COMMAND.COM Part of the operating system, this file interprets and executes all of the Internal Commands, listed above.

AUTOEXEC.BAT A batch file with this special name will execute all of the DOS commands within it automatically upon power-up of the computer. One of the important commands to include in this file is the location of your utility programs, a line beginning with the PATH command.

CONFIG.SYS A file containing information as to how the computer should be customized for the operator's software and hardware. If using a hard disk, this file should include command lines such as BUFFERS=25 and FILES=20.

Dedicated devices

CON: The console, the keyboard, and monitor as one unit.

LPT1: or PRN: The first parallel port (by default, the printer port of a PC).

LPT2: and LPT3: are the designations for the second and third possible parallel ports.

COM1: or AUX: Refers to the first serial port. COM2: is the second possible serial I/O port.

A:, B:, C:, etc. Refers to the storage media drives. Most commonly, A: and B: refer to the first two diskette drives and C: is the first hard drive.

Appendix XV

The ASCII Chart

A computer manages information by a series of bits, which may be set or reset (high or low). While this allows the computer to manipulate numbers easily once they are converted into this binary (two-state) format, numerical manipulation does not apply to letters. Letters are not added or subtracted. Rather, their presence is acknowledged and they are manipulated and moved around within the computer as coded groups of bits. There are several different standards for encoding letters into binary combinations. The code most often used is called the ASCII code. ASCII stands for the American Standard Code for Information Interchange.

The ASCII code requires seven bits to express any given character. In addition to letter characters, controlling codes are also available. While only seven bits are required to code an ASCII character, an extra, eighth bit is usually present but is set by default to a value of "0." This highest-order, eighth bit is used within word processors to represent special characters required by the program.

To find the bit pattern for a given character, assume a "0" for the highest bit, find the character in Table A-XV-1, and then use the bits represented along the top of the corresponding column for the next three bits, moving from left to right. The remaining low-order bits are found to the left of the character, along the left column of the table.

Note that holding down the CONTROL key of a microcomputer keyboard results in forcing bit D6 low. Thus, one can hold the control key down and hit the "L" key to produce an LF code, a printer line-feed command. This technique works in most CONTROL cases, but not all, due to hardware limitations and programming of the keyboards of microcomputers. Note also that holding the SHIFT key down and hitting a letter forces bit D5 low, producing upper-case rather than lower-case letters.

Most of the characters within the ASCII table can be generated by holding down a computer's ALT key, generating the DECIMAL code for the character with the right-hand number pad, and then releasing the ALT key. When decimal numbers greater than 127 are entered in this manner, you will see the Extended ASCII Codes available within the computer. These will allow you to generate special symbols such as degree signs, foreign characters, symbols, and so forth.

BITS D6 D5 D4 → / D3 D2 D1 D0 ↓	0 0 0	0 0 1	0 1 0	0 1 1	1 0 0	1 0 1	1 1 0	1 1 1
	CONTROL		NUMBERS SYMBOLS		UPPER CASE		LOWER CASE	
0 0 0 0	0 **NUL** 0 0	20 **DLE** 10 16	40 **SP** 20 32	60 **0** 30 48	100 **@** 40 64	120 **P** 50 80	140 60 96	160 **p** 70 112
0 0 0 1	1 GTL **SOH** 1 1	21 LLO **DC1** 11 17	41 **!** 21 33	61 **1** 31 49	101 **A** 41 65	121 **Q** 51 81	141 **a** 61 97	161 **q** 71 113
0 0 1 0	2 **STX** 2 2	22 **DC2** 12 18	42 **"** 22 34	62 **2** 32 50	102 **B** 42 66	122 **R** 52 82	142 **b** 62 98	162 **r** 72 114
0 0 1 1	3 **ETX** 3 3	23 **DC3** 13 19	43 **#** 23 35	63 **3** 33 51	103 **C** 43 67	123 **S** 53 83	143 **c** 63 99	163 **s** 73 115
0 1 0 0	4 SDC **EOT** 4 4	24 DCL **DC4** 14 20	44 **$** 24 36	64 **4** 34 52	104 **D** 44 68	124 **T** 54 84	144 **d** 64 100	164 **t** 74 116
0 1 0 1	5 PPC **ENQ** 5 5	25 PPU **NAK** 15 21	45 **%** 25 37	65 **5** 35 53	105 **E** 45 69	125 **U** 55 85	145 **e** 65 101	165 **u** 75 117
0 1 1 0	6 **ACK** 6 6	26 **SYN** 16 22	46 **&** 26 38	66 **6** 36 54	106 **F** 46 70	126 **V** 56 86	146 **f** 66 102	166 **v** 76 118
0 1 1 1	7 **BEL** 7 7	27 **ETB** 17 23	47 27 39	67 **7** 37 55	107 **G** 47 71	127 **W** 57 87	147 **g** 67 103	167 **w** 77 119
1 0 0 0	10 GET **BS** 8 8	30 SPE **CAN** 18 24	50 **(** 28 40	70 **8** 38 56	110 **H** 48 72	130 **X** 58 88	150 **h** 68 104	170 **x** 78 120
1 0 0 1	11 TCT **HT** 9 9	31 SPD **EM** 19 25	51 **)** 29 41	71 **9** 39 57	111 **I** 49 73	131 **Y** 59 89	151 **i** 69 105	171 **y** 79 121
1 0 1 0	12 **LF** A 10	32 **SUB** 1A 26	52 **•** 2A 42	72 **:** 3A 58	112 **J** 4A 74	132 **Z** 5A 90	152 **j** 6A 106	172 **z** 7A 122
1 0 1 1	13 **VT** B 11	33 **ESC** 1B 27	53 **+** 2B 43	73 3B 59	113 **K** 4B 75	133 **[** 5B 91	153 **k** 6B 107	173 7B 123
1 1 0 0	14 **FF** C 12	34 **FS** 1C 28	54 2C 44	74 **<** 3C 60	114 **L** 4C 76	134 **** 5C 92	154 **l** 6C 108	174 **¦** 7C 124
1 1 0 1	15 **CR** D 13	35 **GS** 1D 29	55 **–** 2D 45	75 **=** 3D 61	115 **M** 4D 77	135 **]** 5D 93	155 **m** 6D 109	175 **}** 7D 125
1 1 1 0	16 **SO** E 14	36 **RS** 1E 30	56 2E 46	76 **>** 3E 62	116 **N** 4E 78	136 **Λ** 5E 94	156 **n** 6E 110	176 **~** 7E 126
1 1 1 1	17 **SI** F 15	37 **US** 1F 31	57 **/** 2F 47	77 UNL **?** 3F 63	117 **O** 4F 79	137 UNT **–** 5F 111	157 **o** 6F 111	177 **RUBOUT (DEL)** 7F 127
	Addressed Commands	Universal Commands	Listen Addresses		Talk Addresses		Secondary Addresses Or Commands	

octal	25 PPU	GPIB code
	NAK	ASCII character
hex	15 21	decimal

Some of the abbreviations in the ASCII table are not obvious, so here they are in more digestible form. Note that these are really single-byte messages that can be used in communications between a computer and a modem, a printer, or other peripheral.

NUL = All zeros. Used for idle marking time without occupying buffer space.

SOH = Start of a heading

STX = Start of the text

ETX = End of the text ("End of data, did you receive it?")

EOT = End of a transmission. May be used as a turn-around for half-duplex.

ENQ = Enquiry. Solicits automatic identification from a remote terminal.

ACK = Acknowledgment ("Data has been received OK")

BEL = Bell or attention signal (nowadays a speaker "beep")

BS = Backspace or <--- key (may or may not erase on the way)

HT = Horizontal Tab or -->| key (normal keyboard Tabulator key)

LF = Line feed on a printer (paper up a line)

VT = Vertical Tab (jump lines on a page)

FF = Form Feed (go to beginning of next page)

CR = Carriage return (Return to left margin of paper)

SO = Shift out (Go to alternate character font set)

SI = Shift in (Shift back to normal character font set)

DLE = Data Link Escape. May be used prior to EOT for an automatic disconnect.

DC1 = Device Control 1 (Also called "XON," used in software handshaking)

DC2 = Device Control 2

DC3 = Device Control 3 (also called "XOFF," used in software handshaking)

DC4 = Device control 4

NAK = Negative acknowledgment

SYN = Synchronous/idle

ETB = End of transmitted block

CAN = Cancel (error in data). May be used to cancel an escape sequence.

EM = End of medium

SUB = A character used in place of a character received in error.

Appendix XVI

Answers to Odd-Numbered Questions

Chapter 1

1. Class A.
3. Class B.
5. 1.5 millihertz; 470 kilohms; 4700 picoFarads; 40,000 nanoseconds.
7. That point from which voltage readings should be taken; it is common to all circuitry in the equipment.
9. The smaller one has a higher internal resistance; thus, it cannot produce as much current.
11. Right next to pin 1, and not across the IC from it.
13. In Appendix I.
15. A fuse (see Appendix I).
17. Both logic highs.
19. The kind of equipment to be repaired.

Chapter 2

1. The internal power supply.
3. Make the problem appear so that it can be traced to its source.
5. Mechanical.
7. Heat gun, circuit cooling spray.
9. Operating at full ratings for long periods; over- or under-voltage operation; over- or under-temperature operation.
11. Look at the plastic parts.
13. Diodes, transistors, ICs, and electrolytic capacitors.
15. Small diameter helps prevent accidental shorts; sharp tips are less likely to slip.
17. Clips high-voltage spikes to safe voltage levels.
19. It compares the distortion levels between what is applied to an amplifier and what comes out.
21. Spray the inside of the control with an aerosol spray intended for the purpose.
23. Check the items on the "frustration list."

Chapter 3

1. The system block diagram.
3. When first working on a system.

5. The voltage level is 10 decibels above a reference level of 1 milliwatt.
7. AC audio-frequency voltmeter.
9. *Substitution!*
11. The equipments must be identical in all respects.
13. Three: ohmmeter, transmitter–dummy load, TDR.
15. Extent or severity.
17. Verify proper system operation.

Chapter 4

1. The ground lead, to prevent having a "hot" lead in the other hand.
3. The shock hazard. Unlock the connectors, then slide at least one hand up onto the insulated cable before pulling the connectors apart.
5. Shock hazard when dealing with high voltage; burn hazard when working on circuits with high current capability.
7. Their length and thread type, to ensure placing them in the proper holes upon reassembly.
9. The block diagram.
11. The wiring diagram.
13. The schematic and the theory of operation.
15. At least 10 times more difficult, depending on your experience level.
17. Compare test readings to one of the other equipments.

Chapter 5

1. Shunt or current-sensing resistor.
3. Never apply ammeter leads to a source of voltage. Break the circuit and insert the meter for a measurement.
5. A vacuum-tube voltmeter.
7. Change scales. If the reading is the same, the meter is not loading the circuit.
9. The DC balance control.
11. a. Is the source low?
    b. Is the meter OK?
    c. Is the meter loading the circuit?
    d. Has Rl decreased, overloading the circuit?
    e. Has Rs increased in resistance?
13. Rs also includes the ground, or return path.

Chapter 6

1. Be sure all switches are closed.
3. In parallel. Series for 240-V AC
5. No more than 140 percent of the RMS AC secondary voltage.
7. To force a more equal division of the DC voltage between the capacitors.
9. A voltage doubler.
11. The normal current produced by the ohmmeter could exceed the instrument fuse rating, blowing the fuse during testing.
13. Near zero volts.
15. Fast-blow.
17. Prevents supply-generated interference from getting back into the power line. Recommended for switching and phasing supplies.
19. Twice the peak of the 120-V AC voltage; about 340-V DC.
21. Shorted input filter capacitor; shorted switching transistor(s).

23. The power supply goes into foldback, idling without blowing the input fuse.
25. The UJT and the PUT.
27. Open SCR or TRIAC.
29. Less than about 2 ohms; between 2 and about 50 ohms; nearly normal resistance.
31. A shorted semiconductor.
33. Only when a semishort or "pseudo-zener" overload is evident; when the load measures more than a few ohms of resistance.
35. Smoke-it-out; current tracer; freezer method; cut-trace-and-try; remove most likely components.

Chapter 7

1. Series and parallel (shunt) regulators.
3. No. The short bypasses the zener and does not harm it directly.
5. The zener has opened.
7. The load is demanding too much current, causing overcurrent protection to take effect; the regulator is overheating and going into thermal shut-down because of it. (Check for a good bond to the the heatsink.)
9. To ensure a more even division of the total current between the transistors.
11. Linear current limiting and foldback.
13. Common base.
15. Common collector or emitter follower.
17. 1.5 volts.
19. To allow for input voltage variation without forcing the base-emitter junction beyond the 0.7-V DC level. Lets the current through the base-emitter junction to vary without substantially changing the base-emitter voltage.
21. The linear regulator wastes energy in the form of heat while the switching regulator is either saturated or cut-off, thus making the switching regulator dissipate far less heat.
23. The step-down regulator, because it could cause overvoltage to the load if the switching transistor shorts.

Chapter 8

1. Use of a solid-state tester.
3. One that feeds back to the input a part of the output.
5. To reduce distortion.
7. Signal injection and signal detection methods.
9. Short the signal to ground to determine its source.

Chapter 9

1. To block any DC from entering the signal generator attenuator.
3. Average, RMS.
5. 9.0 V.
7. Use of this jack places a capacitor in series with one test lead, to block DC.
9. The DMM has internal amplification.
11. Improper bias and overdriving.
13. By using it as an XY plotter, a Lissajous figure.
15. Attenuation, isolation, and impedance matching.
17. A volume control that presents a constant load to the distribution line.

Chapter 10

1. Ohms.
3. Open.
5. Blocks DC voltages.
7. Damage to other components.
9. Insulating sheets used in transformers and electrical motors.
11. The DC resistance of the coil wire.
13. 1:10.
15. Place mylar or mica capacitors in parallel.
17. Phase shift.
19. Isolation.
21. Impedance.
23. Stray or distributed.
25. 1/4.
27. Impedance.
29. L, C.
31. Characteristic (surge) impedance; power.
33. Bandpass filter.
35. Average.
37. Increase.
39. Isolation; impedance matching; polarity inversion.
41. The switching transistor.

Chapter 11

1. No. Refer to Figure 11–1 for the explanation.
3. To prevent an inductive kickback voltage when the coil is suddenly deenergized.
5. The emitter.
7. About 8- to 10-V DC.
9. Current, resistor.
11. Linear.
13. The matching transistor to also be shorted.
15. 0.7 volts.
17. No. The base junction is shorted.
19. Gate, source (see Figure 11–16).
21. Voltage, resistor.
23. Loading.
25. The source.
27. The depletion IGFET.
29. Medium.
31. The enhancement IGFET.
33. Enhancement IGFETs.
35. Array.

Chapter 12

1. a. See the five uses listed at the end of topic 12.2.
3. The input signal is normal at the input end of the input resistor, but the signal should *not* be seen at the input pin.
5. Short the input terminals ahead of the input resistor. Adjust for zero volts' difference between the output and positive input pins.
7. Either the op-amp is inoperative because of internal failure or the IC output circuit is shorted.

9. It is a voltage follower circuit and has a gain of 1.00.
11. No. It is one or the other.
13. Because of internal voltage drops required for operation.
15. Voltage comparator.
17. Inverting (–) pin, noninverting (+) pin.
19. Enhancement, IGFETs.
21. Across the switch from input to output. There should be negligible voltage when "on," and full signal voltage when "off."
23. Pin 2 is an input if triggered; otherwise it would be connected to the timing capacitor.
25. Isolating a circuit from electrical noise or two circuits from each other electrically.
27. About 1.0 volt.
29. Probe the traces, not the ends of the components.

Chapter 13

1. It must be answered in writing.
3. Refer to Appendix IX of this book.
5. SSB, CW (continuous wave, also called Morse Code), TV, Packet, and FM.
7. When about 50 miles or more offshore, out of VHF range.
9. His or her shop manager, supervisor, or foreman as applicable.
11. None.
13. PLL.
15. Emitter, filter.
17. Damage to the final RF amplifier transistor, including shorts and opens.
19. U.S. Bureau of Standards WWV transmissions.
21. Power attenuator.
23. 52 Ω.
25. Disconnect the transceiver when making receiver checks.
27. RF wattmeter, dummy load, receiver, frequency counter, RF signal generator, audio signal generator, spectrum analyzer, and modulation monitor.
29. The vertical amplifier.
31. Yes, but the amplitude indication will decrease rapidly as the frequency increases above that specification.
33. 2 MHz.
35. Detuning of the circuit by the metal; accidental shorting; shock hazard.
37. 20 dB quieting and SINAD tests.
39. DC, discriminator.
41. limiter, HF oscillator.
43. When the receiver has to receive a broad range of frequencies simultaneously.
45. Generally speaking, no. The difference at the receiver would be unnoticeable.
47. An internal power-sensing circuit switches the incoming power off the attenuator into a dummy load instead.
49. A spectrum analyzer.
51. Linear.
53. At VHF frequencies and above.
55. The very high negative voltages produced by the power supply, which are capable of lethal currents.
57. Thermistor.

Chapter 14

1. These devices are only operated fully saturated or cut off.
3. True RMS.

5. 500 volts maximum DC, or 500 volts as the maximum peak value for any other waveform.
7. Capacitance from anode to gate produces a false gate signal.
9. The MT1 terminal.
11. Shorting or opening.
13. Anode.
15. DIAC, SBS.
17. These components are critical to safety and should be replaced only by identical parts.
19. Signal amplitude and polarity.
21. Switch from Auto to Normal or Triggered operation.
23. These are phasing dots and are indicated like instantaneous polarities.
25. Passive radar echoes a signal from the target, while active receives a transmitted reply from the target.
27. Specialized test equipment for that system.

Chapter 15

1. Totem-pole, open-collector, and three-state.
3. Wired NOR circuit.
5. A logic probe indication of activity, principally at a high level, is normal at this point.
7. The bypass capacitors prevent power-bus glitches normally generated by a totem-pole output stage within an IC.
9. Logic "0."
11. One.
13. a. Operate on 5-V DC,
    b. Require relatively high power,
    c. Will interpret an open input as a high,
    d. Use thresholds of <0.8 and >2.4 V, and
    e. Operate at high speeds.
15. a. Operate on from 3 to 18 V.
    b. Logic thresholds of <30 percent and >70 percent of Vcc.
    c. Require very little power.
    d. Interpret an open input erratically.
    e. Slower than TTL.
    f. Sensitive to ESD.
17. Accidental firing of a pseudo-SCR built into a CMOS chip, which was triggered by inadvertently forcing an output pin voltage more than 0.5 V above or below Vcc and ground.
19. ECL, emitter-coupled logic.
21. Changes thc logic thresholds interpreted by the instrument.
23. A floating, or indeterminate logic state between logic low and logic high (*not a voltage of "nothing" or zero*). Indicates a floating, or open, disconnected line.
25. Timing analyzer for hardware problems, state analyzer for software problems.
27. Continues recording data for a predetermined number of steps.
29. a. Plug in the analyzer but leave power off,
    b. Connect the analyzer to the circuit under test,
    c. Determine timing or state analysis,
    d. Determine trigger event, and
    e. Press "Run."
31. Single-stepping.
33. Prevents slipping or shorting of the circuit under test.
35. a. Visual check,

b. Power source check, and
c. Clock check.

37. You are probing an accidently open input line.
39. Confirm that both the timing and the presence of the input logic levels truly call for an output signal before proceeding further.
41. Sometimes. The interpretation of signal levels requires thought, however.
43. The transmitting chip is shorted; the receiving chip is shorted; the trace between the chips is shorted.
45. Bus contention.

Chapter 16

1. Diagnostic.
3. PROM, EPROM.
5. In the program that doesn't run.
7. Power-down to reread the new settings.
9. Hold down one or more switches during power-up.
11. The "Here-Jump-Here" program.
13. It must be configured for the hardware in use.

Chapter 17

1. The ohmmeter and the Tracker™.
3. Batteries, neon indicators.
5. The lowest and the highest ranges.
7. Yes.
9. 1,000 Ω.
11. Diode junction.
13. Pattern recognition; recorded patterns; comparison.
15. When testing a quantity of ICs by comparison.
17. Test for Vcc-to-ground short; test major components; test edge connector; test individual components.
19. Clip the pins and remove the stubs.
21. Leave it out to simplify further testing.
23. 1.0 volts.
25. No! The ohmmeter would force too much current through the meter movement.
27. Yes. The neon will not fire (conduct) at less than about 75 to 90 volts.
29. They should be phased.
31. A temperature-sensitive switch.
33. Two transistors in a simple package, with collectors connected together.

Chapter 18

1. A new one must be obtained from the equipment manufacturer.
3. Equipment make, model, serial number, and circuit symbol; overtone or fundamental mode; frequency of operation; circuit capacitive load; standard or special tolerance, and oven or non-oven operation.
5. 5 seconds.
7. By the copper pole piece under the armature.
9. Equal-or-better generic.
11. Correct part orientation.

Chapter 19

1. Make a final operational check with the covers on.
3. Because it will be easiest to find an unrelated problem now, while the unit is in the shop.
5. In the original container, if available.

Chapter 20

1. Take them to the shipping clerk to confirm receipt of the equipment.
3. A megohmmeter, or megger.
5. A TDR generator.
7. Cleaning, filter replacement, and lubrication.
9. Transformers/inductors and electrolytic capacitors.

Chapter 21

1. Burning.
3. 720 hours.
5. Exceptional shelf life.
7. Diluted sulphuric acid.
9. The ability to be used to full discharge with far less damage than a conventional lead-acid battery.
11. Through the use of a hydrometer.
13. No.
15. The cells begin to heat.
17. To help prevent reverse-charging a discharged cell of the battery.

Chapter 22

1. Four times.
3. Never break, switch, or fuse the neutral line.
5. Delta and Wye (Star).
7. Allows safe voltage monitoring of high-energy lines.
9. The needle could be accidentally clamped by the mechanical "hold" button, thus erroneously and very dangerously indicating a zero voltage on an actually "hot" circuit.
11. Three, in conjunction with three normal rectifiers.
13. By using PWM, pulse width modulation.
15. The series-wound DC motor.
17. The DC motor.
19. A series-wound DC motor with laminated armature core.
21. Toward.
23. By reversing the leads of either of the two windings.
25. By reversing any two supply lines to the motor.

27. Rectifier bank of six diodes.
29. Ladder.
31. Top, bottom.
33. A three-wire control circuit.

Chapter 23

1. a. Turn off power,
   b. Place dead-man on circuit,
   c. Hang dead-man on circuit,
   d. Attach test leads and set up meter,
   e. Remove dead-man,
   f. Reapply power, and
   g. Take a reading without touching the meter or leads.
   h. Remove leads beginning with step a.
3. Bottom.
5. Screen; suppressor.
7. a. Heaters lit?
   b. Plate voltage normal?
   c. Screen voltage normal?
   d. Grid bias correct?
   e. Cathode voltage normal?
9. A transformer magnetic field will deflect the CRT beam.
11. It is the CRT itself.
13. Raster scan.
15. Zener diode.

Chapter 24

1. Accept it or reject it.
3. High-speed automated testing of a large number of identical items.
5. To verify by a personal seal that the equipment meets all quality and performance criteria at that stage of the manufacture.
7. a. Missing components,
   b. Wrong components,
   c. Polarized components reversed in circuit, and
   d. Soldering errors.
9. At the end of Chapter 1.
11. Yes, it can be very hazardous indeed to your employment, unless you are specifically authorized to do so.
13. Talk to the person reporting the problem, if possible.
15. Such parts bear no manufacturer's logo.
17. 2400.
19. Use a liquid locking compound made for that purpose.
21. To interconnect automated test instruments for ATE use.
23. Electromagnetic interference.
25. The difference between the two input channel signals.
27. Vpp (Voltage, Peak-to-Peak), Vrms (Voltage, Root-Mean-Square), Vabs (Voltage, Absolute), Vmax, Vmin, Vmean, frequency, period, pulse width, risetime, or fall time.
29. Real-time, sequential, and random sampling.
31. Chart.
33. An EPROM programmer.

35. If the ports are of different configurations (one a DTE and the other a DCE), a simple extension cable will do the job. If they are of the *same* type (both DTE or both DCE), a cross-over cable must be used.
37. If the no. 2 line shows a flickering light, this is a DTE device. Memory aid: D*T*E *T*ransmits on *T*wo. If line no. 3 shows the flickering, however, the device is configured as a DCE.
39. It is, almost without exception. Your job situation may suddenly change and you may then find that the possession of one or both licenses can make the difference in getting a new job.

Index

C

E

F

G

H

I

J

K

L

M

N

O

P

R

S

T

U

V

W

X

Z